D1297092

Clean Combustion Technologies

Clean Combustion Technologies

A Reference Book on Steam Generation and Emissions Control

FIFTH EDITION

EDITED BY

CARL BOZZUTO

PUBLISHED BY

ALSTOM

2000 Day Hill Road
Windsor, Connecticut 06095

Copyright © 1948, 1966, 1981, 1991, 2009
Alstom Power, Inc.

Copyright under international copyright conventions
and under Pan American copyright convention

All rights reserved. This book, or parts thereof,
may not be reproduced in any form
without written permission of the publishers.

Library of Congress Control Number: 2009920370

ISBN 978-0-615-26919-1

Disclaimer

The information in this book has been obtained by Alstom Power, Inc. from sources that are believed to be reliable. Neither Alstom Power, Inc., nor any of the authors employed thereby, makes any warranty, express or implied, or assumes any legal liability or responsibility for the accuracy, completeness, or usefulness of any information, apparatus, product, or process disclosed in this book, or represents that the use of any such information, apparatus, product, or process would not infringe privately owned rights. Any such information, apparatus, product, or process disclosed in this book is for illustrative purposes only. Any reference to any plant or unit is for historical and illustrative purposes only. Trademarks used in this book including, Alspa™, CFS™, Controlled Circulation®, Combined Circulation®, Dynamic™ Classifier, Combustalloy™, FiCIRC™, Flowpac®, KNX™, Ljungström®, LNCFS™, Mer-Cure™, Raymond®, RSFC™, TFS 2000™, and TFS 2000™ R are trademarks of the Alstom Group. INCONEL® and Teflon® are registered trademarks of Specialty Metals Corporation and the DuPont company, respectively. This book is published with the understanding that Alstom Power, Inc. and the authors employed thereby are supplying information but are not attempting to either provide or render engineering, operational, or any other professional services. If any such advice or services are required, the assistance of an appropriate professional should be sought.

Transcontinental Printing
Printed in Canada

Contents

Foreword

The world today displays a wide spectrum of economic development. This translates into disparate needs, and challenges society to create and implement strategies that promote improved standards of living, sustain and empower growth, and protect the environment. Society requires dependable production of electric power. Electricity provides the ability to increase productivity, comfort, and technological development throughout the world. There are many ways that power is generated including the use of nuclear, hydro, wind, and solar power technologies. However, fossil fuels (coal, natural gas, and oil) are the mainstay of power production, providing more than 70% of power generation. Although all sources of energy will be needed in the future, fossil fuels are expected to dominate energy production for a long time to come, and to provide the diversity of energy supplies needed to provide reliable power delivery.

Fossil power generation has evolved considerably over the years with increased efficiency and reduced emissions through the use of advanced designs and new technologies. Average heat rates (the amount of energy required to generate a kW-h of electricity) improved from 25,000 BTU/kW-h in the early 1900s to 6,600 BTU/kW-h for the best combined cycle plants in the early 21st century. At the heart of these technologies is the combustion process and the associated environmental control processes that allow for clean, efficient power production. This book will provide the reader with an overview of the various design considerations, equipment, and technologies that will maintain fossil power's prominence in supporting society.

In this fifth edition, the subject matter has been broadened to include more of the overall power plant equipment. With the increased emphasis on cleaner generation of electricity, it becomes more important to understand all of the processes that must work together in order to produce electricity to meet increased demand. To that end, there are 15 chapters that cover the primary components of a power plant as well as controls, materials, operations, maintenance, and retrofits. This material represents a compendium of works that provide an overview of the technology intended for students and those that are relatively new to the industry. These chapters are in the hardcover portion of the book. With this edition, a new feature has been added in the form of a CD. The CD includes searchable .pdf files of all 15 chapters and the 7 appendices that go with the book. In this manner, the "look up" type of information that is included in the appendices, as well as in the preceding chapters, will be easily accessible without the need to have the physical book present. In addition, a new feature has been included in the form of an executable file: an emissions calculator. This feature allows the user to perform combustion calculations, make English to metric (or other conversions), compare emissions levels and rates in differing formats, and perform boiler efficiency and draft loss calculations. These features are intended to provide a more valuable resource in a more convenient and easily usable format.

CARL BOZZUTO

Acknowledgements

We dedicate this edition of Clean Combustion Technologies, with thanks, to the many people who contributed their talent and time, in great or small measure, to revising and updating its technical base, and encouraging and supporting its publication.

To **Philippe Joubert** for providing senior management's support and recognition of this project.

To **Joseph Vasile** for recognizing the value of the combustion technology textbook and for helping to continue this legacy for the new engineering challenges ahead.

To **Carl Bozzuto** for his vast knowledge and technical capabilities in the editing, rewriting, and proofreading of the entire book.

To **Anne Guerin-Moens** for her leadership, support, and vision which made Clean Combustion Technologies possible.

To **Hope Dipierro** for creative development and overall project management.

AUTHORS

Stefan Ahman
William Bailey
Donald Bairley
Keith Berger
Jesse Bolinger
Carl Bozzuto
Anisa Brown
Denis Bruno
Bruce Carney
Paul Chapman
Jerry Chase
Chee Loong Chong
Larry Czarnecki
Scott Darling
Rich Donais
Matt Dooley
Jean-Paul Drouin
Rory Eastman
Alan Ferguson
Woody Fiveland
Steve Francis
Frank Gabrielli
Dan Gelbar
Jim Geyer
Charlie Hart
Doug Hart
Bill Herman
Pat Jennings
Lars-Erik Johansson
Kurt Johnson
Peter Kelly
Bob Kunkel
Walt Lacey
Phil Lafave
Paul Lafferty
Dennis Laslo
Leif Lindau
Mark Malo
John Marion
Doug Martin
Roger Martinsen
Thomas Mastronarde
Gary Mattice
Jack Matton
Charles McDaris
Gary Mooney
Brian Morris
Anthony Munisteri
Jack O'Rourke
Edward Ortman
Ian Perrin
Eric Pickering

(continued)

AUTHORS (continued)

Dennis Piontek
Kjell Porle
Mike Rini
Michael Rogers
Gus Shearer
Glenn Selby
Harpreet Singh
George Stamatelopoulos
Richard Stone
Jim Sutton
Kevin Taugher
Marc Thomas
Terry Totemeier
Dave Towle
Charles Tsirovasiles
Mark Wagner
John Wheeldon
Beat Zimmerli

CONTRIBUTORS

Iqbal Abdulally
Arthur Adams
Bevan August
John Banas
Barbara Barberie
Kenneth Barna
Dave Bintz
William Birmingham
Ron Blodgett
John Bona
Mike Borden
Daniel Bradfield
Christian Breton
Oliver Briggs
Lynn Broders
Graham Butt
Ray Chamberland
Michelle Clayton
Tricia Cole
John Crean
Tony Criswell
Lothar Eckert
David Elkins
Allan Ferry
Cathy Fischer
John Flynn
Art Fournier
Tom Gibbons
Luis Gonzales
Hans Haldermann
Glenn Hill
Kelley Huebner
Thomas Hurd
Bill Keegan
Heinrich Klotz
Edwin Kramer
Heinrich Lageder
Chris Lech
Frank-Udo Leidich
Vince Llinares
Gail Marken
Carmen Marrone
Sharon Marshall
Pascal Michelin
Tapan Mukherjee
David Muraskin
Don Mylchreest
Peter Nilsson
Michelle Nowak
Nsakala Nsakala
Kevin O'Boyle
Richard Pangrazzi
Joe Pereira
Allen Pfeffer
Steve Renals
Dan Roberts
Troy Robinson
Christoph Ruchti
Peter Rufli
Benjamin Sargent
Jim Scholze
Hermann Seelinger
Jean-Claude Semedarde
Ted Sharp
Cheryl Smith
Wendy Smith
Charles Soothill
Paul Traccarella
Bill Urko
Rod Vanstone
Anke Vietgen-Zeidler
Bruce Wilhelm
Randy Wilson
Manfred Wirsum
Andrea Woods
John Zeppa

Introduction

The world today faces a critical challenge as all nations strive to satisfy basic human requirements—food, shelter, clothing, and work—which are so dependent on adequate supplies of energy. The great increase in the use of energy has been met mostly by fossil fuels—primarily coal, oil, and gas. Environmental concerns, security of supply, and economic impacts all must be balanced as the demand for energy continues to increase. Real economic growth and energy use are still inextricably linked.

While the search for ultimate solutions to provide adequate energy supplies continues, near term, interim approaches must be considered for meeting the immediate growth in demand for energy. Technological improvements in the mining, drilling, moving, processing, and using of fossil fuels can, of course, stretch energy resource reserves, as can a determined effort at conservation of energy. Similarly, the utilization of advanced clean coal technologies such as coal gasification, fluidized bed combustion, or ultra supercritical pulverized coal technologies is capable of widening the use of the world's vast coal resources. Developing new ways to realize the best possible use of the world's energy supplies is what Alstom traditionally does best.

Alstom represents a significant number of companies with roots going back to the 1880s. Such names as Grieve Grate Company and the American Stoker Company brought together two well-known manufacturers of fuel-burning equipment in 1912 to form what became Combustion Engineering, Inc. With the merger of Société Alsacienne de Constructions Mécaniques (SACM) and Thomson-Houston in 1928, **Alsthom** was born. In 1969, Compagnie General d'Electricite (CGE) became the majority shareholder of Alsthom. During the 1980s, ASEA and Brown Boveri merged to form ABB. In 1990, ABB purchased Combustion Engineering, Inc. During that time, UK GEC merged with Alsthom to form GEC Alsthom. In 1998, GEC and Alcatel sold off part of their shares to allow the company to be publicly listed on the Paris stock exchange as Alstom. In 1999, ABB and Alstom formed a joint venture company for their power businesses (ABB Alstom Power Ltd.). In 2000, Alstom purchased ABB's interest in the joint venture company from ABB, leading to the creation of what Alstom is today in the power industry. The pursuit and realization of technical innovation has led to Alstom becoming a global leader in power generation.

In 1918, Combustion Engineering, Inc. (C-E), initiated the development of pulverized coal firing. Overcoming the limitations imposed upon boiler capacity by virtue of the size restrictions associated with the use of stokers, pulverized coal firing opened the door to making it possible to realize a large increase in the capacity of coal-fired boilers. Capitalizing on the pulverized coal firing system that was being employed for steam locomotives, C-E successfully adapted this pulverized coal-firing technology for use with the stationary utility boilers at the Oneida Street and Lakeside Stations of the Milwaukee Electric Railway and Light Co. This pioneering work, done by C-E jointly with Milwaukee Electric's engineers and the Bureau of Mines, marks one of the most important developments in the history of the art of solid fuel combustion. As a result, in 1980, the Oneida Street Station, where pulverized coal-firing was first employed by a utility, was named an Historic Engineering Landmark by the American Society of Mechanical Engineers. Through the

the operating steam pressure to which the non-welded boiler drum could be subjected. C-E, at its Chattanooga, Tennessee plant, developed and has perfected processes, techniques, and machines for the fusion welding of heavy metal plate in order form cylindrical shells from which boiler drums could then be fabricated. The first such welded boiler drum was dedicated as a National Historic Landmark by ASME on May 2, 1980—50 years after this welded boiler drum was first successfully tested. Welded construction enabled steam pressures to be increased. In 1931, the first boiler to operate at a pressure of 1,800 psig was installed at the Phillip Carey Co. in Lockland, Ohio. By 1953, the first steam generating unit capable of operating at a pressure of 2,650 psig was designed for the Kearny Station of Public Service Electric and Gas of New Jersey (PSE&G).

With improvements in the strength of materials that permitted such materials to be operated at higher temperatures and pressures, the outlet steam temperatures of steam generating units began to climb from the 750°F temperature level. By 1939, the outlet steam temperatures reached 925°F at the River Rouge plant of the Ford Motor Co.

The first steam generating unit to exceed a 1,000°F total steam temperature was sold to PSE&G for its Sewaren Station in 1949. This steam generating unit was designed to be operated at a temperature of 1,050°F at the superheater outlet. In 1953, the Kearny steam generating unit of the same utility was designed to operate at a temperature of 1,100°F and a pressure of 2,376 psig at the superheater outlet and at a temperature of 1,050°F at the reheater outlet. In 1954, C-E supplied the supercritical pressure unit for Philadelphia Electric Co.'s Eddystone Station, which was designed for outlet conditions of a temperature of 1,210°F at a pressure of 5,300 psig. This supercritical pressure unit is still in operation and continues to represent the highest temperature and pressure steam conditions to date at which a steam generating unit has been operated.

In its search for higher efficiencies for steam generating units, the utility industry adopted the reheat cycle. This concept involved the reheating of steam in a section of the steam generating unit after some of the steam's energy had been extracted through the expansion of the steam in the initial section of the turbine. This reheated steam, which is now at or near the steam's initial high temperature, is then returned to the final section of the turbine. Although a few steam generating units that embodied a reheat cycle had been built in the 1920s, it was not until after World War II that the surge toward the use of the reheat cycle in the utility industry began in earnest. The first post-war steam generating unit having a reheat cycle was sold in 1947 to Boston Edison Co. for its Edgar Station. In the following years, designs for steam generating units that had a reheat cycle became the standard.

C-E designed and installed the first Controlled Circulation® steam generating unit at the Montaup Electric Co. in Somerset, Massachusetts, in 1942. In accordance with this design, the circulation of water is ensured and controlled through the utilization of pumps that are designed to provide a positive flow through the heat-absorbing tubes in the walls of the steam generating unit. The available head produced by such pumps enables distribution orifices to be employed in the flow circuits through the heat-absorbing tubes in the walls of the steam generating unit. With the Controlled Circulation® steam generating unit design, it is possible to overcome the problem of decreasing thermal circulation as the operating pressure of the steam generating unit approaches the critical pressure point of 3,208 psia. The Controlled Circulation® steam generating unit design has been well accepted around the world by the utility industry.

A license agreement was executed in 1953 between C-E and Sulzer Brothers of Switzerland giving C-E the rights to build and sell in the United States the Sulzer Brothers' Monotube steam generating unit design. (The Monotube steam generating unit design comprises a once-through type steam generating unit in which the water that is introduced at the inlet of the steam generating unit passes continuously through the tubing in the walls where the water is heated to the desired outlet temperature without being subjected to any other type of internal recirculation.) In 1954, the Philadelphia Electric Company purchased from C-E the first steam generating unit embodying this Monotube technology for the Eddystone Plant. This steam generating unit was designed to operate at a pressure of 5,300 psig and a temperature of 1,210°F at the superheater outlet, which represented the highest pressure and the highest temperature operating conditions for a steam generating unit of commercial size ever. This unit went into operation in 1959, and was followed by several other supercritical and subcritical pressure installations of the Monotube design as well.

The next advancement in high-pressure steam generating unit technology was the Combined Circulation® steam generating unit design, which made use of the principle of pumped circulation of water in the walls of the steam generating unit (recirculation of the fluid by pumps) coupled with the once-through flow employed in the Monotube technology. This technology was followed by sliding pressure, supercritical designs. Current developments are aimed at increased steam temperatures and pressures for higher efficiency and reduced emissions.

BROADENED CAPABILITIES

Air preheaters are capable of providing heat recovery from the hot flue gases that leave steam generating units, thereby improving the efficiency of these units. During the 1920s, the Ljungström® continuous, regenerative-type, air preheater was developed. This development of the Ljungström® air preheater occurred in connection with the development of the first turbine locomotive. In the United States, the first Ljungström® air preheater installations for industrial power plant steam generating units occurred in 1923. In 1925, the Air Preheater Corporation, which was jointly owned by the Ljungström Turbine Manufacturing Co. of Sweden and the James Howden Co., Ltd., was founded. The Air Preheater Corporation was acquired by C-E after the depression, along with an exclusive license to manufacture the Ljungström® air preheater design in the United States and Canada. In accordance with the Ljungström® air preheater design, a rotating heating element, made up of closely spaced metal plates, is packed in baskets through which hot flue gases leaving the steam generating unit and cold combustion air flowing into the steam generating unit are alternately made to pass. This Ljungström® air preheater design, which is manufactured in Alstom's Wellsville, New York facility, has been universally accepted within the power generation industry and has been employed with steam generating units that are supplied by all steam generating unit manufacturers.

C-E was one of the pioneers, along with the Flakt Company in Sweden, in the development of flue gas desulfurization equipment for the removal of sulfur dioxide (SO_2). Research and development work on this technology was begun by C-E in 1963. A pilot facility was constructed in C-E's Windsor, Connecticut development laboratory. This was followed in 1966 and 1967 by experimental field work that was done on a steam generating unit at Detroit Edison Co.'s St. Clair Station. The first commercial scrubber installations in the United States for the removal of SO_2 went into service in 1968 at Union Electric Co's Meramec Station and at Kansas Power and Light Co's. Lawrence Station. In the 1990s, ABB, which had purchased both C-E and the Flakt Company, combined together the operations of these two companies in order to form what is now known as the Alstom Environmental Control Systems group. This group includes electrostatic precipitators, fabric filters, selective catalytic reduction (SCR) systems, mercury capture technology, and presently is now in the process of developing new CO_2 capture technology.

In the latter part of the 1980s, the Brown Boveri Company of Switzerland and Germany and ASEA from Sweden merged to form ABB Ltd. In 1939, BBC introduced the first electrical generating gas turbine in Neuchatel, Switzerland. In 1989, General Electric Corp (UK) and Alcatel Alsthom merged to form GEC Alsthom. ABB subsequently purchased C-E in 1990. In 1998, GEC Alsthom was renamed Alstom. In 1999, ABB and Alstom merged their respective power businesses into a joint venture company known as ABB ALSTOM Power Ltd. In 2000, Alstom purchased from ABB, ABB's interest in the joint venture company, leading to the formation of the present day Alstom S.A., which is headquartered in Paris.

The power generation industry has gone through a lot of consolidation over the years. The advances that have been made over more than a century in the development of energy conversion processes from fossil fuels have been substantial. To this end, energy conversion efficiencies have increased from near 10% to over 40% (HHV basis) during that time frame. Moreover, the amount of emissions from steam generating units has been reduced substantially compared to the amount of emissions produced by earlier designs. Those individuals who have worked in the power generation industry during some part of that time frame have been able to witness not only tremendous growth in the art and science of fuel burning and steam generation, but also remarkable changes in the lifestyles of people throughout the world that have been brought about at least in part because of such growth. Today, new developments are underway that are expected to open up new vistas for the use of fossil fuels for power generation purposes. In this book an attempt will be made to cover many of these new developments.

The Power Systems Sector of Alstom is capable of designing, manufacturing, and supplying a broad range of products, systems and services to the power generation and industrial markets and has at last count a presence in 70 countries around the globe. This range of products, systems, and services, by way of exemplification, includes:

Plant Engineering
Steam Turbines
Gas Turbines
Combined Cycle Plants
Boilers
Environmental Control Equipment
Energy Recovery Systems
Clean Coal Combustion Technology
Controls
Maintenance and Retrofit Services
Repowering and Rehabilitation Capabilities

Throughout this book, these products, systems and services, and their associated technologies will be referred to as Alstom products or Alstom technologies, regardless of their origin.

Alstom continues to embrace the same values that have kept it at the cutting edge of power generation technology. A dedication to service and the courage to lead—attributes that have been major influences throughout the history of the power generation industry—still guide its operations today. As it faces the technical challenges of the future requirements for energy and the environment, Alstom will continue to lead in the development of Clean Combustion Technologies.

Fossil-Fueled Power Plant Design

Chapter **One**

The optimum design of a fossil-fueled power plant requires an evaluation of technical, economic, environmental, and social factors to select an approach that best meets the criteria established by investors, owners, operators, the local community, and those who will use the generated power. Existing fossil-fueled power plants can remain valuable assets for many years through the implementation of upgrades designed to increase the remaining useful life, improve the relative efficiency of power production, and reduce the impact on the environment. In this chapter, the following topics are covered: a typical description of a fossil-fueled power plant, the basic thermodynamic principles on which the operation of such power plants is based, and the elements that contribute to the final design configuration and operation of the actual plant. Other topics, such as possible retrofit approaches that may make an existing fossil-fueled power plant more useful, the economics underlying the operation of such a power plant, and recent industry trends, also are reviewed.

SYSTEM DESCRIPTION

In a typical fossil-fueled power plant, a fossil fuel must be delivered to the plant, where it is typically stored for usage as needed. This is especially true for solid and liquid fossil fuels, which can be easily stored. For gaseous fossil fuels, the delivery pipeline typically acts as the storage system. For natural gas, the pipeline pressure is generally about 2,000 psi. In the thousands of miles of such pipelines, substantial amounts of natural gas can be stored. For solid fossil fuels, the fuel is typically prepared at the plant for delivery to the combustion device that will burn it. In the case of coal firing, for example, coal is usually delivered for long-term storage to a coal pile at the power plant itself. From such a pile, the coal is then transferred to a primary crusher for short-term storage before delivery to a coal bin. Thereafter, the coal is delivered from the coal bin to a feeder, which is designed to continuously feed the coal to a pulverizer. The pulverizer grinds the coal to a very fine, powder-like consistency and delivers this pulverized coal directly to a boiler. *Figure 1-1* shows a coal-fired power plant with the coal-storage portion of the plant visible in the foreground.

The boiler burns the fuel, thus liberating the chemical heat the fuel contains. This released heat is then transferred

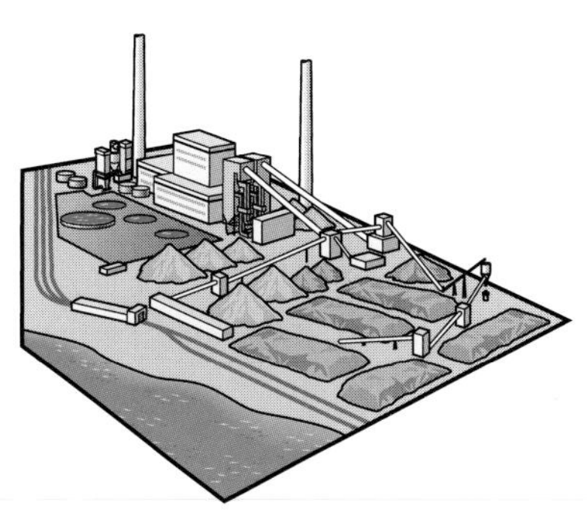

Figure 1-1 | Coal-fired power plant

through the walls of the boiler to water that flows through those walls, thus generating steam. Next, the steam is separated from the water and is sent to a steam turbine. The rotor of the steam turbine rotates as the steam passes over the turbine blades. This rotation in turn causes a generator set, which is connected to the rotor, to rotate as well, thus producing electric power. When the motive force provided by the steam is fully consumed, this steam is sent to a condenser to return the steam to a liquid state so it can be pumped back to the boiler. Thus, the water that flows through the walls of the boiler is continuously reused.

After most of the useful energy has been transferred to the water that flows through the walls of the boiler, the products of the combustion process must be cleaned. In this regard, various emission control devices are employed. Such devices typically include particulate control systems, NOx removal systems, and SO_2 removal systems. Other types of emission control devices could be used for controlling mercury and, eventually, CO_2 as well as other substances. Each of these components and systems will be discussed in later chapters. An isometric view of the major components of a fossil-fueled power plant is shown in *Figure 1-2.*

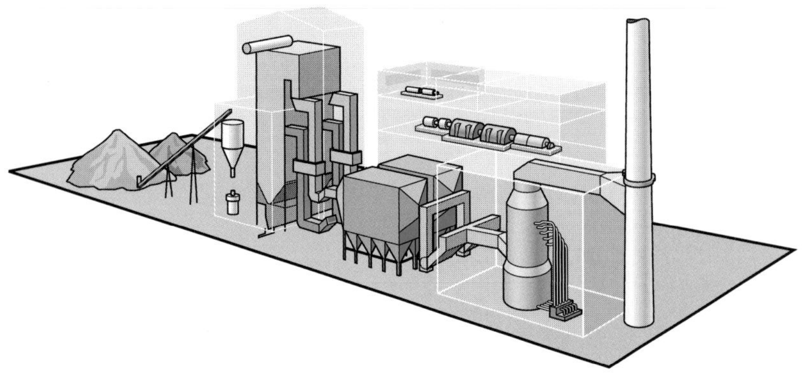

Figure 1-2 | Isometric view of a fossil-fueled power plant

Fossil-fueled power plants can be designed so they are suitable for myriad purposes, including electric power production, thermal energy applications, and standby/emergency power systems. From the early concepts of industrial power to the later, central station designs and back again to designs for smaller, cogeneration systems, power plant technology and its applications have continued to evolve.

The design of a fossil-fueled power plant begins with the application of certain basic, fundamental principles that govern the relationship between the properties of matter, which define the conversion of energy from one form to another. These properties of matter are known as the first and second laws of thermodynamics, and they provide a quantitative method of describing sequentially the processes of a working fluid (predominantly water in liquid or gaseous form [i.e., steam]) as functions of temperature, pressure, enthalpy, and entropy.

The first law of thermodynamics is basically a "conservation" law. It states that matter and energy can be neither created nor destroyed. Thus, the heat that is released during the combustion process must end up somewhere (preferably, mostly in the steam). Moreover, the products that result from the combustion must be accounted for, because they do not just disappear. Simply stated, at steady state, the inputs must equal the outputs. This fact enables heat and mass balances to be created, which provide an accounting as to where all the matter and energy go during the combustion process.

The second law of thermodynamics governs the conversion of heat energy into mechanical work. Regarding this law, physical limits on the conversion of heat energy into mechanical work exist, and these limits are primarily a function of the temperature of the process as well as the temperature of the heat rejection reservoir (with the latter typically comprising the ambient surroundings). The limitation that is imposed insofar as the ambient surroundings are concerned is crucial to understanding how the combustion process works and how the performance of such a combustion process can be improved.

LAWS OF THERMODYNAMICS

By definition, a *thermodynamic cycle* is a series of processes that are combined in such a way that the thermodynamic states at which the working fluid exists are repeated periodically. In a fossil-fueled power plant, this is exemplified by the conversion of water to steam (preferably through environmentally enhanced and efficient combustion of fossil fuel), wherein this steam is then employed to drive a steam turbine to generate electric power. The steam that is exhausted from the turbine is then condensed back to water again (preferably through use of processes that minimize the impact on the surrounding environment) and pumped back to the conversion process (typically a boiler).

FIRST LAW OF THERMODYNAMICS

The first and second laws of thermodynamics govern the thermodynamic analysis of fluid cycles. In equation form, the first law can be stated in the following manner:

$$\Delta E = Q - W + \Sigma(\pm h_i \pm e_{xi})m_i$$

Equation 1-1

where

ΔE = the change in energy content of the system

Q = the heat transferred to the system

W = the work transferred from the system

$(h_i + e_{xi})m_i$ = energy convected into or out of system by mass, m_i, with enthalpy, h_i, and extrinsic energy, e_{xi}

The extrinsic energy, e_{xi}, is dependent on the particular frame of reference. For example, for a fluid system, e_{xi} = kinetic energy + potential energy $= \frac{V_i^2}{2g_i} + z_i$, in which V_i is velocity and z is elevation above a specified datum point.

The latter equation applies equally to processes and cycles and to steady- and transient-flow situations in such processes and cycles. For example, in a closed system where fluid streams do not cross the boundary, $m_i = 0$, and if the process is cyclic, then $\Delta E = 0$ and Equation 1-1 becomes

$$\Sigma Q = \Sigma W$$

Equation 1-2

or

$$\text{input} = \text{output}$$

This implies the existence of an efficiency of 100 percent.

As another example, if the steady-state, adiabatic (no heat loss) expansion in a turbine is being analyzed, then $\Delta E = 0$, $Q = 0$, and Equation 1-1 reduces to

$$\begin{aligned} W &= -\Sigma(h_i + e_{xi})m_i \\ &= m[(h + e_x)_{\text{in}} - (h + e_x)_{\text{out}}] \end{aligned}$$

where in and out refer to input and output, respectively, or

$$W = m\left[\left(h+\frac{V^2}{2g}+z\right)_{\text{in}} - \left(h+\frac{V^2}{2g}+z\right)_{\text{out}}\right]$$

Equation 1-3

When changes in kinetic energy and elevation of the fluid stream may be neglected, Equation 1-3 reduces to the familiar $W = m(h_{\text{in}} - h_{\text{out}})$.

SECOND LAW OF THERMODYNAMICS

In equation form, the second law of thermodynamics can be stated in the following manner:

$$\Delta S = \left(\frac{Q}{T}\right) + I + \Sigma S_i$$

Equation 1-4

where

ΔS = the change in entropy of system

(Q/T), or the sum over the system boundaries of the heat transferred, Q, at a position on the boundary where the local temperature is T

I = irreversibility (for consistency with other second-law statements, $I \geq 0$; for reversible processes or cycles, $I = 0$; and for irreversible processes or cycles, $I > 0$)

In addition, $\Sigma_i S_i$ is the entropy flow into and out of system associated with mass flow, m_i, into and out of system. For a reversible cyclic process involving closed system, $I = 0$, $\Delta S = 0$, $\Sigma_i S_i = 0$, and Equation 1-4 reduces to

$$\frac{Q}{T} = 0$$

Equation 1-5

The steady-flow, adiabatic expansion of a fluid through a turbine is governed by the following equation:

$$I = \Sigma m_i s_i = -m(s_{\text{in}} - s_{\text{out}})$$

Equation 1-6

For reversible, adiabatic expansion, $I = 0$, and the process is characterized by the familiar isentropic property, $s_{\text{out}} = s_{\text{in}}$. Turbine expansion, however, is not wholly isentropic. The non-idealities are taken into account by defining the turbine efficiency. The primary advantage of writing the second law of thermodynamics in the form of an equation (Eq. 1-4), rather than in the form of the usual inequality, is the usefulness of the second law, when written as an equation, for analyzing processes and cycles in a direct and quantitative manner, similar to the analysis with regard to the first law of thermodynamics.[1–6] Because of these irreversibilities, some heat must be rejected to the environment to operate a real cycle.

Equations 1-1 and 1-4, therefore, provide a quantitative means of examining all processes encountered in the analysis of a fossil-fueled power plant, regardless of the nature of the fluids or the specific cycle employed.

CYCLES

CARNOT CYCLE

In 1824, Sadi Carnot, a French engineer, published a small, moderately technical book entitled *Reflections on the Motive Power of Fire.*[7] With publication of this book, Carnot made three important contributions: the concept of reversibility, the concept of a cycle, and the specification of a heat engine capable of producing maximum work when operating cyclicly between two reservoirs that are each at a fixed temperature. The Carnot cycle consists of several reversible isothermal and isentropic processes. *Figure 1-3A* illustrates a flow system for executing the Carnot cycle. The temperature–entropy diagram shown in *Figure 1-3B* depicts the state changes experienced by the working fluid.

The classic Carnot cycle is such that no other cycle can have a better efficiency between the same specified temperature limits. Other cycles may equal the efficiency of the Carnot cycle, but no other cycle may exceed that efficiency. Stated as an equation:

$$\text{Carnot efficiency} = \frac{T_{\text{hot}} - T_{\text{cold}}}{T_{\text{hot}}}$$

Equation 1-7

where

T_{hot} = the absolute temperature of the heat source

T_{cold} = the absolute temperature of the heat sink

Practical attempts have been made to attain the efficiency of the Carnot cycle. Irreversibilities have been encountered during such attempts, however, in the form of finite temperature differences during heat transfer processes and of fluid friction during work transfer processes. In addition, heat losses to the environment occur with practical equipment. Continuing the compression process (denoted as d-a in *Fig. 1-3B*) is difficult to perform on a two-phase mixture and requires an input of work ranging from a fifth to a third of the turbine output. Furthermore, with the Carnot cycle, the high-temperature heat source cannot be defined in terms of maximum temperature. Rather, for the Carnot cycle, the weighted average temperature of the working fluid must be calculated. Consequently, when realistic irreversibilities are introduced into the calculations for the efficiency of the Carnot cycle, the actual efficiency is reduced, and equipment sizes must be increased to attain the desired work output.

RANKINE CYCLE

The cornerstone of the cycle for a modern steam power plant is a modification of the Carnot cycle proposed by W. J. M. Rankine,[8,9] a distinguished Scottish engineering professor of thermodynamics and applied mechanics. The elements comprising the Rankine cycle are the same as those depicted in *Figure 1-3* with one exception. Because the condensation process accompanying the heat-rejection process continues until the saturated liquid state is reached, a simple liquid pump replaces the two-phase compressor of the Carnot cycle. The temperature–entropy diagram and the enthalpy–entropy diagram depicted in *Figures 1-4A* and *1-4B*, respectively, illustrate the changes in state for the Rankine cycle. With the exception that compression terminates (state a) at boiling pressure rather than at boiling temperature (state a′), the Rankine cycle resembles a Carnot cycle. The triangle bounded by a-a′ and the line connecting to the temperature–entropy curve in *Figure 1-4A* are representative

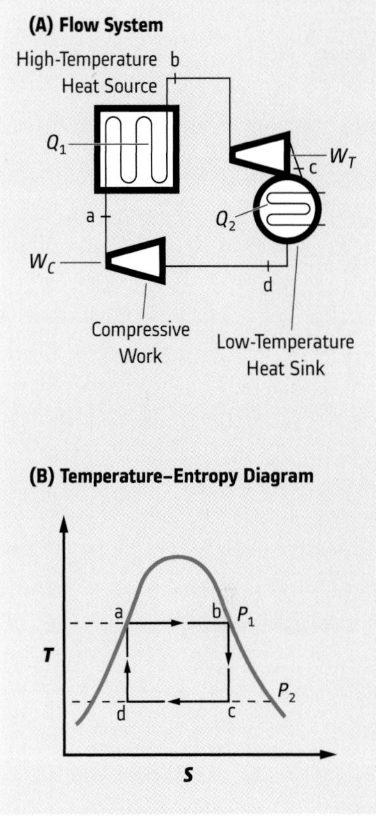

Figure 1-3 | Flow system for a Carnot cycle

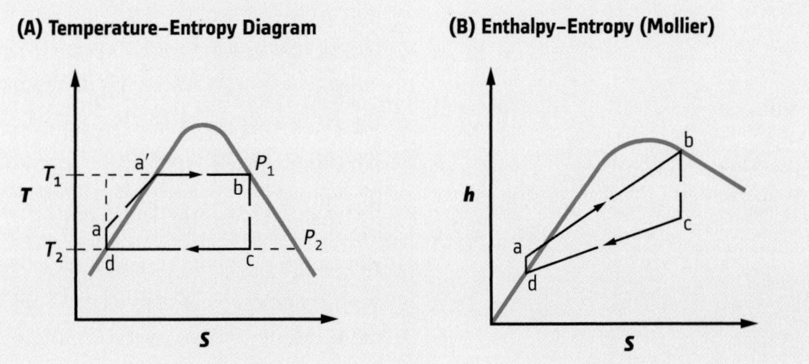

Figure 1-4 | Simple Rankine cycle (without superheat)

of the amount of loss of cycle work because of the irreversible heating of the liquid from state a to a saturated liquid. Continuing, the lower pressure at state a compared to the pressure at state a′ thus makes it possible for a much smaller amount of work of compression to be required between d-a. For operating plants, this smaller compression work amounts to 1% or less of the turbine output (compared to the 20–30% of the turbine output in the case of two-phase compression).

This modification eliminates the two-phase vapor compression process, reduces compression work to a negligible amount, and makes the Rankine cycle less sensitive than the Carnot cycle to the irreversibilities that are bound to be present in an actual power plant. As a result, when compared to a Carnot cycle operating between the same temperature limits and with components having realistic efficiencies, the Rankine cycle is capable of producing a larger net work output per unit mass of fluid circulated while enabling the use of smaller-sized equipment and achieving lower cost. In addition, because of its relative insensitivity to irreversibilities, the operating plant thermal efficiencies of the Rankine cycle will exceed those of the Carnot cycle. Note, however, that the limit on maximum efficiency is still governed by the maximum Carnot cycle efficiency, which is solely calculated by the temperatures of the high- and low-temperature reservoirs.

REGENERATIVE RANKINE CYCLE

Refinements in component design soon enabled power plants based on the Rankine cycle to operate at their peak thermal efficiencies, with further increases realized by modifying the basic Rankine cycle. Included in such modifications were increasing the temperature of the saturated steam supplied to the steam turbine, increasing the turbine inlet temperature by use of constant-pressure superheat, reducing the sink temperature, and reheating the working vapor after partial expansion, followed by the continued expansion of the working vapor to the final sink temperature (reheat). In actual practice, all these modifications are employed along with another important modification. To this end, in the previous section, the irreversibility associated with heating the compressed liquid to saturation by a finite temperature difference was indicated as being the primary thermodynamic reason for the lower thermal efficiency of the Rankine cycle. An attempt is made with the Rankine cycle to minimize this irreversibility by making use of a regenerative cycle wherein other parts of the cycle that have temperatures slightly above that of the compressed liquid being heated are employed as heat sources. *Figure 1-5* illustrates an idealized form of a regenerative Rankine cycle wherein the feedwater train is depicted.

The condensed liquid at f is pumped to the pressure P_1 and passes through coils around the turbine, whereupon the liquid receives heat from the fluid that is expanded in the turbine. The liquid and vapor are made to flow counter to one another, and by virtue of the reversible heat transfer to the liquid over the infinitesimal temperature difference d_T, the liquid is made to reach the saturated state at T (process b-c). Then, the liquid rejects heat at the constant temperature T_2 (process e-f). Such an idealized regenerative Rankine cycle, by virtue of the second law of

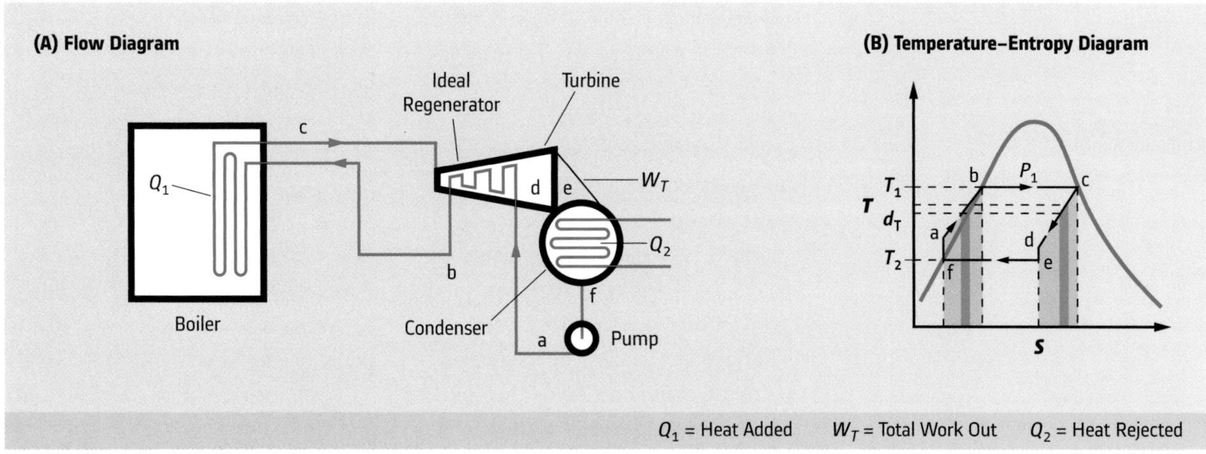

Figure 1-5 | Idealized regenerative Rankine cycle

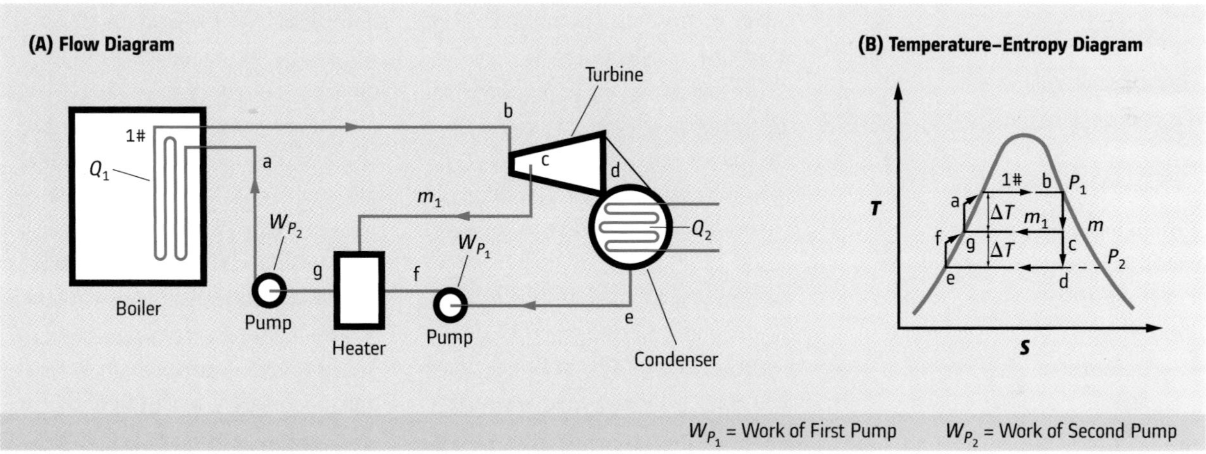

Figure 1-6 | Practical single-extraction regenerative cycle

thermodynamics, will have a thermal efficiency equal to that of a Carnot cycle operating between the same temperatures as the idealized regenerative Rankine cycle.

Such a process of transferring heat from one part of a cycle to another to eliminate or reduce external irreversibilities is termed *regenerative heating*, and it is basic to all regenerative cycles. Although thermodynamically desirable, the idealized regenerative Rankine cycle that has just been described contains several features that preclude the use of such a cycle in practice. To this end, having to locate the heat exchanger around the turbine greatly increases the difficulties associated with the design as well as the cost of the cycle. Even if these problems were capable of being solved, it would not be possible to accomplish reversibly the requisite amount of heat transfer in the time available. Furthermore, the requisite amount of cooling, as described above, causes the vapor to reach an excessive moisture content. The regenerative cycle illustrated in *Figure 1-6* provides a practical approach to regeneration without encountering those problems associated with the idealized regenerative Rankine cycle that was depicted in *Figure 1-5*. Extraction (or "bleeding") of steam at state c for use in the "open" heater provides a means of avoiding excessive cooling of the vapor during expansion in the turbine. In the heater, the liquid from the condenser is subjected to an increase in temperature of ΔT. (Note here that regenerative cycle heaters are referred to as being either "open" or "closed," depending on whether hot and cold fluids are mixed directly to enable energy to be shared between the hot and cold fluids or are kept separate such that an exchange of energy occurs only indirectly, through the use of metal coils.)

The extraction and heating steps in the regenerative cycle (*Fig. 1-6*) cause the finite temperature difference, ΔT, to be substituted for the infinitesimal d_T that is used in the theoretical version of the regeneration cycle. Such a substitution, although failing to attain the full potential of regeneration, nevertheless is capable of halving the temperature difference through which the condensate is required to be heated in accordance with the basic Rankine cycle. Moreover, additional extractions and heaters enable a closer approximation to the maximum efficiency of the idealized regenerative Rankine cycle, thereby providing further improvement over the simple Rankine cycle depicted in *Figure 1-4*.

By reducing the temperature difference between the liquid that enters the boiler and the saturated fluid, it becomes possible to increase the thermal efficiency of the cycle. The price that must be paid to do this is a decrease in the net work that is produced per pound of vapor that enters the turbine as well as the need for increased size, complexity, and initial cost of the power plant. Additional improvements in cycle performance may be attained if the designer can accommodate the consequences associated with an increasing number of feedwater heating stages. To this end, balancing the thermal efficiency of the cycle against the size and complexity of the power plant as well as the cost for production of power by the plant will determine the optimum number of heaters that should be employed.[10–12]

REHEAT CYCLE

Use of superheat offers a simple way to improve the thermal efficiency of the basic Rankine cycle as well as a simple way to reduce the vapor moisture content to acceptable levels in the low-pressure stages of the turbine. With the continual increase in steam temperatures and pressures to achieve an improved cycle efficiency, however, it has been found that in some situations, the available superheat temperatures are insufficient to prevent excessive moisture from forming in the low-pressure stages of the turbine. The solution to this problem is to interrupt the expansion process, remove the vapor for reheat at constant pressure, and then return the vapor to the turbine for continuing the expansion of the vapor to condenser pressure.

The thermodynamic cycle that employs this modification of the Rankine cycle is termed the *reheat cycle*. It is possible to carry out such reheating of the vapor either in a section of the boiler from which primary steam is supplied, in a separately fired heat exchanger, or in a steam-to-steam heat exchanger. In accordance with the design of most present-day utility boiler units, however, the superheater and the reheater are located in the same boiler. Typically, the practice in such power plants is to combine both

the regenerative modification and the reheat modification into the basic Rankine cycle. *Figure 1-7* illustrates a temperature–entropy diagram of a single reheat, regenerative cycle with two stages of feedwater heating. For large power plant installations, reheat makes possible an improvement of approximately 5% in the thermal efficiency of those installations and enables a substantial reduction in the amount of heat that is rejected to the condenser cooling water.[13–16] The operating characteristics and economics of modern power plants normally justify the installation of only one reheat stage, with a possible exception in the case of power plant units operating at supercritical temperatures and pressures.

Figures 1-8 and *1-9* depict a flow diagram for a 600-MW, fossil-fueled reheat cycle, which is designed to be operated with initial turbine conditions of 2,520 psig and 1,000°F (17.4 MPa gage and 538°C) steam. As shown in *Figures 1-8* and *1-9*, six feedwater heaters are supplied with exhaust steam from the high-pressure turbine as well as with extraction steam from the intermediate- and low-pressure turbines. Except for the deaerating heater, which is identified in *Figures 1-8* and *1-9* as the third heater, all of the feedwater heaters that are illustrated are closed heaters. Three pumps are illustrated in *Figures 1-8* and *1-9*:

1. The condensate pump, which pumps the condensate through the oil and hydrogen gas coolers, the vent condenser, the air ejector (or the vacuum pump), the first and second heaters, and the deaerating heater.
2. The condensate booster pump, which pumps the condensate through the fourth and fifth heaters.

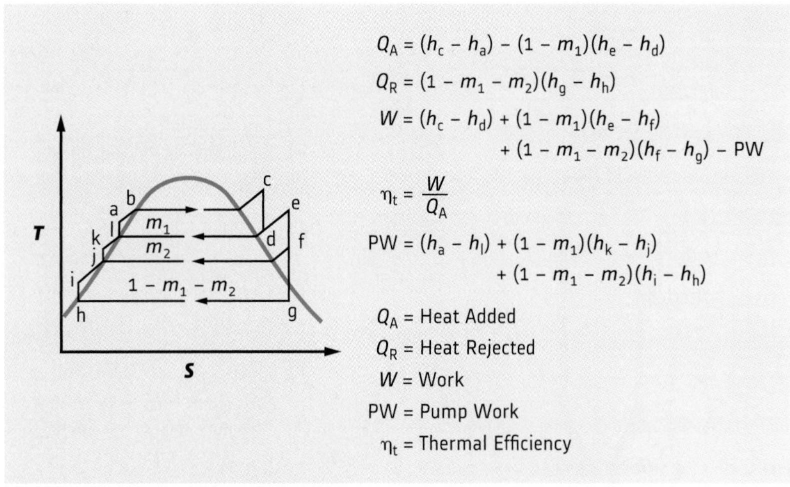

$Q_A = (h_c - h_a) - (1 - m_1)(h_e - h_d)$
$Q_R = (1 - m_1 - m_2)(h_g - h_h)$
$W = (h_c - h_d) + (1 - m_1)(h_e - h_f) + (1 - m_1 - m_2)(h_f - h_g) - PW$
$\eta_t = \frac{W}{Q_A}$
$PW = (h_a - h_l) + (1 - m_1)(h_k - h_j) + (1 - m_1 - m_2)(h_i - h_h)$
Q_A = Heat Added
Q_R = Heat Rejected
W = Work
PW = Pump Work
η_t = Thermal Efficiency
T
S
a
b
c
d
e
f
g
h
i
j
k
l
m_1
m_2
$1 - m_1 - m_2$

Figure 1-7 | Regenerative cycle with a single reheat stage and two feedwater heaters

3. The boiler feed pump, which pumps the condensate through the sixth heater to the economizer and the boiler.

The mass flows noted on the flow diagram in *Figures 1-8* and *1-9* are shown as being at the prescribed conditions for full-load operation.

SUPERCRITICAL PRESSURE CYCLE

A definite relationship exists between the operating temperature and the optimum pressure of a cycle. To this end, the supercritical pressure cycle is used worldwide to obtain the highest possible thermodynamic efficiencies with fossil-fueled steam generation equipment. More specifically, a regenerative, reheat, supercritical pressure cycle is employed, with six to eight stages of feedwater heating. Because of the high inlet temperature and pressure, however, two reheat stages may be justified, and in fact, two such stages have been used in several installations. *Figures 1-10* and *1-11* illustrate a typical supercritical pressure steam turbine heat balance, with seven feedwater heaters and steam extractions from the various turbines that are supplying energy for

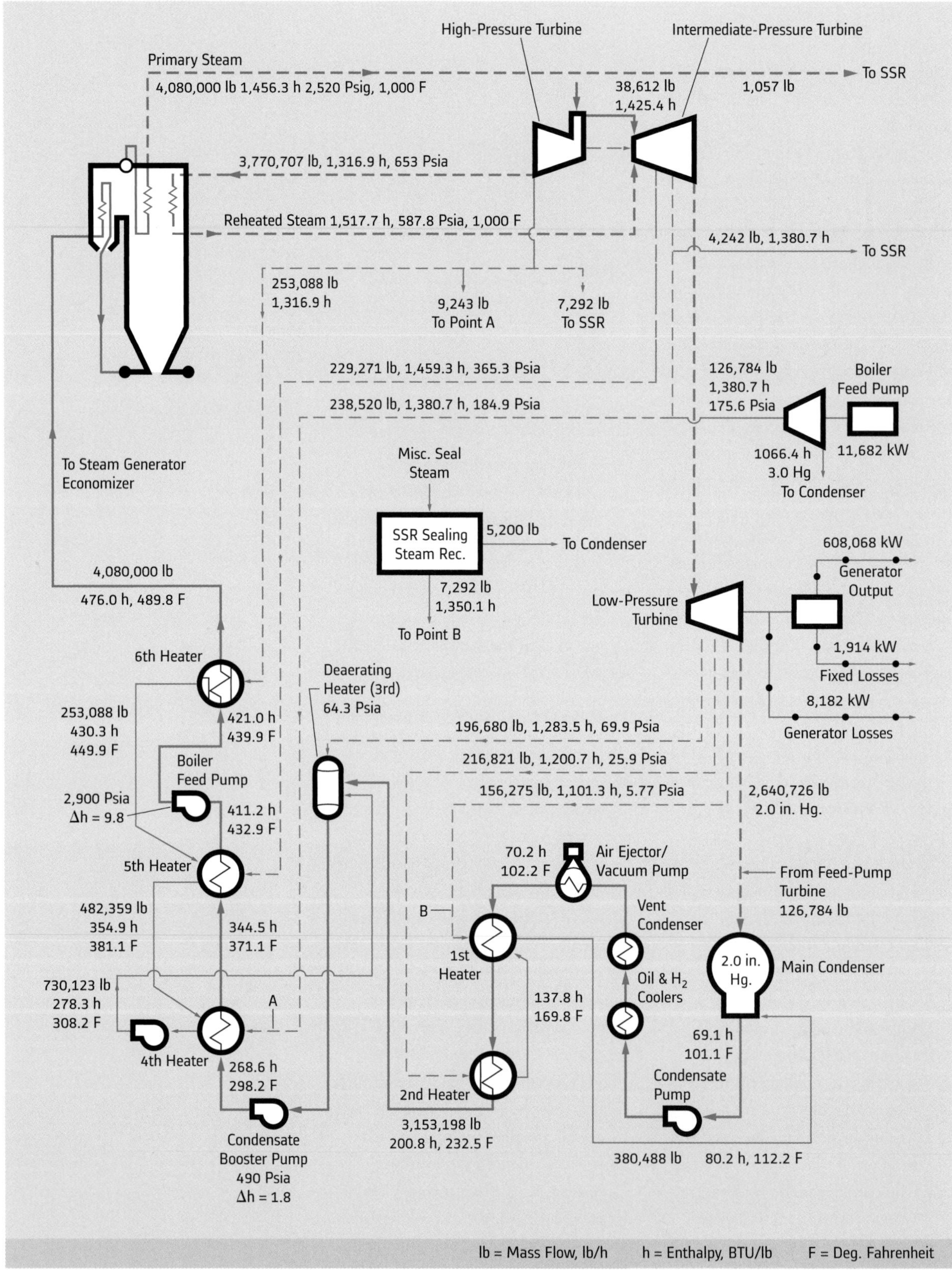

Figure 1-8 | Reheat regenerative cycle for a 600-MW, subcritical-pressure, fossil-fueled power plant (U.S. units)

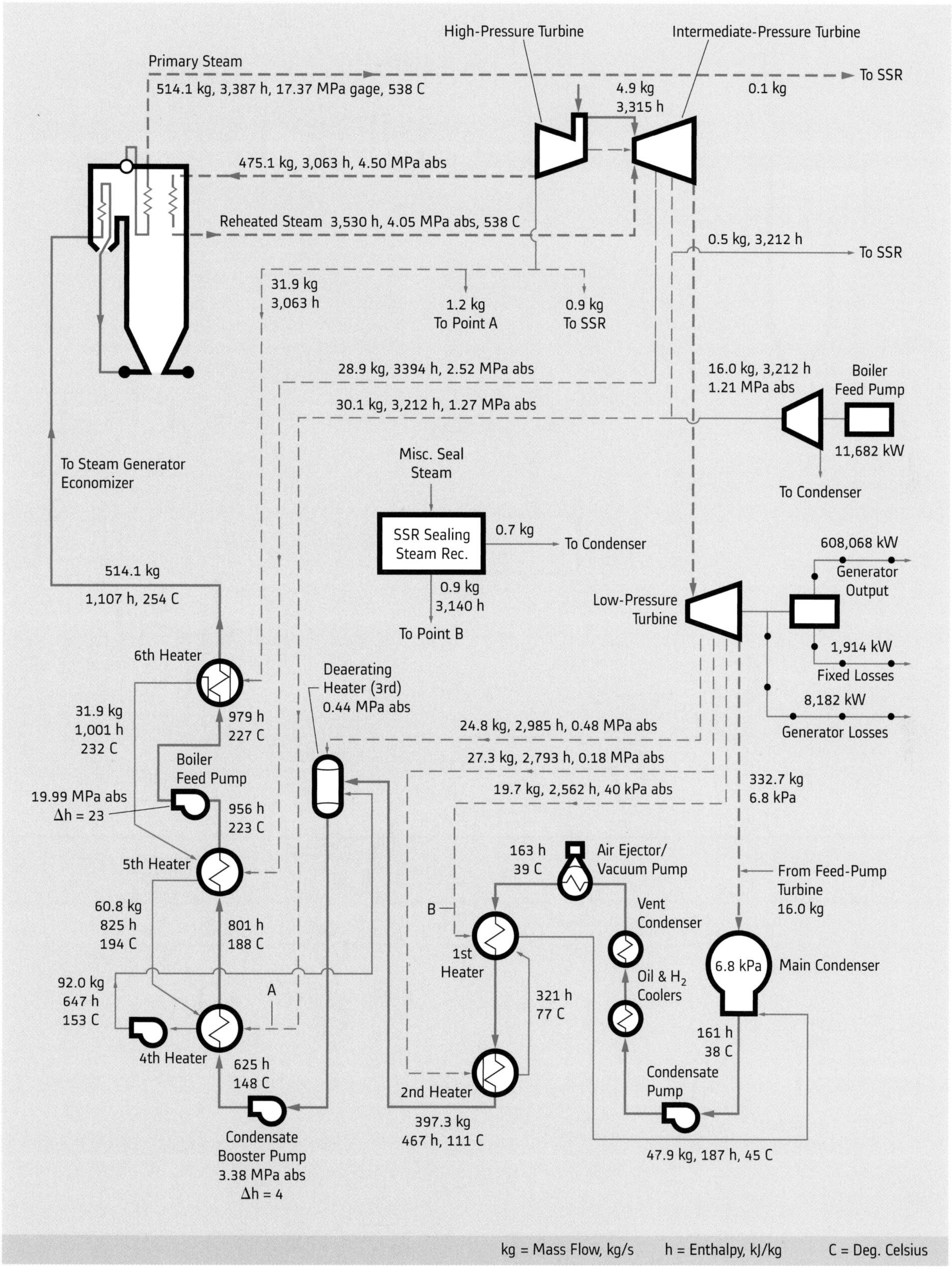

High-Pressure Turbine
Intermediate-Pressure Turbine
Primary Steam
514.1 kg, 3,387 h, 17.37 MPa gage, 538 C
To SSR
4.9 kg
3,315 h
0.1 kg
475.1 kg, 3,063 h, 4.50 MPa abs
Reheated Steam 3,530 h, 4.05 MPa abs, 538 C
0.5 kg, 3,212 h
To SSR
31.9 kg
3,063 h
1.2 kg
To Point A
0.9 kg
To SSR
28.9 kg, 3394 h, 2.52 MPa abs
16.0 kg, 3,212 h
1.21 MPa abs
Boiler
Feed Pump
30.1 kg, 3,212 h, 1.27 MPa abs
11,682 kW
To Condenser
To Steam Generator
Economizer
Misc. Seal
Steam
SSR Sealing
Steam Rec.
0.7 kg
To Condenser
608,068 kW
Generator
Output
514.1 kg
1,107 h, 254 C
0.9 kg
3,140 h
To Point B
Low-Pressure
Turbine
1,914 kW
Fixed Losses
8,182 kW
Generator Losses
6th Heater
Deaerating
Heater (3rd)
0.44 MPa abs
31.9 kg
1,001 h
232 C
979 h
227 C
24.8 kg, 2,985 h, 0.48 MPa abs
Boiler
Feed Pump
27.3 kg, 2,793 h, 0.18 MPa abs
19.99 MPa abs
Δh = 23
956 h
223 C
19.7 kg, 2,562 h, 40 kPa abs
332.7 kg
6.8 kPa
5th Heater
163 h
39 C
Air Ejector/
Vacuum Pump
From Feed-Pump
Turbine
16.0 kg
60.8 kg
825 h
194 C
801 h
188 C
B
Vent
Condenser
1st
Heater
6.8 kPa
Main Condenser
92.0 kg
647 h
153 C
A
Oil & H_2
Coolers
321 h
77 C
4th Heater
625 h
148 C
161 h
38 C
Condensate
Pump
2nd Heater
397.3 kg
467 h, 111 C
Condensate
Booster Pump
3.38 MPa abs
Δh = 4
47.9 kg, 187 h, 45 C

kg = Mass Flow, kg/s h = Enthalpy, kJ/kg C = Deg. Celsius

Figure 1-9 | Reheat regenerative cycle for a 600-MW, subcritical-pressure, fossil-fueled power plant (SI-metric units)

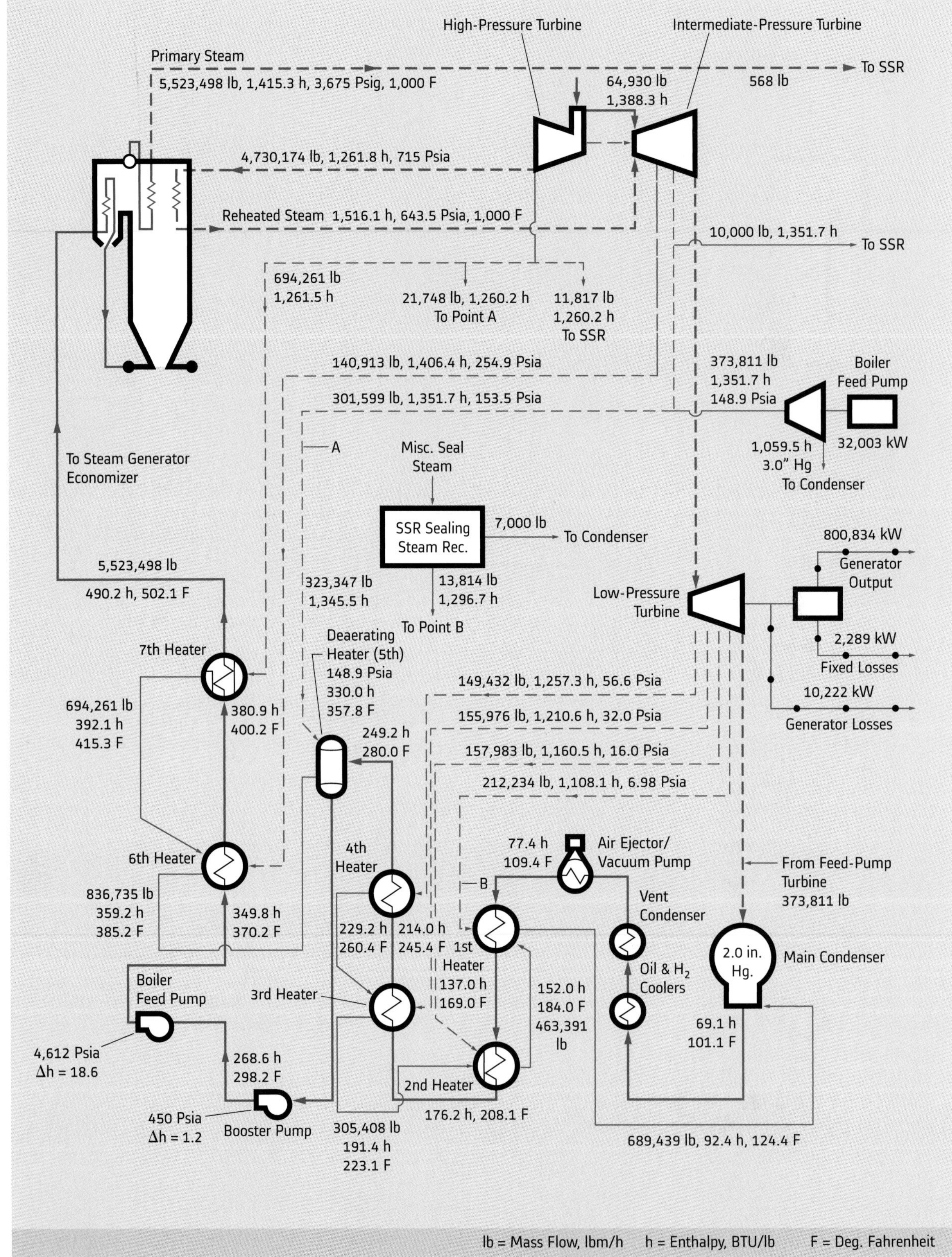

Figure 1-10 | Reheat regenerative cycle for a 800-MW, supercritical pressure, fossil-fueled power plant (U.S. units)

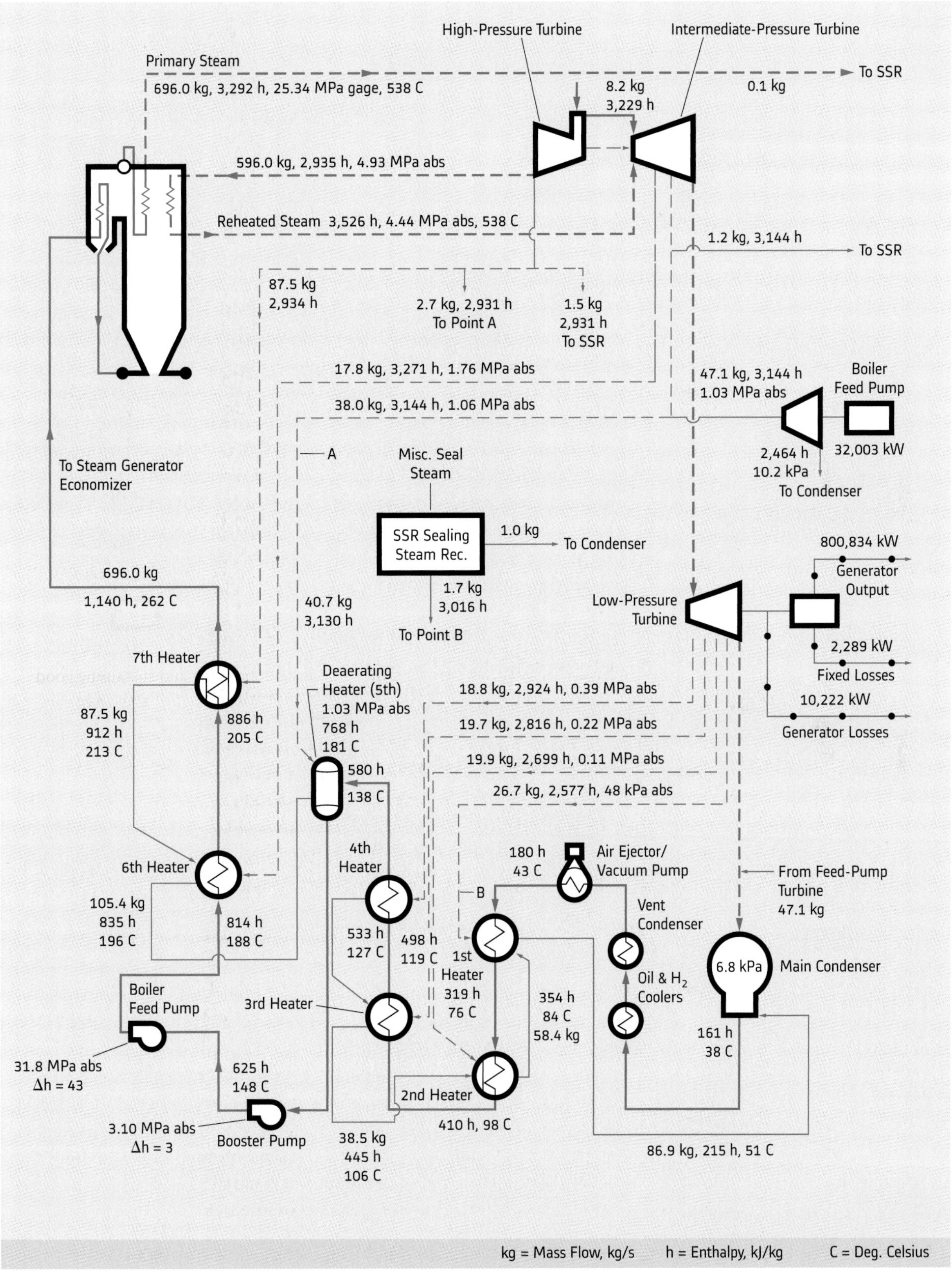

Figure 1-11 | Reheat regenerative cycle for a 800-MW, supercritical pressure, fossil-fueled power plant (SI-metric units)

the regenerative, reheat, supercritical pressure heating processes. With such supercritical pressure plants, cycle efficiencies exceeding 45% (higher heating value basis) have been reached.

COMBINED CYCLE

In combined cycle plants, a Brayton cycle is integrated with a conventional Rankine cycle to recover waste heat. To this end, combined cycle plants use one of a number of possible configurations of combustion turbines, waste heat recovery boilers, and steam turbines. Such combustion turbines are predominantly fired with natural gas but can also be fired with jet fuel, light distillate, or with proper pre-treatment, a wide range of residual and crude oils.

In an open Brayton cycle, a combustion turbine engine is employed in power generation applications. More specifically, the open Brayton cycle consists of the following four processes:

1. A reversible isentropic compression in the inlet air compressor.
2. A constant-pressure fuel combustion.
3. A reversible isentropic expansion in the turbine and exhaust nozzle, which is designed to drive the compressor and the generator.
4. Discharge of the products of combustion.

The discharge of the exhaust products of combustion makes this an "open cycle." The open Brayton cycle is intended to function such that the working fluid temperature is increased as a consequence of the high-temperature capabilities of the combustion turbine, while the steam turbine is employed to reduce the temperature of the heat that is rejected. A penalty is associated with employment of the open Brayton cycle. This penalty comprises the compression work that is required by the air compressor of the combustion turbine. New combined cycle plants generally fall into two categories: a combustion turbine plus an unfired heat recovery steam generator (HRSG), and a combustion turbine plus a supplementary fired HRSG. In the latter, the supplementary firing is designed to occur at atmospheric pressure, and it makes use of the thermal energy and the remaining oxygen that is contained in the exhaust products of combustion to burn additional fuel.

For a combustion turbine plus unfired HRSG (*Fig. 1-12*), all the fuel is subjected to combustion in the turbine, and the HRSG depends entirely on the combustion turbine as the HRSG's heat source. Because the power from the steam turbine is produced without any additional fuel input, and because only a small decrease occurs in the efficiency of the combustion turbine as a result of the increased backpressure of the HRSG, the overall efficiency of the combined cycle plant that employs a combustion turbine plus unfired HRSG is improved over that of the simple (or open) cycle combustion turbine.

The combustion turbine plus supplementary fired HRSG makes use of the oxygen that remains in the exhaust of the combustion turbine through incorporation of a supplemental firing system, which is designed to be located in the connecting duct between the combustion turbine and the HRSG. Depending on the size of the combustion turbine and the temperature limit of the HRSG, it is possible to double

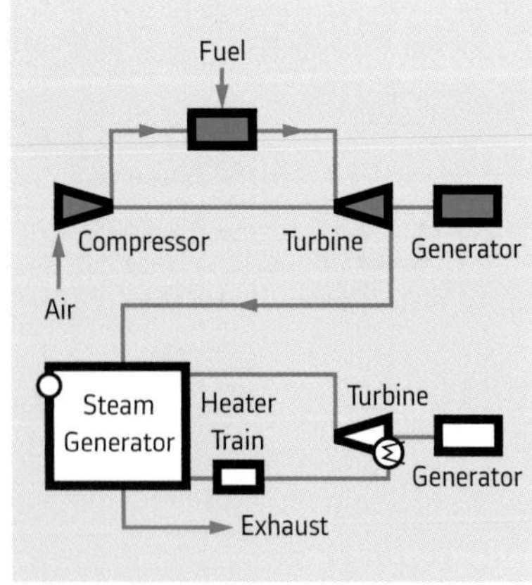

Figure 1-12 | Gas turbine plus unfired heat recovery steam generator (HRSG)

the generation of steam compared to that in a combustion turbine plus unfired HRSG. Because of the higher HRSG temperature, the plant designer is afforded more flexibility in terms of steam turbine design, and the designer can also incorporate reheat into the overall combined cycle (*Fig. 1-13*).

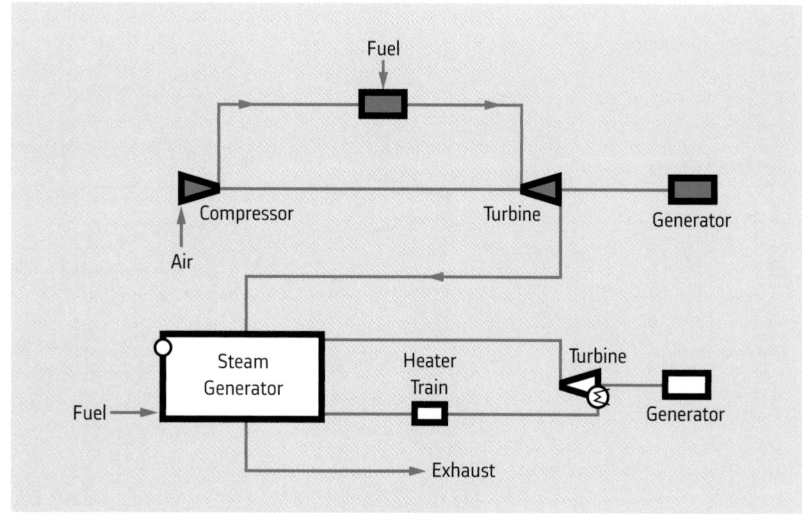

Figure 1-13 | Gas turbine plus furnace fired steam generator

COGENERATION

Cogeneration is the simultaneous production of power (usually electricity) and thermal energy (usually steam or hot water) from a single fuel-consuming process. Cogeneration also is often referred to as "combined heat and power."

Cogeneration plants are most suitable for applications that have coincident electric and thermal loads and that range in size from small industrial and institutional plants to large central stations serving the electric and thermal needs of a municipality or petrochemical installation. Similar electric and thermal load profiles enable cogeneration facilities to operate at a higher annual load factor and higher thermal efficiency than could be obtained by separate plants to handle the power need and the thermal need.

The design of cogeneration facilities differs from that of conventional Rankine cycle plants. The main goal of a Rankine cycle plant is to economically optimize thermal efficiency during the production of electric power, whereas the goal of the cogeneration facility may be to maximize the use of waste heat for heating purposes. The overall efficient use of the heat that is liberated from combustion of the fuel, however, is still greater than what could be achieved with a separate plant for each purpose.

Because of the varying nature of the power needs and the thermal needs of a given facility, the design and configuration of cogeneration plants can vary greatly from site to site. For example, cogeneration plants can use either a topping cycle (electricity is produced first, and the exhausted thermal energy is used thereafter) or a bottoming cycle (electricity is produced through the recovery of waste heat from high-temperature processes). In either case, the prime movers in each such cycle can be conventional boilers, combustion turbines, or reciprocating engines. Moreover, the thermal needs can be met by the turbine exhaust, extraction, or the waste heat that is recovered from the combustion of the fuel. Furthermore, if the amount of energy that is produced by such cycles exceeds the facility's own needs, the excess energy (thermal and/or electric) can be used for other needs.

Figure 1-14 shows a schematic diagram of a basic closed power/process cycle wherein a backpressure turbine is employed. In such a cycle, after

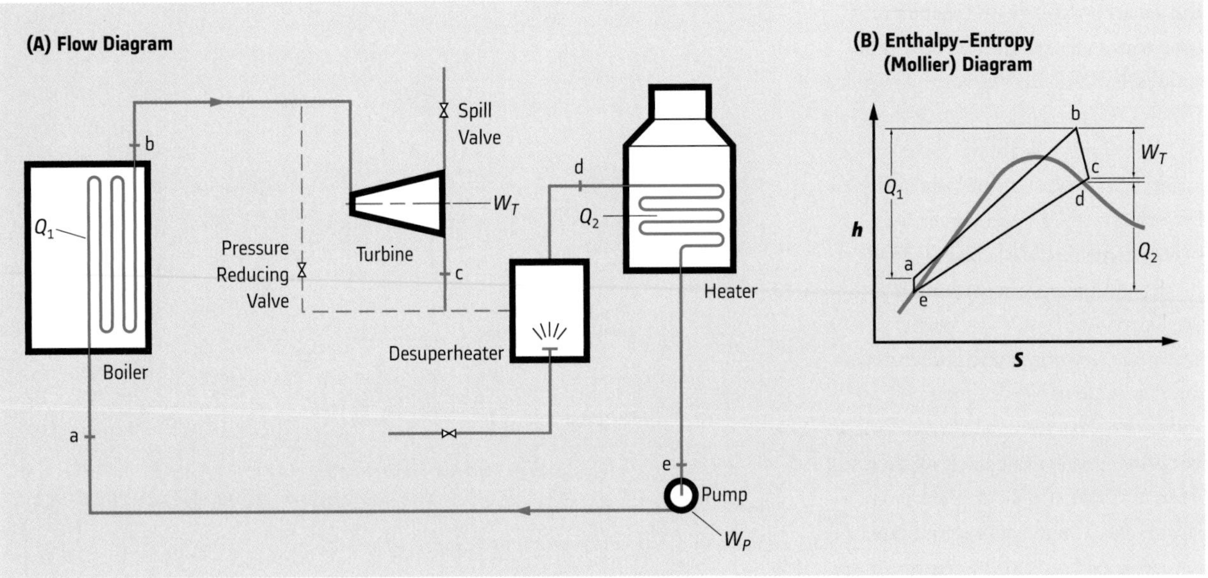

Figure 1-14 | Closed power/process cogenerative cycle using a backpressure turbine

superheated steam has been generated at a suitably high pressure, that steam is admitted to the turbine, where the superheated steam does useful work (W_T). The superheated steam usually emerges from the turbine still in a superheated state (c in *Fig. 1-14*). After being subjected to desuperheating, the saturated steam (d in *Fig. 1-14*) enters the heater, where it is entirely condensed. Because the steam that is required for power generation will not always equal the amount of steam that is required for process work, some means of controlling the exhaust steam pressure must be provided to avoid the creation of pressure variations and, therefore, of variations in the steam saturation temperature. The control method that is employed for this purpose depends on the particular circumstances of the specific application. For example, an ordinary centrifugal governor that is fitted to the backpressure turbine can be designed to control the quantity of available exhaust steam in accordance with the load on the turbine. Should the amount of available exhaust steam be too small, then live steam can be made to pass through a reducing valve into the desuperheater, which is designed to evaporate water to reduce the temperature of the superheated steam. This makes a little more steam at a lower temperature. If there is not enough exhaust steam, additional live steam can be put though the desuperheater to produce the required amount. On the other hand, if the amount of available exhaust steam exceeds the amount required, then the excess amount of exhaust steam may be exhausted to the atmosphere, into an accumulator, or through a spill valve into a feed tank.

Figures 1-15 and *1-16* depict a typical cogeneration system wherein a steam topping cycle is employed. This cogeneration system uses controlled pressure, automatic steam extraction and a controlled backpressure turbine. *Figures 1-15* and *1-16* illustrate the use of three closed feedwater heaters plus a deaerating heater in such a cogeneration system.[17]

DESIGNING A NEW FOSSIL-FUELED POWER PLANT

The specific design of a power plant is intended to be an optimization of the thermodynamic, environmental, regulatory, and economic conditions. Economic conditions include both the initial costs to construct the plant as well as the long-term fixed and variable costs associated with operating the plant, including (but not limited to) such items as fuel, operational and maintenance needs, depreciation, interest, insurance, and taxes.

Many factors must be considered in determining when and where a fossil-fueled power plant will be constructed and what particular design will be used. The need for a new fossil-fueled power plant generally is based on a projection of an increased load demand, which in turn can be attributed to many factors, such as burgeoning populations, new factories, increased use of electronic technological devices, and regulatory impacts. The initial activities in the development of a fossil-fueled power plant design normally focus on addressing both the capacity of the power plant and the date of its projected initial commercial operation. From load demand projections, one can estimate when the existing plants will have insufficient capacity to support the projected demand with adequate reserve margins for acceptable reliability. Further projections can provide the estimated quantity of power that will be needed.

The location at which the fossil-fueled power plant will be constructed is generally determined through a

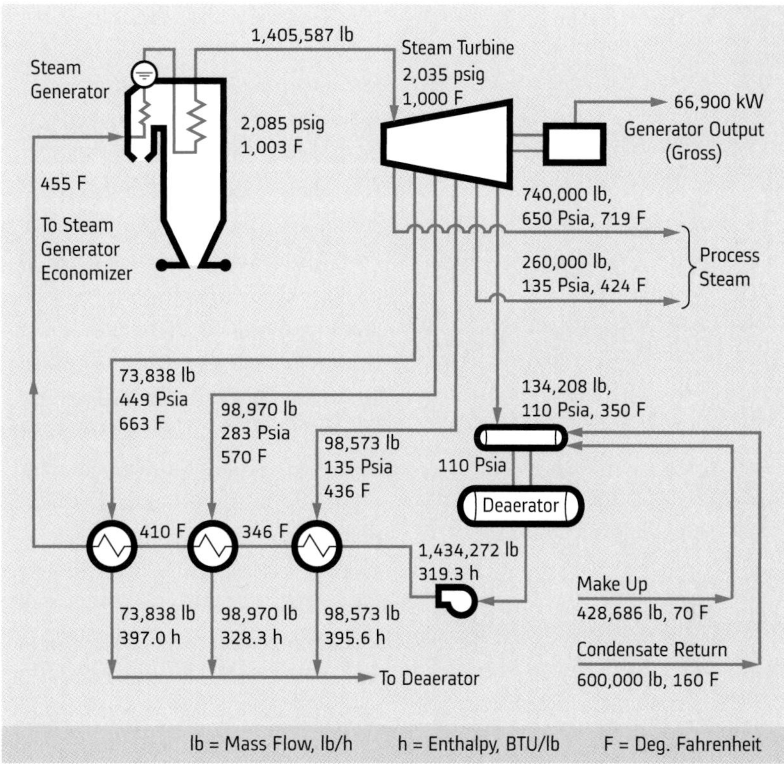

Figure 1-15 | Heat balances of a steam topping cogeneration cycle (U.S. units)

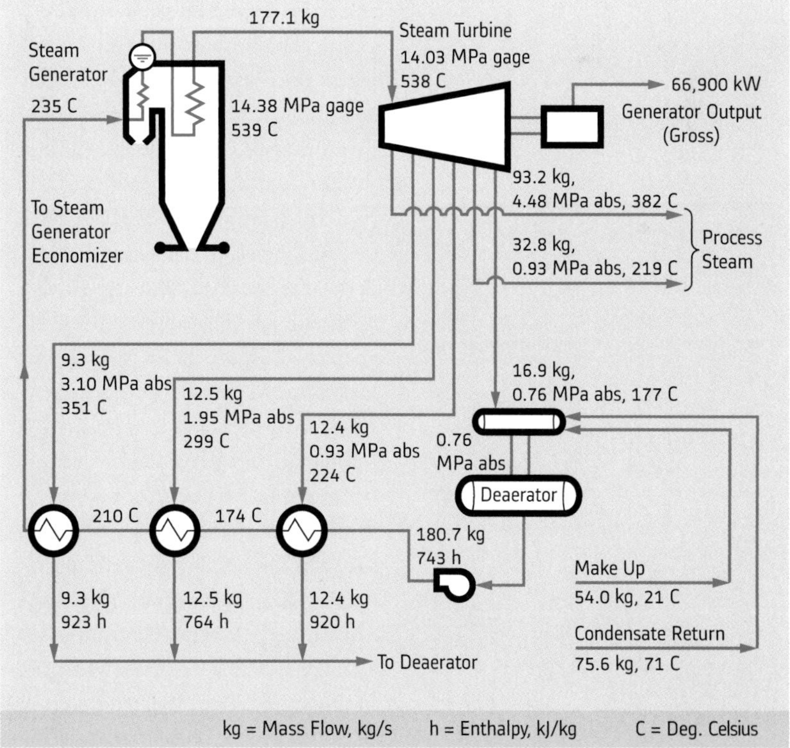

Figure 1-16 | Heat balances of a steam topping cogeneration cycle (SI-metric units)

life-cycle cost analysis for each potential site. Such a life-cycle cost analysis focuses on a number of contributing factors, including (but not limited to) available real estate, proximity and robustness of the closest electrical transmission lines, sources of fuel and cooling water, environmental considerations, and any relevant public opinion. Additional considerations include such matters as availability of municipal services, availability of labor (construction and operation), any relevant zoning regulations, present use of any adjacent properties (i.e., airport), access to the potential site, climate at the potential site, and tax treatment applicable to the potential site. Room for possible growth at the potential site as well as freedom from events such as flood and earthquake are also deemed to be essential.

Life cycle cost analysis considers all of the important factors in selecting a power plant, leading to the lowest cost and environmentally sound choice.

When considered in conjunction with an operating cost analysis, which compares the proposed fossil-fueled power plant with existing power plants, load profiles will indicate in which portion of the dispatch curve and under which scenario the new plant will operate—namely, whether the new facility will be employed as a baseload plant, an intermediate plant, or a peaking plant. Operating scenarios, as the term is used here, are generally defined in terms of how many hours annually the fossil-fueled power plant is expected to operate. To this end, baseload fossil-fueled power plants commonly operate 6,000 or more hours annually, intermediate power plants between 2,000 and 6,000 hours annually, and peaking power plants less than 2,000 hours annually. Note that no clear-cut line of demarcation exists among these three operating scenarios. In this regard, fossil-fueled power plants that have, for instance, been designed for use in accordance with one operating scenario may, in practice, later be required to operate in accordance with another operating scenario that had not been contemplated when the plant was originally designed.

The major factors that determine what cycle should be used—that is, the conventional Rankine cycle, open Brayton cycle, or combined cycle—are generally the operating scenario, fuel availability, and cost. Typically, the open Brayton cycle (i.e., the simple cycle) is used for peaking service, whereas the Rankine cycle or combined cycle are normally selected for intermediate or baseload service. Fuel availability and cost are generally the drivers insofar as selection of the prime mover is concerned. For example, fluidized bed combustors are most commonly considered for use when the fuel being employed is waste coal. Combined cycle plants are most commonly considered for use when natural gas is the lowest-cost fuel. Conventional boilers are most commonly considered for use if coal is the most cost-effective fuel. When comparing fuel costs, consider the following: base price of the fuel; cost of the fuel delivered; cost of fuel handling; cost of labor; cost of plant services, including (but not limited to) auxiliary power loads; and fixed charges associated with operation and maintenance (O&M) of the fuel handling and firing equipment. The type of cycle will drive the selection of the main cycle components, such as the boiler, steam turbine, combustion turbine, and/or HRSG. Each one of these main cycle components needs to be designed to match the operating scenario of the proposed fossil-fueled power plant as well as the fuel to be employed in that plant.

In addition to the main cycle components, the remaining systems for the proposed fossil-fueled power plant are normally selected based on the economic, environmental, and life-cycle cost analyses. For example, the water systems that will provide the heat sink for the thermal energy rejected in the cycle after all useful work has been performed can involve the use of natural water bodies in a once-through arrangement, cooling towers, or air-cooled condensers. In this case, the actual selection is based on consideration of both environmental and economic factors. As discussed previously, an opportunity often exists to increase the thermal efficiency of a particular cycle by increasing the number of stages of feedwater heating. The optimum number of feedwater heaters that should be employed is determined based on balancing the cycle thermal efficiency against the size of the fossil-fueled power plant, the complexity of the power plant, and the cost of power production from the plant. A decision that must be made is whether to use a steam turbine rather than electric motor drives for the rotating equipment in the balance of the plant. Steam turbine drives offer opportunities for improving heat rate and provide reliability of operation as well as guaranteed start-up in the event of a loss of electrical distribution. On the other hand, electric motor drives offer simplicity and generally are lower in cost. Other areas that need to be considered include water and wastewater treatment, nature of the fuel and ash handling, and plant/instrument air systems. Therefore, to summarize, many, many variables need to be considered, and trade-offs must always be made.

Great advancements have been made in emission control systems, and their use enables efficient and environmentally benign generation of electric power. Federal, state, and local regulations have established emissions levels for a number of combustion product constituents. These regulations determine the extent of as well as the configuration of the emission control systems that are required to limit the amount of these emissions from fossil-fueled power plants. To this end, pre-combustion, combustion, as well as post-combustion emission control systems have been developed. The design of the fossil-fueled power plant will determine the appropriate mix of technology that should be used to achieve minimal emissions for all load levels at which the proposed power plant is expected to operate.

Another important consideration is the electrical transmission system. Appropriate transformers and switch gear are required to deliver the power generated by the plant to the grid while simultaneously distributing power within the plant for driving the electric motors, for lighting purposes, and for the control and communication systems. The design of the electrical interconnect between the power plant and the electrical transmission system requires close coordination with the grid operator to establish the requirements for connection voltage, breaker configuration, and relay protection. Electrical distribution from the fossil-fueled power plant is designed to provide reliability through redundant power feeds and backup power sources in the event of a failure.

Emissions control systems have made substantial progress since the installation of the first SO_2 scrubber system in the late '60s, leading to a cleaner environment.

Tying together the intricate components and systems associated with operation of a fossil-fueled power plant is the control system. The control system is normally interconnected with the power plant operations through field monitoring instrumentation and final control devices. The control system is designed to provide indications, alarms, and an automatic response to certain critical operating conditions. In addition, the control systems are designed to provide trending and reporting capabilities, to assess plant and equipment performance, and to enable the operator to take manual control of the operation of the plant should this become necessary. Larger fossil-fueled power plants have typically used distributed control systems that are integrally connected with a combination of smaller (programmable logic controller) control systems for discrete systems within the power plant, such as water/wastewater treatment and emission control systems. Smaller fossil-fueled power plants that are designed as peaking stations may even be designed to allow remote operation with no dedicated operating staff at the plant site. As with the electrical distribution system, the control system of the fossil-fueled power plant embodies sufficient levels of redundancy to allow continuous operation of the power plant under the most stringent of failure scenarios.

The design for industrial and commercial fossil-fueled power plants is very similar to what has been described above for such power plants that are operated as central stations. The major difference between such plants that are operated as central stations and industrial and commercial plants is that the industrial and commercial plants are typically designed for electrical and thermal loads that may differ between daytime and nighttime operation, between weekday and weekend/holiday operation, and between seasons. To address marked swings in the demand to which industrial and commercial fossil-fueled power plants can be subjected, first consider making alterations in production to smooth the peaks in generation before moving on to implement changes in sizing and/or selection of equipment. To this end, by referencing electric and thermal load curves, it is possible to determine what changes, if any, should be implemented in the size of the boiler, turbines, and auxiliaries that are normally employed in industrial and commercial fossil-fueled power plants. Other issues that come into play commonly involve consideration of reliability of service (in terms of life cycle, safety, or high-cost production environments) as well as regulatory requirements.

RETROFITTING AN EXISTING FOSSIL-FUELED POWER PLANT

An existing, operational fossil-fueled power plant can be a most valued asset for the owner. The owner's most prized possessions, generally speaking, are the power plant's valid operating permits. Any improvements to such an existing power plant that do not cause the operation to exceed the limits of the existing, valid operating permits will be a benefit to the present infrastructure of the plant. The most important aspect to consider in evaluating the economic benefit of a retrofit is the expected operating life of the existing power plant after the retrofit has been implemented.

The longer the remaining life of the power plant after the retrofit, the longer the potential revenue streams from the retrofitted plant can be used to offset the initial capital cost of that retrofit.

Many objectives may serve as drivers for retrofitting of an existing fossil-fueled power plant. These include improved environmental performance, improved reliability and efficiency, and increased capacity. Replacing aged equipment can improve the overall reliability of the existing power plant. Through implementation of technological improvements, it has been possible to realize improved efficiencies as well as increased generating capacities from the steam and combustion turbines that are associated with existing fossil-fueled power plants. Likewise, through the use of improved materials, it has been possible to achieve increased heat transfer as well as longer operating lives for the components of existing power plants. Because so many improvements can be made to these plants, it is not feasible to list them all here. The same degree of care should be taken, however, when evaluating the feasibility of a retrofit as when determining the feasibility of the design for a new fossil-fueled power plant.

Repowering is a unique type of retrofit for an existing fossil-fueled power plant. Moreover, repowering enjoys the benefit of employing the existing infrastructure and the permitted site. An existing power plant that employs a Rankine cycle can be repowered in a variety of ways. Such variations may include the following:

1. Installing a combustion turbine plus HRSG, and delivering the steam from the HRSG to the existing steam turbine or an upgraded steam turbine.
2. Installing a combustion turbine, and delivering the exhaust from the combustion turbine to the existing boiler, where such exhaust can be used as combustion air. (Note that typical combustion turbines operate with 250–400% excess air and, thus, can support combustion within a conventional boiler by virtue of their functioning as forced draft fans [see *Figure 1-13*].)
3. Installing a combined cycle unit, and using the existing power plant infrastructure, including the cooling water system, which can support a much higher capacity because of the increased efficiency of the combined cycle over that of the existing Rankine cycle.
4. Maintaining the existing steam turbine, but replacing the existing boiler with one boiler having a different design and capable of being fired with a different fuel.

The design considerations that are available for retrofitting of an existing fossil-fueled power plant provide great flexibility in taking advantage of the present infrastructure and valid operating permits. This is provided, of course, that the economic conditions are sufficient to support the investment required to accomplish the proposed retrofit.

Retrofits often lead to improved environmental performance and greater efficiency, thus providing for a cleaner environment and saving fuel resources.

DOCUMENTATION

Fossil-fueled power plant documentation, as the term is used here, is a series of documents that are used to procure the necessary equipment and, thereafter, to construct, operate, and maintain the power plant. Of this documentation, the governing document is the design criteria document. This document identifies the basis on which all the engineering and design for the power plant are performed, including (but not limited to) all the applicable code and regulatory requirements. Furthermore, all the engineering drawings are derived from the design criteria document. Such engineering drawings provide a clear insight regarding what the fossil-fueled power plant should look like when it has been constructed, and they enable a quality oversight of the construction efforts performed during building of the plant. Procurement specifications for equipment are also developed during the course of the designing of the power plant to allow competitive bidding by multiple vendors and to ensure compliance with all the design criteria requirements that have been established. Such procurement specifications are intended to clearly describe all the requirements that the equipment must meet and, in addition, may specify the construction materials as well as other specific requirements. At other times, particularly when an engineered system is being purchased for the fossil-fueled power plant, a performance specification is written with only such descriptions or limitations that may be applicable to such an engineered system as are necessary to provide the desired quality of materials and workmanship. Within this framework, the original equipment manufacturer is provided as much freedom as possible to deliver an engineered system that will best fulfill the functional requirements. Because of the specialized experience of the original equipment manufacturer, that organization is frequently best able to determine the desired, detailed design of that particular engineered system given all the factors involved with performing economic analyses of the available alternates. Service specifications, such as construction, commissioning, and certification testing, commonly are also prepared in accordance with the design criteria document. Note here that it is important to ensure the drawings and specifications correlate with one another to describe the work needed to construct the fossil-fueled power plant without any gaps or overlap. Close scrutiny is required of the interfaces between the power plant equipment and systems as well as between the various contractors working on the plant to ensure effective installation during construction of the equipment and systems by the various contractors involved.

Generally, a separate set of documents will be prepared for governing the long-term O&M of the fossil-fueled power plant. Certain engineering drawings assist the power plant operators in understanding how the plant is designed to work under both normal and off-normal conditions. Other drawings, which may be provided by the equipment and/or system vendors, represent how the equipment and/or systems are designed to operate. Normally, maintenance documentation is prepared that includes recommendations by the original equipment manufacturer; such recommendations are frequently augmented through programs established by the power plant operator.

ECONOMICS

The costs associated with acquisition as well as with O&M of equipment for a fossil-fueled power plant are a basic concern of both the design engineer and the power plant owner. To this end, the initial cost of such equipment must be balanced against the cost associated with operating such equipment over the lifetime of the power plant. Before discussing how such comparisons are made, it is necessary to consider the two general categories of power plant costs.

Much of the money spent by the owner of a fossil-fueled power plant is for goods and services that are intended to be consumed within a relatively short time after their acquisition. This category of costs includes outlays for wages and salaries, operating and maintenance supplies, and fuel. Such costs are most commonly termed *expenses*, and the payments for these costs are normally made from the revenue generated by the operation of the power plant.

The other category of costs for the owner of the power plant are items with a useful life that continues for an extended period of time and that normally produce revenue in the future. The money spent to construct a power plant is a typical example of such an expenditure, and such costs are generally termed *capital investments*. Expenditures of this nature are not ordinarily paid directly from the revenue that is generated from operation of the power plant. The basic reason is that the current revenue being generated from operation of the power plant would most often be insufficient to cover large capital expenditures. In addition, the equipment for the power plant is expected to provide service well into the future.

Critical to the decision making and performance monitoring that are associated with owning a fossil-fueled power plant is a life-cycle cost analysis. Initial capital costs as well as long-term operating, maintenance, and replacement costs need to be balanced against the predicted revenue streams that will be generated by the power plant. By the application of economic discount factors, the present worth of the asset (i.e., the fossil-fueled power plant) can be established. This methodology is most often termed *discounted cash flow analysis*. To account for the time value of money, the value of the future revenue streams from and the costs for the power plant need to be discounted insofar as time is concerned. Initial capital costs include such items as licensing, permitting, engineering, design, procurement, construction, legal, owner's oversight, and interest during construction on the funding raised to build the plant. On the other hand, the long-term operating, maintenance, and replacement costs include such items as fuel, plant labor, third-party services, and maintenance activities. Note here that cash flow analysis can account for any number of variables, including inflation, taxes, interest rates, construction times, risk, maintenance outages, and so on. A positive net present value indicates the construction and operation of the asset will provide a net benefit to the owner based on the assumptions that have been made. Variations on the assumptions that have a major effect on the present worth that is determined for an asset include the financing method, discount factor, timing and the magnitude of the projected revenue/cost streams, and the projected operating life for the power plant. Unfortunately, it is not always possible to know every detail of the factors used in these assumptions.

Proper economic analysis provides information needed to make decisions to provide electric power or steam at the lowest cost to the consumer.

As an alternative to using the discounted cash flow analysis, it is possible to develop an estimate for the cost of electricity, or the bus bar cost. To this end, bus bar costs are generally considered to consist of the sum of the fixed costs and the variable costs, divided by the projected power generation from the plant for a given period of time (usually in terms of mills/kWh), which by virtue of its use enables all power plant units, regardless of their capacity, to be put on an equal basis. Initial capital costs are translated into fixed costs by applying an appropriate capital charge rate to the initial capital costs. Such a capital charge rate combines many of the unknown future rates (e.g., inflation, interest rates, taxes, and risks) into one figure. Other items that fall under the category of fixed charges include property insurance and allocations for replacement of equipment. In general, the fixed costs for a fossil-fueled power plant bear no relation to the amount of power that plant is projected to generate in a given period of time. Variable costs include fuel, income taxes, consumables, and the salaries and benefits for the plant operations and maintenance staff. By considering such variable costs, the levels of operation of the power plant that are economically feasible can be determined. By considering the combination of variable costs, fixed costs, and the required rate of return, it can be determined whether long-term operation of the power plant will be economical. From time to time, owners of fossil-fueled power plants may need to relax the required rate of return to ensure that operating the plant remains feasible under different possible load scenarios.

In addition to the tangible variables discussed above, which make up the core of the economic analysis, other significant aspects of the design for a fossil-fueled power plant have a powerful effect on the overall economics associated with the construction, operation, and maintenance of that plant. These include reliability of the main cycle components and of the fuel supply, regulatory obligations (current and future), and societal trends, which may affect the acceptance by the public of the proposed fossil-fueled power plant.

FIXED CHARGES

Fixed charges are normally considered to be those costs associated with the fossil-fueled power plant that are incurred each year during the lifetime of the plant. These costs are independent of how much energy is produced by the plant each year. Fixed charges usually include all the costs that are proportional to the capital investment in the power plant; such fixed costs include depreciation, required return on the capital investment, property insurance, federal income taxes, and state and local taxes.

The fixed charge rate is the proportionality constant that converts the initial capital cost of the power plant to the annual fixed charges. Some components of the fixed charge rate, such as depreciation, are bookkeeping expenses, which do not represent an outflow of cash during the operation period. Other components of the fixed charge rate, such as property taxes, insurance, and ad valorem taxes, represent annual outlays of cash, which normally are in direct proportion to part or all the initial capital investment. The required return on such a capital investment and the income taxes associated with this required return generally comprise a major part of the annual fixed charges. Also commonly included in the fixed charge rate is an interim replacement allowance, which provides for any intermittent replacement of equipment that might be required before the end of the scheduled life of the plant. Normally *not* included in the annual fixed charge rate are the relatively constant fixed costs, such as liability insurance or staffing expenses, which bear no direct relation to the plant's capital investment and are somewhat independent of the amount of power that the plant produces. (Such expenses are instead commonly included in the category of O&M expenses.)

As indicated previously, the proportionality constant that converts the initial capital cost of the power plant to the annual fixed charges is the fixed charge rate. Therefore, the fixed charges applicable to the fossil-fueled power plant can be expressed in the following manner:

$$C = \frac{IC \times FCR}{100}$$

Equation 1-8

where

C = fixed charges, \$/year
IC = initial capital cost, \$
FCR = annual fixed charge rate, %

or

$$c = \frac{(IC \times 1{,}000 \times FCR)/100}{G} = \frac{IC \times FCR \times 10}{G}$$

Equation 1-9

where

c = fixed charges, mills/kWh
G = energy generation, kWh/year

By adding the fixed charges to the fixed and variable operation costs (all in mills/kWh), a cost of electricity for the fossil-fueled power plant can be calculated. This cost of electricity can be compared to the prevailing rates or the cost from other power plants to indicate the economic performance of the proposed power plant. By using a constant fixed charge rate, this approach does not yield the year-by-year forecast of costs that would be given with a more detailed approach. Nevertheless, such annual breakdowns of the individual costs are not usually required for making evaluations. A conceptual approach that can be employed for developing a fixed charge rate is illustrated in *Table 1-1*.

FUEL COSTS

For most economic evaluations, the conversion of fuel costs on an as-received basis at the fossil-fueled

TABLE 1-1 | TYPICAL FIXED CHARGE RATE ESTIMATES, UTILITY FINANCING*

Component	Percentage
Interest	8–10
Return on equity	10–12
Depreciation	2.5–3.3
Interim replacements	0.2–0.4
Property insurance	0.2–0.5
Federal income tax	2–3
State and local taxes	2–3
Inflation	2–4
Total	17.9–25.3

*50/50 debt/equity, straight line depreciation.

power plant to the fuel costs per kilowatt-hour of power produced by the plant is generally sufficient. The equation that is normally employed is the following:

$$F = \frac{FC \times NPHR}{10{,}000}$$

Equation 1-10

where

F = the operating fuel cost in cents/kWh

FC = the purchased fuel cost in \$/million BTU

NPHR = the net plant heat rate in BTU/kWh

Thus, if the purchased fuel costs for a coal-fired power plant are \$1.80/million BTU and the net plant heat rate is 9,300 BTU/kWh, then the operating fuel cost, F, for such a power plant would be 1.7 cents/kWh.

ECONOMIES OF SCALE

Many of the components that make up the total costs for a fossil-fueled power plant are relatively independent of plant size or have been found to increase slowly as the size of the power plant increases. Examples of this might include a guard shack at the entrance to the power plant or a control room. These items might have the same cost for a 300-MW power plant as they would for a 600-MW plant. Likewise, as the size of the equipment used in the power plant increases, the surface to volume ratio of such equipment normally decreases. As such, this means it generally takes less material per unit of volume to fabricate a large piece of equipment than it does to fabricate a smaller piece.

When the total power plant costs increase at a slower rate, percentage-wise, than the rate at which the designed output increases, then economies of scale are possible. Experience in the construction of fossil-fueled power plants indicates that economies of scale can be realized in terms of the steam generating plant, the steam turbine generator set, the condenser, the switchgear, and consequently, in total costs.

This type of cost behavior is often represented by some form of power relationship, in which the power relationship is less than unity and, more specifically, usually between 0.7 and 0.9. If this power relationship is denoted by k, then this type of cost behavior can be expressed as follows:

$$\frac{IC_1}{IC_2} = \left(\frac{S_1}{S_2}\right)^k$$

Equation 1-11

where

IC_1 = the capital cost of a fossil-fueled power plant that is of size 1

IC_2 = the capital cost of a fossil-fueled power plant that is of size 2

S_1 = the size of fossil-fueled power plant 1

S_2 = the size of fossil-fueled power plant 2

For example, if the cost of a 300-MW fossil-fueled power generating unit is expected to be \$2,000/kWh (\$600 million), then the total cost for a 500-MW fossil-fueled power generating unit will, when $k = 0.8$, be

$$\left(\frac{500\text{ MW}}{300\text{ MW}}\right)^{0.8} \times \$2{,}000/\text{kWh} \times 300{,}000\text{ kWh} = \$903{,}000{,}000$$

Based on the above calculation, the cost per kilowatt-hour of the larger fossil-fueled power plant is now $1,806/kWh. As such, economies of scale can be an important factor in selecting the size of a power plant for a given application. Of course, this is not the only factor that needs to be considered. Other factors include financing requirements, environmental impacts, site considerations (e.g., amount of space available for construction), electrical grid requirements, proposed mode of operation, and any applicable regulations.

PRESENT WORTH AND LEVELIZED COSTS

Present worth and levelized costs are often employed in discussions relating to planning, evaluation, and engineering economics in general. The concept of present worth costs is frequently explained through the following statement: "A dollar today is worth more than a dollar tomorrow." This sounds reasonable, but it is important to understand the basis for the statement. First, this statement has nothing to do with inflation or escalation of costs. Rather, it simply means that a dollar received today can be invested and, by "tomorrow," should be equal to a dollar plus interest.

The concept of present worth, or present value, is intended to be a corollary. To this end, the present worth of some future expense (or revenue) is intended to comprise the amount that one would need to have to eventually equal that future expense (or revenue). The total amount of present worth costs are simply a way of combining the payments that are made at different times to account for the value of the interest that may be applicable. All large fossil-fueled power plant payments are deemed to fall into this category of present worth costs. Commonly, present worth costs are calculated simply by reversing the process employed for calculating compound interest. Thus, in Equation 1-12 below, C_0 represents the present worth of some cost, C_1, that occurs at a time, t, in the future:

$$C_0 = \frac{C_1}{(1+r)^t}$$

Equation 1-12

where

r = the interest rate or the discount rate

The expression $\frac{1}{(1+r)^t}$ is most often termed the *discount factor*, or the *present worth factor*. As such, the present worth for a payment of $100,000 that is to be made 3 years later, assuming a discount rate of 9% per year, would be calculated as follows:

$$\$100{,}000 \times \frac{1}{(1.09)^3} = \$77{,}200$$

Equation 1-13

In other words, a payment of $77,200 that is made now is equivalent to a payment of $100,000 that is made 3 years later, assuming that the $77,200 would be capable of being invested to generate a rate of return of 9% per year.

The total present worth costs is equivalent to the sum of all the costs associated with a fossil-fueled power plant project that have been properly discounted to a common point in time. As such, the total present worth costs can be used to compare two different possible implementations of the power plant project, each of which involve different cost expenditures at different points in time.

A concept closely related to total present worth costs is that of levelized costs. The concept of levelized costs is an averaging process that uses levelizing, wherein more weight is given to costs that occur early in the life of the power plant. To obtain levelized costs, it is only necessary to divide the total present worth of the payments that will be required by the sum of the total present worth costs. For instance, levelized total costs (LC) can be expressed as follows:

$$LC = \frac{\Sigma \frac{C_i}{(1+r)^t}}{\Sigma \frac{1}{(1+r)^t}}$$

Equation 1-14

The levelized cost that results from Equation 1-14 is a constant, annual value designed to be equivalent to (i.e., have the same total present worth costs as) that of the non-uniform series of actual annual costs for the fossil-fueled power plant project. Thus, if the non-uniform annual expenses for the power plant were assumed to be $157 million, $165 million, $167 million, $163 million, and $170 million, respectively, over the first 5 years of operation, then the total present worth costs and the levelized costs, using a 9% per year discount rate, would be as shown in *Table 1-2*.

Note here that the discount rate designed to be used in such equations is usually equivalent to the after-tax return that is desired from the investment in the fossil-fueled power plant project. This discount rate generally is the minimum return that any plant project must provide for it to be deemed acceptable from a financial standpoint. Also note, however, that different discount rates can be

TABLE 1-2 | LEVELIZED COSTS AND PRESENT-WORTH COSTS OF A NEW GENERATING UNIT

Year	Present-Worth Factor	Expenses 10^6\$	Present-Worth Expenses, 10^6\$
1	0.917	157	143.9
2	0.842	165	138.9
3	0.772	167	128.9
4	0.708	163	115.4
5	0.650	170	110.5
Totals	3.889		637.6

$$\text{Levelized Expenses} = \frac{\$637.6 \times 10^6}{3.889} = \$164 \times 10^6 / \text{yr}$$

employed in different situations. To this end, interest rates, risks, inflation, and other factors are obviously capable of influencing the discount rate that is ultimately selected.

ECONOMIC ANALYSES

Most economic analyses involve comparisons between different power plant designs, alternative components, or various modes of operation. To perform a consistent evaluation, everything that affects the owner's cost of constructing, operating, and maintaining the fossil-fueled power plant must be taken into account. Usually, this requires a study to determine which of the various alternatives available for implementation would have the lowest combination of capital costs (or fixed charges), fuel costs, and O&M costs.

This discussion involves the evaluation of two different fossil-fueled power plants in their entirety, but it could equally well apply to the evaluation of steam supply systems, alternative pump designs, or operating cycles. Most such evaluations normally can be classified into one of two categories. The first is commonly termed the *revenue requirements method*, which is designed to compare the generating costs (or revenue requirements) of the different alternatives on a cents/kWh basis. An equivalent revenue requirements comparison, however, can also be made by contrasting the total present worth of all the costs for the power plant (i.e., the present worth of the fixed charges on the capital investment plus the present worth of the fuel and the O&M costs). Note here that a comparison of total present worth costs, instead of a comparison of cents/kWh, is only deemed to be valid when each alternative is designed to be capable of producing the same amount of power.

The revenue requirements method, therefore, requires that all the capital costs first be converted to annual fixed charges, and then that all such annual fixed charges be combined with the annual revenue requirements for fuel as well as O&M of the power plant. Then, it is possible to calculate either the total present worth revenue requirements for each of the alternatives or the levelized annual revenue requirements. The alternative with the lowest revenue requirements is the preferred choice based on this evaluation.

The second method of performing an economic evaluation of the fossil-fueled power plant is termed the *capitalized cost method*. In accordance with the revenue requirements approach, the capital costs are first converted to annual costs by means of the fixed charge rate. In the revenue requirements approach, these annual costs can then be combined with the fuel as well as the O&M costs for the power plant, because these costs are already on an annual basis. In the capitalized cost method, however, just the opposite is done. Annual costs, such as those for fuel and for O&M, for the fossil power plant are divided by the fixed charge rate (i.e., are capitalized) so that the result can be combined with the capital costs for the power plant. The capitalized cost method provides a quick way of comparing the difference in operating costs with the difference in capital costs for the various alternatives.

OTHER CONSIDERATIONS

Intensive economic and cost analyses of the type described in the preceding section are very important in selecting the size, type, and equipment for power and steam generation. Other important variables, however, can influence the eventual economics of a given fossil-fueled power plant. The engineer performing the evaluation should also take into account the following:

1. Reliability of the many critical components directly associated with the power generating process employed.
2. Reliability of the fuel supply of a specific type and heating value that will be used during the lifetime of the power plant.
3. Regulatory obligations, present and/or future, that the power plant will need to observe during its operation or in the event of the equipment failure that may have an actual or alleged effect on the health or safety of the public.
4. Compatibility with the future regulatory requirements, which need to be anticipated during the siting and equipment selection process.
5. Compatibility with applicable future social and political requirements.

Thus, in addition to the effects of inflation (i.e., the possible escalation and changes in interest rates) presented earlier, large but uncertain capital cost increases must be anticipated in the construction of all fossil-fueled power producing plants because of the possible impact of future federal and state regulations. Should they be enacted, laws regarding clean air, clean water, conservation, resource recovery, public safety, public health, aesthetics (i.e., the power plant's visual impact), and product liability may affect the decision making process even more profoundly than the purely economic and equipment availability considerations.

ANTHONY MUNISTERI
CARL BOZZUTO

SUMMARIZING

The remaining chapters in this book go on to describe the various major components of the power plant in more detail, as well as provide information on the controls, materials, water chemistry, operations, construction, maintenance, retrofit, and testing of fossil-fired power plants. The principal goal of these plants is to provide steam and electric power at the lowest cost to the consumer commensurate with the cleanest possible operation.

Chapter 2 discusses the combustion processes and the means to oxidize the fuel efficiently while reducing unwanted emissions from the process. The importance of excess air and mixing in the combustion process is described to emphasize the types of issues the designer has to consider in the selection of fuel burning equipment.

Chapter 3 covers the boilers. These large-scale devices provide the envelope around the combustion process so that the heat that is liberated can be transformed into the high temperature and pressure steam needed to operate the prime mover in the generation of electricity. Advances in steam conditions continue. While the majority of the plants in operation today are at steam conditions of either 2,400 psig/1,005°F/1,005°F (16.5 MPa/540°C/540°C) or 3,500 psig/1,050°F/1,050°F (24.1 MPa/565°C/565°C), new units are going into operation with steam conditions as high as 4,000 psig/1100°F/1,150°F (27.6 MPa/600°C/620°C). Further development and testing is being carried out to reach temperatures of 1,300°F (700°C) and even 1,400°F (760°C) with commensurate pressure increases. These higher temperatures and pressures improve the overall efficiency of the conversion of the fuel's chemical energy into electric power. This increased efficiency translates into less fuel being used and lower emissions being produced for the same amount of electricity or, basically, cleaner power generation. This is one way of providing clean combustion technologies.

Chapter 4 is about steam turbines and generators. It would do no good to produce high temperature and pressure steam if the steam turbine was not able to utilize that steam without failure. The steam turbine and the boiler have to work together in the production and utilization of higher temperature and pressure steam. Not withstanding that requirement, the steam turbine and the generator set can enhance the overall efficiency of the system by converting the steam more efficiently into electricity. Advanced aerodynamic shapes for the turbine blades along with optimum designs of last stage blades provide the platform for increasing the output and thus the efficiency from the same amount of steam at the same steam conditions. Again, this improvement in efficiency translates into more electricity for less emissions and cleaner power.

Chapter 5 describes the vast array of equipment that reduces or minimizes emissions from fossil-fired power plants. This equipment provides the major contribution to clean combustion technologies. To the extent that these processes can be made more efficient in reducing emissions, more power can be generated more cost effectively. Not only are conventional substances covered, but mercury and CO_2 capture are discussed as well. While efficiency is the least cost means of reducing CO_2 emissions, this approach may not be sufficient to reach the levels of reduction that may be necessary for the future. CO_2 capture processes are being developed in order to address this issue.

Chapter 6 goes on to address the principal auxiliary equipment. In order to continuously burn fuel, the fuel must be fed to the system and the ash must be removed from the system. The water in the system must remain in balance. The appropriate amount of air must be introduced and the product gases must be exhausted. These steps all require auxiliary equipment. As these pieces of equipment all require energy to operate, design for performance and efficiency is a key to clean combustion technology.

Chapter 7 covers the controls for a modern plant. The operation and control of such large pieces of equipment involves special considerations in order to achieve the desired levels of efficiency, emissions, reliability, load following, and safety for the clean production of electric power.

Chapter 8 describes some of the materials that are used in large power plants operating at high temperatures and pressures. Suffice it to say that these plants have to be built out of something that is available at reasonable cost and still capable of withstanding years of operation under demanding conditions. As steam conditions are increased to improve efficiency and reduce emissions, improved materials will need to be demonstrated.

Chapter 9 provides some insights into the needs of the water chemistry for these plants. Water chemistry is important for both the boiler and the steam turbine, as well as for some of the auxiliary equipment. Poor maintenance of the water chemistry is still one of the leading causes of outages for boilers. Good maintenance of water chemistry reduces forced outages, which reduces the number of startups and shut downs. This, in turn, reduces the amount of fuel that is wasted and the emissions associated with that fuel use.

Chapter 10 describes some of the operating considerations involved in large fossil-fired power plants. These plants have to be able to start up and shut down safely as well as operate at peak performance during periods of high load demand. Operating at peak performance maximizes efficiency, which reduces the level of emissions per unit of output.

Chapter 11 describes the construction and maintenance practices needed to build an efficient plant and maintain such a plant over decades of operation. Proper maintenance allows the plant to operate at an effective performance level, which reduces overall emissions, leading to cleaner power generation.

Chapter 12 discusses retrofit applications. Technology does not stand still. As advances are made, retrofit possibilities emerge. These retrofits may be added on to existing equipment to reduce emissions or substituted for older equipment to improve efficiency, which lowers overall emissions as well.

Chapter 13 provides some of the test procedures used on such large equipment. It would be difficult to know if a unit was performing at peak efficiency if it could not be tested and measured. As noted in chapter 10, peak efficiency minimizes fuel use and associated emissions.

Chapter 14 describes some of the considerations for improving the maintainability and reliability of the plant equipment. These practices are important because power plants must last a long time. Maintaining these plants in a safe and efficient operating condition provides for more production of electricity with fewer additional plants. Efficient operating conditions also reduce overall emissions.

Chapter 15 provides some information on alternatives to the more traditional fossil fuels. These alternative fuels are of interest both for cost considerations and environmental reasons. Biomass-type fuels can be produced sustainably. To the extent that they can be utilized to produce energy, less CO_2 is generated overall, leading to a cleaner environment overall.

REFERENCES

1. E. A. Bruges, *Available Energy and the Second Law Analysis*. New York: Academic Press, 1959.
2. J. H. Keenan, "A Steam Chart for Second Law Analysis," *Mechanical Engineering*, 54: 195–204, 1932.
3. M. W. Thring, "The Virtue of Energy, Its Meaning and Practical Significance," *Institute of Fuel Journal*, 17: 116–123, 1944.
4. C. Birnie and E. F. Obert, "Evaluation and Location of the Losses in a 60,000 KW Power Station," *Proceedings of the Midwest Power Conference*. Chicago: Illinois Institute of Technology, 1949, pp. 187–193.
5. A. Keller, "Evaluation of Steam-Power-Plant Losses by Means of the Entropy-Balance Diagram," *Transactions of the ASME*, 72: 949–953, 1950.
6. C. A. Meyer et al., "Availability Balance of Steam Power Plants," *Transactions of the ASME. Journal of Engineering for Power*, 81, Series A: 35–42, 1959.
7. E. Clapeyron and R. Clausius, "Memoir on the Motive Power of Heat," in S. Nicolas, L. Carnot, E. Clapeyron, and R. Clausius, *Reflections on the Motive Power of Fire; and Other Papers on the Second Law of Thermodynamics*. Gloucester, MA: Peter Smith, 1962.
8. E. F. Obert and R. A. Gaggioli, *Thermodynamics*, latest edition. New York: McGraw-Hill.
9. N. A. Hall and W. E. Ibele, *Engineering Thermodynamics*. Englewood Cliffs, NJ: Prentice-Hall, 1960, pp. 447–520.
10. C. D. Weir, "Optimization of Heater Enthalpy Rises in Feed-Heating Trains," *Institution of Mechanical Engineers. Proceedings*, 174: 769–796, 1960. [Discussion by R. W. Haywood, pp. 784–787.]
11. G. Chiantore et al., "Optimizing A Regenerative Steam-Turbine Cycle," *Transactions of the ASME. Journal of Engineering for Power*, 83, Series A: 433–443, 1961.
12. J. K. Salisbury, *Steam Turbines and their Cycles*. Huntington, NY: Robert E. Krieger, 1974, Part 3: Cycle Analysis.
13. "The Reheat Cycle—A Re-Evaluation." *Combustion*, 21 (12): 38–40, 1950.
14. Papers given at the Symposium on the Reheat Cycle sponsored by the ASME and held in New York, November 29–December 3, 1948. *Transactions of the ASME*, 71: 673–749, 1949.
15. J. K. Salisbury, "Analysis of the Steam-Turbine Reheat Cycle," *Transactions of the ASME* 80: 1629–1642, 1958.
16. J. K. Salisbury, "Power-Plant Performance Monitoring," *Transactions of the ASME. Journal of Engineering for Power*, 83, Series A: 409–422, 1961.
17. M. S. Reddy, F. Afshar, and R. J. Hollmeier, "Evaluation of Alternative System Designs in a Cogeneration Plant," *Proceedings of the American Power Conference*. Chicago: Illinois Institute of Technology, 1982.

Combustion Technology

Chapter **Two**

The basic equations used to describe how fuel and air are transformed into gaseous products of combustion are discussed in the first part of this chapter. Fuel-firing systems for burning coal and other solid fossil fuels are described in the second part.

The control and utilization of heat energy has been a fundamental underpinning of civilization. The combustion of fossil fuels has provided the principal means for the liberation of heat energy from this natural resource.

HISTORICAL INTRODUCTION

From our earliest existence on earth, humans have been fascinated by fire, but we did not achieve a quantitative understanding of the combustion process until about the year 1880. Before that date, one can trace the development of many hypotheses concerning the nature and properties of fire, including some that were expressed in supernatural terms of fear and awe. Even the now-discredited phlogiston theory of combustion, however, did not prevent enterprising engineers from designing and constructing boilers to generate steam for the earliest steam engines.

Phlogiston was a hypothetical, mysterious substance. It sometimes was presumed to have the property of negative weight and combined with a body to render it combustible. First proposed by G. E. Stahl in 1697, the phlogiston theory dominated the chemical thought of the eighteenth century. Even such a perceptive observer as Joseph Priestly, who in 1774 discovered the unique power of oxygen for supporting combustion, accepted the phlogiston theory. In the years between 1775 and 1781, Antoine L. Lavoisier substituted the theory of oxygenation for the theory of phlogiston and provided experimental evidence that combustion was the union of the substance burned with the oxygen of the atmosphere.

In 1755, Joseph Black discovered carbon dioxide, and, in 1781, Henry Cavendish demonstrated the compound nature of water. At about the same time, Lavoisier made the precise measurements and formulated the volume and weight relationships that underlie the modern theory of combustion.

Beyond this, Amedeo Avogadro established in 1811 that the number of molecules in a unit volume under standard conditions is the same for all gases. During this same period, John Dalton enunciated the law of partial pressures, and, in 1803, his study of the physical properties of gases led to formulation of the atomic theory, including the law of combining weights. A related observation was made by Joseph Louis Gay-Lussac in 1808—that gases always combine in volumes that bear simple ratios to each other.

COMBUSTION FUNDAMENTALS

To the engineer concerned with boiler design and performance, combustion may be considered as the chemical union of the combustible constituents of a fuel and the oxygen of the air, controlled at such a rate as to produce useful heat energy. The principal combustible constituents are elemental carbon, hydrogen, and their compounds. In the combustion process, the compounds and elements are burned to carbon dioxide and water vapor. Small quantities of sulfur are present in most fuels, and, although sulfur is combustible and contributes slightly to the heating value of the fuel, its presence is generally detrimental because of the corrosive nature of its compounds. Air, the usual source of oxygen for combustion in boilers, is a mixture of oxygen, nitrogen, and small amounts of water vapor, carbon dioxide, argon, and other elements. The compositions of dry and wet atmospheric air are given in *Table 2-1*.

In an ideal situation, the combustion process would occur with the exact proportions of oxygen and a combustible that are called for in theory (the stoichiometric quantities). It is impracticable to operate a boiler at the theoretical level of 0% excess oxygen, however. In practice, this condition is approached by providing an excess of oxygen in the form of excess air from the atmosphere. The amount of excess air varies with the fuel, boiler load, and type of firing equipment.

COMBUSTION EQUATIONS

For combustion calculations, it is customary to write the combustion reaction equations on the basis of theoretical oxygen only, notwithstanding the presence of excess air and nitrogen. A partial list of these combustion equations and the approximate heat released in the reactions are given in *Table 2-2*.

All combustion calculations are based on fundamental chemical reactions (*Table 2-2*). Not only do the equations indicate what substances are involved in the reaction, they also show the molecular proportions in which these substances take part in the reaction.

Each molecule has a numerical value that represents its relative weight or molecular weight. This molecular weight is the sum of the atomic weights of the atoms composing the molecule. For example, carbon, C, has a molecular weight of 12; oxygen, O_2, has a molecular weight of $2 \times 16 = 32$; and carbon dioxide, CO_2, has a molecular weight of $12 + (2 \times 16) = 44$. These molecular weights are only relative values, and they may be expressed in any units. Note that the molecular weights in *Table 2-2*

TABLE 2-1 | COMPOSITION OF COMBUSTION AIR

DRY ATMOSPHERIC AIR

The volumetric composition of dry atmospheric air given in National Advisory Committee for Aeronautics (NACA) Report 1235[1] and the molecular weights of the gases constituting dry air are as follows:

Gas*	Volume, %	Mol. Wt.
Nitrogen	78.09	28.016
Oxygen	20.95	32.000
Argon	0.93	39.944
Carbon dioxide	0.03	44.010

Dry air with this composition has an apparent molecular weight of 28.97 lb/lb-mol and a density at 32°F and 14.7 psia of 28.97/359 = 0.0807 lb/ft^3.
359 is the Ideal Gas Constant. The units are:
Ft lb/lb-mol °R (Reads foot pound over pound-mole degree R)
The oxygen content is 23.14% by weight. The value for lb dry air/lb oxygen = 1/0.2314 = 4.32.

WET ATMOSPHERIC AIR

Wet atmospheric air is defined in this text as the above air plus 0.013 lb water vapor/lb dry air. (Air at 80°F, 60% relative humidity, and 14.7 psia contains 1.3% water vapor by weight; see Figure 2-4.)

Wet air with this amount of water vapor has an apparent molecular weight of 28.74 lb/lb-mol and a density at 32°F and 14.7 psia of 0.0801 lb/ft^3. The oxygen content is 22.84% by weight. The value for lb wet atmospheric air/lb oxygen = 1/0.2284 = 4.38.

The content of nitrogen, argon, carbon dioxide, and water per lb oxygen = 77.16/22.84 = 3.38 lb.

*Neon, helium, krypton, hydrogen, xenon, ozone, and radon, combined, are less than 0.003%.

are the whole-number values for the main isotopes of each substance.

A molecular weight of any substance in the gaseous state and under the same conditions of temperature and pressure will occupy the same volume. This relationship is very significant. The volume will, of course, vary numerically for different units of weight and for different conditions of temperature and pressure. For combustion calculations, the pound (lb) and the cubic foot (ft^3) are the units commonly used in the United States, and unless otherwise stated, the temperature and pressure are understood to be 32°F and 14.7 psia (atmospheric pressure). Thus, a molecular weight of 32 lb of oxygen at 32°F and atmospheric pressure will have the same volume as a molecular weight of 44 lb of carbon dioxide under the same conditions. This volume is 359 ft^3.

CONCEPT OF THE MOLE

A molecular weight expressed in pounds is termed a *pound mole*, or simply a *mole*, and the volume that it occupies is termed a *molal volume*. Molal volume varies with changes in temperature and pressure according to Charles' and Boyle's laws and may be corrected to any desired conditions. Volume is directly proportional to the absolute temperature and inversely proportional to the absolute pressure. Because combustion processes in steam boiler furnaces usually take place at practically constant atmospheric pressure, pressure corrections are seldom necessary.

Returning to the combustion equation for carbon and oxygen and applying these concepts, it is possible to write this reaction in several ways. For purposes of molar analysis, carbon may be treated as a gas:

$$C + O_2 \rightarrow CO_2$$

Equation 2-1

TABLE 2-2 | COMBUSTION EQUATIONS

Combustible Constituent	Molecular Weight	Reaction		Heat Release,* BTU/lb
Carbon	12	$C + O_2$	$\rightarrow CO_2$	14,100
Hydrogen	2	$H_2 + 0.5O_2$	$\rightarrow H_2O$	61,000
Sulfur	32	$S + O_2$	$\rightarrow SO_2$	4,000
Hydrogen sulfide	34	$H_2S + 1.5O_2$	$\rightarrow SO_2 + H_2O$	7,100
Methane	16	$CH_4 + 2O_2$	$\rightarrow CO_2 + 2H_2O$	23,900
Ethane	30	$C_2H_6 + 3.5O_2$	$\rightarrow 2CO_2 + 3H_2O$	22,300
Propane	44	$C_3H_8 + 5O_2$	$\rightarrow 3CO_2 + 4H_2O$	21,500
Butane	58	$C_4H_{10} + 6.5O_2$	$\rightarrow 4CO_2 + 5H_2O$	21,300
Pentane	72	$C_5H_{12} + 8O_2$	$\rightarrow 5CO_2 + 6H_2O$	22,000

*Higher heating value/lb combustible

$$1 \text{ mol C} + 1 \text{ mol } O_2 \rightarrow 1 \text{ mol } CO_2$$

Equation 2-2

$$12 \text{ lb C} + 32 \text{ lb } O_2 \rightarrow 44 \text{ lb } CO_2$$

Equation 2-3

Dividing through by 12,

$$1 \text{ lb C} + 2.67 \text{ lb } O_2 \rightarrow 3.67 \text{ lb } CO_2$$

Equation 2-4

$$1 \text{ volume C} + 1 \text{ volume } O_2 \rightarrow 1 \text{ volume } CO_2$$

Equation 2-5

Because there are 4.32 lb dry air/lb oxygen, the stoichiometric combustion of 1 lb of carbon requires 11.52 lb of dry air, or 11.68 lb of wet air (with 1.3% water vapor).

Each equation balances. There are the same number of atoms of each element and the same weight of reacting substances on each side of the arrow, but not necessarily the same number of molecules, moles, or volumes. Thus, one atom of carbon combined with one molecule of oxygen gives only one molecule of carbon dioxide, and two moles of hydrogen plus one mole of oxygen yield two moles of water vapor. It will be evident from a consideration of the mole–volume relationship that percentage by volume is numerically the same as mole percentage.

Because a mole represents a definite weight as well as a definite volume, it is a means of converting analyses by weight into analyses by volume, and vice versa. Volumetric fractions of the several constituents of a gas can be multiplied by their respective molecular weights, with the sum of the products then being equal to the apparent molecular weight of one mole of gas. The percentage by weight of each component can then be determined.

Finally, the density of any gas at any temperature is found by dividing the molecular weight of the gas by the molal volume at that temperature (*Fig. 2-1*).

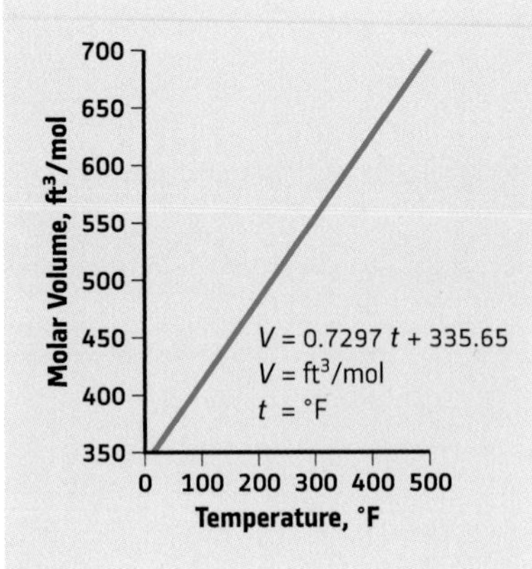

Figure 2-1 | Gas density determination

METHODS OF COMBUSTION CALCULATIONS

Two methods of combustion calculations are presented in this text. The first is known as the mole method and is based on the chemical relationships previously explained. The second uses the firing of a million BTU as a basis for calculation.

The Mole Method

Table 2-2 gives the basic combustion reactions for the carbon, hydrogen, and sulfur in coal. In the following analysis, assume a high-volatile bituminous coal burned at 23% excess air, and perform calculations on the basis of 100 lb of as-fired fuel. The fuel analysis as fired is given in *Table 2-3*.

The calculation of air weight for combustion must be made on the basis of an oxygen balance, because oxygen is the only element common to all oxidizing reactions. Oxygen contained in the fuel must be deducted from the calculated quantity needed, because it is already combined with carbon, hydrogen, or other combustible constituents of the coal.

The molar relations are as given in *Table 2-4*.

TABLE 2-3 | FUEL ANALYSIS

	% by Weight	Mole Weight
C	63.50	12
H_2	4.07	2
S	1.53	32
O_2	7.46	32
N_2	1.28	28
H_2O	15.00	18
Ash	7.16	
Higher Heating Value	11,200 BTU/lb	

TABLE 2-4 | MOLAR RELATIONS

	Mol O_2	Mol CO_2	Mol H_2O	Mol SO_2
Mol C	1	1		
Mol H_2	0.5		1	
Mol S	1			1
AIR FOR COMBUSTION				
O_2 for C	63.5/12 = 5.29 lb-mol			
O_2 for H_2	(4.07 × 0.5)/2 = 1.02 lb-mol			
O_2 for S	1.53/32 = 0.05 lb-mol			
Total for 100 lb of fuel:	**6.36 lb-mol**			
Less O_2 in fuel	7.46/32 = 0.23 lb-mol			
O_2 required	= 6.13 lb-mol			
O_2 in excess air	6.13 × 0.23 = 1.41 lb-mol			
Total O_2 required/100 lb fuel = 7.54 lb-mol				

$$\text{Dry air required} = \left[(7.54 \text{ lb-mol } O_2) \times \frac{(100 \text{ lb mol air})}{20.95 \text{ lb mol } O_2}\right] = 36.0 \text{ lb-mol/100 lb fuel}$$

36.0 × 28.97 = 1,043 lb dry air/100 lb fuel

Weight of Dry Products of Combustion

The weight of gaseous products of combustion can be calculated from the volumetric analysis of flue gas. Not only the weight of the flue gas per 100 lb of coal but also its analysis and volume can be calculated from the information given in the preceding example.

To obtain the wet products of combustion, or total wet gas when a fuel burns completely, the weight of the fuel is added to the weight of atmospheric air supplied for its combustion. If some of the fuel is ash or, because of incomplete combustion, some of the fuel does not leave the furnace with the gases, then there will be less burned-out fuel in the products. The wet products of combustion in the above example, then, are the fuel (100 lb – 7.16 lb ash = 92.84 lb/100 lb) plus the air required for combustion, or (rounded) 93 + 1,043 = 1,136 lb/100 lb fuel.

The Million-BTU Method

The million-BTU method for combustion calculations is based on the concept that the weight of air required in the combustion of a unit weight of any commercial fuel is more nearly proportional to the unit heat value than to the unit weight of the fuel. Consequently, the weights of air, dry gas, moisture, wet gas, and other quantities are expressed in pounds per million BTU fired.

In connection with this calculation method, the following items will be discussed:

1. Fuel in products, F
2. Atmospheric air for combustion, A
3. Effect of unburned combustible
4. Products of combustion, P
5. Moisture in the combustion air, W_a
6. Moisture from fuel in products of combustion, W_f
7. Dry gas content of combustion products, P_d

The first four items are necessary for calculation of the gas and air quantities. The final three items form the basis of heat balance calculations in the design or testing of a steam generating unit.

FUEL IN PRODUCTS, *F*. As defined earlier, F is that portion of the fired fuel that appears in the gaseous products of combustion. Because all quantities are to be those required for, or resulting from, the firing of a million BTU, F must be calculated on that basis. If a fuel contains no ash, then F is obtained through dividing 1,000,000 by the as-fired heating value of the fuel. For solid fuels, where ash and/or solid combustible loss must be considered,

$$F = \frac{10^4(100 - \%\text{ ash} - \%\text{ solid combustible loss})}{\text{HHV}}$$

Equation 2-6

where

F	= lb/10^6 BTU fired
% ash	= percentage by weight in fuel as fired
% solid combustible loss	= percentage by weight in fuel as fired
HHV	= higher heating value as fired, BTU/lb

ATMOSPHERIC AIR FOR COMBUSTION, *A*. In accordance with the mole method, the theoretical weight of dry air (zero excess) may be calculated from the fuel analysis and the formula:

$$A_{dry} = \left[\frac{11.51(\%C) + 34.57(\%H - \%O/8) + 4.32(\%S)}{HHV} \right] \times 10^4$$

Equation 2-7

in which the numerator and denominator are on the same basis—as-fired, moisture-free, or moisture- and ash-free—and A_{dry} is in lb/10^6 BTU fired. For air with 1.3% moisture by weight (80°F and 60% relative humidity), the formula becomes

$$A_{wet} = \left[\frac{11.68(\%C) + 35.03(\%H - \%O/8) + 4.38(\%S)}{HHV} \right] \times 10^4$$

Equation 2-8

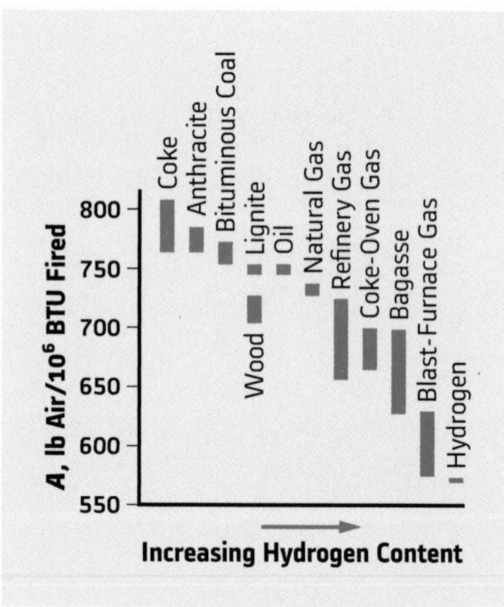

Figure 2-2 | Combustion-air requirements for various fuels at zero excess-air: a range of values as an approximate function of hydrogen content

Values of A_{wet} range from 570 lb/10^6 BTU for pure hydrogen to greater than 800 lb/10^6 BTU for certain cokes and meta-anthracite coals, as shown in *Figure 2-2* for various fuels burned in steam generators. Any calculated values of wet air for combustion that differ substantially from these values should lead to cross-verification of the ultimate analysis and the observed HHV. The analysis and HHV of the fuel have to be from the same sample to avoid errors in determinations of air and gas weight.

Effect of Unburned Combustible Constituents

In the combustion of solid fuels, even in pulverized form, it is not feasible to burn the available combustible constituents completely. Thus, the air requirement per million BTU fired has to be reduced to the air required per million BTU burned. This is done by multiplying the combustion air, *A*, by the combustible-loss correction factor, C. The unburned combustible loss can be expressed either as percentage carbon heat loss or percentage combustible weight loss. These are related by the following expression:

$$\%\text{ carbon heat loss} = \frac{14{,}600}{HHV} \times \%\text{ solid combustible weight loss}$$

Equation 2-9

in which 14,600 is the heat value for combustibles in refuse recommended by American Society of Mechanical Engineers (ASME) Performance Test Code and HHV is the higher heating value of the as-fired fuel. If a fuel has carbon as its only combustible constituent, then C equals

$$1-\frac{\%\text{ solid combustible weight loss}}{100}$$

Equation 2-10

If, however, all heat in the fuel does not come from carbon alone (so that the air is not strictly proportional to the carbon burned), C will not be exact. For high-carbon, low-volatile fuels, it will be nearly exact and will result in only a small error—even for fuels that are low in fixed carbon and high in hydrogen. In all cases, the error involved by using Equation 2-10 is quite within the limits of accuracy for all other combustion calculations. Finally, C can be expressed as a function of percentage heat loss by combining the above relationships:

$$C=1-\frac{\%\text{ carbon heat loss}}{100}\times\frac{\text{HHV}}{14{,}600}$$

Equation 2-11

Figure 2-3 is a graphical solution of this equation.

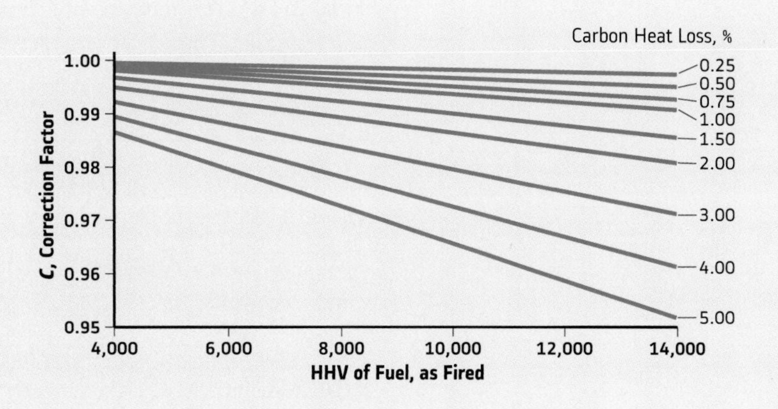

Figure 2-3 | Graphical solution of Equation 2-11

Products of Combustion, *P*

The total gaseous products of combustion, *P*, become the sum of *F* and *A* (as corrected for combustible loss). Thus,

$$P=F+CA$$

Equation 2-12

where

P = total gaseous products of combustion, lb/10^6 BTU fired

F = fuel fired exclusive of ash or solid carbon loss, lb/10^6 BTU fired

A = atmospheric air consumed, lb/10^6 BTU fired

C = combustible loss correction factor

Moisture in Combustion Air, W_a

For heat balance calculations, the moisture in air will be 1.3% of air weight/10^6 BTU, or $W_a = 0.013A$, for ambient conditions of 80°F and 60% relative humidity. For air at a higher or lower temperature or relative humidity, the moisture content will be as shown in *Figure 2-4*; air per million BTU, *A*, and W_a must be adjusted appropriately.

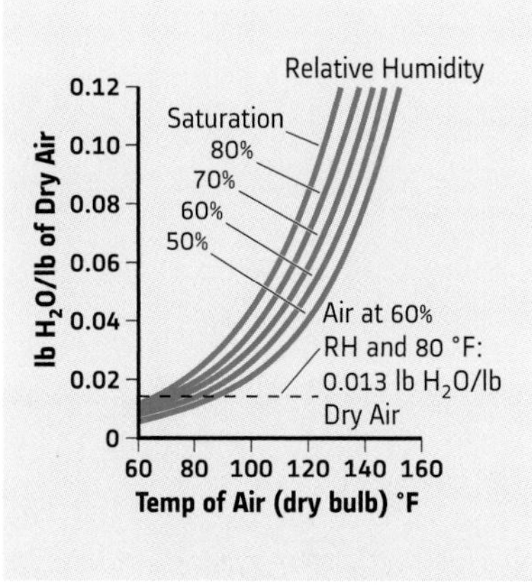

Figure 2-4 | Moisture content of dry air as a function of dry-bulb temperature and relative humidity (RH)

Moisture from Fuel, W_f

This item is separately reported both in an ASME Performance Test Codes heat balance and in a predicted heat balance. In the case of some fuels (e.g., natural and refinery gases), the heat loss because of this moisture may be the largest single item in the heat balance. The value of W_f includes the combined surface and inherent moisture, W_c, from a fuel plus the moisture formed by the combustion of hydrogen, W_h. The value of W_c will vary from zero, or a mere trace in fuel oil, to more than 115 lb/10^6 BTU fired in the case of green wood, and W_h will vary from zero or a trace in lampblack to 100 lb/10^6 BTU fired in the case of some refinery gases. Thus,

$$W_f = W_c + W_h$$

Equation 2-13

where

$W_c = H_2O \times 10^4/HHV$
$W_h = 9 \times H \times 10^4/HHV$

where, in turn, both W_c and W_h are in lb/10^6 BTU fired, H_2O is the percentage water by weight in the as-fired fuel, H is the hydrogen in the fuel (% by weight as fired), and HHV is the higher heating value of the as-fired fuel in BTU/lb.

Dry Gas, P_d

The dry gas content of the combustion products is used in the calculation of the dry gas loss item of a boiler heat balance. The dry gas may be determined by subtracting the water vapor from the total products; thus,

$$P_d = P - (W_a + W_f)$$

Equation 2-14

where

P_d = dry gas, lb/10^6 BTU fired
P = total products of combustion
W_a = moisture in air
W_f = moisture from fuel

COMBUSTION SYSTEMS

In the process of steam generation, fuel-burning systems provide controlled, efficient conversion of the chemical energy of fuel into heat energy, which in turn is transferred to the heat-absorbing surfaces of the steam generator. To do this, fuel-burning systems introduce the fuel and air for combustion, mix these reactants, ignite the combustible mixture, and distribute the flame envelope and the products of combustion.

An ideal fuel-burning system fulfilling these functions would have the following characteristics:

- No excess oxygen or unburned combustibles in the end products of combustion
- A low rate of auxiliary ignition-energy input to initiate the combustion reaction
- An economical reaction rate between fuel and oxygen compatible with acceptable nitrogen and sulfur oxide formation
- An effective method of handling and disposing of the solid impurities introduced with the fuel
- Uniform distribution of the product weight and temperature in relation to the parallel circuits of the heat-absorbing surface
- A wide and stable firing range
- Fast response to changes in firing rate
- Equipment with high availability and low maintenance requirements

In actual practice, some of these characteristics must be compromised to achieve a reasonable balance between combustion efficiency and cost. For example, firing a fuel with the stoichiometric air quantity (no excess above the theoretical amount) would require an infinite residence time at temperatures above the ignition point at which complete burnout of the combustibles takes place. Thus, every firing system requires a quantity of air in excess of stoichiometry to attain an acceptable level of unburned carbon in the products of combustion leaving the furnace. This amount of excess air is an indicator of the burning efficiency of the firing system.

THE COMBUSTION REACTION

The rate and degree of completion of a chemical reaction, such as in the combustion process, are greatly influenced by temperature, concentration, preparation, and distribution of the reactants. The rate and degree are also greatly influenced by catalysts and by mechanical turbulence. All these factors have one effect in common: to increase contacts between molecules of the reactants.

Higher temperature, for instance, increases the velocity of molecular movement, permitting harder and more frequent contact between molecules. A temperature rise of 200°F at some stages can increase the possible rate of reaction a million-fold.

At a given pressure, three factors limit the temperature that can be attained to provide the greatest intermolecular contact. These are the heat absorbed by the combustion chamber enclosure, the heat absorbed by the reactants in bringing them to ignition temperature, and the heat absorbed by the nitrogen in the air.

The concentration and distribution of the reactants in a given volume are directly related to the opportunity for contact between interacting molecules. In an atmosphere containing 21% oxygen (the amount present in air), this rate is much less than it would be with 90% oxygen. As the reaction nears completion, the distribution and concentration of reactants assume even greater importance. Because of the dilution of reactants by the inert products of combustion, the relative distribution—and opportunity for contact—approaches zero.

Both preparation of the reactants and mechanical turbulence greatly influence the reaction rate. These are the primary factors available to the designer of a fuel-burning system who is attempting to provide a desirable reaction rate.

The beneficial effect of mechanical turbulence on the combustion reaction becomes apparent when it is realized that agitation permits greater opportunity for molecular contact. Agitation improves both the relative distribution and the energy imparted. Agitation assumes greater significance if it is achieved later in the combustion process, when the relative concentration of the reactants is approaching zero.

SUSPENSION FIRING

Most large steam generators producing power through burning solid fuels are of the entrained-flow reactor type (most frequently called suspension-fired generators). In pulverized firing, coal is ground to the fineness of face powder, which a stream of primary air transports into the furnace. The pulverized coal ignites as the fuel–air mixture enters the furnace, where it is joined by the bulk of combustion air (called the secondary air), which is heated to temperatures between 500 to 800°F (260–425°C). Residence time of the burning fuel in the furnace is measured in seconds; solid-particle recirculation is not used; and radiation of heat to the furnace-wall tubing is the principal mode of heat transfer.

The following variables affect the average temperature of both gas and solid particles in a suspension-fired or entrained-flow furnace:

- Type of firing (corner/tangential/vortex or multiple wall burners)
- Excess-air percentage
- Fuel reactivity and moisture content
- Air distribution in the furnace
- Firing density (either heat released in the active firing volume, or per square foot or square meter of furnace-plan area)
- Furnace geometry

The introduction of pulverized coal firing in 1918 allowed for the vast electrification of major parts of the world using a low cost, readily available, natural resource.

- Preheated-air temperature
- Dirtiness of the furnace wall (partially a function of the soot-blowing cycle)

Although the maximum attainable temperature (i.e., the adiabatic flame temperature) in such a furnace can be calculated, it will not be achieved in practice.

DESIGN OF A PRACTICAL FUEL-FIRING SYSTEM

In the practical application of a burner and fuel-burning system to a boiler, all fundamental factors influencing the rate and completeness of combustion must be considered along with the degree of heat-transfer efficiency.

There are two methods of producing a total flow pattern in a combustion chamber to provide successful molecular contacts of reactants through mechanical turbulence. The first is to divide and distribute fuel and air into many similar streams and to treat each stream independently. This provides multiple flame envelopes. In contrast, the second provides interaction among all streams of air and fuel introduced into the combustion chamber to produce a single flame envelope.

The first concept requires that the total fuel and air supplied to a common combustion chamber be accurately subdivided. It also limits the opportunity for sustained mechanical mixing or turbulence—particularly during the early stages of combustion. The necessity of obtaining and sustaining good distribution of fuel and air is a design as well as an operating concern. There must be sufficient opportunity for contact of fuel and oxygen molecules as well as uniform distribution of product temperature and mass in relation to the combustion chamber. On the other hand, the single-flame-envelope technique provides interaction between all streams of fuel and air introduced into a common mixture between all fuel and air molecules, and mechanical turbulence is sustained throughout the chamber. This avoids stringent accuracy requirements for fuel and air distribution.

Firing systems representative of these two concepts are horizontally wall-fired systems (characterized by individual flames) and tangentially fired systems (which have a single flame envelope). There are other types and combinations; one such as the vertically fired system, which uses characteristics of both previously described systems.

HORIZONTALLY FIRED SYSTEMS

In horizontally fired systems, the fuel is mixed with combustion air in individual burner registers (*Fig. 2-5*). In this design, the coal and primary air are introduced tangentially to the coal nozzle, thus imparting strong rotation within the nozzle. Adjustable inlet vanes impart a rotation to the preheated secondary air from the windbox. The degree of air swirl, coupled with

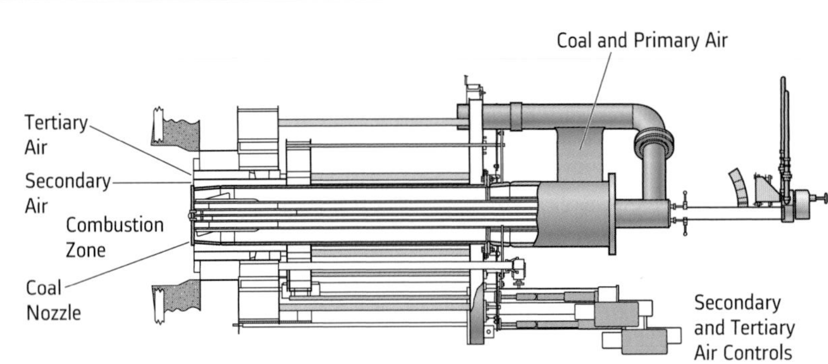

Figure 2-5 | Burner for horizontal firing of coal

the flow-shaping contour of the burner throat, establishes a recirculation pattern extending several throat diameters into the furnace. Once the coal is ignited, the hot products of combustion propagate back toward the nozzle to provide the ignition energy necessary for stable combustion.

The burners are located in rows, either on a single wall only (*Fig. 2-6*) or on both the front and rear walls. The latter is termed *opposed firing*.

Because the major portion of the combustion process must take place within the recirculation zone, it is imperative that the air/fuel ratio to each burner is within close tolerances. The rate of combustion drops off rapidly as the reactants leave the recirculation zone, and interaction between flames occurs only after that point. The degree of interaction depends on burner and furnace configuration.

TANGENTIALLY FIRED SYSTEMS

The tangentially fired system is based on the concept of a single flame envelope (*Fig. 2-7*). Both fuel and combustion air are injected from the corners of the furnace along a line that is tangential to a small circle, lying in a horizontal plane, at the center of the furnace. Intensive mixing occurs where these streams meet. A rotative motion, similar to that of a cyclone, is imparted to the flame body, which spreads out and fills the furnace area.

Tangentially fired boilers have moderate turbulence and mixing intensities compared to those of horizontally fired systems. This is because the turbulent zone does not continue for any great distance as a result of the expanding gas soon being forced into a streamline flow. (The significance of this factor on the production of nitrogen oxides is discussed later in this chapter.) As one stream impinges on another in the center of the furnace during the intermediate stages of combustion, it creates a high degree of turbulence for effective mixing.

The fuel and air are admitted from the vertical furnace corner windboxes (*Fig. 2-8*). Dampers, which control the air to each compartment, make it possible to vary the distribution of air over the height of the windbox. It is also possible to vary the velocities of the air streams, to change the mixing rate of fuel and air, and to control the distance from the nozzle at which the coal ignites.

The vertical arrangement of fuel and air nozzles provides great flexibility for multiple-fuel firing. It is possible to provide for full-load capability with gas or oil by locating the additional nozzles for these fuels in the secondary-air compartments adjacent to the coal nozzles. In addition, separate nozzles for injecting municipal refuse and other waste fuels are frequently provided in both utility and industrial boilers.

As illustrated in *Figure 2-9*, fuel and air nozzles most commonly tilt in unison to raise and lower the flame to control heat absorption in the furnace and, thus, heat absorption in the superheater and reheater sections. In addition to controlling the furnace exit-gas temperature for variations in load, the tilts on coal-fired units automatically compensate for the effects of ash deposits on furnace-wall heat absorption.

As wall blowers clean ash deposits from the furnace walls, the

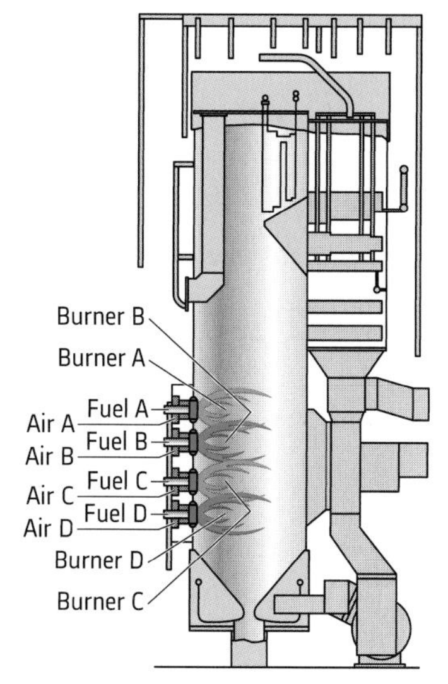

Figure 2-6 | Flow pattern of horizontal (wall) firing

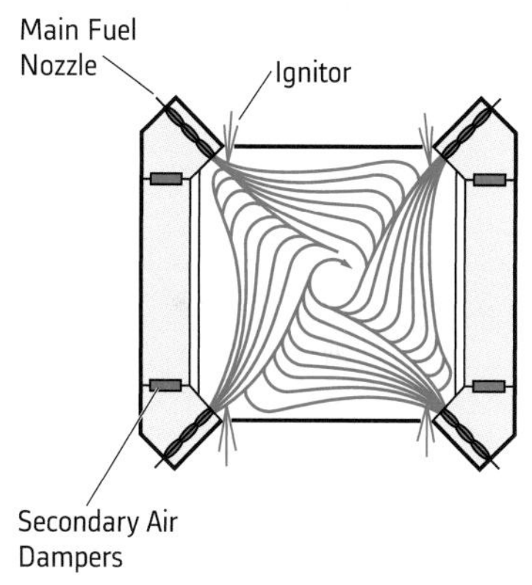

Figure 2-7 | Tangential firing pattern

furnace exit-gas temperature tends to decrease because of the increase in overall furnace absorption. The windbox nozzles are then automatically tilted upward at a controlled rate, and combustion is completed higher in the furnace. The repositioning effectively reduces the absorption in the lower part of the furnace and increases the furnace exit-gas heat content to maintain steam at design temperatures.

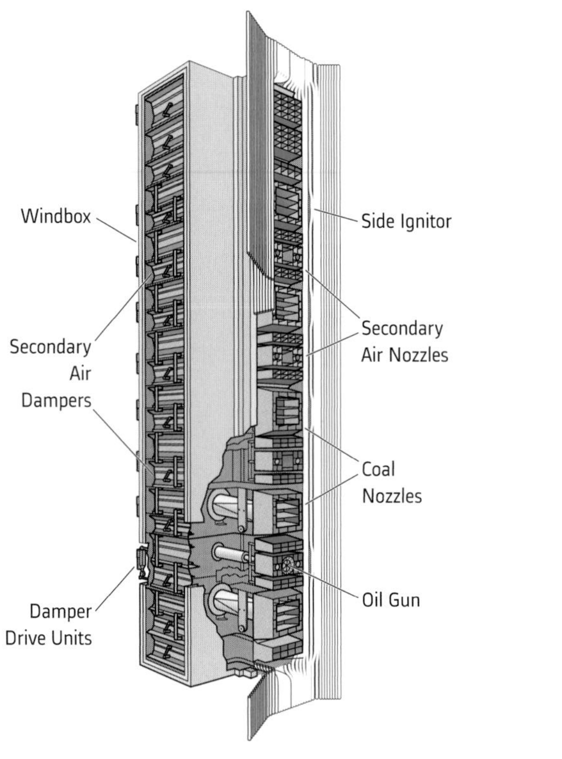

Figure 2-8 | Arrangement of corner windbox for tangential firing of coal

Conversely, as furnace walls are again gradually covered with ash deposits and furnace heat absorption decreases because of the insulating effects of the ash, the tilts are gradually depressed, and combustion is completed lower in the furnace. This exposes the hot gases to a greater proportion of the furnace-wall surface and effectively controls furnace exit-gas temperature and steam temperature until ash is again removed from the furnace walls.

VERTICALLY FIRED SYSTEMS

The first pulverized-coal systems had a configuration called vertical (or arch) firing. These systems are now used principally to fire coals with a moisture- and ash-free volatile matter

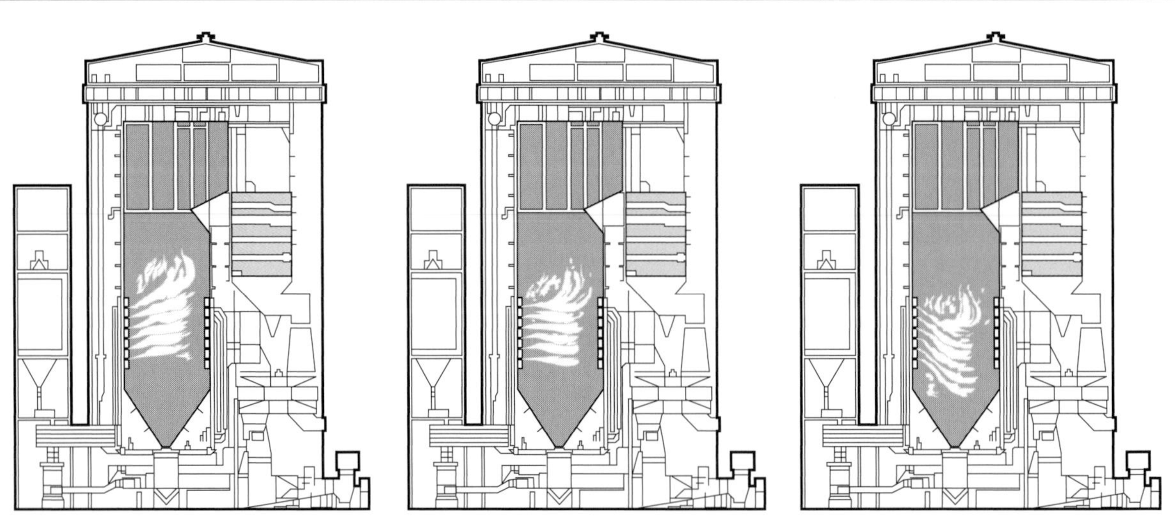

Figure 2-9 | Selective furnace utilization and steam temperature control are accomplished by tilting nozzles in a tangentially fired system

content of between 9 and 13% (i.e., anthracite coals). They require less stabilizing fuel than horizontally or tangentially fired systems, but they have more complex firing equipment and, therefore, more complex operating characteristics.

The firing concept and the arrangement of the burners in the arches are shown in *Figures 2-10* and *2-11*. Pulverized coal is discharged through the nozzles. A portion of the heated combustion air is introduced around the fuel nozzles and through adjacent auxiliary ports. High-pressure jets are used to avoid short-circuiting the fuel/air streams to the furnace discharge. Tertiary air ports are located in a row along the front and rear walls of the lower furnace.

The firing system produces a long, looping flame in the lower furnace, with the hot gases discharging up the center. A portion of the total combustion air is withheld from the fuel stream until it projects well down into the furnace. This arrangement has the advantage of heating the fuel stream separately from a significant portion of its combustion air, thus providing good ignition stability. The delayed introduction of the tertiary air provides needed turbulence at a point in the flame where partial dilution from the products of combustion has occurred. The furnace flow pattern passes the hot product gases immediately in front of the fuel nozzles to provide a ready source of inherent ignition energy, which raises the primary fuel stream to ignition temperature. The flow pattern also ensures that the largest entrained solid-fuel particles, with the lowest ratio of surface area to weight, have the longest residence time in the combustion chamber.

FORMATION AND CONTROL OF NOx IN STEAM GENERATING EQUIPMENT

Nitrogen monoxide (NO) and nitrogen dioxide (NO_2) are by-products of the combustion process of virtually all fossil fuels. Historically, the quantity of these inorganic compounds in the products of combustion was not sufficient to affect boiler performance, and their presence was largely ignored. Now, however, the emissions of NO_2 and NO (collectively referred to as "NOx") are regulated by both state and federal authorities in the United States as well as in most developed countries. NOx emissions have become an important consideration in the design of fuel-firing equipment.

Thermal NOx

The formation of NOx in the combustion process is often explained in terms of the source of nitrogen required for the reaction. The N_2 can originate from the atmospheric air, in which case the product is referred to as "thermal NOx," or from the organically bound nitrogen components found in all coals and fuel oils, in which case the product is referred to as "fuel NOx." It is important to note that even though NOx usually consists of 95% NO and only 5% NO_2,

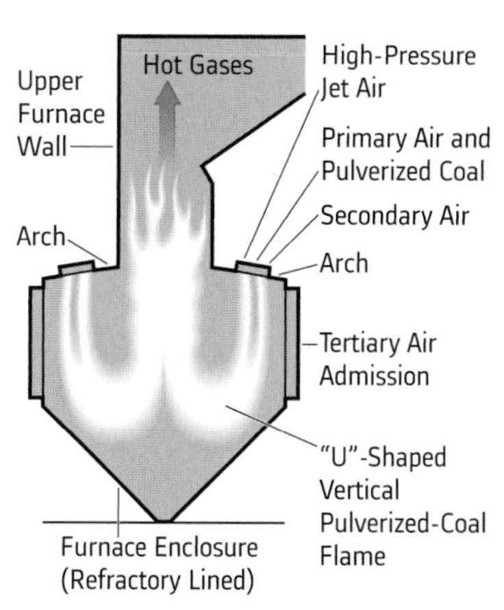

Figure 2-10 | Flow pattern of vertical firing

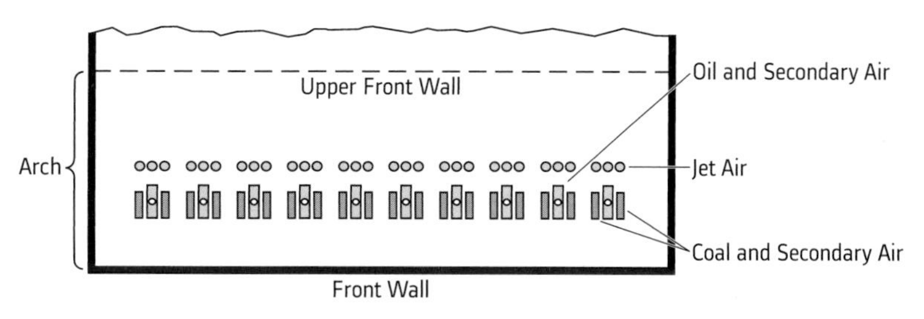

Figure 2-11 | Burner arrangement on the front arch of the furnace shown in Figure 2-10.

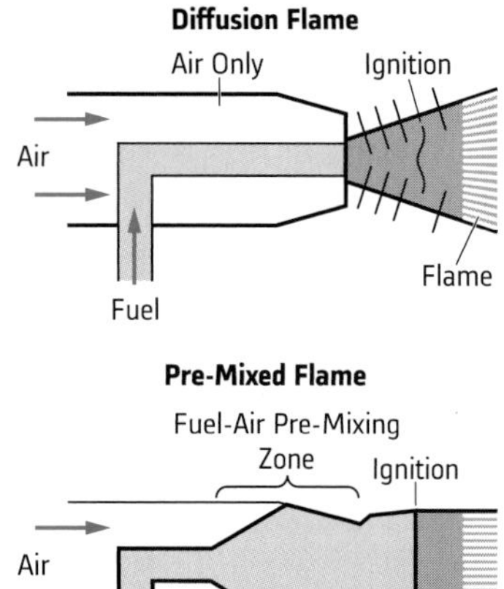

Figure 2-12 | Diffusion-flame and pre-mixed-flame mechanisms

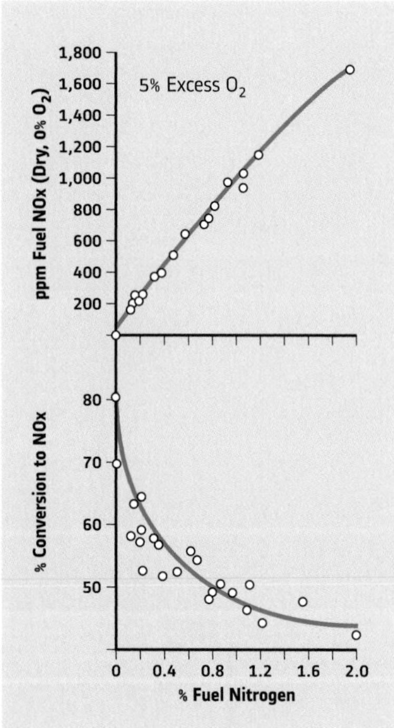

Figure 2-13 | Fuel NO and percentage conversion of fuel nitrogen to fuel NO: liquid fuels

the normal practice is to calculate concentrations of NOx as 100% NO_2.

The mechanisms involving thermal NOx were first described by Zel'Dovich and later modified to what is termed the *extended Zel'Dovich mechanism*[2]:

$$N_2 + O \rightarrow NO + N$$

Equation 2-15

$$N + O_2 \rightarrow NO + O$$

Equation 2-16

$$N + OH \rightarrow NO + H$$

Equation 2-17

Because the equilibrium values predicted by this mechanism are higher than those that are actually measured, it is generally assumed that Equation 2-15 is rate determining as a result of its high activation energy of 317 kJ/mol. A better understanding of thermal NOx can be derived from bench-scale tests that measure NOx in a heated mixture of N_2, O_2, and argon.[3] These tests show that thermal NOx can be predicted by the following equation:

$$d\left[NO\right] = K_1 e^{(-K_2/T)}\left[N_2\right]\left[O_2\right]^{1/2} dt$$

Equation 2-18

where

$[\ldots]$ = mole fraction
T = temperature
t = time
K_1, K_2 = constants

From this equation, it can be seen that thermal NO can be decreased by reducing time, temperature, and concentrations of N_2 and O_2. The fact that temperature in this equation is an exponential clearly demonstrates its importance in the control of thermal NOx. In practice, the Zel'Dovich mechanisms demonstrated by Equation 2-18 are sufficient for predicting NOx only in regions that are downstream of the flame front.

Fenimore coined the phase "prompt NO" to describe the NO generated within the "near" flame-front region, for which, because of the very short residence time, the Zel'Dovich reactions proved to be inadequate.[4] Prompt NO results from the rapid reaction of hydrocarbon radicals with molecular nitrogen, forming compounds that can subsequently convert to NOx. Subsequent investigation by De Soete showed that, as in the Zel'Dovich reactions, temperature in all cases reduced prompt NO.[5] Additional O_2 increased NO for fuel-rich diffusion flame fronts, however, but decreased NO for fuel-lean, premixed flame fronts (*Fig. 2-12*).

Fuel NOx

Although the kinetics involved in the conversion of organically bound nitrogen compounds found in fossil fuels are not yet well understood, numerous investigators have shown fuel NOx to be an important mechanism in NOx formation from fuel oil as well as the dominant mechanism in NOx generated from the combustion of coal. Bench-scale tests (*Fig. 2-13*) burning fuel oils in a mixture of oxygen and carbon dioxide (to exclude thermal NOx) have shown a remarkable correlation between the percentage N in the fuel oil versus NOx.[6] *Figure 2-13* also illustrates that the percentage of fuel-nitrogen conversion is not constant but, rather, decreases with increasing fuel nitrogen.

Similar bench-scale tests with various coals have not produced similar results.

Figure 2-14 illustrates the large contribution of fuel NOx, yet no apparent correlation is observed between the quantity of fuel-bound nitrogen and fuel NOx. Clearly, the fuel-nitrogen conversion rate is not constant. It will instead vary widely, depending more on coal rank than on actual nitrogen content.

At least one study has shown that fuel NOx can account for up to 80% of the total exhaust NOx in uncontrolled (unstaged) combustion.[7] Under these conditions, the fuel NOx contribution is greatest for those coals that evolve the most reactive volatile nitrogen, generally in proportion to volatile matter content, and is least when the nitrogen is retained in the solid (char) phase.[8,9]

A significant property of fuel-nitrogen conversion that affects the design of fuel-firing equipment relates to the availability of oxygen to react with the fuel-nitrogen compounds in their gaseous state. Simply stated, the compounds that evolve from a coal particle, such as HCN and NH_3, are relatively unstable and will reduce to harmless N_2 under fuel-rich conditions or to NO under air-rich conditions. Low-NOx, pulverized-coal firing systems are primarily designed to minimize volatile nitrogen conversion to NOx by establishing early ignition and controlling O_2 availability by using air- and fuel-staging techniques.

In air staging, a portion of the total air required to complete combustion is withheld initially, and the balance of the air is mixed with the incomplete products of combustion only after the oxygen content of the first-stage air is consumed. By varying the amount of first-stage air, the suspension-fired combustion of a coal particle or oil droplet can be interrupted at different stages of the reaction because of lack of oxygen, then allowed to proceed further at such time as the balance of air (second-stage air) is introduced. For NOx control, the ideal quantity of first-stage air would be that which is sufficient to generate the temperatures necessary to drive the gaseous state but insufficient to provide enough oxidant to complete a reaction to NO.

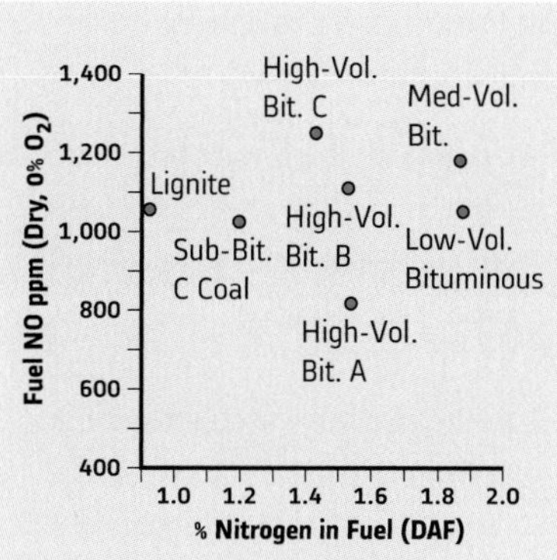

Figure 2-14 | Fuel NO versus percent nitrogen in fuel (Bit., bituminous; DAF, dry ash free)

Figure 2-15 shows the effect of first-stage stoichiometric ratio on outlet NOx levels for liquid fuels with various nitrogen levels. The tests shown in the figure used air for an oxidant, and the total NOx levels represent both thermal and fuel NOx. However, the increased effectiveness of staging with higher fuel-nitrogen content is clear. *Figure 2-16* shows a similar but less dramatic effect on a Utah bituminous coal. This and other tests have shown that for coal, unlike oil, decreasing the first-stage stoichiometric air below an optimum level will increase NOx levels, which suggests the possible requirement of an oxidant to reduce the intermediate HCN, NH_3, and other radicals.

The most important design criteria relevant to the control of both thermal

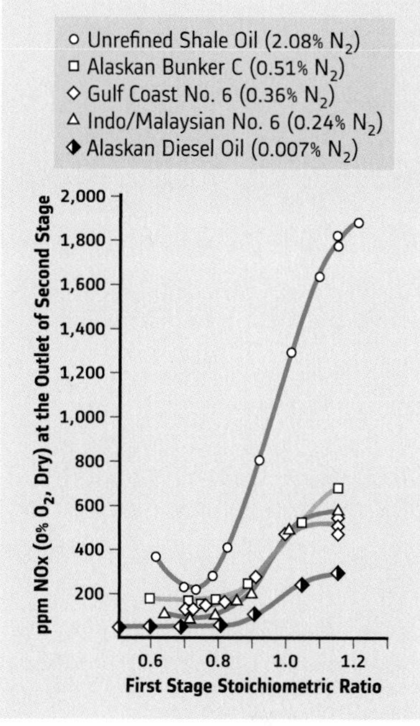

Figure 2-15 | Effect of liquid fuel composition on emissions: staged suspension firing

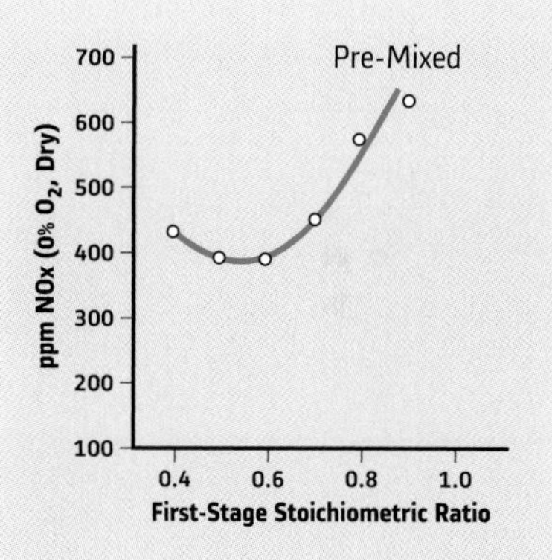

Figure 2-16 | Effect of initial fuel–air mixing: staged, Utah bituminous coal

and fuel NOx for coal firing can be summarized as follows:

- Coals with the lowest fuel-nitrogen content and the lowest fuel oxygen/nitrogen ratios generally will produce the lowest NOx.
- The fuel NOx can be minimized by controlling the quantity of air permitted to mix with the fuel in the early stages of combustion.
- The contribution of thermal NOx to total NOx can be reduced by operating at the lowest practical excess-air percentages as well as by minimizing gas temperatures throughout the furnace by using low-turbulence diffusion flames and large, water-cooled furnaces.

FIRING SYSTEMS THAT MINIMIZE NOx FORMATION

Firing systems designed to minimize NOx formation operate to control nitrogen conversion by driving the major fraction of the fuel-nitrogen compounds into the gas phase under overall fuel-rich conditions. In this atmosphere of oxygen deficiency, there occurs a maximum rate of decay of the evolved intermediate nitrogen compounds to N_2. Following the admission of the remaining air, the slow burning rate reduces the peak flame temperature to curtail the thermal NOx production in the latter stages of combustion.

Early studies of NOx emissions from all types of steam generators indicated that those from tangentially fired units were about half those from horizontally fired systems. Tangentially fired steam generators inject the fuel and air streams from the furnace corners, tangential to an imaginary circle in the center of the furnace. The impingement of laterally adjacent streams creates a single, rotating flame envelope that promotes bulk mixing for complete combustion. The long diffusion flames emanating from each corner, plus the large amount of internal gas recirculation generated by the cyclonic fireball, moderate fuel and air mixing and form the basis of an inherently low NOx combustion system.

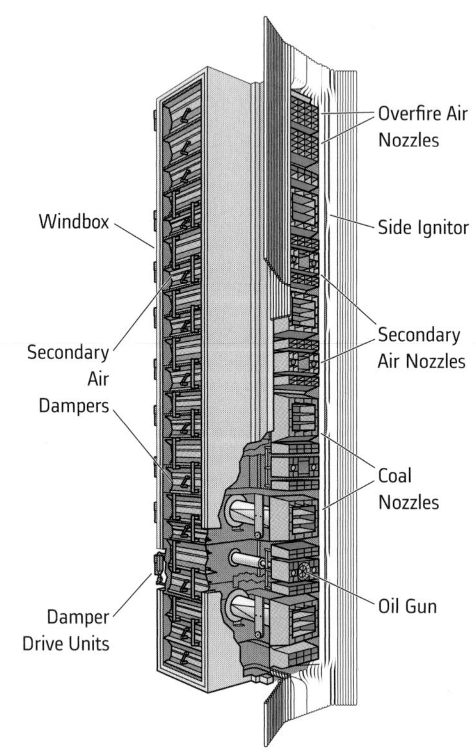

Figure 2-17 | Tangentially firing windbox with overfire air ports

Low-NOx, Tangential Firing with Overfire Air

As shown in *Figure 2-17*, the first modification added air compartments within the windbox above the uppermost coal nozzle. Termed *overfire air (OFA) ports*, these compartments divert approximately 20% of the total combustion air to a burning zone above the windboxes. As a result, the fireball at windbox level is at or near stoichiometric air conditions.

Figure 2-18 shows the effect on NOx production of varying quantities of OFA. Note the effect of total excess air on NOx levels. This results primarily from the reduction in available oxygen within

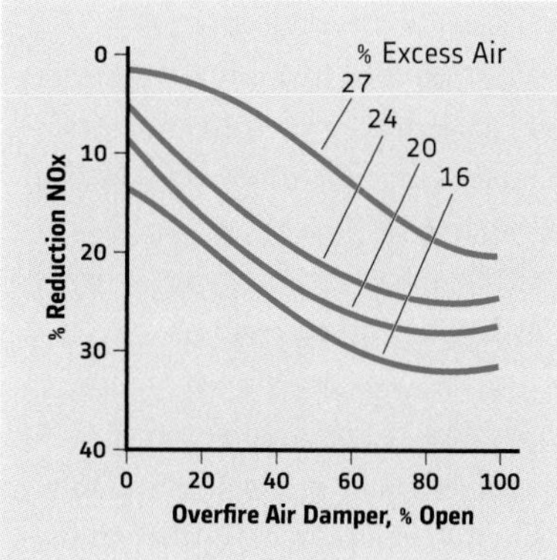

Figure 2-18 | Effect of overfire air on NOx production

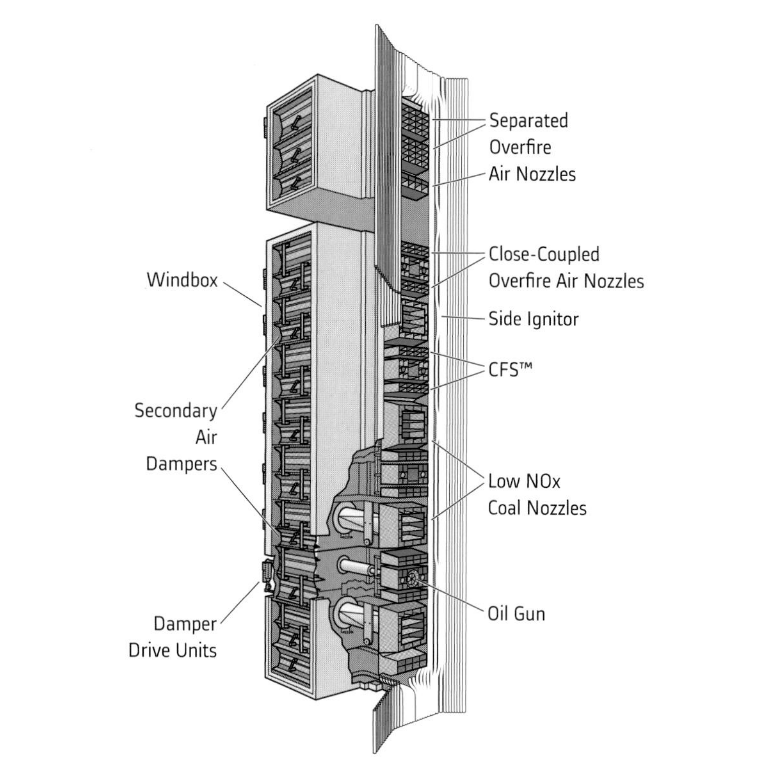

Figure 2-19 | Windbox for low-NOx, tangentially fired system (CFS™, Concentric Firing System)

the fireball adjacent to the windboxes. With a constant windbox-to-furnace differential, reducing total excess air increases the proportion of OFA at any given OFA damper position. This decreases the available oxygen below the OFA ports in even greater proportion to the change in total excess air.

Global and local staging techniques have progressively developed and are designed to minimize the availability of O_2 during the critical early phases of combustion, when the volatile nitrogen species are formed. Staged combustion has minimized NOx emissions, because the initial, fuel-rich conditions promote the formation of N_2 from the volatile nitrogen species.[10] Overfire air staging, which sets the global firing zone stoichiometry, has been used for more than 30 years.

Research efforts have advanced the original concept of "close-coupled" OFA to the next logical step: vertical staging of the OFA with one or more separated OFA windbox elevations to maximize the time at sub- or near-stoichiometric conditions (*Figs. 2-19* and *2-20*). Pilot-scale testing (*Fig. 2-21*) and field demonstrations have proven that some combination of close-coupled OFA and separated OFA is superior to either one alone.[11,12]

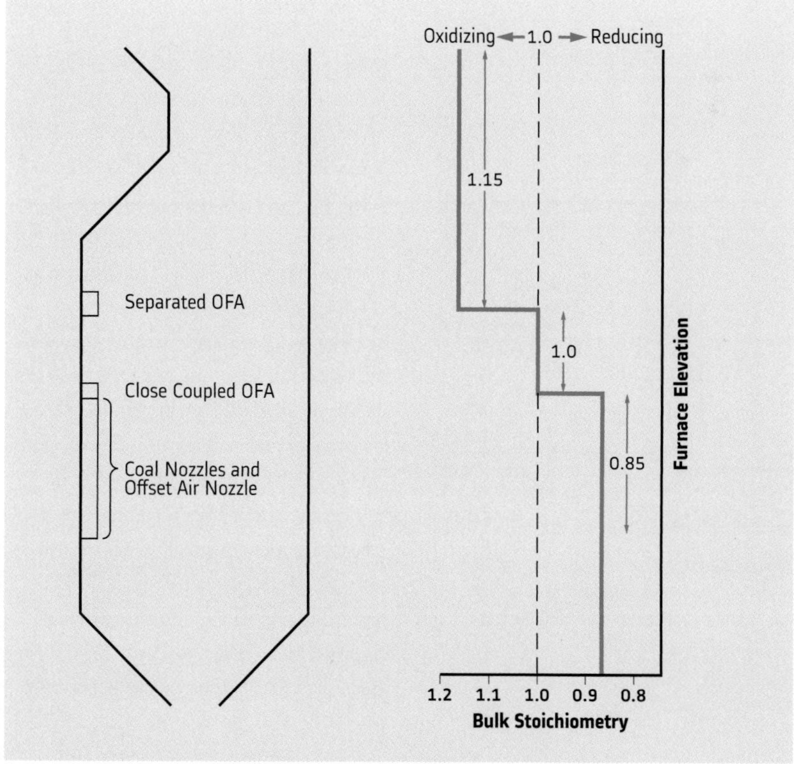

Figure 2-20 | Low-NOx, tangentially fired system (OFA, overfire air)

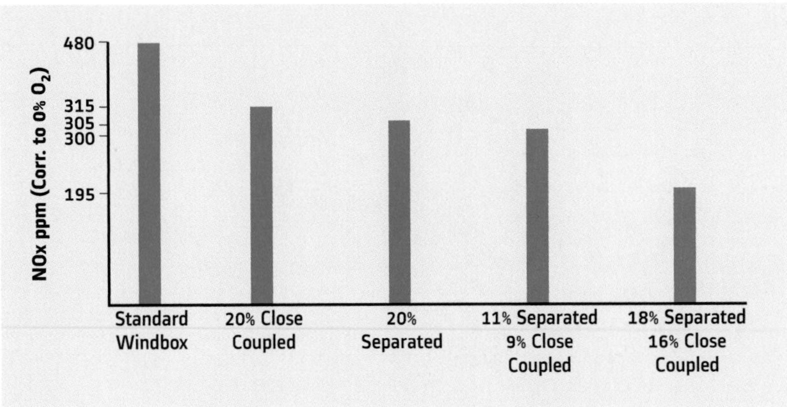

Figure 2-21 | NOx vs. overfire air quantity and elevation

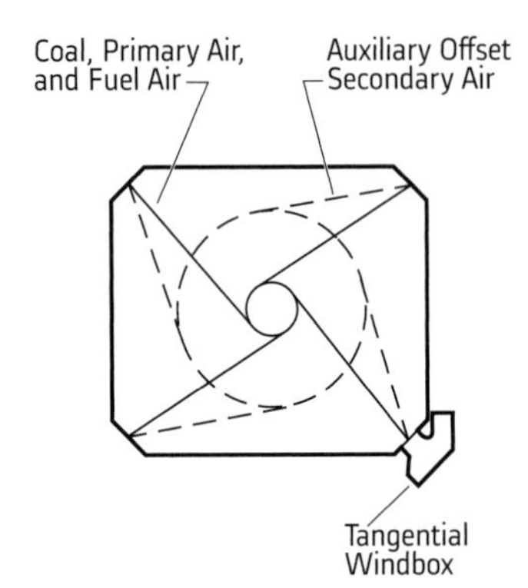

Figure 2-22 | Offset secondary air

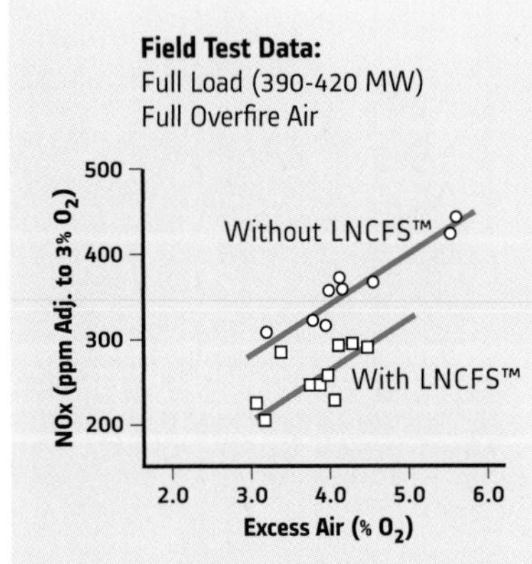

Figure 2-23 | NOx vs. excess air with and without the Low-NOx Concentric Firing System (LNCFS™)

Local staging contributes to NOx reduction via rapid ignition and depletion of near-burner oxygen. This is imperative to achieve maximum conversion of the volatile nitrogen to HCN and NH_3, followed by subsequent reduction to N_2 in the fuel-rich global regime. Flame attachment coal nozzles and rich/lean fuel streams are two local staging concepts currently being used.

Low NOx Concentric Firing System

In 1980, Alstom developed a firing system design called the Low-NOx Concentric Firing System (LNCFS™). In addition to close-coupled OFA and flame attachment coal nozzles, the LNCFS™ horizontally offsets, or stages, the secondary air streams relative to the fuel jets (*Fig. 2-22*). This delays air entrainment into the expanding fuel/primary air streams, and it provides more favorable conditions for low NOx in the pre-fireball flames (*Fig. 2-23*). Furnace aerodynamics are such that the stream separation is short-lived. The concept remains advantageous, however, because it increases oxygen concentration along the furnace waterwalls in the firing zone. In 1983, offset air was commercialized as the Concentric Firing System (CFS™). Units retrofitted with CFS™ had cleaner furnace waterwalls compared to pre-installation as well as slightly lower furnace outlet temperature. Horizontal air staging is particularly important when firing coals that have ash with high potential for slagging and corrosion.

In 1992, Alstom introduced the TFS2000™ system. This system combined many of the concepts that helped to reduce NOx formation in the furnace, including overfire air, concentric firing, yaw control, air staging, and finer grinding. These factors when combined together support each other in the minimization of NOx formation. The air staging allows the fuel to enter the furnace and initiate combustion in a manner that allows the fuel to release its nitrogen content in a relatively low oxygen environment. The concentric firing assures the wall of an adequate oxygen concentration to minimize corrosion potential. The overfire air with yaw control provides the air needed to complete combustion with adequate mixing. The finer grinding of coal provides a smaller particle that needs less residence time for burnout, allowing for adequate staging to lower NOx while still maintaining good combustion efficiency. This system provides for the lowest in-furnace control of NOx without the use of post-combustion treatment. The combination of in-furnace control and post-combustion treatment allows the design engineer the opportunity to meet emissions requirements at a lower cost.

STOKERS

Stokers are firing systems that feed and burn solid fuels in a bed at the bottom of a furnace. In all cases, the fuel is burned on some form of grate,

through which some or all of the air for combustion passes. The grate surface can be stationary or moving. Stokers are classified according to the way fuel is fed to the grate; the three general classes in use today are underfeed stokers, overfeed stokers, and spreader stokers.

Underfeed Stokers

In an underfeed stoker, the incoming fuel (usually coal) is pushed through one or more troughs, called retorts, that are located below the burning fuel bed and air-emission grates. Here, moisture is driven off, and volatile constituents are distilled, passing up through the incandescent bed. As the retorts are recharged, the char from the previous fill is pushed into and becomes part of the burning bed. On both sides of the retort, the "overflow" burns to completion on air-admitting grates, or tuyeres. Ash is removed by dumping grate sections (*Fig. 2-24*). Boilers with underfeed stokers of the single-retort design have been built in capacities ranging from 5,000 to 50,000 lb/h steam flow. Multiple-retort stoker units have been built for capacities ranging from 40,000 to 300,000 lb/h steam flow.

Overfeed Stokers

In an overfeed or traveling-grate stoker, gravity feeds the fuel (again, primarily coal) at one end of the air-admitting grate surface (*Fig. 2-25*). The incoming bed depth is adjusted by a gate under which the coal passes before entering the furnace. The rotating grate surface moves away from the feed end through the furnace; combustion is completed as air passes up through the grate. The ash residue is continuously discharged as the grate rotates around to its return run. Traveling-grate stokers can burn every type of coal that is mined, with the exception of caking bituminous coal. In addition, by-product and waste fuels, such as coke breeze or anthracite dredged from river bottoms, can be burned effectively. This machine has also been used as a part of chemical process operations that produce coke and CO_2. Steaming rates ranging from 10,000 to 300,000 lb/h are achievable.

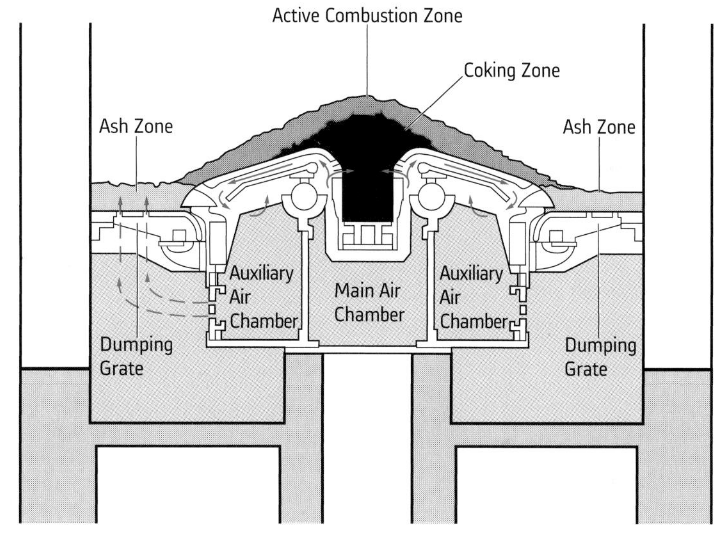

Figure 2-24 | Cross-section through underfeed stoker showing stages of combustion

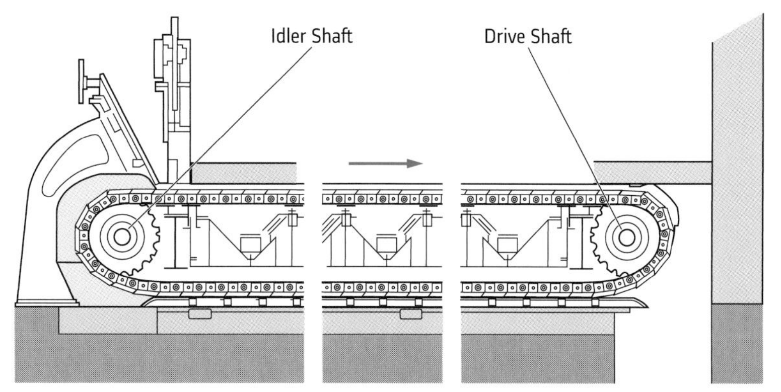

Figure 2-25 | Arrangement of traveling-grate stoker

For more detailed discussions about the designs and performance of these first two classes of stokers, the reader is referred to the first edition of *Combustion Engineering: A Reference Book on Fuel Burning and Steam Generation*.[13]

Spreader Stokers

The third major class of stokers—and the machine of choice in modern steam generation applications—is the spreader stoker (*Fig. 2-26*). This class combines the principles of suspension burning and thin-bed combustion. Feeder/distributor devices continuously project fuel into the furnace above an ignited fuel bed on the grate. Fines are burned in suspension, while larger particles fall and burn on the grate.

The spreader stoker method of fuel firing provides quick response to changes in boiler demand, and it generally never has more than a few minutes of fuel inventory on the grate. Flash drying and rapid release of tarry hydrocarbons enable this system to fire caking-type coals without concern for matting or clinkering. The air-cooled, non-agitated ash bed forms few clinkers despite low-fusion-temperature fuels. Particulate loadings for spreader stokers are higher than those for previously described designs, in which the fuel quiescently enters the burning zone. Practically all types of coal (except anthracite) and a wide variety of cellulosic fuels, including wood wastes, bagasse, furfural residue sludge, rice hulls, and coffee grounds, have been successfully burned on spreader stokers.

The most popular type of spreader stoker is that incorporating a continuous ash discharge grate (*Fig. 2-26*). This machine, unlike the traveling-grate stoker, moves toward the fuel feeders, which are throwing new fuel toward the back of the unit. All the fuel is burned before reaching the front end, from which ash is continuously dumped. The return side of the grate carries siftings, which fall through the top side of the grate to the rear and discharges them into a hopper. Grate speed is regulated to maintain an ash-bed depth of 2 to 4 inches at the discharge. Typical operating speed ranges from 2 to 20 ft/h and is varied via gear or hydraulic drive units.

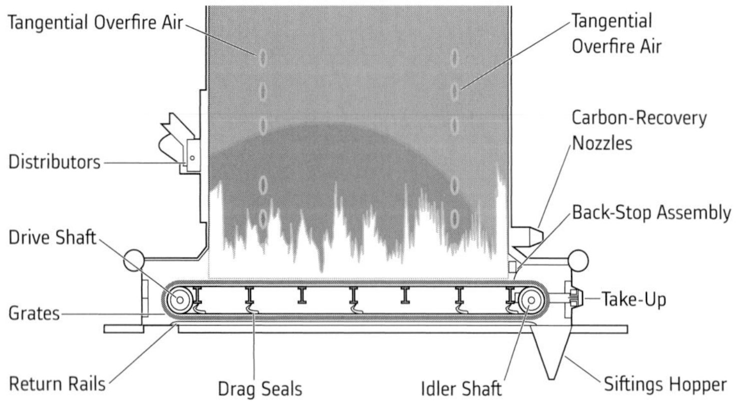

Tangential Overfire Air
Distributors
Drive Shaft
Grates
Return Rails
Drag Seals
Idler Shaft
Siftings Hopper
Take-Up
Back-Stop Assembly
Carbon-Recovery Nozzles
Tangential Overfire Air

Figure 2-26 | Spreader stoker with continuous ash discharge grate

Coal Size Specifications for Spreader-Stoker Firing

Spreader stokers were developed to burn the lower grades of coal, but they are capable of handling all ranks, from semi-anthracite to lignite as well as numerous waste and by-product fuels. As might be expected, spreader-stoker performance is best when fuel quality and sizing are good. The thin, quick-burning fuel bed requires a relatively small-size fuel. Because 25 to 50% of the fuel is burned in suspension, the size consistency of coal for spreader stokers has a direct bearing on boiler efficiency and on the tendency of the installation to emit particulates. Coal with a large percentage of fines will have high particulate emissions and high carbon loss. If the coal is coarse, with only a small percentage of fines, then boiler response to load variations will be affected, because fuel ignition depends on the fines. In general, the spreader-stoker coal consistency should follow the American Boiler Manufacturers Association (ABMA) recommendation per *Figure 2-27*, which shows that 95% of the coal delivered to the coal spreader will pass through a ¼-inch round-hole screen. Top size should not exceed 1-¼ inches.

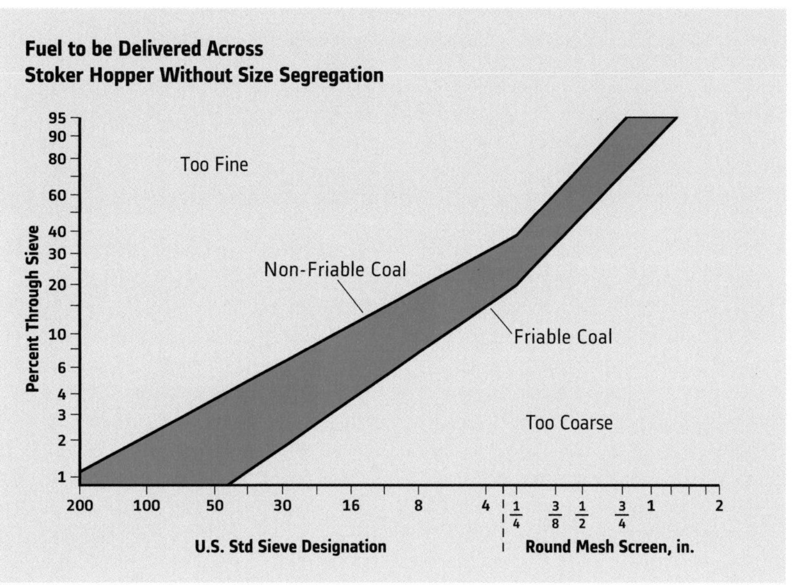

Figure 2-27 | American Boiler Manufacturers Association (ABMA)–recommended limits of coal sizing for spreader stokers

Overfire Air

In stoker-fired furnaces that burn bituminous coals, OFA is necessary to improve combustion efficiency by turbulent mixing of air with the unburned gases. Optimum mixing results are achieved through proper pressure and volume of the air. The quantity of OFA should be between 5 and 20% of the total quantity of air needed for fuel combustion. The amount of OFA will be a function of the coal rank and the amount of excess air in the furnace. Relatively small jets of air at pressures up to 25 or 30″ water gage are used in most installations for improving combustion in the furnace and for reducing visible emissions and cinder carryover.

IGNITION SYSTEMS

Modern steam generators are very dependent on their ignition systems for safe start-up and shutdown operations. The need to ensure reliable and safe firing conditions has caused the evolution from simple ignitors to highly sophisticated ignition systems. Such advanced systems require the following features:

- A timed spark-ignition sequence
- A device to create turbulent fuel/air mixing and sufficient hot-gas recirculation to insure flame stability
- A device to detect and monitor the ignitor flame
- A device to monitor ignitor fuel flow as an indication of ignitor heat energy release

The primary function of the ignition system is to light the main fuel. Often, the ignition system is also designed to stabilize the main fuel flame under potentially unstable firing conditions. Determining the correct amount of ignition energy to fulfill either function is a challenging task. The correct combination of ignition-energy quantity, quality, and location is affected by many factors, some of which vary with time; what constitutes sufficient

IGNITOR FUNCTIONAL DEFINITIONS

To fully understand the hardware, it may be necessary to review the definitions contained in NFPA 85E, "Standard for Prevention of Furnace Explosions in Pulverized Coal-Fired Multiple Burner Boiler-Furnaces, 1985 Edition."[14]

CLASS 1 (CONTINUOUS IGNITOR)

An ignitor applied to ignite the fuel input through the burner and to support ignition under any burner light-off or operating conditions. Its location and capacity are such that it will provide sufficient ignition energy (generally in excess of 10% of full load burner input) at its associated burner to raise any credible combination of burner inputs of both fuel and air above the minimum ignition temperature.[15]

CLASS 2 (INTERMITTENT IGNITOR)

An ignitor applied to ignite the fuel input through the burner under prescribed light-off conditions. It is also used to support ignition under low load or certain adverse operating conditions. The range of capacity of such ignitors is generally 4 to 10% of the full load burner fuel input. It shall not be used to ignite main fuel under uncontrolled or abnormal conditions. The burner shall be operated under controlled conditions to limit the potential for abnormal operation, as well as to limit the charge of fuel to the furnace in the event that ignition does not occur during light-off. Class 2 ignitors may be operated as Class 3 ignitors.[16]

CLASS 3 (INTERRUPTED IGNITOR)

A small ignitor applied particularly to gas and oil burners to ignite the fuel input to the burner under prescribed light-off conditions. The capacity of such ignitors generally does not exceed 4% of full load burner fuel input. As a part of the burner light-off procedure, the ignitor is turned off when the timed trial for ignition of the main burner has expired. This is to ensure that the main flame is self-supporting, is stable, and is not dependent upon ignition support from the ignitor. The use of such ignitors to support ignition or to extend the burner control range shall be prohibited.[17]

CLASS 3 SPECIAL (DIRECT ELECTRIC IGNITOR)

A special Class 3 high-energy electrical ignitor capable of directly igniting the main burner fuel. This type ignitor shall not be used unless supervision of the individual main burner flame is provided.[18]

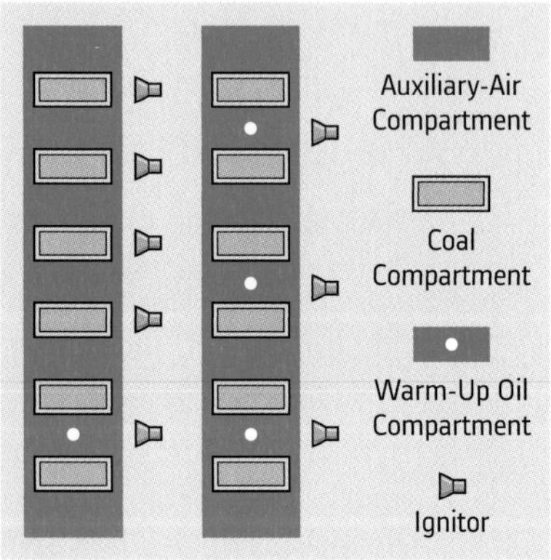

Figure 2-28 | Alternative step ignition processes for tangential firing

ignition energy at one instant may be insufficient the next. From the rate-igniting standpoint, there is never excess ignition energy: The more stable a fire, the more likely the ignition energy substantially exceeds the minimum necessary to maintain ignition.

Years of experience with various fuels and firing systems have led the National Fire Protection Association (NFPA) to establish practical guidelines for defining ignition-energy requirements based on fuel type and ignition-system function. For NFPA definitions, see the accompanying box *Ignitor Functional Definitions*.

Ignition-System Design

An electrical spark is the typical initiating source of fuel ignition. High-voltage, free-air sparks can reliably ignite high-calorific-value gases and light (distillate) oils. High-energy, surface-shunted arcs are used to reliably ignite distillate and heavy (residual) oils. Safety considerations dictate that because of its relatively low ignition energy, only a limited quantity of fuel be exposed to the electrical spark. The heat released from this initial fuel input then becomes the ignition energy for a different and/or larger fuel input. Essentially, the ignition system provides a controlled transition from spark to main-fuel firing through an incremental increase in the ignition energy.

Not making too large of a step-increase in fuel input is also important to avoid undesirable furnace pressurization during light-off. *Figure 2-28* shows two methods of achieving a step-increase in fuel input for tangential firing. In the example shown on the left of *Figure 2-28*, the lowest elevation of ignitors is fired first, and after a suitable period of time, the elevation of oil warm-up guns is ignited. As the furnace temperature stabilizes, the main coal nozzles adjacent to the oil guns are brought into operation. Thereafter, additional ignitors can come into service to light off elevations of main coal nozzles directly.

In the alternative example shown on the right of *Figure 2-28*, ignitors light off successive elevations of warm-up oil guns. Adjacent elevations of main coal nozzles are then ignited by the oil guns.

Experience indicates that firing by these steps/input methods will minimize furnace pressurization and unnecessary overpressure trips.

Ignition Systems

Ignitors available for tangentially and horizontally fired systems include the Ionic Flame Monitoring (IFM) and High Energy Arc (HEA) ignitors. These ignitors use a wide variety of gas and oil fuels. The IFM ignitor fires medium to high HHV oils and/or natural gas or propane. The HEA ignitor sparks/ignites distillate through residual oils. The type of system selected depends on fuel availability and cost. High-quality gas and distillate oil are preferred for both ignition systems and for boiler warm-up, because such gas and oil are easier to handle and burn more cleanly in cold furnaces.

IFM IGNITORS. An IFM ignitor is a complete ignition system containing an electrical spark source, a self-stabilizing burner device, flame detection, and fuel-input monitoring. A high-voltage spark or high energy arc source as defined can be used for ignition. Either gas, ranging from coke-oven gas to butane, or No. 2 fuel oil is used with this type of system. Flame detection is achieved with the IFM device. Flow switches monitor fuel input. The IFM design (*Fig. 2-29*) follows the traditional Alstom philosophy of providing both qualitative and quantitative indication of flame.

The IFM system takes advantage of the production of ions and charged particles during the combustion of hydrocarbon fuels. A hydrocarbon-fuel flame, then, will conduct electricity. Another characteristic of turbulent flames is that they continuously pulsate at some constant frequency. The quantity of ions and charged particles generated varies as the flame pulsates. Thus, the conductivity of the flame also changes with the pulsation of the flame.

When a DC potential is placed across a flame, the electric current flow varies at the same frequency as the flame pulsation. The IFM system operates by imposing a DC potential on an electrode called the flame rod, which is in contact with the flame. When there is "no flame," the DC voltage remains at the originally imposed level, and no current flows. When there is "flame," the DC voltage drops as current flows, generating an AC feedback signal. This AC signal is filtered, amplified, and modified by the IFM electronics to drive a flame-indication relay. The electronics are designed to be fail-safe. If a component failure occurs (e.g., a short circuit in the flame rod or signal lead wire, or an external AC interference), a "no flame" indication will occur.

The most common application of IFM ignitors is consistent with the NFPA Class 2 definition. The IFM ignitors have been used as Class 1 devices and could be used as Class 3 devices; however, additional burner-control

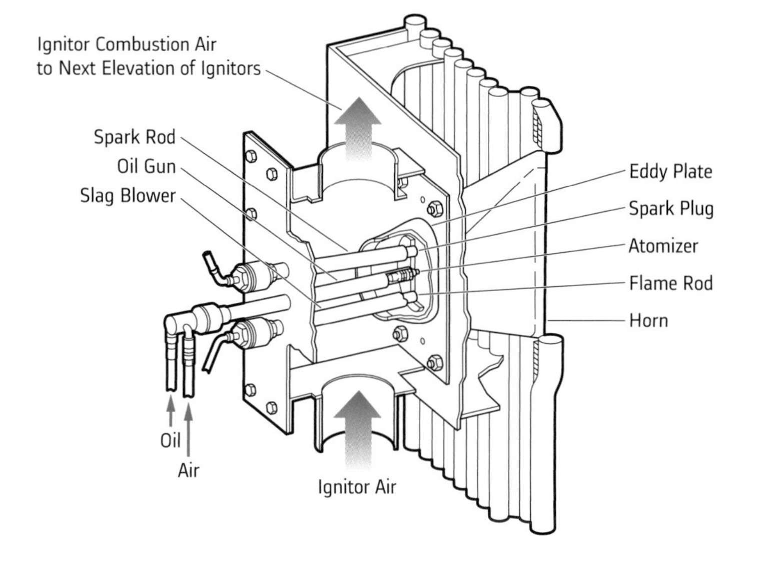

Figure 2-29 | Ionic Flame Monitoring (IFM) side ignitor

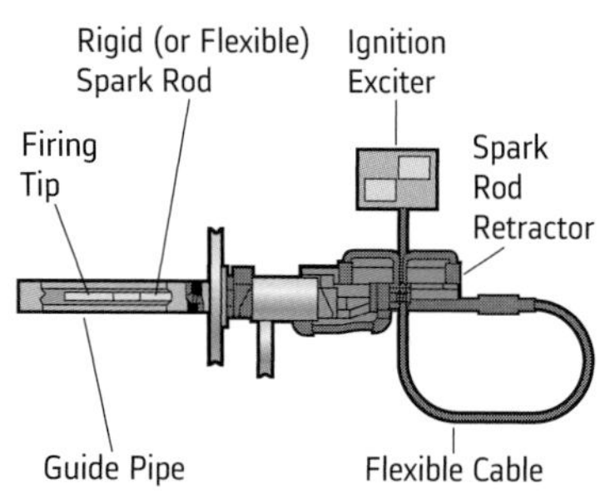

Figure 2-30 | High Energy Arc (HEA) ignitor

(A) Flame Pocket is Created on Ignitor Tip

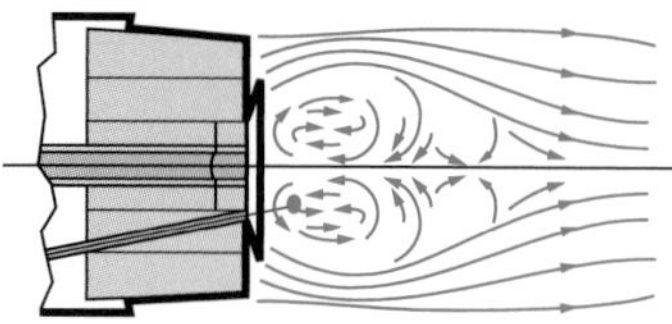

(B) Flame Pocket Becomes Entrained in Recirculation Zone and Expands Towards Oil-Gun Tip

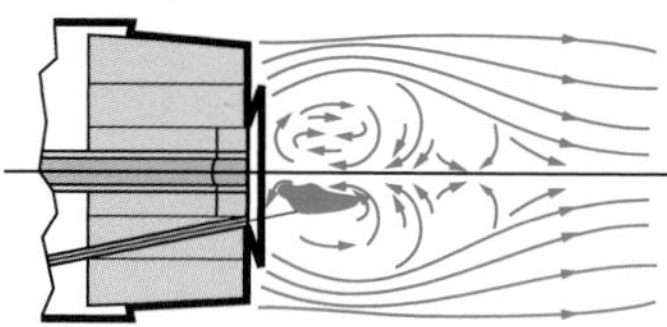

(C) Flame Pocket Reaches Oil-Gun Tip and Stabilizes

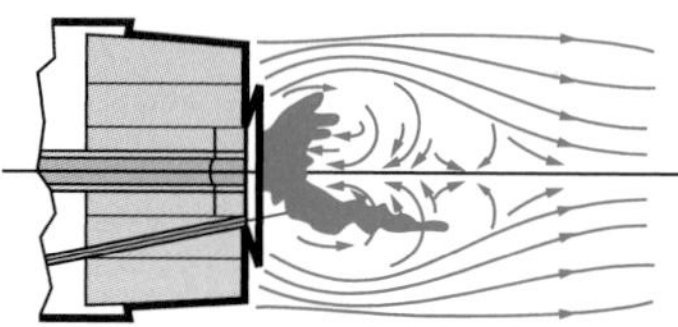

Figure 2-31 | High Energy Arc (HEA) ignition sequence

logic and discriminating flame scanners would be required. (Refer to Chapter 7 for more information on flame scanners.) A Class 3 application would be made only when a limited amount of ignition fuel is available, such as with a bottled-gas supply system.

HEA IGNITORS. The HEA ignitor was developed specifically for residual oils. It eliminates dependence on premium fuels, such as natural gas and No. 2 fuel oil for main-fuel ignition and boiler warm-up. The HEA ignitor directly spark-ignites a heavy-oil warm-up gun, which in turn ignites the main coal nozzles. The HEA ignitor is used with a discriminating scanner that verifies the operation of the warm-up gun. The warm-up gun is sized for an oil flow of about 10% of the energy capacity of an adjacent coal nozzle, with the discriminating scanner proving the presence of a flame. The combination of an HEA ignitor and a No. 6 fuel oil-fired warm-up gun satisfies the NFPA definition of a Class 1 or Class 2 ignitor. The HEA ignitor alone would be a Class 3 ignitor.

The complete HEA ignition system consists of:

- An HEA ignitor
- A warm-up oil compartment capable of producing a stable flame at all loads
- A flame-detecting system sensitive only to its associated oil gun
- A control system coordinating all the components and providing unit safety

The HEA ignitor can ignite warm-up fuel oils ranging from No. 2 to No. 6 and also crude oils. The ignitor is a self-contained electrical discharge device that produces a high-intensity spark. Use of a high-resistance transformer (to produce a full wave charging circuit and control spark rate) enables the sealed power supply to store maximum energy and then deliver a greater percentage of this energy through insulated cables to the ignitor tip. A high spark energy also eliminates coking of the ignitor tip. The HEA ignitor consists of four basic components: an exciter, a flexible cable, a spark tube and guide pipe, and a retractor assembly (*Fig. 2-30*).

A key to the successful application of spark-ignition is the presence of a strong recirculation pattern in the primary combustion zone (*Fig. 2-31*). The recirculation provides the energy required to vaporize and heat the oil to its ignition point, thus maintaining stable ignition after the spark has been deactivated.

The discriminating flame scanners operate in the visible-light range, which provides excellent sensitivity to the presence of a flame. These scanners therefore can discriminate between different flames based on both frequency and intensity. This insures safe operation of the overall HEA system.

DOUG HART
BOB KUNKEL

REFERENCES

1. "Standard Atmosphere Tables and Data for Altitudes to 65,800 feet," National Advisory Committee for Aeronautics Report 1235 International Civil Aviation Organization (ICAO), Montreal, Canada, and Langley Aeronautical Laboratory, Langley Field, VA. 1952.
2. Ya. B. Zel'Dovich, "The Oxidation of Nitrogen in Combustion and Explosions," *Acta Physicochimica (USSR)*, 21: 577–628, 1946.
3. D. J. MacKinnon, "Nitric Oxide Formation at High Temperature," *Air Pollution Control Association Journal*, 24: 237–239, 1974.
4. C. P. Fenimore, "Formation of Nitric Oxide from Fuel Nitrogen in Ethylene Flames," *Combustion and Flame*, 19: 289–296, 1972.
5. G. De Soete, "Mechanism of Nitric Oxide Formation from Ammonia and Amines in Hydrocarbon Flames," *Revue de L-Institut Français du Petrole et Annuales Des Combustible Liquides*, 28: 95–108, 1973.
6. W. W. Habelt, "The Influence of Coal Oxygen to Coal Nitrogen Ratio on NOx Formation," Presented at the 70th Annual American Institute of Chemical Engineers Meeting, New York, November 13–17, 1977.
7. D. W. Pershing and J. O. L. Wendt, "Pulverized Coal Combustion: The Influence of Flame Temperature and Coal Composition on Thermal and Fuel NOx," 16th Symposium (International) on Combustion, The Combustion Institute, 1976, p. 389
8. J. D. Freihaut, W. M. Proscia, and J. D. Seery, "Fuel-Bound Nitrogen Evolution During Devolitilization and Pyrolysis of Coals of Varying Rank," Joint Symposium on Stationary Combustion NOx Sources, New Orleans, 1987.
9. S. L. Chen, M. P. Heap, D. W. Pershing, and G. B. Martin, "Influence of Coal Composition on the Fate of Volatile and Char Nitrogen During Combustion," 19th Symposium (International) on Combustion, The Combustion Institute, 1982, p. 1271.
10. Ibid, p. 1271.
11. M. S. McCartney and J. Grusha, "Development and Evolution of the ABB Combustion Engineering Low NOx Concentric Firing System," 1991 Joint Symposium on Stationary Combustion NOx Control, Washington, D.C., 1991, Vol. 1.
12. R. A. Buchs, L. K. Bailey, J. V. Dallen, T. D. Hellewell, and C. W. Smith, "Results from a Commercial Installation of Low NOx Concentric Firing System (LNCFS™)," International Joint Power Generation Conference, Boston, MA, 1990.
13. Otto De Lorenzi, ed., "Combustion Engineering: A Reference Book on Fuel Burning and Steam Generation," First Edition, New York: Combustion Engineering-Superheater, Inc., 1947.
14. NFPA 85E, "Standard for Prevention of Furnace Explosions in Pulverized Coal-Fired Multiple Burner Boiler-Furnaces, 1985 Edition," p. 85E-9.
15. Ibid, p. 85E-9.
16. Ibid, p. 85E-9.
17. Ibid, p. 85E-9.
18. Ibid, p. 85E-9.

Boilers

Chapter **Three**

PULVERIZED COAL-FIRED BOILERS

One of the most significant engineering achievements of the twentieth century was the commercial development of methods for firing coal in pulverized form. In fact, this development made possible the extremely large, modern, steam-generating unit with its high thermal efficiency, reliability, and safety. This is graphically illustrated in *Figure 3-1*, which shows the increase in boiler capacity after World War I, when pulverized coal firing achieved widespread adoption in the central station industry.

Practically every type of coal mined in the United States and throughout the world is now being burned successfully in pulverized form. Many other types of low-grade, waste, and by-product solid fuels also may be fired economically and efficiently in this manner. Pulverized fuel firing has contributed to the reduction of labor costs in steam power plants, increased the flexibility of operation, and allowed use of an extremely wide range of fuels.

Since World War II, manufacturers have developed diverse designs for generating steam at high subcritical and supercritical pressures. This diversity is particularly apparent in large, high-pressure (HP) units, for which the individual proprietary designs become the hallmark of each manufacturer. It is for the development of its large, HP, high-temperature steam generators that Alstom has built and staffed some of the finest research laboratories in the world, dedicated solely to the development and improvement of equipment for steam generation (see Appendix G).

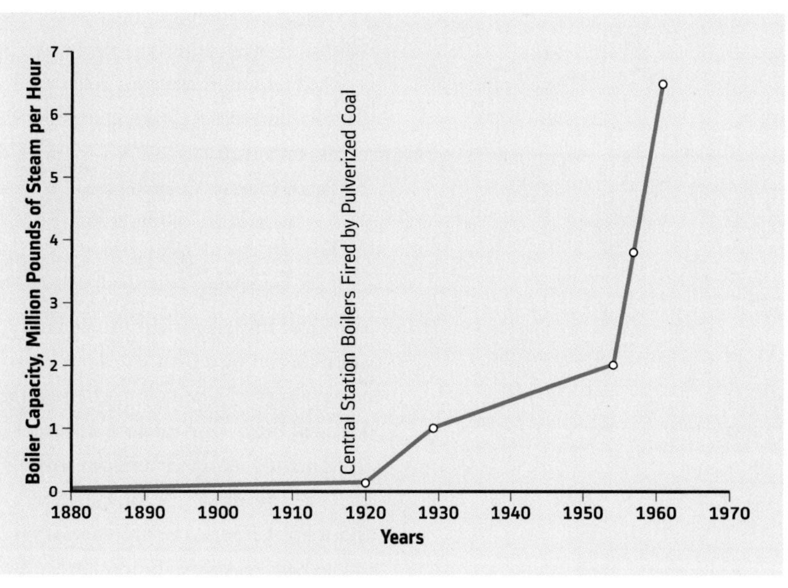

Figure 3-1 | Increase in boiler capacity, showing the effect of the introduction of pulverized coal firing to central stations in 1919

CONVERTING COAL'S ENERGY TO ELECTRIC POWER

The boiler designer has the difficult task of converting the many forms of coal into HP and high-temperature steam, which powers steam turbines to drive generators that make electricity. A very wide range of coal properties, combustion properties, ash eutectics, corrosive characteristics, and environmental implications need to be considered.

The thermodynamics of steam generation demand steam at the highest possible temperatures and pressures for the best cycle efficiency. Progress in boiler design throughout the twentieth century resulted in tremendous improvements in both coal combustion and advanced steam cycles. Boiler design has to balance breakthroughs in combustion and metallurgy in the development of new designs expected to last for at least three decades.

Advances in emission control processes and equipment have reduced the environmental impact of this large-scale equipment (see Chapter 5). Since the early applications of pulverized coal-fired boilers, emissions rates have been reduced more than 300 fold on a kilowatt-hour basis. Ongoing improvements are anticipated that will improve this figure to more than 700 fold.

IMPACT OF FUEL ON BOILER DESIGN

The most important item to consider when designing a utility or large industrial steam generator is the fuel the unit will burn. The furnace size, the equipment to prepare and burn the fuel, the amount of heating surface and its placement, the type and size of the heat recovery equipment, and the flue gas treatment devices are all fuel dependent. The major differences among those boilers that burn coal or oil or natural gas result from the ash in the products of combustion (see Appendix B). Firing oil in a furnace results in relatively small amounts of ash; there is almost no ash from natural gas. For the same output, because of the ash, coal-burning boilers must have larger furnaces. The velocities of the combustion gases in the convection passes must be lower as well. In addition, coal-burning boilers need ash-handling and particulate control equipment, which adds to the overall cost and requires considerable space.

Table 3-1 lists the variation in calorific values and moisture contents of several coals as well as the mass of fuel that must be handled and fired to generate the same output of electric power. These values are important, because the quantity of fuel required helps to determine the size of the coal storage yard as well as the handling, crushing, and pulverizing equipment needed for the various coals. The amount of ash in the coal directly affects the sizing of the ash-handling and particulate control equipment.

FURNACE SIZING

The most important step in designing a coal-fired unit is to properly size the furnace. Furnace size has a first-order influence on the size and cost of the convective heat-transfer surface, the structural steel framing, the boiler building and its foundations, the quantity and length of soot blowers, the extent of platforms and stairways, and the arrangement of steam piping and ductwork.

Three very important parametric influences on furnace sizing are:

- Fuel reactivity
- Gaseous emission limitations (particularly those concerning nitrogen oxides)
- Fuel ash properties

TABLE 3-1 | REPRESENTATIVE COAL ANALYSES

	Med.-Vol. Bituminous	High-Vol. Bituminous	Sub-bituminous C	Low-Sodium Lignite	Med.-Sodium Lignite	High-Sodium Lignite
Total H_2O, %	5.0	15.4	30.0	31.0	30.0	39.6
Ash, %	10.3	15.0	5.8	10.4	28.4	6.3
VM, %	31.6	33.1	32.6	31.7	23.2	27.5
FC, %	53.1	36.5	36.6	26.9	18.4	26.6
ASH ANALYSIS, %						
SiO_2	40.0	46.4	29.5	46.1	62.9	23.1
Al_2O_3	24.0	16.2	16.0	15.2	17.5	11.3
Fe_2O_3	16.8	20.0	4.1	3.7	2.8	8.5
CaO	5.8	7.1	26.5	16.6	4.8	23.8
MgO	2.0	0.8	4.2	3.2	0.7	5.9
Na_2O	0.8	0.7	1.4	0.4	3.1	7.4
K_2O	2.4	1.5	0.5	0.6	2.0	0.7
TiO_2	1.3	1.0	1.3	1.2	0.8	0.5
P_2O_5	0.1	0.1	1.1	0.1	0.1	0.2
SO_3	5.3	6.0	14.8	12.7	4.6	17.7
Sulfur, %	1.8	3.2	0.3	0.6	1.7	0.8
FUSION (REDUCING), °F						
Initial Deformation	2,170	1,990	2,200	2,080	2,120	2,030
Softening	2,250	2,120	2,250	2,200	2,380	2,090
Fluid	2,440	2,290	2,290	2,310	2,700	2,200
FUSION (REDUCING), °C						
Initial Deformation	1,190	1,090	1,200	1,140	1,160	1,110
Softening	1,230	1,160	1,230	1,200	1,300	1,140
Fluid	1,340	1,250	1,250	1,270	1,480	1,200
BTU/lb, as fired	13,240	10,500	8,125	7,590	5,000	6,520
BTU/lb, MAF	15,640	15,100	12,650	12,940	12,020	12,050
Lb Ash/Million BTU	7.8	14.3	7.1	13.7	56.8	9.7
***Fuel Fired, 1,000 lb/h**	405	520	705	750	1,175	900
***Ash Fired, 1,000 lb/h**	42	78	41	78	334	57
MJ/kg, as fired	30.8	24.4	18.9	17.7	11.6	15.2
MJ/kg, MAF	36.4	35.1	29.4	30.1	28.0	28.0
kg Ash/Million kJ	3.3	6.1	3.1	5.9	24.4	4.2
***Fuel Fired, kg/s**	51.0	65.5	88.8	94.5	148.0	113.4
***Ash Fired, kg/s**	5.3	9.8	5.2	9.8	42.0	7.1

*Constant Heat Output, Nominal 600-MWe Unit, Adjusted for Effect of Moisture Content on Efficiency
MAF, moisture and ash free

Among the ash properties described in Appendix B, those that Alstom considers to be particularly important when designing and establishing the size of coal-fired furnaces include:

- The ash fusibility temperatures (both in terms of their absolute values and in terms of the spread or difference between initial deformation temperature and fluid temperature)

- The ratio of basic to acidic ash constituents
- The iron/calcium ratio
- The fuel ash content in terms of lb ash/million BTU (kg ash/million J)
- The ash friability

These characteristics translate into the typical furnace sizes shown in *Figure 3-2*, which are based on the six coal ranks shown in *Table 3-1*. This size comparison illustrates the philosophy of increasing the furnace plan area, volume, and the fuel burnout zone (the distance from the top fuel nozzle to the furnace arch) as lower-grade coals with poorer ash characteristics are fired.

Figure 3-2 is a simplified characterization of actual furnaces built to burn the fuels listed in *Table 3-1*. Wide variations exist in fuel properties within coal ranks as well as within several sub-classifications (e.g., sub-bituminous A, B, and C), each of which may require a different size of furnace. Note that in general, high-sodium lignite also tends to have high slagging tendencies.

Among the most important design criteria in large, pulverized-fuel, tangentially fired furnaces are the net heat input in BTU/h-ft^2 (W/m^2) over furnace plan area (NHI/PA) and the vertical distance from the top fuel nozzle to the furnace arch in ft (m). Furnace dimensions must be adequate to establish the necessary furnace retention time to properly burn the fuel as well as to cool the gaseous combustion products. This cooling must be adequate to ensure that the gas temperature at the furnace outlet plane is well below the ash-softening temperature of the lowest-quality coal that is burned. Specifically, the furnace outlet plane is the entrance to the close-spaced convection surface. The latter is defined as non-platen surface on less than 12 inch (300 mm) horizontal centers. In addition to the tilting of fuel and air nozzles, the heat absorption characteristics of the walls are maintained using properly placed wall blowers to control the furnace outlet gas temperature by removing ash that has been deposited on the furnace walls below the furnace outlet plane.

To arrive at an appropriate value of NHI/PA and furnace plan area, a thorough evaluation of all fuels expected to be burned in the unit is required. Depending on the analyses and range of coals to be burned, large, pulverized fuel-burning units have an NHI/PA that generally varies from 1.4 to 2.0 × 10^6 BTU/h-ft^2 (4.4 to 6.3 × 10^6 W/m^2). The distance from the upper fuel nozzle to the furnace arch is a function of furnace width and depth, the upper furnace superheater and reheater surface arrangement, and of course, the fuel and ash characteristics.

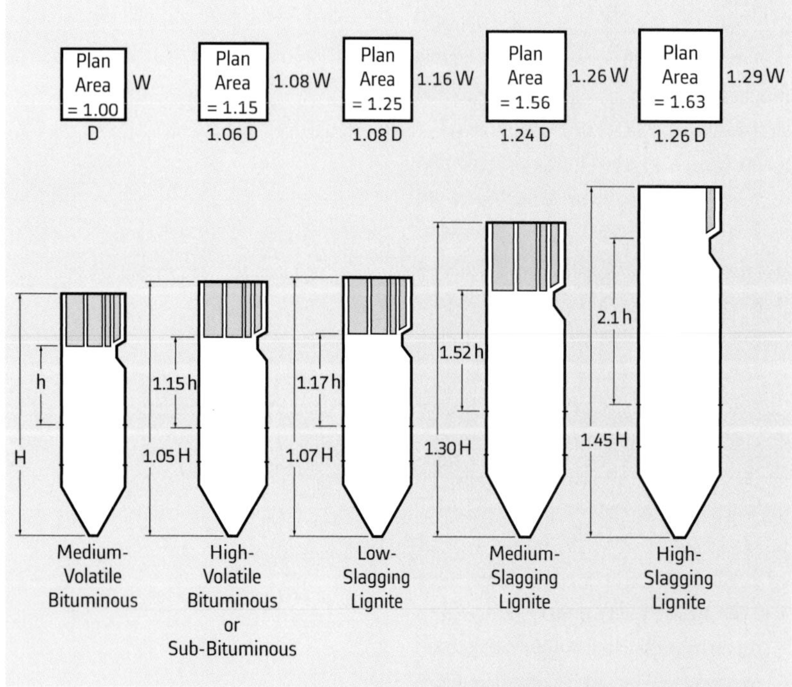

Figure 3-2 | Effect of coal rank on sizing of a pulverized-fuel furnace (constant heat output)

A widely spaced, steam-cooled, platen-type heating surface is usually required in the upper furnace to provide further cooling of furnace gases before those gases enter the convection surface. These sections potentially are subject to the most severe fouling conditions, and wide spacing helps to prevent ash plugging caused by bridging. To perform satisfactorily in this environment, the platens are constructed with the tubes at a tangent to each other in the direction of gas flow to minimize ash deposition.

A furnace design parameter known as "burner zone heat release" is sometimes specified. This term does not have the same significance in tangential firing as it does in other firing systems. In tangential firing, not all of the fuel is consumed in the windbox zone because of the manner in which the fuel and air are introduced into the furnace. In a unit designed for wall firing, the fuel and air are intimately mixed at the burner throat and are consumed directly in front of the burner. A wall-fired boiler may have its burners moved farther apart, or more burners can be added, to give any value of burner zone release rate, because little interaction occurs between rows of burners. The vertical distance from the lowest coal nozzle to the point where the furnace walls are bent to form the hopper section of the furnace is a function of the furnace width and depth and of the slagging potential of the fuel. This dimension generally is between 12 and 20 ft (between 3.7 and 6 m) in a tangentially fired furnace. The hopper section typically slopes at 50° to the horizontal.

With the exception of dry-bottom, pulverized coal-fired units with sizes of between approximately 50 and 100 MWe, the furnace volumetric heat release rate in BTU/h-ft^3 (W/m^3) generally is not a controlling design parameter. For such units, the release rate range is from 15,000 BTU/h-ft^3 for very good bituminous coals to approximately 10,000 BTU/h-ft^3 for lignite (from 150,000 to ~100,000 W/m^3). Similarly, the burner zone, volumetric heat release rate in BTU/h-ft^3 (W/m^3) is not a meaningful design parameter for tangentially fired boilers.

DRY-BOTTOM VERSUS WET-BOTTOM FURNACES

All current pulverized-coal reheat units are of the dry-bottom type. The ash dislodged from the furnace walls is below the ash melting point and leaves the furnace bottom in a substantially dry condition. The wet-bottom, or slagging-bottom, furnaces are offered today only for very special applications, such as in furnaces for gasifying coal.

In the wet-bottom design, the lower part of the flame has to sweep the furnace floor at all loads to maintain the fluidity of the ash. This requirement imposes a definite limitation in the use of slag-tap furnaces. Slag-tap freezing can occur during operation at low load or when fuel is fired only in the upper furnace for steam temperature control. In addition, wet-bottom units have higher nitrogen oxide production. The dry-bottom furnace, on the other hand, and particularly those designs using tilting fuel nozzles, can provide a wider control range for steam temperature and can handle coals with widely varying ash characteristics. This latter characteristic, more than any other, originally was responsible for the greater application of dry-bottom units.
In the typical dry-bottom furnace, bending the front- and rear-wall tubes

at their lower ends forms the hopper. The tube slope is greater than the angle of repose of the ash and, thus, forms a self-cleaning, water-cooled hopper. Ash is discharged to the ash receiver through a transverse opening in the hopper that on large units is approximately 4 ft (1.2 m) wide.

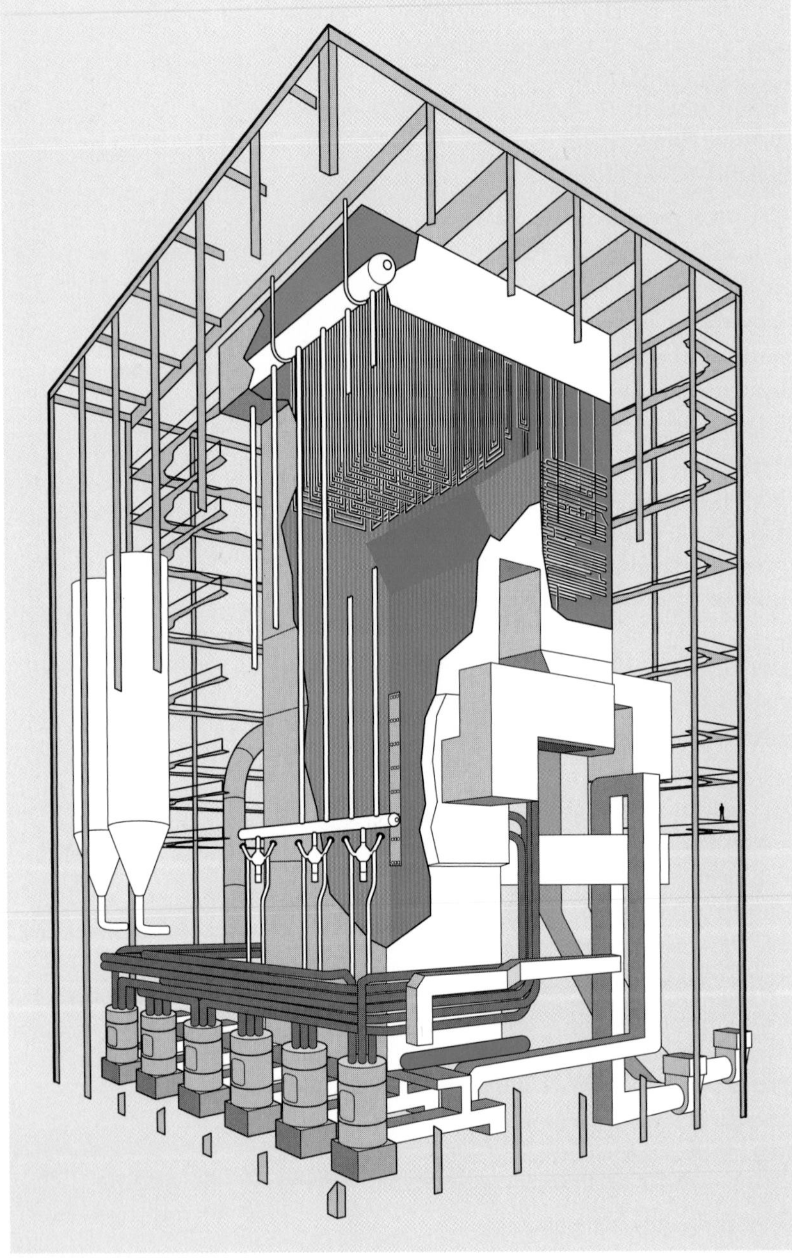

Figure 3-3 | Typical coal-burning central station reheat steam generator of the Alstom tangentially fired Controlled Circulation® design

ARRANGEMENT OF UPPER FURNACE HEATING SURFACE

Alstom uses two principal arrangements of upper furnace heating surface, which can be termed the *two-pass design* (or *pendant panel design*) and the *tower design* (or *horizontal surface design*). The reheat steam generators shown in *Figures 3-3, 3-8, 3-13, 3-19,* and *3-24* illustrate the two-pass design as it is applied to large, coal-fired units. The boilers shown in *Figures 3-4, 3-25,* and *3-26* also are large, coal-fired units but use the horizontal arrangement of superheater and reheater surfaces in the top of the furnace (tower units). Each of these configurations has its advantages, and each allows customer preference as a factor in the final arrangement of heating surface.

Advantages of the Two-Pass Design

Advantages of the two-pass design include:

- The support elements for the pendant surface are out of the gas stream, above the furnace roof; this eliminates the exposure of load supports and seals to high gas temperatures and fly ash erosion. Superheater and reheater tubes are free to expand downward and have only simple alignment devices in the gas stream.
- No relative motion occurs between the furnace tubing and the superheater or reheater tubes where the latter penetrate the enclosure. Thus, the area of penetration can be seal-welded for maximum gas tightness, eliminating the need for pressurized header enclosures.
- The above support and sealing arrangement favors shop modularization of tubes, headers,

attachments, and supports. Field construction consists of lifting these modules into position, butt-welding adjacent header sections, and seal-welding small areas of skin casing after the horizontal furnace roof tubes are in place.
- The lower height of the pendant boiler can be expected to result in lower costs for the boiler building, elevators, platforms and stairways, structural steel framing, steam piping, and foundations, particularly in high seismic and wind-load areas.
- In field erection, construction of major pressure parts can be carried out in several areas simultaneously. Also, the pendant panel steam generator is not as tall as the horizontal type, which reduces construction costs.
- Any required replacement of or modifications to heating surfaces are greatly simplified.
- Widely spaced panels (6 to 8 ft [1.8 to 2.4 m] horizontal centers), along with steam-cooled wall sections in the upper furnace, have high radiant-heat absorption, resulting in an improved control range for steam temperature.

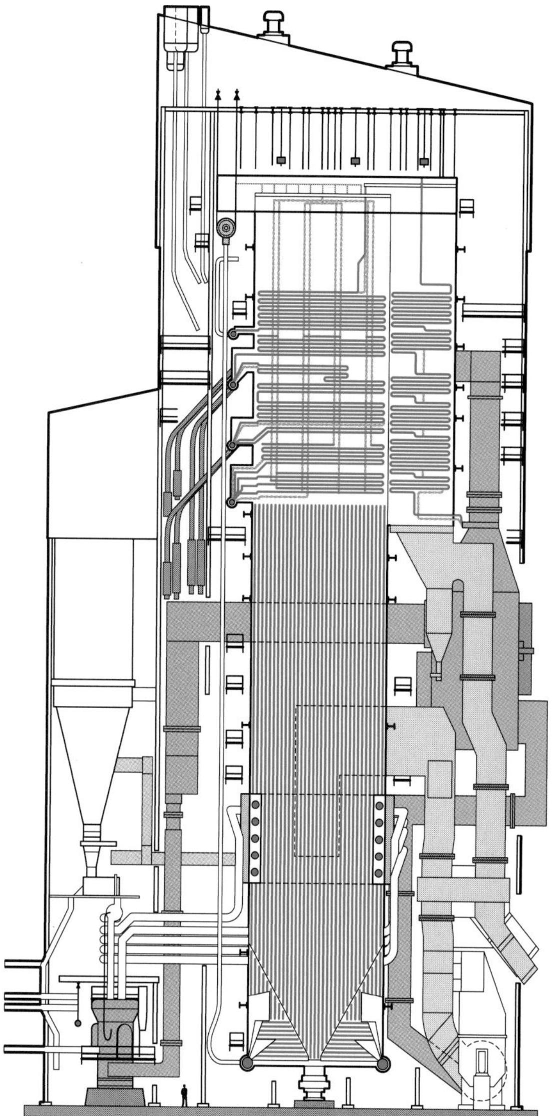

Figure 3-4 | Large pulverized coal-fired Controlled Circulation® unit with horizontal superheater and reheater surface in the top of the furnace

Advantages of the Tower Design

The tower boiler design originally was developed for brown coal-fired boilers, in which the asymmetric temperature distribution of the flue gas side and the high slagging tendency of the fuel intensified the problems of the two-pass boiler associated stresses caused by different temperatures of the waterwalls and the more complex structural design of two-pass boilers. The positive feedback gained from the operation of brown coal-fired boilers was then transferred to bituminous coal-fired boilers. The main advantages of the tower-type boiler are summarized below.

FURNACE WALL TEMPERATURES AND BOILER EXPANSION. The water/steam flows uniformly through the waterwall of the tower boiler from the bottom to the top.

In all cases, the medium temperature at a given height is identical over the entire boiler volume. As a consequence, all connected components have the same temperature (i.e., inadmissible stresses induced by temperature differentials cannot occur). Even in those cases when, because of special circumstances, a part of the waterwalls is arranged as a superheater, the temperature jumps that occur during start-up can be accommodated without problems since there are only minor differences in rigidity within the waterwalls. The geometry of the tower boiler enables use of a very simple but nonetheless effective system of boiler guides. The entire boiler body can expand freely in all directions. Thus, even under extreme modes of operation, defects resulting from expansion forces can be safely avoided.

HORIZONTAL HEATING SURFACE ARRANGEMENT. In the tower boiler, all convective heating surfaces can be arranged horizontally. This offers considerable advantages for the operation of the plant:

- The heating surfaces are fully drainable (no problems caused by condensate accumulations during start-up or longer boiler outages).
- The heating surfaces are uniformly heated by the hot flue gas, because no change occurs in the flow direction of the flue gas.
- Homogeneous velocity and temperature profiles improve the heat absorption of the heating surfaces.
- Low temperature imbalance of the water/steam side occurs, allowing lower design margins for the metal temperatures.
- The wall penetrations of the heating surfaces can be executed very simply, with sufficiently long expansion legs. Differences in expansion between the wall and the headers can thus be accommodated without excessive stresses.
- The horizontal arrangement enables inclusion of the convective section in the general acid-cleaning process. This leads to shorter boiler cleaning times.

Note that the horizontal arrangement requires that operators take care during start-up to ensure adequate cooling flow through the vertical hanger tubes that support and align the horizontal tube bundles. Thermocouples should be used to monitor hanger tube temperatures on start-up, especially in tubes with a downward flow.

EROSION AND FOULING. In the tower boiler, the flue gas flows vertically through the heating surfaces. No great differences in dust concentration occur; thus, stratification is avoided. Furthermore, because of gravitation, the velocity of the ash particles is lower than the respective flue gas velocity. This leads to a reduction of erosion in the heating surfaces. The uniform temperature profiles at the inlet of the heating surfaces also prevent local temperature peaks. Consequently, the margin to the ash-softening point of the particles can be maintained more safely. Caking with softened ash particles or slagging on the heating surfaces can be significantly reduced. Because the transverse pitch of the heating surfaces increases from the top to the bottom of the boiler, slag or ash that is removed through soot blowing from the convective heating surfaces can fall into the hopper. The next heating surface has little risk of blockage.

Convection Pass Design for Two-Pass and Tower Boilers

A number of coal ash properties have a significant influence on superheater, reheater, and economizer convection surface design and on the associated considerations of fouling and erosion. These include:

- Ash-softening temperature
- Base/acid ratio
- Iron/calcium ratio
- Sodium and potassium content
- Silica and alumina content
- Chlorine content
- Ash friability

In sizing and locating these sections within the unit, a proper balance is required to maintain a thermal head with which to transfer heat from gas to steam while optimizing heating surface use and avoiding undesirably high metal temperatures. Also, to limit erosion of pressure parts from fly ash, the flue gas velocity must not exceed reasonable limits. Depending on the ash quantity and abrasiveness, the design velocity generally is 40 to 60 ft/s (12 to 18 m/s). A boiler that burns coal yielding a heavy loading of erosive ash (usually indicated by a high silica/alumina content) would use the lower velocities. Such velocities are based on the predicted average gas temperature entering the tube section at the maximum continuous rating of the steam generator fired at normal percentage of excess air.

Considering these factors in furnace sizing and convection pass design, it is not impractical to propose a steam generator capable of burning any kind of coal in the same unit. However, such a unit would not usually be economically feasible. For example, consider the wide variation in pulverizer size and primary air temperature requirements for a high-calorific-value, low-moisture, low-ash coal versus a sub-bituminous coal or lignite with high moisture and ash contents. Selecting an optimum preparation and firing system for one rank of fuel can result in a much less favorable situation for some other rank of fuel.

Operating experience on units firing certain coals shows the need for wide transverse tube spacing throughout the unit to reduce the fouling rate and possible bridging of ash deposits between adjacent assemblies. This arrangement minimizes serious fouling problems, which have an adverse effect on fan power requirements and unit availability. Because the gas temperature is reduced along its flow path to well below the ash-softening temperature of the worst coal that is expected to be burned, the transverse spacing of the banks of convection pass tubes also is reduced, depending on the fuel type and the ash characteristics. The tube spacing selected at the entrance to the convection pass depends mainly on the maximum gas temperature that is possible in this zone under upset conditions and the propensity of the ash to adhere.

In the superheater and reheater sections beyond the ash adhesion temperature zone, the tube spacing is further reduced to the minimum required for effective penetration of soot blower jets. In addition, gas velocities are maintained sufficiently low to prevent erosion. To avoid serious plugging, the transverse spacing in this area must be wide enough to allow pieces of accumulated ash that are loosened by

Coal ash properties have a major influence on the design of any coal-fired boiler. Thorough consideration of these properties is the key to successful performance and operation.

soot blowers to pass through the tube bank and not bridge the span between adjacent rows of tubes. *Table 3-2* is a guide for establishing transverse clearances for platen and spaced convection surfaces. This guide is based on fouling and non-fouling coals and on gas temperatures at maximum boiler load.

TABLE 3-2 | TRANSVERSE CLEARANCE GUIDE

Temperature Range		Inches (cm) of Clearance	
°F	°C	Non-fouling Coal	Fouling Coal
2,000–2,400	1,093–1,316	Platen–22 (56)	Platen–22 (56)
1,750–2,000	954–1,093	Spaced–7 (18)	Spaced–12 (30)
1,450–1,750	788–954	Spaced–3 (8)	Spaced–6 (15)
Up to 1,450	Up to 788	Spaced–2 (5)	Spaced–3 (8)

Coal Properties Used for Design

Properties of the coal to be used in a boiler design are established by the purchaser's specifications. It is preferable to show an analysis that represents an actual coal as the performance coal and to include low, average, and high analyses to confirm limits for the boiler design. Important items of the analysis are calorific value, moisture and ash contents, grindability index, and the ash analysis. If the fuel specifications are stated as ranges, it is customary to consider the average as the performance fuel but to design the unit to handle fuels with the worst analysis. If coals from two or more sources may be fired, individual analyses rather than a calculated average are desirable, with "low" and "high" representing the composite. Justification for using individual analyses comes from the necessity to evaluate pulverizer capabilities as well as ash influences on unit performance. The "worst" coal can become the design coal when a good probability exists that the power plant will use a significant amount of the "worst" coal. Finally, if coals are to be blended, information must be provided on both the separate analyses and the possible blends, including values for eutectic fusibility temperatures.

DESIGN OF LARGE, HP FURNACE WALL SYSTEMS

The design of various heat-absorbing equipment involves a finite pressure drop or resistance to fluid flow. Air heaters, economizers, superheaters, and reheaters all have a multiplicity of parallel flow paths or circuits through which the fluid being heated must pass. The uniformity of the flow distribution largely depends on the magnitude of the pressure drop across the apparatus. The water-cooled furnace generally handles the fluid it is heating in many more parallel circuits than are found in other heat-transfer devices. Therefore, the problem of distributing water to each tube, and providing adequate circulation for cooling all the tubes, is correspondingly more difficult.

The tubes that form the furnace walls are of different lengths and are subject to varying rates of heat absorption. Great care must be exercised to ensure that each tube receives a sufficient flow of water to prevent the overheating of individual waterwall tubes as well as an excessive difference in temperature between adjacent tubes. Flow instability, which can occur in furnace circuits, is considerably more difficult to control when a large number of tubes operate in parallel. The designer must calculate the heat absorption per furnace tube from a forecast of the normal absorption pattern for the entire furnace.

This forecast depends on the height and width of the furnace and, most of all, on the manner in which the fuel is fired. This anticipated pattern of heat absorption might not, however, be reproduced in service. Moreover, the pattern will fluctuate from time to time because of load changes, transient conditions, and variation in the thickness of the ash covering the walls. With certain firing systems, the number of pulverizers and burners in service also will vary the pattern. At intervals, ash deposits will drop off or be removed by soot blowing, which will give rise to further considerable variations. Misjudging the intensity or distribution of heat absorption may cause circulation difficulties that are impossible to correct except by decreasing the rating and operating pressure of the boiler.

As the boiler operating pressure approaches the critical point, the difference in the density of water and steam to produce circulation approaches zero. Designing tube circuits with low enough resistance to ensure adequate velocities and adequate water/steam ratios in all tubes, at all loads, with all fuels, under varying slagging conditions, and at all firing rates becomes proportionately more complex. Achieving proper circulation becomes increasingly difficult not only with higher operating pressures but also with increased unit capacity. In units with high-megawatt ratings, the fuel fired per lineal foot of furnace perimeter increases markedly compared to earlier, 100- to 200-MWe units. This has led the boiler industry to adopt internally rifled tubes for straight furnace walls, because higher percentages of steam can be tolerated in the steam–water mixture in rifled furnace tubes at lower mass velocities. In any case, the difficulties of designing a satisfactory furnace-wall circulating system involve:

- Operating pressure level
- Furnace physical arrangement
- The presence of non-heat-absorbing tubes near the fuel nozzles or burners
- Manufacturing tolerances of commercially available tubing (which affect the inside diameter and consequent pressure drop from tube to tube)
- Allowance for different heat pickup in different portions of the furnace
- The possibility of internal or external deposits
- Provision for the necessary pressure drop for steam–water separation in the drum

TANGENTIAL FIRING AND CIRCULATION SYSTEM DESIGN

With tangential firing and its mode of introducing the fuel, the furnace is used as the burner. Thus, heat absorption patterns in this design are much more uniform and more definable than with any other type of firing. The fuel and combustion air are introduced in the corners of the furnace, but the actual burning process takes place in the main body of the furnace. Therefore, heat is not liberated in a concentrated form within the area of the fuel admission assemblies, nor is it concentrated on one side of the furnace. As the load on the steam generating unit varies, the amount of heat admitted into the furnace is either increased or decreased uniformly and in such a manner that the heat absorption pattern remains basically unchanged. This is because each pulverizer feeds one horizontal level of fuel nozzles. These two features of Alstom's tangential firing, coupled with inherently low flame temperatures, are an asset to the successful design and operation of the furnace circulation system.

Furnace Wall Circulation in Subcritical-Pressure Steam Generators

Alstom customarily uses three types of circulating systems for subcritical pressure applications: thermal (thermosyphonic or "natural") circulation, Controlled Circulation® system (*Fig.* 3-5), and once-through flow. Each is designed to meet specific power-plant requirements and to provide certain advantages. *Figure* 3-6 shows various boiler circulation principles.

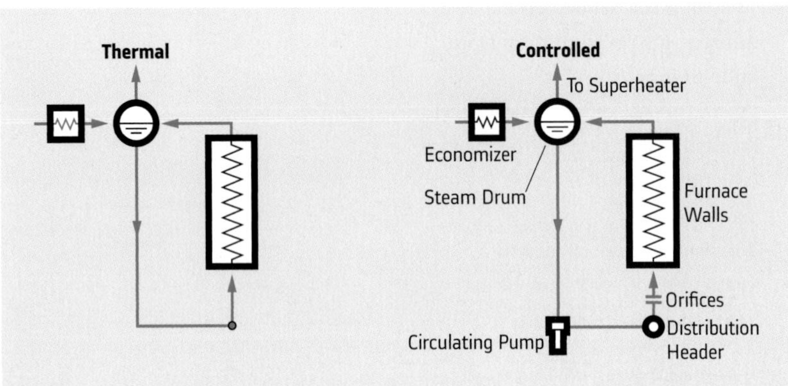

Figure 3-5 | Drum-type subcritical-pressure circulating systems

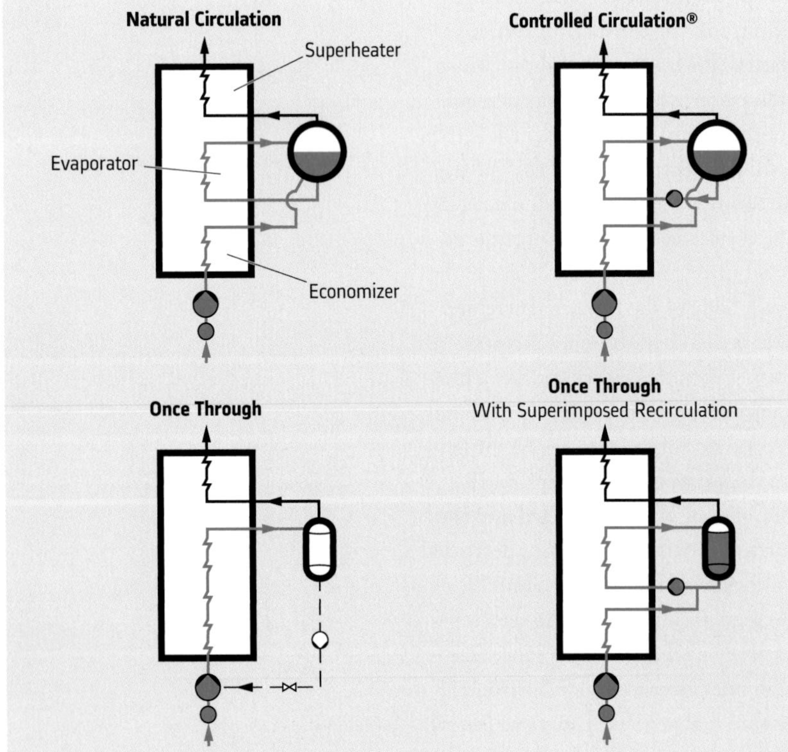

Figure 3-6 | Boiler circulation systems

THERMAL CIRCULATION. Thermally induced circulation, in theory, could be used in the design of a boiler that approaches the critical pressure of 3,208 psia (22.1 MPa abs). This could be done only by going to extremely large-diameter furnace wall tubes of high-alloy materials and essentially zero pressure-drop downcomer systems, risers, and drum internals. For thermal circulation designs, particularly drum and waterwall circuitry, 2,800 psig (19.3 MPa gage) is the maximum *practical* system pressure. This limits the available pressure drop for superheater cooling when the required superheater outlet pressure is above 2,650 psig (18.3 MPa gage). As furnace wall operating pressures and furnace sizes increase, a designer must have substantially greater knowledge of the waterwall heat absorption patterns that result from the firing system characteristics. Predictability and repeatability of such heat flux patterns must be achievable on a positive, long-term basis. Operator intervention or equipment malfunction must not permit a different distribution of heat input to the furnace walls other than that for which the unit was designed.

CONTROLLED FORCED RECIRCULATION. A boiler with a controlled, forced-circulation system incorporates a recirculating pump between the drum and the waterwalls, freeing the designer from dependence on the difference in steam and water densities to provide circulating head. Using a recirculating pump means that the designer is ensured of positive circulation even before heat is applied. Because the pump helps to overcome friction loss in the waterwall tubes, it is possible to substitute smaller-diameter tubes for the larger-diameter tubes that are required with a limited thermal circulation head. The net result is a lower-tube-weight, lower-metal-temperature wall with lower thermal stresses.

Another advantage to incorporating a recirculating pump is the greater flexibility of boiler layout. More freedom exists in the arrangement of boiler heating surface, because with ensured positive circulation, a horizontal evaporation surface may be used to any extent desired. The Alstom system for controlled, forced recirculation at the high-subcritical-pressure level is called a Controlled Circulation® system. A 2,850 psig (19.7 MPa gage) drum pressure limit has been established for Controlled Circulation® steam generators. This limit permits operation of the 2,400 psig (16.6 MPa gage) throttle pressure cycle at 5% overpressure, or 2,520 psig (17.4 MPa gage) at the turbine, and as high as 2,680 psig (18.5 MPa gage) at the boiler superheater outlet.

THERMAL CIRCULATION FURNACE DESIGN. Thermal circulation results from a density difference between the mixture of saturated water and feedwater in the downcomers (downtakes) and the lighter steam–water mixture in the furnace wall tubes. The temperature and corresponding density in the downtakes can be changed somewhat in the initial design of a unit by varying the water temperature leaving the economizer. *Figure 3-7* shows how the furnace wall operating pressure and the percentage steam in the mixture in the wall tube affect the available thermal head for circulation. The available head is the difference between the weight of water in the unheated downcomer and the static head of the steam–water mixture in the heated waterwall tubes. *Figure 3-8* shows a typical Alstom thermal circulation, reheat steam generator for burning pulverized subbituminous coal for low to medium subcritical pressures.

Tangential fuel nozzles are located at five elevations in the four corners of the boiler furnace. Vertical downcomers, connecting the steam drum to the bottom waterwall header system, supply the boiler water. The lower ends of the front, rear, and side wall tubes connect to the bottom waterwall headers, and the upper ends connect to the upper headers. Relief (riser) tubes transport the mixture of steam and water from the waterwalls to the drum, where the steam is separated from the boiler water.

To ensure uniform distribution of steam and water, the connecting tubes are spaced evenly along the drum and

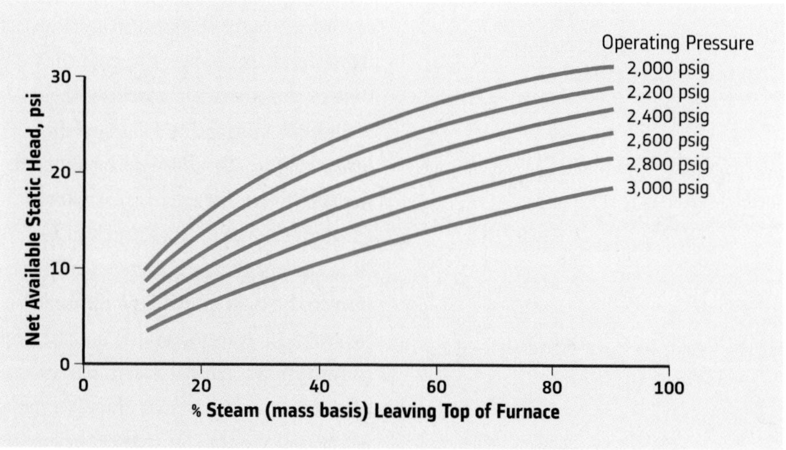

Figure 3-7 | Typical available static head for circulation based on a 200-ft high furnace; this available head is independent of the type of circulation

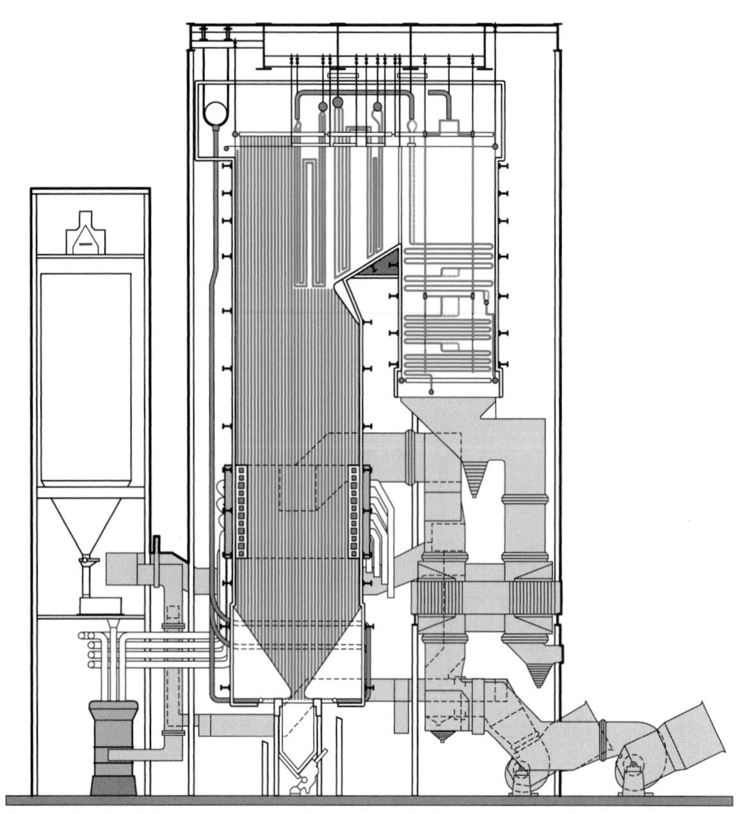

Figure 3-8 | A thermal circulation, tangentially firing, pulverized coal-fired steam generator

headers. Steam that has been separated from the steam–water mixture in the drum passes on to the first superheater stage. The first superheater stage is located in the vertical gas pass to the rear of the furnace. Saturated steam from the drum passes through the roof of the furnace, then down the walls enclosing the rear pass to the lower ring header. From this point on, the slightly superheated steam flows through the horizontal superheater tubes in a generally counter-flow direction to the downward flow of the products of combustion. From the first superheater stage, the steam passes to the finishing or outlet stage, which is a platen section, located at the gas outlet of the furnace. The reheater is located between the finishing platen superheater and the initial superheater stage. The flow of furnace gas over the reheater is essentially counter to the flow of steam. The economizer is located directly below the first stage superheater. Water flows upward in the economizer to provide counter-flow of furnace gas and feedwater. Outlet tubes of the economizer section extend vertically upward to form the supporting hanger tubes for the horizontal superheater and the economizer. These tubes then connect to a header above the roof. Connecting piping conducts the feedwater from this header to the steam drum.

This boiler is of the balanced-draft type. Primary air fans pressurize the pulverizers. Ljungström® trisector air pre-heaters with vertical shafts are located at the economizer gas outlet. The gas ducts connecting the economizer to the air pre-heater and at the air pre-heater outlet are arranged with hoppers to collect ash as well as any drain-off washwater. With the exception of the air pre-heaters, the entire boiler is supported by steel located at the roof elevation. Expansion joints are provided in the gas duct below the economizer and in the air ducts between the air pre-heaters and the windboxes to accommodate the downward expansion of the boiler pressure parts in their heated condition.

Shown in *Figure 3-9* is a cross section of a steam drum used in thermal circulation boilers. In this drum, the steam–water mixture from the furnace passes through the centrifugal separators, where a spin is imparted. This forces the water to the outer edge of the centrifugal separator,

where it is separated from the steam. Nearly dried, the steam passes through corrugated plates, where, through low-velocity surface contact, the remaining moisture is removed by wetting action on the plates and final screen dryers. The cross-sectional area of the drum limits the size and arrangement of the internal steam separators and dryers and, consequently, the acceptable rating in terms of mass flow per hour per unit of length. A drum with a large diameter affords more free area for water content at normal water level and reduced moisture entrainment in the larger steam space. Within the limits of the available pressure drop for steam–water separation, higher-capacity separators and increased dryer surface can be provided to achieve a higher rating per unit of length. For a specific diameter and arrangement of internal components, the drum capacity is proportional to its length. The diameter and length, then, are determined by:

- Unit generating capacity
- Operating pressure in the drum
- Practical considerations in the spacing and arrangement of connecting tubes and piping with respect to drum shell ligaments
- Requirements for uniform distribution of steam and water flow entering and leaving the drum

The percentage of boiler-water solids that will be carried over by moisture entrained in the steam leaving the drum is proportional to the concentration of boiler-water solids and to the percentage moisture carried over. Moisture is removed sequentially by the steam separators, followed by gravitational separation of droplets in the steam space, and finally, by the

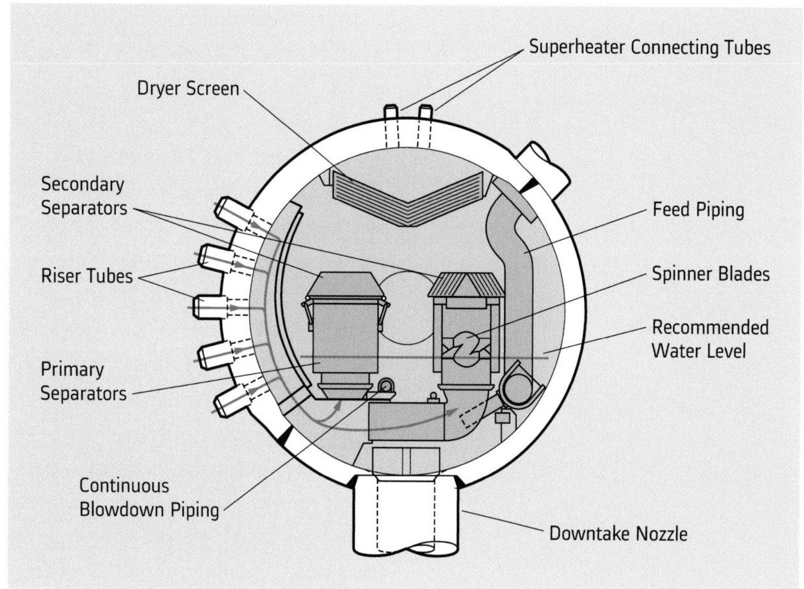

Figure 3-9 | Steam-drum internals for Alstom thermal circulation radiant and reheat steam generators

steam dryers which are arranged to prevent moisture re-entrainment. A high water level in the drum reduces the steam space available for gravitational separation of moisture. An excessively high level can impair the efficiency of primary and secondary separators, resulting in an increased moisture content entering the dryers and a corresponding increase in carryover moisture containing entrained solids. The concentration of dissolved solids in the boiler water should be held as low as practicable, consistent with the recommended chemical treatment for protection of boiler tubes against corrosion. This ensures that the carryover of solids during high-water-level excursions will be negligible. Vaporous carryover of certain boiler-water constituents, such as silica and sodium, is determined by the respective volatility of these unwanted constituents or their solubility in steam. Limiting the concentration of boiler-water solids at high drum pressures must control them (Chapter 9).

THE CONTROLLED CIRCULATION® BOILER. The first Controlled Circulation® boiler in an American central station entered service in 1942 at the Somerset Station of Montaup Electric Company in Somerset, Massachusetts. Since then, the Controlled Circulation® principle has been widely accepted for boilers ranging from waste heat, marine, and industrial units up to the largest central station installations. The reliability and safe operating records of Controlled Circulation® boilers have justified their selection in power stations throughout the world.

THE CONTROLLED CIRCULATION® SYSTEM. Water flow through the economizer generally is the same with either a thermal circulation or a Controlled Circulation® boiler. Water from the economizer enters the drum, is mixed with the water discharged from the steam–water separators, and is directed to the large downcomers, which are evenly spaced along the drum. From this point on, a Controlled Circulation® unit (*Fig.* 3-3) differs from a thermal circulation boiler in five respects:

1. Circulating pumps are placed in the downcomer circuit to provide sufficient head to ensure adequate, positive upward circulation under all operating conditions.
2. Orifices are installed in the inlets of waterwall circuits to assist in obtaining a predetermined, proportioned flow of water to tubes of varying length and heat absorption.
3. Furnace wall tubing is of smaller diameter and lower metal temperature than tubing for thermal circulation, all made possible by the head available from the pumps.
4. The drums are internally shrouded to provide uniform heating and cooling of the drum shell for maximum maneuverability during start-up, load changes, and shutdown.
5. Controlled Circulation® boilers have an economizer recirculation line that provides a positive flow from the boiler water circulating pump discharge through the economizer to the drum. Under start-up conditions, with the feedwater valve closed, this feature minimizes any steaming in the economizer and precludes the need for blowdown with its associated heat loss.

The boiler circulating pump suction is taken from a suction manifold, which is supplied by the downcomers. From the boiler circulating pumps, the water discharges into the waterwall inlet ring header through the pump discharge lines. In the inlet header, the water passes through strainers and then through orifices feeding the furnace wall tubes, the extended sidewall tubes, and the water-cooled, element spacers. The mixture of steam and water leaving the evaporative circuits is discharged into the upper drum, where the steam is separated from the water.

In the drum of a Controlled Circulation® unit, as shown in *Figure 3-10*, the basic separation process is similar to that of thermal circulation drums, except that the available pump head permits more efficient use of the centrifugal devices. One distinct advantage of the Controlled Circulation® design is the internal shrouding of the drum. This watertight shrouding directs the flow of steam and water returning from the furnace around the inside surface of the drum, providing uniform heating. This uniform heating effectively eliminates thermal stresses from temperature differences through the thick wall of the drum, between the submerged and unsubmerged portion of the shell, and from end to end. This facilitates more rapid start-ups, shutdowns, and cyclic operations. In operation, a Controlled Circulation® boiler has positive circulation established before any heat is introduced into the furnace, which then permits a more rapid start-up, with virtually no time restrictions because of circulation in the pressure part system.

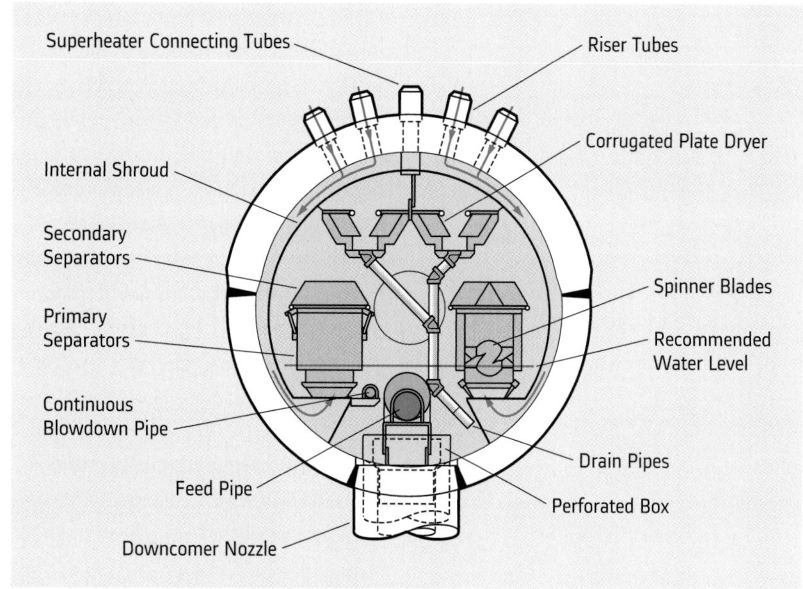

Figure 3-10 | Steam-drum internals for Controlled Circulation® steam generators

CONTROLLED CIRCULATION® PUMP AND PIPING SYSTEM. *Figure 3-3* shows the overall arrangement of the boiler circulating pump and downcomer piping system. Downcomers installed on the steam drum carry the recirculated boiler water, mixed with the feedwater, into the circulating pumps. These pumps are connected through a common suction manifold that ensures flow through all the downcomers regardless of the number or location of circulating pumps in service. This feature minimizes the difference in water level along the length of the steam drum, and it contributes to good performance of the steam–water separation equipment, independent of the number of pumps in service. The downcomers are straight, vertical pipes connecting the steam drum and the suction manifold. The circulating pumps are mounted on the suction manifold. Using the boiler as the support for the pumps is a feature that eliminates any need for external supports and that prevents undue stresses, which might affect pump alignment. The head developed by the circulating pumps is only that required to supplement the thermal head and, for a typical Controlled Circulation® boiler, is 25 psi (172 kPa) or less. A single-stage impeller is adequate. Boiler water circulating pumps and their design are described further in Chapter 6.

ORIFICES FOR FURNACE WALL TUBES. The orifices used for optimizing flow distribution to the furnace wall tubes are shop-fitted to adapters that are welded to the internal header wall. A keying arrangement ensures that each orifice is installed in its proper tube circuit once the correctness of the initial installation of the orifice mount adapter has been established. Orifice size varies for different circuits, or groups of circuits, depending on their length, arrangement, and heat absorption. Strainers or screens between the circulating pump discharge and the orifices prevent large particles of foreign material from plugging the orifices at the entrance to the generating circuits. The strainers are particularly valuable during the initial start-up of a new unit because, during this period of operation, foreign material is brought into the boiler from preboiler-cycle, feedwater piping and auxiliary equipment.

DESIGN OF A CONTROLLED CIRCULATION® FURNACE WALL SYSTEM. The orificing and selection of the pump head for a Controlled Circulation® boiler are best understood by first reviewing a non-pump-assisted, thermal circulation unit design. The designer of a thermal circulation furnace of a given plan area determines the total number of parallel vertical tubes making up the outer walls of the furnace. A common selection is to use 2½-inch (6.4 cm) (outer diameter) tubes on 3-inch (7.6 cm) centers. The next step, based on experience with units of similar physical size and heat duty, is to establish the size and number of unheated downcomers from the steam drum to the lower waterwall header system. Along with this, it is necessary to establish the arrangement, diameter, and number of relief tubes connecting the upper waterwall headers to the drum. An average is then calculated for the overall percentage of steam leaving the furnace, based on the heat absorbed by the "average" furnace tube and on the flow resistances in that tube, the downcomers, the relief tubes, the drum internals, and all associated entrance and exit losses. Within the limits of available thermal head and physical space, adjustments in downcomer and relief tube size and flow resistances can be made at this time to increase or decrease the average circulation and so achieve satisfactory cooling of the furnace-wall.

Tubes in the furnace enclosure have different lengths and dissimilar configurations, and they receive varying amounts of heat. Any tube absorbing more heat than the average tube has a higher circulating water flow but probably also a high percentage of steam leaving. Typically, a 50% increase in absorption above the average, equally received throughout the length of a tube, produces a 10 to 20% increase in water flow entering the tube. For every tube receiving more than the average tube, another tube is receiving less water. Thus, each tube must be analyzed on the basis of its individual heat absorption to arrive at its own mass percentage of steam (quality) leaving. Realize that in designing a waterwall section (i.e., a group of parallel tubes having a common [bottom] inlet header and a common upper [outlet] header), such as that shown in *Figure 3-11*, the pressure drop or head loss between the headers must be identical for every tube. This situation exists irrespective of any pump assistance. The flow in each tube and the percentage steam in the mixture leaving differ, depending on the following factors:

- Heat absorption (overall and local)
- Effective inside diameter of tubing (as affected by manufacturing tolerances)
- Effective tube length (accounting for bends)
- Amount of tubing "shaded" from heat
- Location relative to feeder tubes
- Orifices (if used)

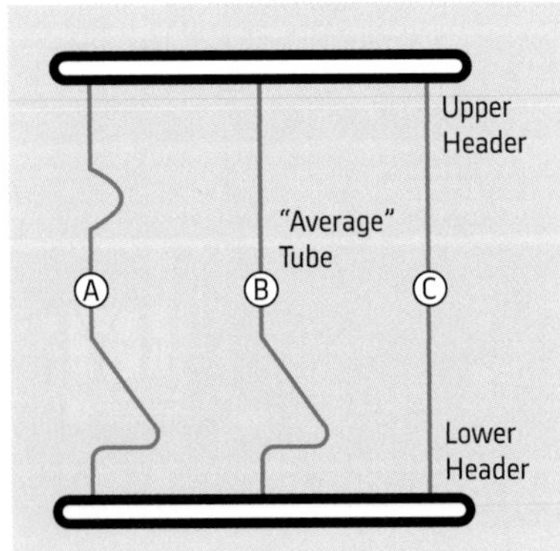

Figure 3-11 | Schematic of furnace-wall section; head loss between headers is identical for each tube

Tube A, for instance, may be longer but have a lower overall heat absorption than the "average" tube B. Without orificing, tube A will have a lower flow than tube B. Tube C, if shorter than tube B but fully exposed for its entire length to high heat, will have a higher flow than the average tube (i.e., tube B). All tubes, however, must have the same differential pressure from header to header. An equilibrium condition will always result in the flow-plus-orifice losses being additive to the weight of the saturated mixture in each tube at any given moment. This is because the header-to-header differential consists of the following components:

- The weight of the steam–water mixture in each tube
- The pressure drop caused by the resistance to flow of the steam–water mixture in each tube
- The orifice pressure drop (if any)

The flow may or may not be enough to cool the tube properly, and it may even reverse (from upward to downward, and vice versa) from time to time, depending on the variables acting on it. In tubes where mass flow is lower because of lower heat absorption, the specific volume is correspondingly higher to compensate for the flow resistance of a high-absorption tube with higher mass flow. For any given overall steam content, water between the lower and upper headers redistributes from tube to tube according to the above relationships.

Figure 3-12 gives a comparison between thermal circulation and Controlled Circulation® performance. In the upper curve, average mass flow in furnace wall tubes is shown as a function of design heat absorption. Note that the circulating pumps move the maximum mass of water before firing commences, because the water is most dense at that time. The lower curve shows that the designer of a Controlled Circulation® unit can preferentially increase the flow in tubes with less favorable configurations to provide more cooling at all loads. The orifice pressure drop designed into Controlled Circulation® circuits is additive to the heated circuit resistance loss and static head. Orificing individual tubes, or groups of tubes, provides either adequate mass flow or a desired exit quality under a wide range of postulated operating conditions. The orifice pressure drop has a dampening effect on the almost-random behavior of a purely thermal circulation unit. Because the orifice drop occurs at the beginning of a circuit, before heat has been added in the furnace, the principal variable is mass flow through the opening, with no effect of differential specific volume. This is a very significant difference between pure forced circulation, in which most of the pressure drop is in the heated tube circuits themselves, and Alstom's selectively orificed, pump-assisted, Controlled Circulation® units.

CONTROLLED CIRCULATION® STEAM GENERATORS. *Figure 3-13* shows a Controlled Circulation® reheat boiler designed to provide steam to a large, high-subcritical-pressure, turbine generator. This is a single, open-furnace unit. It has a superheater with both pendant and horizontal surfaces and a reheater with both radiant wall and pendant surfaces. This boiler has superheater outlet conditions of 2,620 psig and 1,005°F (18.1 MPa gage and 541°C), with single reheat to 1,005°F (541°C). It is designed to

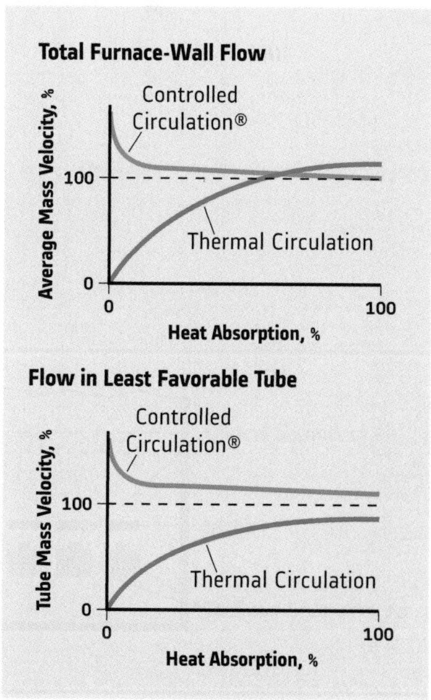

Figure 3-12 | Comparison of furnace-wall performance: thermal circulation versus Controlled Circulation® systems

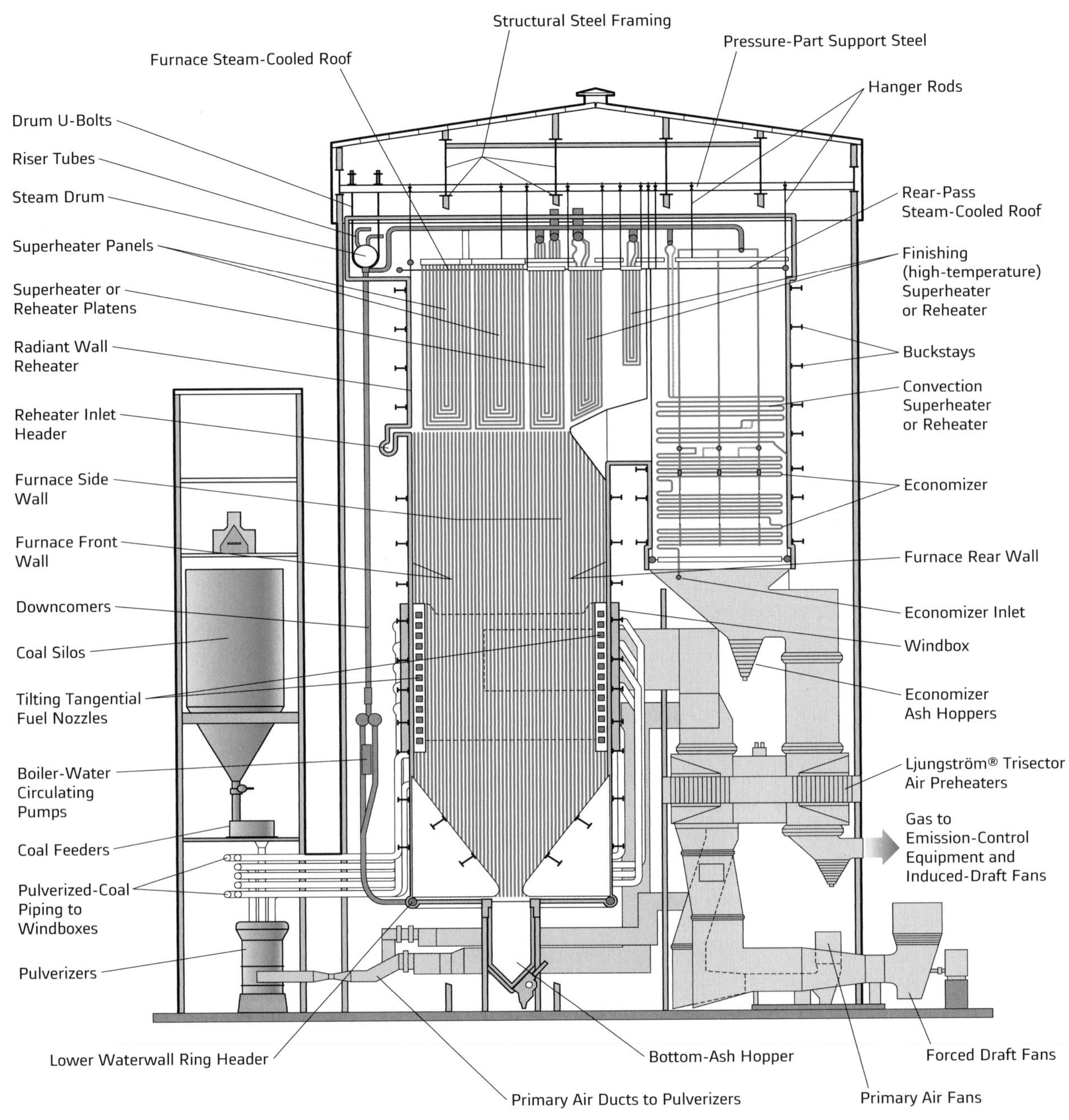

Figure 3-13 | Large Controlled Circulation®, tangentially firing, pulverized coal-fired reheat steam generator

burn high-volatile bituminous coal and is of the balanced-draft type, with forced and induced draft and primary air fans.

Six pulverizers supply coal to tangential fuel nozzles located in each of the four corners of the furnace. The supply of water to the waterwalls begins with the steam drum. The water travels down through the downcomers to the suction manifold and into the circulating pumps, from which it is discharged to the lower ring header, which has flow-distributing orifices. The mixture of steam and water that flows up through the various heated circuits is collected in an arrangement of waterwall outlet headers located just above the furnace roof. The steam–water mixture passes through connecting tubes to the drum, where steam is separated from boiler water and passes on to the superheater. The first-stage superheater is located in the vertical pass at the rear of the furnace. Saturated steam from the drum passes through the furnace radiant roof, through the backpass roof and walls, and then enters the lower inlet header of the first stage. The steam flows upward through the first-stage superheater and into the second stage, which consists of pendant, double-loop panels located at the top of the furnace. The final superheater is of the vertical pendant-platen type and also is in the upper furnace, between the panels and the furnace nose. Reheat steam enters the radiant wall reheater inlet header and travels upward through the radiant wall tubes. After leaving the radiant wall outlet header, the reheat steam enters the low-temperature rear pendant and continues into the finishing reheat pendant. The horizontal, bare-tube economizer is located directly below the first-stage superheater. Vertical outlet tubes from the economizer serve to support both the economizer banks and first-stage superheater. The tubes then terminate in an economizer outlet header above the roof, from which connecting piping transports the water to the drum. Two vertical shaft, regenerative-type (Ljungström®), trisector air pre-heaters are located beneath the economizer.

ADVANTAGES OF A CONTROLLED CIRCULATION® SYSTEM. A primary reason for selecting a steam generator of the Controlled Circulation® type is its characteristic of high dynamic maneuverability. The fact that furnace wall flow is positively established, in an upward direction, before heat is applied enables an operator to fire such a furnace at any desired rate. Controlled Circulation® furnace walls and steam drums are not a limiting factor in building or changing load. Thus, Controlled Circulation® units are inherently better suited for operation under cycling conditions (particularly those demanded by two-shift operation) compared with other boiler types.

OPERATION WITH WATERWALL TUBE LEAKS. Because of the available pump head, Controlled Circulation® units use smaller-diameter tubing than thermal circulation boilers do, and they incorporate orifices at the entrance to the tubes for optimum flow distribution. The smaller-diameter tubing and orifices at the entrance to the tubes act to control and reduce the amount of water that can pass through a tube leak of a given size, resulting in a significantly lower

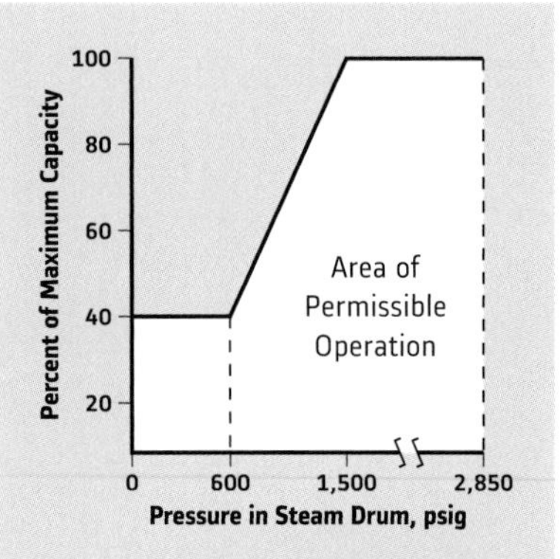

Figure 3-14 | Maximum permissible capacity as a function of operating pressure in the drum for Controlled Circulation® boilers

potential for damage to adjacent tubes compared with that in a thermal unit. There are many recorded instances in which an operator has kept a Controlled Circulation® unit in service through a peak period, or until a weekend, when it became more convenient to shut down. An additional capability, that of forced furnace wall cooling with the pumps, allows boiler cooldown with uniform stresses without using the feedwater pump or dumping feedwater to the condenser.

OPERATING PRESSURE FLEXIBILITY. The curve shown in *Figure 3-14* shows that a Controlled Circulation® steam generator can be operated through a wide range of pressures at full load. Operation within the permissible area allows great latitude in establishing a desirable sliding-pressure pattern.

THERMAL CIRCULATION VERSUS CONTROLLED CIRCULATION® SYSTEMS. In choosing between thermally induced circulation and a Controlled Circulation® system, the following must be taken into account:

- Although thermal circulation does increase in response to heat applied, the increase in flow is not directly proportional to the increase in heat flux. That is, although a larger amount of water usually circulates in an individual tube when more heat is applied, the increase may not be completely adequate to provide proper tube protection.
- Slag can form heavily—and does form unpredictably—on different areas of the furnace at different times. It can be removed by soot blowers or shed, equally unpredictably, because of its mass. It is common to have a major part of the heat input to a furnace wall tube in its upper half because of soot blower cleaning or shedding, which can result in a calculable decrease in the circulation rate within an individual tube or group of tubes. Flow reversal can occur, with local overheating becoming a possibility.
- Controlled Circulation® and thermal circulation boilers have the same thermal circulating head available if they have the same furnace height, the same economizer water leaving temperature, and the same circulation ratio (*Fig. 3-7*). The pumps and orifices incorporated in Controlled Circulation® units do not destroy the available thermal head or lessen the difference in density between furnace wall tubes and unheated downcomers.
- To ensure adequate available head under all operations of firing and maneuvering the boiler, Alstom adds orifices so that all tubes will receive water under all conditions, and Alstom shrouds the thick-walled steam drum to cool or heat it in a controlled manner under all rates of load change. The circulating pumps complement these engineered modifications to the basic thermal circulation design, and they provide the pressure head to overcome the incrementally increased resistance. A most important point is that increases in flow are created with pump assistance that are much greater than those available through the thermosyphonic phenomenon. This point is illustrated in *Figure 3-15* by comparing the pressure drops in the various components of typical

thermal circulation and Controlled Circulation® steam generators.

- The net power consumption of the circulating pumps is small compared to that in other circuitry of the boiler for accomplishing basically the same objective of equalized flow distribution with variation in load, firing conditions, and heat absorption patterns. The feedwater pump power charged to a unit, because of its superheater and economizer pressure drops, is substantially higher than the small power loss of the circulating pumps.

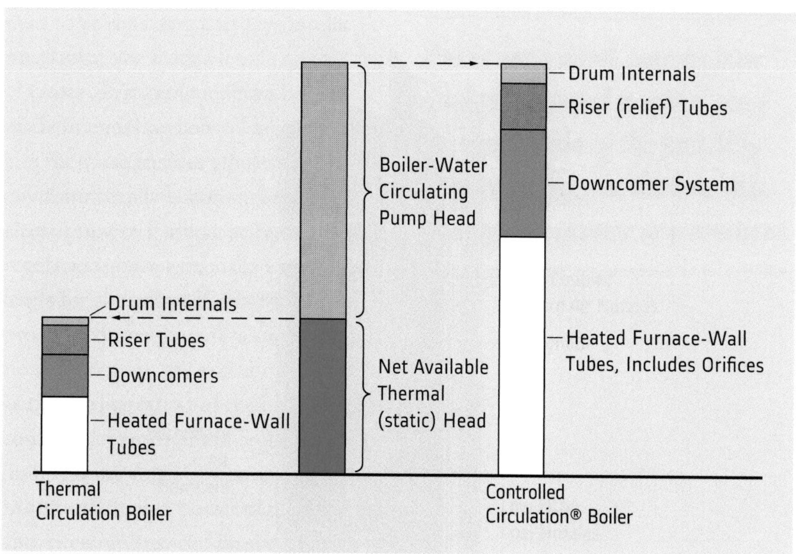

Figure 3-15 | Comparison of component pressure drops and available static head: Thermal circulation boiler versus Controlled Circulation® boiler

SUPERCRITICAL-PRESSURE STEAM GENERATORS

Alstom supercritical-pressure steam generators can be classified in three basic design categories according to their operating pressure regimes. In the first, which includes units designed for constant-pressure operation, supercritical pressures are maintained in both furnace walls and superheater over the normal operating range. The furnace wall arrangement and the use of boiler throttling valves are as described later under Typical Combined Circulation® Unit. For units that are to have partial sliding-pressure capability, supercritical pressures are maintained in the furnace walls. Only the superheater follows a sliding-pressure program. The boiler throttling-valve arrangement is modified from the basic Combined Circulation® design to allow increased throttling. For units designed to have full sliding pressure, the furnace wall and superheater pressures may vary with load, including operation at subcritical pressure.

Sliding pressure is a highly desirable way to operate central station steam generators at both high-subcritical pressures and in the supercritical-pressure range. A later section of this chapter addresses the subject of sliding (or "variable") pressure operation in detail and covers the significant advantages to the steam generator and turbine while operating in such a mode. The three designs to meet user requirements for throttle pressures above the 3,800 psig (26 MPa gage) level are described in the following sections.

Constant-Pressure Supercritical Units

The Combined Circulation® system is a once-through steam generator with a superimposed, controlled, forced-recirculation system for the furnace walls. When once-through flow is insufficient at low loads, the furnace wall system is automatically protected by recirculation of fluid with a boiler circulating pump. The recirculation pump eliminates the need for a high-capacity bypass system for furnace wall protection while still allowing once-through supercritical flow at higher output. This type of design permits furnace wall tubes of sufficient inside diameter to maintain an adequate mass flow at all operating conditions. The recirculating pump handles both recirculated flow and feedwater flow and, thereby, assists the feed pump, reducing some of its power requirement.

In the Combined Circulation® design, all furnace walls are single-pass upflow, with no mixing headers. Proper design tolerances and use of tube orifices compensate for flow unbalance or uneven heat absorption. The mixing vessel or sphere is substituted for the conventional drum to properly mix the recirculated flow from the furnace walls with the unit throughput. The constant-pressure, Combined Circulation® supercritical units, then, are capable of operating with once-through flow, but they cannot be operated with full sliding pressure. The furnace walls must be kept above the supercritical pressure (3,208 psia [22.1 MPa abs]) to avoid the film boiling and tube overheating that can occur during the transition to subcritical pressure. Boiler throttling valves are used at the furnace wall outlet to keep the wall system pressurized (*Fig. 3-16*). The superheater operates in the sliding-pressure mode below approximately 30% load. Above that range, turbine load control is accomplished by using the turbine throttle valves.

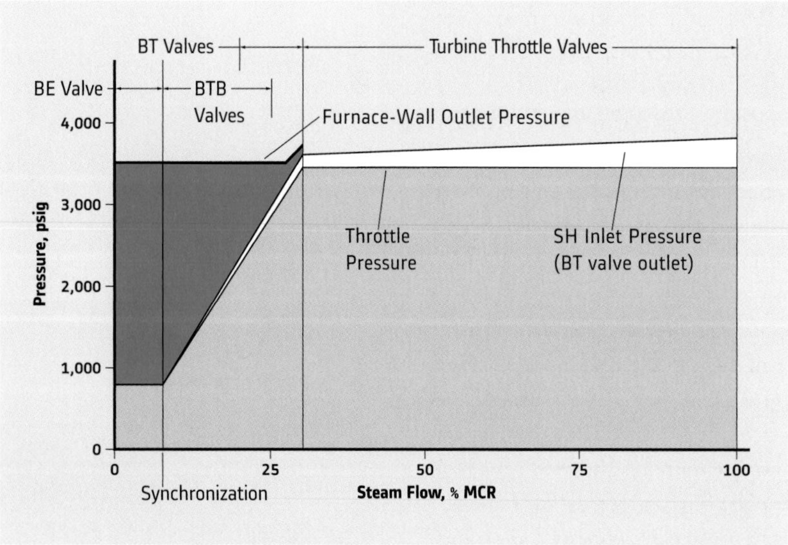

SYSTEM INTEGRATION. The simplified flow diagram (*Fig. 3-17*) illustrates several features that have significantly advanced system integration. First, the supercritical, once-through steam generator closes the steam and feedwater connections of the steam power cycle in a continuous, heat-addition loop without the division established by the water level in the drum of subcritical recirculating units. This fact is recognized by an automatic, non-interacting, feed-forward control system geared to the dynamic characteristics of the entire plant. Second, system integration permits starting the turbine and steam generator simultaneously under conditions that provide an optimum of turbine protection for accelerated cold and hot starts. This facility is combined with unique features to remove solids and oxides from both pre-boiler and boiler systems. Third, the Combined Circulation® principle eliminates the basic requirement of other once-through systems for minimum feedwater flow through the furnace. Heat removed from the steam generating system during any operation is determined only by functions other than furnace wall protection. The feedwater heating system, therefore, need not be used to reduce start-up heat losses. This, in turn, avoids contamination of this system by start-up flow and makes the system very simple. Eliminating the minimum

Figure 3-16 | Constant-pressure program for Combined Circulation® steam generators (BE, boiler extraction; BT, boiler throttling; BTB, boiler throttling bypass; MCR, maximum continuous rating; SH, superheater)

flow requirement also greatly facilitates use of turbine-driven feed pumps for start-up and avoids complications from separate start-up pumps.

BOILER TURBINE SYSTEM. In *Figure 3-17*, the feedwater enters the steam generator through the feedwater valve. From the economizer, the feedwater passes through the recirculating pump and its associated isolating valves to the furnace, where it flows in series through the center and outer walls and then through the enclosure walls of the rear gas pass. At this point, the steam passes through a system of throttling valves (boiler throttling bypass [BTB] and boiler throttling [BT]) and continues through four sections of horizontal and pendant superheater before reaching the steam leads to the turbine through an outlet piping system. Steam is returned to the steam generator for reheating in a two-section reheater and then returned to the turbine. The condensate passes through a demineralizer and a series of low-pressure (LP) heaters to an open deaerator. The turbine-driven feed pump then returns the feedwater through a string of HP heaters to the feedwater valve.

Figure 3-17 also shows the main components of a simple start-up system within which the throttling valves (BT and BTB) belong. Upstream of these valves, piping connects the furnace wall system with the extraction valves and the start-up separator. The steam side of the separator is connected to the superheater system through a steam admission valve and to the condenser through a spillover valve. Water from the separator is discharged to the condenser through the water drain valve. The steam drain valve, which is close to the turbine valve chest and discharges

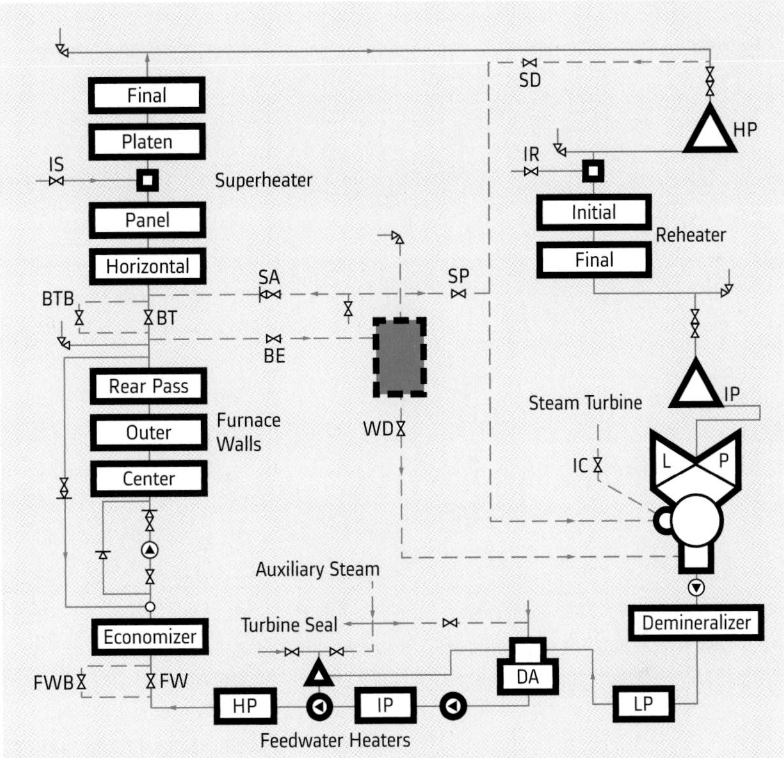

Figure 3-17 | Simplified flow diagram of a Combined Circulation® steam generator (BE, boiler extraction; BT, boiler throttling; BTB, boiler throttling bypass; DA, deaerator; FW, feedwater; FWB, feedwater bypass; HP, high pressure; IC, injection condenser; IP, intermediate pressure; IR, injection reheater; IS, injection superheater; LP, low pressure; SA, steam admission; SD, steam drain; SP, spillover; WD, water drain)

the steam for superheater cooling and heating of steam, leads to the condenser, and an injection valve regulates desuperheating water flow for condenser protection. Auxiliary superheated steam is furnished to turbine seals, the deaerator, and the main feed pump turbine from separate start-up boilers.

COMBINED CIRCULATION® RECIRCULATING SYSTEM. The components of the Combined Circulation® recirculating system are shown in a simplified isometric view in *Figure 3-18*. Mixing feedwater flow with recirculated flow (as takes place in the drum of a subcritical unit)

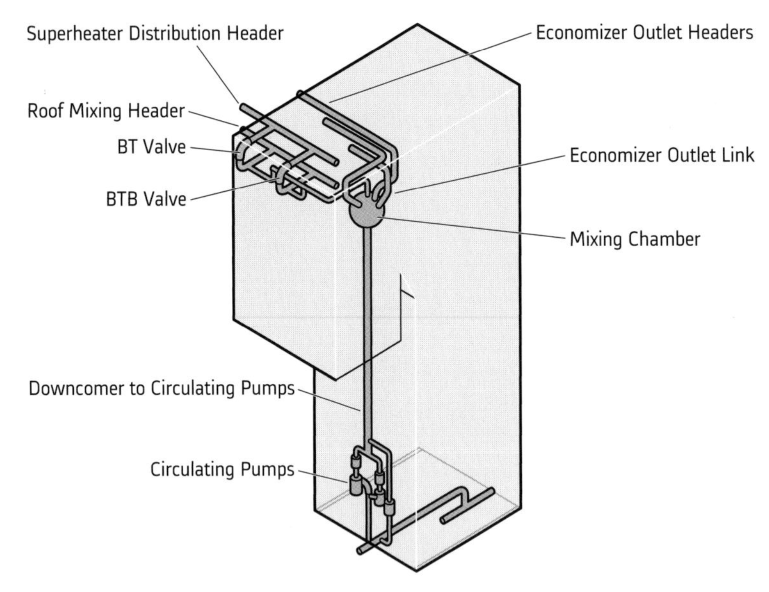

Figure 3-18 | Flow diagram of furnace-wall and start-up system for Combined Circulation® centerwall unit (BT, boiler throttling; BTB, boiler throttling bypass)

occurs here in the spherical mixing vessel. A single downcomer brings the fluid to the two recirculating pumps, which hang from a symmetrical tee connection on the downcomer. Only one pump is needed for low-load operation, with the other being a spare on hot standby. Neither is required at high loads. The pumps discharge to a common header, from which supply piping runs directly to the furnace wall headers. The subcritical-pressure drum, which functions to separate steam and water, is eliminated at supercritical pressure. The recirculated flow is returned from the outlet of the furnace wall enclosure to the mixing vessel through a single recirculating line. A stop-check valve in this line automatically prevents bypassing the furnace wall system when recirculation has ceased at the upper load range. Because downcomer, pumps, and piping to the centerwall all handle mixed or through flow at low temperatures, they are fabricated of carbon steel. The recirculating line and the mixing vessel use chrome alloy material. From the furnace wall outlet headers, the fluid is piped to the backpass, where it cools the walls. From the backpass outlet header, the total boiler through flow goes through the BT and BTB valve complex to the superheater. During waterwall recirculation conditions, a portion of flow in excess of the steam generator through flow is recirculated back to the mixing chamber. This flow is extracted ahead of the BT/BTB valve complex.

TYPICAL COMBINED CIRCULATION® UNIT. The most common type of supercritical steam generator in operation in the United States is the Combined Circulation® design. A Combined Circulation® unit in the size range of 600 to 900 MWe is shown in *Figure 3-19*. It is designed for balanced-draft firing of sub-bituminous A coal, and it has superheater outlet conditions of 3,590 psig and 1,005°F (24.8 MPa gage and 541°C). The reheated steam has an outlet temperature of 1,005°F (541°C) from inlet conditions of 583°F and 676 psig (306°C and 4.7 MPa gage). Seven pulverizers supply coal to the seven elevations of fuel nozzles in each of eight corners. Two centrifugal fans furnish the primary air to the pulverizers.

FURNACE WALL SYSTEM. The arrangement of the Combined Circulation® furnace wall system has several characteristics:

- Flow in all furnace and backpass enclosure walls is in the upward direction only.
- With single-pass flow, all tubes in a welded panel have the same inlet temperature.
- Centerwall flow and outerwall flow are in series on divided furnace units.

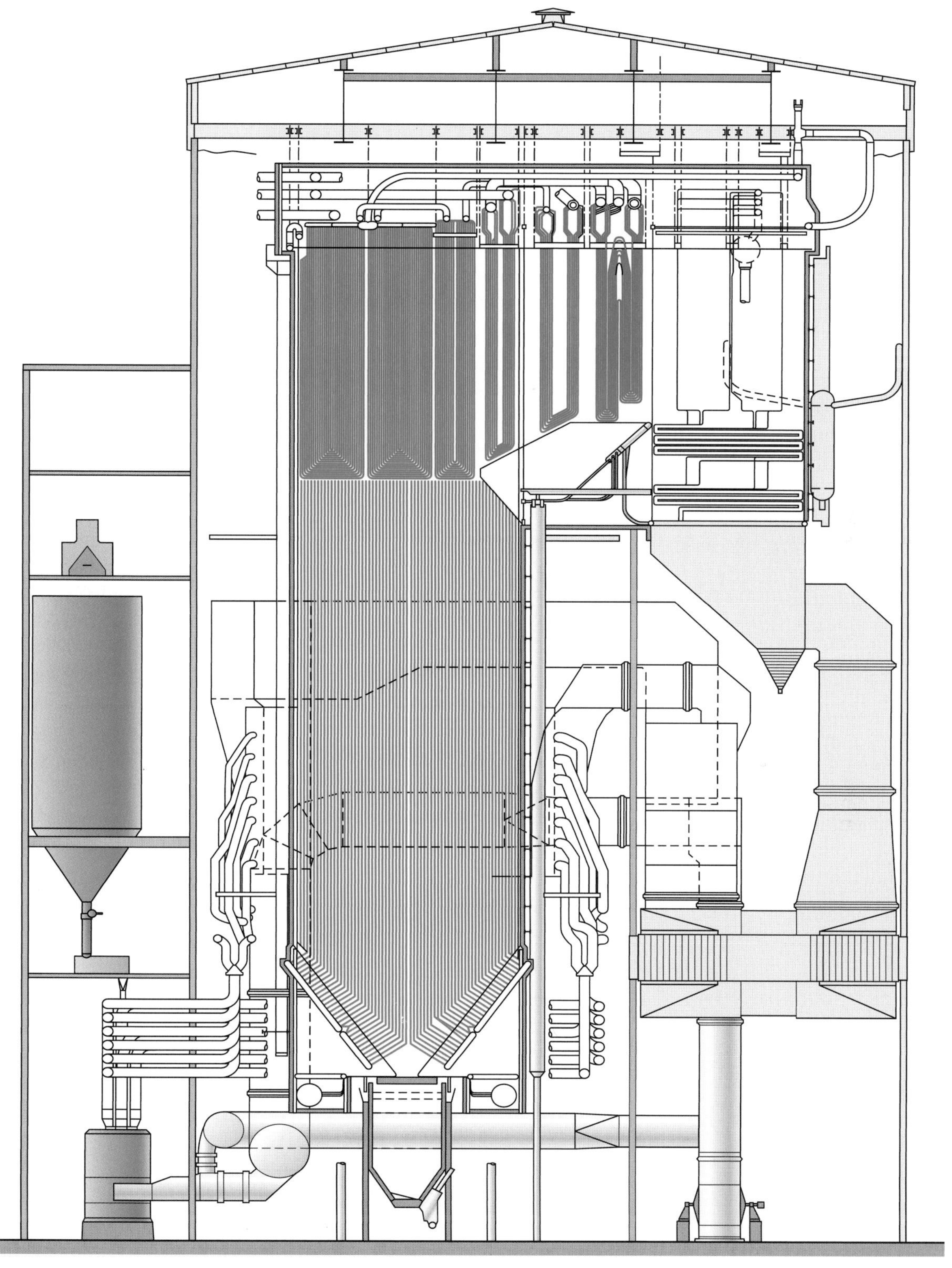

Figure 3-19 | A Combined Circulation® tangentially firing, coal-fired reheat steam generator

- All components of the recirculating system, except for the recirculating line, are in series with the once-through flow.
- Drainable, welded tube panels form all the walls.

These characteristics provide a number of important advantages, among which is the design flexibility available from the presence of a circulating pump, with which the flow quantity through the parallel tubes around the furnace periphery can be distributed. Other benefits are improved temperature performance over the entire load range and elimination of the bypass system as a requirement of the furnace wall.

These advantages will be understood most clearly after considering the flow performance of a typical furnace wall system, with the volumetric flow at the furnace wall inlet being a function of load (*Fig. 3-20*). The through flow, as maintained by the feed pump, increases in direct proportion to load. The recirculated flow, as maintained by the circulating pumps, supplements the through flow over the low-load range in a manner that protects the furnace walls

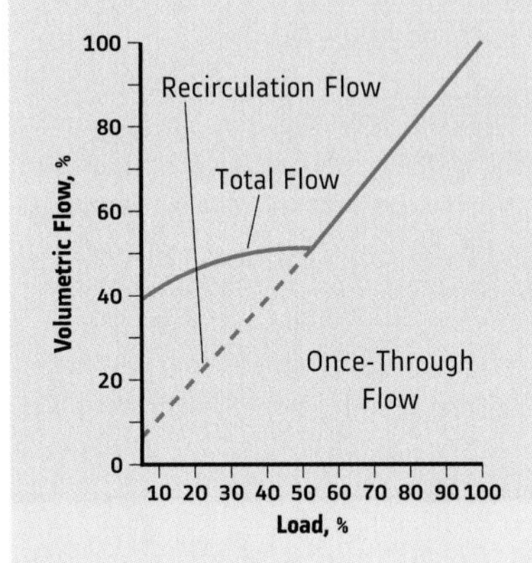

Figure 3-20 | Flow in typical Combined Circulation® furnace-wall system

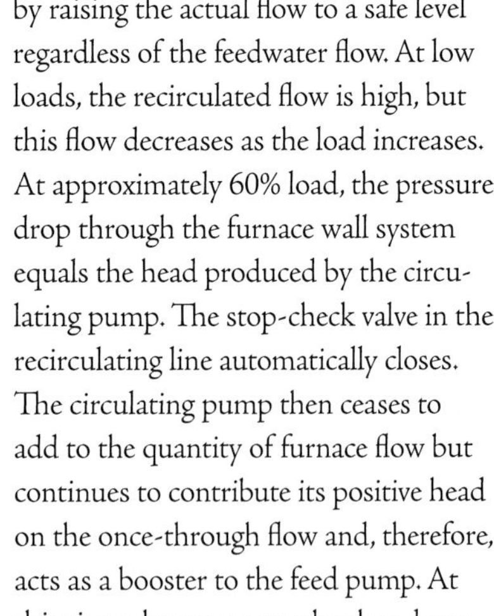

by raising the actual flow to a safe level regardless of the feedwater flow. At low loads, the recirculated flow is high, but this flow decreases as the load increases. At approximately 60% load, the pressure drop through the furnace wall system equals the head produced by the circulating pump. The stop-check valve in the recirculating line automatically closes. The circulating pump then ceases to add to the quantity of furnace flow but continues to contribute its positive head on the once-through flow and, therefore, acts as a booster to the feed pump. At this time, the pump may be shut down.

COMBINED CIRCULATION® PERFORMANCE. In *Figure 3-21*, fluid temperatures, both primary and reheat, throughout a typical Combined Circulation® supercritical steam generator at maximum continuous load are plotted against the percentage of heat absorption. The primary fluid takes approximately 83% of total output, showing a gradual and continuous rise of fluid temperature from the feedwater inlet to the superheater outlet. The curve of these temperatures follows the characteristic line of supercritical fluid, in which any heat absorption or change of heat content is accompanied by a change in fluid temperature. Desuperheating, occurring at the outlet of the panel superheater, provides precise control of the average steam temperature. It also adjusts for unbalance of pickup across the width of the unit through four individual, temperature-controlled sections that are installed in each furnace. The platen and finishing superheater sections add the balance of superheat.

PARTIAL SLIDING PRESSURE DESIGN. Combined Circulation® supercritical designs with boiler throttle valves (to keep the

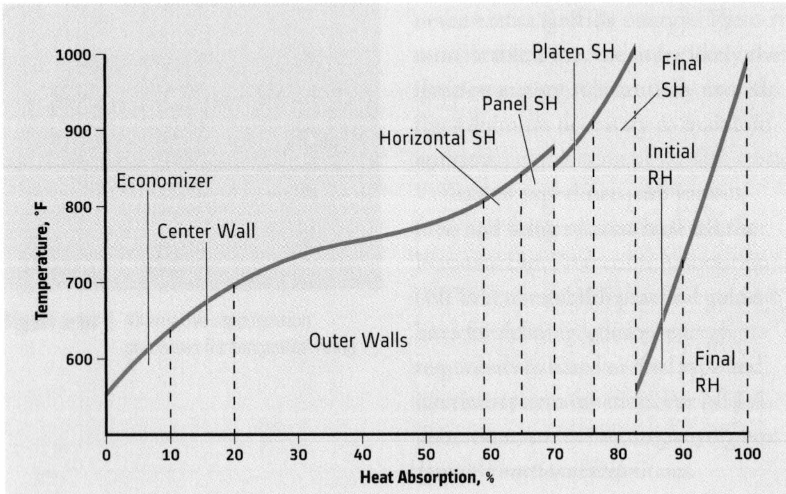

Figure 3-21 | Fluid temperatures through Combined Circulation® steam generator at full load (SH, superheater; RH, reheater)

furnace wall system pressurized above, e.g., 3,500 psig [24 MPa gage]) can operate in the sliding-pressure mode only below approximately 30% rating (*Fig. 3-16*). Above this point, turbine load control is achieved through the steam turbine throttle valves. This causes the usual temperature changes in the first stage of the turbine and is a factor in establishing permissible rates of load change. This design is extremely well suited for base load operation. Cycling and two-shifting operation, however, may require greater flexibility at reduced unit load to protect the steam generator and turbine during the increased number of load swings.

Figure 3-22 shows the rearrangement of a constant-pressure, boiler-throttle-valve set to obtain sliding-pressure turbine operation to 80% rating while maintaining the furnace walls at supercritical pressure. This design has the usual advantages of operating the turbine in a sliding-pressure mode, including increased range of reheat temperature control, reduced thermal stresses, and improved turbine heat rates as a result of variable-pressure operation with full arc admission below 80% load. Note that the boiler feed-pump power is the same for this modified design as for constant-pressure operation. With use of boiler throttle valves at all loads below 80%, however, some increased wear and maintenance can be expected. This design, then, often is well suited as a field modification to existing Combined Circulation® units that are now required to cycle or for new units that will cycle a minimal number of times during their operating lives.

Full Sliding-Pressure Design

The third once-through design eliminates the boiler throttling valves and adopts a full sliding-pressure approach (*Fig. 3-23*). The furnace walls are allowed to enter the subcritical pressure range, along with the superheater circuits, over the entire load range as shown. Benefits to plant operation, in addition to those described above, include:

1. Reduced pressure levels at lower loads that unload all cycle components in terms of pressure, from the feedwater pump to the HP turbine, thereby prolonging life span.
2. Improved overall power plant heat rates when considering power consumption of the boiler feed pump and other auxiliaries.
3. Simplified and faster start-up procedures that can be employed in the design.

The superheater circuitry for the full sliding-pressure design, as well as the start-up system, the operational controls, and the auxiliary equipment, are essentially the same as those for

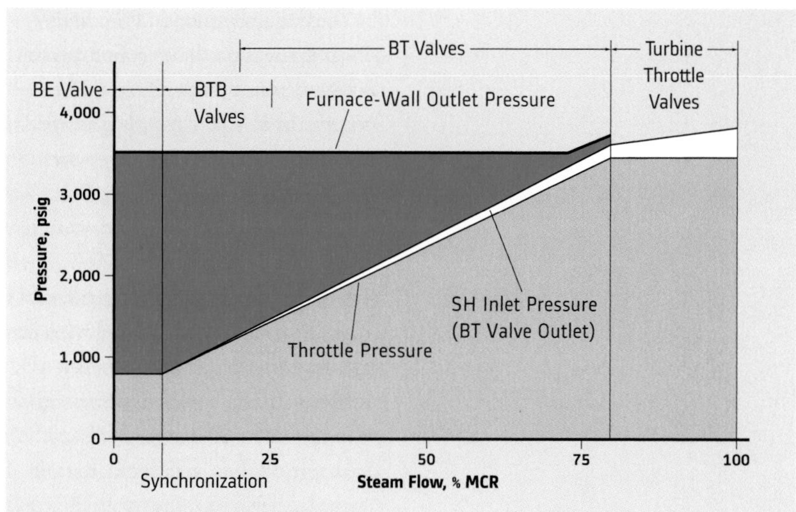

Figure 3-22 | Sliding pressure operation of Combined Circulation® steam generators (BE, boiler extraction; BT, boiler throttling; BTB, boiler throttling bypass; MCR, maximum continuous rating; SH, superheater)

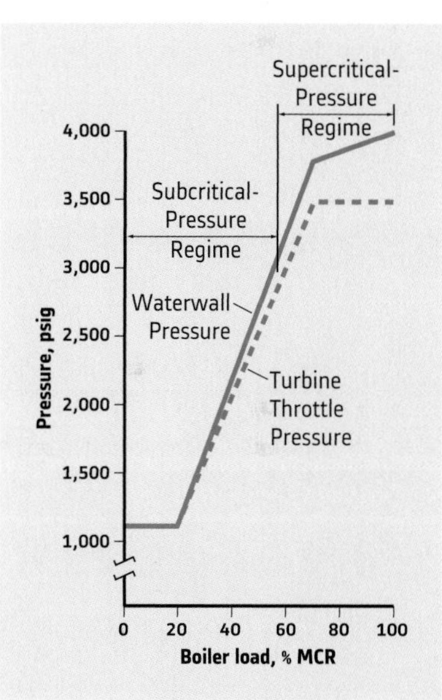

Figure 3-23 | Pressure versus load for full sliding-pressure supercritical design (MCR, maximum continuous rating)

the constant-pressure and modified-constant-pressure designs. For start-up and low-load operation below 30 to 35%, the unit makes use of a pumped recirculation system (similar to the Combined Circulation® unit) to provide an adequate mass flow through the furnace walls and the economizer. This mass flow is required to provide satisfactory cooling of the furnace wall tubes and to avoid circuit stability problems. It also avoids flashing and steaming in the economizer. The basic advantage of a pumped recirculation system is that no heat is rejected in the recirculated water; it is all returned to the system.

Figures 3-24, 3-25, and 3-26 show side elevations of the Alstom super-critical-pressure, steam generating unit for full sliding-pressure operation with both two-pass and tower arrangements. The units have the following features:

- An integral water separator is placed between the furnace wall outlet and the superheater inlet. During start-up and low-load conditions, the separator operates with a water level, or wet. Under these conditions, the excess water from the furnace walls is recirculated through the furnace walls and the economizer.
- In the once-through mode of operation, the water separator is dry and serves as a junction header between the furnace walls and the superheater. The principal advantage of this arrangement is that the water separator remains in the circuit at all times, eliminating the multitude of valves associated with previous designs.

The furnace wall configuration of a full sliding-pressure, supercritical steam generator can be designed for two different arrangements: the vertical tube wall, and the spiral wound or helical tube furnace. Vertical tube walls are shown in the steam generator in *Figure 3-24*. The spiral wound design is shown conceptually in *Figures 3-27* and 3-28. Each has its own design, performance, and cost advantages that must be considered in selecting one or the other for any given application.

Once-Through Technology

Evaporator systems with a fixed water vapor phase transition point, both natural circulation and forced circulation, can be only realized up to drum pressures of approximately 2,850 psig (19.6 MPa). For once-through systems, however, the pressure can be increased to supercritical or advanced super-critical steam conditions. The basic principle of any evaporator design is that the mass flow must be sufficient in each tube and under all operation conditions such that overheating of any tube in the furnace enclosure does not occur. The secondary priority of the furnace wall design is to minimize the temperature differences of the fluid leaving the tubes. The former holds true for both drum-type and once-through designs; the latter is mainly a design criterion for once-through units. *Figure* 3-6 shows various principles of boiler circulation. Drum units maintain the proper mass flows by the use of either natural or forced circulation. These boilers are designed to generate steam in the furnace under nucleate boiling conditions.

In a once-through boiler, waterwall mass flow changes in direct proportion

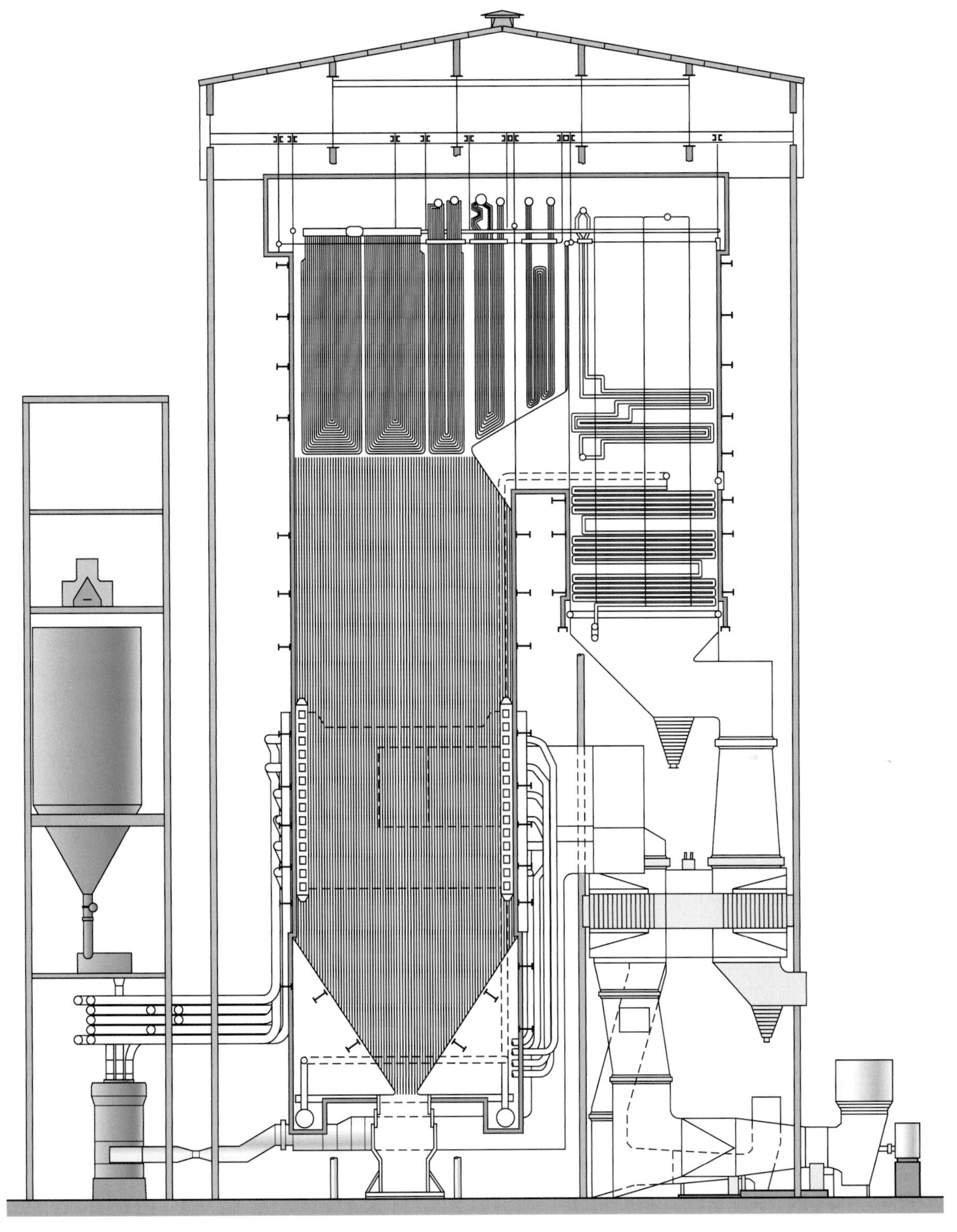

Figure 3-24 | A supercritical-pressure, coal-fired steam generator for full sliding-pressure operation

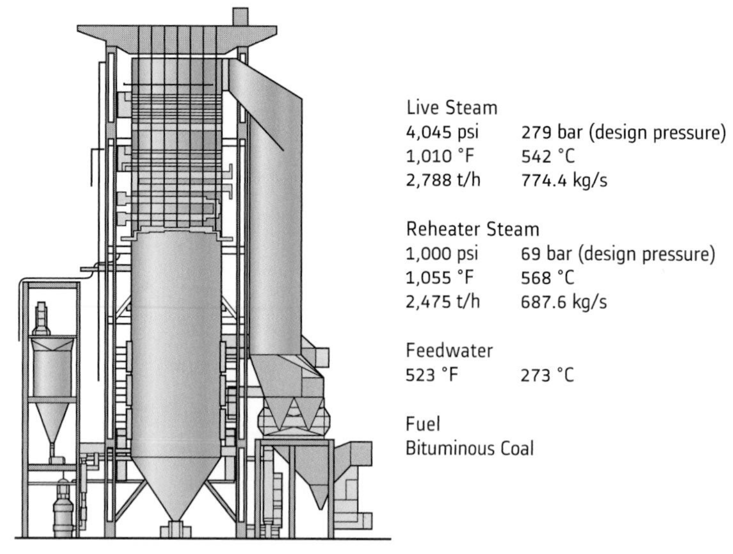

Live Steam
4,045 psi 279 bar (design pressure)
1,010 °F 542 °C
2,788 t/h 774.4 kg/s
Reheater Steam
1,000 psi 69 bar (design pressure)
1,055 °F 568 °C
2,475 t/h 687.6 kg/s
Feedwater
523 °F 273 °C
Fuel
Bituminous Coal

Figure 3-25 | Wai Gao Qiao (2 × 980 MWe)

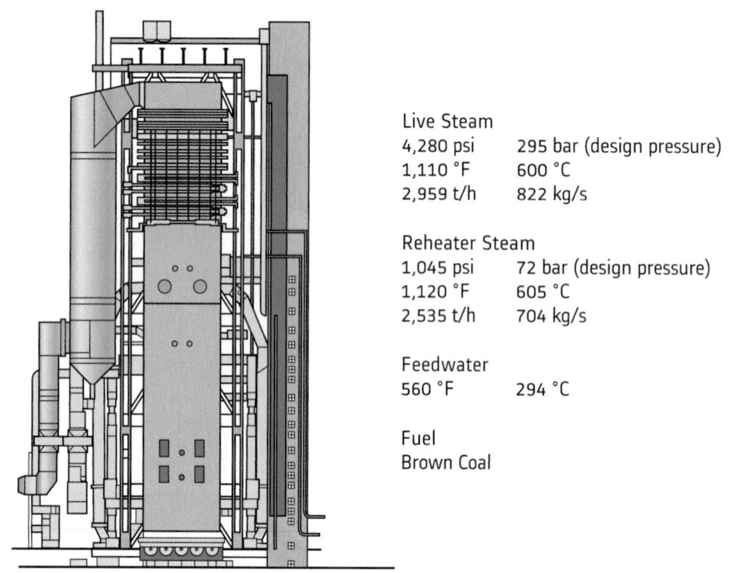

Figure 3-26 | Neurath F/G Steam Generator (2 × 1,100 MWe)

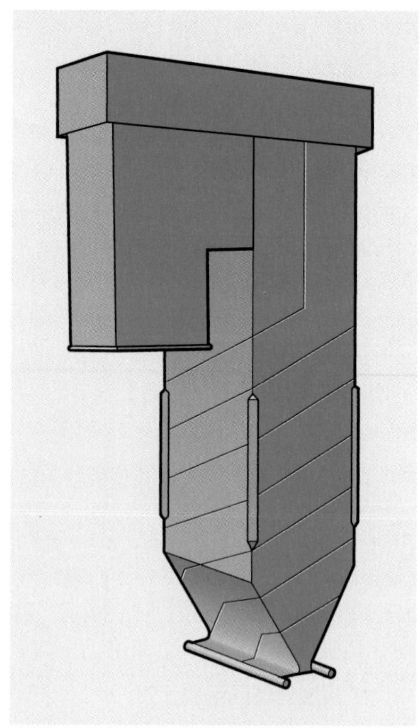

Figure 3-27 | Spiral-wall furnace for supercritical pressure

to steam flow. In the supercritical-pressure region, the fluid inside the tubes is heated, and the heat is directly converted into a higher temperature. In the subcritical, once-through pressure region, the process of heat transfer is more complicated and involves a change in phase from liquid to steam as well as superheating. The fluid enters the furnace tubes with a temperature below its boiling point and then is heated so that progressive vaporization and slight superheating occurs. The process of heat transfer during vaporization depends on many variables. As the quantity of the steam–liquid mixture increases, various two-phase flow patterns are encountered.

Boiler designers must be concerned with two conditions that may occur when a boiler operates in the subcritical-pressure region: departure from nucleate boiling (DNB), and dryout. Both DNB and dryout are characterized by formation of a layer of steam that covers the inner surface of a tube, resulting in a sharp decrease in heat-transfer coefficient and, consequently, a high rise in metal temperature. Theoretically, DNB can only occur at high subcritical pressures with very high heat fluxes and low flow velocities inside the tubes at low steam content. Design analysis for each once-through boiler type checks this, and the possibility of DNB must be avoided in any case by an adequate furnace waterwall design. Dryout occurs at relatively high steam content. Because of the once-through operation principle, dryout cannot be avoided when the boiler operates in subcritical conditions. Therefore, the mass flux in the waterwall tubes is selected in such a manner that a proper cooling of the evaporator tubes is guaranteed under all operating conditions. In addition to the cooling aspects, the once-through system also has to deal with a second design challenge. To avoid potential stresses, differences in steam temperature at the outlets of the tubes must be maintained within acceptable limits.

Start-Up System

The start-up system consists of the water–steam separating system with cyclone separators, the leveling vessel, the recirculation system back to the feedwater line upstream economizer, and the discharge system via the atmospheric flash tank to the condenser (*Fig. 3-29*). The purpose of the recirculation system is to provide an adequate mass flow in the furnace walls during start-up and at low loads. Depending on the type of low-load system, more or less energy of the separated, saturated water can be recovered. The preferred solution is a recirculation system with a low-load recirculation pump (*Fig. 3-30, left*). This boiler internal recirculation system avoids any water losses during start-up, with the exception of the necessary discharge

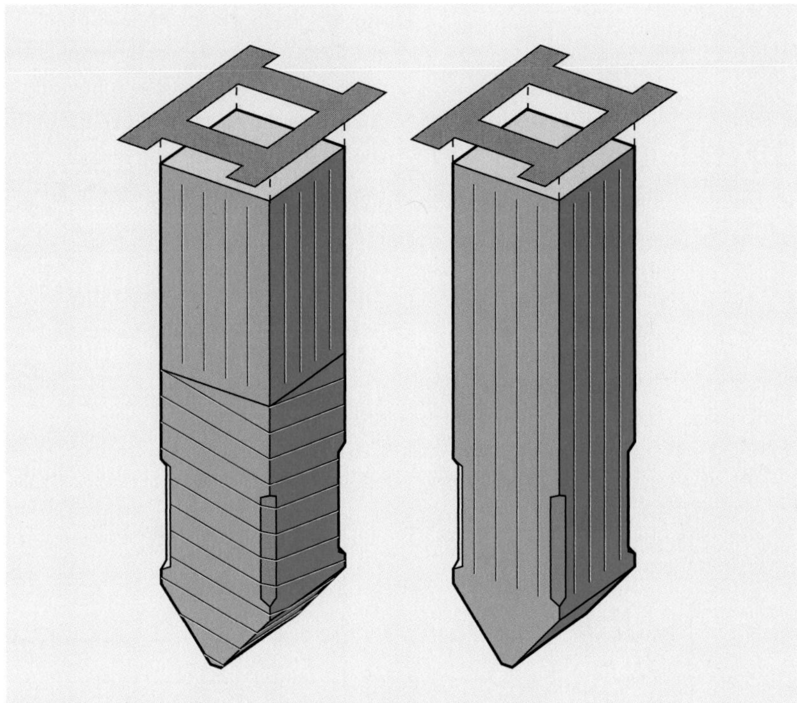

Figure 3-28 | Evaporator wall design

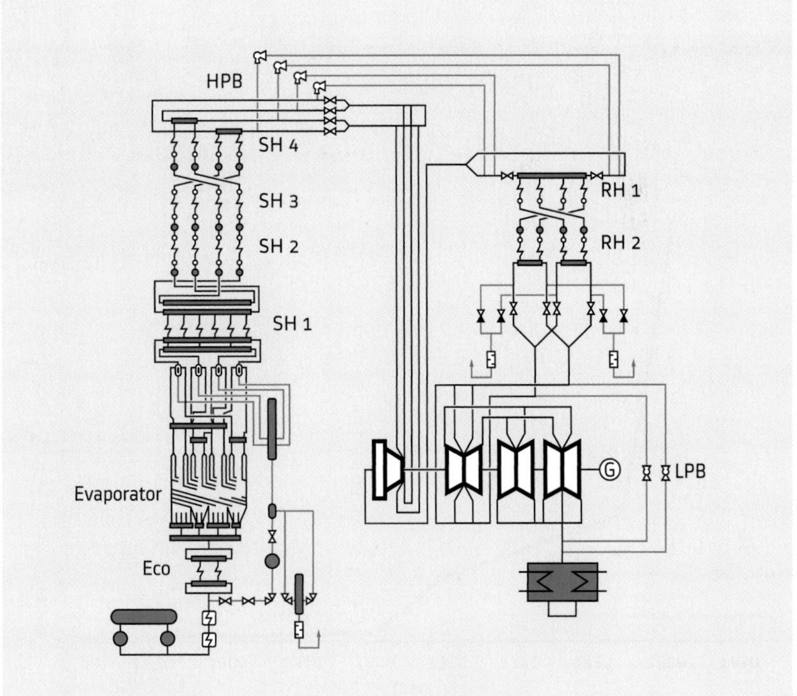

Figure 3-29 | Water–steam diagram (Eco, economizer; HPB, high pressure bypass; LPB, low pressure bypass; RH, reheater; SH, superheater)

flow via the flash tank because of the sudden volume increase during start-up (i.e., swelling phenomenon). Another solution is to return the condensate to the feedwater tank (*Fig. 3-30, right*). In this case, the condensate, or a part of it, is recirculated to the boiler via the feedwater pump. This type of start-up system should be used for boilers that are operated mainly at base load. Especially during a hot start-up, the feedwater tank is not able to recover all the energy; consequently, water and energy losses cannot be totally avoided. In addition, the system increases the start-up times compared to those with a start-up system via the recirculation pump.

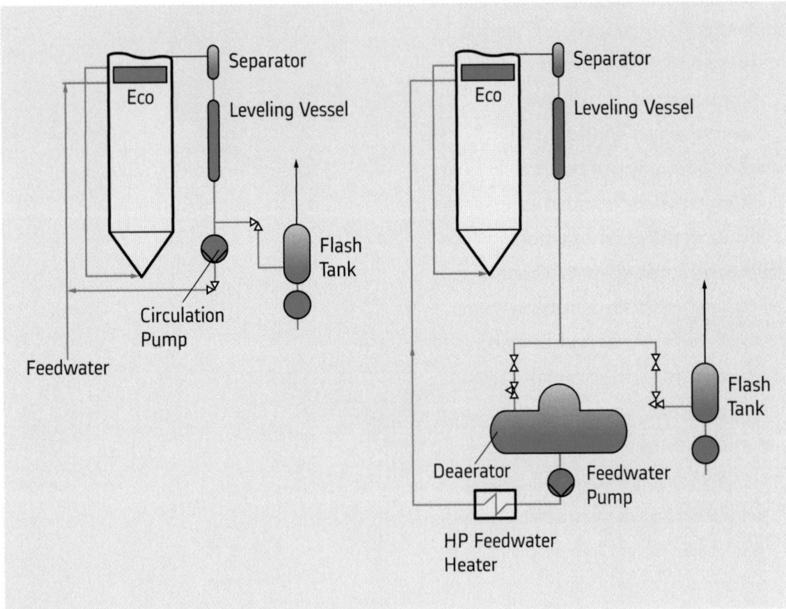

Figure 3-30 | Start-up and low-load system (Eco, economizer; HP, high pressure)

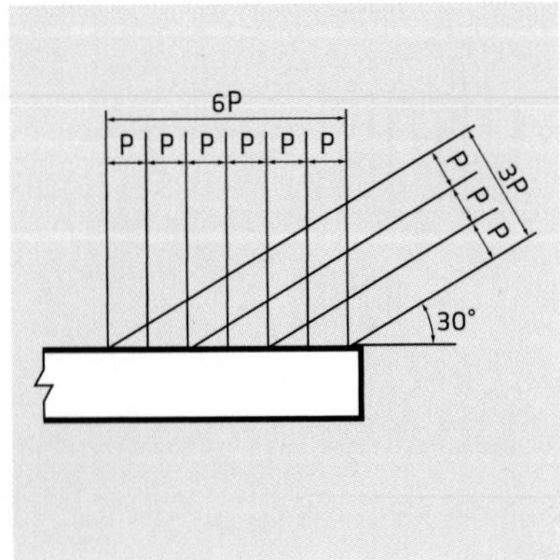

Figure 3-31 | Basic principle of spiral-wall furnace (P, pitch)

Bypass Design

The main function of the HP and LP bypass systems is to lead the superheated steam to the reheater inlet and the reheater steam to the condenser in all operational situations where the turbine is not able to take the whole steam flow (*Fig. 3-29*). This usually is necessary during start-up or shutdown of the unit or during operational malfunctions (i.e., turbine trip). In these operating cases, the HP/LP bypass systems take over the pressure control of the boiler and also ensure sufficient flow through the superheater and reheater heating surfaces. Furthermore, the HP bypass valves can serve as a pressure relief (safety) device. Protection of the boiler reheater part must be accomplished by separate safety valves.

Vertical Versus Spiral or Helical Furnace Walls

The principal concern with a sliding-pressure, supercritical-pressure design is the requirement for once-through operation. The mass flow in the furnace wall tubes must be sufficiently high to avoid overheating or DNB while generating steam at subcritical pressures and to avoid excessive metal temperatures as well as uneven steam outlet temperatures when operating at supercritical pressure at higher boiler loads.

To accomplish these objectives, the spiral wall design can be used. The principle of the spiral or helical wall furnace is to increase the mass flow per tube by reducing the number of tubes that are needed to envelop the furnace without increasing the spacing between the tubes. This is done by arranging the tubes at an angle and spiraling them around the furnace. For instance, the number of tubes required to cover the furnace wall can be reduced in half by putting the tubes at a 30° angle (*Fig. 3-31*). Note that the centerline spacing, or pitch, is made the same as that on a vertical wall to prevent fin overheating. In addition, by spiraling around the furnace, every tube is part of all the walls, which means that each tube acts as a heat integrator around the four walls of the combustion chamber (*Fig. 3-27*). The spiral wall concept thus addresses two major challenges of the full sliding pressure, supercritical pressure boiler:

1. Achieving the required mass flows to avoid overheating and excessive metal temperatures by reducing the number of tube circuits
2. Minimizing differences in tube-to-tube heat absorption by exposing each tube to all four furnace walls

Spiral wall furnaces have been in operation worldwide for many years and have given satisfactory performance. Spiral wound furnace designs, however, involve one performance penalty. Because of the high mass flow, the pressure drop in the lower furnace walls generally is higher than that for vertical wall supercritical or subcritical units, which increases the boiler feed pump power requirements.

While on the process side the spiral wall design achieves all of the required performance parameters, the furnace wall tubes are at an angle. Thus, the furnace wall support system is more difficult to build. The load must be transmitted through the fins between the tubes by means of weld attachments and tension strips. Consequently, the spiral wound furnace is somewhat more expensive to manufacture and erect compared with a vertical tube unit. There typically are fourfold as many tube-to-tube butt welds in the furnace walls as a result of the spiral arrangement. With this design, it is customary to revert to vertical tube construction in the upper portions of the furnace, where the heat absorption rates are lower. This requires use of bifurcated/trifurcated sections of tubing or an intermediate header. Spiral wall configurations also entail difficult tube routing around all openings for the firing equipment in the lower furnace.

In larger sizes, the mass flow per tube increases such that cooling flow can be adequate. Vertical walls can be used under these conditions. In order to ensure low temperature differences at the evaporator outlet and sufficient cooling throughout the furnace walls, rifled tubing is used, as in the Controlled Circulation® design. The vertical wall design has individual tube orifices to control the heat absorption in each circuit (in the same manner as in Combined Circulation® units). Analyses based on operating experience and design practices for Combined Circulation® units have demonstrated that satisfactory temperature differentials throughout the entire operating load range can be achieved. Thus, the two problems of DNB (tube overheating) and waterwall steam-temperature unbalance can be addressed in a vertical wall design by employing a tangentially fired system and rifled tubing.

Heat Rate: The Why of Supercritical Pressure

In Chapter 1, it was noted that improved thermodynamic cycle efficiency can be gained by using high steam pressures and temperatures. The data in *Table 3-3* give some insight regarding the relative improvement of net plant heat rate for several steam cycles.

TABLE 3-3 | NET PLANT HEAT RATE IMPROVEMENT

	2,400 PSI	3,500 PSI
Temperature, °F	—BTU/kWhr—	
1,000/1,000	9,000	8,860
1,050/1,000	8,930	8,800
1,000/1,025/1,050	—	8,630

For 4,500 psi/1,110°F/1,150°F the heat rate would approach 7,600 BTU/KWhr

Large incremental decreases in plant heat rate (improved efficiency) are very difficult to achieve. Increasing the superheat temperature of a subcritical unit to 1,050°F (565°C) in lieu of 1,000°F (540°C) provides only 0.8% improvement in the heat rate. Increasing pressure to 3,500 psi (24 MPa) at 1,000°F/1,000°F (540°C/540°C) yields an improvement of 1.5%, and the double-reheat ramp cycle improves 4.1% above 2,400 psi (17 MPa) at 1,000°F/1,000°F (540°C/540°C). Many factors affect plant heat rate besides the cycle itself, such as load regime, fuel, condenser temperature, and steam generator exit gas temperature. These and other items noted in Chapters 1 through 6 must all be considered when selecting a pressure and temperature. A detailed history regarding development of the once-through steam generator and large supercritical units is given in Chapter 25 of the 1966 edition of *Combustion*.

Advances in overall power station efficiency have received considerable attention in Europe as well (*Fig.* 3-32). The European power plant industry has been steadily increasing the cycle conditions as well as further optimizing various power plant components. The various contributions to achieve this significant increase in net plant efficiency from, as a percentage, the mid-thirties to the mid-forties are shown in *Figure* 3-33. Most bituminous coal-fired units that were built in the 1980s were characterized by moderate steam conditions. Power plants built in the 1990s were typically designed with supercritical steam parameters of 3,800 psig/1,000°F/1,050°F (260 bar/542°C/568°C).

Figure 3-25 shows the bituminous coal-fired, once-through boilers at Wai Gao Qiao in Shanghai, China, with a capacity of 2 × 980 MWe. The two boilers were designed for a broad range of Chinese coals, some with high slagging potential. The further step of the lignite-fired power station renewal program led to the two units at the Neurath power station in Germany (*Fig.* 3-26), with a total gross output of 2,200 MWe. This project has steam conditions of 4,280 psig/1,110°F/1,120°F (295 bar/600°C/605°C).

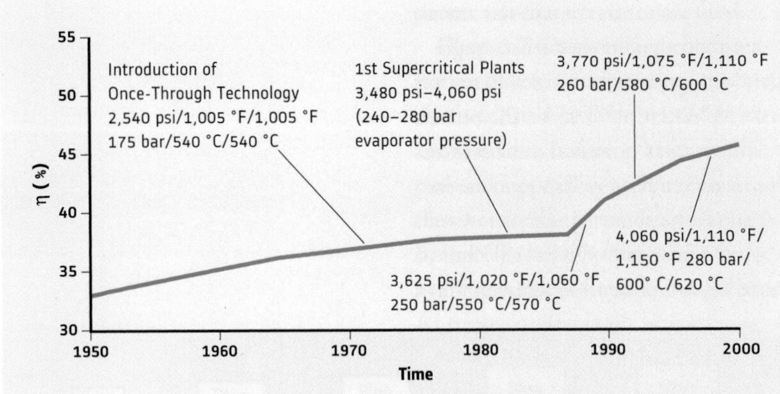

Figure 3-32 | Efficiencies of steam power stations in Europe

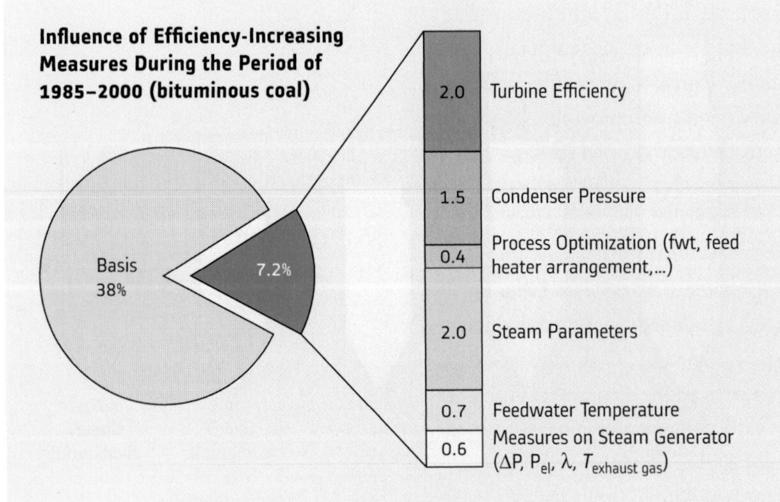

Figure 3-33 | Efficiency increase of steam power plants in Europe

BOILERS FOR PROCESS USE AND POWER PRODUCTION

A typical pulverized coal-fired industrial power plant boiler is a thermal circulation, water tube steam generator, without steam reheat, with a steam drum operating pressure below 2,000 psig (13.8 MPa gage) and an electrical generating capability of less than 100 MWe. The lower design pressure, lower steam flow, and lack of a reheater alter design considerations to some degree from those of the utility boilers already discussed. Operating pressures are selected to supply the process steam requirements of the industrial facility. Typical applications are to provide an easily controlled source of heat for driving chemical reactors or drying products. Many applications generate steam at higher pressures and temperatures to operate a "topping" steam turbine generator, in which the exhaust from the turbine has sufficient energy for the industrial process. These cogeneration applications provide a substantial increase in overall energy efficiency compared with providing these quantities of steam and electricity separately.

Boiler Design as a Function of Operating Pressure

A common feature of most industrial boilers is a convective section of heating surface known as a "boiler bank." A boiler bank consists of several hundred vertically oriented tubes connected to the steam drum at their top and to a lower drum at their bottom. These tubes are a very effective means of absorbing heat from the flue gas to heat the boiler water, generating a significant amount of steam in the hottest tubes where the flue gas enters the bank. The effectiveness of this surface is a function of the boiler operating pressure and the superheater outlet temperature. As *Figure 3-34* shows, the percentage of total heat absorbed in a boiler bank is reduced significantly at higher pressures by two factors:

1. In the superheater, the greater heat absorption required to heat the steam to a higher temperature reduces the temperature of gas entering the boiler bank.
2. The water temperature in the boiler bank is essentially at the saturation temperature corresponding to the boiler operating pressure. As the pressure increases, the temperature of the water inside the tubes rises, thereby reducing the logarithmic mean temperature available for heat transfer.

Evaluating Pulverized Coal-Fired Systems for Industrial Boilers

Reduced efficiency caused by carbon loss is a major factor in the selection of a solid fuel firing system. A properly designed pulverized coal-fired boiler can maintain an efficiency loss resulting from unburned carbon of less than 0.4%. On the other hand, a continuous-ash-discharge spreader-stoker fired unit will typically have a carbon loss of 4 to 8%, depending on the amount of reinjection. The pulverized coal-fired unit offers a lower carbon loss because of the increased combustion efficiency obtained with the finer coal particles that enter the furnace (normally, 70–80% will pass through a 200-mesh screen.)

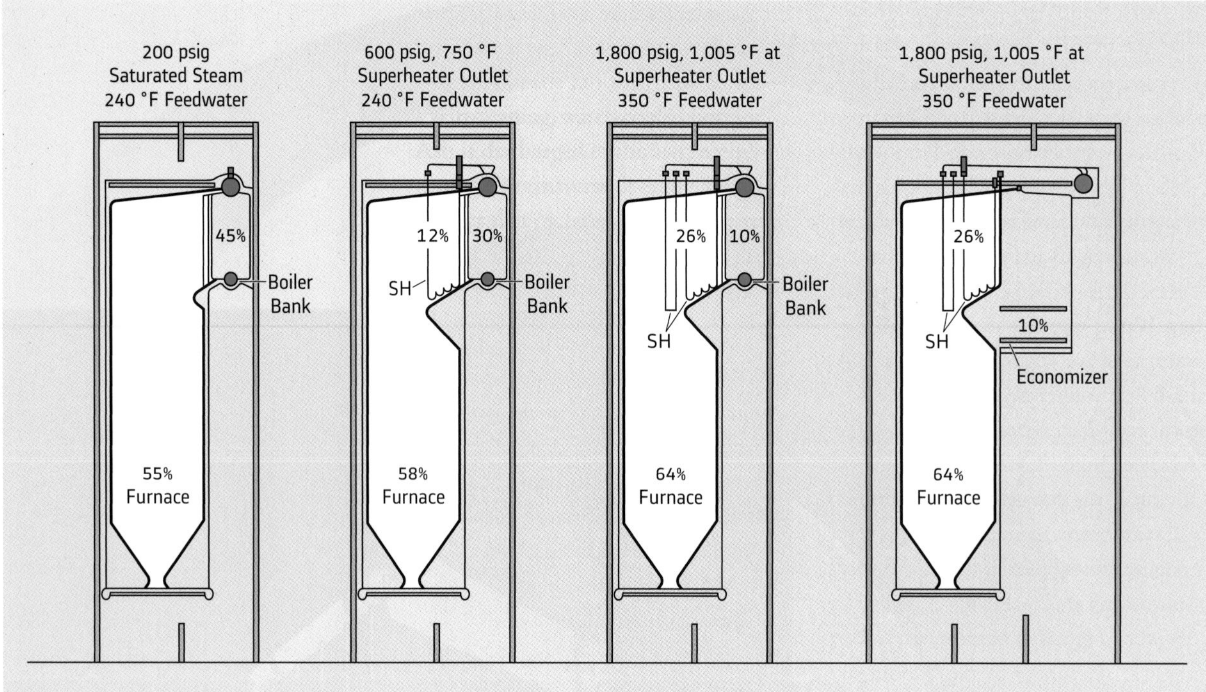

Figure 3-34 | Heat absorption distribution for pulverized coal suspension-fired boilers (SH, superheater)

ADVANCED TECHNOLOGY FOR LIGNITE-FIRED BOILERS

Brown coal and lignites typically are medium- and high-volatile coals (50–60% of volatile matter on daf [dry ash free] basis) that are used either in circulating fluidized bed or in modern, highly efficient, pulverized coal-fired boilers with tangentially fired systems. They are characterized by a relatively low heating value of 1,750 to 4,750 BTU/lb (4–11 MJ/kg, as received), mainly because of the high moisture content, which can vary between 20 and 70%, whereas the ash content can be very low (2%) or very high (up to 35%). Other typical characteristics of the fuel are the low ash-softening point (typically between 1,830 and 2,190°F [1,000 and 1,200°C]) and, very often, the xylite content, resulting in a fibrous structure of the fuel.

Because of its high moisture content, brown coal needs to be dried before being ignited to ensure a good ignition and burnout behavior in pulverized coal-fired units. The drying is combined with the grinding process in special milling equipment, the beater wheel mill. Unlike with bituminous coal, hot flue gas is used as a drying medium instead of hot primary air. The origin of the beater wheel mill is the KSG Lopulco firing system, shown in *Figure 3-35*, developed in the early 1920s by KSG, an Alstom predecessor company.

Depending on the moisture content of the brown coal and the requirements for stable coal firing at part load, three different firing system arrangements, which are shown schematically in *Figure 3-36*, are applied:

1. **Direct injection without vapor separation:** The raw coal is transferred via belt conveyors into the mills, where it is mixed

with recirculated flue gas from the top of the combustion chamber, having a temperature of approximately 1,800°F (1,000°C). Hot and cold air are used to temper the mill. In the beater wheel mill, the coal is dried and ground. Then, the mixture of dried coal, vapor, recirculated flue gas, and air is led directly to the burner openings.

2. **Direct injection with vapor separation:** Same as above, except for the installation of a separator at the outlet of the mill that separates the fine particles, which are led to the reburning burners located on the top of the main jet burners. This system is applied in cases when coal-firing stability at low loads is important.
3. **Semi-direct injection:** Same as the system with vapor separation, except for the fine particles being separated from the carrying gas via fabric filter, or electrostatic precipitator, and stored in a bunker. From the bunker, the pulverized lignite is then transferred pneumatically via hot air to the burners. This system is applied in cases of very high moisture content to achieve adequate ignition stability throughout the entire load range.

In all firing system arrangements, the drying and milling of the lignite takes place in beater wheel mills, as shown in *Figure 3-37*. The top of the mill is connected with the recirculation duct, from where the raw lignite, together with the recirculating flue gas, enters the mill. Depending on the configuration of the mill, the brown coal–gas mixture either enters a pre-beater stage

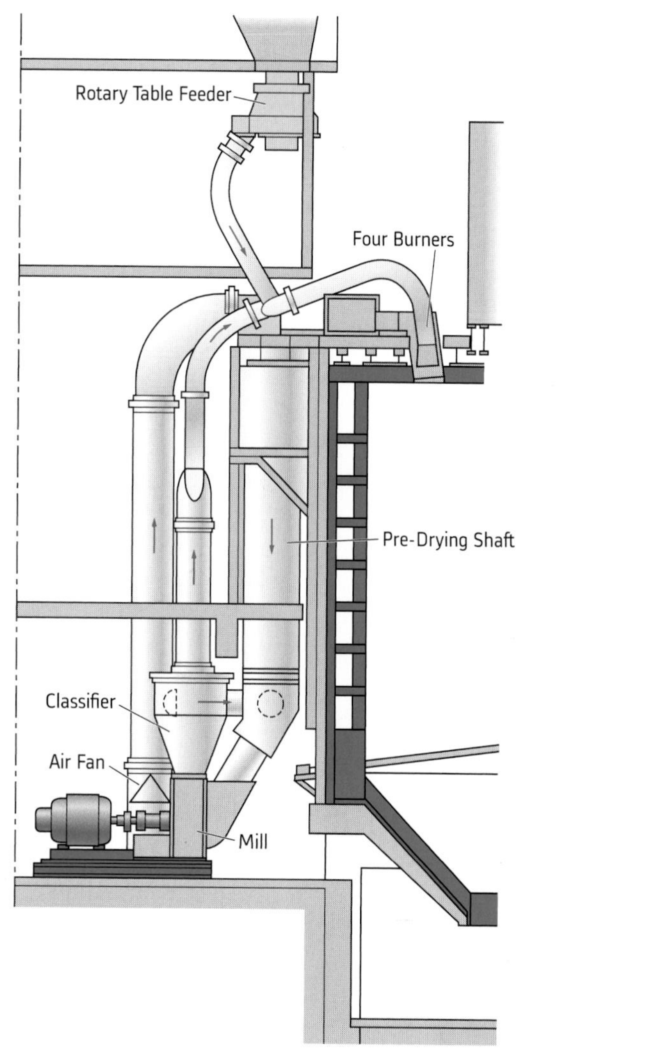

Figure 3-35 | KSG Lopulco firing system with wet coal burner

and then the beater wheel or enters directly into the beater wheel. For lignites with high xylite content, or for generally difficult-to-grind coals, the configuration with the pre-beater stage is applied.

The beater wheel consists of beater plates, which grind the lignite via impact forces. The wheel is turning at constant or variable speed, depending on the fuel properties and the load. Similar to a fan, the flow of the coal particles follows a spiral path and is led

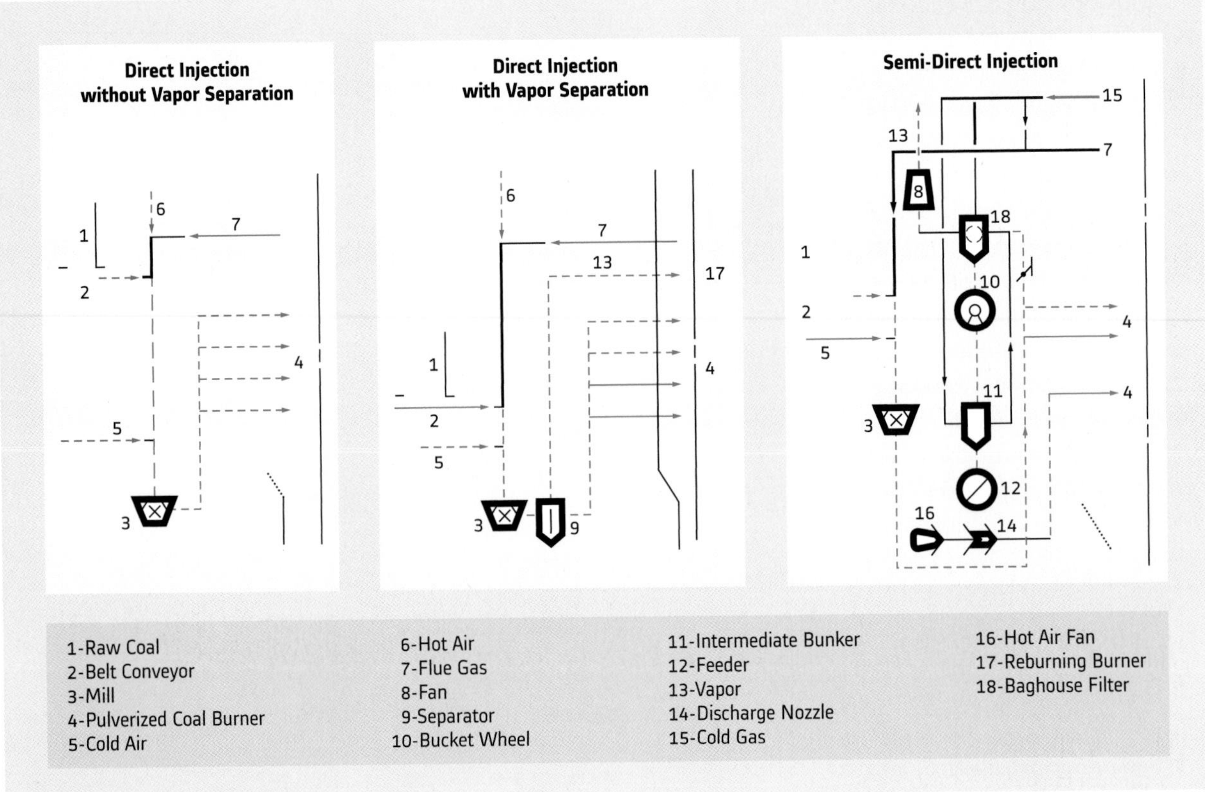

Figure 3-36 | Lignite firing systems

into a classifier, where coarse particles are separated and led back to the beater wheel and fine particles exit the mill and are carried by the transporting gas, consisting of a mixture of recirculated flue gas, air, and volatile matter to the burner openings. In brown coal-fired units, no primary air fan is installed. The beater wheel mill takes over the role of the primary air fan. The pre-drying and grinding capacity are the main design parameters to be matched with the layout of the firing system design. In modern designs, the beater wheel speed can be adjusted according to the demand for drying, either by hydraulic coupling or by frequency converter. Such measures significantly improve the service and maintenance cycles for these types of mills.

In brown coal-fired units, six or eight beater wheel mills are arranged circumferentially around the combustion chamber, as shown in *Figure 3-38*. Full load is achieved with $(n - 1)$ or $(n - 2)$ mills in operation, with the mills that are out of service undergoing inspection or maintenance. Tangential firing has proven to be the preferred option for the burner arrangement because of the homogeneous temperature distribution of the gases inside the furnace. Each mill serves one burner compartment at each corner of the furnace. Unlike bituminous coal, tangentially fired system arrangements, because of the position of the gas recirculation ducts, the burners are located close to, but not directly at, the corner of the furnace. Each burner array consists of two or three compartments, depending on the capacity of each burner compartment and on the application of vapor separation. Correspondingly, two or three coal pipe fingers connect the mills with the burner compartments, as shown in *Figure 3-39*.

Recently, the tower-type design has dominated brown coal-fired boilers. Besides the other known advantages, tower units offer special advantages for brown coal:

- Arrangement advantages, because it supports the symmetrical arrangement of the gas recirculation ducts
- Less temperature and flue gas velocity imbalances, because no change of the flue gas flow occurs in an area including heating surfaces
- Easier cleaning of the heating surfaces, because the transverse pitch of the convective heating surfaces increases from the top to the bottom of the boiler, allowing the removed ash to fall into the hopper without being trapped in the heating surfaces underneath
- Simple and symmetrical hanging and support structure, without the need for expansion joints between heating surfaces, especially for large-capacity boilers

Figure 3-40 shows the most modern current lignite-fired boiler, which is installed as Unit K in Niederaussem, Germany. It has been in commercial operation since 2002. The dimensions of the boiler are the largest for any boiler in the world. The steam parameters are the highest for any brown coal-fired unit.

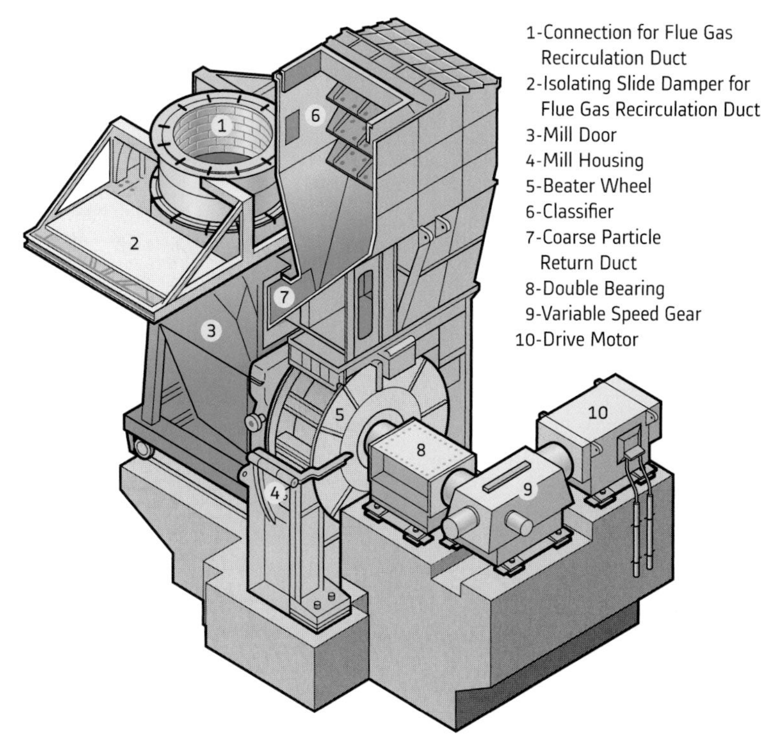

Figure 3-37 | Beater Wheel Mill Type N 400.42

The high moisture content of brown coal and lignite has a positive impact on NOx formation. For most modern brown coal-fired units, NOx emissions of less than 0.16 lb/MMBTU (200 mg/Nm^3) at 6% O_2, dry, are obtained with only primary measures. This value is currently the European Union (EU) limit for NOx emissions from new coal-fired power plants; therefore, lignite-fired boilers are the only coal-fired boilers using pulverized coal technology that can be permitted in the EU without the need for a selective catalytic reduction (SCR) system. A proven, compact burner design maintains

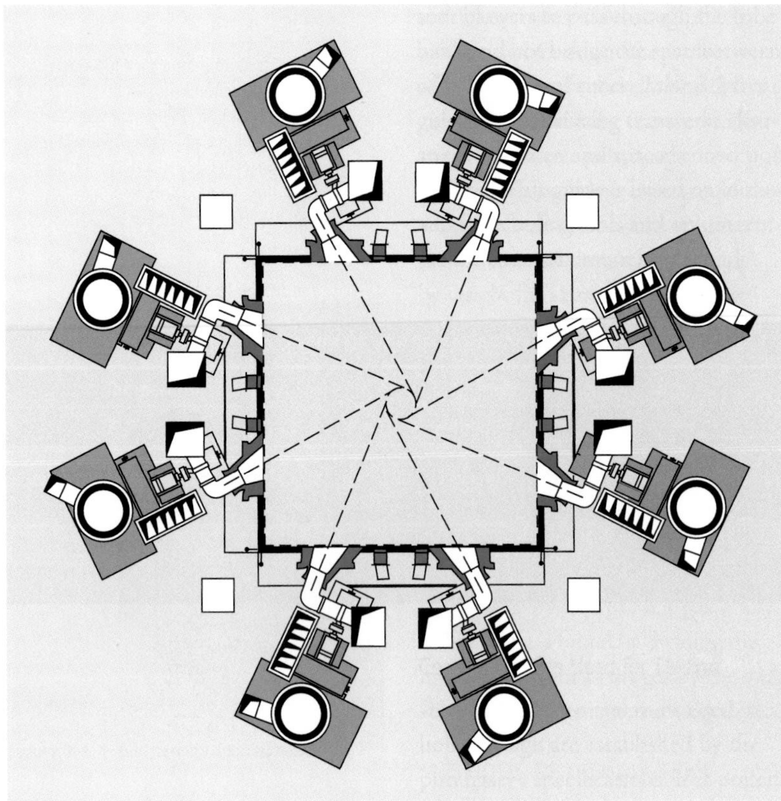

Figure 3-38 | Burner and mill arrangement of a lignite-fired boiler

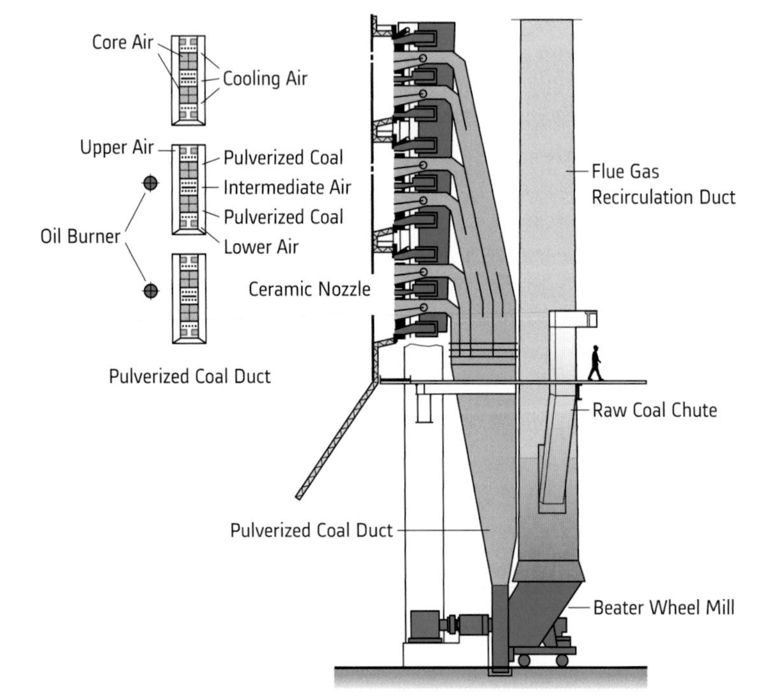

Figure 3-39 | Pulverized brown coal firing

an optimum residence time to reduce NOx emissions. By providing enough time for the burnout of coal particles, the combustion efficiency is further optimized. Based on these measures, the amount of excess air can be reduced significantly, resulting in lower stack losses and increased boiler efficiency. The slagging tendency of brown coal often led to forced part load operation and outages. Specifically for these coals, a firing system consisting of a compact burner design was developed that significantly improves the slagging behavior, as shown in *Figure 3-41 (left)*.

Since the 1960s, the capacity of lignite-fired units (along with their steam parameters) has continuously increased. Unit sizes have increased from 300 MWe to the 1,100 MWe of today. Similarly, the steam parameters have increased from subcritical 2,650 psig, 995°F/995°F (180 bar, 535°C/535°C) in the 1960s to the supercritical 4,200 psig, 1,110°F/1,120°F (285 bar, 600°C/605°C) of today. *Figure 3-42* gives an overview of the development of lignite-fired boilers.

The improvement of power plant efficiency was recognized to reduce greenhouse gas emissions and provide fuel cost savings. The two 800-MWe boilers for the power station in Schwarze Pumpe, Germany, were commissioned in 1997 and 1998. These boilers were the first of the new 800-MWe-or-greater series with supercritical steam conditions. The 1,000-MWe unit located in thes Niederaussem, Germany, power station is another example of increased efficiency. Plant optimization led to the selection of steam parameters of 1,080°F (580°C) and 1,110°F (600°C) and an advanced flue gas heat

recovery system that helped to achieve an overall efficiency in excess of 43% LHV (lower heating value) on brown coal. The unit was commissioned in 2002 and is now in successful commercial operation. This unit is being followed by the Neurath, Germany, site (2 × 1,100 MWe).

The next technological milestone for brown coal utilization is the drying of the high-moisture fuel with a low-temperature energy source. The most advanced technology for brown coal drying is the WTA technology (WTA technology is the German abbreviation for Wirbelschicht-Trocknung mit interner Abwärmenutzung) developed by RWE. The application of advanced drying technologies for brown coal-fired power plant boilers is planned for the post-2012 time frame. This technology comprises the following features:

- Drying in a stationary, fluidized bed with superheated steam
- Supplying the drying energy via heat exchangers installed in the drier
- Utilizing the drying exhaust gases by means of a heat pump process for drier heating
- Utilizing the vapor condensate for coal, or condensate pre-heating in the power plant
- Feeding the raw coal at a particle size of less than 0.08 inch (<2 mm)

The main advantage in pre-drying via atmospheric, fine-grain, fluidized bed technology is that the latent heat of evaporation can be recovered and used to continue the evaporation process in lieu of combustion energy. This, in turn, increases the overall efficiency of the power cycle. Depending on the moisture content of the fuel, the increase in efficiency can reach up to 4 percentage points (i.e., 32% becomes 36%).

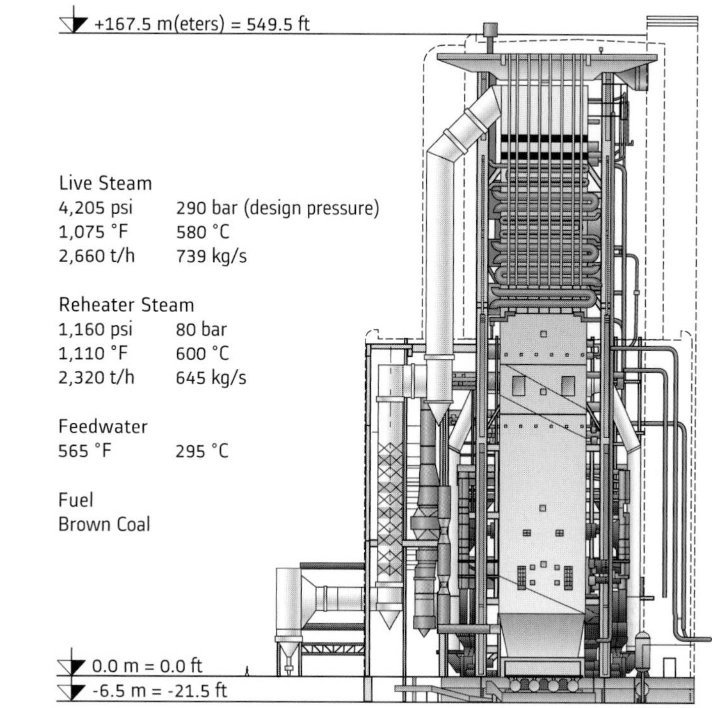

Figure 3-40 | Power Station Niederaussem K

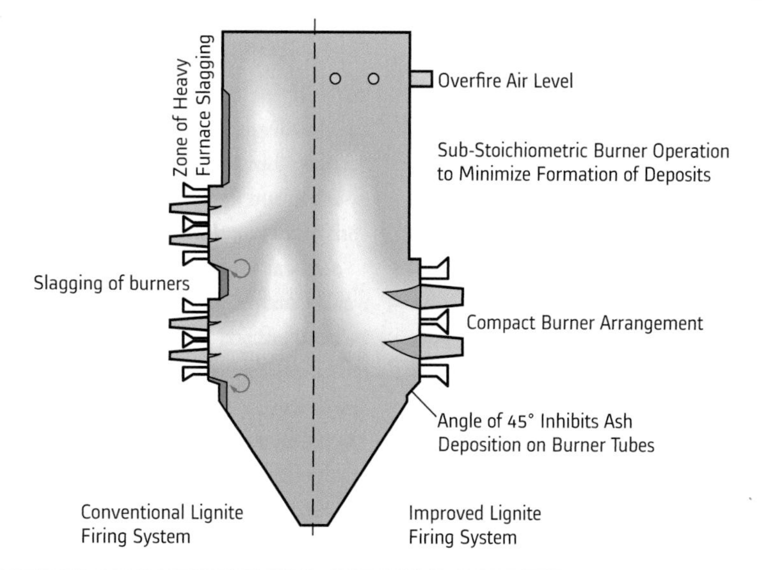

Figure 3-41 | Low NOx Firing System and measures against furnace slagging

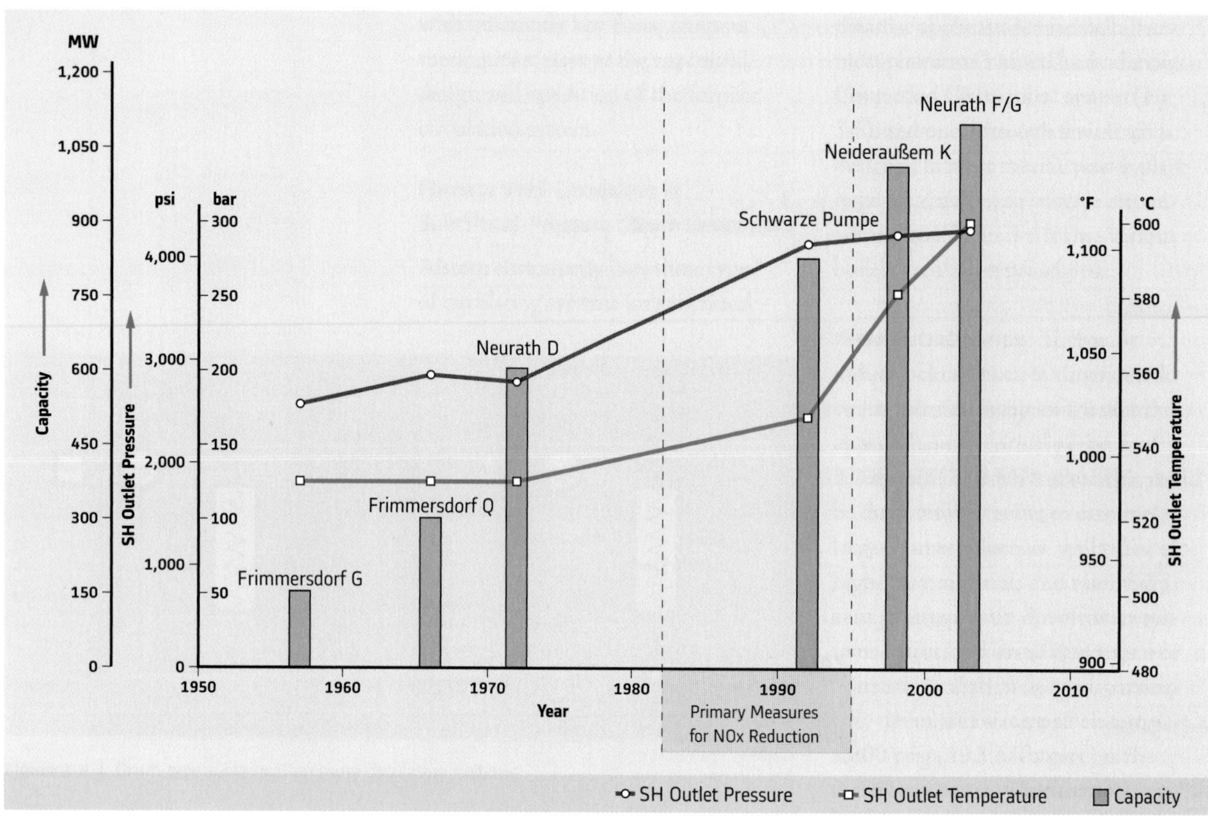

Figure 3-42 | Development of brown coal-fired boilers

FLUIDIZED BED STEAM GENERATORS

For decades, fluidized bed reactors have been used for non-combustion applications in which the thorough mixing and intimate contact of the reactants in a fluidized bed result in high product yield with improved economies of time and energy. Although other methods of burning fuels also can provide very high combustion efficiency, fluidized bed combustion (FBC) can burn nearly any fuel efficiently at a temperature low enough to avoid many of the problems encountered when using other technologies.

HISTORICAL PERSPECTIVE

Fluidization and observations of phenomena related to fluidization have been referenced in the literature since the late 1800s. The person most often cited as initiating fluidized bed technology is Fritz Winkler, who in the 1920s developed the Winkler coal gasifier, which employed fluid bed concepts. He received a patent for his work in 1928.

With a knowledge of Winkler's work and a wartime demand for petroleum products, a Fluidized Catalytic Cracking (FCC) process was developed during the early 1940s. This process greatly increased both the quantity and quality of the refined product. Over the years, many improvements were made to the original FCC process, and today, various types of fluid bed processes are used in the refining of petroleum and the production of other chemical feedstocks.

Various fluidized bed processes for roasting of ores and other materials also were developed.

During the early 1960s, much of the work in applying fluidized bed technology to steam generation was carried out in England by the Central Electricity Generating Board (CEGB) and the British Coal Utilization Research Association (BCURA). The overall emphasis was to develop FBC for industrial steam production from coal while meeting low SO_2/NOx emissions requirements without additional equipment. The technology developed in England found its way to the United States in the late 1960s. Pilot plant research work was conducted and later used to develop concepts for the construction of a 30 MWe, fluidized bed boiler demonstration plant at Rivesville, West Virginia, in 1975. This plant was about 15 fold larger than any other fluidized bed boiler facility then operating.

Spurred on by the oil crises of the 1970s, FBC technology was considered to be a potential solution. Many studies and several demonstration projects were funded in the United States by government agencies, some based on the Rivesville technology (called bubbling fluidized bed [BFB]) and others based on a newer technology adapted from a fluidized bed process developed by Lurgi initially used for aluminum calcination (called circulating fluidized bed [CFB]). In 1984, two key demonstration projects were initiated. One was the 160 MWe demonstration boiler at the Tennessee Valley Authority's Shawnee Steam Plant in Paducah, Kentucky.[1] This project utilized BFB technology for coal firing and began operation in 1988. The other was the 110 MWe demonstration boiler at Colorado-Ute's (now Tri-State Generation and Transmission) Nucla Station in Nucla, Colorado. This project utilized CFB technology for coal firing and also began operation in 1988. Both demonstration plants can be considered successful, but the BFB technology (despite subsequent operation of a 350 MWe, coal-fired demonstration unit in Japan in 1995) has not been applied commercially in sizes above approximately 100 MWe. BFB technology is used mainly for smaller, biomass-fired, industrial applications. On the other hand, CFB technology has been applied commercially in sizes over 300 MWe, firing a range of fuels, and has become the dominant FBC technology for industrial and utility applications worldwide.

GENERAL DESCRIPTION OF FBC

"Fluidization" refers to the condition in which solid materials are given free-flowing, fluid-like behavior. As a gas is passed upward through a bed of solid particles, the flow of gas produces forces that tend to separate the particles from one another. At low gas flows, the particles remain in contact with each other and tend to resist movement. This condition is referred to as a "fixed bed." As the gas flow is increased, a point is reached at which the forces on the particles are just sufficient to cause separation. This condition is referred to as a fluidized bed. The gas cushion between the solids allows the particles to move freely, giving the bed a liquid-like, or fluid, characteristic.

The transition from fixed bed to fluid bed is illustrated in *Figure 3-43*, which plots the drop in gas pressure through the bed versus the gas velocity. For a

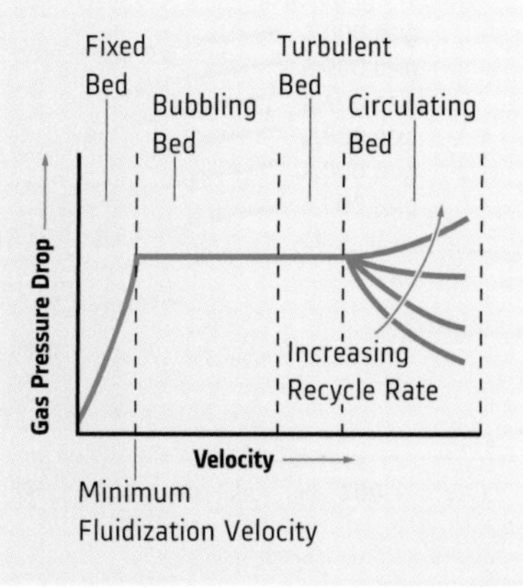

Figure 3-43 | Plot of gas pressure drop through a fluidized bed versus gas velocity

fixed bed, the pressure drop is proportional to the square of the velocity. As velocity is increased, the bed becomes fluidized, and the velocity at which this transition occurs is called the "minimum fluidization velocity" (V_{mf}). The V_{mf} depends on many factors, including particle diameter, gas and particle density, particle shape, gas viscosity, and bed void fraction.[2,3] At velocities above V_{mf}, the pressure drop through the bed remains nearly constant and is equal to the weight of solids per unit area, because the drag forces on the particles just overcome the gravitational forces. Further increases in velocity bring about changes in the state of fluidization (discussed later in this chapter).

CHARACTERISTICS OF FBC

FBC offers the power engineer the ability to efficiently utilize a wide variety of fuels, including fuels with high ash, high moisture, high sulfur, low volatiles, and low heating value that are unsuitable for other firing systems. Furthermore, FBC can utilize such fuels while meeting stringent stack emission limits. This unique combination of fuel flexibility and low emissions is responsible for the development and growth of FBC technology.

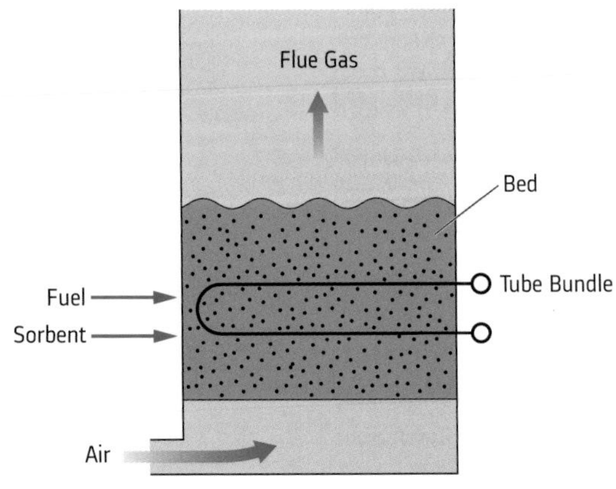

Figure 3-44 | Generalized fluidized bed combustor

Figure 3-44 shows a generalized fluidized bed combustor, in which fuel is burned in a bed of hot, non-combustible particles suspended by an upward flow of fluidizing gas. Typically, the fuel is a solid such as coal, although liquid and gaseous fuels can be readily used. The fluidizing gas typically is the combustion air and the gaseous products of combustion. Where sulfur capture is not required, the ash may be supplemented by an inert material, such as sand. For applications that require sulfur capture, limestone is used as the sulfur sorbent and forms a portion of the bed. Bed temperature is maintained in the range of 1,550 to 1,650°F (850–900°C) by the use of a heat-absorbing surface within or enclosing the bed. This temperature range is optimal for the chemical processes needed to capture sulfur and minimize NOx emissions, and also avoids ash softening in nearly all fuels. Efficient combustion can be achieved at this relatively low temperature range because of the long fuel residence time and high gas–solid mixing rates in the bed.

The characteristics of fluidized bed firing also can be illustrated by comparison to the other key combustion technologies—stoker and pulverized firing—as shown in *Figure 3-45*. With stoker firing, fuel feed size is relatively large and gas velocity low, with fuel burned in the resulting fixed bed. Furnace temperatures and fuel residence times are high to provide efficient combustion with the given fuel feed size and low bed mixing rates. With pulverized firing, fuel feed size is very small and gas velocity high, with the fuel burned in the resulting entrained bed (also called "suspension firing"). Furnace temperatures are very high to provide efficient combustion with

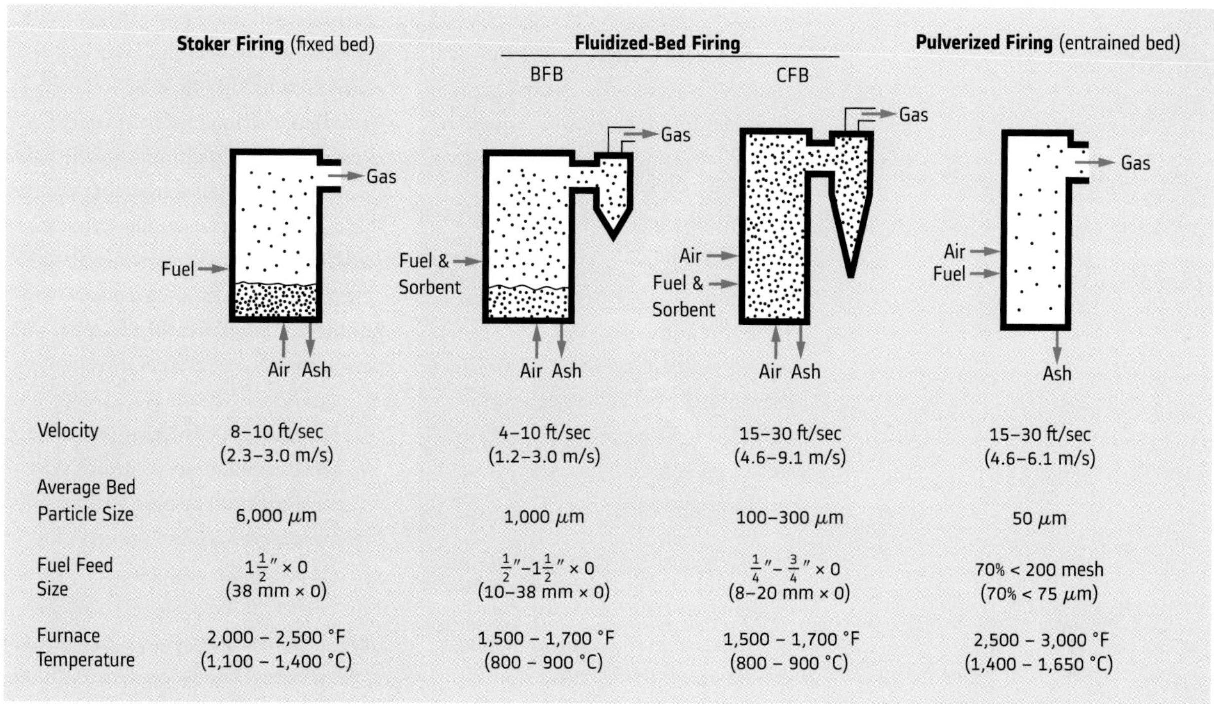

Figure 3-45 | Relationships between stoker, fluidized bed, and pulverized firing of solid fuels (BFB, bubbling fluidized bed; CFB, circulating fluidized bed)

the low solids residence time, which is equal to the gas residence time (a few seconds). With fluidized bed firing, fuel sizing and gas velocity are nominally between those for stoker and pulverized firing, but furnace temperatures are much lower. In addition, fluidized bed firing systems typically use solids recycle to maintain bed inventory and increase solids residence time (calculated as bed solids inventory/throughput) to values on the order of hours. The high solids residence time and high mixing rates in the bed allow efficient combustion at the relatively low furnace temperatures with FBC. These characteristics of fluidized bed firing lead to the advantages described below.

Ability to Burn Low-Grade Fuels

The high thermal inertia of the bed mass allows stable ignition and combustion of very-low-grade fuels, such as those high in ash and/or moisture. Fuels with over 70% ash and over 60% moisture have been successfully burned in a fluid bed. The high thermal inertia of the bed also allows good performance when firing low-volatile fuels, such as anthracite, anthracite culm, and petroleum coke.

Fuel Flexibility

Because furnace temperatures are below the ash-softening temperature of most fuels, FBC boilers are not as sensitive to fuel ash characteristics. A wide range of fuels with varying ash content and ash properties can be fired in a given boiler.

Low NOx Production

Emissions of NOx are considered to come from two sources: oxidation of nitrogen in the air (thermal NOx) and oxidation of nitrogen and/or nitrogen components in the fuel (fuel NOx). At the low furnace temperatures in FBC, thermal NOx is essentially zero. Design features such as staged combustion can significantly reduce fuel NOx. Furthermore, selective non-catalytic reduction (SNCR) systems can be added, leading to very low NOx emissions.

Low SO_2 Emissions

Emissions of SO_2 can be controlled within the combustor by addition of a sorbent material, typically limestone. The sulfur sorbent also can react with other fuel constituents, such as vanadium, reducing the downstream corrosion potential.

TYPES OF FBC SYSTEMS

As shown in *Figure 3-45*, there are two basic types of fluid bed firing systems, each operating in a different state of fluidization. The state of fluidization depends mainly on the bed particle diameter and the fluidizing velocity. At relatively low velocities and coarse bed particle size, the fluid bed is dense, with a uniform solids concentration and a well-defined surface. This type of fluidized bed is called a "bubbling fluid bed" (BFB), because the air in excess of that required to fluidize the bed passes through the bed in the form of bubbles. The BFB is further characterized by modest bed solids mixing rates and relatively low solids entrainment in the flue gas. Little recycle of the entrained material to the bed is needed to maintain bed inventory, but substantial recycle rates may be used to enhance performance.

At higher velocities and with finer bed particle sizes, the fluid bed surface becomes diffuse as the solids entrainment increases, such that a defined bed surface no longer is present. Recycle of entrained material to the bed at high rates is required to maintain bed inventory. The local density of the bed decreases with increasing height in the furnace. This type of fluidized bed is called a "circulating fluid bed" (CFB) because of the high rate of material circulating from the furnace to the particle recycle system and then back to the furnace. The CFB is further characterized by very high solids mixing rates. The difference in fluidization state will be reflected in different applications and performance of BFB and CFB.

CHEMICAL PROCESSES

Within the bed, several interrelated chemical processes occur, including combustion, sulfur capture, and nitrogen–oxygen conversion.

Fuel Combustion

Even at the relatively low temperatures associated with FBC, the combustion of fuel in a fluid bed is a rapid process. The combustion rate is a function of the reactivity of the fuel and the available fuel surface area. The combustible portion of solid fuel can be considered to consist of volatile matter (the gaseous components driven off as the fuel is heated) and fixed carbon (the solid remaining, called "char"). Volatile combustible matter generally burns more rapidly than the residual char and can be viewed as a separate process from char combustion. Char combustion is a much slower process and requires substantial solids residence time and mixing. With sufficient residence time and mixing, the concentration of char within the fluidized bed at any given time is a small percentage of the total bed material. The combustible loss is determined by the amount of char that escapes the system without burning, because the loss from unburned volatiles is insignificant. Both the fly ash and bottom ash streams will contain some char, but the majority of combustible loss is typically in the fly ash stream.

In a BFB, the carbon loss by entrainment from the bed (elutriation) can be on the order of 10% when firing a fuel such as coal. Recycle of elutriated material back to the bed is an effective means for retaining the char within the system long enough for efficient combustion. In a CFB, the high fluidizing velocity produces vigorous mixing, and the recycle rates that are attainable with a high-efficiency particle separator allow a long solids residence time. For CFB, combustion efficiencies of 98% for less reactive fuels such as coal, and of more than 99% for more reactive fuels such as biomass, can be achieved. For BFB with sufficient recycle, combustion efficiencies approaching that of a CFB can be achieved for most solid fuels.

Sulfur Capture

The use of limestone as a sorbent allows sulfur emissions to be controlled within the fluidized bed during the combustion process. Limestone consists of calcium carbonate ($CaCO_3$) and various impurities, such as magnesium carbonate ($MgCO_3$). Lime (CaO) is formed by calcining the limestone to drive off carbon dioxide (CO_2):

$$CaCO_3 \rightarrow CaO + CO_2 \text{ (endothermic)}$$

Equation 3-1

Sulfur in the fuel is converted to SO_2 during the combustion process. Although nearly all the sulfur is oxidized, some of the inorganically bound sulfur may be retained in the ash. The SO_2 combines with the calcined lime in the reaction:

$$SO_2 + CaO + \tfrac{1}{2}O_2 \rightarrow CaSO_4 \text{ (exothermic)}$$

Equation 3-2

Equations 3-1 and 3-2 indicate that a mole of calcium is required to capture one mole of sulfur. Then, defining the Ca/S molar ratio as moles of calcium in the limestone feed to moles of sulfur in the fuel feed, Ca/S = 1/1 could theoretically provide 100% sulfur capture. In practice, however, this is not possible for two reasons. First, the sulfation process takes place on the surface of the lime particles, and the resulting sulfate shell prevents access to the lime in the particle core. Second, the time available for the sulfation reaction is limited (equal to the furnace gas residence time of ~3–6 seconds), inevitably allowing some SO_2 to escape capture.

The porosity of the particle surface formed during calcination is a strong factor in sulfur capture and results from the CO_2 vacating the $CaCO_3$ structure. Ideally, calcination results in a highly porous particle with an exposed surface area that is much higher than that of a smooth particle having a similar diameter. As sulfur capture proceeds, calcium sulfate tends to block the pores. Optimum porosity provides the maximum surface that can be fully sulfated. The presence of $MgCO_3$ tends to enhance porosity and, therefore, limestone utilization (that fraction of calcium reacting with sulfur), even though it does not participate in the sulfur capture process. This is because, in calcining to MgO, the $MgCO_3$ increases porosity without contributing to pore blockage.

The calcination and sulfation processes begin at around 1,300°F (700°C), and the reaction rates increase with increasing temperature. The most favorable temperature for simultaneous calcination and sulfation, however, is approximately 1,550°F (840°C). Above

The ability to capture sulfur during the combustion process is a key feature of fluid bed combustion.

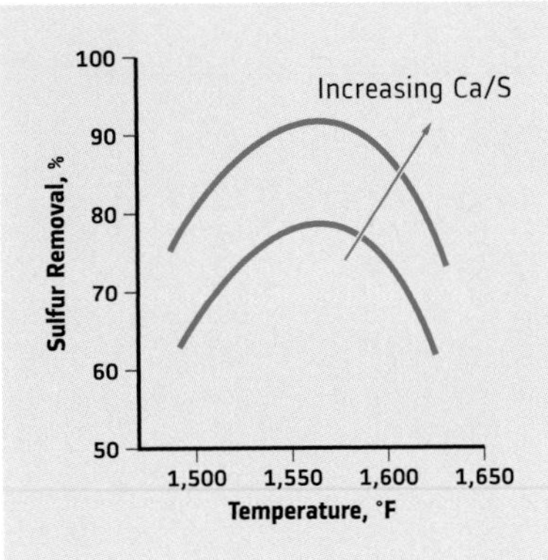

Figure 3-46 | Sulfur removal versus fluidized bed temperature

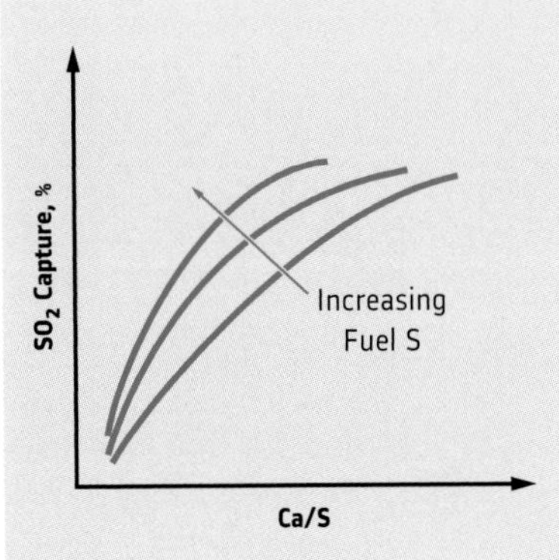

Figure 3-47 | Percentage SO_2 capture versus sulfur content

this temperature, less-than-optimum porosity forms during calcination (in extreme cases, the limestone particle surface can become glazed, called "dead-burned"), limiting sulfation capacity. Also, at high temperatures, the sulfation reaction can reverse. *Figure 3-46* indicates the dependence of sulfur capture on temperature.

The amount of limestone needed for sulfur capture depends on several factors, including the required sulfur capture, fuel sulfur content, limestone reactivity, limestone particle size, and limestone calcium content. Sulfur capture in an FBC boiler typically is in the range 85 to 95%, although capture rates of more than 98% have been demonstrated. As the capture rate increases, limestone utilization decreases such that high sulfur capture can require high Ca/S. *Figure 3-47* shows the dependence of sulfur capture on Ca/S. Higher fuel sulfur content increases the SO_2 concentration in the furnace and the sulfur capture reaction rate, reducing the Ca/S required for a given capture (see also *Fig. 3-47*). Limestone reactivity is a measure of the ability of a given limestone to capture sulfur. Reactivity is measured via bench tests intended to simulate conditions in a commercial FBC, with most boiler suppliers having their own test methods. Limestone particle size determines its residence time. Particles that are too fine will escape as fly ash; particles that are too coarse will escape as bottom ash, with any escaping material increasing the required limestone feed rate. Limestone requirements are proportional to limestone calcium content, because calcium carbonate is the only active constituent for sulfur capture. Sorbent utilization generally is better in a CFB than in a BFB, because the smaller sorbent particle size exposes more surface area per unit mass. The BFB units with high recycle rates, however, can closely approach the sorbent utilization of a CFB.

NOx Production

Emissions of NOx are generated from conversion of atmospheric nitrogen in the combustion air (thermal NOx) and/or from conversion of nitrogen in the fuel (fuel NOx). In FBC, the furnace temperatures are low enough to avoid thermal NOx, and the proper staging of combustion in the furnace can significantly reduce fuel NOx.

In a CFB, staged combustion is provided by introducing a significant portion of the total air above the fuel feed ports, creating a sub-stoichiometric zone in the lower furnace. This, in turn, results in some char and carbon monoxide (CO), which strip oxygen from a portion of the fuel NOx to produce elemental nitrogen (N_2). A similar condition can be established in a BFB by diverting some of the total air above the bed as overfire air. Evidence also indicates that NOx emissions increase with increasing Ca/S, where the CaO catalyzes the production of fuel nitrogen to NOx.[4] Thus, minimizing Ca/S is important to minimizing NOx emissions as well as limestone cost.

Additional NOx reduction can be accomplished by adding an SNCR system, which injects ammonia into the flue gas at an appropriate point. The ammonia reacts with NOx to form elemental nitrogen and water:

$$4NO + 4NH_3 + O_2 \rightarrow 4N_2 + 6H_2O$$

Equation 3-3

$$4NO_2 + 8NH_3 + 2O_2 \rightarrow 6N_2 + 12H_2O$$

Equation 3-4

Ammonia can be injected at the inlet or outlet of the particle separator, where higher gas velocity and the associated smaller gas duct cross section aids in mixing. As with limestone, the amount of ammonia required is greater than the theoretical minimum because of imperfect mixing, thermal decomposition of the ammonia, and other factors. A small amount of ammonia may be present at the stack, where it is called "ammonia slip" (see Chapter 5).

HEAT TRANSFER IN FBC BOILERS

Heat transfer to surfaces immersed in, or bounding, an active fluidized bed occurs by means of three mechanisms acting in parallel: gas convection, particle–gas radiation, and particle convection. The heat-transfer coefficient to the bed-touched surface is

$$H_o = H_{gc} + H_{rad} + H_{pc}$$

Equation 3-5

where

H_o = total outside heat-transfer coefficient
H_{gc} = coefficient of gas convection
H_{rad} = coefficient of particle and gas radiation
H_{pc} = coefficient of particle convection

The gas convection term is the smallest and refers to the transfer of heat from the gas to the surface, assuming that no solids are present. The radiation term usually is the second-largest term and treats the particle "cloud" as a gray body of given emissivity radiating to the surface. The particle convection term usually is the largest term, and it describes the heat transferred to the surface by particle contact. In practice, the overall heat-transfer coefficient is measured, the gas convection and particle–gas radiation terms are calculated, and the particle convection term is determined by difference. Then, the particle convective component is correlated to certain physical variables for design purposes. *Table 3-4* indicates the relative magnitude of the various heat-transfer components in, and bounding, the bed in typical BFB and CFB steam boilers.

TABLE 3-4 | RELATIVE MAGNITUDE OF HEAT TRANSFER COMPONENTS IN FLUIDIZED-BED STEAM BOILERS

	BFB	CFB	
		Furnace	FBHE/FBAC
H_{gc}, BTU/h-ft^2-F (W/m^2-K)	0–2 (0–11)	1–3 (6–17)	0–1 (0–6)
H_{rad}	8–12 (45–68)	8–12 (45–68)	2–10 (11–57)
H_{pc}	30–50 (170–284)	5–20 (28–114)	30–90 (170–511)

BFB, bubbling fluidized bed; CFB, circulating fluidized bed; FBHE/FBAC, fluid bed heat exchanger/fluid bed ash cooler; H_{gc}, coefficient of gas convection; H_{pc}, coefficient of particle convection; H_{rad}, coefficient of particle and gas radiation.

Note that CFB boilers sometimes use bubbling bed heat exchangers to cool ash, called a "fluid bed heat exchanger" (FBHE) when used in the main ash recirculation loop and a "fluid bed ash cooler" (FBAC) when used to cool bottom ash. Although not combustors, these devices are similar in layout and fluidization regime to many BFB combustors; thus, the associated heat-transfer rates are similar. Gas velocities in the backpass of a BFB and a CFB are essentially the same as those in stoker and pulverized firing, so the heat-transfer correlations describing convection and radiation that have been developed for those boilers can be applied directly to BFB and CFB boilers.

FBC BOILER EFFICIENCY

Calculating the boiler efficiency for a fluid bed boiler is different in several respects compared to calculating the boiler efficiency for a stoker or pulverized fuel boiler. For this discussion, the loss method is used, as described in Chapter 13. An additional loss term is required for the net heat loss or gain from the calcination and sulfation processes. The calcination loss is the heat that is lost in calcining $CaCO_3$ to CaO, an endothermic reaction. The sulfation heat gain is the heat that is gained from combining the SO_2 with O_2 and CaO to form $CaSO_4$, an exothermic reaction. Typically, at Ca/S ratios of greater than two, the calcination/sulfation term is a net heat loss, whereas at Ca/S ratios of less than two, the term is a net heat gain.

The ash sensible heat loss can be large, considering the high-ash fuels that frequently are fired and the presence of sorbent products in the ash. For a high-ash fuel, the ash sensible heat loss can exceed 5% of heat input. Therefore, the ash sensible heat loss should be calculated rather than included as an unaccountable loss. For very-high-ash fuels, an FBAC can be used to recover some of the sensible heat in the bottom ash to improve the overall efficiency.

For the efficiency calculation according to the American Society of Mechanical Engineers (ASME) Performance Test Codes (PTC), the use of refractory lined components, such as cyclones and ash coolers, increases the radiation loss above that estimated from the American Boiler Manufacturers Association (ABMA) standard curve. Recent versions of the test code include methods for measuring this loss, which is calculated based on the surface area and skin temperature of the refractory lined components. Fan heat credits also should be determined and included in the heat balance. The relatively high fan discharge pressures used with fluidized bed boilers result in significant addition of thermal energy to the boilers. All other loss terms are the same for fluidized bed boilers as for other types of boilers and covered in detail in Chapter 13.

BFB VERSUS CFB

The question of which system, BFB or CFB, is best for a given application is frequently asked. The answer depends mainly on boiler capacity and fuel.

BFB technology does not scale particularly well, because the relatively low bed velocity requires a large furnace cross section. Also, in-bed tube bundles, which are required to maintain bed temperature when firing relatively low-volatile fuels, such as coal, are prone to erosion/corrosion and to problems involving bundle support because of the large forces imposed by the dense bed. These issues were identified in the early coal-fired BFBs, including the 160-MWe demonstration unit. Today, BFBs are offered for firing biomass, a fuel that does not typically require in-bed tubing, in sizes up to approximately 100 MWe.

CFB technology scales much more readily. CFBs have been built in sizes of 300 MWe and larger, and are commercially available in sizes up to 600 MWe. With the expanded nature of the bed and the high internal mixing rates, tube bundles are not needed in the dense part of the bed. Thus, CFBs can handle most fuels in essentially any size. Furthermore, there currently is more commercial experience with CFB over a wider range of boiler capacities, steam cycles, and fuels, all of which can influence user selection for new projects. The one disadvantage of CFBs compared with BFBs is cost: For the size range and fuels with which a BFB is feasible, the BFB usually is lower in cost.

BFB STEAM GENERATORS

Figure 3-48 illustrates a general form of BFB steam generator. Crushed fuel and sorbent are fed to the top or bottom of the bed. Fluidizing air is supplied to the bottom of the bed through a plenum and air distributor. Combustion and sulfur capture (presuming a sulfur sorbent is used) take place in the bed, with the flue gas and some entrained solids passing into the section of the combustor above the bed surface, called the "freeboard." In the freeboard, additional combustion and sulfur capture can take place. From the freeboard, the gas and solids enter the convective pass, where they are cooled before entering a mechanical dust collector. Collected solids are recycled to the bed or sent for disposal, and the flue gas then passes to an air heater, fine particulate collector, and induced draft fan. Bed temperature is maintained at the optimum for sulfur capture and combustion efficiency, usually by means of the water-cooled walls of the furnace and/or a tube bundle immersed in the bed. The bed level is controlled by draining an appropriate amount of material from the bed.

Process Considerations

At V_{mf}, a cushion of gas separates the bed particles from one another. Increasing the gas velocity does not significantly increase the separation distance. Rather, the gas volume in excess of that required for minimum fluidization forms bubbles in the bed. Bubble formation provides

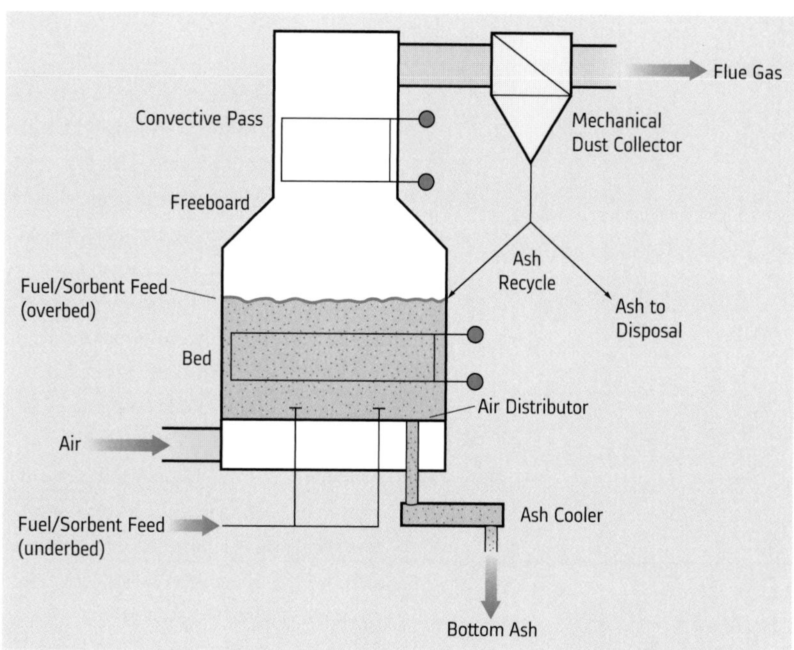

Figure 3-48 | Typical bubbling fluidized bed steam generator

a lower-resistance path for gas flow. The volume of the bubbles causes the bed depth to increase over that of minimum fluidization. The ratio of the operating bed depth to the depth at minimum fluidization is called the "expansion factor." An expansion factor of 1.5 to 2.0 is typical.

The bubbles provide an important function. At V_{mf}, very little particle movement occurs. Therefore, reactive feed materials, such as coal and limestone, would not be well dispersed within the bed. The bubbles agitate the bed and induce mixing. On the other hand, the bubbles can provide a path for gases to bypass the bed. If the system is designed improperly, a major portion of the air that is required for combustion can pass through the bed as bubbles without adequately contacting the fuel. The SO_2 and NOx that are released from the fuel also can escape through the bubbles without fully contacting the sorbent materials in the bed.

For proper performance, the designer must provide for good mixing without promoting gas bypassing. This is accomplished by ensuring that the gases in the bubbles are rapidly exchanged with gases from the non-bubbling regions of the bed. The non-bubbling part of the bed is essentially at the minimum fluidization condition and is referred to as being in the "emulsion phase." The bubbles rise through the emulsion and produce agitation. The effectiveness of gas interchange between the bubbles and emulsion is a function of the bubble size and the apparent viscosity of the emulsion phase.

One parameter that can be adjusted to provide for efficient gas mixing is the mean bed particle size. At a given gas velocity, the volume of gas in the bubbles depends on the V_{mf}, which is affected by particle characteristics. The particle size and density both influence the apparent viscosity of the bed, which in turn affects the average bubble size and the rate of bubble growth. With a mean bed particle size of 1,000 microns, near-optimum conditions can be maintained over a range of operating conditions with fluidizing velocities from approximately 2 to approximately 10 ft/s (~0.6 to 3.0 m/s).

For a specific application, it may be desirable to choose a finer or a coarser bed particle size. For example, a low-reactivity, high-sulfur fuel, such as petroleum coke, may require a deep bed with a low design superficial velocity. This would increase the solids residence time for both the fuel burning and the sulfur capture processes. In such instances, the bed particle size could be reduced while still maintaining desirable bubble conditions. As a secondary benefit, the smaller particle size results in greater sorbent surface area, improving sulfur capture.

In the freeboard, large solids that are ejected (elutriated) from the bed surface separate from the gas flow and then fall back into the bed. The freeboard is considered to terminate at the level where the gas velocity significantly increases, usually on entering a convective heat-transfer section. The freeboard can be considered as a second reactor in series with the fluidized bed. The freeboard serves as an important region in which additional combustion and sulfur capture occur.

For coal-fired applications, the fly ash can contain significant amounts of unburned carbon and underutilized limestone. Typically, fly ash is collected and recycled back to the bed to enhance combustion efficiency and sorbent utilization. The amount of recycle generally is described as a recycle ratio, equal to the recycle mass flow divided by the fuel mass flow. For BFB systems burning bituminous coals, the recycle ratio usually is selected in the range of from 1:1 to 3:1. When firing a bituminous coal, with the flue gas flow approximately 10-fold the coal flow, a recycle ratio of 1:1 gives a solids concentration in the freeboard of approximately 10% by weight. This solids concentration provides high sulfur capture and combustion efficiency. For biomass-fired applications, fuel reactivity is very high and fuel sulfur low (generally not requiring sulfur capture or limestone feed), so fly ash recyle is not required.

Bed material usually consists of fuel ash and the products of limestone calcination and sulfation. For fuels with little or no ash or sulfur, such as biomass, an inert material must be added to form the bed. Properly sized sand typically is used for this purpose. This sand also can serve another important purpose: control of bed alkali content. Biomass can contain significant amounts of sodium and potassium, which lower the softening temperature of the bed material to near-bed-operating temperatures, which can lead to bed agglomeration. Feeding and draining sand at an appropriate rate can limit bed alkali content and avoid bed agglomeration.

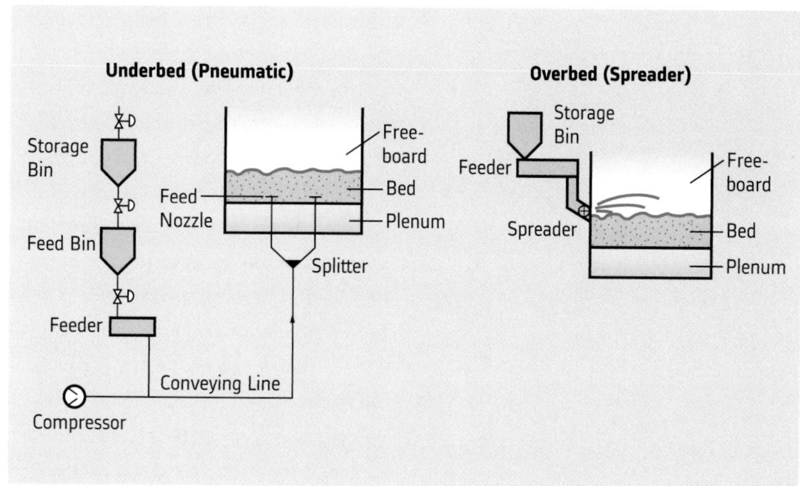

Figure 3-49 | Fuel/sorbent feed systems for bubbling fluidized bed boilers

Feed Systems

The fuel feed system has a major impact on the performance and design of BFB units. Two basic types of feed systems are used: underbed and overbed. Underbed systems include pneumatic as well as mechanical means, such as screw feeders and ram injectors, and are used with relatively low-volatile fuels, such as coal and petroleum coke. The common feature is the introduction of fuel at the bottom of the bed. On the other hand, overbed systems use devices, such as spreaders, to throw the fuel onto the bed surface and are used with both the relatively low-volatile fuels and the relatively high-volatile fuels, such as biomass. Both types of feed systems are shown in *Figure 3-49*.

Underbed feed is the method that takes best advantage of the bubbling bed dynamics. The fuel typically is introduced by a pneumatic feed system through nozzles located just above the air distributor. For adequate fuel distribution, generally one feed nozzle is provided for each 20 ft^2 (1.9 m^2) of bed area. The nozzles are designed to inject the fuel laterally, with a velocity of approximately 50 ft/s (15 m/s), to increase dispersion. The fuel usually is limited to a topsize in the range of ¼ to ½ inch (6 to 13 mm) to facilitate pneumatic conveying. This size range also provides a large number of fuel particles per unit mass, which contributes to a nearly uniform distribution of fuel within the bed.

The advantage of underbed feed is improved performance, particularly in terms of sulfur capture. With the fuel introduced upstream of the bed, most SO_2 (especially that from the fuel fines) is released in the bed and has an opportunity to contact the sorbent in the bed. Thus, sorbent utilization generally is better with underbed feed. Also, underbed feed is more tolerant of fuel fines, which generally are burned in the bed. Furthermore, increasing bed depth can provide acceptable performance with fuels of low reactivity and/or high sulfur content.

The disadvantage of underbed feed is added complexity. Relatively small pneumatic conveying lines limit the surface moisture of the material being transported to approximately 6% maximum to avoid line pluggage, which may require fuel drying. Also, the point of fuel introduction at the base of the bed typically is at a high positive pressure of 40 to 50 inches of water gage (1½ to 2 psi [10 to 12.5 kPa]). Considering the pressure that is lost in the conveying lines and splitters, the feed system must move the fuel from atmospheric pressure to between 5 and 10 psig (35 and 70 kPa gage).

The advantage of overbed feed is that it is much simpler than underbed feed. The fuel is sized as in a typical spreader stoker application to 1 to 2 inches (25 to 50 mm) topsize. With the type of equipment involved, this size of material is much easier to feed when wet, so fuel drying is not required.

The principal limitations in using overbed feed arise where high performance is required, especially with fuels such as coal and coke, which require sulfur capture. From a process point of view, overbed feed injects the coal downstream of the primary reactor. For combustion, this may not be a major problem, because high recycle rates and overfire air can enhance fuel burnout in the freeboard. The bed, however, is ineffectively used. Larger particles that settle on the bed will liberate volatiles, a large source of SO_2, at the top of the bed. Fines will burn before reaching the bed and liberate SO_2 in the freeboard. All this SO_2 bypasses the sorbent in the bed. Screening of the coal to eliminate fines as well as water sprays to avoid fines burning in the freeboard have been tried to offset this limitation. Overbed feed also requires closer attention to the removal of rock and other inert material being fed to the bed. This material can be quite large and, along with any ash particles formed during combustion, will sink to the bottom of the bed. A layer of large, dense particles can then form at the bottom of the bed and disrupt fluidization.

Overbed feed is most appropriate for highly reactive fuels with low sulfur content and for fuels very high in ash. With reactive, low-sulfur fuels (e.g., certain sub-bituminous coals, lignite, and biomass), the combustion efficiency can be quite high, even with minimal or no recycle. Also, because the required sulfur capture is low, SO_2 bypassing the bed may not be a concern. With high-ash coals, the fuel is relatively dense and contains sufficient inerts so that a small particle, such as ¾ inch (20 mm) or smaller, can be uniformly spread. Efficiency of sulfur capture can still be a problem, but the fuel ash can often contain a large amount of calcium. The amount of limestone additive required for sulfur capture may then be negligible or no greater than that in the system designed for high-sulfur fuel. Overbed feed is more is appropriate when simplicity and reliability, rather than performance, are the main concerns.

Distribution of Heat Release

Within the BFB combustor, fuel heat is released both in the bed and in the freeboard. Bed temperature is maintained at the desired level by heat transfer to furnace wall tubes and, if needed, to tubes immersed in the bed. Because the heat-transfer rate to these tubes is very high, it usually is cost-effective to maximize the amount of heat released in the bed. For fuels such as coal and an underbed feed system, 85 to 90% of fuel heat is released in the bed. With an overbed feed system, 70 to 80% of fuel heat is released in the bed, shifting heat release to the freeboard, where heat-transfer rates are much lower. For fuels such as biomass, with relatively high moisture and volatile content, and an overbed feed system, only 30 to 40% of fuel heat is released in the bed, with the remainder being released in the freeboard. For this reason, BFBs that fire biomass do not require in-bed tubes. Also, such boilers typically have an extended freeboard region, with several levels of air feed, to provide for adequate combustion of the fuel volatiles and a relatively uniform gas temperature profile.

Heat Duty Distribution

The locations of evaporator, superheater, and reheater heating surfaces within the combustor and convection pass are designed to minimize total cost while providing the proper performance characteristics over the complete operating range. Usually, the combustor (furnace) enclosure is composed of welded, water-cooled tubing and performs evaporative duty. In-bed tube bundles, if required, are used for evaporation and for superheater and reheater service. The convective pass typically contains superheater, reheater, economizer, and air heater surfaces.

Process Parameters

Table 3-5 contains a list of typical BFB process design parameters. Feed size affects both operation and performance. With overbed feed, fines must be limited, because they will be entrained in the gases leaving the bed and not contact the sorbent in the bed, leading to higher SO_2 emissions. Excessive fines can produce higher-than-expected freeboard heat release or localized hot spots near the feeder, which can lead to bed agglomeration. An overbed feed system typically is used for firing biomass, with a fuel topsize of 2 to 3 inches (50 to 75 mm). Both overbed and underbed feed systems have been used for firing coal, although the relative simplicity and reliability of overbed feed has led to its much more extensive use. For coal firing, overbed feed requires fuel sizing in the range of 1 to 2 inches (25 to 50 mm) topsize and can accommodate 10% or greater fuel surface moisture.

With underbed feed, the fuel must be properly sized for pneumatic conveyance. High topsize leads to a requirement for excessive transport line velocity and, as a result, a potential for erosion. With coal, topsize typically is limited to ¼ inch (6 mm). Furthermore, the fuel must have a surface moisture of less than 6% to avoid pluggage in the transport lines. Sorbent size is selected to maximize sorbent utilization, striking

TABLE 3-5 | TYPICAL BUBBLING FLUID BED PROCESS PARAMETERS

Fuel	Overbed Feed	Underbed Feed
Topsize	1–2″ (25–50 mm)	⅜″ (10 mm)
Moisture	–	< 6 percent (surface)
Fines	< 25 percent minus 16 mesh	< 20 percent minus 30 mesh
SORBENT		
Topsize	$^3/_{16}$″ (5 mm)	
*d_{50}	800–1,400 microns	
COMBUSTOR		
Bed Temperature	1,560–1,650°F (850–900°C)	
Bed Velocity	4–10 ft/s (1.2–3 m/s)	
Bed Particle Size	500–1,200 microns	
Bed Depth (slumped/active)	24″/48″ (0.6 m/1.2 m)	
Bed Pressure Drop	20–50″ WG (5–12.5 kPa)	
Recycle Ratio	0 to 5/1	
PERFORMANCE		
Carbon Loss	2 to 5 percent or lower	
Ca/S	2.3 to 3.0 (for 90 percent SO_2 capture)	
SO_2	300 ppm or less	
CO	250 ppm	
NOx	150 ppm or less	

*d_{50} is the diameter at the 50 percent point of a Rosin-Rammler logarithmic probability plot of particle size versus percent passing through a given sieve size

a balance between bed solids residence time and surface area. Bed makeup material, usually sand, is sized equal to the desired bed sizing (typically 1,000 microns d_{50}), because this material is essentially inert and has a relatively low attrition rate.

In the furnace, bed temperature is controlled in the range of 1,550 to 1,650°F (850 to 900°C) for good combustion efficiency and sulfur capture. Freeboard temperature is designed for the same temperature range as the bed. Design bed velocity is typically 6 to 8 ft/s (1.8 to 2.4 m/s). This velocity provides a reasonable plan area, avoids excessive air/gas bypassing via the bubbles, avoids excessive erosion, and retains a margin in fluidization velocity above minimum fluidization for turndown purposes. Bed particle size depends on the fuel and sorbent sizing and on the decrepitation characteristics in the bed. For a given design velocity, bed particle size then determines the state of bed fluidization.

Bed depth typically is set at 1.5 to 2 ft (0.5 to 0.6 m) in the slumped condition, which results in an active bed height of approximately 3 to 4 ft (1.0 to 1.2 m) and an expansion factor of two. Design bed depth is adjusted (along with bed velocity) to match fuel characteristics. A deeper bed and a lower velocity are used with harder-to-burn fuels or with fuels requiring high sulfur capture. Bed pressure drop is mainly a function of bed depth. Deeper beds, while yielding better performance, also require more fan power. Recycle of entrained material to the bed improves carbon burnout and sorbent utilization. Given the fineness of the entrained material and the multi-cyclone collection efficiency, optimum recycle rates are in the range of 1:1 to 5:1.

Part Load Operation

Part load operation of a BFB is achieved using one or more of several methods. The simplest is called "velocity turndown," wherein fuel and air flow are reduced to the entire bed. This method allows operation without support fuel down to 70% load for units with in-bed bundles and to lower loads for units without in-bed bundles. Another method, called "bed removal," drains bed inventory into a tank as load is reduced, more effectively reducing heat transfer to the in-bed surface (if any) and extending the load range without support fuel to between 25 and 35% load on units with in-bed surface. A third method is called "bed zone slumping." The air plenum is divided into zones so that the air supply to each zone is separately controlled. As load is reduced, sections of the bed are slumped (defluidized). This allows the bed temperature to be maintained at the required levels in the active zones. With this method, turndown to 25% load or less without support fuel is easily achieved.

Start-Up

Start-up of the unit is accomplished via burners, which typically fire oil or gas. These burners can be located underbed in the air plenum or overbed. Underbed burners heat the bed to solid fuel ignition temperature (typically 1,000°F [540°C] for coal) by first pre-heating the air to between 1,200 and 1,400°F (650 to 760°C). Overbed burners fire onto the bed surface, heating the bed material directly. Because only a portion of the bed usually is heated during start-up, the gas or oil heat input requirement is minimized. The start-up section may or may not have in-bed surface.

If an in-bed surface is present, the bed level generally is reduced before start-up to avoid having the tube bundles in the active bed. This minimizes both heat losses from the bed and bed heat-up time.

When the start-up section is heated adequately, solid fuel feed is started. An increase in bed temperature verifies solid fuel ignition, and both fuel and air flows are raised to bring the bed temperature up to design. With a multi-zone bed, load is increased by fluidizing a zone adjacent to the start-up zone, bringing the newly fluidized zone to the solid fuel ignition temperature, and then firing additional solid fuel. This process is repeated until all zones of the bed are at temperature on solid fuel.

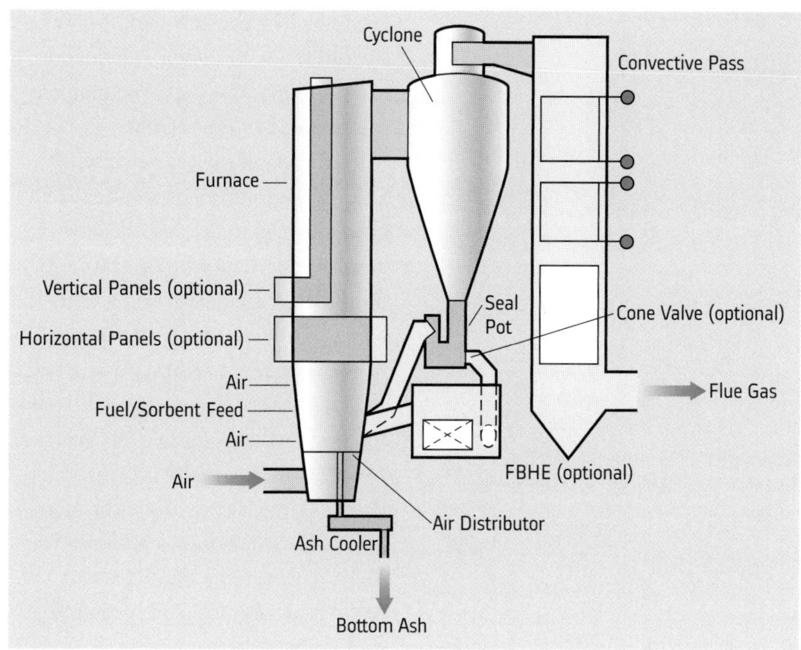

Figure 3-50 | Typical circulating fluidized bed steam generator (FBHE, fluid bed heat exchanger)

CFB STEAM GENERATORS

Figure 3-50 shows a typical CFB steam generator. Crushed fuel and sorbent are fed mechanically or pneumatically to the lower portion of the furnace. Primary air is supplied to the bottom of the furnace through an air distributor, with secondary air fed through one or more elevations of air ports in the lower furnace. Combustion takes place throughout the furnace, which is filled with bed material. Flue gas and entrained solids leave the furnace and enter one or more cyclones, where the solids are separated and fall to a seal pot. From the seal pot, the solids are recycled to the furnace. Optionally, some solids may be diverted through a plug valve to an external FBHE and back to the furnace. In the FBHE, tube bundles absorb heat from the fluidized solids.

Bed temperature in the furnace is essentially uniform and is maintained at an optimum level for sulfur capture and combustion efficiency by heat absorption in the furnace and the FBHE (if used). Flue gas leaving the cyclones enters a convection pass, air heater, baghouse, and ID fan (induced draft fan). Solids inventory in the furnace is controlled by draining hot solids through an ash cooler.

Process Considerations

The CFB conditions (also called "fast fluidization" or "lean phase fluidization") are achieved as fluidization velocity is increased past the bubbling regime (see *Fig. 3-43*). The CFB conditions generally are attained at velocities greater than 10 ft/s (3 m/s), with a mean bed particle size smaller than 500 microns. A large fraction of the bed mass is small enough to be entrained in the gas stream. This material must be collected and recycled to maintain bed inventory. The distinction between bed and freeboard has faded, and bubbles are no longer

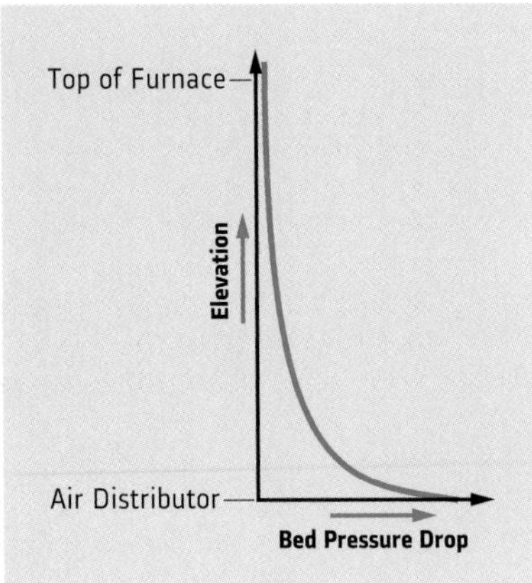

Figure 3-51 | Circulating fluidized bed combustor pressure profile

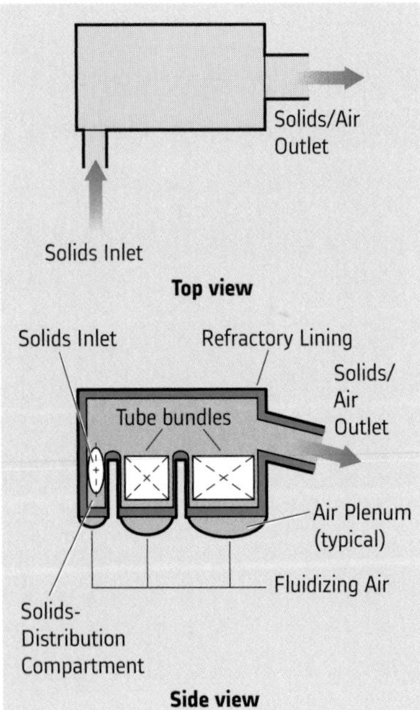

Figure 3-52 | Typical fluidized bed heat exchanger (FBHE) with refractory-lined steel-plate enclosure

apparent. The pressure drop from the bottom to the top of the combustor follows a smoothly declining gradient, as illustrated in *Figure 3-51.*

Even though the gas velocity is above the entrainment velocity of most particles in the bed, the entire bed is not entrained out of the combustor. This is because the particles tend to form "clusters" that break up, reform, and move up and down within the combustor. Clusters in a CFB are somewhat analogous to bubbles in a BFB. The gas velocity is below the entrainment velocity of the clusters. The clusters thus allow considerable bed inventory to be maintained at usual CFB velocities and account for considerable internal bed recirculation. The size of the entrained material is large enough to be captured by a cyclone for transport back to the bed. This process results in substantial external recycle and leads to excellent mixing and gas–solids contact, with high performance in terms of combustion efficiency and sorbent utilization. Recycle ratios of 10:1 to 100:1 and greater are typical, and these ratios are required to maintain the desired high solids concentration in the furnace. When firing a typical bituminous coal with flue gas flow tenfold the fuel flow, a recycle ratio of 10:1 provides a solids loading of 1 kg solids/kg gas at the combustor outlet, whereas a recycle ratio of 100:1 provides a solids loading of 10 kg solids/kg gas at the combustor outlet. At these solids loadings, the temperature is essentially uniform throughout the furnace, cyclone, and seal pot. The mixing rates are extremely high. Because of the high mixing rates, only a simple fuel–sorbent feed system, with a minimal number of feed points, is required.

Heat Duty Distribution

In smaller CFBs (e.g., steam flow < 300,000 lb/h [40 kg/s]), the proper furnace temperatures can be maintained via heat absorption by the furnace walls. Because furnace wall surface area does not increase linearly with boiler capacity, larger boiler sizes require heat-absorbing surface in addition to the furnace walls to maintain proper bed temperatures. Here, the designer has two basic options:

1. Internal surface in the furnace
2. External FBHE

Internal surface can take many forms, but the predominant are vertical tube panels (wingwalls) and horizontal tube panels. The vertical panels can be used for evaporative, superheat, or reheat duty. The horizontal panels can be used for superheat or reheat duty. Some very early applications of internal surface experienced rapid erosion; however, successful designs have evolved such that erosion is no longer a major concern. The two key features of successful internal surface applications are proper location (high enough in the furnace to avoid the dense part of the bed) (see *Fig. 3-51*) and local shielding (in the form of a thin, refractory lining on the lower-most part of the wingwalls and metallic [or refractory] shields on the leading edge of the horizontal panels).

The FBHE is a bubbling bed heat exchanger with one or more compartments containing immersed tube bundles, as illustrated in *Figure 3-52.* A flow of solids from the loop seal, controlled by a plug valve, enters the FBHE and is cooled by the immersed tube bundles before exiting to the furnace. Early FBHE designs experienced problems with the tube bundle supports, but recent designs have successfully addressed those issues. The tube bundles can be used for evaporative, superheat, or reheat duty. If multiple FBHEs are provided, solids flow to one or more can be used to control furnace temperature. This feature allows furnace temperature to be maintained at a desired level over a wide range of load as well as fuels. Furthermore, if one FBHE contains a finishing reheat surface, solids flow to that FBHE can be used to control reheat steam temperature, more or less independently of the other temperatures.

The advantage of internal surface is lower cost, in that the complexity of the FBHE (e.g., plug valve, solids transfer ducts, and fluidizing blower/piping/controls) is avoided. The advantage of the FBHE is in the potential control of furnace temperature, enhancing emission control at part loads and with a range of fuels. For large CFBs (e.g., >350 MWe), however, there may not be room in the furnace for the internal surface that is needed, so an FBHE may be required in any case.

The distribution of evaporator, superheater, and reheater duty within the primary solids recirculation loop (primary loop) and convective pass is set to minimize cost while providing the required performance over the load range. The major considerations in selecting the heat duty distribution have been described by Gottung et al.[5] In a unit without an FBHE, the furnace walls (and wingwalls, if needed) perform evaporative duty, the internal surface (if needed) handles superheat duty, and the convective pass contains the superheater, economizer, and air heater. In a unit with an FBHE, the furnace does evaporative duty, and the convective pass typically contains the superheater and economizer, plus the air heater. The FBHE contains the superheater surface and may contain an additional evaporator surface. When fluid cooled, the walls of the FBHE perform evaporative duty.

For reheat cycles in a unit without an FBHE, a portion of the reheater is in the convection pass, and a portion is in the furnace. Reheat steam temperature control is via a split backpass with gas biasing dampers or steam bypass around the convective pass reheat surface. In a unit with an FBHE, there usually are at least two FBHEs. A portion of the reheater is in the convective pass, and a portion is in one of the FBHEs. Reheat steam temperature control is via solids flow to the FBHE containing the reheat surface. The split reheater (with part in convective pass and part in the FBHE) is designed to put heat into the reheat circuit at low loads, when hot solids may not be available to the FBHE, for matching the turbine steam temperature without requiring a turbine bypass.

The heat duty distribution described above minimizes the heating surface and cost in a subcritical, drum-type cycle without a turbine bypass (the most common cycle in the United States). Other heat duty distributions may be best for other cycles and for meeting certain special performance requirements.

Process Parameters

Table 3-6 lists typical CFB process design parameters. Proper fuel feed size is extremely important to both operation and performance. If the feed is too coarse, there will be insufficient material entrained in the gas leaving the furnace, leading to insufficient solids recirculation. This results

TABLE 3-6 | TYPICAL CIRCULATING FLUID BED PROCESS PARAMETERS

FUEL	
Top size	3–20 millimeters
d_{50}	500–1,000 microns
SORBENT	
Topsize	1,000 microns
d_{50}	100–300 microns
FURNACE	
Temperature	1,560–1,650°F (850–900°C)
Velocity	16–20 ft/s (5–6 m/s)
Particle Size	100–1,000 microns
Pressure Drop	30–50″ WG (10–20 kPa)
Recycle Rate	10 to 100/1
PERFORMANCE	
Carbon Loss	1–2 percent or less
Ca/S	1.5–2.5 (for 90 percent SO_2 capture)
SO_2	100 ppm or less
CO	100 ppm or less
NOx	100 ppm or less

in reduced carbon burnout, sorbent utilization, and furnace heat transfer. In the extreme, the solids circulation rate will be low enough to cause large temperature gradients in the furnace. This condition can lead to agglomeration and defluidization. If the feed is too fine, excessive material will be entrained from the furnace, but escape the cyclone, producing insufficient material in circulation and a resultant negative impact on performance.

Solids inventory is a major factor in good performance of a CFB.

In general, low-volatile and/or high-ash fuels must be crushed finer than other fuels for two reasons. First, these fuels tend to decrepitate less, so smaller feed size is required to produce the optimum bed particle size. Second, if high-ash fuels are not adequately crushed, carbon will be encapsulated by the ash, and the carbon loss will be unnecessarily high. Low-volatile and high-ash fuels, such as anthracite culm (which may contain up to 70% ash), typically are crushed to ⅛ inch (3 mm) topsize, whereas lower-ash fuels, such as bituminous coals, typically are crushed to ¼ to ½ inch (6 to 12 mm) topsize. More reactive fuels, such as lignites, typically are crushed to ⅜ to ¾ inch (10 to 20 mm) topsize. Biomass typically is sized at 2 inches (50 mm) topsize. These figures are typical values for orientation purposes. Normally, for fuels to be applied in CFBs, specific decrepitation tests are conducted to determine the required PSD (particle size distribution) for the specific fuel.

Proper sorbent size also is important for good performance. Limestone is crushed to 1,000 microns topsize, although the optimum sizing depends on the actual decrepitation and sulfur capture characteristics of a given limestone. The combuster (bed) particle size shown in *Table 3-6* is that which can be circulated through the system at the design velocity. Larger particles must be drained from the furnace; finer particles escape the cyclone. The feed material undergoes a variety of size reduction processes, including decrepitation, attrition, and combustion. The key is to set the feed size such that the resulting bed particle size falls within the indicated range, maximizing the solids residence time.

Within the furnace, gas–solids temperatures typically are maintained in the range of 1,550 to 1,650°F (840 to 900°C), with fuel characteristics affecting the selection of design temperature within this range. For example, high-ash fuels, such as anthracite culm and bituminous gob, generally are fired at 1,650°F (900°C) for improved carbon burnout. Design combustor velocity usually is in the range of 16 to 20 ft/s (5 to 6m/s). This velocity level provides a reasonable furnace heat-transfer surface for a given height, low erosion rates, and an acceptable turndown range with adequate bed stability.

Bed pressure drop generally is in the range of 30 to 50″ WG (7.5 to 12.5 kPa). The inventory provides for high internal and external rates of solids recycle and leads, in turn, to good carbon burnout, effective sorbent utilization, and bed stability. Performance in terms of carbon burnout and emissions is excellent. For high-ash, low-reactivity fuels, such as anthracite culm, carbon loss can be as low as 1 to 2%, whereas for high-reactivity fuels, such as lignite, carbon loss typically is below 0.5%. Emissions of SO_2 can be reduced below 100 ppm, with 90% or more SO_2 capture at a Ca/S ratio of 1.5 to 2.5 (depending on fuel sulfur levels, limestone reactivity, and so on). Sulfur capture above 95% has been achieved in several commercial plants. Levels of CO generally are in the range of 100 to 200 ppm, and levels of NOx below 100 ppm are typical with SNCR.

Part Load Operation

Turndown over the load range from 100 to 60% is accomplished by reducing both fuel and air flows. In the process, grate and furnace velocity are sufficient to produce adequate mixing and solids recirculation and to avoid temperature maldistribution and backsifting of bed material into the air plenum. Furnace temperatures drop moderately. At loads below approximately 60%, fuel flow is decreased, but airflows are held constant to maintain velocity. Furnace temperatures drop more rapidly. At some load, usually in the range of 25 to 35%, furnace temperatures drop low enough that support fuel, via a start-up burner, must be added to maintain stable combustion.

With an FBHE, furnace temperatures can be maintained through a given load range. As load is reduced, solids flow to the FBHE can be lowered, reducing primary loop heat absorption and maintaining furnace temperature. At some load, either all solids flow is stopped or a further reduction in solids flow would produce an undesirable drop in steam temperatures. Below this load, furnace temperatures will drop with decreasing load.

Start-Up

Start-up is accomplished by means of start-up burners located in the lower furnace walls and/or in the primary air duct. Minimum primary air flow is established. The start-up burners are used to heat the bed material slowly, at a rate dictated either by the allowable rate of drum metal temperature increase by or the allowable rate of refractory temperature increase. Both limitations typically are in the range of 100 to 200°F/h (55 to 110°C/h). When solid fuel permissive temperature is reached (typically 1,000–1,300°F [540–700°C] for coal), solid fuel is added. Furnace temperature is further increased by adding solid fuel and backing out start-up fuel. Above a load of 25 to 35%, the boiler can run on solid fuel alone.

CFB System and Components

The following sections describe the major subsystems within the CFB boiler and discuss typical equipment and major performance criteria.

FUEL PREPARATION. As with a BFB, the CFB fuel preparation system is dependent on fuel type, fuel characteristics, range of fuels to be fired, incoming fuel size, and required fuel sizing to the boiler. With the variety of fuels fired in CFBs and the subsequent variety in fuel preparation systems that is required, a complete treatment here is not possible. Only general remarks can be provided.

For coals and waste coals, the preparation system usually consists of one or more stages of crushing. Many types of crushers, including impact mills, hammer mills, rod mills, and cage mills, have been applied. For coals, the system usually is straightforward. For waste coals, the need to limit oversize material can add complexity via the addition of screening and recycle steps. Drying has been utilized occasionally, but justifying the added costs through savings in operating costs and improved reliability typically is difficult.

For biomass, the preparation system also is very dependent on the fuel type and source. Again, the system may need to consider separation/removal of non-combustibles.

SORBENT PREPARATION. Sorbent can be purchased at the proper size and delivered via truck to the site, where it is loaded into a day bin. Alternatively, coarse limestone can be stored on site, then crushed to the proper size, dried, and loaded into the day bin. Various types of crushers, including rod mills, roll crushers, and air-swept roller mills, have been used. Because the sized material is relatively fine and typically will be conveyed pneumatically from the day bin to the furnace, the sized limestone must be dried to no more than 1% moisture. This is accomplished via oil- or gas-fired burners feeding hot gas to the crushers. To reduce cost and complexity, Alstom has developed an alternate system that combines the limestone preparation and feeding systems into a single system, called the "Just-In-Time (JIT) limestone system," which is described under *Sorbent Feed* on the next page.

FUEL FEED. The solid fuel feed system usually consists of a belt feeder (typically gravimetric) followed by a fuel chute or pipe leading to the lower furnace. Fuel from the feeder falls by gravity into the furnace. The feeder is pressurized with cold primary or secondary air, and the head of fuel in the standpipe at the feeder inlet forms the pressure seal between the day bin and the feeder. An isolation valve at the feeder discharge protects the feeder from furnace gases if the pressure seal is lost.

Fuel also can be fed to the solids return from the seal pot using the same system as described above. This location is advantageous when firing high-moisture fuels, such as lignite and biomass, because this mixes the fuel with hot solids, partially pre-drying the fuel. This feed location also has the advantage of eliminating a separate fuel feed opening in the furnace. The seal-pot feed may be used for any solid fuel when deemed to be convenient and economical.

Because of the high internal mixing rates, only a few feed points are required for adequate mixing and dispersion of the solid fuel within the furnace. Typically, one feed point is provided for every 250 to 500 ft^2 (23 to 46 m^2) of furnace plan area. For example, a 150-MWe unit with a furnace plan area of 985 ft^2 (92 m^2) has four feed points. It is important to note that CFB combustion technology evolved from other industrial applications, including calcination of alumina hydrate to alumina. The CFB calciners are fired with oil or gas, because any fuel ash would contaminate the alumina product. This experience indicates that CFB boilers, although generally designed to fire solid fuel, can very easily handle liquid or gaseous fuels.

Liquid and gaseous fuels for load carrying are fired in what are called "lances." Lances are fuel feed pipes that carry only fuel plus an atomizing medium—these pipes carry no combustion air—and are located in the lower furnace. The lance is intended to disperse the fuel within the bed, where it is combusted in the fluidizing air stream. Full load can thus be obtained on liquid or gaseous fuels with adequate lance capacity. Because these fuels have much shorter bed residence times compared with solid fuels, they require more feed points for proper fuel distribution and performance. The lances can be either retractable or stationary. In either case, the lance fuel feed can be initiated very quickly on a switch from solid fuel to liquid/gas or to regain load on a temporary loss of a portion of the solid fuel feed system. Liquid and gaseous fuels for start-up are fired in start-up burners, either in the lower furnace or in the primary air ductwork. The burners located in the lower furnace are retractable.

SORBENT FEED. The sorbent feed system usually consists of a day bin containing sized/dried limestone followed by two rotary valves in series (the first controls the feed rate and the second functions as a pressure seal) that drop the sorbent into a pneumatic conveying line for transport to the lower furnace. Gravimetric feeders can be used in place of the first rotary valve for more accurate measurement of limestone flow. To provide the desired number of feed points to the combustor, multiple bin outlets and feed systems can be used, or the conveying line from a given feed system can be split.

An alternate to the above is the JIT limestone system shown in *Figure* 3-53. The JIT system combines the limestone preparation and feed systems into one system. Coarse limestone from a storage silo is fed to an air-swept roller mill, where the limestone is crushed, dried, and conveyed from the mill directly to the lower furnace. Hot primary air from the air heater, tempered with cold primary air, provides the heat for drying. The advantages of the JIT system (also called a "direct feed system") are:

- Reduced capital cost, because the sized limestone storage/feed system plus the separate oil/gas-fired dryer are eliminated

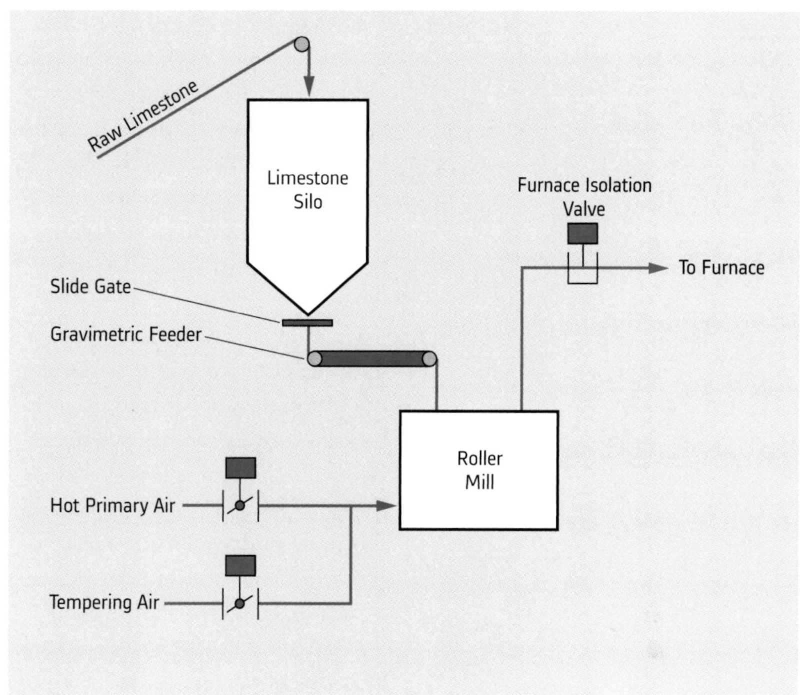

Figure 3-53 | Just-In-Time limestone feed system

- Reduced operating cost, because heat from solid fuel firing instead of that from oil or gas firing is used for drying
- Reduced maintenance, because less equipment is required

Raymond® roller mills have been used successfully for JIT applications.

AIR SUPPLY. Primary air and secondary air are supplied to the furnace by separate fans, which are generally arranged in parallel. Primary air fan discharge pressure is typically 60 to 90″ WG (15 to 22 kPa); secondary air fan discharge pressure is typically 40 to 50″ WG (10 to 12.5 kPa). Both air streams are usually pre-heated in an air heater. Fluidizing air for the seal pot, FBHE (if used), and FBAC (if used), is typically supplied by centrifugal blowers, with a discharge pressure of 250 to

300″ WG (62 to 75 kPa). Note that if these streams are significant and not pre-heated in the air heater, the air heater performance is affected, because less air is available to cool the flue gas. A positive displacement blower supplies conveying air at the higher pressures required for pneumatic transport of material.

Fluidizing air nozzles are located in the furnace floor for proper air distribution. The nozzles are designed to avoid backsifting of bed material into the air plenum and pluggage during both operation and shutdowns. Nozzle pressure drop is selected to minimize auxiliary power requirements while ensuring adequate air distribution during low-load operation. Secondary air ports are located along the furnace walls at one or more elevations above the floor.

FURNACE. The furnace consists of two zones: the lower furnace and the upper furnace. The lower furnace is that portion containing the fluidizing nozzles, secondary air ports, fuel feed ports, and solids recycle ports. The density of the bed in this region is relatively high, with density decreasing rather rapidly with increasing furnace height (see *Fig.* 3-51). Because of the staged air feed, this region is sub-stoichiometric. Physically, this section usually is rectangular, tapered, formed from finned or fusion-welded waterwall tubing, and lined with refractory material to protect the tubing from erosion by the dense bed and corrosion in the sub-stoichiometric atmosphere. The optimum refractory lining is hard (to minimize erosion), thin (to minimize weight), and reasonably conductive (to maximize furnace heat absorption). The refractory lining typically is 1 to 2 inches (25 to 50 mm) thick over the tube crown and is held in place with short metal studs.

The upper furnace contains the in-furnace surface (if used) and the gas outlet(s) to the cyclone(s). The density of the bed in this region is relatively low, and the density drops off very slowly with increasing furnace height. Because all the air has been fed in the lower furnace, the upper furnace operates under excess air (oxidizing) conditions. Physically, this section usually is rectangular, straight walled, formed from finned or fusion-welded waterwall tubing, and unlined to maximize heat absorption.

The furnace floor, containing the fluidizing nozzles (also called the "grate"), typically is water cooled. The air plenum below the floor can be either water cooled or formed from plate. If necessary for large units, two tapered, lower furnace sections can be used with a single upper furnace, forming the dual grate (or "pantleg"[5]) configuration (see *Fig.* 3-54). This configuration allows secondary air feed to the center of the furnace, a problem that is encountered when scaling CFBs to large sizes. The dual-grate configuration is used for Alstom CFBs in sizes of greater than 350 MWe. In small sizes, the furnace can be bottom supported, but in larger sizes (>50 MWe), top support nearly always is used.

CIRCULATION SYSTEM. The walls of the furnace are cooled by natural circulation for subcritical units. When provided, an FBHE evaporator bundle can be cooled using natural circulation or pumped circulation. Use of natural circulation generally requires inclined tubing and, therefore, less bundle surface per unit of bed plan area.

CYCLONE COLLECTOR. One or more high-temperature cyclones are used to collect the solids entrained in the gas leaving the furnace. The cyclone is designed to collect essentially all particles with a diameter of greater than approximately 100 microns. Given the relatively large size of particles entering the cyclone, the separation efficiency typically is well over 99%. A vortex finder usually is added to the cyclone gas outlet to improve collection efficiency by preventing solids bypassing from inlet to outlet. The vortex finder, which is exposed to the hot gases leaving the furnace, typically is uncooled and, therefore, must be made from high-grade materials.

CYCLONE CONSTRUCTION. Two types of cyclone construction are available:

1. **Steam-cooled tubes** (*Fig.* 3-55): The cyclone is formed from tubing that is cooled with steam. The cyclone interior has a thin layer of refractory lining for erosion protection, using the same materials and construction as in the lower furnace. The exterior is covered with insulation and lagging, like the furnace.
2. **Plate/refractory** (*Fig.* 3-56): The cyclone is formed from steel plate with a thick, two-layer refractory lining. The hot face of the lining is a dense, erosion-resistant material that is backed up by lighter-weight, insulating materials. Proper selection, installation, and subsequent operational care of the refractory materials are essential to ensure long-term

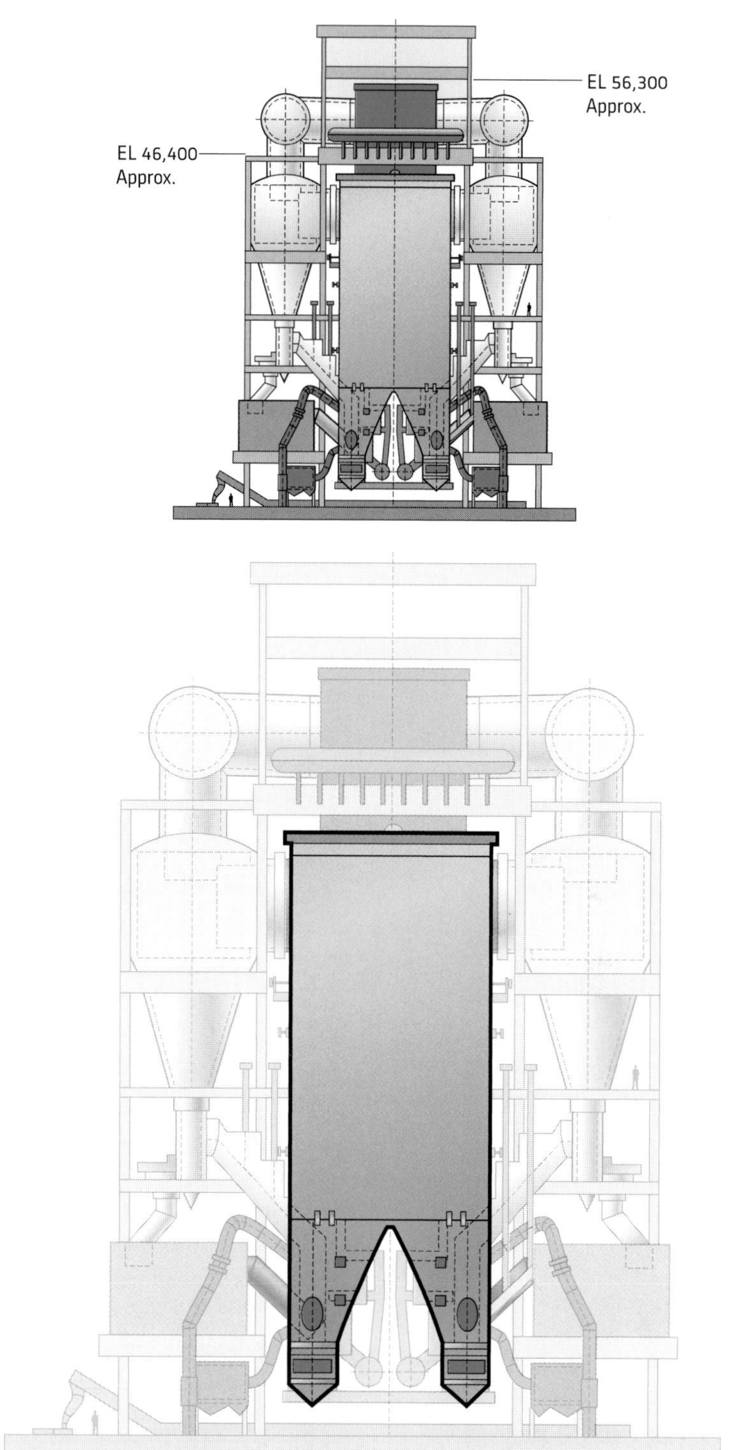

Figure 3-54 | Dual grate (pantleg) configuration

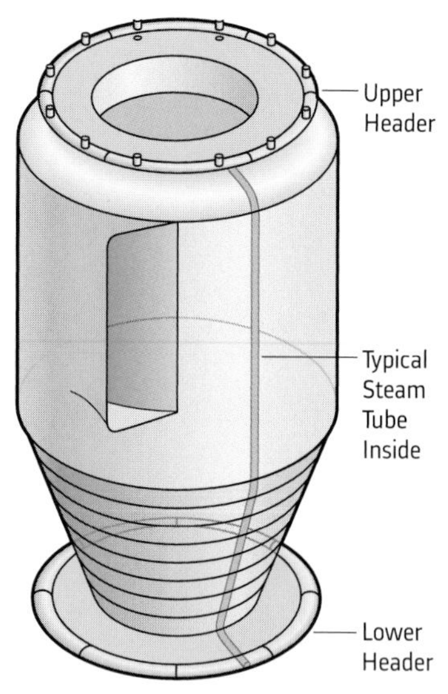

Figure 3-55 | Steam-cooled cyclone

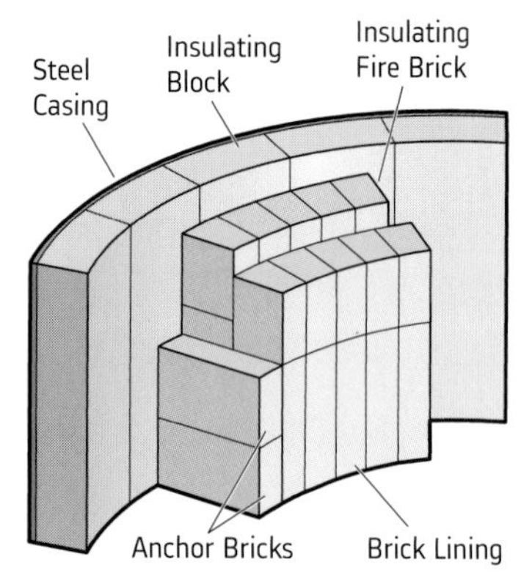

Figure 3-56 | Plate-refractory cyclone construction

viability of the lining. The exterior must be left uncovered to avoid problems with refractory anchors.

The advantages of the steam-cooled cyclone are reduced weight, reduced refractory maintenance, and reduced heat losses. The advantage of the plate/refractory cyclone is reduced capital cost.

SEAL POT. The seal pot is a non-mechanical valve that moves the solids collected by the cyclone back into the furnace against the furnace back-pressure. Solids flow down the inlet side, up the outlet side, then back to the furnace. The bottom portion of the seal is fluidized so that material in the seal can seek different levels on each side of the seal. The difference in level corresponds to the pressure difference across the seal. Then, solids entering the seal inlet displace solids out of the seal on the outlet side. The seal pot is constructed of steel plate or pipe with a multiple-layer, refractory lining. Fluidizing nozzles along the bottom of the seal provide the required fluidizing air. On units with an FBHE, a plug valve is located in the lower portion of the seal pot to regulate the flow of solids from the seal pot to the FBHE.

FBHE. The FBHE is a bubbling bed heat exchanger consisting of one or more compartments separated by weirs and containing immersed tube bundles (see *Fig.* 3-52). Hot solids from the seal pot enter the FBHE, where they are fluidized, transfer heat to the tube bundles, and flow back to the furnace. The tube bundles can be an evaporator, superheater, or reheater surface. Again, proper design of the tube bundle supports is essential. Fluidizing velocity is low (1–2 ft/s [0.3–0.6 m/s]). The fluidizing medium is air. The particle size is small, and the carbon content of the material is low. All these conditions lead to essentially no erosion or corrosion of the in-bed tube bundles. Also, because of the high bed density, rates of heat transfer are very high. The enclosure can have either refractory lined steel plate or water-cooled tubing.

SNCR. Even though NOx emissions from the furnace are low because of low furnace temperatures and staged combustion, emission regulations may require additional NOx control. In a CFB, this is accomplished using an SNCR system. This system uses an ammonia-based reagent (anhydrous ammonia, aqueous ammonia, or urea) to reduce NOx emissions. The reagent is injected into the gas stream at the cyclone inlet duct and/or outlet duct using nozzles located on the side of the duct. NOx reductions of 50% and higher can be achieved. The required gas temperature range for effective NOx reduction is 1,400 to 1,700°F (760 to 925°C). This becomes an issue at part loads, when gas temperatures at the cyclone can become too low. At these loads, ammonia flow is stopped to avoid excessive ammonia slip.

CONVECTIVE PASS. The convective pass is of the same basic design as that used in pulverized fuel- or stoker-fired boilers. The enclosure walls are usually formed from finned or fusion-welded tubing and are steam or water cooled. Where gas temperatures are sufficiently low, duct plate can be used to form the enclosure. The convection pass can contain superheater, reheater, evaportive, and economizer surface. Gas velocities are typical of solid fuel-fired boilers. Retractable or rotary soot blowers can be used to keep the heat-transfer surfaces clean.

AIR HEATER. A prime consideration in selecting an air heater type for CFB applications is the high air-to-gas pressure differential resulting from the high primary air pressures required plus the draft loss across the cyclone separator and backpass. Low leakage designs, such as tubular and heat pipe air heaters, have been used. The development of advanced leakage control systems for Ljungström® regenerative air heaters, as described in Chapter 6, has led to their use on most large (>200 MWe) CFBs.

Because of the different air pressures, the primary and secondary air streams are heated separately, in series or in parallel, with the gas stream. With large amounts of fluidizing air for FBHEs and FBACs, it sometimes is economical to provide a separate air heater for this fluidizing air. This is because the primary and secondary air heaters become large to achieve a given stack temperature if a significant amount of the total air bypasses the air heaters.

With tubular air heaters, the most common design for CFB applications is a gas-over-tubes/air-through-tubes design. The dust-laden gas passes over the tubes and, because the tubes are arranged in-line, they can be easily cleaned with soot blowers. Gas-through/air-over designs, although potentially more difficult to clean, also have been used successfully.

Use of steam or hot-water preheaters, or of a cold-air bypass, usually is recommended to increase the air heater average cold-end temperature to minimize acid (H_2SO_4) condensation/corrosion in colder climates and/or at low loads. The air-bypass option offers the advantage of cooling the unit faster on a shutdown. Note that because of the low SO_2/SO_3 in the flue gas (from limestone injection in the furnace), the acid dew-point temperature (and the associated average cold-end temperature) is relatively low. The CFB boiler can operate at relatively low exit gas temperatures, offering the potential for higher boiler efficiency than with other boiler types.

ASH REMOVAL/COOLING. The ash removal system includes both the bottom ash and fly ash systems.

BOTTOM ASH. The main functions of the bottom ash removal system are to control the flow of bottom ash to maintain the desired bed inventory and to cool the ash to a temperature suitable for the bottom ash conveying system. Bed pressure, measured just above the furnace floor, is the indicator of inventory, and bottom ash flow is adjusted to maintain desired bed pressure. The bottom ash system also can help control accumulation of oversize material. In a CFB, such accumulation can produce an unfavorable pressure profile with excessive material in the lower furnace and little in the upper furnace, resulting in poor performance. The best and most direct way to control oversize accumulation, however, is with proper design of the fuel-sizing equipment to avoid oversize feed. A limited number of ash drains usually are sufficient, depending on the capacity of the unit and the ash content of the fuel. Ash classifiers also may be used to remove oversize material and reinject properly sized material, thereby adjusting the bed pressure profile without requiring excessive rates of bottom ash flow. Such classifiers can operate continuously or in batch mode, and they can cool the ash as well.

The bottom ash must be cooled from furnace temperature to between 250 and 500°F (120 to 240°C) before entering the bottom ash conveying system. The ash cooler options typically considered are:

- **Screw coolers, a screw feeder with water cooled casing, auger, and shaft:** These have been used successfully on many units. With relatively low ash flows, the wear rates on the auger and casing are reasonable. With high ash flows, however, auger size and/or speed are increased, and wear rates can become excessive, requiring frequent maintenance.
- **FBACs, a bubbling bed heat exchanger identical in design to the FBHE:** Cooling coils immersed in the bed cool the ash and transfer heat to the fluidizing air, condensate/feedwater, or service water. A cone valve typically controls ash flow to the FBAC, as with the FBHE. The FBAC ash flow capacity is much higher than that with screw coolers. The FBAC design must accommodate the accumulation of coarse material that can lead to sintering and/or defluidization; this typically is done by adding gravel screws to drain coarse material as required.
- **Rotary coolers, a relatively new option consisting of a slowly rotating cylinder with a water cooling jacket:** Ash from the furnace enters one end of the cooler. The interior has short metal fins that trap ash against the cooling jacket. These fins are arranged in a spiral pattern so that the ash is transported from inlet to outlet as the cylinder rotates. This cooler design has an ash cooling capacity higher than that of a screw cooler but lower than that of an FBAC.

The key advantage of the screw cooler is simplicity, with the disadvantage being low capacity. The key advantage of the FBAC is high capacity, with the disadvantages of susceptibility to oversize material and high auxiliary power (from the fluidizing air required). The key advantages of the rotary cooler are the ability to handle oversize material, low auxiliary power, and low maintenance.

Cooled ash from the ash cooler passes to the bottom ash-handling system for transport to storage. This usually is a mechanical system consisting of flight conveyors or a pressure pneumatic system. Alternatively, a mechanical system can be used to transport bottom ash to an intermediate hopper, from which a pneumatic system conveys the material to storage.

FLY ASH. Fabric filters (baghouses) and electrostatic precipitators are used for final particulate cleanup. Fly ash, from the economizer and air heater hoppers and the fabric filter or electrostatic precipitators, typically is handled with a vacuum pneumatic system, although flight conveyors also are used. No ash cooling is necessary.

ASH STORAGE. The bottom ash and fly ash streams can be stored for disposal together in the same silo or in separate silos. Ash conditioners then mix in sufficient water for proper handling and transport to the ultimate disposal area.

ASH UTILIZATION. Many studies have examined the possible uses for fly ash and bottom ash from a CFB, and with similar results. To maximize potential reuse, it is helpful to have separate fly ash and bottom ash silos rather than a single ash silo. This allows the plant to take advantage of the different properties of each stream.

FLASH DRYER ABSORBER. Recent emission regulations may require the use of secondary SO_2 scrubbers (also called "polishing scrubbers") to reduce the low levels of SO_2 emissions from the boiler even further. Because the SO_2 levels in the flue gas leaving the CFB are low even with high-sulfur fuels, dry scrubbers have been used for this purpose. Dry scrubbers typically use lime as the sulfur sorbent, which is approximately tenfold the cost of limestone. To reduce operating cost, a dry scrubber technology called the Flash Dryer Absorber (FDA), that utilizes unspent lime in the fly ash from the CFB, rather than fresh lime, has been developed. The FDA consists of a vertical duct, baghouse, fly ash recycle system, and mixer/feeder. Fly ash containing unused lime from the CFB is captured in the baghouse, sent to a feeder/mixer, where a small amount of water is added, and then dropped into the vertical duct upstream of the baghouse. The moisture added to the ash increases humidity and reduces gas temperature, leading to the capture of SO_2 by the lime in the fly ash, both in the duct and in the baghouse filter cake. The extent of sulfur capture in the furnace versus that in the FDA can be adjusted to minimize total operating cost. Overall SO_2 removal of 98% or greater has been demonstrated. A more detailed description of the FDA is provided in Chapter 5.

Polishing scrubbers can reduce SO_2 emissions to very low levels.

SCALE-UP. Since CFB boilers were first commercialized in the early 1980s, boiler size has been scaled from the 10 to 25 MWe size range to the 300 MWe size of the early 2000s. To control scale-up risk, the scale-up process involves two main steps:

1. Establish the key parameters for proper boiler performance.
2. Limit the scale-up in those parameters to small increments beyond then-current experience.

The parameters considered to be most important involve the furnace and cyclone, because these are unique to CFB boilers. All other aspects of the boiler (e.g., backpass sizing and design as well as auxiliary equipment sizing and design) have been proven in sizes to 1,000 MWe or more on pulverized coal-fired boilers. The bulk of that experience can be applied to CFB boilers. Those parameters are:

- **Furnace height:** This has an impact because of the reduction in bed particle density with height in the furnace. At excessive height, the bed density will be too low and unpredictable, leading to low rates of heat transfer, high furnace temperatures, insufficient loading of the FBHEs (especially at part load), and excessive NOx/SOx emissions.

- **Furnace depth:** This impacts secondary air penetration into the center of the furnace. Solids (including fuel) residence times in a CFB are very high, meaning that fuel particles will find their way to all parts of the furnace, including the center. With excessive furnace depth, secondary air (fed from the walls of the furnace) cannot penetrate the bed and reach the fuel in the furnace center, decreasing combustion efficiency.
- **Fuel feed points per furnace plan area:** This impacts combustion efficiency and emissions. An inadequate number of feed points limits fuel distribution and mixing, creating zones of low O_2 near the feed nozzles that reduce combustion efficiency and SO_2 capture, both of which need O_2.
- **Cyclone diameter:** This impacts collection efficiency. Excessive diameter reduces collection efficiency. Inadequate collection efficiency reduces solids recirculated to the furnace and bed density, increasing furnace temperature and NOx/SOx emissions.

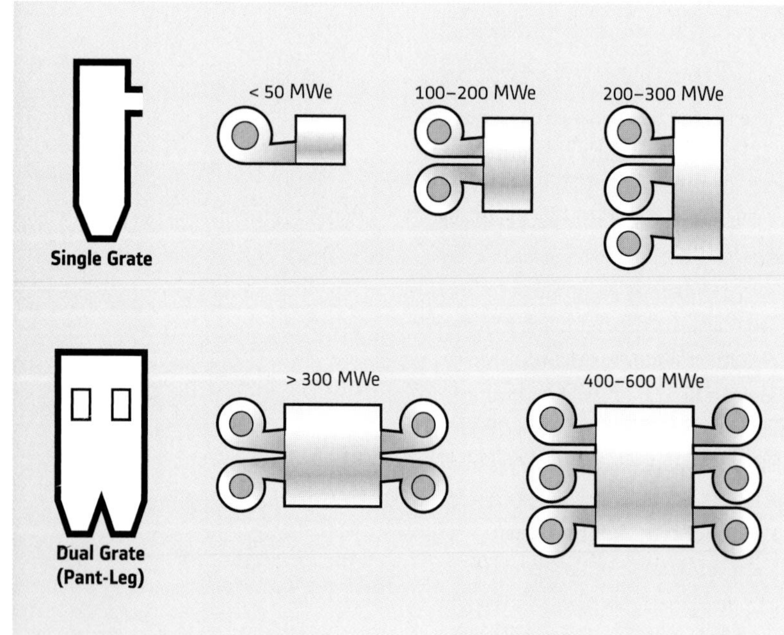

Figure 3-57 | Scale-up (modular approach)

Alstom's approach to scale-up has been to design larger boilers using "modules" that have been proven on smaller boilers, as illustrated in *Figure* 3-57. Thus, a 300 MWe unit essentially consists of three 100 MWe furnace/cyclone "modules" without increasing furnace height, furnace depth, feed points/plan, or cyclone diameter beyond the values proven at the 100 MWe scale. For more compact layout of larger units, the dual grate (pantleg) configuration is used while avoiding excessive furnace depth. This configuration allows secondary air feed to the center of the furnace on either side of each grate, ensuring high combustion efficiency. This configuration can be scaled to 600 MWe and larger.

Supercritical CFB

Supercritical steam conditions allow an increase in power plant efficiency in accordance with the selected steam conditions. Combining this increased efficiency with the inherent fuel flexibility and emission control of CFB technology offers obvious advantages. Design of a supercritical CFB involves bringing together two technologies: supercritical boiler design and CFB

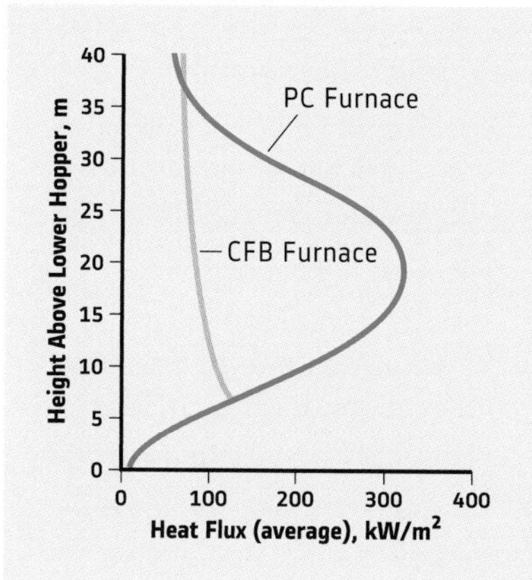

Figure 3-58 | Heat flux profile: Pulverized coal versus circulating fluidized bed

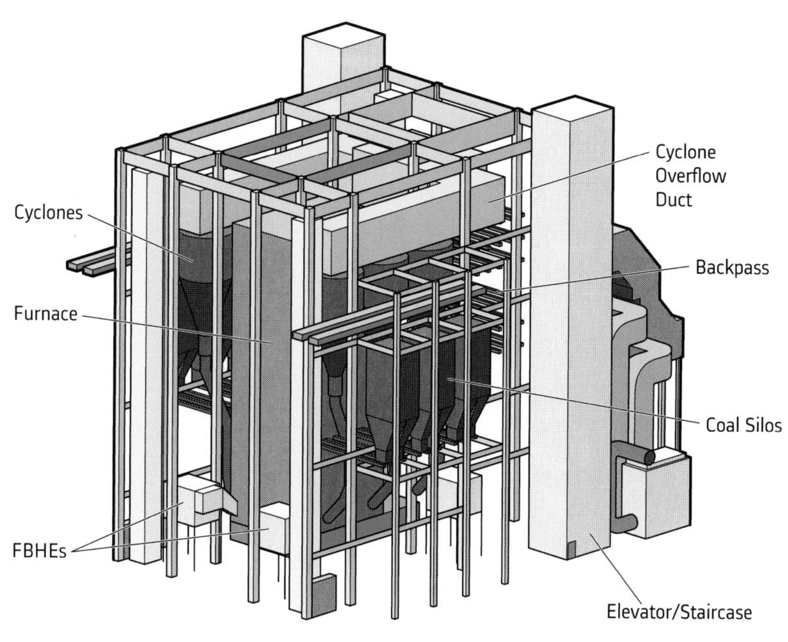

Figure 3-59 | Supercritical circulating fluidized bed design (FBHE, fluid bed heat exchanger)

boiler design. Experience with these technologies has been described earlier in this chapter.

A key issue in the design of any supercritical boiler is that the flow available for cooling the furnace is the feedwater flow only. Because of the relatively high heat flux to the furnace walls in a pulverized coal-fired boiler, various means must be employed to ensure adequate furnace cooling, such as increasing flow per tube via a spiral tube layout or use of internally rifled, vertical tubes to reduce the needed cooling flow. CFB boilers have a much lower furnace heat flux (*Fig. 3-58*). Thus, neither of the above is required. The furnace can be constructed of vertical, smooth-bore tubing, just as for subcritical steam conditions. As with a pulverized coal-fired boiler, a supercritical CFB boiler requires a recirculation system to supply the extra cooling flow that is needed during start-up and low-load operation. Boiler size for supercritical applications is on the larger side, typically above 300 MWe, to match the size of available steam turbines.

Alstom has developed a supercritical CFB boiler design (*Fig. 3-59*). This 600 MWe version includes a dual-grate furnace with internal surface, six cyclones, six seal pots, and four or six FBHEs (evaporative, superheat, and reheat), depending on the design fuel. The convective pass contains a superheater, reheater, and economizer. A regenerative air heater also is included.

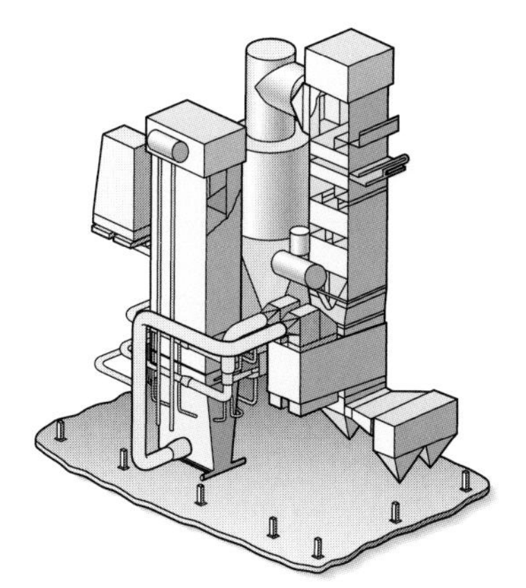

Figure 3-60 | A 220,000-lb/h circulating fluidized bed for biomass firing

Industrial Application

Two examples of CFB designs for industrial-scale applications are described here to illustrate major component design and arrangement. The first is a boiler of 220,000 lb/h, 1,255 psig, and 955°F (28 kg/s, 8.7 MPa gage, and 513°C) designed to fire wood (*Fig. 3-60*). The unit has a single-grate furnace, with one

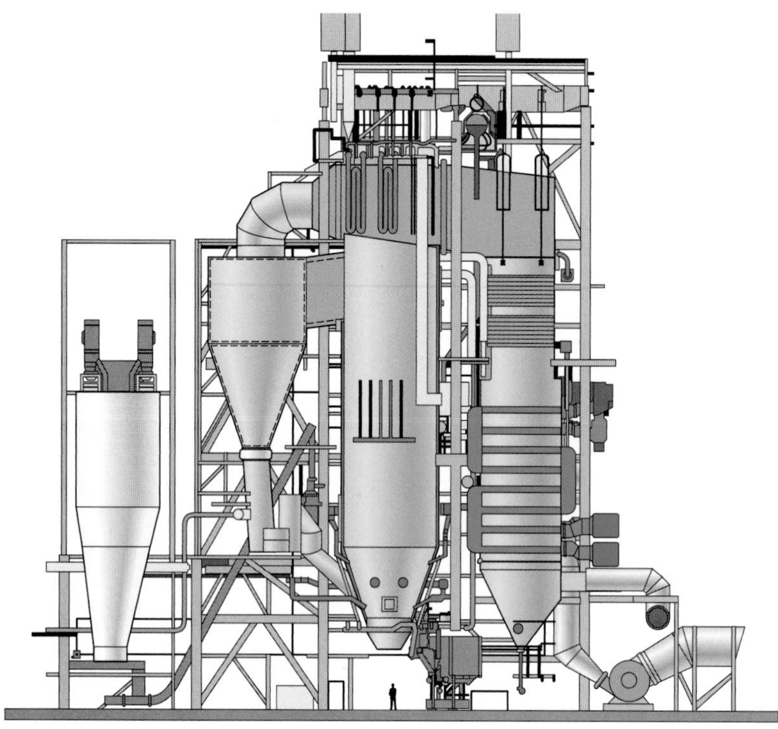

Figure 3-61 | A 524,000 lb/hr circulating fluidized bed

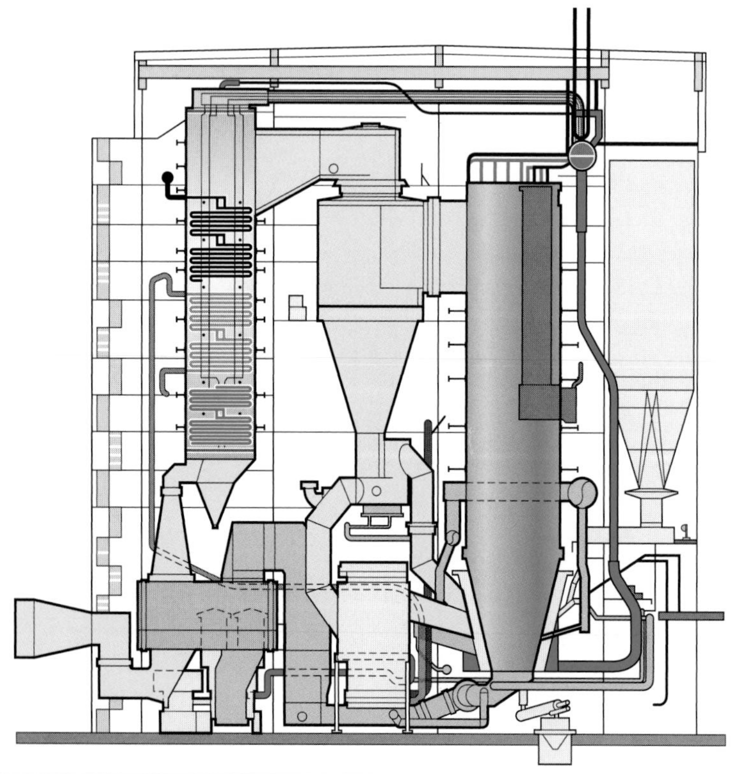

Figure 3-62 | A 1,922,000 lb/h circulating fluidized bed with reheat

cyclone and seal pot. The convective pass includes a superheater, evaporator, and economizer. Also included are screw coolers for the bottom ash and a heat pipe air heater.

The second is a boiler of 524,000 lb/h, 1,421 psig, and 1,000°F (67 kg/s, 9.8 MPa gage, and 540°C) designed to fire semi-anthracite (*Fig. 3-61*). The unit has a single-grate furnace, with one cyclone and seal pot. The furnace contains an internal surface wingwall evaporator and horizontal panel superheater. The convective pass includes a superheater and economizer. Also included are FBACs and a tubular air heater.

Utility Application

Two examples of CFB designs for utility applications also are described. The first boiler is a 1,922,000 lb/h, 2,524 psig, and 1,005°F (244 kg/s, 17.5 MPa gage, and 541°C), with reheat, designed to fire bituminous coal (*Fig. 3-62*). This design has a single-grate furnace with wingwall surface, three cyclones, three seal pots, and two FBHEs (one with a superheat surface and one with a reheat surface). The convective pass contains a superheater, reheater, and economizer surface. A regenerative air heater and FDA also are included.

The second boiler is a 2,260,000 lb/h, 2,524 psig, and 1,004°F (287 kg/s, 17.5 MPa gage, and 540°C), with reheat, designed to fire a high-ash anthracite (*Fig. 3-63*). This design has a dual grate furnace, four cyclones, four seal pots, and four FBHEs (two containing a superheat surface and two containing a superheat and reheat surface). The convective pass contains a superheater, reheater, and economizer surface. Also included are four rotary ash coolers and a regenerative air heater.

HYBRID CFB

The hybrid CFB, called the FiCIRC™ CFB, combines a BFB with a recirculation loop of fines to increase performance over that attainable with a BFB alone. The basic FiCIRC™ module is shown in *Figure 3-64* and includes a bubbling bed furnace, an air plenum, an air distributor with fluidizing nozzles (tuyeres), an in-bed tube bundle, and a cyclone/standpipe. The use of relatively small-diameter cyclones with direct return of collected material to the bed produces a large amount of fine material circulating through the freeboard. The result is high combustion efficiency, high limestone utilization, and low NOx/CO emissions. Ammonia injection into the freeboard is very effective in further reducing NOx.

The boiler design is relatively simple, with a plate/refractory furnace enclosure and cyclones plus removable in-bed evaporator tube bundles bolted to the furnace enclosure. Fuel feed is over the bed via spreader or in-bed via pneumatic injectors from the sidewalls. Hot gases from the cyclones enter a convective pass containing a superheat and economizer surface, tubular air heater, and baghouse/electrostatic precipitators (see *Fig. 3-64*). Boiler height is relatively low, and the boiler typically is bottom supported.

Larger boilers are designed using multiple furnace/cyclones modules. Because of this modular approach and the relatively small size of the basic module, maximum FiCIRC™ boiler size is in the range of 50 to 70 MWe.

PRESSURIZED FBC SYSTEMS

This chapter has introduced the various concepts involved in the design of

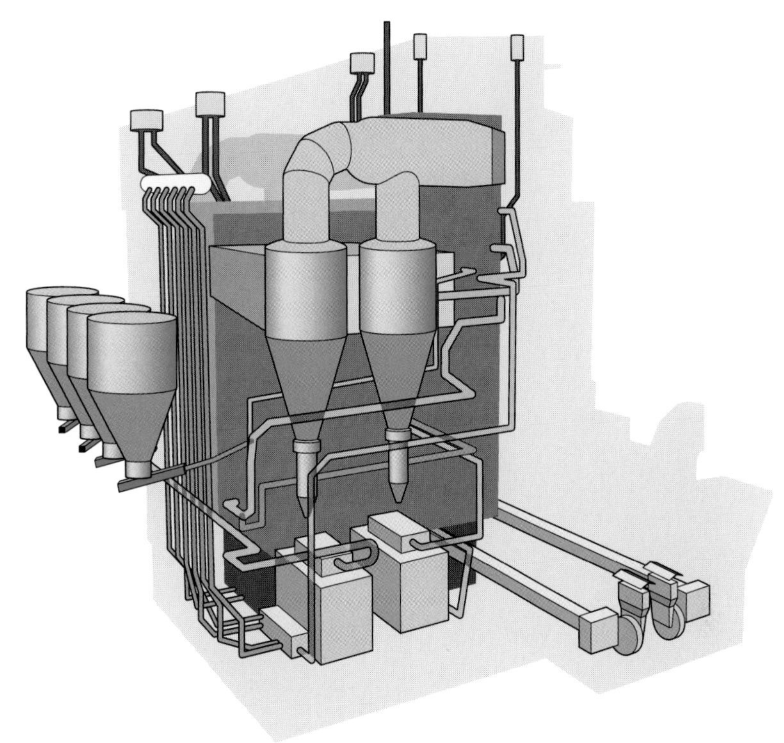

Figure 3-63 | A 2,260,000 lb/hr circulating fluidized bed with FBHEs and reheat

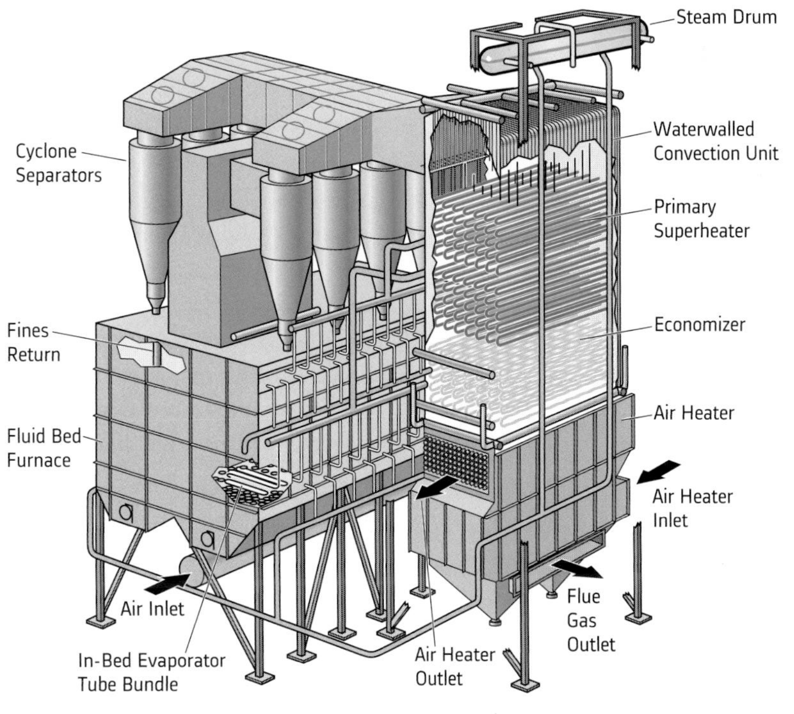

Figure 3-64 | FiCIRC™ Hybrid circulating fluidized bed

fluidized bed steam generators, and it has described the implementation of designs for boilers operating at or near atmospheric pressure. Combustion in that regime is referred to as "atmospheric FBC" (AFBC). Fluidized bed operation at pressures 10 to 20 fold atmospheric pressure, taking place in large cylindrical or spherical pressure vessels, in combination with axial compressors and gas turbines is termed "pressurized FBC" (PFBC).

In addition to the reduced emissions of SOx and NOx that are possible with fluid bed combustion, PFBC offers the potential for a gain in overall thermal efficiency because of the incorporation of a gas turbine in the cycle. Another potential advantage of the PFBC system is that all the equipment operating above atmospheric pressure is smaller in size than it would be at atmospheric pressure, making shop assembly and barge delivery of components an attractive option.

Two of the many approaches to the pressurized cycle are the PFBC turbocharged cycle and the PFBC combined cycle. Each has many possible variations that are being investigated throughout the world in both design studies and operational units. In the turbocharged cycle, hot flue gas from a PFBC boiler (~800°F [~425°C]) is expanded through a gas turbine that produces enough power to drive the turbocharging compressor. One version of the higher efficiency power-producing PFBC concept has the gas leaving the pressurized fluidized bed combustor at approximately 1,600°F (~870°C). The gas is cleaned in tandem, high-temperature cyclones and then sent to the gas turbine. The turbine exhaust is further reduced in temperature by passing through heat recovery equipment, such as evaporative and feedwater-heating surface.

The commercialization of this technology has been difficult, mainly for two reasons:

1. The optimal furnace temperature of the FBC process is lower than today's state-of-the-art combustion temperature of gas turbines. Thus, the efficiency advantage achievable by combined cycle operation cannot be fully exploited.
2. Difficulties in adequate cleaning of the flue gas entering the gas turbine blades from particles and alkalies, as well as the extended outage time required to repair equipment inside the pressurized vessel, led to lower availability during commercial operation of PFBC units.

HEAT RECOVERY STEAM GENERATORS

OVERVIEW OF COMBINED CYCLE

Gas turbine (GT) combined cycles account for almost one-fifth of global electrical capacity and electrical production. Much of this capacity is relatively new, having been installed in the 1990s and 2000s. North America, Asia, and Europe account for most of the capacity. Because they can be built relatively quickly, combined cycles are responsive to the power industry's business cycles. Typically, 30 to 40 GW are added each year, but annual orders have run as high as 100 GW during market cycle peaks.

Key drivers leading to the selection of combined cycles are their low capital cost, quick delivery time, high efficiency, low emissions, and compact footprint. This includes not only low conventional emissions (NOx, SOx, and particulates) but also relatively low CO_2. Combined cycles have the lowest CO_2 profile of any fossil fuel technology, as a consequence of their high efficiency and the lower carbon content of natural gas compared to other fossil fuels. Combined cycle plants occupy a small fraction of the land that coal and nuclear plants do (about an order of magnitude less). Their compact nature and low emissions enable them to be sited in urban, suburban, and rural areas.

About one-fifth of combined cycles are employed for cogeneration. In this process, not only is power produced but a portion of the steam is used to provide heat. Examples include process steam for petrochemical plants, desalination, and/or district heating. By using lower-energy steam, these processes further improve the already high efficiencies of combined cycles.

Most combined cycle power plants use natural gas as the primary fuel, with light oil as a backup fuel. The current generation of combined cycle power plants is based on the introduction and deployment of utility-scale, large-frame, gas turbines in the early 1990s. These gas turbines have a power output capacity of 180 to 260 MWe and are optimized to use natural gas as the primary fuel. Very large gas turbines producing 250 to 320 MW and up are part of the trend toward increasing the size of the GT and heat recovery steam generator (HRSG) enabling even higher plant efficiencies. The HRSG coupled with the steam turbine produces power equal to approximately 50% of the gas turbine output. A basic combined cycle is configured with a combustion turbine (gas turbine), an exhaust HRSG, and a steam turbine, as shown in *Figure 3-65*.

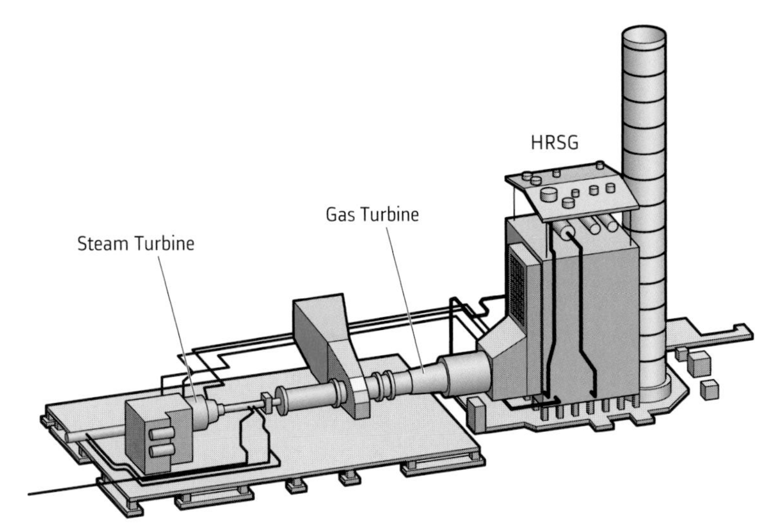

Figure 3-65 | Basic combined cycle configuration (HRSG, heat recovery steam generator)

RELATED PARAMETERS

Gas turbine exhaust-gas outlet conditions are the primary input for the HRSG design. The exhaust gas flow rate leaving large gas turbines ranges up to 1,400 lb/s (640 kg/s). Exhaust gas temperatures range from 930 to 1200°F (500 to 650°C). Static backpressure imposed on the gas turbine by the HRSG heat exchanger tubing, SCR, CO catalyst, silencer, and stack is limited by the gas turbine manufacturer. Excessive backpressure degrades gas turbine performance. Typical HRSG backpressure is in the range of 0.3 to 0.7 psi (20 to 50 mbar).

Large, industrial gas turbines employ a Brayton cycle and operate in the 32 to 39% efficiency range. Exhaust heat is captured in the HRSG and, with the addition of a steam turbine, condenser, and pump, is used to drive a Rankine cycle. Total combined cycle plant efficiency in higher pressure cycles approaches 60% (LHV). Steam in the HRSG is produced at multiple pressure levels, typically up to three. Steam leaving the HP steam turbine may be returned to the HRSG and reheated to improve efficiency. This is referred to as a "reheat system." HP steam is produced at a pressure of 870 to 2,600 psi (60 to 180 bar). HP and reheat steam temperature is between 930 and 1,100°F (500 and 600°C). Higher steam pressure and temperature correspond to improved efficiency at increased cost.

Steam turbine power output can be increased by supplementary firing of the HRSG to produce more steam flow. The gas turbine exhaust contains oxygen at high enough levels to support combustion of additional fuel. However, augmenting combustion air may be required. The duct burner may be located between the gas turbine and the HRSG or within the HRSG. The duct burner can increase the exhaust gas temperature up to 1,650°F (900°C). The additional steam generated by supplemental firing also can be used for processes in cogeneration applications.

HRSG DESIGNS

Types of HRSGs

HRSGs consist of heat exchanger sections that are typically arranged in a counter flow direction relative to gas turbine exhaust flow. The surface is arranged to provide the various steam and water process requirements stipulated by the customer in terms of pressure, temperature, and flow rate. The HRSGs can be configured so that the turbine's exhaust gas flow passes through the boiler in either a horizontal or a vertical direction. Both types of units have a variety of common physical design characteristics, but differ in how these characteristics are put into practice.

Vertical gas flow path HRSGs are composed of individual heat exchanger sections made up of horizontal tubes that pass water back and forth through the gas turbine exhaust-gas flow, as shown in *Figure 3-66*. The tubes in these sections are connected by return bends. Larger horizontal inlet and outlet distribution header pipes serve as central connection points between heat exchanger sections. Heat exchanger sections, such as HP superheaters and reheaters that require the hottest available gas flow, are located at the bottom of the vertical arrangement. Economizers are located at the top of the unit near the stack.

Pressure parts in vertical HRSGs are top supported, meaning that all the unit's heat exchanger sections are hung one under another from the uppermost steel structure. The support steel must then be sized to accommodate this loading. This arrangement may permit the required components of the boiler to be situated in a slightly smaller overall footprint, but it requires a significant amount of steel support structure compared to the horizontal gas flow arrangement. The unit's structure also must be designed to accommodate a significant downward growth of the pressure parts because of thermal expansion. This combination of vertical orientation and top support makes the inclusion of additional equipment, such as SCR systems and duct burners, within the gas path of a vertical HRSG extremely difficult.

Horizontal gas flow path HRSGs are composed of vertical tubes that pass water back and forth through the gas flow as shown in *Figure 3-67*. Unlike a vertical HRSG, tubes in these sections are connected directly to top and bottom horizontal header pipes. This header-tube arrangement typically is called a "harp," and one or more rows of tubing may be connected to the headers in a single harp. Connecting piping, or links, serve to pass the steam/water between individual harps and between heat exchanger sections.

Pressure parts in horizontal HRSGs may be either top or bottom supported. For bottom-supported units, the weight of the individual harps will be carried by the lower support steel. Thermal expansion of the pressure parts takes place in the upward vertical direction. Steam drums also may be supported by, and expand with, the tubes. For top-supported units, the weight of the individual harps is hung from the upper support structure. Thermal expansion of the pressure parts takes place in the downward vertical direction. In this case, tubes also may be supported by the steam drum. The support structure for horizontal HRSGs must still be sized to accommodate the loading it experiences. The total load that any given column is required to support is much lower than

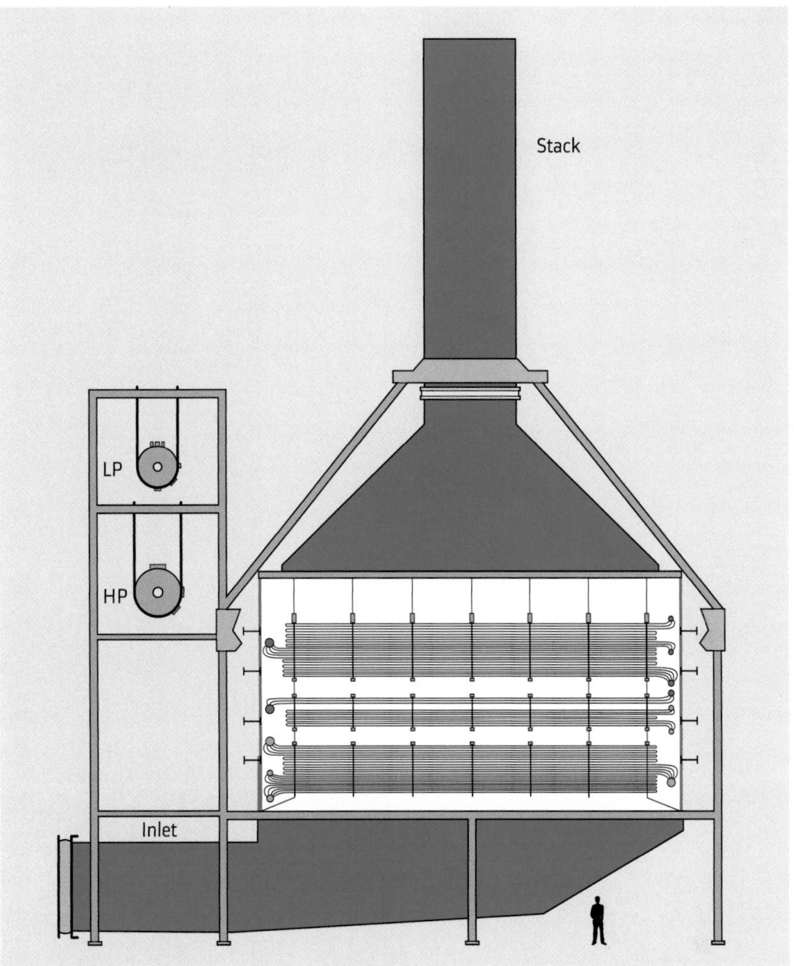

Figure 3-66 | Cutaway view of vertical heat recovery steam generator (HP, high pressure; LP, low pressure)

that in a vertical HRSG because the weight of the pressure parts is distributed over the length of the HRSG. The combination of horizontal orientation and top/bottom support makes the inclusion of additional equipment, such as SCR systems and duct burners, within the HRSG's gas path relatively simple. Also, the horizontal exhaust path configuration affords easier overall access for maintenance to the various boiler components, such as pressure parts, duct burners, catalysts, valves, and

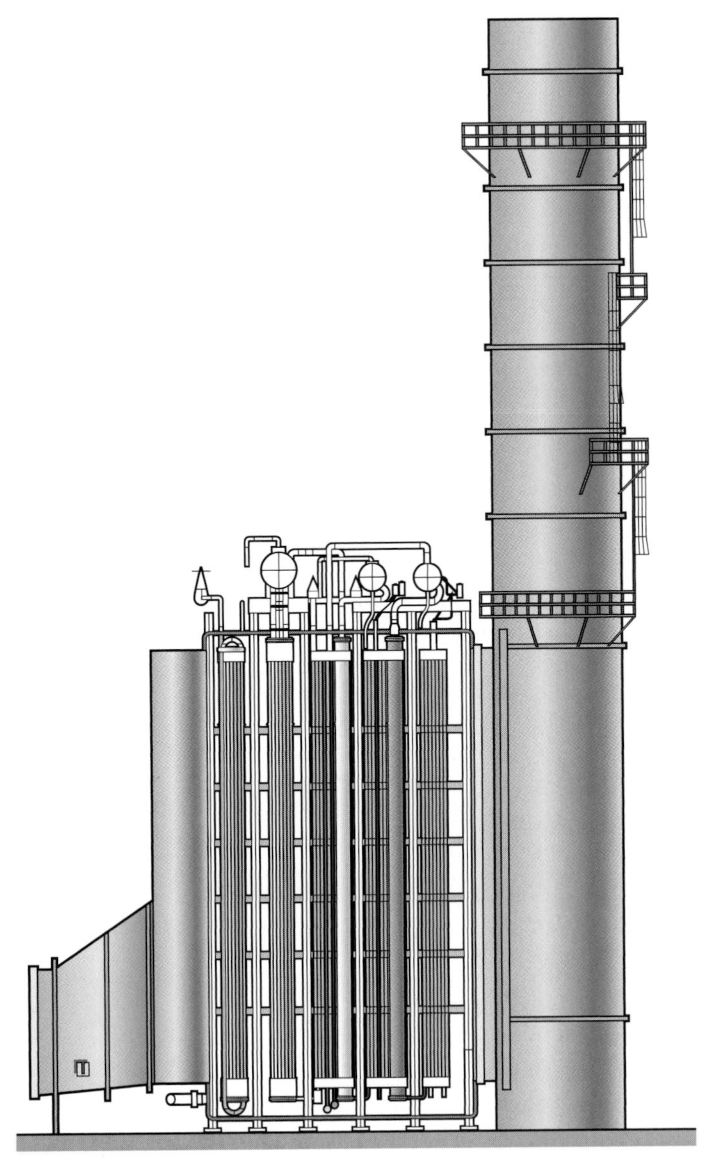

Figure 3-67 | Cutaway view of horizontal heat recovery steam generator

instruments, compared to vertical units.

The last two design characteristics to be discussed pertain to how the water is moved through the evaporative heat exchanger sections on its way to becoming steam. There are two methods of circulating water through an HRSG's evaporators: natural circulation and forced (or assisted) circulation. Natural circulation typically is employed in horizontal HRSGs, where the heat exchanger tubes are vertical (*Fig. 3-68*). Water is fed from the steam drum to the bottom of the evaporator section, and circulation of the steam–water mixture within the evaporator tubes is accomplished by the natural buoyancy forces of the fluid as it absorbs heat, boils to form steam (bubbles), and decreases in density. The rate at which the steam–water mixture passes through the various tubing and piping sections is determined by a number of variables, including the internal diameters of these sections. Forced circulation typically is employed in vertical HRSGs, where the heat exchanger tubes are horizontal (*Fig. 3-69*). With this type of circulation, a pump, located at ground level, forces circulation of the water–steam mixture through the evaporator tubes. It is possible for vertical HRSGs to function properly using only natural circulation; however, circulation pumps typically are still included to provide assistance during transient operating conditions, such as start-up.

There are also two different types of evaporator sections: the drum-type section and the once-through section. In a majority of HRSG installations, evaporator systems are topped by a steam drum. This is called a "drum-type evaporator" (see *Fig. 3-68*). Steam drums serve as a central collection point for the steam and water in the evaporator system, and they function as both a fluid reservoir and a phase separator. Steam is taken off the top of the drum to be superheated, and water is returned to the bottom of the evaporator. Drum-type evaporators may employ natural or forced circulation and may be included in vertical and horizontal HRSGs. The second type of evaporator is called a "once-through evaporator" (*Fig. 3-70*). As the name suggests, this type of evaporator does not include a steam drum but, instead, is arranged so that the water makes one pass through the system on its way to becoming steam. Once-through evaporators may be constructed of either horizontal or vertical tubes. One major advantage of once-through evaporators is elimination of the steam drum, which because of its thickness may limit start-up rates as a result of transient stresses. Recently, the industry trend has been to construct more HRSGs that include once-through evaporators as customers demand faster start-up times, improved flexibility in choosing plant loading, and higher pressures leading to higher overall thermal efficiencies.

Factors Influencing HRSG Design

Several factors influence design of the HRSG on a project basis. One factor is the desired output of the HRSG in terms of pressure, temperature, and flow rate. Another is how the HRSG is integrated with the plant's overall design. Determination of these parameters is accomplished by the plant designer or architect engineer. The architect engineer's function is to integrate all systems that comprise the plant (e.g., gas turbine, HRSG, and steam turbine) to satisfy the needs of the end customer. Projects that include HRSGs may be constructed for power generation (combined cycle) or industrial (cogeneration) applications. Once the process requirements have been established, it is up to the HRSG design engineer to arrange HRSG components to satisfy those requirements. In some situations, the design is as simple as meeting the direct needs of a steam turbine to generate electricity. In others, the design may involve close integration with the customer's process, including intermediate requirements where steam and/or water are extracted from and returned to the HRSG at various points in the thermal design.

Another set of factors influencing design of the HRSG and its systems relates to environmental considerations. Components such as silencers and shrouds may need to be included to meet local noise restrictions as measured at either near field (3 ft. [1 m]) or far field (400 ft. [120 m]). There also may be the need for emission reduction catalysts to reduce the emission of certain compounds into the air. Dampers and auxiliary heating systems may need to be included to protect an idle HRSG from cold-weather conditions. In addition, a stack damper is provided to keep the HRSG warm during a plant shutdown by not allowing heat to escape out of the stack. Lastly, the HRSG needs to be designed to meet elevation, weather, and seismic conditions.

Once the parameters of the plant have been identified, the HRSG design engineer will need to examine these items and determine their impact on specifics of the HRSG design. The type of fuel used in the gas turbine will directly impact the main source of heat for the HRSG. Currently, natural gas is the fuel of choice and imposes few design restrictions on the HRSG. Some units are designed to work with gas turbine exhaust produced by fuel oil or

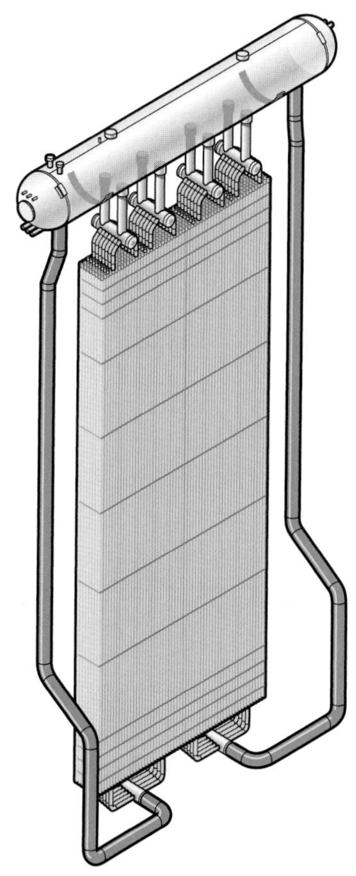

Figure 3-68 | Natural circulation evaporator with vertical tubes

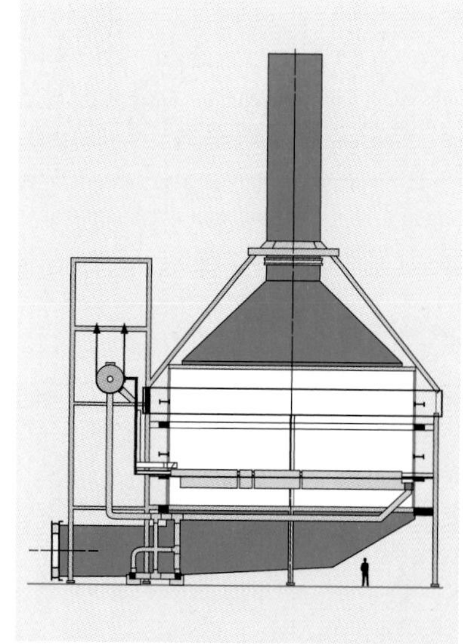

Figure 3-69 | Forced circulation evaporator with horizontal tubes

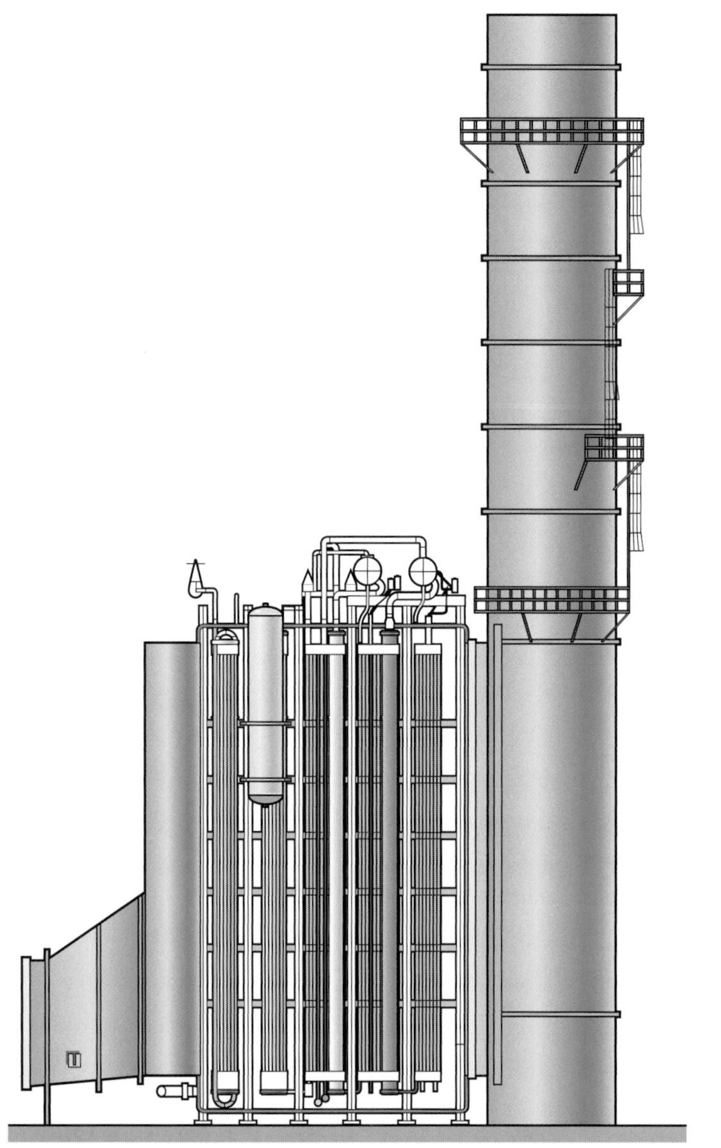

Figure 3-70 | Once-through evaporator system

synthetic gas created by the gasification of coal in the IGCC (Integrated Gasification Combined Cycle) process. Emissions present in the gas turbine exhaust because of fuel constituents may impact the physical arrangements of HRSG pressure parts. Tubes may need to be spaced to accommodate cleaning procedures, such as water washing and soot blowing when firing oil. The geometry of finned surfaces will need to be designed to account for these conditions, even to the point that typical fin spacing and serrating for optimal heat transfer may not be permissible. Finally, steps may need to be taken to protect the back end of the HRSG against excessive particulate formation or acid and/or water dew-point corrosion. This will impact the types of materials used to construct the HRSG as well as the water flow path arrangements made to keep temperatures above critical levels for forming these products.

The type of loading is another significant factor influencing HRSG design. The HRSG may experience steady base load, daily cycling, or peaking service loads, each of which will affect the design details of the HRSG. Physical arrangement of the HRSG pressure parts determines the thermal stress, fatigue, and creep that the equipment will experience over time. By knowing the type of service that the HRSG will experience, the engineer can adjust the equipment's design to minimize the impacts of these factors through proper choice of materials and arrangements.

FUNDAMENTALS OF HOW HRSG EQUIPMENT WORKS

Steam–Water Flow Path

The basic principles for selecting HRSG equipment are similar to those for conventional utility and industrial boilers. To integrate the HRSG properly within the overall plant, the designer must be aware of the entire system arrangement. Although cycle efficiency and economics generally determine basic cycle conditions, the designer typically is faced with a matrix of conditions that determine the optimum design. These conditions include a wide range of thermal performance parameters dictated by varying ambient conditions and steam load requirements, limitations on capital cost, and restrictions on available space. In pursuing a solution to the demands of a specific application, three aspects of the HRSG design process dominate:

1. Extensive use of externally finned tubing for maximum convective heat recovery
2. An emphasis on low gas side pressure loss to limit the gas turbine fuel-rate penalty associated with increased backpressure on the gas turbine
3. Distribution of heat-transfer surface in multiple sections to achieve optimum heat transfer at each temperature level through the boiler.

The HRSGs are composed of cylindrical pressure parts in the form of tube, pipe, and plate-formed vessels, some of which are also heat exchangers. In top supported horizontal HRSGs, these heat exchangers are vertically hung tube bundles (harps), which are arranged in the flow path with gas turbine exhaust-gas flowing horizontally past them. The heat exchangers are divided into different heat-absorbing sections, depending on their function in the HRSG. These heat-absorbing sections operate at certain temperature levels, depending on their location in the gas path. The goal of an efficient design is to minimize the amount of heat-transfer surface that is required based on the gas temperature available and the fluid temperature requirements. Thermal energy in the gas turbine exhaust gas is transferred to thermal energy in water or steam in the HRSG.

The most common HRSG configuration is three pressure levels: high pressure (HP), intermediate pressure (IP), and LP. In addition, most HRSGs for advanced cycles have a reheat section of the boiler that takes steam from the steam turbine and recirculates it through the HRSG to increase thermal efficiency. Some designs only require one or two pressure levels; the number of pressure levels is dictated by the plant's overall design. Each pressure level is made up of the following pressure-containing components: economizer/feedwater pre-heater, evaporator (coupled to a steam drum), and superheater. *Figure 3-71* shows a typical HP steam–water circuit.

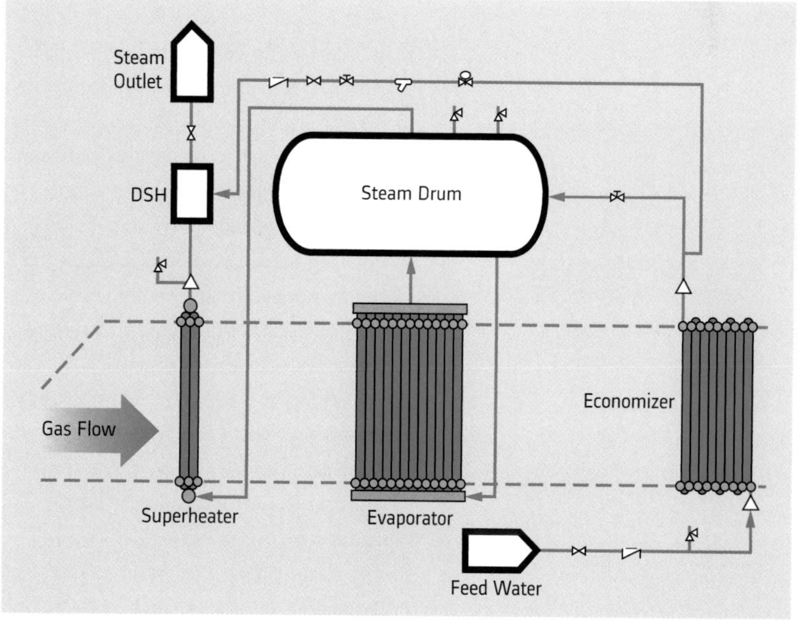

Figure 3-71 | Typical steam–water flow path: high-pressure system; DSH (DeSuper Heater)

Feedwater pumps supply water to the HRSG. The water supply for these pumps comes either from the LP drum or from the feedwater storage tank. The pump discharges into a feedwater inlet pipe, which is connected to the economizer (HRSG inlet).

Each pressure level has a dedicated economizer circuit, arranged in harps, connected by link pipes to form economizer sections. The tubes are inline or staggered, perpendicular to gas flow. The LP economizer is referred to as a feedwater pre-heater when the LP drum provides pump water supply for the HP and IP feedwater pump. Most economizers use a series design, in which all water flows through each harp. In order to reduce velocity and pressure drop in an economizer section, a parallel flow design is used, wherein only a portion of the water flows through each row of tubes. Water flows from the economizer inlet pipe of the first economizer section and discharges into the next economizer section or to the steam drum. The coldest feedwater enters the HRSG closest to the stack. The feedwater temperature is increased by convective heat transfer from the hot combustion gas passing by the water-filled tubes. The purpose of the economizer is to raise the feedwater temperature close to the saturation temperature. If the water temperature entering the LP economizer/feedwater pre-heater is not high enough (i.e. close to the water dew point), then a recirculation system can be provided.

Feedwater enters the steam drum, mixes with the water in the drum, is directed to the drum's downcomers, and then is fed to lower harp headers by means of a manifold and circulator pipes. The water passes through the evaporator tubes with all the flow directed up toward the steam drum in a single pass. At this point, the water is at its boiling point, and convective heat transfer causes steam to be generated. As a result of buoyancy forces, natural circulation is developed, and a circulating pump is not needed. Control valves, located between the economizer outlet and the drum or upstream of the economizer inlet, regulate the level in the drum by modulating open and closed, depending on boiler demand.

In the steam drum, the water–steam mixture is directed through a series of separation devices consisting of baffles and vane/mesh demisters. The water drains from the vane and mesh sections back into the drum, and steam is directed upward, to a dry box. Dry steam exits the top of the drum and travels to the superheater section at saturation temperature. In a once-through HRSG, the HP steam drum is not used. This design allows the plant to increase pressure and, therefore, efficiency and to endure more thermal cycles.

The superheater section increases steam temperature to a superheated state, raising the steam's thermal energy. Similar to the economizer and evaporator sections, the superheaters are composed of an inlet manifold, finned tubes, and an outlet manifold. The number and location of superheater tubes varies, depending on the required superheat temperature. Superheater tubes are physically located upstream of the evaporator section in the gas path. The HP superheater sections are located close to the gas turbine. The IP and LP superheaters are located downstream of the HP evaporator in the gas path. Steam flow leaves the superheater and is routed to the steam line supplying the steam turbine.

The IP steam leaves the IP superheater and most often combines with the HP turbine return (cold reheat) steam line. This line then flows into the reheat section of the boiler. The reheat section of the HRSG functions the same as a superheater. Superheated steam that leaves the reheat section of the HRSG is referred to as "hot reheat."

Because of downstream metal temperature limits, the steam temperature leaving the superheater/reheater sections is controlled through the use of a desuperheater. The desuperheater can be between superheater/reheater sections (inter-stage), in the steam line supplying the steam turbine (exit stage), or in both locations, depending on the design of the HRSG. The desuperheater takes feedwater from the HP and IP economizer inlets or outlets and sprays enough water to control the outlet steam to the desired temperature. The water sprays into a pipe containing a liner that protects the pipe from thermal fatigue.

Gas Side Flow Path

The gas turbine exhaust gas enters the HRSG through an inlet duct section that is designed to evenly distribute gas turbine exhaust flow over the frontal area of the HRSG finned tubing. The height and width of the inlet duct is a function of the gas turbine being used. A fabric expansion joint connects the gas turbine with the HRSG to isolate the two structures. *Figure* 3-72 shows a typical gas side flow path.

The highest-temperature exhaust gases are in the inlet duct, and the lowest temperature is at the inlet to the stack. The design objective of the HRSG is to absorb as much heat as possible in the heat-transfer surface and leave the stack at the lowest possible temperature. The HP superheater and reheater sections are located close to the gas turbine in the first and second sections (inter bank). The layout of the pressure parts is based on the steam temperature and pressure requirements of the customer.

Supplementary firing or duct burners supply additional heating input to the HRSG to meet electrical load or steam flow requirements. The duct burner may be located in the inlet duct, upstream of the superheater and reheater sections, or between heat-transfer sections (inter bank). The most common location is between reheater 1 and HP superheater 2. Tubes downstream of the duct burner normally are bare or have low fins. A space of approximately 20 to 26 ft (6 to 8 m) is provided between the duct burner elements and the tubes to avoid flame impingement on the tubes.

Emission reduction equipment—namely, CO and SCR catalysts—are considered to be optional equipment. The location of any emission reduction equipment requires specific gas path temperature ranges to perform the proper conversions. The CO catalyst is a passive, honeycombed structure or coated foil substrate in the gas path that converts CO to CO_2. If the HRSG has no supplementary firing, it can be placed in the inlet duct or downstream of the HP evaporator. If the HRSG is supplementary fired,

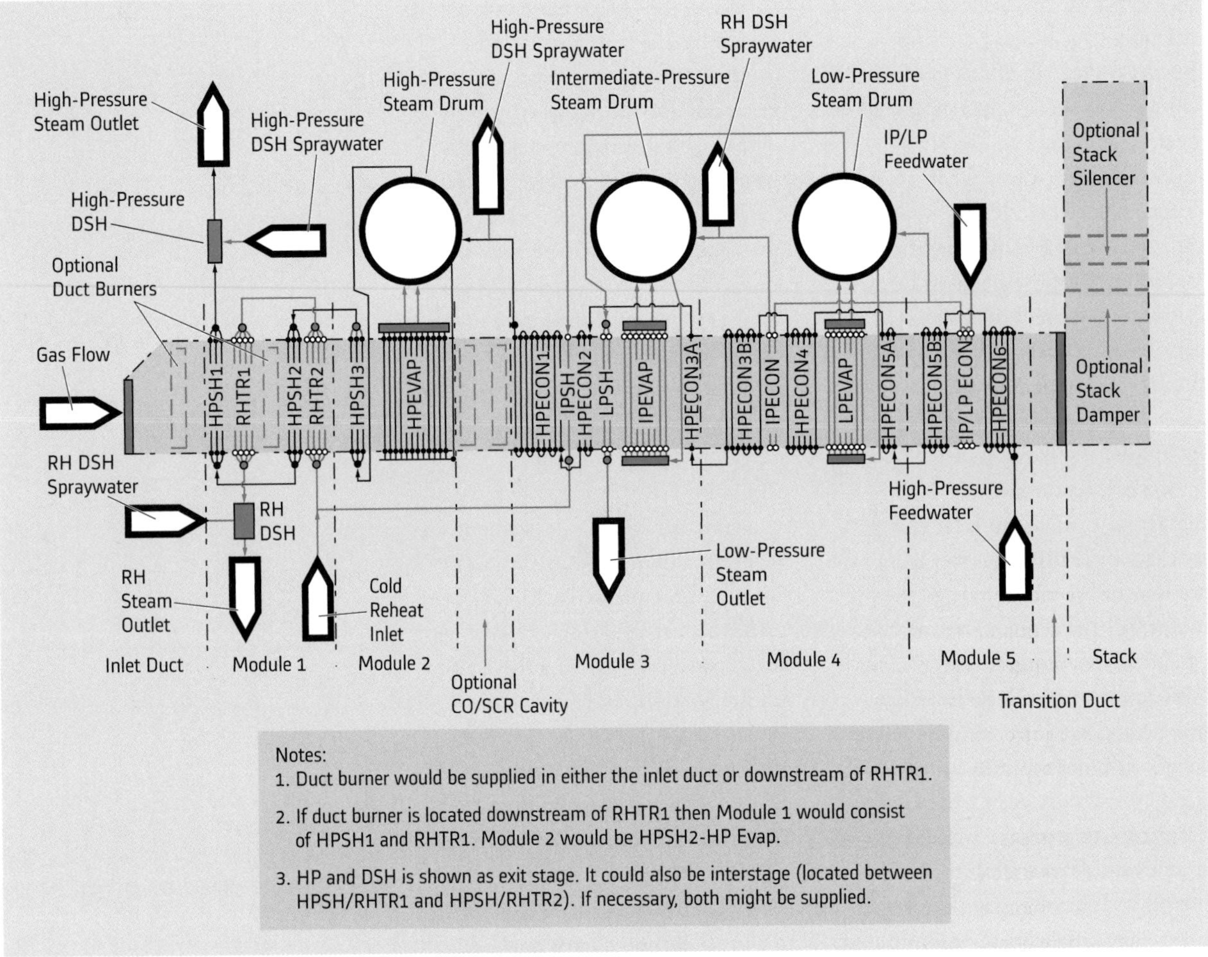

Figure 3-72 | Triple pressure with reheat HRSG (HP, high pressure; IP, intermediate pressure; LP, low pressure)

it would be placed downstream of the duct burner. The SCR reduces NOx into molecular nitrogen (N_2) and water (H_2O). The NOx breaks down when it reacts with a reducing agent, usually ammonia (NH_3), in the presence of a catalyst. The ammonia injection grid is installed upstream of the SCR to provide ammonia as the reducing agent. The SCR normally is located downstream of the HP evaporator.

After the last heat-transfer section, a piece of ducting connects the boiler to the stack. This is referred to as the "outlet duct" or "transition duct." A fabric expansion joint connects the outlet duct to the stack. Most stack designs contain optional dampers and silencers.

Economizers, Evaporators, Superheaters, and Reheaters

ARRANGEMENT OF PRESSURE PART SECTIONS. A simplified flow diagram (*Fig. 3-73*) for a triple-pressure-with-reheat HRSG illustrates the way in which heat-absorbing sections operating at certain temperature levels are located in the gas stream to minimize the amount of heat-transfer surface. Often twenty discrete heat exchange sections are distributed in descending order based on the gas temperature available and the fluid temperature requirements. Note that the LP and IP economizer, evaporator, and superheater sections are arranged in an alternating sequence with sections of the HP economizer to optimize boiler performance. Furthermore, note that the HP superheater and IP reheater sections are arranged in an alternating sequence to meet the temperatures required at the HP and IP steam turbines, respectively, as temperature requirements at these steam turbines typically are similar.

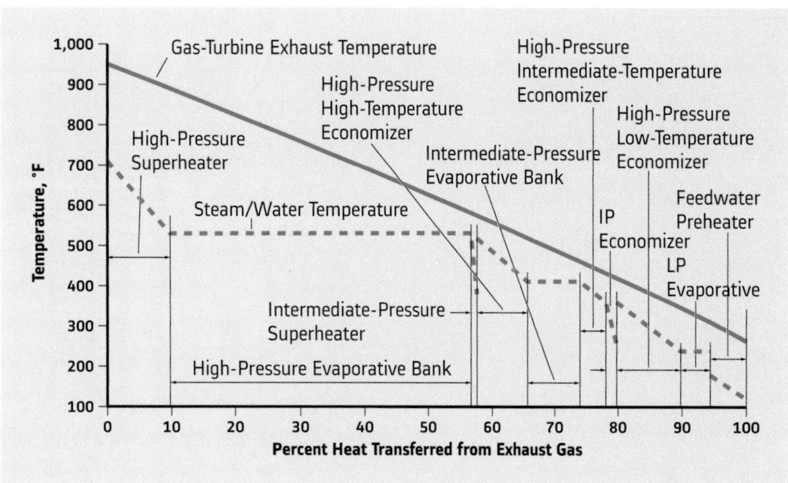

Figure 3-73 | Temperature profile of unfired HRSG with three operating pressure levels

ISOLATED ECONOMIZERS

HOT WATER EXTRACTIONS. The HRSGs may have one or more hot water extractions where hot water is extracted from an economizer for use in another process in the plant. These extractions can be used for processes such as fuel pre-heating or combustion turbine rotor air cooling. To provide water at the desired temperature, the extraction is located downstream of one or more economizer sections. The extraction flow typically is required at all operating conditions. To ensure the availability of the extraction flow when the feedwater control valve is closed, the feedwater control valve is located downstream of the extraction point. Locating the feedwater control valve downstream of an economizer means the economizer can be isolated from the water flow path and become a fired pressure vessel. The isolatable economizer must be protected by a pressure relief device.

PRESSURE RELIEF VALVES FOR ISOLATABLE ECONOMIZERS. Traditional sizing criteria for pressure relief devices on isolatable economizers in Section I of the ASME Boiler and Pressure Vessel Code (B&PVC) is based on relieving steam. Although the calculation is based on steam relief, the valve typically will relieve water, which will then flash to steam as the pressure is quickly reduced across the valve. Water is not compressible. If the economizer is isolated, changes in temperature cause quick increases in pressure, lifting the valve. Unless the economizer is steaming, the pressure is quickly relieved, and the valve closes. If the pressure relief valve is relieving water, it will not reseat quickly. Operation of all valves in the feedwater system should be reviewed to make sure the valve is not being held in a relieving condition by the discharge flow and pressure of the feedwater pump.

Design of the pressure relief valve must accommodate relieving either steam or water. If a traditional, spring-loaded safety valve is used, it will be quickly damaged when relieving water. Spring-loaded safety valves are designed for relieving steam. Steam is compressible and acts as a cushion when the valve closes, preventing the disk from slamming into the seat. Water is not compressible, and so does not provide this cushion. When a spring-loaded safety valve relieves water, the disk and seat are damaged after few cycles. A pilot-operated valve limits differential pressure across the seat to minimize the impact between the disk and seat and, therefore, is appropriate for either steam or water service.

RECIRCULATION. If the overall plant design requires the HRSG to include an LP drum acting as a storage tank for the HP and IP feedwater pumps, care must be taken to avoid corrosion in the "cold end" of the HRSG. In this arrangement, cold condensate flows through a condensate pre-heater heat exchanger located in the gas path before entering the LP drum. Typically, a recirculation pump is supplied to recirculate the hot water from the condensate pre-heater outlet back to the condensate pre-heater inlet. The recirculation flow is varied such that the mixed temperature of the condensate flow and the recirculation flow is greater than the water dew point of the exhaust gas. With a higher-sulfur fuel, such as conventional No. 2 fuel oil, the condensate pre-heater may have to be bypassed.

Operation and Control

The typical HRSG comprises a unit in the functional hierarchy of the power plant that generally is controlled by a Distributed Control System (DCS). Depending on the plant configuration and operating philosophy, the HRSG operation can be a combined cycle, with or without a steam turbine functional unit. In general, HRSG operation is coordinated with a specific gas turbine functional unit and may be coordinated with a specific steam turbine unit, steam header system, or a combined cogeneration steam turbine and process steam header system.

The hierarchy of control is broken down into the following function group controls: drum level, steam temperature, blowdown tank level, steam vent, and steam drain control. Optionally, additional function group control can be provided for feedwater pre-heater temperature control, duct burner firing rate control, HRSG inlet damper bypass control, and so on. The direct control interface to the process is the DRIVE control level, made up of the actuators for control valves (feedwater and fuel flow), motor-operated valves (high-energy steam vents and drains, dampers), and solenoid air-operated power block valves (desuperheater spray water).

START-UP. Typically, the gas turbine and the HRSG are started together. If a diverter damper is between the gas turbine and the HRSG, the HRSG can be started at a later time. The following permissives must be met in order to initiate HRSG start-up: stack damper open, ready lists complete (gas turbine ready list, steam turbine ready list, electrical ready list, balance-of-plant ready list, HRSG ready list), and HRSG cold-start valve alignment table complete. Once all pressure sections of the HRSG are filled with water and levels are verified to be at start-up set points, the gas turbine start can be initiated, followed by the HRSG start-up. For combined cycle start-up, the gas turbine starts using its normal start-up procedure and loading curve.

For a start-up to proceed, the following systems related to the HRSG must be in operation:

1. Feedwater storage and feedwater pump systems
2. Drain and vent system
3. Blowdown system

In addition, the following function groups in the HRSG control system must be enabled:

1. LP drum level control
2. IP drum level control
3. HP drum level control
4. Blowdown tank level control
5. HRSG drains
6. HRSG vents

The gas turbine and HRSG gas path also must be purged of all gaseous, or suspended, combustibles before gas turbine flame is initiated. The purge will be in accordance with local codes.

The control system drum water level set points are set to start-up set points. The drum level set points may be lower than the normal operating set points to allow drum level "swell" (i.e., a rise in drum water level associated with increased water volume in the evaporator section because of increased temperature and steam content). During start-up, the drum level set points are reset to normal operating condition. Typically, the set points are automatically reset at specific steam flow rates. The start-up set point flow rate will be monitored by single-element measurement via HP steam flow. Three-element measurement drum control will automatically take over when the respective steam flow is greater than approximately 30% of normal steam flow (typically the lowest repeatable and accurate steam flow measurement available). As the HRSG is brought up to the normal operating pressures and temperatures, steam vents and drains are cycled. The intent is to warm up the HRSG unit, remove any condensate, and minimize pressure losses and waste heat releases through the vents and drains. The duct burner is permitted to operate above a determined gas turbine load.

Faster start-up times allow combined cycle plants to respond to load demand in a timely fashion.

DRUM LEVEL CONTROL FOR ALL DRUM LEVEL CONTROL SYSTEMS

NORMAL LEVEL CONTROL. The drum level will be corrected by the drum pressure. Level control is maintained by monitoring drum level and adjusting the feedwater control valves to provide more or less feedwater to the system.

Measurement devices used in level control include:

- Steam outlet flow (pressure and temperature compensated)
- Feedwater to drum flow (pressure and temperature compensated)

- Desuperheater feedwater flow (pressure and temperature compensated)
- Drum level (pressure compensated, 2 out of 3 voting logic)

The drum level controls will regulate the rate of feedwater flow to maintain a proper drum level throughout the operation range of the steam generator (HRSG). To get the maximum benefit from a three-element system, the feedwater flow should be proportional to the steam flow, with reset action on drum level. This means that the mass of feedwater entering should always be equal to the mass of steam leaving, with continuous corrections made for deviations from level set points. The best drum level control is achieved through mass flow balance:

1. **Feedwater control valves:** The feedwater control valves will open and close (modulate) to maintain drum normal water level set points.
2. **Single element:** At a steam flow of less than approximately 30% of normal, single-element measurement drum level control at the feedwater inlet will be implemented.
3. **Three element:** At a steam flow of greater than approximately 30% of normal, three-element system measurement drum level control will take over. Steam flow minus feedwater flow is compared in a mass balance calculation. Split-range feedwater control valves may be used to increase the turndown control range of the drum level control system. When split-range feedwater control valves are used, the feedwater control valve (30%) controls the feedwater flow from 0 to 30% of the drum level/feedwater flow control system demand. The feedwater control valve (100%) controls the feedwater flow from 30% to 100% of the drum level/feedwater flow control system demand.

STEAM TEMPERATURE CONTROL. Steam outlet temperature can be controlled either with a final-stage desuperheater before the steam outlet header or with an inter-stage desuperheater, between the superheaters, or both. To prevent damage to the HRSG because of operation without the required steam flow, the desuperheater block valves and control valves open above a specific steam outlet flow or steam temperature and also if the outlet temperature is greater than a specific amount over the calculated saturation temperature.

DESIGN CONSIDERATIONS

Tube Length and Diameter

The tube length and the number of tubes wide are selected based on the gas side pressure loss allowed in the overall plant design (i.e., permissible gas turbine backpressure). Once the number of tubes wide is determined, an increase in tube length will decrease the gas side pressure loss but may significantly increase the overall cost of the tubes because of manufacturing and transportation constraints. Maximum tube lengths of 82 ft (25 m) are feasible in a horizontal gas flow, vertical tube design.

Tube diameter is selected based on velocity, pressure drop, and heat-transfer requirements. Smaller-diameter tubes yield the lowest weight; however, there are limitations on material availability and manufacturing. Most HRSG manufacturers have found 1½ inches (38 mm) to be the optimal tube diameter. For any given HRSG design, it is typical for the tube diameter of the reheater heat-transfer sections to be greater than the tube diameter of other heat-transfer surface sections, because minimizing steam side pressure drop in this section dramatically improves steam turbine power output. Maximum tube diameters of 2 inches (50.8 mm) are common in a horizontal gas flow, vertical tube design.

Water and Steam Velocity

Selection of tube and pipe sizes must take into account the full range of operating cases, including continuous operation and of peak load/partial pressure operation. Permissible values for maximum velocity during peak load or partial pressure operation cases are typically 25 to 30% higher for steam and 40 to 65% higher for water compared with the permissible values for maximum velocity during cases of continuous operation. Larger pipe sizes with lower values for velocity may be required to meet the pressure drop requirements of individual pipe systems.

Metal Temperature

Selection of tube and pipe materials must also take into account the full range of operating cases. Once the design case has been established, tube and pipe materials can be chosen based on maximum allowable metal temperature, and thickness can be chosen based on design code and mechanical design calculations.

The maximum allowable metal temperatures are established by considering the following factors:

- Surface oxidation (wastage) as determined by behavior analysis of ferritic and austenitic materials under operating conditions. The limits are based on achieving satisfactory life even though some wastage is expected.
- Metallurgical instability, such as graphitization (carbon and carbon-moly), in relation to several factors, including the current use of steel mill deoxidation processes and heat treatment after fabrication.

Flow Distribution Economizers and Superheaters

To ensure proper distribution between adjacent economizers and between adjacent superheaters, an adequate number of links connecting the headers must be installed to limit the velocity to a value within the maximum velocity guidelines. The velocity in the economizer tubes must be great enough, however, to overcome the buoyancy effect in downflow tube rows and to achieve equal distribution in the tubes that are transverse to the gas flow.

Pinch and Approach

The two critical temperature differences that influence the amount of heat-transfer surface and the overall steam generated at each pressure level are:

- **The pinch point:** The difference between the gas temperature leaving an evaporating section and the temperature at which boiling is occurring (saturated-water temperature).

- **The approach temperature:** The difference between the saturated-water temperature in an evaporating section and the incoming feedwater temperature.

The pinch point strongly influences the amount of heat-transfer surface in the evaporating section. Current HRSG designs use pinch points in the range of 9 to 27°F (5 to 15°C). In general, these boilers have 50% more surface in the evaporating section compared with boilers having pinch points of 36 to 54°F (20 to 30°C).

The approach temperature also influences the amount of surface required for an economizer section, with exponentially increasing amounts required for very low approach temperatures. Current HRSG economizers have approach temperatures in the range of 9 to 27°F (5 to 15°C) at the design point. Many other operating conditions can occur at off-design points, including start-up. Some conditions will result in steaming at the exit of the economizer, so that it acts as evaporative surface. Specific provisions to accommodate steaming in an economizer include:

1. Careful control of water distribution in the last downflow passes of the economizer to cause that portion of the economizer to behave as a forced circulation evaporator
2. Configuring the last pass of the economizer as entirely upflow.

The triple-pressure with reheat HRSG temperature profile shown in *Figure 3-73* illustrates the distribution of heat exchanger sections and the associated temperature differences between exhaust gas and water and steam temperatures. Pinch points can be observed as a relatively small temperature difference at the right-hand side of each evaporating bank section. Approach temperatures are illustrated as the difference between the water temperature leaving the last section of each economizer and the saturated-water temperature. Note in *Figure 3-72* that the HP economizer is divided into six separate sections to provide appropriate temperature zones for the LP and IP superheater, evaporator, and economizer.

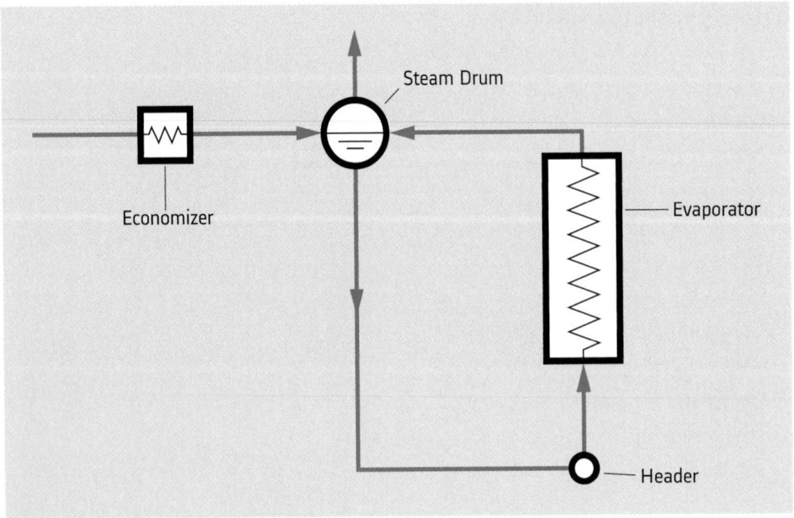

Circulation Ratio

In natural circulation boilers, circulation is accomplished without the use of a circulating pump. The density difference between steam and water (thermal head) is the driving force in a natural circulation boiler (*Fig. 3-74*):

- **Cold side:** The density of saturated water in the downcomers will range between 60 lb/ft^3 and 30 lb/ft^3 (960 and 480 kg/m^3), depending on the corresponding

Figure 3-74 | Natural circulation boiler

- pressure and temperature in the boiler steam drum.
- **Hot side:** The steam–water mixture density in the evaporator will be approximately 25 lb/ft^3 (400 kg/m^3). Variations in boiler pressure have a lesser effect on the mixture density.

As boiler pressure increases, the difference between the densities of water and steam, which is the motive force for natural circulation boilers, becomes smaller. Thermal head differential is the resulting differential and ranges between approximately 25 psi and 10 psi (1.7 and 0.7 bar), with the greater differential being possible in lower pressure boilers.

Circulation ratio is defined as the mass flow of water entering the downcomer divided by the mass flow of steam in the water–steam mixture leaving the evaporator tube circuits. Because circulation is dependent on the thermal head, which is dependent on boiler pressure, the flow of water into the downcomer increases as load decreases. At low loads of 50% of the maximum continuous rating or less, the circulation ratio will be much higher, because less steam is being generated. Natural circulation boilers generally are designed for circulation ratios ranging from 3:1 up to 10:1.

HRSG Materials

The HRSGs have water temperatures and pressures similar to those encountered in subcritical utility and industrial boilers, but the gas temperatures are considerably lower, precluding most common overheating incidents unless supplemental firing with duct burners is employed. Turbine exhaust gas is much cleaner than that associated with other fossil fuels, such as coal and heavy oil. Thus, HRSGs do not have to contend with erosion and fouling, and unless a corrodent-laden oil is being fired, corrosion problems are minimal.

Materials are almost always iron-base alloys, ranging from plain carbon steels through low-alloy steels to the creep strength-enhanced ferritics and stainless steels. Other high-alloy iron-base alloys, erosion-resistant materials, and the nickel-base materials have not frequently been used in HRSGs because of the relatively low gas temperatures and ease of fuel handling. The product forms used are also common to other boilers with:

- Tubing for heat-absorbing surfaces
- Piping for headers, manifolds, links, and lines
- Plate and sheet for drums, casings, and ductwork
- Structural members for support
- Castings and forgings for valves and pipe fittings

In contrast to other utility and industrial boilers, HRSGs do not use heat-absorbing waterwalls for gas containment and flow direction. Typically either a cold casing or a hot casing design is used. In the more common cold casing design the duct is formed from carbon steel outer plates, a layer of insulation, and a system of overlapped inner liner sheets. Both the insulation thickness and the liner sheet material are varied as the gas temperature changes from 1,100 to 1,200°F (600 to 650°C) at the inlet to between 212 and 300°F (100 and 150°C) at the stack. All of the heat-absorbing tubes have extended external surfaces in the form of spiral wound fins. Because the turbine exhaust gas has very little

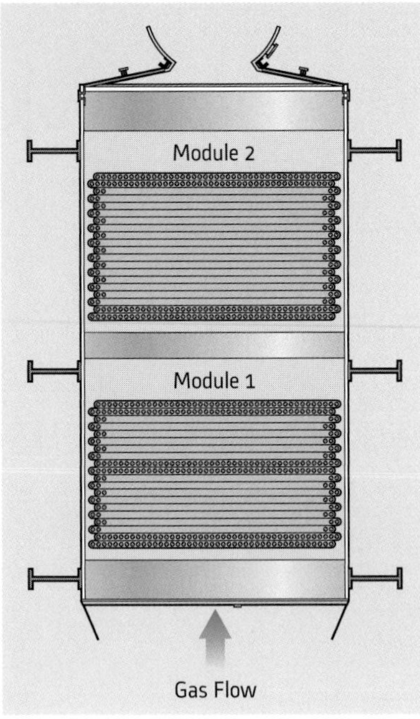

Figure 3-75 | Single wide × two modules deep HRSG, top view

particulate, these fins are not prone to pluggage and can be closely spaced, which results in the HRSG being a very compact steam generator.

Material selections follow standard industry practices for structural and non-pressure containing components and boiler code limitations for pressure parts. The structurals can nearly always utilize plain-carbon steels in readily available product forms. Pressure parts (basically plates for large drums, tubes and pipes for the remaining cylindrical components, and forgings and castings for fittings) employ carbon steels for low-temperature sections, chromium–molybdenum low alloys (1¼Cr-½Mo and 2¼Cr-1Mo) for the next level, and creep strength-enhanced ferritics (9Cr-1Mo-V) or type 304 stainless steel for the hottest sections.

Construction is effected mainly through cutting, forming, and welding. Machining is mostly limited to that required for generating appropriate weld preparations. All welding utilizes fusion processes with filler metal additions except for the tube finning process, during which an electric resistance process is used. The fusion processes include gas metal arc, gas tungsten arc, submerged arc, and shielded metal arc.

Shipping Considerations

In addition to all the performance and structural inputs, the HRSG designer must be aware of shipping limitations, loads, and requirements. These practical issues often create hard design constraints that change the configuration of HRSG components. Available modes of transport, infrastructure, and economics are all factors influencing design. Transportation limitations or requirement oversights lead to costly delays and, potentially, damage to the product before it is delivered to the customer.

When shop fabricated pressure part modules are supplied, these are the largest and heaviest HRSG components for the project. A pressure part module is assembled by connecting from 3 to 30 harps. The number of pressure part modules per HRSG can vary from two modules for small HRSGs (single wide, two modules deep) (*Fig. 3-75*) to up to 18 modules for the largest HRSGs (triple wide, six modules deep) (*Fig. 3-76*). Depending on the degree of shop fabrication, module weights can range from 20 to more than 300 tons, with approximate dimensions of 18 × 13 × 98 ft (5.5 × 4 × 30 m). If the infrastructure, including roads, bridges, docks. and so on, cannot support the weight or accommodate the size of a module, then the module will have to be split into two or more parts during the initial design phase.

Shipping limitations also must be considered when designing other HRSG components. The HRSG structure, inlet duct, stack, platforms, stair towers, steam drums, and piping all have to be designed with these limitations in mind. For the HRSG structure, large shop assemblies are required to reduce construction costs. These assemblies can be as large as 4.9 × 13 × 98 ft (1.5 × 4 × 30 m) and weigh over 50 tons. Special trucks and rigging equipment are required to move steel assemblies of this size. Inlet duct panels follow the same rules as the main HRSG structure but typically are smaller. The HRSG stack can be split into 180, 120, 90, or 72° sections, depending on the diameter and over-the-road width clearance. If the stack shell section is too wide, it will have to be split to the next smaller size until it can be transported to the site. For

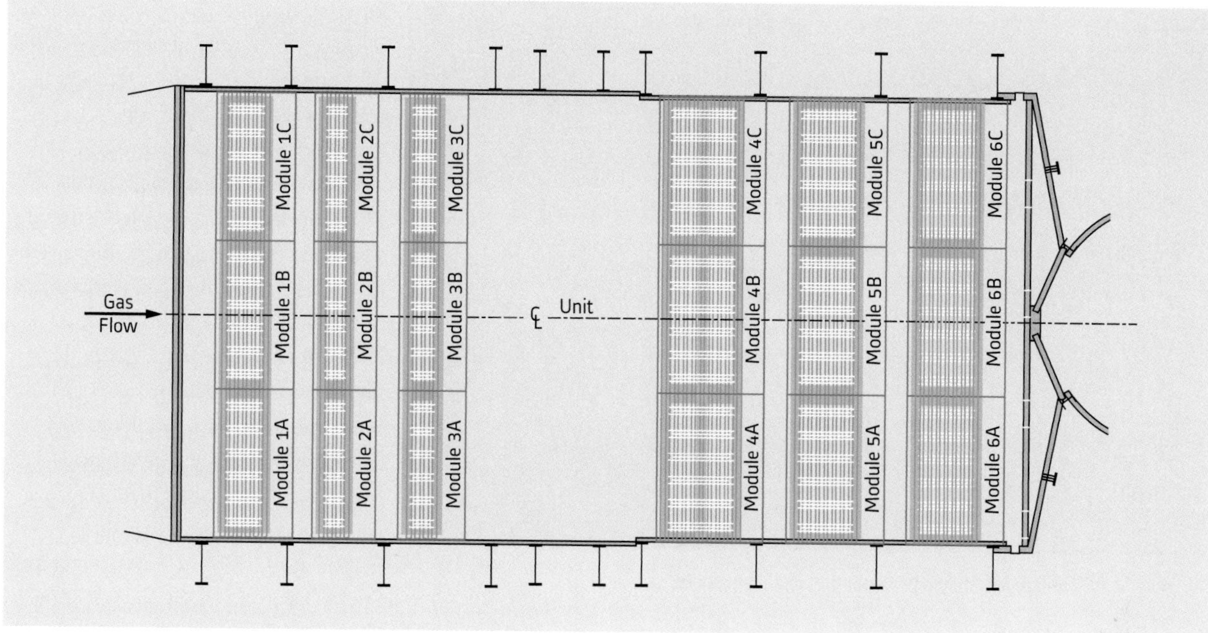

Figure 3-76 | Triple wide × six deep heat recovery steam generator

steam drums, weight is the primary concern, with HP drums typically weighing up to 130 tons. For other components, such as platforms, stair towers, piping, valves, and so on, the challenge is to transport for the lowest cost without damage. The recent trend has been for increased use of shipping containers, which offer the lowest cost, regular schedules, short transit times, and a high level of protection for the cargo. The size of such cargo, however, is limited to 8.2 × 8.2 × 39 ft (2.5 × 2.5 × 12 m), and the weight is limited to 20 tons.

Construction

A significant economic consideration for the power plant developer is HRSG construction cost. The HRSG can consume from 20 to 25% of the labor required to construct the entire power plant. The term *constructability* has been used to describe the ease with which an erector can build the HRSG. Therefore, the HRSG designer must always be aware of constructability when producing a new design to remain competitive. There are restrictions based on available equipment, capability of labor, and safety. On today's construction site, safety is truly "job number 1." If equipment, structures, or procedures are not sufficiently safe, as determined by compliance with the erector's quality procedures, work on the construction site will stop until the engineer resolves the issue.

The HRSG pressure part modules are one of the key determinants of constructability. The number and type of module selected has a significant impact on the labor required for construction. In general, larger modules with the highest degree of shop content will decrease field labor requirements but increase the need for equipment, such as cranes and lifting gear. At sites where labor costs are low, equipment usually is less available, and the preference is for small, lightweight modules.

Figure 3-77 | Heat recovery steam generator pressure part bundles

Figure 3-78 | Heat recovery steam generator pressure part modules

In contrast, locations with high labor costs usually can provide equipment for lifting and prefer the largest, heaviest, most shop-assembled modules that can be economically transported. A range of options is available for pressure part modules. The same HRSG can have pressure parts shipped in 20 ton bundles (*Fig. 3-77*), 200 ton modules (*Fig. 3-78*), 300 ton modules with integral structure called "C-Frames" (*Fig. 3-79*), or 2,500 ton, complete boilers (*Fig. 3-80*).

Preferences for other HRSG components, such as stacks, inlet ducts, outlet ducts, and platforms, are similar, with the degree of shop fabrication being proportional to the cost of field labor and equipment availability. At locations with extremely high labor costs, usually metropolitan areas, the designer is challenged to consider shipping and construction loads associated with moving complete components. For example, a stack measuring 23 ft (7 m) in diameter and 260 ft (80 m) in height and weighing hundreds of tons may be shipped in one piece.

ESSENTIAL COMPONENTS

Duct Burner System

Temperature limits at the gas turbine inlet force the turbine to use excess air, above the optimal stoichiometric ratio to burn the fuel. The excess oxygen may be used for supplementary firing of fuel gas after the gas turbine to increase flow or temperature of the steam generated. Supplementary burners also are called "duct burners," since they are located either in the inlet duct or in the interbank duct after the superheater section. The duct burners in HRSGs typically use natural gas as fuel, but they also may fire oil.

The duct burner consists of burner elements designed to withstand flue gas temperatures and typically are made of stainless steel. The number of burner elements is dependent on firing capacity and the duct dimension. Each burner element comes equipped with flame stabilizers or baffles to ensure that proper flame length is maintained. The duct burner assembly consists of the following equipment:

- Natural gas distribution header that distributes fuel to burner elements.
- Pneumatically actuated fuel shutoff valves, one per natural gas burner element. These valves are used to provide automatic isolation of any element upon loss of flame, without affecting the remaining elements. These valves also prevent condensation in the gas lines from the water vapor contained in the turbine exhaust.
- Flame scanner blowers and cooling air distribution header and piping.
- Ultraviolet flame scanners for each element.
- High-stability, spark-ignited gas pilot for each element.
- Pilot gas distribution header.
- Fuel skid, consisting of the control valve, safety valves, shutoff valves, and instrumentation for the fuel gas and pilot gas system.
- Burner Management System, which is equipped to cope with all burner safety signals and to provide an interface with the DCS.

Figure 3-79 | Heat recovery steam generator pressure part C-Frame modules

Figure 3-80 | Complete heat recovery steam generator shipped

Control of Gas Bypass

Gas bypass plays a significant—and detrimental—role in heat recovery efficiency and overall boiler performance. Gaps are designed into HRSGs to permit free thermal expansion of hot parts. Therefore, gas turbine exhaust gas also has an opportunity to bypass the heat-transfer tubing by following the gaps and exiting the stack at high temperature. For optimized performance, the HRSG employs a complex system of flow baffles to ensure that turbine exhaust gas is directed over the finned tubes. Only a complete baffle installation can ensure overall system integrity.

These baffles must address leakage at sidewalls, between side-by-side modules, above upper headers and below lower headers, and in gaps between headers.

Tube Supports

Finned tubes are held in place by passing them through tube restraints located at several elevations vertically in the boiler. Tube restraints are sized to the specific diameter of the finned tube. The restraints serve to restrict lateral movement of the tubes and to limit vibrations induced by exhaust gas flow. Vortices are produced at regular frequencies, depending on the gas properties and velocity at each tube row, when the gas turbine exhaust flows over the finned tubes. The resulting differential pressure loads excite the finned tubes. If the excitation frequency is close to a natural frequency of the tubes, destructive vibrations will occur. Tube restraints are located such that the first natural frequency of the tubes is significantly higher than the vortex shedding frequency. Tube restraints are designed according to the mechanical loading placed on them, and materials are selected based on the local exhaust gas temperature. The tube restraining system also includes restraint stops, which coincide with main column locations in the HRSG steel structure. In so doing, seismic loads from the finned tubes are transferred to the main steel at the tube restraint elevations. *Figure 3-81* illustrates a typical HRSG tube restraint.

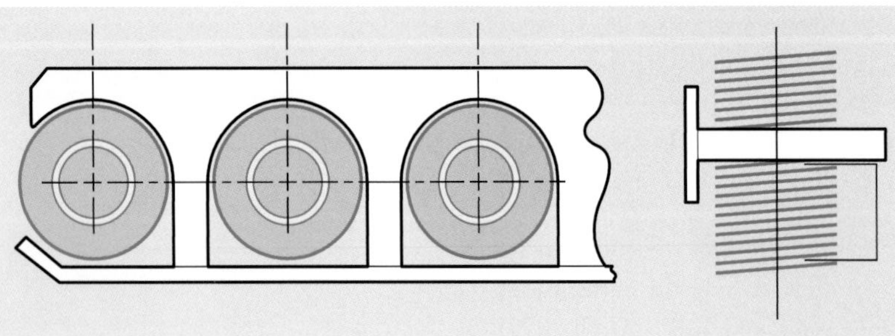

Figure 3-81 | Heat recovery steam generator tube restraint

HRSG Structure

The steel structure consists of two main sections: the inlet duct and the HRSG. Each section is made up of a series of parallel steel moment frames connected together by a continuous, ¼ inch (6 mm) thick steel duct casing. A substantial portion of the pressure part mass is supported at the roof elevation. The steel frames serve as the vertical load carrying system. Occasional loads, wind and seismic, are resisted by moment frames and casing plate in transverse and gas flow directions, respectively. Internal and external HRSG components are attached to wide flange roof beams, which are then supported by wide flange columns that bear on a foundation system.

Cold Casing Design

The HRSG incorporates "cold casing" construction. Internal insulation is selected to ensure the external casing has a typical surface temperature of 140°F (60°C), allowing the use of carbon steel casing plate and stiffeners and minimizing the need for expansion provisions for the overall boiler structure. Insulation materials are selected for low casing temperature, safe and efficient operation, and minimum maintenance. The floor of the HRSG is sloped, has drains, and insulation suitable for water washing.

An internal liner is utilized at the internal surface of the insulation to protect it from gas flow. Liner plates are segmented for free thermal expansion. They are overlapped in the direction of gas flow in turbulent areas near the gas turbine to prevent the gas from lifting the liner sheet away from the HRSG casing. Liner materials are selected based on local gas temperatures and flue gas flow conditions.

Liner plates are supported by studs protruding through oversize holes in the liner. On the gas side, the liner is secured with an oversize washer welded to the stud. Sound construction includes studs welded to the inside of the casing plate. An insulating blanket is laid out on the inside surface of the casing and held in place with wire insulation pins. An oversize washer is placed on the stud under the liner. Compression of the insulation is limited by the stud. *Figure 3-82* shows a cross-sectional view of duct casing.

Acoustic Resonance

Acoustic resonance occurs when the frequency of vortex shedding within a tube bank coincides with the frequency of an acoustic standing wave in the HRSG. Acoustic resonance causes high-intensity sound, at low frequencies, which is not attenuated by conventional silencers installed in the stack. Acoustic baffles eliminate resonance. Baffles are placed parallel to the main flow direction and perpendicular to the acoustic standing wave. *Figure 3-83* illustrates a representative position of baffles in a typical HRSG. The most important characteristic of a baffle is that it should have limited "open area," through which acoustic pressure can be transmitted. Good acoustic performance generally is ensured if the baffle meets mechanical design considerations and constraints as follows:

- Adequate service life at high temperature
- Thermal distortion
- Vibration and wear

Noise Abatement

In certain circumstances, the HRSG can itself be a generator of noise (see Acoustic Resonance discussed previously). For the most part, however, the noise attributed to a combined cycle power plant is caused by the sound power emanating from the gas turbine via the exhaust. As a result, measures must be taken in the HRSG design and ducting system for noise abatement.

Gas path silencing equipment includes silencers installed in inlet ductwork (rarely applied to gas turbines in the 150 to 260 MWe range), outlet ductwork, or HRSG exhaust

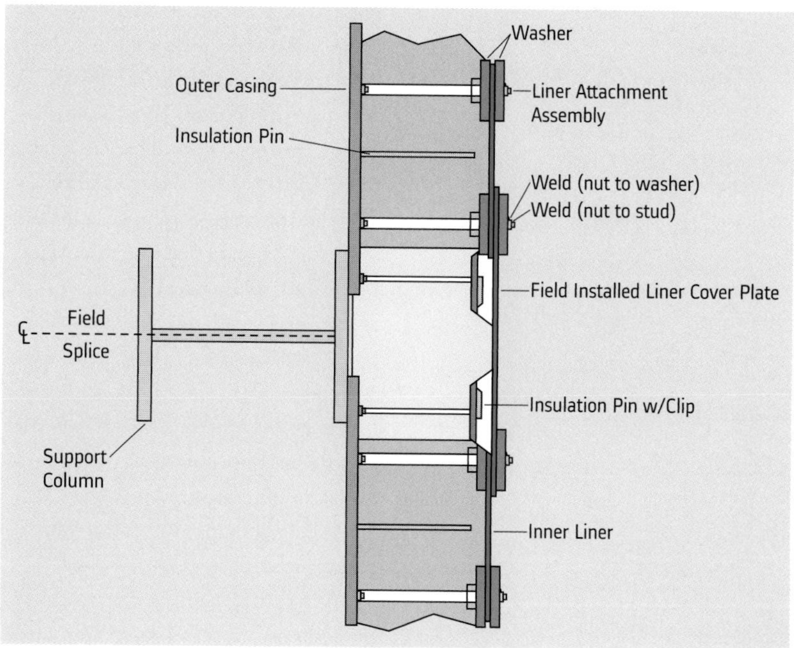

Figure 3-82 | Cross sectional view of heat recovery steam generator cold casing design

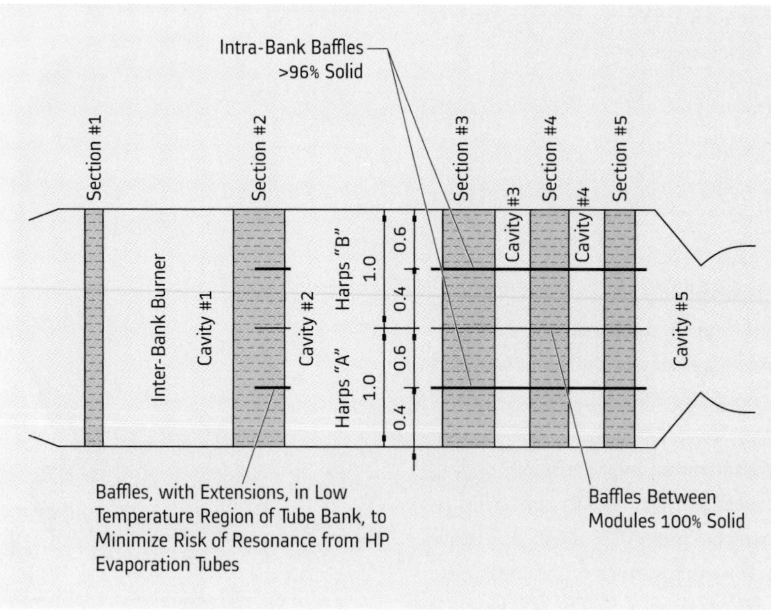

Figure 3-83 | Acoustic baffle positioning

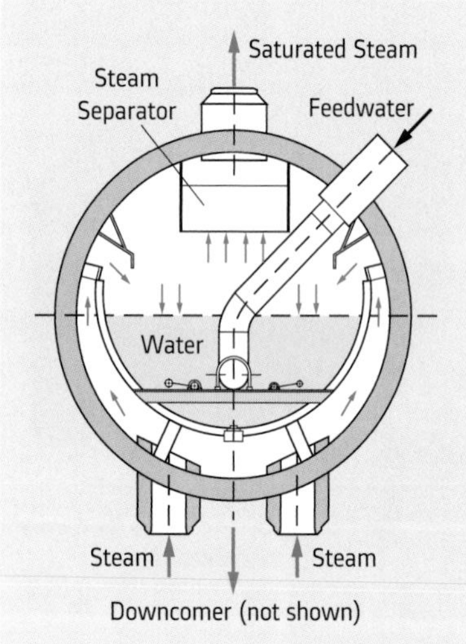

Figure 3-84 | Typical heat recovery steam generator drum arrangement

stack. These silencers are effective at attenuating noise in the exhaust gas of the HRSG system. Noise emanating from HRSG walls is addressed via duct design or shrouding. Adding mass to duct walls can attenuate noise and usually is accomplished by increasing the thickness of the external casing plate. To a greater extent, however, shrouds are employed to attenuate wall noise from HRSGs. Typically, shrouds can be designed as side-wall shrouds that use existing HRSG structural steel for support or as full, free-standing enclosures that effectively cover the HRSG sidewalls and roof.

Aside from gas turbine exhaust, the HRSG designer also must consider a number of intermittent noise sources, including start-up vents, safety valve exhaust systems, pumps, and other operating equipment. Vents typically are addressed with commercially available silencing equipment, sized for the specific flow, pressure, and temperature conditions of the application. Pumps and other operating equipment generally are addressed as well by local means, including, but not limited to, sound barriers and enclosures.

Drums

HRSG evaporative circuits incorporate steam drums, which ensure steam purity and reduce the potential for water surges encountered during cold starts. *Figure 3-84* shows a typical drum arrangement. On the water side, incoming feedwater is distributed along the length of the drum by a feedwater distribution header. Nozzles in the distribution header direct the feedwater in the downward direction to minimize turbulence and aid in circulation. The water in the drum is then directed to downcomers.

On the steam side, the saturated steam–water mixture from the evaporative circuit enters the drum through risers and is directed through separation devices and dryers to remove the water from the steam. Dry saturated steam leaves the drum exiting through saturated steam outlets located on the top of the drum.

Other aspects of drums include:

- **Construction:** The drum is fusion welded, fabricated from carbon steel plate, and equipped with two manway openings, one at each end of the drum.
- **Downcomers:** Dedicated external downcomers are used for proper circulation in the evaporative steam generating sections.
- **Safety Valves:** The drum is fitted with safety valves, each rated at a percentage of the drum's design evaporation rate as required by boiler design code.

- **Internals:** The steam drum includes baffles and commercially available mist/vane separators to achieve required steam purity.
- **Connections:** Typical connections on the steam drums include steam outlet, feed inlet, riser and downcomer, vents, safety valves, blowdown, pressure measurement, water columns, chemical feed, and nitrogen blanketing.

Desuperheaters

Spray-type desuperheaters are used to control steam temperature in HRSG superheater and reheater steam circuits. Spray water is taken from the appropriate feed pump discharge or economizer outlet, depending on the potential for thermal shock in the spray system. A typical desuperheating system includes the necessary control valve, piping, isolation and check valves, and control temperature indicators. A spray-type desuperheater employs water as a medium for cooling superheated steam. Water is sprayed directly into the steam flow, adjusting the steam temperature. A replaceable liner is installed for protection against erosion and thermal shocking of the desuperheater that would otherwise occur with intermittent desuperheater spray. Spray water desuperheaters must utilize boiler feedwater-quality water because of the location of the device in the steam circuitry. By design, the desuperheater is located within the steam piping system to ensure sufficient time for evaporation of the spray water over the control range of the unit before the steam reaches the steam turbine (for exit-stage installations) or the superheat/reheat elements (for inter-stage installations). *Figure 3-85* illustrates a typical desuperheating installation.

Ductwork

The HRSG consists of two major duct sections:

1. The HRSG inlet transition duct from the outlet flange of the gas turbine expansion joint to the first row of tubes (the inlet duct).
2. The HRSG outlet transition duct from the last row of tubes to the opening in the exhaust stack (the breech).

Inlet ducts of HRSGs (*Fig. 3-86*) typically diverge rapidly in the vertical direction between the gas turbine and first row of tubes. Often, the inlet duct also diverges in the horizontal direction, but at a much smaller angle. It is desirable to make the inlet duct as short as possible, both to minimize cost and space requirements and to eliminate dead air space, where purge procedures

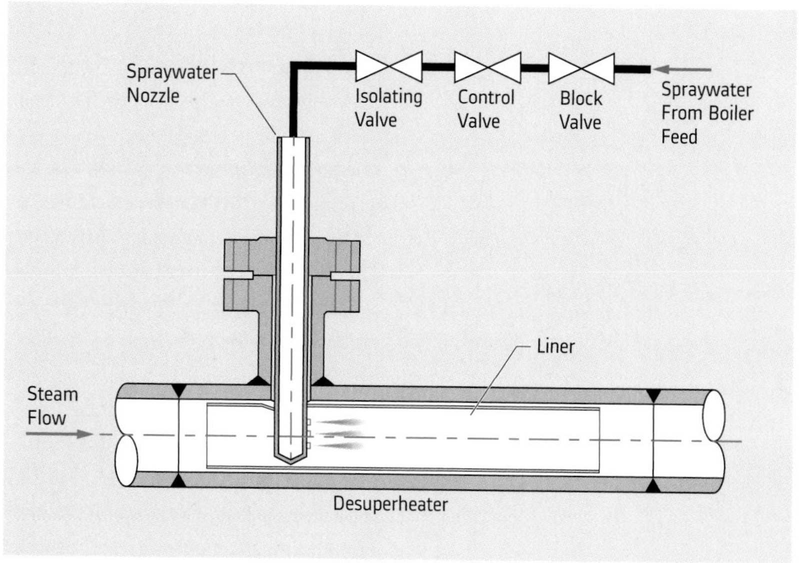

Figure 3-85 | Desuperheater

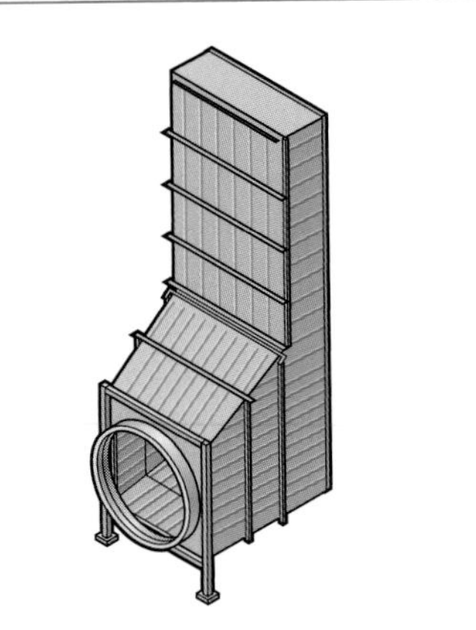

Figure 3-86 | Compact heat recovery steam generator inlet duct

may not remove undesirable gases. It also is required that the flow entering the HRSG be as uniform as possible to ensure good thermal performance. The inlet ductwork is fabricated as shop-assembled panels consisting of a carbon steel outer casing, insulation, and internal liner. Design and fabrication is similar to that of the casing panels.

The outlet duct serves as the transition from the HRSG to the exhaust stack. The typical geometry is a reducing cross section as the exhaust gas makes the turn from horizontal to vertical, coupled with a geometry change from rectangular cross section (HRSG) to a circular cross section (exhaust stack). *Figure 3-87* shows a representative outlet duct. The ductwork from the HRSG to the stack is carbon steel casing, reinforced with stiffeners, provided with expanded metal standoffs for personnel protection from the hot surfaces. The ductwork is complete with necessary doors and expansion joints. Internal insulation and liners are not typically used in outlet ductwork, because exhaust gas temperature typically is 212 to 300°F (100 to 150°C) when it enters the outlet duct.

Steel Stack

The final component in the exhaust gas system of the HRSG, the stack directs turbine exhaust gas to the atmosphere. The stack is the primary location for emissions compliance testing and validation. *Figure 3-88* shows a typical HRSG stack.

Stacks are configured as straight cylinders, with typical heights from 130 to 200 ft (40 to 60 m) for HRSG applications. Stack height is largely dependent on air permit requirements for release of exhaust gas to the atmosphere. For large HRSG installations, stack diameters range from 20 to 23 ft (6 to 7 m). Diameter, too, is dependent on air permit requirements but also includes consideration for velocity and draft loss as critical design inputs. Typically, HRSG stacks are fabricated from carbon steel, because operating temperatures range from 212 to 300°F (100 to 150°C), with operating pressures in the range of 2″ WG to 4.8″ WG (5 to 12 mbar). The stack is bottom supported from its base using a series of anchor bolts around a stiffened base ring. The stack is not normally insulated, but insulation can be used in cold environments or where corrosion may be a concern.

Stacks may include a variety of additional equipment:

- **Silencer:** Reduces gas turbine exhaust noise to acceptable levels
- **Damper:** Provides protection for internal parts during unit standstill periods
- **Platforms:** Provides access to emission testing locations
- **Access doors:** Provides access to the HRSG or damper
- **Trolley:** Can be used for painting trolleys or other accessibility devices

EMISSIONS REDUCTION

Selective Catalytic Reduction (SCR) Process

The process of SCR involves the catalytic reaction of ammonia (NH_3), which is injected into the flue gas containing NOx to produce molecular nitrogen (N_2) and water vapor (H_2O). These reactions take place on the SCR catalyst, which is coated with vanadium oxides as the catalytic agent. The SCR catalyst is housed in the HRSG casing, where the flue gas temperatures ranges between 500 and 700°F (260 and 370°C). The reaction depends primarily on available active sites (a function of geometric surface area, pore volume, and concentration of active catalyst component), flue gas temperature, and reducing agent concentration (see Chapter 5).

The primary reactions describing the process are:

$$4NO + 4NH_3 + O_2 \rightarrow 4N_2 + 6H_2O$$
$$NO + NO_2 + 2NH_3 \rightarrow 2N_2 + 3H_2O$$
$$6NO_2 + 8NH_3 \rightarrow 7N_2 + 12H_2O$$

Equation 3-6

The first reaction is the predominant reaction. It shows that one mole of ammonia is consumed for each mole of NO removed. In an actual system, however, slightly more ammonia is injected than necessary for the desired NO removal (to account for imperfect mixing). The excess ammonia, which passes through the catalyst bed non-reacted, is called "ammonia slip." A well-balanced process will maintain appropriate output levels of residual NOx and NH_3. The SCR is designed to provide an outlet NOx concentration set point. Three reducing agent forms can be used in the SCR system:

- Anhydrous Ammonia
- Aqueous Ammonia
- Urea

The most commonly used reducing agent form in HRSG applications is aqueous ammonia.

An aqueous ammonia-based SCR system typically consists of the following components in addition to the catalyst:

1. **Storage and Handling System.**
2. **Ammonia Flow Control Unit:** The ammonia flow control unit regulates the amount of reagent (ammonia) to the system, properly dilutes the ammonia for injection into the system, and vaporizes the ammonia if necessary. The ammonia flow control unit skid consists of the following:
   a. **Centrifugal Blowers:** Blowers are designed to provide sufficient air to deliver the ammonia in proper concentration for the optimum reaction without ammonia slip.
   b. **Vaporizer:** The vaporizer consists of heaters that heat the dilution air, which in turn vaporizes the aqueous ammonia for injection into the flue gases.
   c. **Control Skid:** The control skid consists of instrumentation and valves to control ammonia injection into the flue gases.
3. **Ammonia Injection Grid:** The air–water vapor–ammonia mixture is sprayed into the flue gases using an arrangement of nozzles to ensure even distribution throughout the flue gas. Insufficient mixing of ammonia in flue gas results in higher ammonia slip.

CO Catalyst

Catalytic oxidation is a process using precious metal to combine CO with oxygen to form CO_2. The gas turbine's exhaust stream is directed into the catalytic oxidizer, and when the CO molecules in the stream hit a catalyst site, the oxygen and carbon bonds are

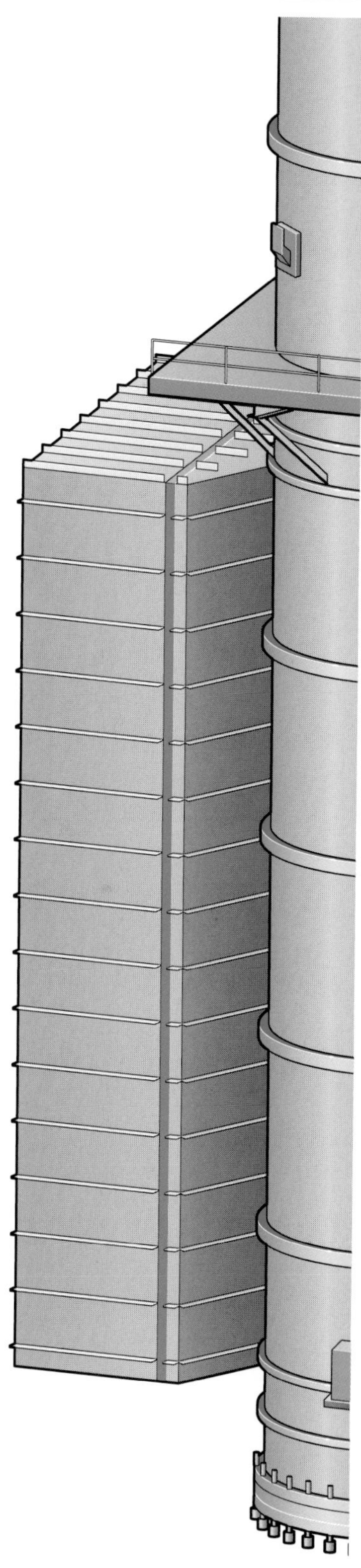

Figure 3-87 | Heat recovery steam generator outlet duct

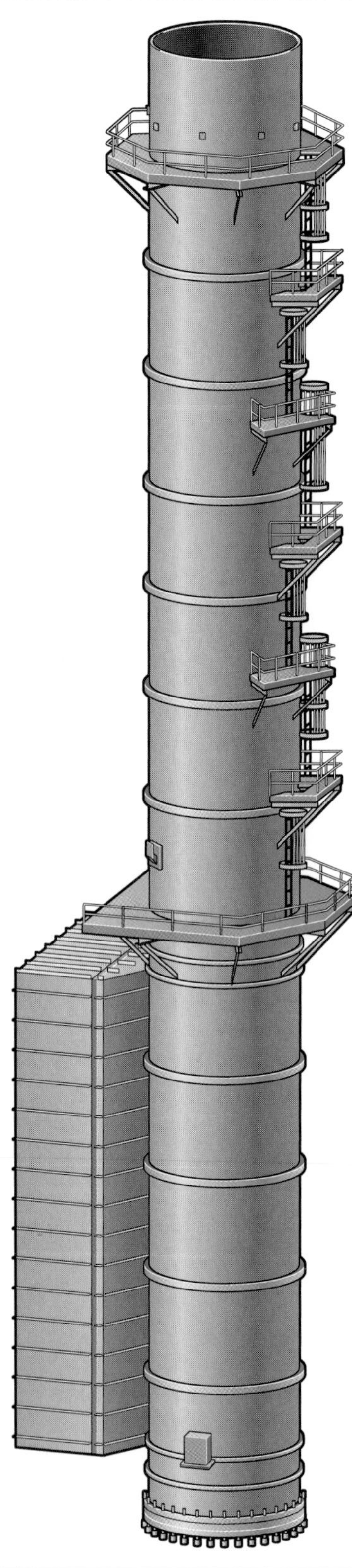

Figure 3-88 | Heat recovery steam generator steel stack

broken, allowing the free atoms to recombine, forming CO_2:

$$2CO + O_2 \rightarrow 2CO_2$$

Equation 3-7

The catalyst is composed of stainless-steel foil substrate, which is corrugated and coated with alumina wash coat. The wash coat is impregnated with platinum group metals. The catalyzed foil is folded and encased in welded steel frames to form individual modules weighing approximately 44 lb (20 kg). The individual CO catalyst modules are installed in the frame structure within the HRSG casing. The CO catalyst frame is installed in the HRSG inter-bank upstream of the SCR catalyst, where the flue gas temperature is predicted to be between 500 and 1,000°F (260 and 540°C) for maximum efficiency of CO destruction.

FUTURE TRENDS

Gas-fired combined cycle technology is available now for base load, for peaking, and as a bridge between the older, coal-fired steam plants of the past and the high-efficiency, coal-fired plants of the future designed with CO_2 capture and sequestration as an essential consideration. For the near term, the dominant technologies for production of electricity that will support reduced CO_2 emissions will be nuclear, gas-fired combined cycle, large-scale wind farms, and solar applications. Continued technical advancement of utility-scale gas turbines will drive increasingly efficient combined cycles. For the HRSG, this means that exhaust gas flows will increase, requiring larger boilers. Steam cycle parameters also will increase, requiring higher steam temperatures and pressures from the HP section of the HRSG.

The HRSGs operating at higher pressures (2,300–3,200 psi [160–220 bar]), requiring that the HP evaporator be based on once-through circulation principles, are an emerging trend. Higher steam temperatures (1,100–1,160°F [600–625°C]) will require use of the same high-strength alloys that are currently being developed for advanced, supercritical, coal-fired boilers. The combined cycle plant will continue to support a range of load applications and often will be required to cycle on and off daily as well as to support grid frequency with rapid-response loading characteristics. The mechanical design of HRSGs must continue to evolve to improve fatigue tolerance, even as the size, temperature, and pressure of the boiler continues to increase.

KEVIN TAUGHER
GEORGE STAMATELOPOULOS
SCOTT DARLING
GLENN SELBY
DONALD BAIRLEY
JESSE BOLINGER
DENIS BRUNO
MARK MALO
THOMAS MASTRONARDE
EDWARD ORTMAN
HARPREET SINGH
CHARLES TSIROVASILES
ANISA BROWN

REFERENCES

1. Combustion Engineering, Inc.,"TVA Utility AFBC Project, Phase II, Final Report: Volume 1—200-MW Demonstration Plant Final Design; Volume 2—800-MW Commercial Plant, Proposed Design and AFBC Research and Development Requirements"; prepared under TVA Contract 51863A, January 18, 1981. Windsor, CT: Combustion Engineering, 1981.

2. S. L. Goodstine et al.,"Industrial Application of Fluidized Bed Combustion, Phase 1, Task 4—Sub-Scale Unit Testing and Data Analysis, Final Report, Volume 1," prepared for the U.S. Department of Energy under Contract EX-76-C-01-2473, December 1979; published by the U.S. Department of Energy (NTIS) DOE/ET10389-T3.

3. D. Kuni and O. Levenspiel, *Fluidization Engineering*. Malabar, FL: Robert E. Krieger Publishing Co., Inc., 1969.

4. B. Lecker and L.-E. Amand,"Emissions from a Circulating and a Stationary Fluidized Bed Boiler: A Comparison," *Proceedings of the Ninth International Conference on Fluidized Bed Combustion*, Boston, MA, May 4–7, 1987.

5. E. J. Gottung et al.,"Design Considerations for Circulating Fluidized Bed Steam Generators," *Proceedings of the Tenth International Conference on Fluidized Bed Combustion*, San Francisco, CA, May 1–4, 1989.

Steam Turbines for Electric Power Generation

Chapter **Four**

The first demonstration of a steam turbine was the Hero engine, which was developed as a novelty. Although first invented two millenia ago, useful application of the steam turbine did not occur until the nineteenth century, with the work by pioneers such as Gustav Delaval and Charles Parsons.

Steam turbines evolved at the end of the nineteenth century as the most common prime mover in the generation of electricity. Steam turbines also commonly are used for marine propulsion, industrial drives, and large pump drives. Because Alstom provides steam turbines primarily for generation of electric power, this chapter focuses principally on this application.

Steam turbines convert the heat energy from steam into mechanical energy. The source of heat to generate the steam is irrelevant to the steam turbine, making these turbines applicable to almost any fuel source. Heat sources range from coal, biomass, solar, nuclear, natural gas, and combustion turbine exhaust (combined cycle) to waste products.

The steam turbine has many advantages for electric power generation. Because turbines favor relatively high speeds, they are suitable for direct drive of alternating current (AC) generators. High speeds also allow large flows and result in a relatively compact generating device—the steam turbine generator. Therefore, the steam turbine generator is the preferred generating device for central station applications.

In addition to electric power generation, steam turbines play an important role in the supply of steam and heat for industrial and district heating applications. By passing steam through the steam turbine and then using the exhaust steam for other applications, both steam and electricity are cogenerated, resulting in very efficient use of energy.

THE BASICS

The steam turbine converts moving steam to mechanical energy aerodynamically, through a circular arrangement of stationary and rotating airfoils (blades) as shown in *Figure 4-1*. Each stationary and rotating row set is called a "stage." The stationary blades direct the steam into the rotating blades. Lift on the rotating blades turns the rotor and generates power. A bladed rotor is shown in *Figure 4-2*.

From humble beginnings as a desktop novelty, modern turbines have grown to sizes of up to 1,600 MW or more for nuclear applications. Fossil fuel applications of up to 1,300 MW are operating in North America. These machines may be more than 100 ft in length and weigh thousands of tons. Large machines typically consist of multiple casings (modules) arranged on a single shaft (tandem compound) connected directly to a generator. Less common turbo sets consist of multiple shafts driving one or more generators (cross compound). *Figure 4-3* shows an example of a tandem compound steam turbine. A typical utility reheat turbine would consist of a high-pressure (HP) section, an intermediate-pressure (IP) section, and one or more low-pressure (LP) sections (*Fig. 4-4*).

Because utility turbines typically are connected directly to the generator, their speed is governed by the

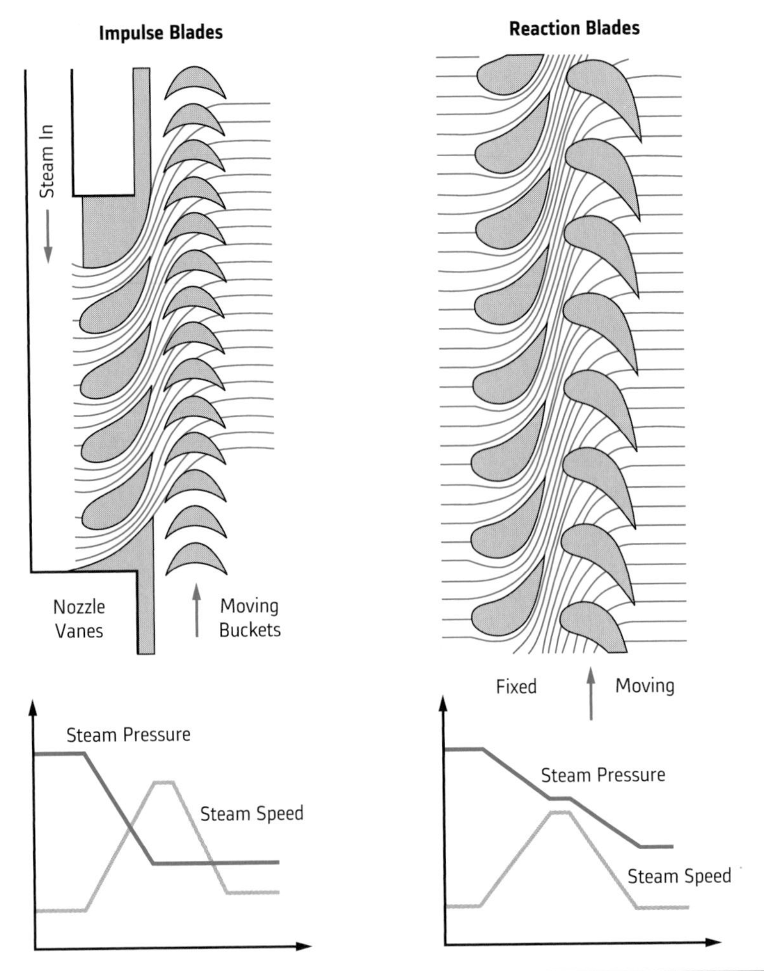

Figure 4-1 | Steam flow through stationary and rotating blades

Figure 4-2 | Bladed rotor

frequency of the grid on which they operate. Modern fossil fuel units of larger than 100 MW operate at 3,600 rpm in 60-Hz applications and 3,000 rpm in 50-Hz applications. Because of their large size, nuclear units typically drive four pole generators that operate at 1,800 and 1,500 rpm (i.e.,"half-speed") for 60- and 50-Hz applications, respectively. Some small industrial generation units drive the generator through a reduction gear, allowing them to operate at higher speeds. Most units are limited to ±5% of their nominal speed and, hence, are not interchangeable between 50- and 60-Hz applications.

STEAM TURBINE THERMODYNAMICS

Steam plants operate on the Rankine cycle (see Chapter 1). The ideal Rankine cycle is a closed loop consisting of (a) isentropic compression of liquid water (feedwater); (b) constant-pressure heating, boiling, and superheating of the liquid to steam; (c) isentropic expansion of the steam through the turbine; and (d) condensing of the exhaust steam to 100% liquid water (condensate), as shown in *Figure 4-5*. Heat is introduced into the cycle in Step b via a steam generator (boiler) and is rejected from the cycle in Step d via the condenser. Boiler pressure is generated by the boiler feed pump in Step a. Pressure is reduced in the turbine as it generates power.

Cycle efficiency in a power plant is influenced by the steam parameters (steam temperature and pressure), the cycle design, and the efficiency of the turbine. Advantages of the Rankine cycle are that the cycle efficiency is more affected by the former and less affected by the turbine efficiency itself.

Major parameters affecting cycle efficiency are:

1. Live (inlet) steam temperature and pressure
2. Reheat steam temperature and pressure (if applicable)
3. Final feedwater temperature
4. Number of feedwater heaters
5. Exhaust pressure
6. Exhaust annulus area
7. Steam path (blading) efficiency

These factors, along with other minor factors, will be discussed throughout this chapter.

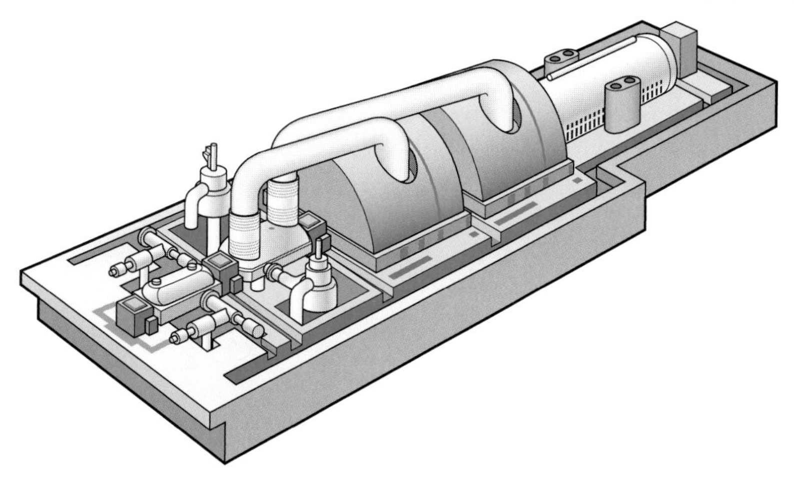

Figure 4-3 | Tandem compound turbine

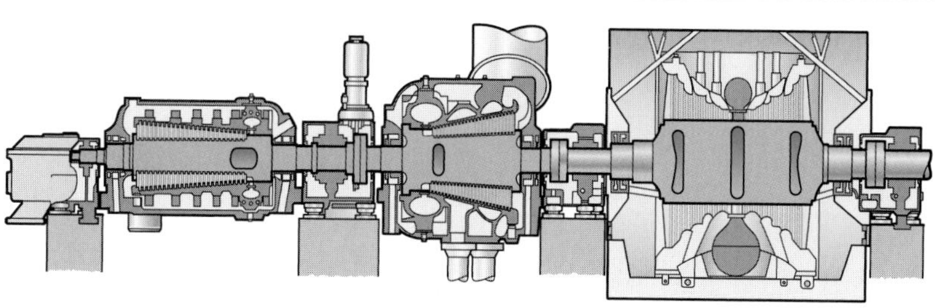

Figure 4-4 | Cross section of a typical reheat steam turbine

DEVELOPMENT OF THE MODERN STEAM CYCLE

Cycle efficiency is improved by increasing the length of the expansion line (Step c), as shown in *Figure 4-5*. This is accomplished by increasing the steam temperature and pressure (live steam) at the turbine inlet, by reducing the exhaust pressure at the condenser, or both. The inlet temperature and pressure are limited by the material properties of the casings, blading, and rotors. The temperature of the cooling medium (typically water) removing heat from the condenser determines the exhaust pressure.

During the 1920s and 1930s, power plant designers quickly determined that further efficiency could be gained through reducing the amount of heat rejected to the condenser by using steam extracted from the turbine to heat condensate/feedwater (regenerative heating). Effectively, regenerative heating reduces both the heat rejected to the condenser (i.e., lost to the cycle) and the heat required to bring feedwater to the boiling point. Steam extracted from the turbine is piped either to closed heat exchangers (where extracted steam and feedwater are kept separate) or to an open heater (where extracted steam and feedwater are mixed).

At 3,206.2 psia (22.106 MPa),no phase change between water and steam occurs. Therefore, no heat of evaporation is present above this pressure. Cycles with live steam pressures below this point are called "subcritical," and those with live steam pressures above this point are called "supercritical." This has a profound effect on the design and operation of the boiler, but there are no inherent conceptual design effects on the steam turbine other than the higher stresses.

During the 1950s and 1960s, live steam temperatures steadily increased to approximately 1,000°F (540°C) (*Fig. 4-6*). Designers effectively increased

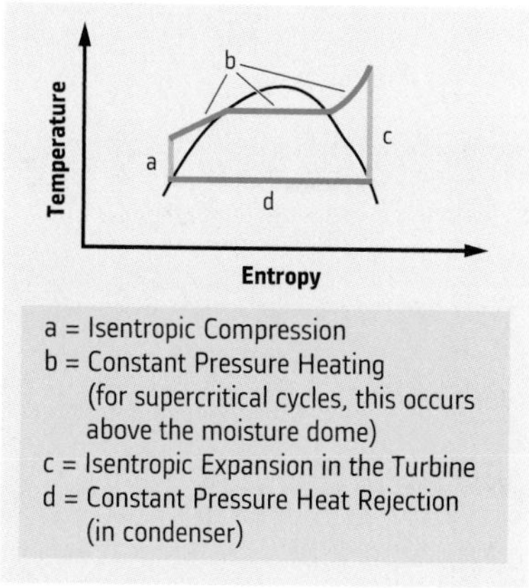

Figure 4-5 | Ideal Rankine cycle

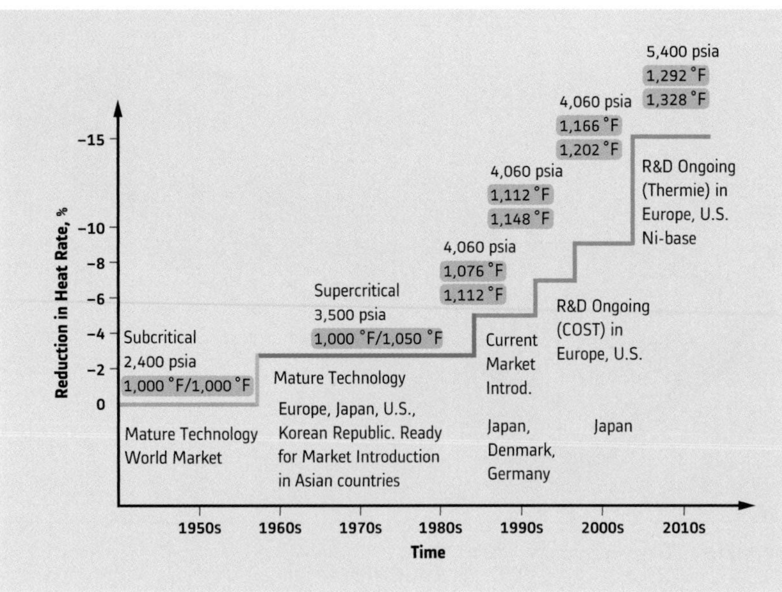

Figure 4-6 | Development of main steam temperatures and pressures for steam turbines (HR, Heat Rate)

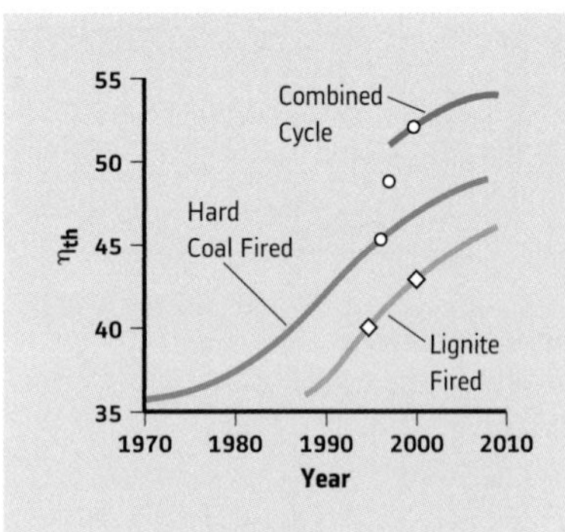

Figure 4-7 | Plant efficiency has improved significantly

the expansion line by reheating steam from the HP turbine exhaust before readmitting into the IP turbine. Reheating HP exhaust steam typically results in a 5% increase in cycle efficiency and has the benefit of reducing moisture in the LP turbine exhaust. By the end of the 1960s, typical subcritical cycles had inlet steam parameters of 2,415 psia and 1,000°F (16.65 MPa and 540°C) and reheat temperatures of 1,000°F (540°C). In the United States, these cycle parameters were typical of utility coal plants through the 1990s.

During the 1960s, supercritical and double reheat cycles also were introduced. Supercritical cycles had some acceptance in the United States but generally were used in Europe and Japan because of the higher efficiency. Double reheat units have been limited in application since that time, however, because of their higher capital costs and more complex operation.

STEAM CYCLES

STEAM CYCLES FOR COAL/FOSSIL FUEL APPLICATIONS

Live steam temperatures continue to increase with the development of advanced casing, blade, and rotor materials. Contemporary live and reheat steam temperatures for supercritical plants often exceed 1,100°F (595°C) for large (>500 MW) utility units. Development programs in Europe are expected to achieve inlet temperatures of 1,290°F (700°C). Materials studies in the United States are looking at 1,400°F (760°C). These advanced cycle parameters result in a steam cycle efficiency of greater than 50% and a plant efficiency of 48% (based on Lower Heating Value [LHV]) (*Fig. 4-7*).

For smaller units (<400 to 500 MW), the gains in efficiency for supercritical cycles are less than those for larger units. Traditionally, cycles for medium-sized units have remained subcritical. Increased temperatures of 1,050°F (565°C), however, are common.

Subcritical cycles typically have six or seven feedwater heaters, and supercritical cycles typically have seven or, more commonly, eight. If an extraction is taken from the HP turbine, this is known as a HARP (Heater Above Reheat Pressure) cycle. Typical final feedwater temperatures range from approximately 500°F (260°C) for small subcritical cycles to nearly 700°F (370°C) for some high-temperature, supercritical applications.

COMBINED CYCLE APPLICATIONS

During the 1980s and 1990s, development of larger, more efficient combustion turbines resulted in the common use of heat recovery steam generators and steam turbines to extract energy from the combustion turbine exhaust. In this way, plant cycle efficiencies approaching 60% (LHV) can be achieved.

Because ample low-grade energy is available in the exhaust stream of the combustion turbine, a combined cycle typically does not use regenerative heating (feedwater heating extraction). Conversely, the available low-grade energy can be used to generate additional IP and LP steam that can be admitted to the IP and LP turbine. As a result, a combined cycle steam turbine application may have 35% more mass flow at the LP exhaust compared with the HP inlet. A conventional boiler steam cycle may have 35% less steam flow at the LP exhaust because of feedwater heating extraction.

NON-REHEAT APPLICATIONS

For smaller industrial plants or other cycles with generally lower available steam temperatures, turbine inlet pressures are limited to approximately 2,000 psig (14 MPa(s)) because of the high moisture content (i.e., wetness) in the exhaust steam. Typically, these units are smaller and use lower steam parameters for ease of operation and reduced capital cost.

COMPONENT IMPACTS ON EFFICIENCY AND DESIGN

EFFECT OF EXHAUST PRESSURE

The turbine exhaust pressure (condenser pressure) profoundly affects both the cycle efficiency and the turbine component design. By lowering the exhaust pressure, more energy can be extracted from the steam. This results in less energy being rejected to the condenser and in a higher cycle efficiency. The variation of the design condenser pressure may be more significant than cycle changes from subcritical to supercritical steam parameters. By lowering the exhaust pressure, the expansion line of the steam extends further into the moisture zone, increasing the exhaust moisture. At lower pressure, the steam also has a much higher specific volume, so the LP turbine exhaust area must be much larger. Therefore, the LP turbine must be designed and sized to handle the volume flows for the design cycle. Aspects of the LP turbine component design will be discussed later.

BOILER FEED PUMP DRIVE (TURBINE OR ELECTRIC MOTOR)

Other associated cycle equipment also affects the cycle efficiency. The boiler feed pump drive can be a major plant load—in some cases, more than 40 MW (mechanical) for a large supercritical unit. Therefore, this drive must be carefully considered in the overall plant concept.

Boiler feed pumps are driven by either a turbine or an electric motor. Motor drives may be variable-speed, synchronous drives or conventional AC motors driving the pump through a variable hydraulic drive. Synchronous motors are more efficient than conventional AC but have higher capital cost. Electrical motors have advantages during facility start-up, provided that electric power is available. For smaller facilities, motor-driven drives are a less expensive solution than turbine drives. Because the motor requires electric power, however, the main generator must be larger.

Boiler feed pump turbine (BFPT) drives more commonly are used for large units. The BFPT is driven with steam extracted from the cold reheat (HP turbine exhaust) or from the IP turbine. With increasing load, more steam is available from the main turbine, matching the steam available with the steam required by the BFPT. Use of a BFPT reduces the LP steam flow, in turn reducing the exhaust losses in the LP turbine (exhaust losses will be discussed later), making the cycle more efficient. Because the BFPT drive does not require electric power, the generator can be smaller. For very large units, BFPT drives can be less expensive than motor drives.

REACTION/IMPULSE BLADING

The more detailed theory of blade type will not be discussed in this text, but some explanation regarding the impact of reaction and impulse blading is necessary for understanding steam turbine technology. By definition, a purely impulse stage has a pressure drop only across the stationary blade (sometimes called a "nozzle"). Pressure drop across the rotating blade (sometimes called a "bucket") is, by definition, zero. Impulse stages, as the name implies, rely only upon the transfer of momentum to the rotating element.

A purely reaction stage has an equal pressure drop across the stationary and rotating blade row. Energy is transferred by momentum transfer and by acceleration of the steam out of the rotating blade (also called a "nozzle effect").

Impulse blading generally is much heavier than reaction blading, and more energy can be extracted per stage from the steam. In practical terms, this means that fewer stages are required. Because of the higher pressure drop across the nozzle assembly (called a "diaphragm"), however, impulse stages require a reduced diameter at the stationary stage to reduce leakage. Additionally, a heavier root attachment is required to hold the heavier blade. *Figure 4-8* shows the relative difference between the types of blade technology.

Reaction blading generally is lighter but requires more stages. With reaction blading, a drum-type rotor can be used (*Fig. 4-9*), and both rotating and stationary blades can be directly mounted in T-slots in an inner casing or blade carrier. Because of the pressure drop across the rotating blades, substantial axial thrust is created on the rotor. Therefore, reaction turbines typically require a balance piston for single-flow sections.

Comparing the two technologies (impulse blading and reaction blading), both of which have been successfully employed for more than 100 years, usually is more theoretical than practical. To summarize, however, impulse technology requires fewer stages, which can result in a shorter section length. Reaction stages tend to have less leakage loss across each stage, but some leakage results from the balance piston.

Control stages (discussed below) utilize impulse technology. Downstream blading for Alstom designs typically use predominantly reaction

Typical Low Reaction (Impulse) Fixed & Rotating Blades

Fixed blade diaphragm

Typical Reaction Type Fixed & Rotating Blades

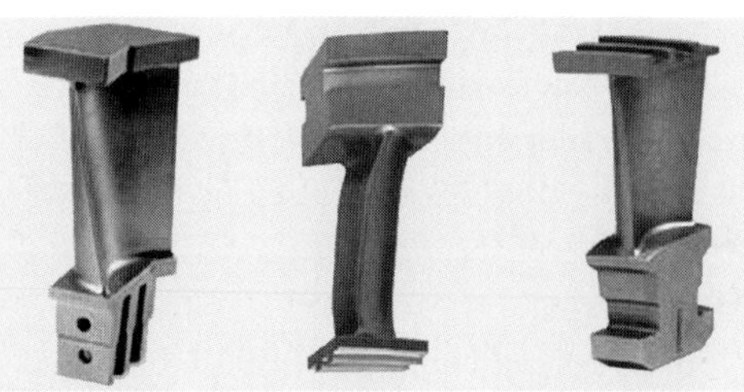

Rotating blade | Fixed blade | Rotating blade

Figure 4-8 | A typical impulse stage has a heavier stationary element (often a diaphragm assembly), whereas the reaction stage has similar profiles for both stages

blading for new equipment. Increasingly, however, blades through the steam path involve some component of both reaction and impulse technologies.

THREE-DIMENSIONAL BLADING

Early blade profiles were uniform throughout the length of the blade. With the evolution of three-dimensional modeling technology and multi-axis machining capability, the ability to manufacture blades with different curvature and profile at the root versus the tip became possible. Because the velocity at the tip is different than the velocity at the root, optimum performance can only be obtained by varying the profile along its length (*Fig. 4-10*). This is particularly important with lower-pressure blades, for which the greater blade length causes significant variations in blade velocity along the length of the blade.

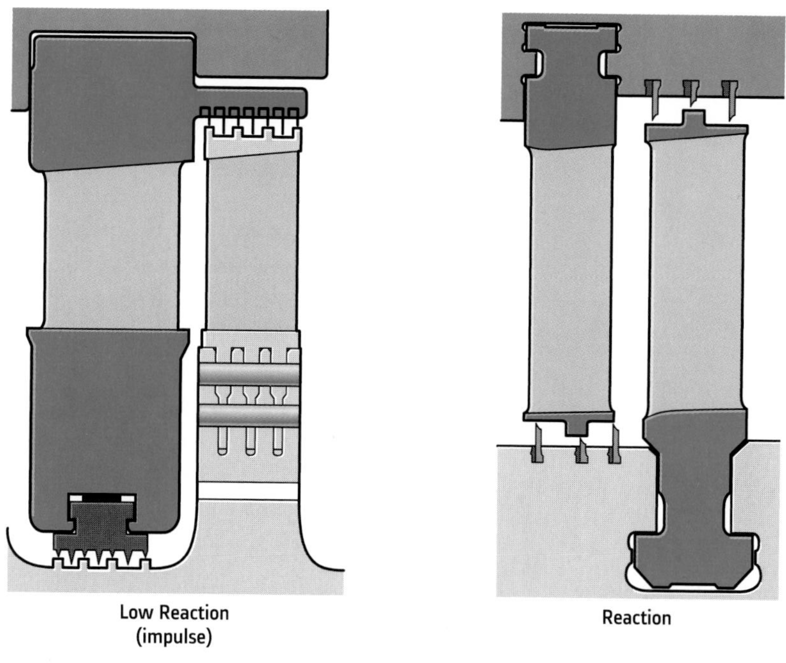

Figure 4-9 | Smaller reaction blades typically use a T-root attachment to secure the blade to the rotor

PARTIAL/FULL ARC ADMISSION

Steam flow into the turbine is controlled by throttling the steam with valves upstream of the HP turbine (live steam valves) and IP turbine (intercept valves) inlets. Both inlets have stop and control valves in series. Stop valves are used mainly to stop all steam flow into the turbine during normal shut down or emergency stops. Stop valves are fully open during normal operation. Control valves are used to control steam flow and, thus, the speed or load generated.

Intercept stop and control valves typically are left fully open during operation. Intercept control valves are only used during start-up and shutdown at very low loads. Contemporary designs use individually hydraulically actuated valves. Some older designs are mechanically actuated via cams and levers.

Live steam inlets to the steam turbine have two main configurations—full arc and partial arc. With full arc admission, steam is admitted to the entire circumference of the inlet annulus. For partial arc admission, steam is admitted into discrete arc segments of the inlet by sequentially opened control valves.

Full Arc Admission

With full arc admission, all steam entering the turbine is admitted around the entire first-stage inlet annulus. Control is accomplished through 1) lowering the pressure at the first row of blades, either by lowering the pressure from the boiler (typically via boiler feed pump control [i.e., sliding pressure]) or 2) throttling steam to a lower pressure through the control valves (i.e., constant pressure). Lowering this pressure naturally lowers the steam flow through the turbine and,

Figure 4-10 | A state-of-the-art, three-dimensionally designed blade varies in profile along its length, resulting in a twisted shape

thus, the output of the turbine. Sliding- and constant-pressure control modes will be discussed in more detail later.

Partial Arc Admission

By sequentially opening the control valves, steam can be admitted to only one arc segment of the turbine inlet annulus. At the inlet, only the blades being struck in areas where the valve is open will generate power. In this mode, it is possible to open some valves entirely, negating the pressure drop across that valve (i.e., no throttling), while other valves are completely closed. This maintains the steam velocity—and, thus, efficiency—across this stage. Partial arc admission requires the use of a control stage. The control stage uses impulse blades, so there is minimal pressure drop across the rotating blades. If a pressure drop were to occur across the control stage, the steam would tend to flow around the inlet annulus rather than where it is directed by the inlet nozzles when operating with only one inlet section open.

Comparing Partial Versus Full Arc Admission

Each mode has advantages shown in *Table 4-1*. Full arc admission designs not using a control stage result in a higher full load (valves wide open) efficiency. An improvement of approximately 0.2 to 0.5% in heat rate can be achieved compared to a typical control stage design. Full arc admission designs can be used with constant pressure. They are less efficient in this mode at part load, however, because all of the steam is throttled.

TABLE 4-1 | PARTIAL VERSUS FULL ARC ADMISSION

	Advantages	Disadvantages
Partial Arc (Nozzle Control)	No throttling across fully open valves when at part load Higher part load efficiency for subcritical cycles Faster response to step load changes	Lower efficiency of first stage Higher cost (more control valves)
Full Arc	Higher full load efficiency	Lower efficiency in throttle control mode

SLIDING- AND CONSTANT-PRESSURE OPERATION

Sliding- and constant-pressure operating modes refer to the pressure within the boiler. In the sliding-pressure mode, the pressure within the boiler is allowed to increase or decrease with load changes. Constant-pressure operation requires that the pressure within the boiler be kept constant. It also is possible to operate using both of these modes (hybrid operation).

In sliding-pressure operation, live steam pressure typically is maintained by a variable-speed, boiler feed pump drive (turbine or motor). The heat rate advantage here is that at lower loads, the boiler feed pump power requirements are substantially reduced. Most combined cycle and modern supercritical applications use sliding pressure. Because there is no need for partial arc control with sliding-pressure operation, these steam turbines do not normally have control stages.

Subcritical, drum-type boilers typically have constraints on the operating pressure of the boiler, so constant-pressure or hybrid operation is desired. In the United States, most older, subcritical fossil fuel units use constant-pressure operation in combination with partial arc admission. Often, however, larger, base load units have no control stage to achieve better full load performance.

In some cases, the turbine valves are operated partially closed to respond quickly to load increases and frequency control. The required step change capability will vary with electrical grid requirements. The difference between the valves wide open load and the operating load is called the "throttling margin." Without a control stage, all control valves open in parallel to admit more steam; with a control stage, control valves open sequentially. Sequential operation with partial arc admission gives a finer degree of control and, hence, better response. Residual energy in the boiler and piping provide the instantaneous energy for a step load change. At the new load point or for ramp load changes, steam pressure must be maintained by the boiler feed pump during this response.

Sequential operation also yields a series of valve points where all valves are either fully open or closed. Operation at the valve point is more efficient than at load points adjacent to it (*Fig. 4-11*). Therefore, operation at these points is desirable. If the valve points at a nominal pressure do not exactly match the load point, it is possible to slide the pressure down or up to obtain the flow necessary to achieve the desired output at the valve point (valves fully open or closed). This combined use of sequential valve control and sliding pressure is called "hybrid control." For units operating at a variety of load conditions, this may be the most efficient mode across the load range (see *Fig. 4-11*).

MECHANICAL DESIGN OF THE TURBINE

WELDED ROTORS

The rotors of Alstom steam turbines (and gas turbines) typically are built from forged disks that are welded together using a combination of the gas tungsten arc and submerged arc welding procedures (*Fig. 4-12*). After welding, the shafts are stress relieved under controlled temperature conditions.

The resulting rotor is a robust, drum-type rotor. Stresses at the welds and throughout the rotor are low for this design compared with disk or mono-block designs. This allows the

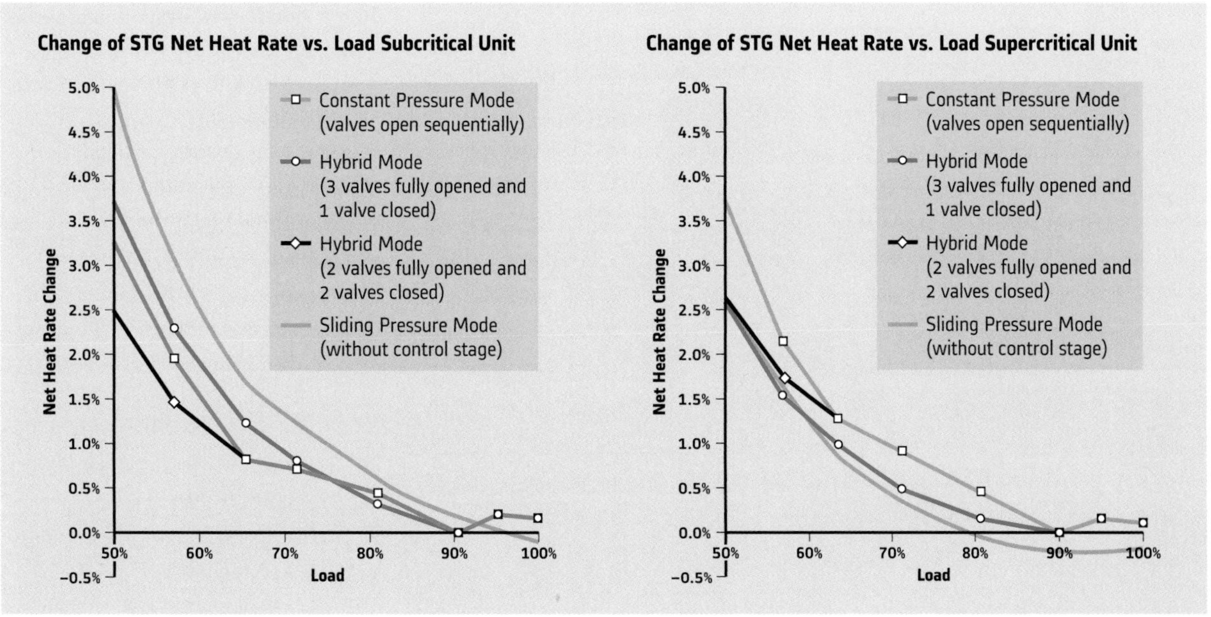

Figure 4-11 | Efficiency varies with turbine inlet configuration and valve operation. Maximum efficiency occurs at the valve points (STG; steam turbine generator)

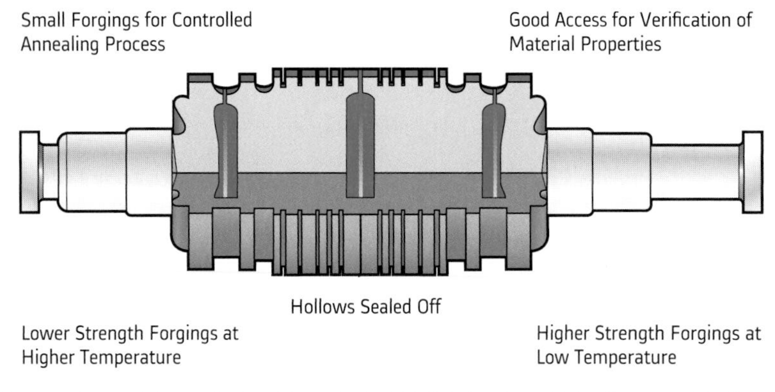

Figure 4-12 | Welded rotors are constructed of separate disks

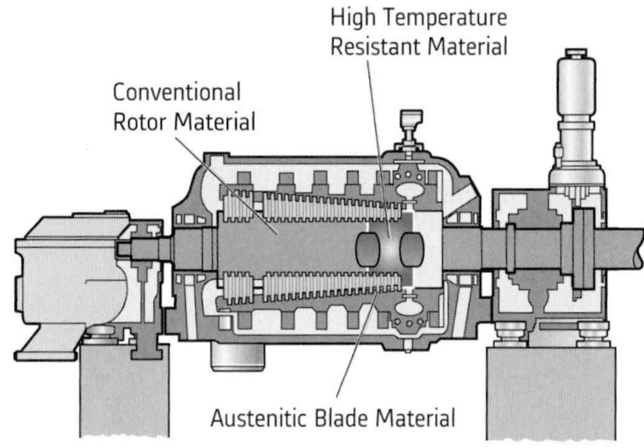

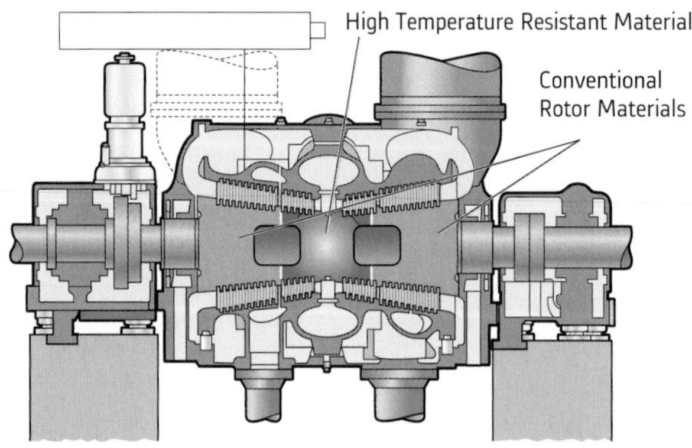

Figure 4-13 | Welded rotors can be assembled from different alloys to match the material needs required at specific locations

use of low-carbon steels, which are not susceptible to stress corrosion cracking. This is a major improvement over other mono-block or shrunk-on disk designs.

With the development of higher live and reheat steam temperatures, it is possible to assemble the rotor from different materials so that high-temperature materials are used only where required, as shown in *Figure 4-13*. This optimizes the use of appropriate materials throughout the rotor.

Thousands of rotors have been welded in this manner since Alstom initiated this technique in 1929 for a plant in Japan. There has not been any case of rupture or comparable failure using this design. This high inherent safety is particularly important for nuclear power plants, with their extremely stringent safety requirements.

THE HP TURBINE

The HP section of the turbine expands the live steam from the boiler superheater outlet down to the reheat pressure (cold reheat), where it is piped back to the boiler reheater. The high temperatures and pressures combine to create high stresses in the blading, inlet valves, and inner casings. Because of the high pressures, thicker materials are required. Therefore, care must be taken to accommodate thermal stresses induced by transient loading conditions.

HP Turbine Shrink Rings

The HP turbine inner casings of Alstom reheat units are held together by 5 to 10 shrink rings rather than by large flanges and bolts (*Fig. 4-14*). To

erect the HP turbine, the rotor is first installed inside the inner casing halves. The shrink rings are then heated to approximately 400°F (200°C) using a ring burner (*Fig. 4-15*) and are subsequently slipped over the inner casing. After cooling, the shrinkage compresses the inner casing to hold it together.

Figure 4-16 compares the shrink ring design with a typical flanged design. The advantage of the shrink ring over a flanged design is principally in the elimination of the flange and associated bolts. A bolted casing varies in thickness around its circumference and, therefore, is subject to variable stresses during transients. This is significant for combined cycle or other load-following applications. A bolted casing, by design, has different portions of the casing in compression, bending, or tension. These variable stresses result in distortion (ovalization) because of high temperature creep over the life of the turbine. Resulting leakage can significantly affect performance. Because shrink rings maintain the inner casing in compression, no distortion occurs. This ensures long-term, leak-free operation under steady-state and transient operating conditions.

Additionally, reduced distortion makes reassembly after major overhauls easier. The use of ring burners and hydraulic jacks for assembling and dismantling the shrink rings enables rapid removal and refitting of the shrink rings during overhauls. The maintenance time required with the shrink ring connection is less than that with flange connections. It also is not necessary to return the HP casing to the manufacturer's workshop.

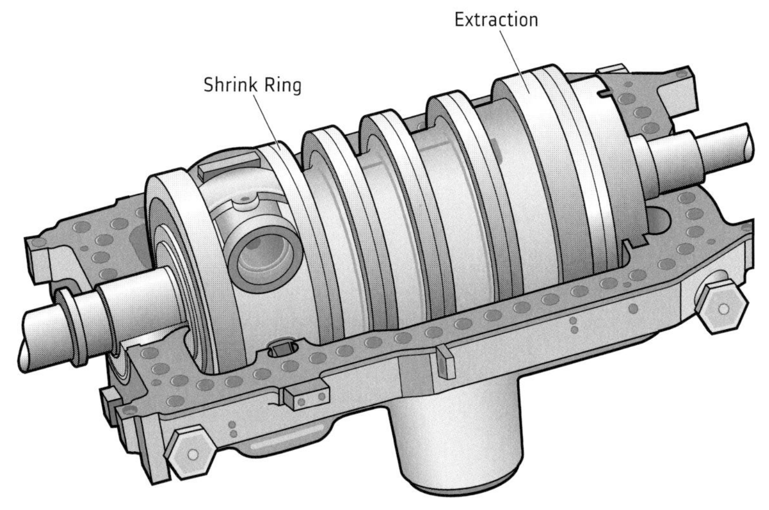

Figure 4-14 | High-pressure (HP) inner casings for Alstom HP turbines are held together with shrunk-on rings (shrink rings) as shown in this opened HP turbine. The HP extraction is possible via a hollow extraction shrink ring

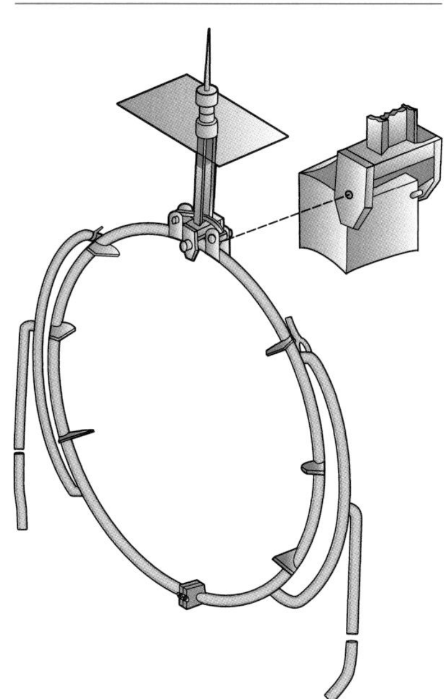

Figure 4-15 | Shrink rings are heated before installation with a ring burner. The rings shrink into place after installation

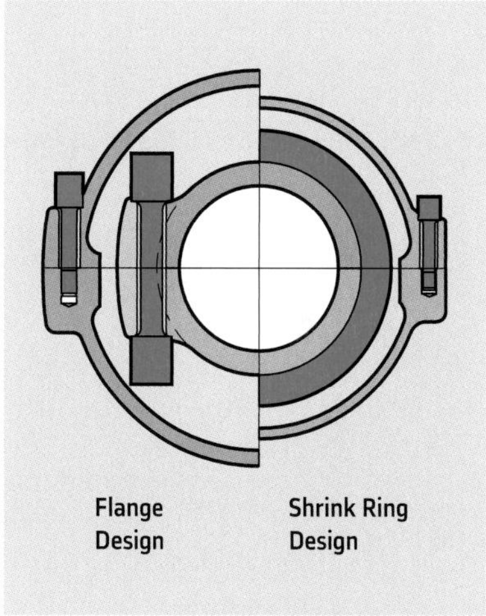

Figure 4-16 | Inner casings using shrink rings can be thinner, because the casing is entirely held in compression. Faster start-ups can therefore be accomplished

A summary of benefits of shrink ring design follows:

- Low stresses in flange area
- Rapid start-up and shutdown capability
- Stable operation during load changes
- Ideal for two-shift or load-following applications
- Simple dismantling and reassembly after major overhauls

Inlet Scrolls

The inlet duct of all turbine sections (HP, IP, and LP) consists of inlet scrolls. Because of the stop/control valve arrangement, the larger HP and IP turbines use 2 × 180 inlet scrolls (*Fig. 4-17*). Some smaller HP turbine modules with low inlet volume flows use a 1 × 360 inlet scroll. All LP turbine sections have vertical steam admission and, therefore, are equipped with a 1 × 360 inlet scroll.

This scroll design enables a low-loss flow characteristic and, together with the first axial radial blading stage, enables an optimal outlet in the axial blade path. The steam is brought right up to the blading with no abrupt changes in speed and direction. The flow losses in the scroll are considerably reduced, yielding higher efficiency.

Control/Stop Valves

The construction of the stop and control valves varies among manufacturers. Alstom uses a combined stop and control valve that is flanged to the steam turbine generator body. This eliminates piping between the valve body and turbine, saving floor space and making erection and maintenance simpler. *Figure 4-18* shows a typical combined stop and control valve in which both valves are in the same body. For modern HP turbines, Alstom uses separate control and stop valves in a common casing that is flanged to the steam turbine.

THE IP TURBINE

The IP turbine admits hot, reheated steam from the boiler reheater. Although reheat temperatures are equal to and often higher than the live steam temperature going to the HP turbine, the lower pressures and stresses generally do not require the same features as used in the HP turbine. Like the HP turbine, the IP turbine typically has an inner and an outer casing. Because the stresses are lower, however, a bolted flange design is acceptable. Larger units may have a split flow (two-flow) IP turbine with an exhaust at either end. Smaller turbines typically have a single-flow IP turbine.

THE LP TURBINE

Figure 4-19 shows a cross section of an Alstom LP turbine. A typical LP turbine is a two-flow design; however, smaller units often have a

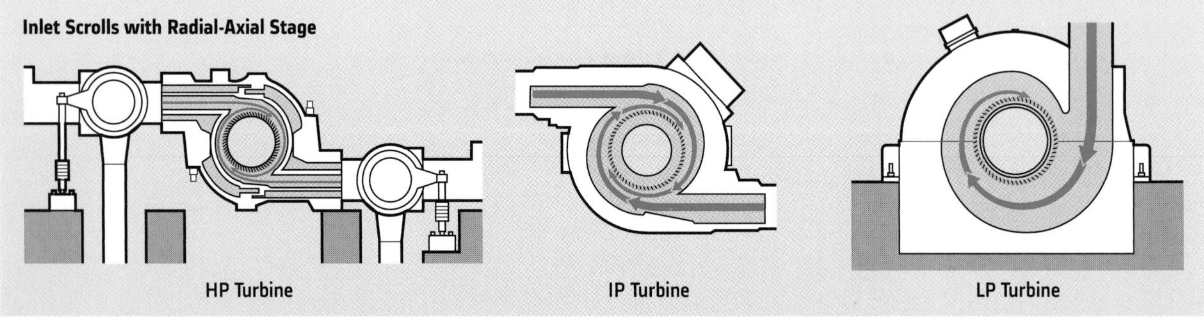

Figure 4-17 | Steam is guided smoothly into the blading via inlet scrolls (HP, high-pressure; IP, intermediate-pressure; LP, low-pressure)

Steam Turbine Inlet Valves

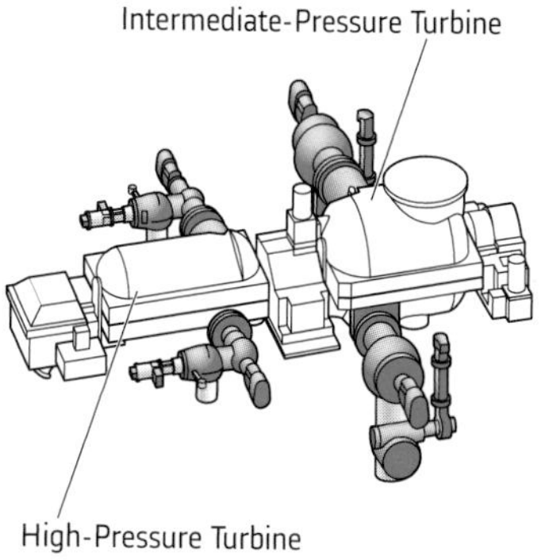

Intermediate-Pressure Turbine

High-Pressure Turbine

Figure 4-18 | The high-pressure and intermediate-pressure combined stop and control valve assembly is directly flanged to the turbine casing

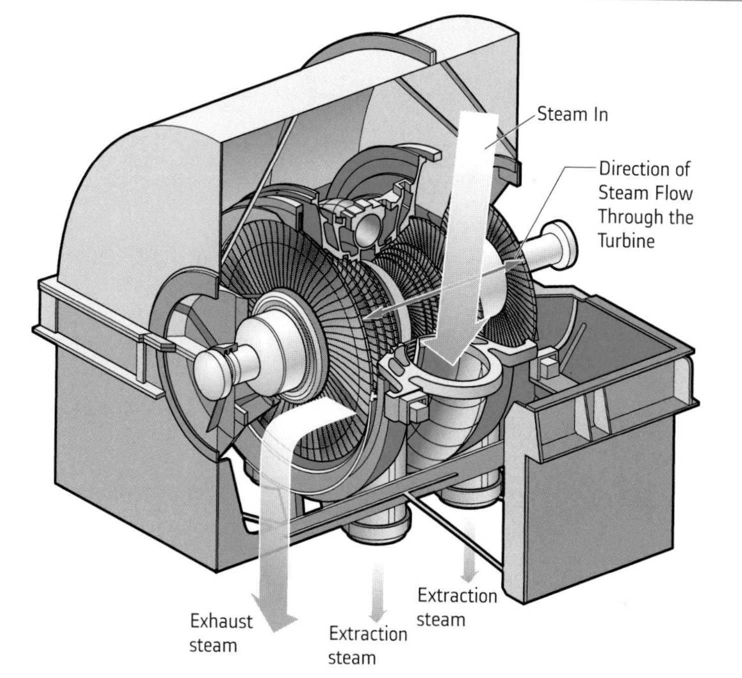

Figure 4-19 | Steam is admitted into the center and flows outward for typical two-flow low-pressure designs. Normal exhaust is downward, but side exhaust also is available

single-flow LP turbine design. This is very common on non-reheat units. Alstom also offers IP/LP combination turbines (see *Fig. 4-20*) for smaller reheat applications.

The two-flow LP turbine receives its steam supply from the IP turbine exhaust via a crossover pipe and exhausts to the condenser. The LP turbine exhaust is the only significant thermodynamic interface with the external environment. Lower available cooling water or air temperatures yield lower absolute exhaust pressures. As noted in the earlier discussion of thermodynamics, it is desirable to achieve as low an exhaust pressure as possible to extract more energy from the steam, resulting in higher cycle efficiency. Typical utility condenser pressures vary between 0.25 and 2.0 psia (1.7 KPa and 14 KPa) for surface condensers but may be higher for dry (air-cooled) condensers. The lowest exhaust pressures are only achieved with direct cooling from relatively cold water sources (e.g., northern lakes or oceans).

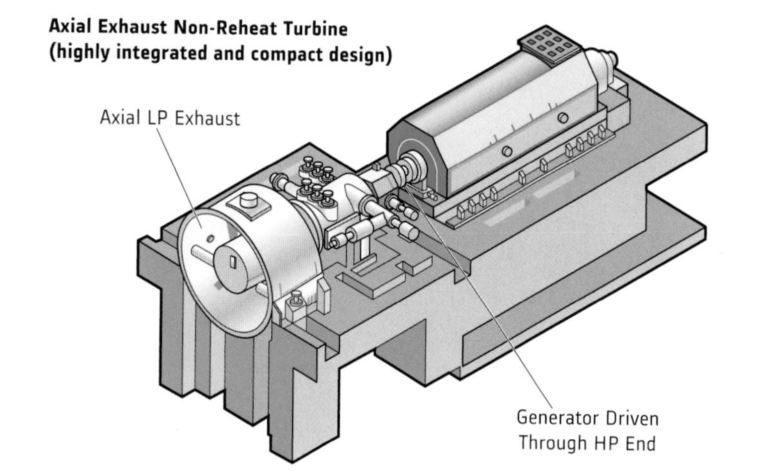

Figure 4-20 | Single-flow low-pressure (LP) turbines can exhaust axially (shown here) or downward (HP, high-pressure)

As the steam pressure decreases through the turbine, the steam volume increases. Therefore, the LP turbine must be designed to pass a large volume of steam through to the condenser. Issues with this large LP exhaust volume flow are two-fold: efficiency, and choking. High-volume flow through a fixed area translates into high velocity. The kinetic energy leaving the last-stage blades is lost to the condenser, reducing cycle efficiency. (Note that the kinetic energy in the steam leaving any upstream stage can be recovered in the downstream stages. This lost kinetic energy is the major component of the combined exhaust losses that will be discussed later.)

Steam, like any gas, has a sonic velocity (speed of sound). As the steam velocity reaches the sonic velocity, a shock wave forms in the blading. Once the shock wave is formed, steam flow cannot be increased by downstream conditions. This point is appropriately called the "choke point," and it represents a maximum volume flow condition for a given LP turbine.

If the volume flow and exhaust steam velocity are too low, turbulence and uneven flow result along the length of the last-stage blades. At extremely low flows, partial recirculation of steam may occur, typically along the rotor. These phenomena mechanically add energy back to the steam—that is, energy lost to the condenser. These losses, combined with the kinetic energy losses discussed earlier, represent exhaust losses.

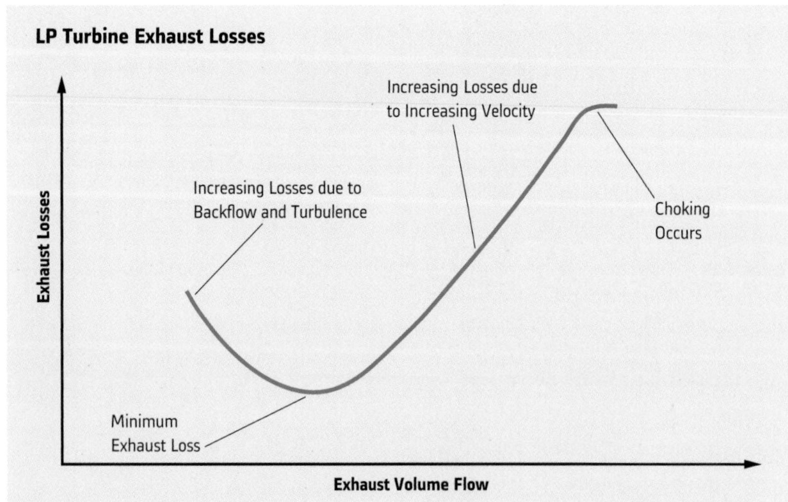

Figure 4-21 | Optimal cycle efficiency occurs where exhaust losses are minimized at the lowest point of the exhaust loss curve

LP Selection

Exhaust losses can be plotted versus volume flow, as shown in *Figure 4-21*. The right side of the curve (high volume per flow) parabolically increases because of increasing kinetic energy losses. Typically, however, the left side (low volume per flow) is more vertical and less defined. Choking will occur at the extreme right end of the curve. Maximum efficiency occurs where the exhaust losses are minimized. For a given steam flow, exhaust volume flow will increase with decreasing exhaust pressure.

Because the LP exhaust pressure will vary seasonally with the condenser cooling medium (water or air), the size of the total LP annulus area must be selected to match that experienced throughout the year. Ideally, the LP exhaust area should be selected to operate at or near the minimum exhaust loss point. Because the left side of the curve is more vertical, the LP should be selected to avoid operation too far below the minimum exhaust loss.

The LP annulus area can be increased by increasing the last-stage blade length or by increasing the number of flows. Increasing the LP annulus area effectively reduces the specific volume flow on the exhaust loss curve, moving to the left on the curve. Large, utility-size turbines typically use one, two, or three double-flow LP turbines in tandem to achieve the desired exhaust flow area. Using the longest blades available enables the designer to use fewer LP modules, reducing cost.

Moisture Protection

Steam in the last stages of the LP turbine is starting to condense to liquid (sometimes called the "wet zone"). This liquid can collect into droplets that can severely damage the LP blading and casings because of impact or erosion. Additionally, corrosion and deposition caused by impurities in the steam occur in this zone. Therefore, materials and designs must be carefully selected to accommodate this moisture. There are orifice drains on some of the stationary blades to remove moisture. On very large last-stage blades, such as those used for nuclear applications, moisture removal devices are used on the stationary blades. The leading edges of last-stage blades are induction hardened to improve erosion resistance. Finally, water–steam chemistry must be carefully controlled to ensure that corrosive or adhesive deposits do not occur.

MAJOR TURBINE AUXILIARY SYSTEMS

LUBE OIL SYSTEM (BEARINGS)

The rotating turbine shaft is supported by hydrodynamic sleeve bearings. The turbine shaft journal is supported by a film of oil between the journal (shaft) and the bearing sleeve. Failure to maintain this oil film during operation would be catastrophic. Therefore, reliability is critical for this component.

Alstom designs use a shaft-driven, positive-displacement, lube oil pump. Because the pump is shaft driven, a reliable supply of oil is maintained whenever the unit is running. Because the pump is positive displacement, oil flow is always maintained during rundown from a black trip (loss of all electric power). An auxiliary (backup) AC electric pump and a direct current (DC) electrical pump also are used for start-up or emergencies.

Pressure and flow for the bearing oil is provided from the main lube oil pump. Because the oil is heated by friction in the bearings and by the main pump, the oil temperature must be controlled with oil coolers downstream of the pump. A reserve of oil is maintained in the lube oil tank. Auxiliary lube oil pumps are mounted on the lube oil tank. Features include skid-mounted pumps, self-priming mechanical pumps, and redundant pumps.

GLAND STEAM SYSTEM

Because the steam inside each turbine module is at a different pressure than the atmosphere, the steam must be sealed, at the end of each casing, with shaft seals to prevent steam from leaking out or air from leaking in. Gland seals (*Fig. 4-22*) are highly effective but must be supplied with steam slightly above and below atmospheric pressure. These seals ensure that no steam leaks from the turbine to the atmosphere. Steam from higher-pressure seals can be used to supply lower pressure seals.

The LP turbine shaft seals are below atmospheric pressure, so exhaust steam from this point must be collected in a separate condenser (because it contains some air). A typical system is shown in *Figure 4-23*.

CONTROL FLUID/HYDRAULIC SYSTEM

Large turbine control valves require substantial force to actuate. Some older systems used a large hydraulic actuator to mechanically move a cam or rack to control the valves sequentially, but modern designs use individual hydraulic actuators. This allows individual control of each valve position. Even with partial arc designs, it is possible to operate

Water quality is important for both the boiler and the steam turbine.

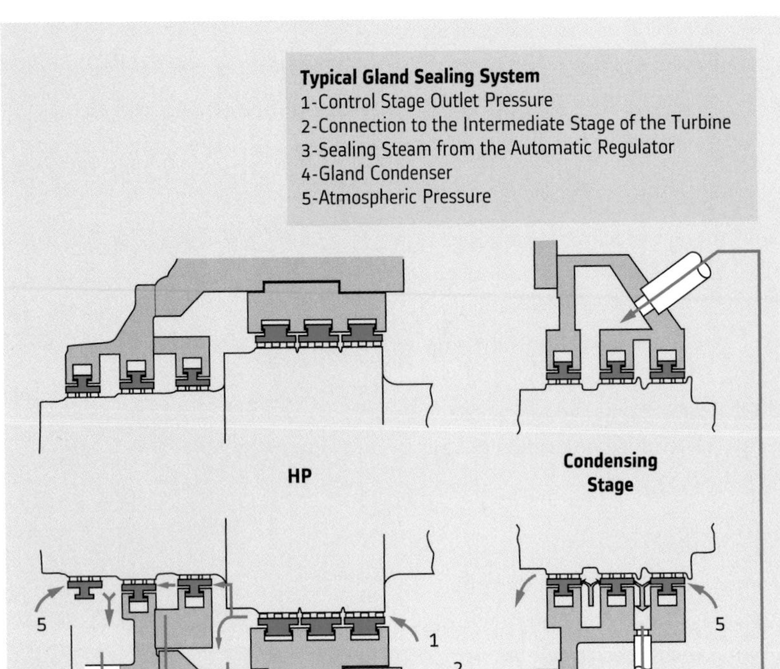

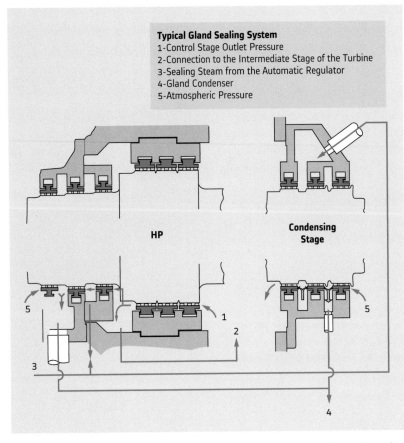

Figure 4-22 | The typical gland seals shown here prevent leakage into or out of the turbine casing along the shaft. Positive pressure on the inner gland leakage port at Point 3 and vacuum at Point 4 prevent leakage of steam out of or air into the turbine casing along the shaft. Sealing steam is supplied from the high-pressure (HP) seals to lower-pressure seals

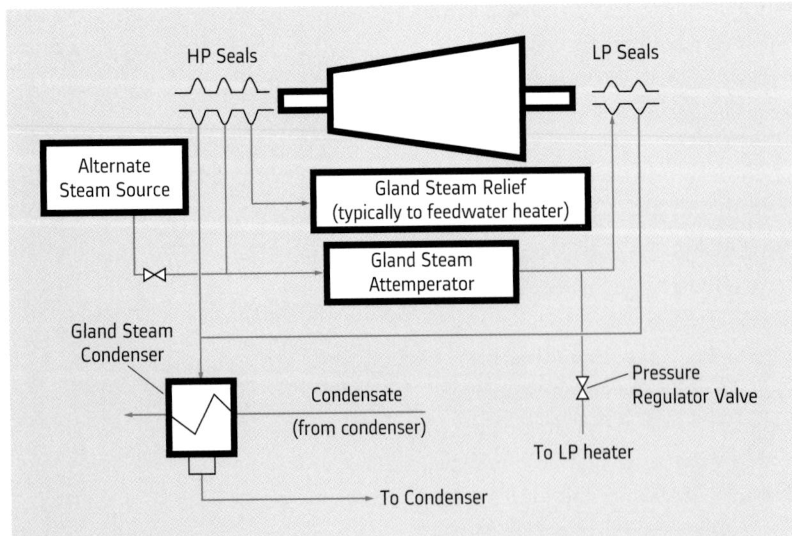

Figure 4-23 | The gland steam system uses steam extracted from the turbine to seal the shafts. A typical, simple sealing system for a single-casing turbine is shown (HP, high-pressure; LP, low-pressure)

valves in parallel or sequentially. Hydraulic systems can operate at pressures from a few hundred psi (~20 bar) to several thousand psi (~200 bar). Large Alstom turbines use a 590-psi (40 bar) system for control. This gives a balance in terms of the safety and reliability of an IP system while maintaining the response of an HP system.

Hydraulic systems often use a reservoir combined with the lube oil system. In this case, the hydraulic fluid is a mineral oil-based fluid suitable for lubrication of the bearings. If a fireretardant hydraulic fluid is used, a separate tank is required for the hydraulic system.

A typical control oil schematic is shown in *Figure 4-24*. Generally, two hydraulic pumps are installed in parallel. The main steam and reheat intercept stop valves usually are held open by the hydraulic force, so only one pump is sufficient to operate the turbine. Should both pumps fail, lack of control oil pressure would allow the stop valves to close, and the turbine would shut down (trip).

TURBINE ELECTRONIC CONTROLS

A large steam turbine has many systems that require continuous monitoring and regulation during start-up and operation. The controls serve to operate the turbine generator while protecting the unit from damage. Among the basic functions of the control system are:

- Speed control
- Load control
- Start-up sequencing
- Synchronization
- Auxiliary system control
- Equipment condition monitoring
- Emergency trip functions
- Extraction pressure control (for cogeneration applications)

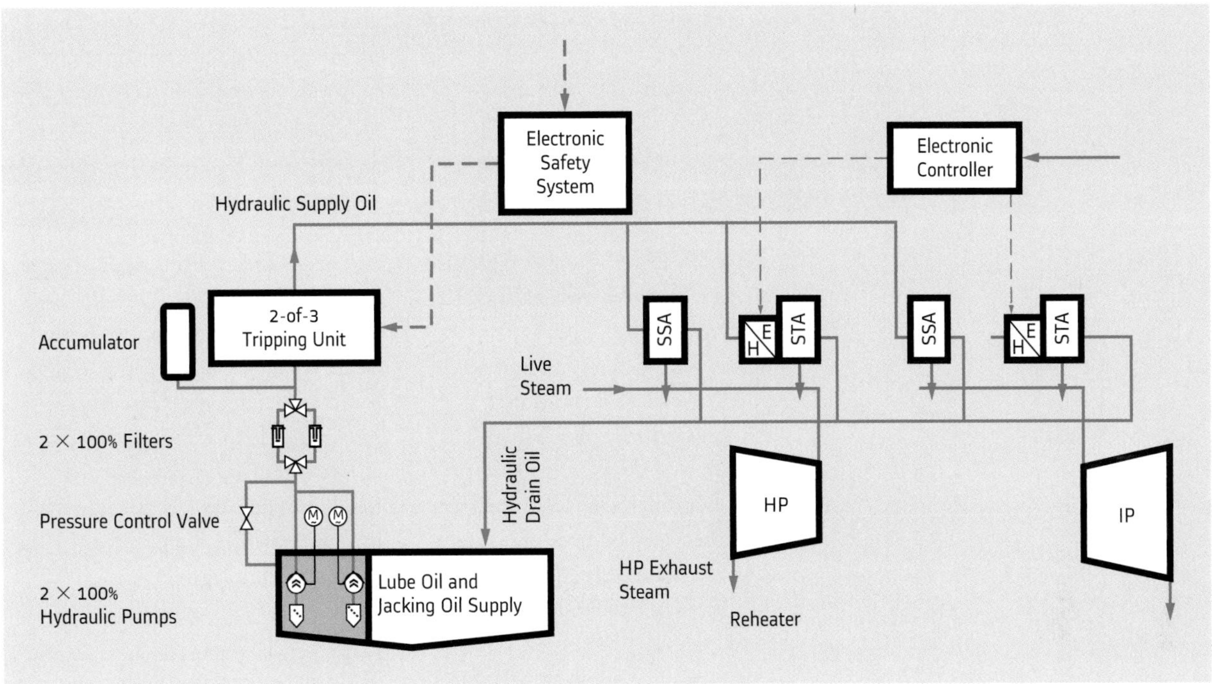

Figure 4-24 | The control oil system (hydraulic system) supplies the valve actuators with pressurized fluid to actuate the valves and control the turbine. If control oil pressure is lost, the stop valves will automatically close (E, open; H, closed; HP, high pressure; IP, intermediate pressure; SSA, control valve; STA, stop valve)

Some of these systems are included in the base control system. Others, such as vibration monitoring and synchronization, may be in specialized subsystems. Critical functions and parameters will have triple redundancy, with two out of three voting among the channels to ensure safety while preventing inadvertent trips. Less critical parameters may have only double redundancy, and non-critical parameters may be monitored only on a single channel. The central processor itself is redundant on the same bus to ensure system reliability.

The speed of the system is important in regulating the turbine. The control system must respond quickly to load and system requirements as well as to emergency situations requiring systematic, controlled shutdown. As the "nerve center" of the turbine generator system, the control system also is the main interface with the plant distributed control systems (see Chapter 7). Modern systems also can monitor turbine stress and turbine life. Communications systems also allow remote monitoring of systems and condition assessment. All of these can generate increased reliability and equipment lifetime.

TURNING GEAR AND JACKING OIL SYSTEMS

Large steam turbines and generators have extremely heavy rotors with long bearing spans. Over long periods of storage, these rotors can develop a set sag. Also, at elevated temperatures as the turbine cools, thermal gradients can cause a bow in the rotor. Therefore, turbines have a turning gear to maintain a low rpm that keeps the temperature of the rotor constant while the unit cools.

Turning gears have various mechanical means to engage with the rotor. Some units utilize a ratchet mechanism; others use a pinion gear to turn the rotor. These can be motor or hydraulically driven. Smaller units also have manual backup mechanisms.

As long as a film of oil is maintained in the bearings, the force required to maintain rotation is relatively small. At operating speeds, the rotation of the shaft generates enough hydrodynamic force such that the required lube oil pressure is minimal. In case of an extended outage or from a standstill, more oil pressure is required than can be supplied from the auxiliary lube oil pumps. The jacking oil system provides HP oil to the bearings during start-up or turning gear operation.

In case of a black trip and extended outage, special consideration must be given to maintaining power to the turning gear and jacking oil systems to protect the turbine. This can be accomplished with battery-powered, DC motor-driven pumps or via an emergency diesel generator.

THE FUTURE OF STEAM TURBINES

Because steam turbines can use virtually any high-quality energy source to develop power, they will remain an important part of our electric power generating portfolio for the foreseeable future. Increasing demands for better efficiency are driving steam parameters to higher levels. For the conventional steam cycle, this means higher inlet temperatures and pressures.

For the steam turbine, increased steam temperatures require materials that can survive the environment for an extended lifetime. Currently, materials are available to accommodate inlet temperatures of approximately 1,150°F (620°C). Efforts are underway, however, to develop steam cycles using inlet temperatures of 1,290°F (700°C), and materials programs are looking at materials for 1,400°F (760°C). These elevated temperatures may require steam or water cooling. Other energy sources may introduce new requirements as well. In addition to traditional energy sources, such as nuclear, fossil, and gas, new technologies may introduce further requirements to this "mature" technology.

GENERATORS

The generator (or turbogenerator) converts mechanical energy supplied by the turbine(s) into electrical energy. The generator consists of a stationary active part, the stator; a rotating part, the rotor; and the generator externals. The electrical energy is generated in the key component of the generator, the stator winding (armature winding) (*Fig. 4-25, 1*), which connects to the generator terminals (bushings) (*Fig. 4-25, 2*).

The stator winding outputs a three-phase AC current at the power frequency (50–60 Hz) and a voltage of 10 to 27 kV, depending on the power rating. Bus ducts (*Fig. 4-25, 3*) connect the generator terminals to the step-up transformer, which adapts the power to the grid voltage (*Fig. 4-25, 4*). By the synchronous generator principle, the speed of the turbo set is locked to the power frequency. The speed for full-speed generators is 3,000/3,600 rpm; that for half-speed generators is 1,500/1,800 rpm.

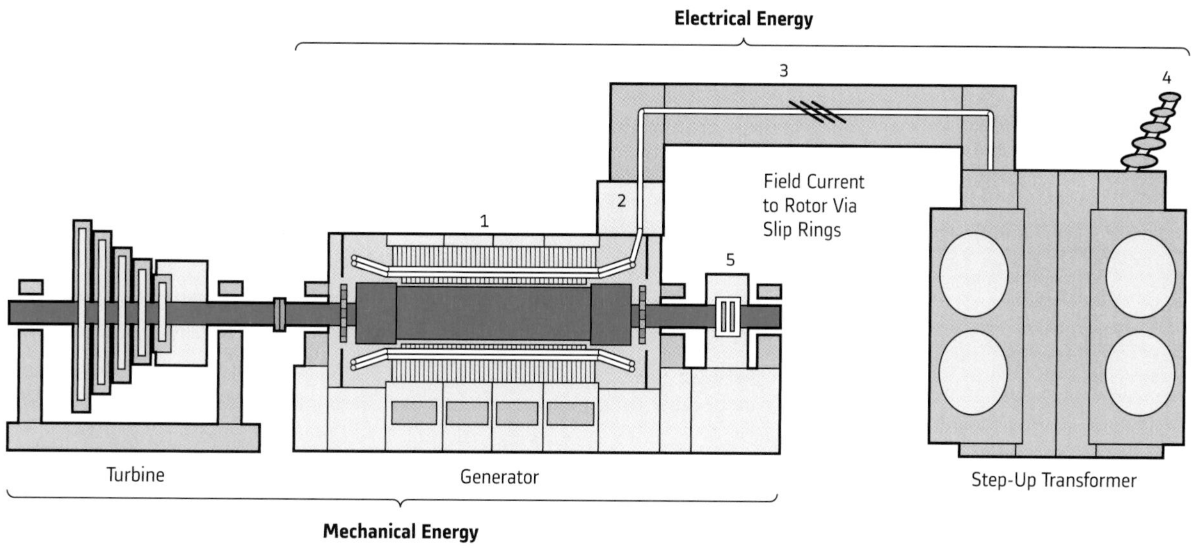

Figure 4-25 | Turbine and generator set

For steam turbine and open cycle gas turbine sets, the generator rotor is connected at the main drive end to the turbine. Smaller units may connect to turbine drives via a speed-reducing gearbox. Larger units connect directly to the steam or gas turbine. For single-shaft, combined-cycle sets, the rotor is coupled at the main drive end to the gas turbine and on its other drive end to the steam turbine. The stator, like the turbines, is bolted to the foundation to sustain the reaction torque (*Fig. 4-26*).

The rotor is fitted with its own winding (rotor winding or field winding). The electric power for the rotor winding supply is either tapped from the generator terminals and passed to the rotor via slip rings (static excitation) or is produced by a small additional generator connected to the generator rotor (rotating or brushless excitation). The current in the rotor winding is controlled by a stationary control unit called the "automated voltage regulator" (AVR). The rotor winding and the AVR provide voltage control and reactive power control.

The generator requires a number of auxiliary systems, such as bearing oil and jacking oil supply, plant cooling water, and on larger units, hydrogen and stator water auxiliaries. For gas turbine start-up, the generator also may operate as a drive motor, supplied from a static frequency converter (static starting device) connected to the generator terminals during start-up.

PRINCIPLES OF CONTROL

The common operation for power plants is to deliver power into the grid. Normally, several units are acting on the grid. The unit operator ensures that the sum of the generated power is balanced against the sum of the consumed power. The grid parameters

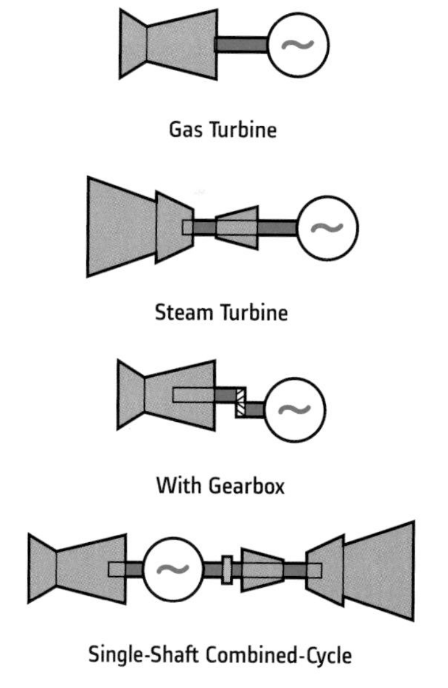

Figure 4-26 | Turbine and generator connections

of concern are voltage and frequency. The plant parameter to influence the frequency is the active power delivered into the grid. In the grids, which usually are large in size, the turbine valve is governed by continuously comparing the actual grid frequency with a reference value (50/60 Hz) (*Fig. 4-27*).

If the demand for power from the grid increases, then the speed of the turbines supplying the grid slows down. Because the synchronous generator locks the speed with the grid frequency, this frequency decreases. The response of the turbine governor is to open the steam or fuel valves to increase the power output from the turbines and so restore grid frequency to the reference value.

The plant parameter to control the grid voltage is the reactive power delivered into the grid. The reactive power results from the current component, which is out of phase with the voltage. Reactive power normally is associated with AC systems. In an AC system (single phase), the voltage and the current alternate up and down (60 times per second in the United States and 50 times per second in Europe). This power goes up and down around some average power. The average is called the "active power," and the variation around the average is the reactive power (commonly referred to as volts-amperes reactive or var). An analogy would be climbing up and down a hill. In climbing up and down a hill without carrying anything, no net work is done, and no active power is required. If, however, some cargo is carried up the hill and left there, then net work is done, and active power is required. Reactive power is required to get up the hill; this power is recovered in the absence of friction going back down the hill. Active power cannot be delivered without reactive power. Thus, reactive power is needed to start motors or activate devices, and is a key consideration in the design requirements of a steam turbine and generator.

The generator excitation is responsible for the control of reactive power. The excitation current can be controlled such that the grid current is in phase with the voltage (power factor = 1). Increasing the excitation current results in a phase shift of grid current to voltage (power factor < 1; overexcited or lagging current mode). Decreasing the excitation current results in a reverse phase (power factor < 1; underexcited or leading current mode). Overexcited mode tends to increase the grid voltage, and underexcited mode tends to lower it. Stability of the turbo set on the grid is heavily influenced by the excitation; usually, an overexcited mode makes the system more stable. This is the reason why, in case of a disturbance on the grid, the generator excitation is driven to a ceiling value for a short duration. In case of severe disturbances on the grid, the generator may fall out of step; in that

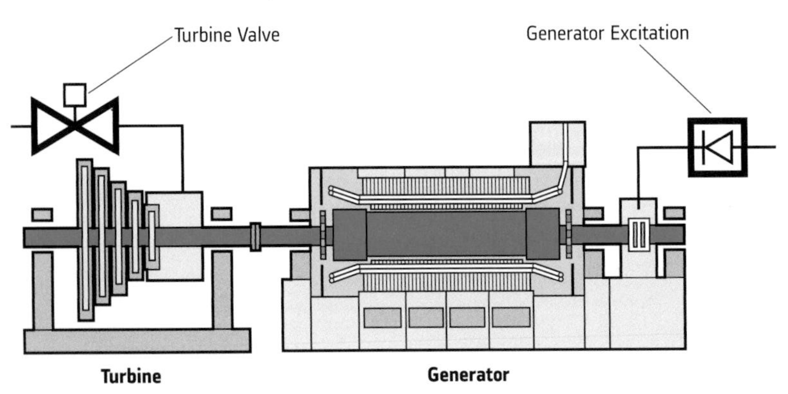

Figure 4-27 | Turbine valve and generator excitation

case, the generator is switched off the grid and resynchronized.

The control for generator excitation is the AVR. It is a closed loop that senses the generator terminal voltage, compares it with a set value, and controls the excitation current to counteract any deviation in voltage. An important additional component is the power system stabilizer, which dynamically modulates the excitation current to counteract low-frequency oscillations between the grid and the turbine generator. Operation of a single generator supplying a local grid is called "island-operating mode." In that mode, the turbine valve governor acts directly to maintain constant speed of the turbo set and, thus, constant frequency. The AVR maintains the grid voltage.

GENERATOR OPTIONS

Basic generator features, such as speed, cooling system, and excitation, are determined by the various turbine ratings and plant requirements. The generator speed is determined by the number of magnetic poles (a basic generator design feature) and the grid frequency of 50/60 Hz. Two-pole generators run at 3,000/3,600 rpm and are the general choice for gas and steam turbines in the power range of 40 to 1,000 MW. Four-pole generators (half-speed generators) run at 1,500/1,800 rpm and often are used for small generators (less than ~40 MW) with geared drives. They also are found on the large half-speed steam turbines, which are common in nuclear power plants.

The cooling of the generator depends mainly on rated power. The simplest coolant is air. The open ventilation system uses ambient air, feeds it straight through the machine, and exhausts it back to ambient. The advantage is that the generator efficiently matches the gas turbine output at low temperatures (*Fig. 4-28*).

More common is the totally enclosed water–air cooling system (TEWAC), in which air circulates in the generator and is cooled by heat exchangers (coolers) integrated in the generator casing. The advantage is the clean air inside, an important feature for reliability (*Fig. 4-29*).

The rotor winding is directly cooled, which means the air passes through the rotor winding and removes the heat by direct contact with the conductors.

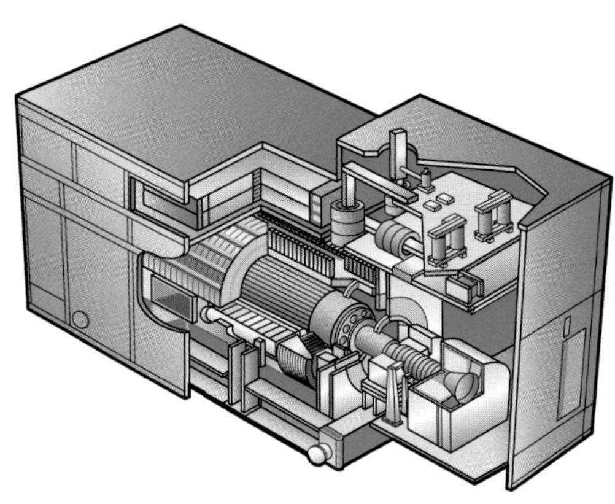

Figure 4-28 | Open ventilation system

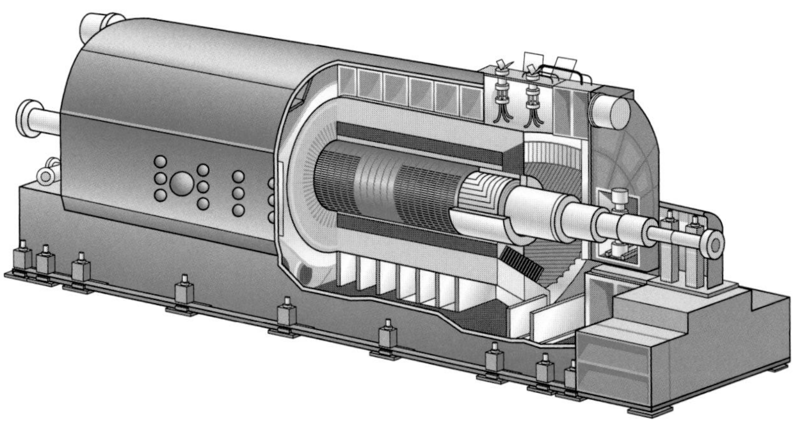

Figure 4-29 | Totally enclosed water–air cooling system

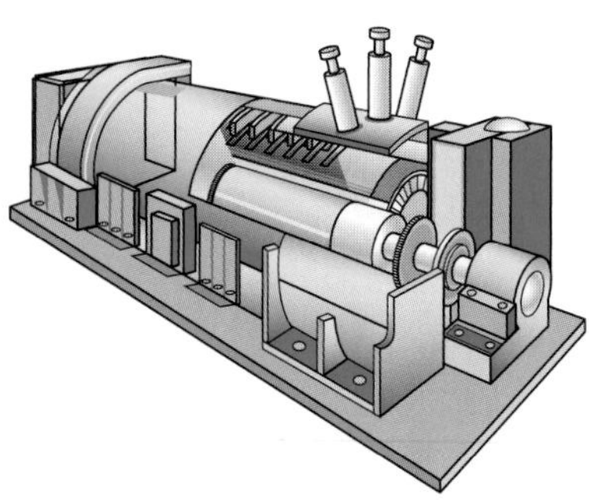

Figure 4-30 | Hydrogen cooling

Figure 4-31 | Brush gear compartment

The stator winding is indirectly cooled. This means the heat from the stator winding is removed by conduction through the main insulation to the stator core. The stator core is then directly cooled by air passing through cooling ducts in the core.

Hydrogen cooling is applied above a certain output level. Hydrogen combines high cooling capacity with low gas friction loss (*Fig. 4-30*).

Optimum cooling is achieved by pressurizing the hydrogen cooling gas to about four- to six-fold the atmospheric pressure. The generator housing is designed to contain pressurized hydrogen gas and is filled with shaft seals near the generator bearings. Auxiliary systems are required to control the hydrogen supply and to supply seal oil to the shaft seals.

On larger generators (above ~400 MW), the stator winding is directly cooled by deionized water flowing in the stator conductors, but the rotor winding and stator core are still cooled by hydrogen. Here, an additional auxiliary for deionized water supply is provided. Depending on design constraints, generators are equipped with either static excitation or rotating (brushless) excitation. Design rules vary between manufacturers, and both systems can be found at all ratings.

MAIN EXCITATION SYSTEM

Static Excitation

The power for the generator excitation is tapped from the generator bus ducts and fed to an excitation transformer, which steps down the voltage. The low-voltage side of the excitation transformer is connected to a thyristor-controlled rectifier, which is located in the rectifier compartment. The DC output is fed by cables, or bus bars, to the generator brush gear (*Fig. 4-31*). In the brush gear, an array of graphite brushes contacts the two slip rings on the rotor and carries the excitation current to the rotor winding. The AVR, which controls the rectifier, normally is integrated in the rectifier compartment. The outstanding feature of the static excitation is the fast response.

Rotating Excitation

The excitation power is produced by the rotating exciter machine, which is flanged to the generator rotor. The rotating armature winding of the exciter feeds into a rotating diode rectifier. The rotating diode rectifier is connected to the rotor winding of the generator. The AVR feeds the exciter stator. Because the exciter power is generated mainly by the exciter machine running as a small generator taking the power from the main shaft, the required control power of the AVR is quite small and can be provided by a small, thyristor-controlled rectifier. The rotating excitation is free of the required continuous maintenance of the graphite brushes.

MAIN COMPONENTS

The generator converts the mechanical power provided by the turbines into electric power. The generator consists mainly of a static part (stator), which is supported on the foundation, and a rotating part (the rotor), which is coupled to the turbine shaft and located in the bore of the stator. Generators using a cylindrical rotor shape, built up of steel forging, usually are directly coupled to a gas turbine or steam turbine. This kind of

generator is called a "turbogenerator" (i.e., turbine generator). The efficiency of the generator depends mainly on cooling type, size, and frequency and is in the range of 98.3 to 99.0% at full load. This means that up to 99% of the input mechanical power gets converted into electric power.

The rotor carries the rotor winding (field winding), in which the excitation current (DC) flows, provided by an excitation system (*Fig. 4-32*). The rotor winding produces a magnetic field that rotates with the speed of the rotor. The magnetic field lines bridge the air gap between the rotor surface and the stator bore and close in the stator core. The stator core is a cylinder built up from as many as 250,000 insulated steel sheets. Slots are formed in the inner surface to support the stator winding (armature winding), which is built up by series connection of the bars in the stator slot. The stator winding consists of three individual windings, one for each phase (*Fig. 4-33, L1–L3*) of the generator output. It carries the main current in the generator and connects directly to the generator terminals. The stator terminals are connected by bus ducts to the step-up transformer, which matches the grid voltage.

The outer cylindrical part of the core is called the "yoke." It carries the cylindrical component of the magnetic fields.

The rotating magnetic field induces an alternating voltage in the stator winding (see *Fig. 4-33*). When the speed of the generator rotor is synchronized with the grid frequency, connection is made via the transformer to the grid. As the load on the generator increases and the stator current rises, the current in the rotor winding must be increased to maintain the voltage in the stator winding.

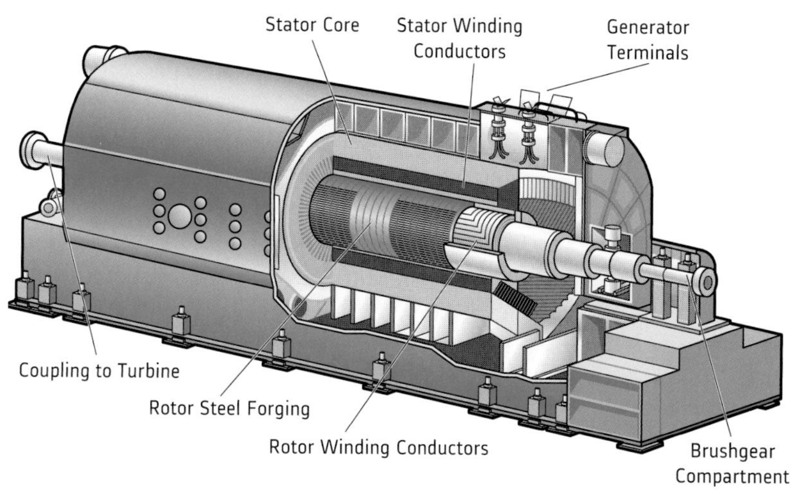

Figure 4-32 | Alstom TOPAIR generator

The stability of the generator is controlled by the AVR, which senses the generator voltage and acts on the excitation (rotor current) to maintain a pre-set voltage under all load conditions (for constant-voltage regime). For static excitation, the AVR controls a stationary, thyristor-controlled rectifier, which feeds the excitation current via brush gear and slip rings (collectors) to the rotor winding. For brushless excitation (rotating excitation), the AVR controls the input of an exciter machine, which is mounted on the non-turbine end of the main generator and in which a rotating diode wheel is integrated.

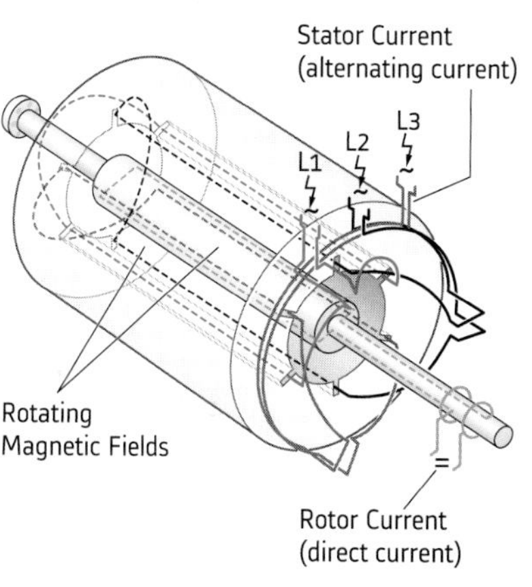

Figure 4-33 | Generator working principle

GENERATOR EXTERNALS

For air-cooled turbogenerators, the stator and rotor are supported on a common frame. This design allows transport with the rotor installed.

Small units have a rectangular base

frame on which the generator stator pedestal bearings and exciter stator are mounted. The base frame transfers all mechanical forces of the bearings and stators to the foundation (*Fig. 4-34*). The base frame supports a box-shaped enclosure (acoustic cover), which serves for internal air flow, noise protection, and when requested, weather protection. The top of the enclosure is prepared both for open ventilation (air filters) and for a totally enclosed air circuit with air–water heat exchangers (i.e., TEWAC). All essential components are inside the enclosure. This applies to the bearings, the exciter, and the wiring and piping. Further components may be integrated inside the enclosure, including a gearbox to the turbine and medium-voltage equipment, such as voltage and current transformers, neutral point circuitry, and overvoltage protections. The only external component is the generator excitation control module (i.e., the AVR).

Larger air-cooled units consist of a two-part housing: the housing frame and the housing cover. The housing frame carries the heat exchangers, the inner stator, and on integral housing extensions, the bearing pedestals and the brush gear or rotating exciter. To keep the railway profile, the housing cover and bushings are installed on site. The normal cooling is TEWAC, with the heat exchangers located at the bottom of the housing frame. An additional outer cubicle can be provided for noise protection. The main interfaces to the plant surroundings are the stator winding terminals mounted on top of the housing, the individual bearing oil supplies, and the excitation current leads of the brush gear. The external components are the AVR and the static excitation cubicles, where applicable. Current and potential transformers also are mounted outside the generator.

Hydrogen and hydrogen/water-cooled turbogenerators (except four-pole generators) are all equipped with bearing pedestals supported on the foundation. Transport is by components, with the main components being the stator central housing and rotor.

Hydrogen-cooled units consist of a central housing part that contains the inner stator and rotor, two end covers that support the gas–water heat exchangers, and pedestal bearings. Because the housing contains the hydrogen, it is of heavy design and contributes significantly to the overall weight of the generator. The openings for the shaft in the end covers are fitted with hydrogen-tight oil seals located inboard of the generator bearings. The generator is designed for table mounting and needs a recess

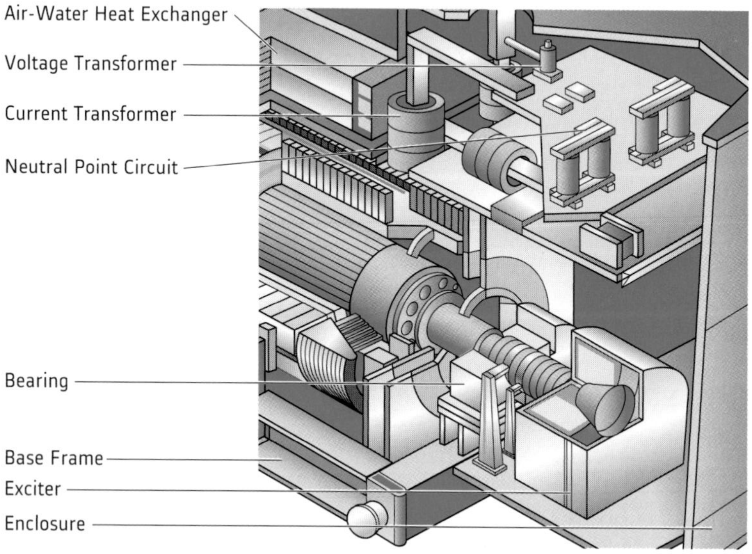

Air-Water Heat Exchanger
Voltage Transformer
Current Transformer
Neutral Point Circuit
Bearing
Base Frame
Exciter
Enclosure

Figure 4-34 | Totally enclosed water–air cooled generator

in the foundations to clear its lower half. Flanges on each side of the central housing transmit the static and dynamic forces in the table. Three generator terminals are mounted on top and three below, allowing flexibility in bus duct arrangement. A brush gear compartment is arranged separately on the foundation, which connects to an external static excitation supply (*Fig. 4-35*).

Hydrogen-cooled generators require an additional auxiliary unit to control the hydrogen supply and the CO_2 used for purging. Furthermore, an external source of hydrogen is needed, usually a battery of bottled gas in a safe area. A second auxiliary unit is fitted to circulate oil and to control pressure differentials in the shaft seals. This unit continuously degasses the oil recirculating from the seal units.

Hydrogen/water-cooled units differ from the hydrogen-cooled units by having central housing extensions for the heat exchangers (two-pole generators) and end shield bearings (four-pole generators). In addition, a deionized water auxiliary is needed for the supply of cooling water to the stator winding. The generator terminals normally are arranged in a bottom housing extension.

STATOR

The inner stator consists of a cylindrical magnetic core with the stator winding embedded in the slots in the inner surface of the core. The stator core consists of stacked silicon-steel laminations. The laminations typically are 0.01 inches (0.5 mm) thick and chosen to balance magnetic properties, core loss, and mechanical properties (*Fig. 4-36*).

The laminations are overlapped, like bricks in a wall, and clamped in the axial direction by keybars at the core

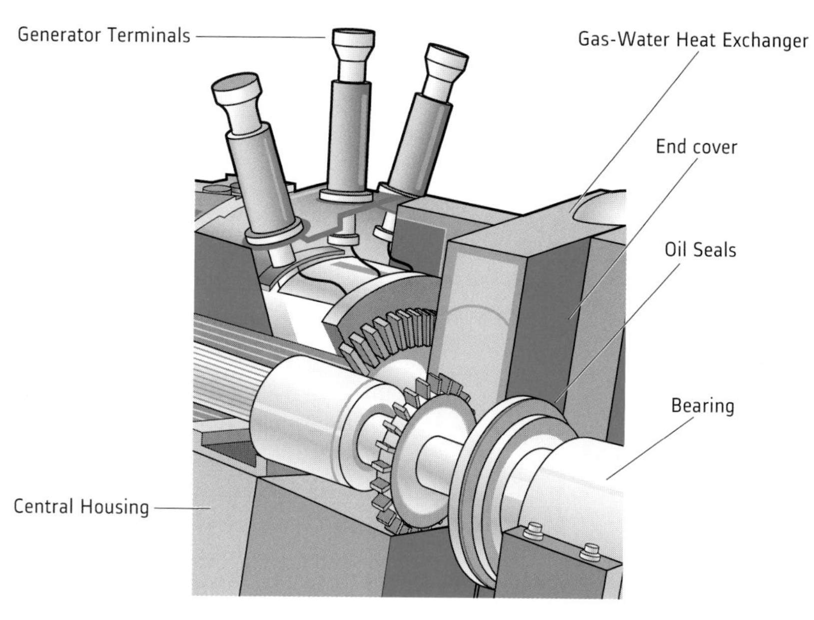

Figure 4-35 | Hydrogen-cooled generator

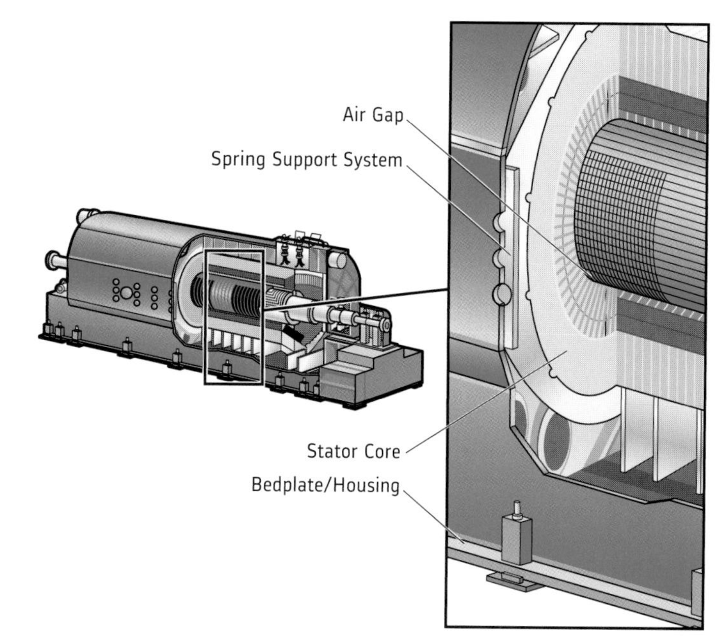

Figure 4-36 | Stator core connection to the housing

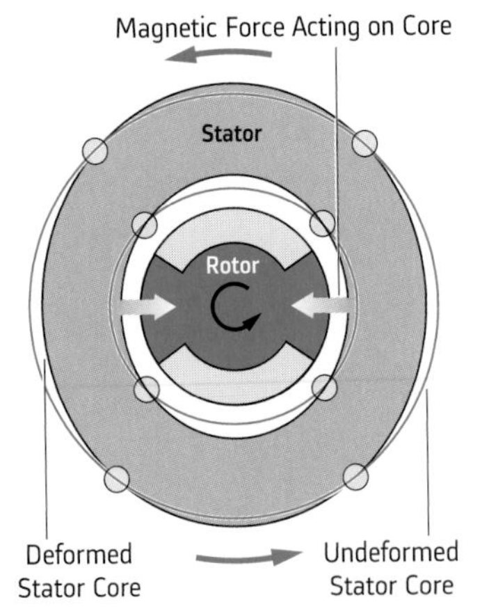

Figure 4-37 | 2f Ovalization (2f, double frequency)

back and, in some designs, by tie bolts through the core. This forms a rigid cylindrical structure to resist the rotating 2f ovalization forces produced by the magnetic fields in the air gap (*Fig. 4-37*).

The stator core connects to the bedplate or housing via a spring support system to attenuate vibrations transmitted to the foundation. Press plates are fitted at the ends of the core to transmit axial pressure from the keybars and tie rods and to protect the end laminations from axial magnetic fields that induce eddy currents in the core ends. Various designs of the press plate and core end screen are available, including steel plates with a copper screen, aluminum plates, or conical rings of bonded lamination material.

The stator winding system consists of a two-layer arrangement of Roebel bars located in the slots. Each slot carries a lower and an upper bar (*Fig. 4-38*). The Roebel bars are built up from two (or four) parallel stacks of insulated strands, which are twisted together to minimize eddy current and circulating current heating in the winding. The bars are series connected, upper bar to lower bar, to form coils. For two-pole windings, the connection is made between nearly opposite slots. Thus, the array of all connections forms a cone-shaped end winding. The line and neutral ends of the three phases of the stator winding are connected to the generator terminals by the phase ring connections. Usually, rated generator voltage is defined phase to phase and, depending on size, is in the range of 10 to 27 kV. Terminal currents are in the range of 2 to 30 kA.

To support the bars against magnetic forces, the slot is closed by fiberglass wedges. The tightness of these wedges is maintained either by fiber-reinforced ripple springs between the top bar and wedge or by a double-tapered wedge, which inherently acts as a spring.

The main insulation of the bars consists of a mica-tape wound around the bar in several overlapping layers to produce a ground wall insulation thickness according to the rated generator voltage. The bars are impregnated with resin, either by vacuum pressure impregnation or by using resin-rich tape. After curing, the bars are inserted in the stator slots and connected together in the end form stator windings to coils. Some air-cooled generators are manufactured using a global vacuum pressure impregnation process. To achieve this, the stator is fully wound, including end winding support. The insulation is dry (without resin). Resin impregnation is made by submerging the wound stator in a large, resin-filled pressure vessel.

The stator bars are provided with a

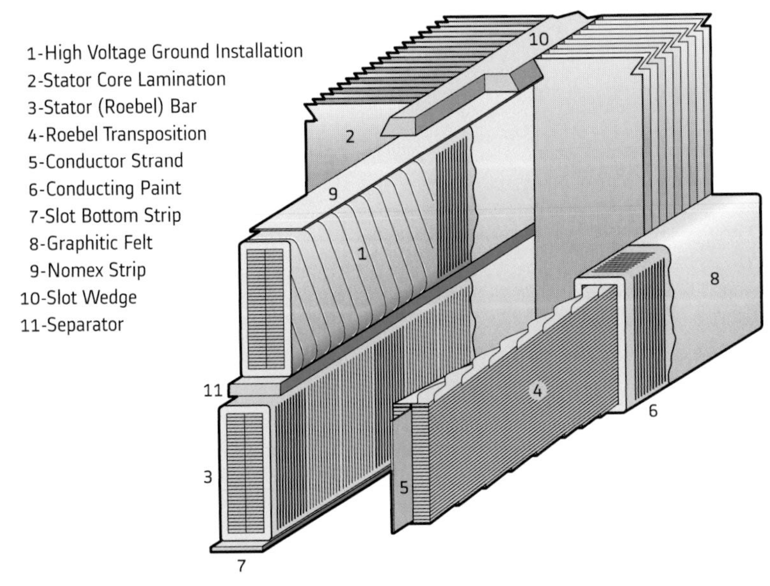

Figure 4-38 | Stator winding system

conductive coating around the main insulation, which prevents electric surface discharges that might erode the main insulation. In the slot region, this is done by conductive paint or taping (slot corona protection); in the end winding region, a coating of non-linear, voltage-dependent resistance is applied (grading paint or taping).

At each end of the stator, the bars form the typical conical end winding. Like the other sections of the bar, the stator end winding is subject to double-frequency magnetic forces. To keep the vibrations within acceptable levels and to prevent deformation under short-circuit condition, the bars are fixed to an end winding support structure. For indirectly cooled windings, the support must allow enough space for coolant flow around the bars. In general, this is done by taping the bars in the cone to triangular brackets, which in turn are suspended by a system of concentric rings. A well-designed support structure allows axial expansion of the bars while keeping the end winding stiff in the radial and tangential directions. In larger air-cooled machines and in hydrogen-cooled machines, the cone inner surface is additionally supported by an inner ring.

For larger generators with water-cooled (directly cooled) windings, the bracket support structure may be replaced by a massive, cone-shaped, fiberglass ring. Usually, the phase ring connections also are supported by the end winding support (*Fig. 4-39*).

The stator winding insulation materials are specified to allow conductor temperatures up to at least 311°F (155°C), according to Class F (311°F [155°C]) of the electric machine standards. According to long-standing practice, rated thermal utilization is well below 266°F (130°C; Class B).

ROTOR

The main components of the rotor of a turbogenerator are a cylindrical steel forging (rotor body), the rotor winding contained in slots in the rotor body, the retaining rings (end bells) to support the winding heads, and one or two fans for coolant drive. The rotor body consists of a steel forging with shaft extensions on both sides. The drive end is fitted with a coupling to the turbine; the non-drive end carries the slip rings or the rotating exciter (*Fig. 4-40*).

On two-pole units, the center part

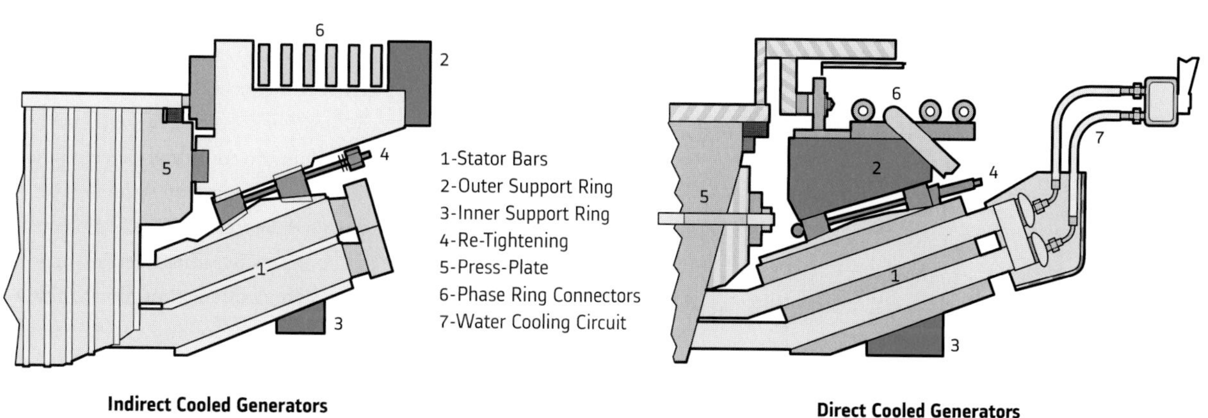

Figure 4-39 | Indirectly and directly cooled generators

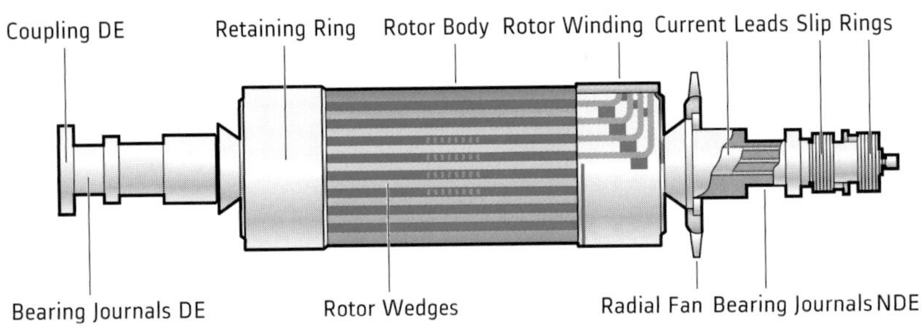

Figure 4-40 | Rotor details (DE, drive end; NDE, non-driven end)

of the rotor is divided circumferentially into two pole zones, with winding zones in between. The winding zones are provided with axial slots, which contain the rotor winding. The pole zones usually have transversal slots (inertia slits) to equalize the stiffness in bending on the pole and quadrature axis. On four-pole rotors, the circumference is divided into four pole zones, with winding sections in between.

The rotor winding consists of a stack of copper conductors (temperature-resistant, silver-alloyed copper) in each slot. The slot ends are connected together in series across the pole faces to form the rotor coils and winding. The conductors are insulated from the rotor body by the slot wall insulation, and the stacked conductors are separated by layers of an inter-turn insulation. The excitation current is supplied via copper D-leads in the center of the shaft on the non-drive end. Connection to the winding is made via radial studs through the shaft with flexible connectors to the ends of the winding. Depending on unit size, the rated field current is in the range 1,000 to 6,000 A, and the rated field voltage is in the range 200 to 750 V (DC). The slots are closed by metallic wedges, usually of non-magnetic steel, a high-strength copper-nickel alloy, or aluminum. The latter two normally consist of single-piece wedges running the full length of the rotor. The rotor is fitted with a damper winding to limit rotor heating under system fault conditions. This can be achieved by single conductors located beneath the slot wedges, closed by a circumferential copper coronet at the slot ends or formed by connecting full-length slot wedges to a copper coronet or to the retaining ring at the slot ends.

The winding conductors usually are provided with ducts or openings for cooling gas flow. Depending on the design, the slots are equipped with subslots between the copper and slot bottom to feed cooling gas into the conductors. The cooling gas escapes through an array of openings in the wedges. Additional baffling is provided in the rotor end windings to direct gas into the conductors.

The rotor end windings are enclosed by a retaining ring, which is held in place by a shrink fit on the rotor body (*Fig. 4-41*). The retaining ring serves to hold the winding heads against the centrifugal forces. It is made of non-magnetic, cold-worked, austenitic steel (18Mn-18Cr). Older units may be operating with ring material that is susceptible to stress corrosion cracking and may need special supervision.

Usually, the rotor is equipped with a fan on one or both shaft ends to circulate the air or hydrogen cooling gas within the generator. Normally, this is an axial fan, but larger units may be equipped with radial fans or multi-stage axial blowers. Modern rotor insulation materials are specified to allow conductor temperatures of up to at least 311°F (155°C), according to Class F of the electric machine standards. According

to long-standing practice, the rated operating temperatures are much lower, corresponding to Class B.

EXCITER

Static Excitation

In general the power for the generator excitation is tapped from the generator bus ducts and is fed to an excitation transformer (*Fig. 4-42*). The excitation transformer steps down the voltage to the level required by the rated field voltage and specified margin (ceiling factor). The output of the excitation transformer is connected to a thyristor-controlled rectifier, which is located in the excitation compartment.

The DC output is fed by cables or bus bars to the generator brush gear (*Fig. 4-43*). In the brush gear, an array of brushes contact two slip rings located on a rotor shaft extension, which carries the excitation current to the rotor winding. The slip rings normally are of steel, but some older units may use bronze. The brushes are of natural graphite and are mounted in brush holders, which allows an exchange of worn brushes in operation. The normal lifetime of brushes is one year, but this may be considerably lower with non-optimal air conditions (e.g., humidity, salt, and chemical contamination). Usually, a small fan provides air flow in the brush gear. Large units have air-conditioned brush gear with closed air circulation and built-in, air–water heat exchangers. Depending on shaft dynamics, a third bearing is needed behind the slip rings. The AVR, which controls the rectifier, normally is integrated in the rectifier cubicle. In operation, the static excitation is characterized by its fast response under system fault conditions.

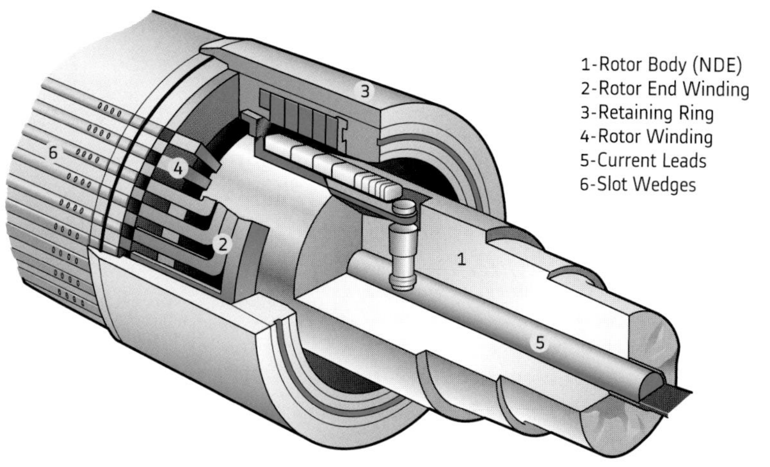

Figure 4-41 | Rotor end windings (NDE, non-driven end)

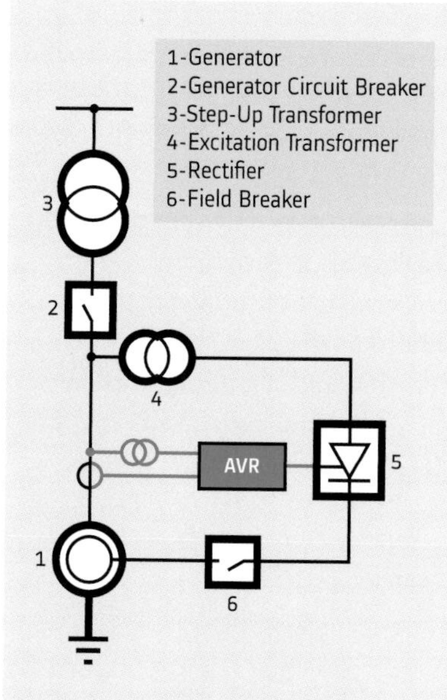

Figure 4-42 | Static excitation (AVR, automated voltage regulator)

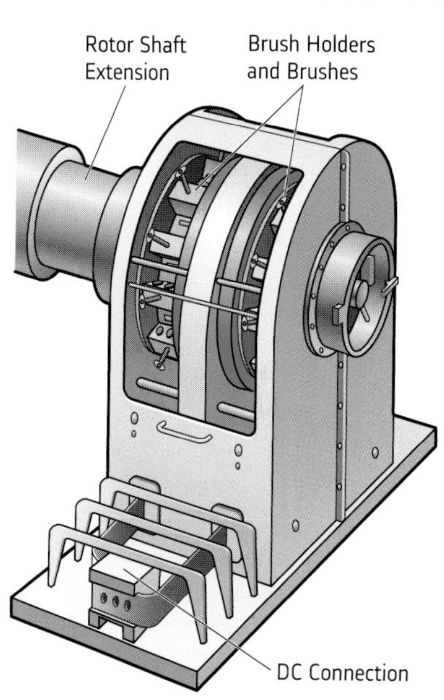

Figure 4-43 | Brush gear compartment (DC, direct current)

Rotating Excitation

The excitation power is produced by a rotating exciter machine, which is driven from the generator shaft end. The rotating winding of the exciter feeds into a rectifier equipped with silicon diodes. The rotating rectifier supplies the rotor winding of the generator.

There are two basic designs of rotating exciter: the conventional exciter, in which a three-phase winding supplies a rectifier bridge with fused parallel diodes in the branches, and an overhung bell exciter, in which a multi-phase winding supplies a multi-phase bridge of individual diodes (*Fig. 4-44*). The latter generally is without fuses and is characterized by its short axial extension, which eliminates the need for a third bearing. In a conventional exciter, the stator surrounds the exciter rotor. In the overhung bell design, the stator is arranged inside the exciter rotor and extends into the cavity of the overhung bell. The AVR supplies the field current to the exciter stator (*Fig. 4-45*).

Because the exciter power is generated mainly by the exciter running as a small generator, the required control power from the AVR is quite low and can be provided by a small, thyristor-controlled rectifier. Rotating exciters require no on-load maintenance.

COOLING GAS CIRCUITS

The cooling gas removes the losses produced in the stator and rotor. It also maintains the conductor temperatures at acceptable levels.

In small air-cooled generators, the air is driven by axial fans located at the rotor shaft ends. The air flows through the rotor conductors (direct cooling) and radially out through the slot wedges into the air gap, where it mixes with cold air coming from the open ends of the air gap (*Fig. 4-46*). This air mix enters the stator core through a multitude of radial cooling ducts. By means of this system, the air cools the stator core and, thus, removes the losses from the stator core and winding. Losses from the stator winding conductors are all removed through the main insulation (indirect cooling). The hot air escapes through the core back. On open air ventilated units, ambient air is drawn into the fans

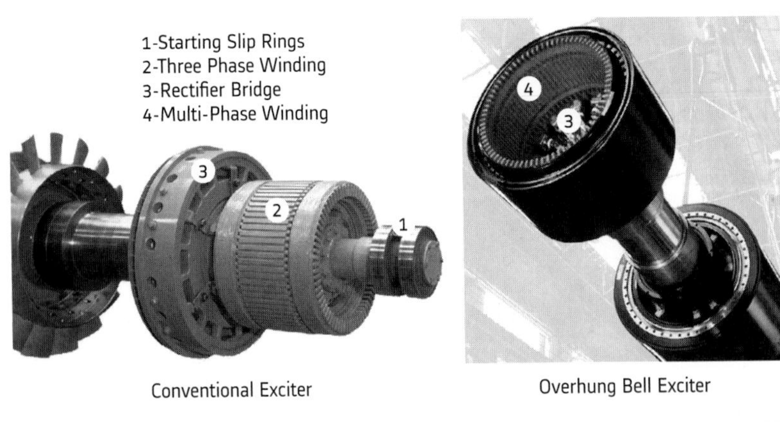

Figure 4-44 | Conventional and overhung bell exciters

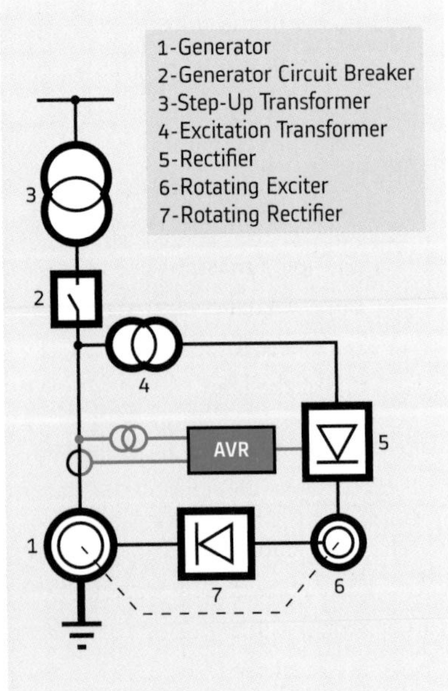

Figure 4-45 | Rotating excitation (AVR, automated voltage regulator)

through filters, and the hot air from the core back is exhausted through silencers. On closed air flow machines (TEWAC), the hot air from the core back is passed through air–water heat exchangers, and the cooled air returns to the fan.

In larger air-cooled generators, the stator core is equipped with a series of cold and warm air chambers. Fresh air is supplied into the air gap by centripetal flow in the cold air chambers. The warm air chambers expel the heated air at the core back, where it is fed by a series of ducts to the air–water heat exchangers. The system results in uniform stator winding temperatures and reduces the total air flow, increasing efficiency.

Hydrogen-cooled generators are similar in cooling to the largest air-cooled generators. The hydrogen is subject to a static overpressure in the range of 58 to 87 psia (4–6 bar) and, thus, combines highly efficient cooling with low windage loss.

Hydrogen/water-cooled turbo-generators have independent, direct water cooling of the stator winding. The ventilation of the rotor is similar to that of indirectly cooled machines (*Fig. 4-47*). The ventilation of the stator core, however, can vary. Some designs use radial cooling ducts, similar to indirectly cooled machines, whereas others employ axial cooling channels in the stator core formed by special punchings of the laminations.

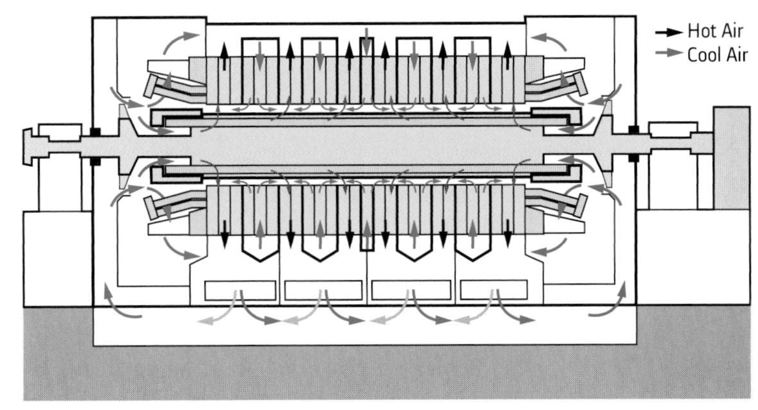

Figure 4-46 | Air-cooled generator

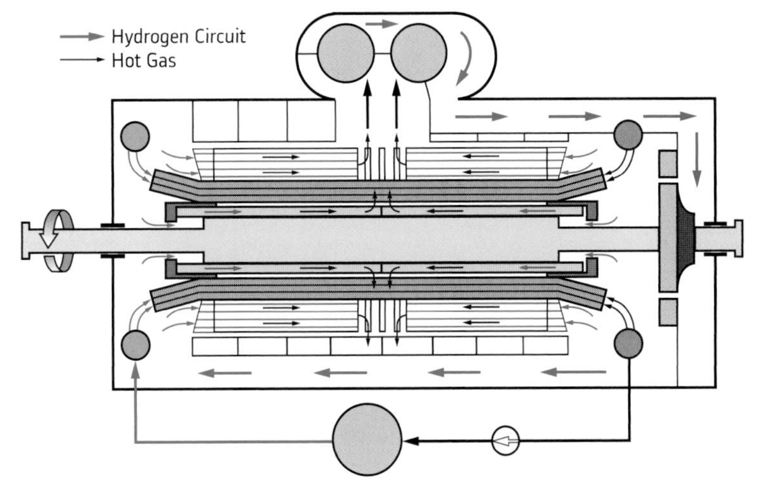

Figure 4-47 | Hydrogen/water-cooled generator

WATER-COOLED STATOR BARS

Large generators are equipped with water-cooled stator bars. Water cooling allows an increase in electrical loading far beyond the values of indirect cooling. To achieve this water flow, rectangular tubes of the same width as the strands are dispersed into the Roebel bar stacks. Most generator designs use copper tubes. This requires rigid control of the cooling water quality to avoid oxidation of the copper, leading to blockage of the cooling tubes. In modern generators, the tubes are made of stainless steel, which avoids the risk of copper corrosion.

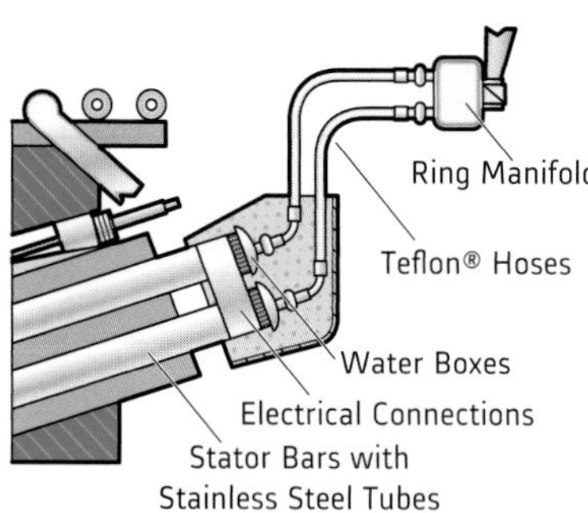

Figure 4-48 | Water-cooled stator bars

The ends of the stator bar connect to water boxes. On bars with conventional copper tubes, the strands and tubes of the stator bar are brazed together to form a combined electrical connection and water box. This brazed connection is a weak point of design on many generators, because microscopic failures in the brazed joint can allow water into the stator winding insulation. This problem is avoided by making the electrical connection of the copper strands between copper plates and hydraulic connection of the stainless-steel tubes in a separate, welded water box (*Fig. 4-48*).

The water passes through all bars in parallel. This is achieved by a ring manifold at one end of the generator, which supplies water via electrically insulated, Teflon® hoses to each bar. The water is collected on the other end in a similar manner. Usually, sensors are fitted to measure the water outlet temperatures to help detect corrosion or blockage of the cooling tubes.

A separate auxiliary unit provides circulation and cooling of the water and maintains the water quality. Regeneration of the water normally is done in an ion exchanger. The water quality is permanently monitored by sensing the electrical conductivity. The water pressure is kept below the hydrogen pressure so that, in case of leaks, water does not leak into the machine.

HYDROGEN MANAGEMENT AND SEALS

Hydrogen-cooled generators need rigid hydrogen management to maintain operational performance and safety. This is achieved by the design of the generator itself and by the auxiliary equipment connected to the generator. The generator housing is pressure tested and equipped with shaft seals. The shaft seals consist of two rings, which are assembled from segments. The rings are floating and close around the shaft with a small clearance. The seal oil enters the gap between the rings and fills the clearance between ring and shaft. Because oil pressure is kept slightly above hydrogen pressure, the seal oil flows through the clearance in the hydrogen side ring and prevents hydrogen from escaping. The same—with more pressure drop and, thus, more flow—applies to the air side ring. An array of baffling rings collects the oil flow. This single-circuit seal is very common, however, because it combines the highest pressure with the lowest hydrogen leakage rate. More complex twin-or triple-circuit seals are available as well.

The drain oil flow from the hydrogen seals passes to the seal oil auxiliary package unit, which essentially consists of a pump and degassing tanks. The degassed seal oil (vacuum oil) is pumped back into the shaft seal. Because the seal oil system is a vital safety issue, its components are arranged with various levels of redundancy. The seal oil unit operates as long as hydrogen is in the generator and when the generator is at a standstill. The seal oil unit generally is a few yards (a few meters) below the generator level, and the drain seal oil returns in slightly inclined ducting to prevent production of foam.

A gas unit is connected to the generator. The gas unit serves for safe filling with hydrogen, for maintaining hydrogen supply, and for evacuation of the hydrogen. The gas unit is connected to a hydrogen supply, commonly consisting of a battery of gas baffles in a free area, and to a purging medium supply, commonly an array of CO_2 bottles. Hydrogen filling of the generator is preceded by a purging of air using CO_2 and then a purging of CO_2 using hydrogen. Evacuation of hydrogen is done the reverse way. This avoids any explosive mixtures of gases. Hydrogen pressure, purity, and consumption (leakage) are continuously monitored when the generator is operational.

AVR AND ELECTRICAL GENERATOR PROTECTION

The electrical output of the generator is continuously monitored by current and voltage (potential) transformers fitted at the generator terminals. The measured current and voltage signals are used for control and protection purposes. Small generators have this equipment integrated within the casing; larger units have this equipment outside the generator.

Some of the current and voltage transformers are used to determine the generator active power output. This value is passed to the turbine control and compared with a set point value. The difference signal is used to control the turbine valves and, hence, output power. The measured voltages are also passed to the AVR. Usually, the signal is compared with a set point value for the voltage, and deviations are acted on by the generator excitation equipment (constant voltage regime). Other practices are to compensate further with an additional current signal to determine the actual reactive power and to work on constant reactive power delivery. The AVR control part often is integrated in the static excitation compartment, where it acts on the gates of a silicon-controlled rectifier (six-pulse thyristor bridge) to control the DC current supplied to the generator rotor. For rotating excitation, the AVR acts on a small, silicon-controlled rectifier, which supplies the DC current to the exciter armature winding, which in turn controls the generator rotor current.

Modern AVRs are prepared to be equipped with an optional power system stabilizer. The power system stabilizer senses low-frequency oscillations in the electric power and counteracts these oscillations by modulating the gating of the thyristor bridge. Some current transformers are used for protection purposes. Currents are compared at each end of the winding (differential protection) and between phases (phase imbalance) as well as being summed over phases (earth leakage current). These signals can indicate different types of electrical faults in the stator winding.

ERIC PICKERING
CHEE LOONG CHONG
BEAT ZIMMERLI

Control of Power Plant Stack Emissions

Chapter **Five**

This chapter presents the various types of commercially available equipment for the control of particulate and gaseous emissions from power plants. No reference is made to national or local legislation or regulations, because these change from year to year. Such regulations are best found in the *Federal Register* in the United States or obtained from local environmental regulatory agencies in other countries.

ENVIRONMENTAL FACTORS IN POWER PRODUCTION

The installation of highly efficient emission control systems including electrostatic precipitators (ESPs), fabric filters (baghouses), selective catalytic reduction (SCR), and flue gas desulfurization (FGD) systems has become increasingly necessary. Power plant owners must include such systems in their planning in order to obtain permission to start construction of a new facility. Additional controls that are applied to other gaseous emissions, such as SO_3, mercury, and condensable particulates, and to liquid and solid wastes that result from the processing, handling, and disposal of fossil fuels and their products of combustion add considerably to the complexity and cost of installation, operation, and maintenance of power plants. The amount and complexity of emission control systems will become even more of an issue as carbon dioxide emissions from power plants are restricted by environmental regulations.

Changes in fuel availability as well as air-quality standards have significantly impacted the electric utility industry. Discounting inflation, the cost of installation for a major facility has more than doubled since the imposition of environmental laws. Because of the permits needed to satisfy environmental statutes and the delays occasioned by debating these in public, the time required to plan and construct a fossil fuel power plant has increased by as much as 2 to 3 years. Besides the emission control equipment described in this chapter, a coal-fired power plant must have:

- Very high static pressure, induced draft fans, or additional booster fans to accommodate draft requirements
- FGD solid waste and ash beneficiation, handling, and disposal systems
- More sophisticated treatment of raw water, makeup water, and wastewater
- Condenser cooling water systems that do not add heat to inland or coastal waters.

The auxiliary power requirements of equipment to satisfy environmental regulations will demand a significant percentage of the total installed capacity of a power plant.

POWER PLANT EMISSIONS

Four types of emissions from fuel-burning processes are judged to be significant from an air-quality standpoint: particulate matter, sulfur oxides, nitrogen oxides, and mercury. Carbon dioxide has recently received a great deal of attention and, while presently unregulated in the United States, likely will be regulated in the future and is already subject to a cap-and-trade program in the European Union.

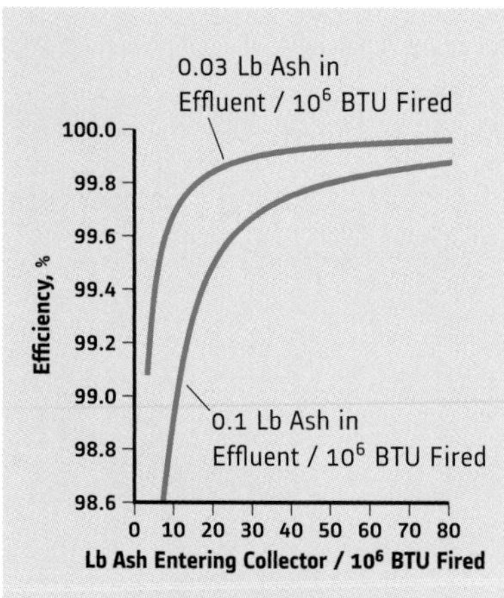

Figure 5-1 | Required particulate collection efficiency

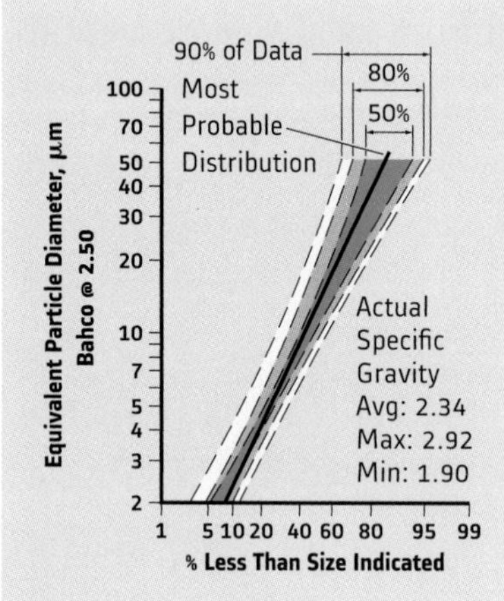

Figure 5-2 | Fly ash distribution

Historically, particulate matter has received the greatest attention, because it is easily seen and often labeled as a public nuisance.

PARTICULATE EMISSIONS

Emissions from coal-fired boilers vary considerably, depending on the ash content of the coal and on the type of firing. A pulverized coal (PC)-fired unit can be expected to have 80 to 90% of the coal ash leaving the furnace with the flue gas. The balance of the ash leaves through the boiler bottom ash removal system, hoppers under economizers and air heaters, and pulverizer reject systems. *Figure 5-1* illustrates the removal efficiency required of particulate-collection equipment for high-ash-content coals and very low levels of effluent ash. The requirement often is expressed as an emission requirement rather than in terms of collection efficiency. Emission levels as low as approximately 0.004 gr/scfm (10 mg/Nm^3) at 6% O_2 are not unusual in Europe for green field plants, whereas older plants may have to meet emissions in the range of 0.015 to 0.040 gr/scfm (35–100 mg/Nm^3).

Because fly ash is not homogeneous, its properties (e.g., specific gravity, particle shape, and particle size) are very difficult to describe in absolute terms. Methods for determining these properties include photomicrographs, sedimentation, elutriation, and inertial impaction devices. Fly ash is the combination of inert or inorganic residue in PC particles with varying amounts of carbon or coke particles resulting from incomplete combustion. In general, the inorganic ash particles consist primarily of silicates, oxides, and sulfates, together with small quantities of phosphates and other trace compounds. Because coal is mined from the ground, the inorganic fraction (or mineral matter content) can be considered to be a local sampling of the earth's crust. As such, trace quantities of numerous elements can be found in coal ash. Particle size varies from less than 0.01 micron in diameter to more than 100 microns. *Figure 5-2*, based on test data,[1] shows the particle size distribution of fly ash at equivalent particle diameters to be between 2 and 50 microns for typical coals used in PC boilers.

SULFUR OXIDE EMISSIONS

The quantity of sulfur varies widely for different coals and may range from less than 0.5 to more than 5%. Sulfur generally is present in two forms: organic and inorganic. The inorganic compound pyrite (FeS_2) is present as discrete particles within the fuel and typically accounts for 20 to 50% of the total sulfur. Pyrite as a percentage of total sulfur is from less than 10 to more than 55% for the low-sulfur Appalachian Basin coal and from approximately 25 to 70% for the higher-sulfur Illinois Basin fuel. The coal milling and classifying operations associated with PC steam generators can separate a substantial portion of the pyritic sulfur from the coal. An additional amount of inorganic sulfur is retained in the bottom ash, and some sulfur is either retained or adsorbed on the alkaline fly ash, leaving the boiler in solid form and eventually captured in the particulate control equipment.

As fuels burn, most of the sulfur is converted to SO_2 and SO_3. In general, 90% or more of the sulfur in the fuel will oxidize to gaseous sulfur oxides. Typically, concentrations will be from 0.05 to 0.30% by volume in the products of combustion. The further conversion of SO_2 to SO_3 ranges from 1 to 4%. The formation of SO_3 in a boiler is a complex process and is influenced by the oxidation of SO_2 by molecular oxygen, the oxidation of SO_2 in the flame by atomic oxygen, and the catalytic oxidation of SO_2. With decreasing temperature, SO_3 progressively becomes the more thermodynamically stable form. The equilibrium conversion in the reaction

$$SO_2 + \frac{1}{2}O_2 \rightarrow SO_3$$

increases with decreasing temperature (*Fig.* 5-3). There is some influence on the conversion of the flue gas oxygen level within the range of practical interest in boilers, with higher oxygen increasing the thermodynamic equilibrium conversion ratio.

Because SO_3/SO_2 conversion rates of only some few percent are observed in practice at the boiler exit, it is safe to assume that the production of SO_3 is kinetically limited during the residence in the boiler system. In a chemical kinetics simulation using the rate constants for nine homogenous, gas-phase reaction paths, modeling both high- and low-sulfur coals,[2] it was calculated that approximately 0.7% of the SO_2 was converted to SO_3. The conversion mechanism is active only during the first 2 seconds of residence time in the boiler, which corresponds to a cooling of the flue gases down to approximately 1,900°F (1,300°K). At lower temperatures, the reaction rates become negligible.

Evidence also indicates catalytic conversion processes based on the catalytic activity of fly ash. Ash deposit iron compounds also can contribute to the production of SO_3 in the temperature range of 800 to 1,200°F (700 to 900°K). This mechanism is less well documented and quantified. The effect also is plant specific, because it is affected by the soot blowing schedule and the boiler surface area. The net effect of the two mechanisms (the gas phase and the catalytic ash effects) is estimated to correspond to a conversion of 0.7 to 1.4%.

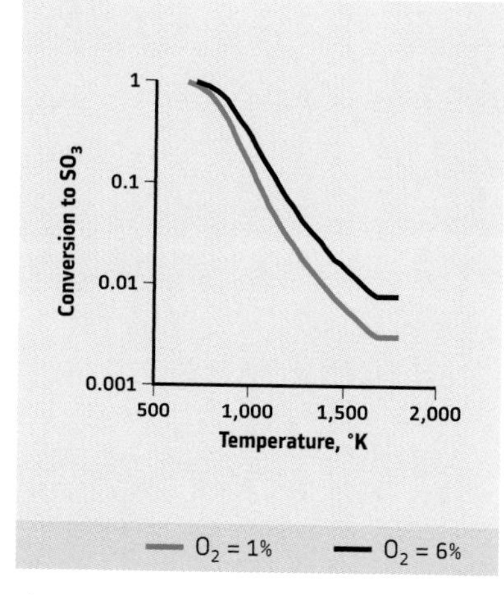

Figure 5-3 | SO_3/SO_2 equilibrium ratio

NITROGEN OXIDE EMISSIONS

During the combustion process in a conventional fossil fuel-fired boiler, oxides of nitrogen (collectively referred to as NOx) form in the high-temperature region both in and around the flame zone. The oxidation of both atmospheric nitrogen (thermal NOx) and nitrogen contained in the fuel (fuel NOx) is the cause. The rate of formation is influenced by the temperature level and the local oxygen concentration. Reducing both the flame temperature and the excess air level can help to control thermal NOx formation. Fuel NOx is related to the available nitrogen in the fuel and is influenced most significantly by the oxygen concentration in the combustion region. (In addition to the information on post-furnace NOx control in this chapter, refer to Chapter 2 for a discussion of NOx formation during combustion and to Chapter 12 for techniques to reduce NOx in furnaces.)

MERCURY EMISSIONS

Mercury often is a trace element in coal. When the coal is burned, some of the mercury is oxidized, and some remains as the element in the vapor state. Mercury has been considered to be a surrogate for other heavy metals that also might be present in the coal. Mercury emissions are being restricted in many areas.

INTEGRATED EMISSION CONTROLS

For decades, utilities and large industrial power producers in the United States have been routinely purchasing ESPs or fabric filters to control particulate emissions from their boilers. Since enactment of the 1970 Clean Air Act requiring control of sulfur dioxide, utilities also have been installing FGD systems. More than 250,000 MW of FDG systems have been purchased in the United States. Wet FGD systems have accounted for approximately 80% of those purchased, dry FGD systems for more than 10%, and all other types of FGD systems for less than 10%. Emissions of NOx have been controlled in the combustion process and through the use of SCR. *Figure 5-4* illustrates the most common and typical integration of the particulate, nitrogen oxide, and sulfur dioxide control systems. If used, SCR equipment can be designed for either high- or low-dust content, thus dictating the position of the ESP.

CONTROL OF PARTICULATE EMISSIONS

Particulate emission control deals with methods of removing particles dispersed in effluent gases of power, industrial process, and commercial plants. These dispersions have come to include all particles in air or other gases. Dispersoids are characterized by their physical, chemical, and electrical properties; their particle size and structure; their rate of settling under gravity; their optical activity; their ability to absorb an electrical charge; their surface-to-volume ratio; and their chemical reaction rate. Particles larger than 100 microns are excluded from consideration, because they settle rapidly.

Dispersoids generally are classified as dust, smoke, fumes, and mists. *Figure 5-5A* indicates the common dispersoids and the typical particle size for each classification. *Figure 5-5B* shows the devices for collecting the various classifications of dispersoids. Note that methods relying on gravity or centrifugal forces are effective for removal of particles larger than 10 microns. Efficient collection of particles 1 micron in size and of submicron particulates requires devices that depend on electrical force, impaction, interception, or inertial diffusion. These are the capture mechanisms at work in ESPs, fabric filters, and high-energy wet scrubbers.

INFLUENCE OF COAL AND COMBUSTION CHARACTERISTICS

The varying coal characteristics described in Chapter 2 and Appendix A have a dominant effect on the efficiency of particle removal. The variation in ash content, ash composition, ash resistivity, and particle size distribution requires an engineering evaluation of collection principles to reduce emissions to required levels.

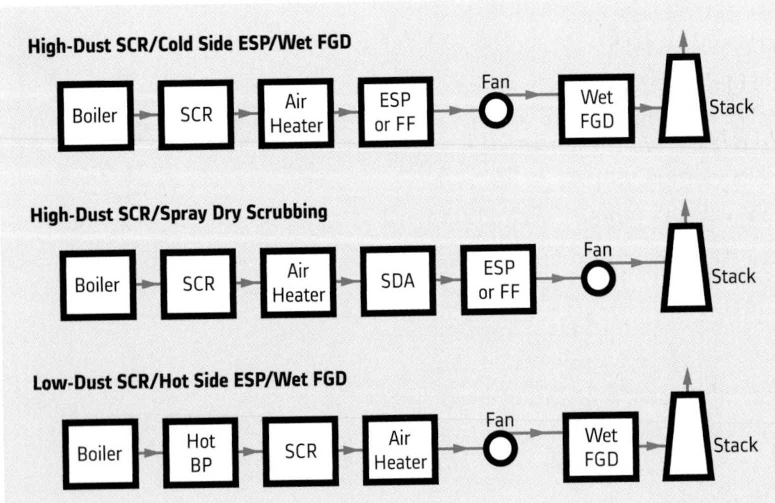

Figure 5-4 | Typical power plant cleaning systems

INFLUENCE OF VOLUMETRIC GAS FLOW

No matter what type of fly ash collector is to be installed on a steam generator, it is essential that it be designed for the correct gas volume. Manufacturers design and size their equipment based on their experience with this same type of equipment. This experience includes tests on both laboratory or pilot-plant equipment and on full-scale equipment. The joint American Boiler Manufacturers Association (ABMA) and Institute of Clean Air Companies (ICAC) survey has shown a difference in the volume of flue gas that is measured by pitot tube and the volume of gas that is calculated from a stoichiometric balance.[3–16]

The pitot-tube measurements consistently indicate a higher gas volume than stoichiometric calculations do. The manufacturer of the dust-collection or desulfurization equipment therefore must ascertain if the gas volume for equipment design has been stoichiometrically calculated and be aware that such a value may differ from a volume measured by pitot tube in the operating installation. It is vital that proper corrections be made for plant elevation and local negative pressure ahead of the induced draft fan to arrive at the actual gas volume (see Chapter 6 and *Code of Federal Regulations*[17]). Performance testing required to demonstrate compliance with air-quality regulations uses pitot-tube techniques as prescribed by U.S. Environmental Protection Agency (EPA) methods stipulated in 40 CFR Part 60, Appendix A (Reference Methods) 1, 5, 17, 201 and 202.[17]

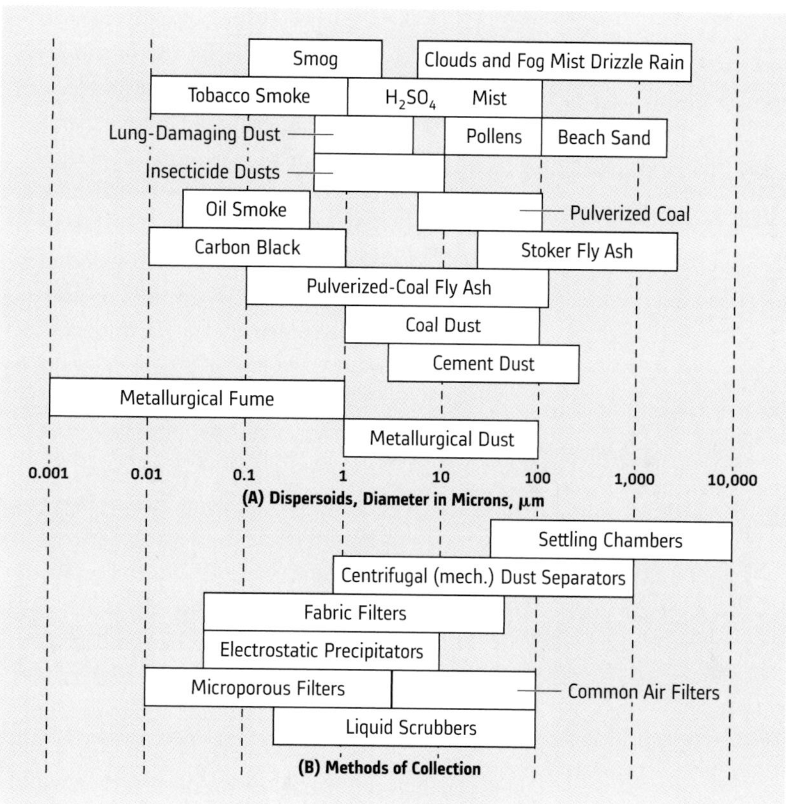

Figure 5-5 | Classification of dispersoids and methods of collection

MEASUREMENT TECHNIQUES

It is difficult to analyze the size distribution of fine particulate matter, because fly ash is not homogeneous. The varying specific gravities and particle shapes make it difficult to describe size in absolute terms. Many methods, including photomicrographs and various sedimentation and elutriation techniques, have been used to determine the size distribution. The American Society of Mechanical Engineers (ASME) Performance Test Code Committee has selected terminal settling velocity to characterize fly ash particulate emissions from furnaces.

Terminal Velocity

Particle terminal velocity is a significant parameter in the design of mechanical separators that use inertial or centrifugal forces to separate dust from a gas stream. It includes the effect of particle shape and specific gravity for each particle. Its determination is important for heterogeneous dusts of varying shape and specific gravity. Determination of terminal velocity for a centrifugal classifier is included in *ASME Performance Test Code 28.* Fly ash characterization also includes methods for bulk electrical resistivity, in situ resistivity, and particle size.

Bulk Electrical Resistivity

Particulate resistivity can be determined using a high-voltage conductivity cell in which a sample of known thickness is placed between two oppositely charged electrodes. Guard rings eliminate fringe effects. A voltage is applied between the two electrodes, and the current is noted. The resistivity is then calculated and reported in ohm-centimeters (Ω-cm). The conductivity cell is placed in an oven, and the resistivity can be measured at different temperatures. The humidity in the oven also should be noted; normally, it is possible to vary the humidity. The effect of temperature and humidity on resistivity thus can be investigated. The influence of other gas components, however, cannot normally be taken into account. *Figure 5-6* illustrates typical bulk resistivity as a function of temperature and humidity as measured in a laboratory.

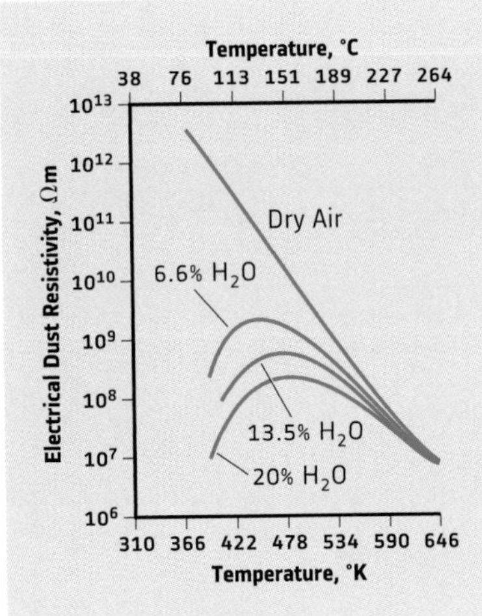

Figure 5-6 | Laboratory measurement of fly ash resistivity for varying humidity (% by volume) in the flue gas

In Situ Resistivity

A combination high-voltage and ground-potential probe, inserted in the gas stream, has a negative high-voltage probe consisting of a flat disk that is concentric about a needle-point electrode. The needle-point electrode precipitates particulates electrically from the dispersoid. The flat, charged disk is separated from the needle point so as not to affect the precipitation of particulate onto a grounded electrode. After a short time, the charged disk is lowered to entrap the precipitated particulate between it and the grounded electrode. Calculation is the same as for bulk electrical resistivity.[18] Real flue gas conditions prevail. The collection efficiency of the apparatus is low, however, and the calculated resistivity may not reflect the resistivity of the total ash. The missing fraction—mainly the fine particles—may change the resistivity substantially.

DUST COLLECTION BY MECHANICAL MEANS

Cyclone-type, mechanical collectors are now used only occasionally as pre-collectors to ESPs and fabric filters. Mechanical collectors can be either dry cyclone collectors or wet scrubbers.

Mechanical Cyclone Collectors

These devices achieve particulate removal by centrifugal, inertial, and gravitational forces developed in a vortex separator. The dust-laden gas is admitted either tangentially or axially over whirl vanes (*Fig. 5-7*) to create a high velocity in the cylindrical portion of the device. Particles are subjected to a centrifugal force and an oppositely directed viscous drag. The balance between these two forces determines whether a particle will move to the wall or be carried into the vortex sink and then passed on to the clean-gas outlet tube.

The high-velocity, downwardly directed vortex is reversed at the bottom of the cylindrical section. In this reversal, inertia and gravity as well as centrifugal force inject the dust into the hopper. The action of the reversed-gas circulation takes place over a small diameter but at relatively great velocity.

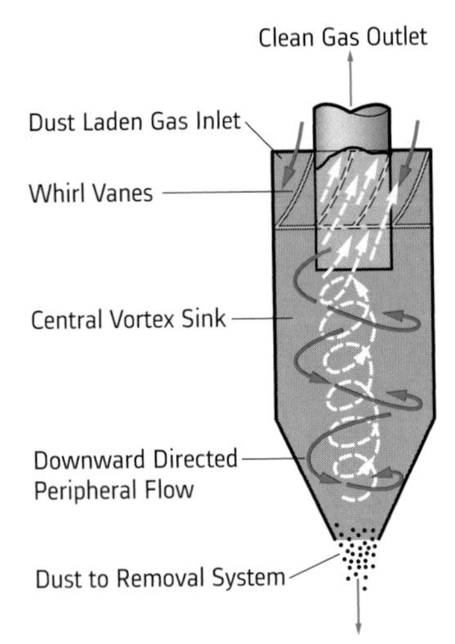

Figure 5-7 | Principle of cyclone-separator operation

This inner vortex has an axially upward component that carries the spirally flowing gas to the outlet pipe at the upper center of the separating unit. Because these collectors depend primarily on differential inertia, collection efficiencies vary with particle size, particle density, gas temperature, and pressure drop through the apparatus. Efficiencies are very high on material greater than 20 microns in size but drop rapidly for smaller particles. The overall collection efficiency of a cyclone can be estimated when the particle size distribution and specific gravity of the dust as well as the allowable pressure drop are known. *Figure 5-8* relates collection efficiency to particle size. In normal boiler operation, differential-pressure requirements for mechanical collectors are from 2 to 5″ WG (0.4–0.9 cm Hg).

An alternative design of mechanical collector has been developed wherein a high-voltage discharge electrode is placed in the center of the internal tube, providing electrical forces to help with the collection of smaller-particle-size matter from the gas stream. A number of parallel units are required when high gas flows prevail.

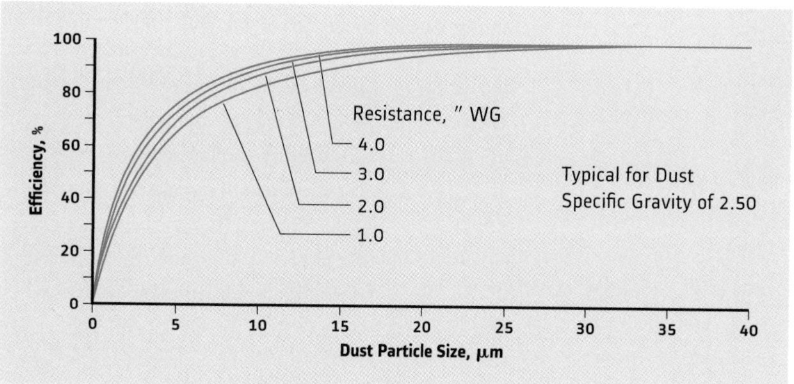

Figure 5-8 | Form of mechanical cyclone dust-collector efficiency curve versus particle size

Wet Scrubbers

In the analysis of wet particulate scrubbing, a number of important facts are known. First, the dust particle must impact on the water droplet. The impaction efficiency is a function of the dimensionless group $\frac{V_r V_s}{Dg}$, where V_r is the relative velocity between the water droplet and the dust particle, V_s is the settling velocity for the dust particle, D is the diameter of the water droplet in microns, and g is the acceleration of gravity. Because g and V_s are constant for a dust particle of given size, target efficiency is a direct function of the relative velocity and an inverse function of the droplet diameter. If the collection efficiency depends critically on relative velocity and droplet size, then collection efficiency also must be a function of the power supplied to the unit.

Capture of small particles requires high-energy inputs, usually in the form of greater pressure drops across the scrubber. Low pressure-drop scrubbers, such as spray towers, collect coarse dust in the range of 2 to 5 microns. High pressure-drop venturi scrubbers are effective in removing particles in the range of 0.1 to 1.0 microns. Typically, a scrubber operating at a 6″ WG (1.1 cm Hg) pressure drop should capture practically all particles greater than 5 microns and approximately 90% of the particles in the range of 1 to 2 microns. *Figure 5-9* shows a typical efficiency curve for a wet scrubber operating at a 6″ WG (1.1 cm Hg) pressure drop.

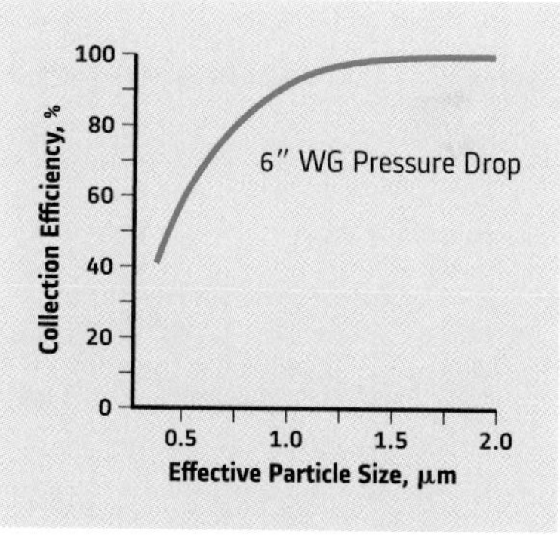

Figure 5-9 | Wet-scrubber fractional efficiency curve

Venturi Scrubbers

In a venturi scrubber, dust-laden gases are wetted continuously at the venturi throat. Flowing at 12,000 to 18,000 fpm (61 to 91 m/sec), the gases produce a shearing force on the scrubbing liquor because of the initial high velocity differential between the two streams. This shearing force causes the liquor to atomize into very fine droplets.

Impaction takes place between the dust entrained in the gas stream and the liquid droplets. As the gas decelerates, collision continues, and agglomerated, dust-laden liquor droplets discharge through a diffuser into the lower chamber of a separator vessel. Impingement of the stream into the liquid reservoir removes most of the particulates. A venturi-type scrubber operating in the pressure range of 30 to 40″ WG (5.6 to 7.5 cm Hg) can collect nearly 100% of particles in the range of 0.2 to 10 microns.

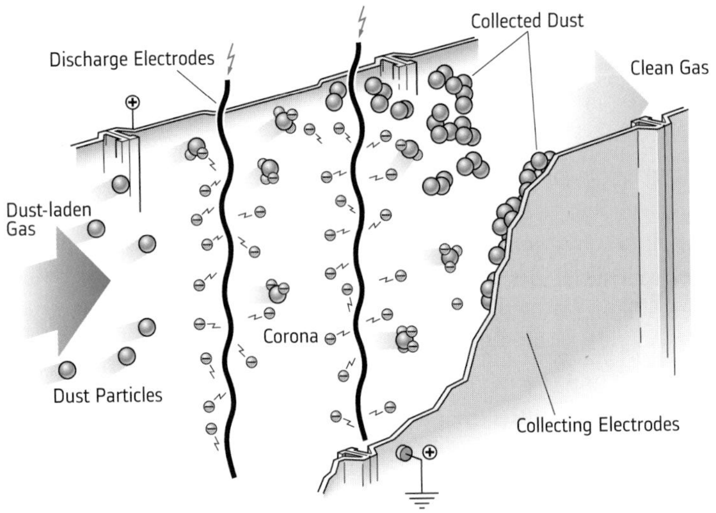

Figure 5-10 | Operating principle of electrostatic precipitation

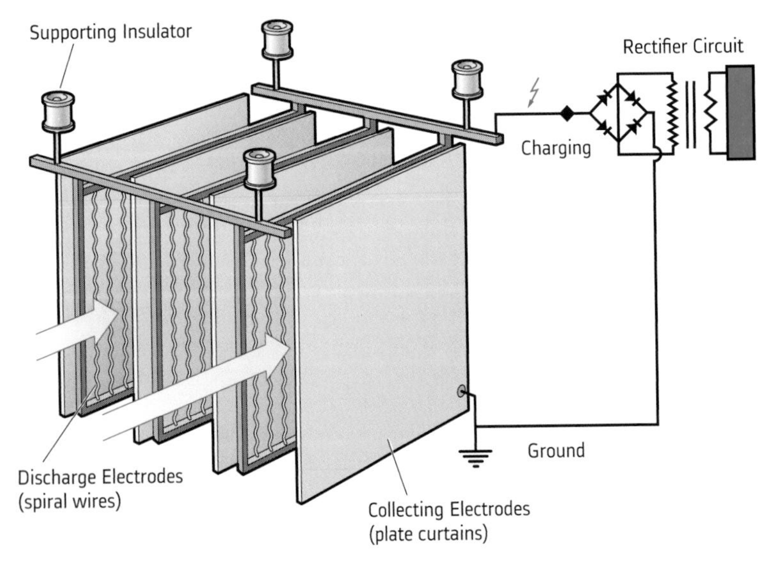

Figure 5-11 | Principal design of a single-stage electrostatic precipitator

ELECTROSTATIC PRECIPITATION OF DUST

In electrostatic precipitation, suspended particles in the gas are electrically charged, then driven to collecting electrodes by an electrical field. The electrodes are rapped to cause the particles to drop into collecting hoppers. The charges and the electrical field are generated by high-voltage discharge electrodes that are placed in between the grounded collecting electrodes (*Fig. 5-10*).

This process differs from mechanical or filtering processes, in which forces are exerted directly on the particulates rather than on the gas as a whole. Effective separation of particles can be achieved with a low power expenditure and with a low draft loss compared to fabric filters and scrubbers and with little or no effect on the composition of the gas.

The most commonly used design is the single-stage ESP—known previously as the Cottrell type—that combines the ionizing and collecting process (*Fig. 5-11*). The discharge electrodes are suspended on insulators connected to a high-voltage source—the power supply.

The dust-laden gas flows horizontally between grounded collecting plates. This system is powered from a transformer rectifier (T/R), and the assembly is called a "bus section." There usually are several independent bus sections in length, and for large plants with high gas flows, there are parallel bus sections. One or several (parallel) casings enclose the sections to form the ESP plant. The T/R sets often are placed on the roof of the ESP. The high voltage is unidirectional—usually negative—and can exceed 100 kV for certain applications.

The unipolar discharge of gas ions starts at a critical voltage—the onset voltage. The ionization is visible as a corona at the discharge electrode. The negative ions move toward the positive collecting electrode; the positive ions migrate toward the discharge electrode. The movement of the ions constitutes the corona current. When a higher voltage is applied, the current increases. The ions become attached to particles carried by the gas stream. The charges on the particles and the electrical field move the fly ash to the appropriate electrode. Higher voltages and currents enhance the precipitation process for most fly ash. The particles attached to the positive electrode dissipate their charge and become electrically neutral. The fly ash layer on the electrodes is removed mechanically by rapping. In a two-stage precipitator, the ionizing and collecting stages are separated. This design is used for low particulate loadings and minimum ozone generation, and it is common for indoor ventilation systems.

Single-stage ESPs can be either hanging, weighted-wire, or rigid-frame units. As initially applied in the United States, precipitators were designed to provide a minimum plate area at low cost. Designs used interlocking collecting plates and weighted-wire discharge electrodes with a maximum height of 36 feet (11 m). Roof-mounted, gang-rapping vibrators removed particulate matter from the collecting plates.

To meet a demand for ultra-high efficiency collectors of rugged construction and high reliability, European manufacturers in possession of the basic patents disseminated by Frederick Gardner Cottrell developed the rigid-frame precipitator. Actually, this design more closely approximated Cottrell's original design than the U.S.-style, weighted-wire designs did. The term *rigid-frame* refers to the rugged pipe-frame or mast-construction discharge electrode, which largely precludes wire breakages and electrical short circuits. The basic design incorporates segmented collecting plate configurations and profiles (for close fabrication tolerances over heights above 50 feet [15 m]), rigid discharge frames and electrodes, and much greater division of rapping (often with individual rapping for each discharge frame). Modern ESPs are robust and have high reliability. Availabilities for new ESPs often exceed 99%.

Precipitator Design Factors

Precipitator designs consider:

- Specific collection area (SCA)
- Treatment time
- Gas velocity
- Spacing
- Electrode configuration and rapping
- Number of bus sections and fields
- Power supply
- Automatic voltage control
- Hopper size and slope

SPECIFIC COLLECTION AREA. The SCA relates the size of one precipitator to another in terms of the effective collecting-electrode surface area in square feet per thousand cfm (square meters per cubic meter per second) of gas treated. The area considered is the flat, projected surface of both sides of the collecting electrodes; the gas volume is the actual volume at the design operating temperature and at the prevailing absolute pressure in the ESP. Depending on the physical, chemical, and electrical characteristics of the coal ash, precipitator SCAs range from 300 to more than 1,000 ft^2/cfm (60 to 200 m^2/cubic meter per sec) for collection efficiencies above 99.5%.[19]

TREATMENT TIME. This refers to the length of time the flue gas will spend in the presence of the electrical field at design gas velocity. The treatment length is not the total front-to-rear dimension of the "box" but, rather, is the horizontal dimension from the plane of the front face of the first collector to the rear plane of the last surface, less any space for walkways, beams, and so on.

GAS VELOCITY. Superficial gas velocity is a critical design parameter. It is calculated by dividing the actual gas volume (at design temperature and absolute pressure) by the face area of the precipitator immediately in front of the first collecting electrode. Effective plate height is multiplied by the inside, face-to-face dimension between the outer two collecting electrodes—one at each side of the sidewall casings—to give the face area. The calculated gas velocity is the average velocity. Real velocity at any spot may deviate somewhat from the average velocity because of imperfections from the distribution of the gas.

Designs for medium- and high-resistivity fly ashes and for low emissions often use average velocities between 3 and 4 ft/s (0.9 and 1.2 m/s). For fly ash particles that easily agglomerate, velocities on the order of 5 ft/s (1.5 m/s) can be used. Excessive gas velocities will cause re-entrainment of collected ash and, thereby, reduce the collecting efficiency.

SPACING. Spacing is the distance between adjacent collecting plates. Through the years, the spacing has been increased, because experience has shown that cost savings can be achieved. Standard spacing is approximately 16 inches (400 mm) for fly ash applications. Many years ago, the spacing normally varied between 9 and 10 inches (230 and 250 mm), and that can still be seen in old ESPs. During the 1970s, it became common to use 12 inches (300 mm). Since the mid-1980s, the common consensus is that the wider spacing (e.g., 16 inches [400 mm]) does not need longer treatment time in order to achieve a certain efficiency compared to the narrower spacing.[20,21] Thus, the actual collecting area is reduced in proportion to the spacing for a given task. For some power plants, a space of 12 inches (300 mm) remains the main alternative; on others, spacings of more than 16 inches (400 mm) are applied.

It should be noted that the SCA value for an ESP depends on the spacing. For example, the SCA value for 16 inches (400 mm) is three-fourths of the SCA for 12 inches (300 mm) for the same treatment time. The wider spacing implies that the ESP weight is reduced for the same "box." Furthermore, fewer components are used inside, and ESP reliability is increased.

ELECTRODE CONFIGURATION AND RAPPING. The shape of the electrodes and the rapping effectiveness can drastically affect the collecting efficiency of a given ESP. Properties such as current distribution along the collecting electrode, the amount of voltage and current achieved in the precipitator before sparking occurs, and the rapping sequences are important parameters in achieving efficient ESPs.[22,23]

NUMBER OF BUS SECTIONS AND FIELDS. For reliability and effectiveness, ESPs are divided into bus sections, each of which normally is energized by one independent, electrical, high-voltage power supply. There may be several bus sections in parallel and in series. Each set of parallel bus sections is called a "field." It is common to have three or more fields in the direction of gas flow. The amount of plate area per power supply—a T/R set—affects the current and voltage achieved in an electrical section. Small bus sections are more efficient per square foot than are large ones because of better control of tolerances and less variations in gas and particulate data. This implies that a lower SCA value can be used for a given task. The ESPs of European design often use large bus section areas (e.g., 60,000–80,000 ft^2 [5,600–7,400 m^2]); the U.S. design has a higher sectionalization (more T/Rs), implying smaller bus sections. Cost estimations, available space, redundancy, or spare capacity might decide the final number of bus sections.

POWER SUPPLY. The conventional T/R set produces a high direct current voltage based on the mains 50/60-Hz frequency. The T/R set charges particles flowing through the ESP. This occurs once during a portion of every half-wave. The result is that the high direct current (DC) voltage has peak and valley voltages—that is, ripple—because there is a continuous corona discharge but an intermittent charging. The collecting efficiency depends on the voltage and current that are used in the ESP. From time to time, sparking or arcing can occur between the high voltage and the grounded parts in the ESP. During a spark, the ESP is short circuited and not efficient. It therefore is important to control the spark rate and power input.

Since the mid-1990s, a new type of T/R set has been available. This T/R converts the main voltage with a frequency of up to 50 kHz to an almost pure DC voltage. The high-frequency power supply is small and lightweight compared to conventional units. The high voltage and the control units are placed together in one box. For many applications, a higher collecting efficiency can be achieved for a given ESP with this type of power supply.[24]

Improved power supplies and T/R sets provide a nearly pure DC voltage, allowing for a higher collection efficiency and reduced emissions.

AUTOMATIC VOLTAGE CONTROL. The automatic voltage control system keeps the precipitator operating at its optimum voltage and current. This digital control system allows a much faster and more reliable control of sparking and other parameters. Advanced microprocessor controls (one for each power supply) can automatically sense the operating conditions and change the set values of the current and voltages in order to achieve the highest possible collecting efficiency. The optimum settings vary with the type of coal and the boiler load, and the controls are able to handle such changes.

Intermittent energization, or semipulse, is a standard feature for modern automatic voltage control systems. The intermittent energization comprises blocking of a selected number of half-waves of the mains. The ripple is then enlarged, which results in improved collecting efficiencies for high-resistivity ashes.[25]

The automatic voltage control systems also can be designed to reduce overall ESP power consumption and can incorporate the rapping control. Sometimes, the electrical setting and rapping sequences are closely interrelated. Power saving is further enhanced for some applications by using intermittent energization.

HOPPER SIZE AND SLOPE. The proper design of the collecting hoppers forming the floor of a precipitator is important, because a breakdown in the hopper outflow that results in overfilling can severely damage the electrical internals. Alstom has made comprehensive recommendations concerning the design and heating of precipitator and fabric filter hoppers and their fly ash removal systems.[26] These recommendations, some of which are detailed later in this chapter, help to avoid costly outages attributable to these portions of the collection/transport complex.

Precipitator Design Analysis

MIGRATION VELOCITY, *w*. It was traditional to consider the semi-empirical Deutsch–Anderson equation, developed in 1922, in the analytical design of a precipitator for low efficiencies (up to 98%). In the 1970s, a modified form of the Deutsch–Anderson formula, the so-called Matts–Ohnfeldt equation,[27] was used to better predict the performance of an ESP for most applications.

The ESP collection efficiency is related to the total surface area of the collecting electrodes per unit volume of gas, or the specific collecting area (SCA). The SCA value is inversely proportional to the particle migration velocity. The expression "particle migration velocity" is the velocity the particle achieves toward the collecting plate and perpendicular to the gas flow because of its charges and the applied electrical field. Efficiency is determined by the Deutsch–Anderson equation:

$$\eta = \left(1 - e^{\frac{-Aw}{V}}\right) \times 100$$

Equation 5-1

where

η = efficiency of collection (%)
e = base of natural logarithms (2.718...)
A = collecting-electrode surface area (ft^2 [m^2])
w = migration velocity (ft/s [m/s])
V = actual volumetric gas flow rate (1,000 ft^3/s [m^3/s] at temperature and absolute pressure)
A/V = SCA

It should be noted that *w* cannot be measured but, instead, must be calculated from the equation. The calculated *w* is furthermore the average particle velocity through the ESP regardless of particle size. A significant discrepancy exists between theoretical and practical values of *w*, with the theoretical value being much higher than the actual value.[28,29] This "loss" of performance is caused by such factors as uneven gas flow, particle diffusion, electrical wind, particle charging time, and loss of particles from collecting surfaces by re-entrainment. Because the value of *w* can hardly be estimated from theory, and because of these uncertainties, it is necessary to rely upon field experience with a variety of precipitator installations.[19,26,30–34] When experience is limited, designs have to be established by means of experimentation and pilot-plant testing.[35–38]

The Deutsch–Anderson equation is important to an understanding of the precipitation process. In reality, however, it is difficult to use. It can be shown both theoretically and through real measurements that w varies with the particle size (*Fig. 5-12*). The drift or migration velocity w, also called the "precipitation rate," is determined by the magnitude of the particle charge, the strength of the electrical field, and by Stokes' law for the drag of the particles.[30,39] A large particle acquires more charges in the electrical field and gets a higher migration velocity than a small particle does. This implies that larger particles are efficiently collected in the front of an ESP but that the fine particles take a longer time to migrate to the collecting electrode. Thus, the migration velocity is not constant for low and high collecting efficiencies, because for a high efficiency, more of the fine particles must be precipitated and the average migration velocity is reduced. In order to use Equation 5-1, the particle size distribution must be known.

The difficulties encountered with Deutsch–Andersen equation led to the development of the modified equation:

$$\eta = \left(1 - e^{\left(\frac{-Aw_k}{V}\right)^k}\right) \times 100$$

Equation 5-2

where w_k is now an empirically observed migration velocity and k is a constant (~0.5, but varying between 0.4 and 0.6 depending on the specific ash and application). The other terms are as defined as for Equation 5-1.

The modified formula reduces the effect of the size distribution, and w is now rather a constant for a wide range of efficiencies for similar ash and gas conditions.

EFFECT OF ELECTRICAL PROPERTIES.

The electrical conductivity, or its inverse resistivity, of fly ash and the electrical field strength of the flue gas are two properties important to the electrostatic-collection process. For effective operation, a small but definite electric current, in the form of charges carried by gas ions and particles, flows between the high-tension discharge electrodes and the collecting electrodes. This current must pass through the layers of collected ash that normally coat the plates. The ash therefore must be able to conduct the ionic current to the grounded metal surfaces of the plates. The electrical conductivity required is very small—approximately 10^{-8} mho/m or S/m (Siemens/m), corresponding to a resistivity of 10^{10} Ω-cm.

The transport of charges through the ash layer produces a voltage or potential drop across the layer in accordance with Ohm's law. When the resistivity of the ash is in the critical zone (in the range from 10^{11} to 10^{12} Ω-cm, depending on conditions and design), the voltage drop across the ash layer can amount to several kilovolts. The existence of this voltage drop may be higher than the breakdown strength across the layer and can be sufficient to cause localized sparking because of ionization of the gas. Positive ions that are generated migrate toward the high-voltage electrode and will cause particle charging of the opposite polarity compared to the original charging. The whole process is called "back corona," and

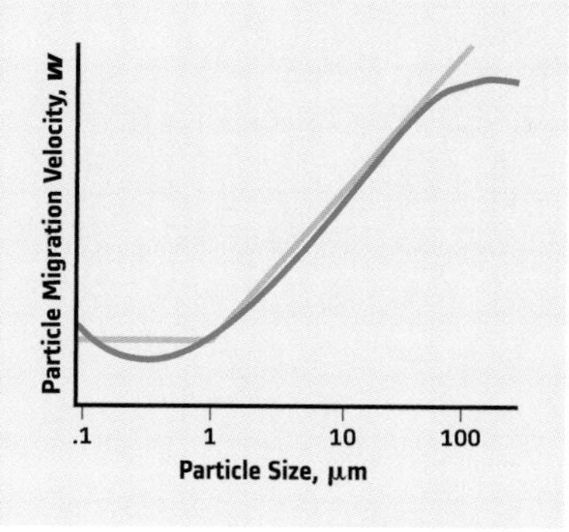

Figure 5-12 | Theoretical migration velocity as a function of particle diameter

collecting efficiency or particle migration velocity is reduced (*Fig. 5-13*).

When back corona happens, sparks flash through the dust layer and may propagate to the discharge electrode. This is the source of the intensified sparking that can occur with dusts of excessive resistivity. Sparking in the ash layer also results in re-entrainment of already-collected ash. Signs of back corona on the collecting plates are uneven ash surfaces covered with small "craters." Clearly, the higher the breakdown strength of the dust layer, the higher the resistivity that may be tolerated for a given amount of corona current.

For fly ash, the breakdown strength of the bulk ash in ¼- to ½-inch (6 to 13 mm) thick layers ranges from as low as a few hundred V/cm up to as high as 20 kV/cm. The average value of dielectric strength is in the range of 5 to 10 kV/cm.

Back-corona can be reduced by either changing the resistivity of the bulk ash (conditioning) or by reducing the corona current to a degree that breakdown does not occur. Lower currents mean a lower migration velocity, however, which must be compensated for with a larger ESP box.

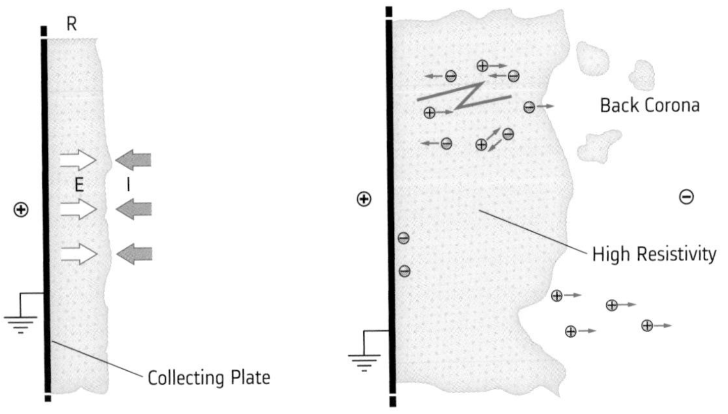

Figure 5-13 | Corona current (I) penetrating the dust layer generates ionization, or back corona, along the collecting plate (E, electrical field; R, dust layer resistivity)

ASH RESISTIVITY. Experience has shown that coal ashes with resistivities above 5×10^{11} Ω-cm could be difficult to collect, implying an increased ESP box. Low resistivity ($<10^9$ Ω-cm) ash may suffer from re-entrainment, because the ash discharges immediately after precipitation and there are no longer any electrical holding forces keeping the ash to the collecting electrodes. The range between 10^9 and 5×10^{11} Ω-cm usually is considered to be easy for fly ash precipitation.

The factors that affect resistivity are the sulfur content of the coal, flue gas temperature and moisture, and ash constituents, such as sodium, potassium, calcium, carbon, alumina, silica, and iron oxide. Ash resistivity decreases with increased concentration of sulfur trioxide and water in the flue gas and with higher sodium, potassium, and carbon in the ash. A higher content of calcium, magnesium, alumina, and silica increases resistivity. Dry fly ash (i.e., no humidity in the gas) shows an ever-increasing resistivity when the temperature is lowered. This reflects the so-called volume resistivity. Because water is always present in flue gases, however, the resistivity is decreasing at lower temperatures as soon as the fly ash is absorbing some moisture. Surface conduction starts to dominate, and a higher water dew point in the flue gas reduces the resistivity further. At high temperatures, such as those above 450 to 550°F (230 to 290°C), the resistivity is not sensitive to the water content. Peak ash resistivities occur between 250 and 450°F (120 to 230°C), depending on coal ash and flue gas characteristics. High-resistivity ash does not readily lose its charge when collected on the plates, and the agglomerated ash can be very difficult to remove. Means to overcome this problem include more efficient rapping (higher rapping forces in the collecting electrodes) or reduced corona current in connection with rapping. There also is a specially developed ESP design in which the collecting electrodes are brushed and, therefore, kept clean. The electrodes comprise a band that is moving up above the discharge frame, turning, then moving down into the hopper area continuously. The brushing is done in the hopper area, where no electrical field is present.

To have any possible value to a precipitator design engineer, dust resistivity must be measured with the dust under the same gas and temperature conditions as those at which the precipitator will operate. Also, the packing density of the dust should be the same as that of the dust layer deposited on the precipitator collectors. It will be appreciated, then, that the measurement of dust resistivity is subject to considerable problems, making it very difficult in practice to relate absolute precipitation efficiency to dust resistivity.

Figure 5-14 indicates the in situ bulk resistivity of a variety of fuels as related to temperature. Although a significant difference is found between many of the ash samples tested at temperatures below 400°F (200°C), it appears that above 600°F (300°C), many ashes will have resistivities below 5×10^{11} Ω-cm. Many Australian coals generate high-resistivity fly ashes because of a high content of silicon and aluminum and a low content of sodium in the coal ash, together with low sulfur in the coal.

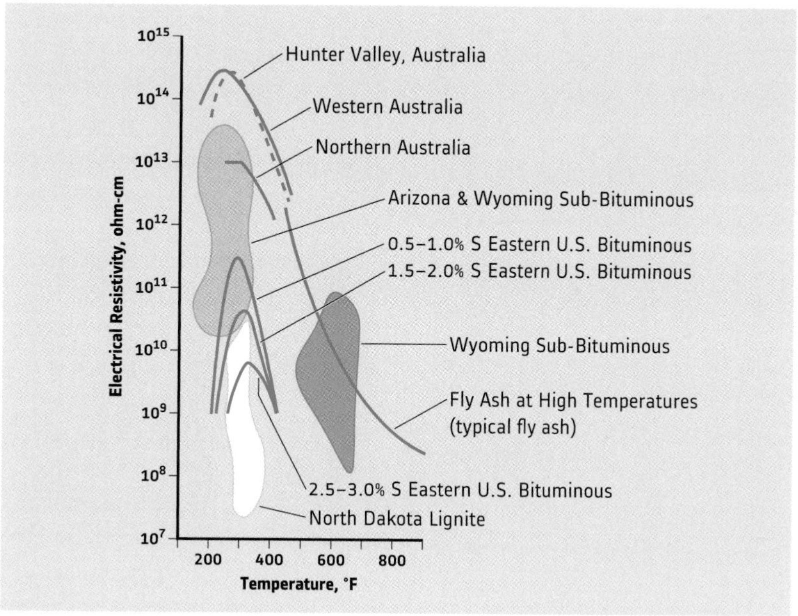

Figure 5-14 | Composite of in situ fly ash resistivity data versus temperature, from several sources[26,35,40,41]

Because of the recorded low resistivities above 600°F (300°C), some precipitators have been located *between* the boiler economizer and the air heaters, in what is called the "hot" position, instead of downstream of the air heaters, in the ordinary "cold" position. Hot precipitators are intended to avoid back-corona, to minimize the heavy rapping that is sometimes needed at lower temperatures, and to increase the effective migration velocity.[42,43]

The structural and mechanical design of hot precipitators is more critical than that of equipment intended to operate at 300°F (150°C). Designs should minimize thermal gradients and, if such temperature gradients cannot be avoided, all differential expansion. It also should be noted that actual gas flow increases because of the higher temperature, implying larger ESP boxes.

Several plants in the United States placed the ESPs upstream of the air

Gas conditioning can reduce ash resistivity, leading to higher collection efficiency and reduced emissions.

pre-heater. The flue gas temperature was approximately 650°F (340°C). Many of these plants could not meet the required emission levels, and investigations revealed that the ash layer on the electrodes developed back corona after some time of operation. The reason was found to be so-called "sodium depletion." In other words, the ash layer on the electrodes became inhomogeneous after some time of operation. Sodium, which reduces resistivity, migrated to the outer ash layers, while the inner ash layer was lacking sodium. Thus, a high-resistivity, thin inner layer was developed, and the corona current had to pass through it. As a result, back corona was generated in this layer. Manual cleaning of the electrodes had to be done frequently. Most of these "hot" ESPs have been rebuilt and are today placed after the air pre-heaters.[44,45]

Another way of overcoming the high-resistivity problem is to use a substantially lower flue gas temperature in the ESP. Since the late 1990s, several large boilers have been equipped with ESPs operating successfully at approximately 200°F (93°C). The use of low-sulfur coal, together with a more alkaline fly ash, prevents clogging and corrosion—no acid dew point can be measured in this flue gas. Such ESPs are characterized by very small collecting areas.

GAS CONDITIONING. Migration velocity declines as resistivity increases, as is characteristic of many low-sulfur bituminous and sub-bituminous coals. Adding SO_3 to flue gas can reduce ash resistivity.[46] For some western-U.S., low-sulfur coals, an increase of 30 ppm of SO_3 in the gas has reduced the fly ash resistivity from between 10^{11} and 10^{12} to 5×10^9 Ω-cm. Experience has revealed that predicting the effect of SO_3 is difficult for very-high-resistivity coals—for example, when the silicon and aluminum oxides exceed 85% of the fly ash. An alternative concept is, then, to use dual conditioning—a combination of SO_3 and NH_3 injection in the flue gas. These two gas components combine and, when mixed into the fly ash, reduce resistivity significantly.

COHESIVE AND ADHESIVE PROPERTIES OF FLY ASH. These properties of fly ash are important for collection by ESPs, where the ash forms in compacted layers on the electrode surfaces. Typically, these layers are less than 0.5 inch (13 mm) thick but, in some cases, may build up to 1 inch (25 mm) or more. Although some ash falls into the hoppers because of either the mechanical vibrations frequently present in plant structures or its own weight, rapping or jarring of the electrodes usually is necessary to effectively remove the collected ash layers. The ash generally breaks away in isolated patches, so the collecting plate surfaces present a somewhat spotty appearance.[29]

Fine solid particles tend to cohere and form agglomerated masses, which have a small but definite stability. The coherence of the particles is caused by molecular attractive forces at the points of contact of the particles. The degree of coherence is appreciable only for relatively fine particles of less than approximately 20 to 40 microns. Coarse or granular particles (e.g., sand) do not cohere in the dry state. On the other hand, fume particles, which typically are less than 1 micron in size, usually show a high degree of coherence.

The adhesion of particles to the collecting electrodes also is the result of molecular attractive forces, and similar to cohesion, the adhesive forces are larger for fine particles. Thus, adhesion and retention of the collected layers of ash on the electrodes are determined basically by particle size, and both increase with decreasing particle size. Other factors, however, such as particle shape and composition, influence the adhesion and cohesion of particles as well. The presence of condensed moisture, with possible cementing effects, also can profoundly influence the buildup of particles on electrodes and other surfaces.

In ESPs, the accumulation of ions on the collected dust layers produces an additional retention force of major importance. These ions tend to charge the collected particles so that they are attracted to the collecting plates by relatively strong electrical forces. Furthermore, any particles that do escape from the collected layers of ash (assuming that no back corona conditions prevail) tend to be immediately recharged electrically by the corona ions and forced back to the collecting plates. The particle-retaining force of the corona current increases with the electrical resistivity of the particles and with the strength of the current. Thus, it often is advantageous to operate precipitators, particularly the outlet sections, at relatively high corona current densities.[29]

Agglomerated masses of particles, removed from the electrodes by rapping, fall into the hoppers by the force of gravity. These agglomerated masses are bound together by molecular cohesive forces. For best performance, these falling agglomerates must be relatively stable and fall with as little loss of particles as possible. If the falling agglomerates have little coherence, some may break up and be redispersed into the gas stream, partially nullifying the collecting action of the precipitator.

The presence of coarse particles tends to reduce the cohesive and adhesive forces and, therefore, the agglomerating effect, which holds masses of fine particles together. Excessive amounts of coarse, gritty particles in an ash make the ash difficult to hold on the collecting plates and also lead to loose, unstable agglomerates when the plates are rapped. On the other hand, the elimination of all coarse particles above 10 to 20 microns may, in some cases, make removal of the ash difficult. There will be a much greater tendency for the particles to build up on the discharge electrodes. A very fine ash containing no coarse particles presents a more difficult rapping problem.[27]

Construction of ESPs

The weighted-wire type of precipitator has been well described elsewhere.[3–16,30,47–49] Features of the rigid-frame design can be found elsewhere as well.[3–16,38,44,49]

In the rigid-frame design, the carbon steel collecting plates are constructed of profiled segments up to 26 inches (660 mm) wide and sometimes more than 50 feet (15 m) long. They attach at the top to back-to-back channels spanning the insulator housing. At the bottom, anvil or spacer bars maintain plate alignment and act as anvils for plate rapping. The collecting electrode plates are rapped individually by mechanical hammers indexed on a shaft driven from outside the precipitator shell. For applications when the ash is easily removed, top rapping with magnetic impact solenoids can be used. Made from steel tubing, the individually suspended and rapped discharge frames typically are from 6 to 26 feet (1.8 to 7.9 m) long. These can be located one above the other or as one single frame from top to bottom, with horizontal beams at selected heights for stability. The discharge electrode itself can be a star-shaped wire (i.e., a round wire of a helical shape creating a spring); a thin, flat ribbon with barbs; or some other profile, depending on the manufacturer. Insulators carrying the high-tension support steel work are located in the insulator housing. The discharge frames are individually rapped by mechanical hammers driven from outside of the precipitator. These are restrained front and rear to maintain electrical clearances. With top suspension for all internals, expansion allowances are provided in the lower-alignment steel work.

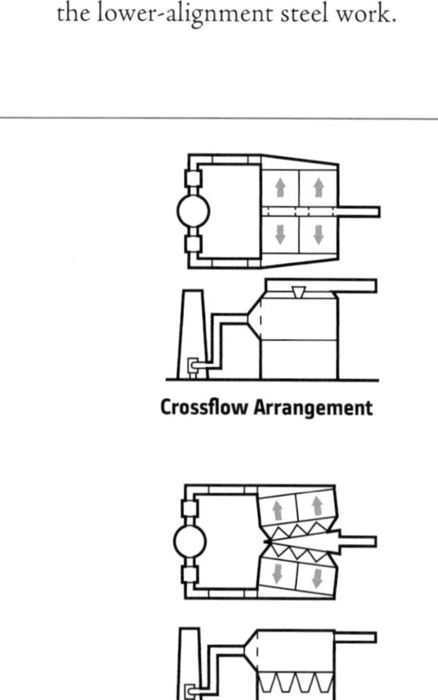

Figure 5-15 | Basic precipitator arrangements

PRECIPITATOR ARRANGEMENT. After calculating the total collecting area of a precipitator, the application engineer must determine the shape of the box required to house the internals. The beginning point is the computation of precipitator frontal area (width × height) using an acceptable gas velocity to the unit—ordinarily, 3 to 5 ft/s (0.9 to 1.5 m/s) for a coal-fired boiler application. Once field height and number of gas passages have been determined, required treatment length is figured. Selection is now complete if the equipment fits the allocated space envelope. Should the equipment extend beyond the width constraints, alternative selections must be made.

There are four basic arrangements for locating precipitators in a given plot plan (*Fig. 5-15*):

- In-line
- Crossflow
- Piggyback
- Chevron

The preferred arrangement is in-line because of such advantages as:

- Lowest capital cost
- Good flow balance between chambers
- Best gas distribution within a chamber
- Lowest system pressure drop
- Easy removal of internals in event of damage from fires, explosion, or corrosion
- Ease of construction and shortest time span to install a precipitator system

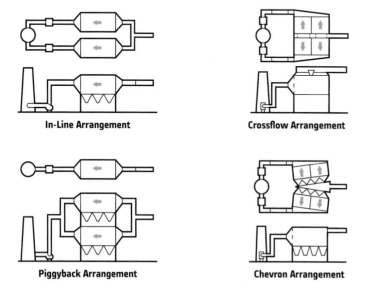

In laying out a plant, rigid-frame precipitators have a decided advantage over weighted-wire units, because field heights can be above 50 feet (15 m) for the rigid-frame and a maximum of 36 feet (11 m) for the weighted-wire unit. In many instances, a rigid-frame unit will fit inline, whereas the weighted-wire design must be arranged in one of the other, less desirable ways.

FLY ASH RECEIVING HOPPERS. During operation, the fly ash accumulated on the collecting surfaces of the precipitator is periodically shaken loose and dropped into the hoppers. The level of dust in each hopper will rise until that particular hopper is emptied. If for any reason emptying the hopper is delayed until the dust level approaches the elevation of the bottom of the discharge electrodes, they will be electrically short circuited to ground through the mass of collected dust. The affected precipitator section will cease functioning in a normal manner but will continue to collect some dust by acting as a settling chamber.

If the dust and flue gas entering the precipitator are reasonably well distributed, all precipitator hoppers in any row perpendicular to the gas flow will collect substantially the same quantity of dust per unit of time. Much more fly ash, however, will be collected in the rows of hoppers closer to the precipitator inlet than in the rows toward the rear of the precipitator. The quantities can be approximated with reasonable accuracy by use of the Deutsch–Anderson equation. An example is shown in *Table 5-1* for four precipitators having overall efficiencies of 99.6% and from three to six rows of hoppers in the direction of gas flow. In modern fly ash precipitators, then, the inlet row of hoppers can collect from 40 to 100 fold as much fly ash as does the rearmost row.[50]

FABRIC FILTRATION

Fabric filters (or baghouses, as they commonly are called) have a long history of application in the capture of particulate matter from process gases. Applications range from nuisance-particulate collection (for the control of silo dust or conveyor transfer station dust) to process applications in which the fabric filter equipment is an integral part of the process equipment used to capture the product (as with carbon-black manufacturing) and to strictly particulate capture for environmental compliance (as with coal-fired boiler applications). In general, fabric filters have found increasing acceptance in applications where gas-borne particulate matter must be efficiently and dependably removed from gas streams.

Fabric filtration presently is considered by many as the best available technology to control particulate emissions from a gas stream. The development of new and improved fabrics and finishes since the early 1970s has had a dramatic effect on the application potential of fabric filters, which in early years were limited primarily to the natural material cloths. These new fabrics and finishes have greatly extended the allowable operating temperature window, the expected service life, the resistance to chemical attack, and the cake release properties.

The preference of fabric filtration over other types of particulate removal equipment generally is attributable to the superior performance of fabric filters in the following areas:

- Outlet emissions are nearly independent of the magnitude of the inlet dust loading as well as the resistivity of the dust.

TABLE 5-1 | PERCENT OF FLY ASH COLLECTED IN EACH ROW OF HOPPERS

	Total number of rows, front to rear			
Row No.	3	4	5	6
1	84.1	74.9	66.9	60.2
2	13.4	18.8	22.2	24.0
3	2.1	4.7	7.3	9.3
4	—	1.2	2.4	3.9
5	—	—	0.8	1.6
6	—	—	—	0.6
TOTAL	99.6	99.6	99.6	99.6

- Special fabrics and fabric finishes can significantly—and cost-effectively—reduce outlet emissions below the capabilities of the ESPs and wet scrubbers.
- Particulate/gas chemical reactions can occur in the fabric filter system. Thus, in the case of dry FGD systems, overall sulfur dioxide removal efficiency is improved by as much as 15 to 20% because of the interaction of the flue gas with the fabric filter dust cake.
- Captured particulate and chemical reaction products removed from the filter bags (cake) remain dry for ease of handling and disposal.

Although fabric filters can be used in a wide variety of applications to control particulate emissions, the emphasis in the following discussion is primarily on those applications in which the fabric filter controls particulate emissions resulting from the combustion process (i.e., boiler applications).

Types of Fabric Filters

Fabric filters have a relatively constant collection efficiency and exhibit a varying pressure drop, depending on the dust properties and the degree of cake thickness at any point of reference. On the other hand, ESPs have a relatively constant pressure drop but will vary in overall removal efficiency, depending on inlet loading and dust properties. Another way of expressing this relationship is to say that the fabric filter is a constant-emission device (as measured by the mass of particulate emitted per unit of fuel fired), whereas the ESP is a constant-efficiency device (as measured by the percentage removal of the inlet dust loading).

When particulate-laden flue gas flows through a fabric, the captured particulate matter forms a cake on the surface of the fabric. This deposit increases both the filtration efficiency of the fabric and its resistance to the gas flow. Thus, for continuous operation, a fabric filter must have some mechanism for periodic cleaning of the deposited cake. The mechanism chosen must be capable of maintaining a reasonable pressure drop, consistent with the operational pressure drop limitations of the system in which it is installed. The cleaning mechanism used frequently represents the generic name of the type of filter equipment.

In addition to the above, the magnitude of the gas flow will have a bearing on the cleaning mechanism or fabric filter design selected. The intended service of the fabric filter also will have an additional influence on equipment selection, with more aggressive cleaning mechanisms being used for a more difficult to dislodge cake. The designer of the system must address the merits of each filter type and choose the appropriate design for the system requirements.

SHAKER-TYPE FABRIC FILTERS. In this oldest of filter designs, the cleaning mechanism is a vigorous shaking of the filter bag to remove the deposited cake. The shaking action causes the cake to fracture and fall into the collection and disposal hopper (*Fig. 5-16*). This method of cleaning has been applied to both inside collectors (those collecting particulate matter on the inside of the individual filter bags) and outside collectors (those collecting the particulate matter on the outside of the individual filter bags).

The cleaning mechanism is a very aggressive system, limiting bag cloth selections to those materials and weaves that can withstand the rigors of such use without premature cloth failure. Alternatively, special precautions must be taken to address the forces acting on the filter bags during the cleaning cycle, such as the amplitude of shake, the frequency of shake, and the bag tension.

Shaker designs, being the oldest type, have been used in a variety of applications, from ambient condition, nuisance dust collection (those typically seen on bin vent filters and dust-suppression systems on conveyor transfer points) to small industrial boiler applications (those using the outside collector-type designs) and large utility applications (those using inside collector-type designs on coal-fired boilers). In all cases, the fabric cloth is carefully selected to be consistent with the cleaning mechanism as well as with the chemistry and temperature of the filtered gas.

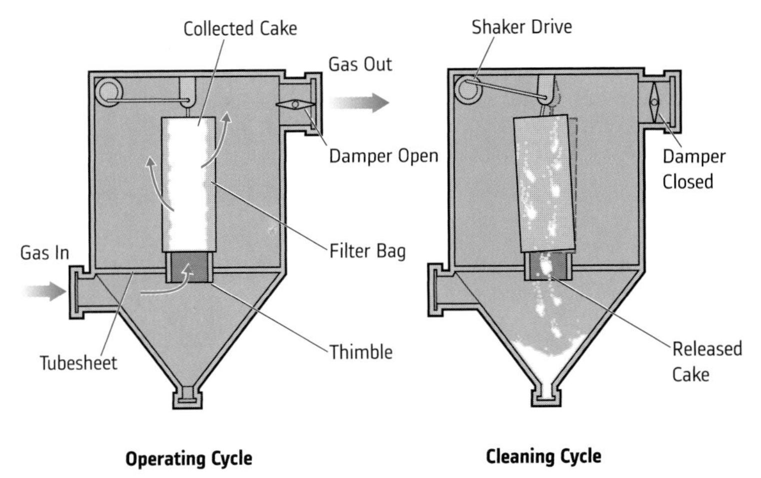

Figure 5-16 | Schematic arrangement of shaker-type fabric filter

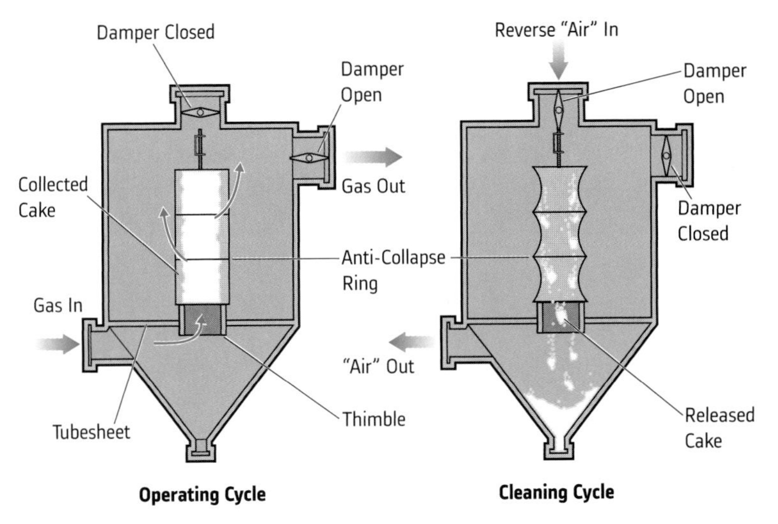

Figure 5-17 | Schematic arrangement of reverse air–type fabric filter

REVERSE AIR–TYPE FABRIC FILTERS. Originally developed to accommodate the relatively fragile, fiberglass cloths selected for fabric filters operating at higher boiler flue gas or process off-gas temperatures, this cleaning method generally is associated with inside-type collection units, although some variation of this design can be found in limited and unique applications. The name "reverse air" is really a misrepresentation. Properly named, the cleaning mechanism should be called "reverse gas," because the cleaning mechanism is a reverse flow of gas through an isolated compartment to cause an inward collapsing of the filter bag and, thus, the fracturing of the filter cake (*Fig. 5-17*).

Low air/cloth ratios characterize reverse air units, with typical gross ratios (with all compartments in service) ranging between 1.5 and 2.0. The air/cloth ratio given for any operating condition represents the cubic feet of actual gas filtered divided by the square feet of effective filter cloth currently in service.

Filter bag attachment hardware consists of a cap installed in the upper-top portion of the bag. This arrangement allows attachment of the bag to the tensioning device that is hung from the compartment bag-hanging frame. An adjustable clamp or sewn-in band fastens the bottom cuff of the bag to the tubesheet located in the lower section of each compartment. Both arrangements allow direct attachment to the tubesheet thimble. Filter bags for reverse air service contain multiple rings sewn in the bag length to prevent total collapse during the cleaning cycle (see *Fig. 5-17*).

Although the bag hardware represents only a small fraction of the total cost of the fabric filter system, this hardware can cause problems if not properly selected with respect to both design and material. Any component that contacts the cloth needs to be carefully chosen to ensure that premature cloth damage will not occur during normal operation of the unit. For example, edges need to be smooth, and excessive corrosion should be prevented.

Depending on the inlet dust loading per unit volume of gas treated and the particle size distribution, the designer of the fabric filter unit will adjust the design air/cloth ratio and/or the total number of system compartments required to ensure a reasonable air/cloth ratio under all operating conditions. Of concern in these calculations is the effective air/cloth ratio during the cleaning mode and the maximum ratio in the event of full load operation with one compartment isolated for any maintenance activity plus one additional compartment in the cleaning mode. Generally, the maximum air/cloth ratio, with two compartments out of service and one of these in the cleaning mode, is limited to 2.5 for these types of units.

The cleaning frequency of the individual compartments will depend, in part, on the particle size of the dust, the cohesive nature of the filter cake that is formed, and the inlet dust loading. All other parameters remaining equal, the frequency of cleaning will also increase as the inlet dust loading increases, which results in a greater time of operation by the filter unit in the net (less than full complement of compartments operating) condition. Ideally, a properly designed fabric filter unit should operate in the gross condition the majority of the time, because this represents the most efficient filtering mode (lowest air/cloth ratio) and lowest differential system pressure drop.

This fabric filter design using appropriate cloth materials has been applied to a wide range of temperatures, from near ambient to more than 500°F (260°C). An advantage of this particular system is the ability to use fiberglass cloth that can withstand wide ranges in temperature without physical damage. The reverse air system, being a gentle method of filter bag cleaning, is compatible with most available bag materials.

One of the most attractive features of this type of fabric filter system is the extended bag life for the fiberglass bags. The typical bag is approximately 12 inches (0.3 m) in diameter, with bag lengths of up to 36 feet (11 m). A large number of operating units have experienced bag life in excess of 10 years between changes. The negative aspects of this design are the increased capital cost associated with the low air/cloth ratio (particularly considering the mandatory off-line cleaning) as well as the required site plan area needed for installation of the filter system.

SHAKE/DEFLATE FABRIC FILTERS. This type of unit combines the features of the shaker unit and the reverse air unit in its design. The unit is an inside type of collector, which uses shaking and mild reverse gas flow during the cleaning cycle.

An advantage of the shake/deflate unit is its ability to operate at somewhat higher air/cloth ratios than pure reverse air units because of the more vigorous cleaning action of the shaking mechanism. Following the shaking sequence, the filter bags are exposed to a mild reverse air deflation that further assists in cake removal from the bags. This type of cleaning system is sensitive to cloth selection and the parameters of the cleaning cycle, as noted previously for the pure shaker units, and generally has not demonstrated the bag life expectancy that is characteristic of pure reverse air units.

PULSE JET FABRIC FILTERS. The pulse jet unit is an outside type of collector wherein the particulate laden flue gas flows from the outside to the inside of the filter bag. *Figure 5-18* shows a comparison between the reverse air and generic pulse jet collector, with the incoming flue gas entering the compartment and flowing upward and through the filter bags. Wire or mesh-frame cages support the filter bags on the pulse jet design to prevent their collapse during the filtering period. Cages vary in both design and construction material, depending on the composition of the gas being filtered, the support requirements necessary for the filter bag construction, and

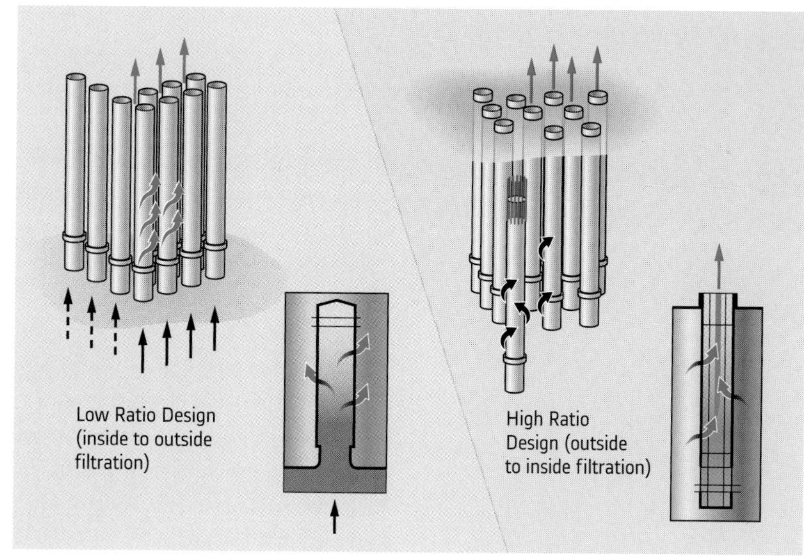

Figure 5-18 | Comparison of reverse air and pulse jet fabric filter designs

customer preference with respect to ease of handling and potential reuse of components.

The filtered particulate (cake) is trapped on the outside of the bags while the clean gas flows through the cake and cloth. It travels up to the inside of the bag through the cage to the clean gas plenum, and it exits through the compartment outlet damper. The individual bags and support cages are installed and removed from the top of the compartment through the clean gas plenum. The clean air plenum can be either a full height "walk-in" type, an extension of the compartment casing, or a top hatch cover design, which has removable top hatch covers to reach the bags and cages.

Bag cleaning is accomplished by short pulses (50–100 ms) of pressurized, clean, dry air directed downward into each bag in the row being cleaned. Radial acceleration of the fabric and dust cake causes a significant portion of the dust to be separated from the bags. Gravity allows the released cake to fall between the bags and into the discharge hopper. Within a single pulse jet unit or single compartment, rows of filter bags are pulsed sequentially under the control of a solid-state programmer, which usually is mounted adjacent to the collector casing.

The original operating concept for all pulse jet types of collector was on-line pulse cleaning, with the gas entering each compartment in the bottom area (or hopper) and flowing upward between and through the bags. The gas flow through the collector is continuously maintained, and the rows of filter bags are pulsed sequentially, either on a timed sequence or under control of the collector differential-pressure monitor. Although still an established arrangement for many nuisance dust collection applications, this gas flow arrangement and cleaning method can be inefficient compared to off-line pulse cleaning. Consider the following points:

- The pressure pulse is from 50 to 100 ms in duration. Only during this period is the gas flow stopped through a row of bags being cleaned.
- Dust pulsed from one bag row is immediately re-entrained on an adjacent bag row because of the upward gas flow direction and, therefore, does not reach the hopper.
- Only after repeated pulsing will the captured cake gravitate to the hopper.

The main reason that dust can be collected using online pulse jet cleaning with gas entering the compartments through the hoppers is dust agglomeration. The dust particles form agglomerates that are heavy and dense enough to resist attraction to adjacent bags and, therefore, can fall through the rising gas stream into the hopper.

With the advent of large collectors to control emissions from hot processes (e.g., boilers), the online pulse jet filter with gas entering the compartment through the hopper has been shown to have several disadvantages:

- Online maintenance and inspections are not practical.
- Compressed air requirements are very large, with increased filter area needed to maintain the required pressure drop.
- Physical properties of the fiberglass fabrics required for hot boiler processes are inconsistent with the harsher cleaning mechanism of online pulsing at high pulse pressures.

Reverse air systems, as previously described, are essentially multicompartment units with off-line cleaning. The carryover of the reverse air operating scheme to smaller industrial boilers produced the modular reverse air systems (i.e., those that are made up of totally shop-assembled compartment modules). These designs substantially reduced field construction labor costs.

This same concept was then applied to the pulse jet units using shop-assembled modular units and off-line cleaning. This allowed pulse jet systems composed of totally shop-assembled modular systems, including the extra module for off-line cleaning. With this method of operation, features include:

- Off-line cleaning, which is more effective, because the dust has little tendency to migrate to adjacent filter bags. Instead, the cake has an

opportunity to fall into the collection hopper(s).
- Reduced pulsing pressure, because there is no need to overcome the forward momentum of the operating system.
- Improved bag life, because lower pulse pressures improve filter bag life without sacrificing fabric filter performance.

The pulse jet fabric filter units, then, can be cleaned in either an on-line mode, in which the compartment is not isolated from the system during the cleaning cycle, or an off-line mode, in which the compartment to be cleaned is removed from on-line service by closing its outlet dampers before and during cleaning. In the off-line mode, multiple compartments are required, including an extra compartment to allow the removal of one compartment without affecting the overall system performance during cleaning. Pulse jet module designs have evolved over the years, with numerous design modifications providing improved performance over the generic design shown in *Figure 5-18*. Some of these major differences are illustrated in *Figure 5-19*.

In place of a particulate-laden flue gas inlet in the module hopper, gas entry is into the side of the module casing. An internal baffle and impact plate protect the filter bags from direct impact of the incoming gas and dust particle stream. The advantages of this arrangement include:

- Better gas and dust distribution to all module filter bags.
- Gravimetric gas flow enhancing on-line cleaning.

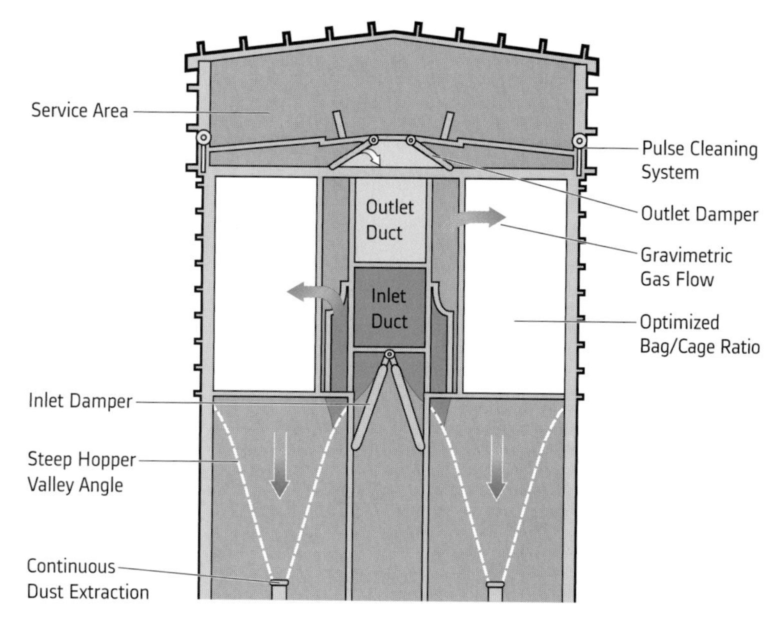

Figure 5-19 | Improved pulse jet fabric filter system arrangement

- A gas inlet location consistent with a combined manifold design, in which the system inlet and outlet manifolds are formed by a single rectangular duct, with a diagonal splitter plate forming the two gas paths.
- Greater hopper storage capacity, which is important on high-inlet-loading systems.

This type of fabric filter system has a number of attractive features. The primary feature is the reduced installed cost of the filter. As a result of the higher air/cloth ratio and use of on-line cleaning, the size and arrangement of the pulse jet filter system results in a lower cost than that with most reverse air–cleaned systems. The total plan area at site for pulse jet–cleaned filters also is less than that with reverse air–cleaned units. With lower cost and size, the pulse jet style of fabric filter often is preferred by many end users. The typical bag diameter is approximately 6 inches (0.15 m) or less, with bag lengths typically of up to 26 feet (7.9 m). Progress is being made on extending the bag length even more based on the quality of the fabrics and finishes available. This increase in filter area per bag will help to further reduce the total installed cost of the filter. The negative aspect of this design is the decreased bag life. Because of the more aggressive cleaning system, a bag life of 3 to 4 years is common in most installations.

Design of Equipment

Overall system designs involve selection of the cleaning mechanism and type of fabric filter to be used for a particular service along with selection of a suitable bag material and bag finish. To make these choices, the designer needs a complete knowledge of the process on which equipment is to be installed and knowledge regarding the limiting factors of the options available for application.[51]

Fabric filter designs have some established criteria, such as typically acceptable air/cloth ratios and bag aspect ratios. As noted previously in the discussion of reverse air systems, the gross air/cloth ratio that generally is acceptable for the reverse air system is at or less than 2.0, with a maximum of 2.5 in the net condition of two compartments off-line and one of those compartments in the cleaning mode. In the design of a reverse air unit, or any off-line cleaning unit, the number of compartments will affect the value of the net condition, because with fewer compartments, the removal of one compartment from service has a greater effect than that in a unit with a greater number of compartments.

In the design of the reverse air unit, bag aspect ratios typically are 32:1, with a maximum of 36:1. Bag aspect ratio is defined as the ratio of the bag length divided by the bag diameter. Here, the concern is the ability to effectively clean the upper section of the bag on this inside type of collector unit if the length becomes too long. Most designs have used the more common bag length of 32 feet (9.8 m) in the typical boiler flue gas application. In recent years, however, many successful units with a ratio of 36:1 have been used.

Similar design criteria also have been developed for the pulse jet units in defining acceptable ratios or component designs. As an example, typical filter bag lengths for most industrial applications range from 12 to 16 feet 3.6 to 4.9 m), although some designs have been up to 20 feet (6.1 m) in length. For larger gas volume applications, such as coal-fired boilers, a bag length of 26 feet (7.9 m) has been used on a large number of installations. The application of felted cloths on pulse jet units is quite typical. The use of woven fiberglass cloth is acceptable, especially for the higher boiler flue gas operating temperatures, provided the method of cleaning the bags is appropriate for this material. As indicated in the section below on filter materials, higher-temperature felts also are available with some limitations. Filter bag cage materials commonly are of carbon steel with a baked-on epoxy coating. Other coatings are available, as is alloy construction. High side inlet collectors have advantages with respect to hopper capacity and hopper re-entrainment. Designs that have the gas entering the hoppers are acceptable in some instances and allow lower equipment setting heights in the overall system design.

The selection of the cleaning mechanism design, the number of compartments needed, the air/cloth ratio necessary, the bag material and finish, the maximum bag length, and a variety of other design considerations are specific to the service intended and to the user's preference. Regardless of the design selected, the majority of emissions from a fabric filter occur either during or immediately after bag cleaning. The cleaning system and the bag material must be properly matched to achieve low emissions from the installed fabric filter system.

FABRIC FILTER MATERIALS. Specification of the weave, thread count, weight, and finish of the cloth for a required filter bag lists only a few of the possible combinations of manufacturing procedures or designs that ultimately will describe the finished filter bag for a particular application. Fabric specifications include such properties as tensile strength, abrasion resistance, chemical attack resistance, and operating temperature limitations (*Table 5-2*). Tensile strength measures the ability of the cloth or fabric to resist breaking when in direct tension. Abrasion resistance is the fabric's ability to withstand externally caused abrasion or abrasion resulting from internal rubbing of the fabric fibers. Some cloths exhibit excellent resistance, and others are damaged quite easily. Coatings applied to some cloths not only improve their abrasion resistance but also their chemical resistance, as in the case of fiberglass cloth, which would self-destruct without a suitable coating.

Fiber manufacturers and felt suppliers have done a large amount of developmental work to improve the performance and features of felts used in fabric filters. Different fiber shapes and sizes, along with varying methods of assembling the fibers into felt material, have been investigated and tested in laboratories and some pilot demonstration units. As more and more fabric filters are requested by end users, the technology will continue to advance.

In addition to the developments in felt material construction, bag suppliers have improved quality control of manufacturing and have increased production capability. This has impacted the cost of bags. Improvements in the quality of coatings and membranes for filter bags also have resulted in improved filter performance and bag life, particularly in very harsh gas environments.

TABLE 5-2 | SUMMARY OF FILTER MEDIA*

Filter media summary						
Material	PES	PAC	PPS	PI	PTFE	GLS
Polymer Common trade name	Polyester	Dolanit Ricem	Ryton Pracon Torcon	P84	Teflon®	Fiberglass
TEMPERATURE °C						
Continuous	275°F (135°C)	257°F (125°C)	347°F (175°C)	312°F (200°C)	461°F (240°C)	461°F (240°C)
Peak	300°F (150°C)	266°F (130°C)	392°F (200°C)	500°F (260°C)	500°F (260°C)	536°F (280°C)
RESISTANCE†						
Acid	3	4	4	3	5	4
Alkali	2	3	4	3	5	3
Hydrolysis (H_2O)	2	4–5	5	3	5	5
Oxidation (O_2)	5	3	3	3–4	5	5
Abrasion	5	3–4	3–4	4	3	1
Price rel. to PES	1	1.5	3.5	6.5	15	2.5

* GLS, fiberglass; PAC, polyacrylic fiber; PES, polyester fiber; PI, polyamide fiber; PPS, polyphenylene sulfide; PTFE, polytetrafluoroethylene.

† 1, low; 2, mediocre; 3, generally good; 4, good; 5, excellent.

FABRIC FILTER PERFORMANCE. Unlike fabric filters, most other particulate emission control devices depend on either pressure drop or collection surface area to reach the required collection efficiencies. Upsets to the predicted gas volumes or particulate loadings typically will cause these other types of equipment to have higher emission rates despite their maintaining the same fractional efficiency. The fabric filter does not behave in this fashion, however, because the material collected on the filter bags is the filtering medium that captures the incoming particulate matter. Although upset conditions may change the flange-to-flange pressure drop, resulting in an excessively fast buildup of cake, these conditions do not materially change the final emission rate. It can be said that a fabric filter represents a constant-emission device.

The actual performance of a fabric filter depends on specific items, such as the air/cloth ratio, the permeability of the fabric/cake (particulate bleed-through), the loading and nature of the particulate (irregularly shaped or spherical), the particle size distribution (fine vs. coarse), and to some extent, the frequency of the cleaning cycle. By careful selection of design components, fabric filters can achieve removal levels of higher than 99.9% of incoming particulates, or an outlet loading of less than 0.005 grain per dry standard ft^3 (0.11 mg/Nm^3).

FABRIC FILTER BAG LIFE. A primary concern in the operation of a fabric filter is the bag life, which affects bag replacement frequency and resultant cost. Because the initial cost of the filter bags, excluding installation, can represent 10% or more of the total cost of the equipment, a significant operating expense can occur if the bag life is shorter than expected. Typical bag life is 3 to 5 years (depending on the type of cleaning mechanism selected and the design parameters used in that selection), so this operating expense item can represent a significant cost over the life of the equipment. In some cases, the shortened bag life also could require an outage to change the bags and, thereby, result in loss of revenues from production. Shortened bag life can be caused by various operating and design problems, among which are the following:

- Bag blinding, usually caused by operating a fabric filter for frequent or long periods at or below the dew point. Such operation tends to plug or blind the cloth. Bag blinding results in unacceptable unit pressure drop that ultimately will become fan or process limiting and require filter bag replacement. The effect on the filter cloth is that material builds up in the passages of the cloth body and restricts the gas passage such that even after repeated cleanings, the lodged material cannot be removed.
- Bag erosion, resulting from high-velocity streams of fly ash-laden gases where the gas enters the filter bag or directly impacts the cloth in any way. Proper selection of the air/cloth ratio and filter bag length controls the high entry velocity at the bag-inlet inside collectors. Higher air/cloth ratios with longer filter bags tend to increase this velocity in the entrance, or "neck" area, of the bag. Velocities generally are

limited to less than 1,500 ft/min (7.6 m/sec) into the bag nest from the side.

- Filter bag deterioration, often caused by poor selection of cloth material or finish or by abnormal operation of the system, resulting in damage to the cloth or components of construction. Abnormal operation would include operation outside the design temperature range (either high or low), operation in excess of the design volumetric flow, or significant variation in the chemistry of the flue gas being filtered. Any of the above could cause premature deterioration of the cloth selected for service.

OPERATING ISSUES

Fly Ash Hopper Plugging

The reliability and availability of ESPs and fabric filters are affected adversely by problems in the dust-receiving hoppers and in the equipment beneath those hoppers for transporting fly ash to disposal. A significant portion of the downtime of such dust-collecting equipment stems from problems with, and malfunctions of, ash evacuation systems.[26]

A paradox exists in the design of equipment for removing the collected fly ash from the bottom of precipitators and fabric filters and then conveying it away. Suppliers of ash-handling systems want to design their equipment for "dry and free-flowing" material at the inlets of the ash removal equipment. Yet, dust-collecting equipment can have mud or water flowing out of hoppers any time the hopper metal temperatures are below the water dew point (100–130°F [38–54°C], depending on fuel type and excess air in the products of combustion). This condition commonly occurs during a cold start-up, when many metal surfaces in the gas stream are at ambient temperature. When sub-dew point conditions occur, the hygroscopic fly ash absorbs the acid or water produced and may agglomerate or cement into large pieces that either cannot pass through the hopper outlets or are too heavy to be conveyed.

EFFECT ON COLLECTING EQUIPMENT. Undetected and/or uncorrected hopper plugging can cause one or more of the following deleterious effects on ESPs:

- Bent or misaligned collecting surfaces
- Discharge-electrode burning
- Distorted or broken discharge-electrode frames
- Broken anvil bars
- Broken shaft or drive insulators
- Shorted high-voltage bus sections
- Lowered electrical power output from bent or misaligned collecting- and discharge-electrode components
- Formation of large, difficult-to-remove clinkers by high-temperature electrical fusing of the ash overflowing a hopper

With fabric filters employing gas flow into the filter through the hoppers, plugging can increase the gas velocities as the hoppers fill above the inlet level, resulting in the possibility of re-entrainment of dust. This can result in excessive bag abrasion. With a completely blocked hopper, the compartment will no longer accept gas flow, and the other compartments

Removing ash from the receiving hoppers as continuously as possible is key to high availability of ash collection equipment.

will have to handle the volume, resulting in increased gas side pressure drop.

With both precipitators and fabric filters, if a plugged hopper cannot be cleared and discharged through the ash system in a normal manner, the ash must be emptied onto the hopper room floor or the ground (creating a fire and safety hazard) and be manually removed.[50]

SOLUTIONS TO FLY ASH HOPPER PLUGGING. The problem can be solved by:

- Removing the ash as continuously as possible so that it can remain hot and uncompacted, thus preventing the hoppers from being used for storage of the hygroscopic fly ash.
- Preventing air-in leakage that cools the fly ash below the acid or water dew point.
- Regularly inspecting and maintaining, or replacing, fly ash intakes.
- Modifying hopper design for improved fly ash outflow.
- Enclosing hopper areas and using adequate insulation thickness to minimize heat losses and cooling of ash system hardware.
- Heating hoppers such that the walls do not drop in temperature and have condensation form.

These suggestions, and other recommendations on the design and sizing of fly ash hoppers, are discussed further below and in the following chapter on ash-handling systems.

Maintenance of Fly Ash Intakes

It is estimated that some fly ash intakes may open and close nearly a quarter of a million times per year. It is completely reasonable to expect, under such conditions, that solenoids will fail and that valve seats will become worn, resulting in an inflow of air into the hopper. With a pressure-pneumatic ash removal system, air can be forced into the hopper at pressures as high as 100 psig (6.9 bar) in a dense-phase system. With vacuum systems, the motive force for inducing air into precipitator hoppers or baghouse hoppers is the suction maintained in the precipitator or baghouse by the boiler induced draft fans, which can create a suction of as much as –20 to –30″ WG (–3.7 to –5.6 cm Hg) in the precipitator or baghouse. With either a pressure or vacuum system, then, a pressure differential can result in the introduction of large quantities of cool air into the hoppers, which can lead to the condensation of moisture from the flue gas.

Actual field temperature measurements on both "hot" and "cold" precipitators have shown that even very active hoppers can have low (essentially ambient) temperatures. One plausible explanation for such a low internal temperature is leakage of air into the hoppers through the fly ash intake valves located at the bottom of the hoppers. Very seldom have such valves been considered "maintenance items" that should be inspected and considered for replacement on a set schedule. It has become apparent in plant after plant, however, that such valves cannot be expected to last forever and that they are a source of the low-temperature conditions occurring in many hoppers.[26]

HEATING OF PRECIPITATOR AND FABRIC FILTER OUTLET HOPPERS. The ABMA/ICAC Committee stated that the heating of hoppers has not been sufficiently emphasized in the purchase, design, and construction of precipitator and baghouse dust outlets. They recommended that along with a redesign of the dust-conveying equipment, improved hopper heating and insulation are needed, all with the purpose of facilitating the emptying of the dust outlets.

The principal variables in the application of hopper heating are:

- External (ambient) design temperature
- Internal design temperature
- Presence of an internal ash layer
- Extent and placement of heating elements
- Design electrical heat density
- Thickness of insulation outside the heating equipment

The design operating temperature of hopper heating equipment for boilers firing low- to medium-sulfur coals should be a minimum of 270°F (132°C), based on an ash layer inside the hopper. This is 10 to 15°F (5.6 to 8.3°C) above the normally expected acid dew point. For units firing high-sulfur coals or oils, the hopper plate should be kept above 325°F (163°C). The heating equipment must be capable of maintaining such temperatures under the worst expected ambient conditions of temperature and wind velocity (for 97–98% of the time) and for the lowest anticipated interior gas temperature.

Test reports of temperature measurements in operating precipitator hoppers indicate that gas or air temperatures as low as 90°F (32°C) sometimes occur inside the hoppers, with the precipitator and boiler operating at essentially full load. Under such conditions, most of the heat loss from the hopper plate is not to the outside atmosphere but, rather, to the inside of the hopper.[50] The heat-transfer and mass-transfer situation in such a precipitator in no way can result in the occurrence of such low temperatures by a normal heat-loss/transfer mechanism. The greatest probability is that the low temperatures in such hoppers result from the in-leakage of relatively cool air from the pneumatic transport system serving the hoppers or from other areas, such as improperly sealed access doors or poke tubes.

Even when bulk gas temperatures in collecting equipment are above the acid dew point (240–350°F [115–177°C]), hopper skin temperatures at the critical throat can be very low, both because of the heat sink effect of the ash system hardware (strike pads, poke holes, and vibrators) and because of the convective transfer of heat from the bottom of the hoppers to the top by chimney action. This situation is aggravated by severe local weather conditions and exposed hoppers facing a prevailing wind, and it can result in localized condensation and wetting of collected ash.[26]

Normally, only the lower one-third or one-half of a hopper is heated, both to minimize costs and to avoid the problem of heating elements obstructing access to the equipment. Most plugging is expected to occur in the constricted outlet region. The hopper plate does not readily conduct heat to other parts of the hopper, especially when the interior gas temperatures are low. If such areas cannot be heat traced, they must be completely insulated, including doors, poke holes, strike pads, and other protrusions.

Because heater vendors may interpret heating needs very differently, precise heater specifications or hopper heat loads in kilowatts must be made

Reduced NOx formation in the combustion zone allows for a lower cost post-combustion system such as an SCR.

directly to the vendor, both to ensure adequate heating and to prevent the possibility of damage from overheating. Heat loads as high as 32 kWh per hopper have been specified on some large coal-fired boiler precipitators. This is two to three-fold as much as that in many existing installations. It is important to properly design and heat the hopper outlets and poke tubes, because these heat sinks have been known to contribute to ash removal problems.

In most current installations, if the flue gas temperature falls below the acid dew point, or if air or gas in the hopper falls below the water dew point, there is little that can be done by hopper heaters to prevent condensation inside either precipitator or fabric filter hoppers. This is because their proper function is to heat the steel wall of the hopper, not the air or gas inside.[26] Following vendor-recommended start-up and shutdown procedures regarding hopper heating and evacuation will help to minimize ash removal problems.

CONTROL OF NOx EMISSIONS

The formation of NOx during the combustion of fossil fuels is discussed in Chapter 2. Briefly, the reactions are as follows:

$$N_2 + O_2 \rightarrow 2NO$$

Equation 5-3, Step 1

$$2NO + O_2 \rightarrow 2NO_2$$

Equation 5-3, Step 2

Two basic strategies commonly are used for controlling or minimizing NOx emissions from combustion sources. The first is to create an environment favoring a minimal amount of NOx formation in the combustion region. Typically, this is done by either lowering the level of O_2 and/or lowering the prevailing temperature. Common technologies for obtaining this environment of low-NOx formation include:

- Flue gas recirculation
- Staged combustion
- Burners out of service
- Overfire air
- Staged air or fuel introduction
- Low-NOx burners

These technologies are discussed in greater detail in other sections of this book. Alternative means of minimizing NOx formation by suppressing the N_2 content via O_2 enrichment or by chemical reactor (non-thermal) combustion are emerging technologies.

The other strategy relies on chemically converting NOx emissions after the formation of NOx in the combustion region. This is accomplished by using a reducing agent to react with the NOx emissions to form atmospheric N_2 and water vapor. For a reducing agent, ammonia species are favored over other chemical reducing compounds because of ammonia's selective nature (ammonia prefers to react with NOx rather than with oxygen), relatively low cost, and water by-product. All of the chemical reaction end products are already present in, and are emitted along with, the exhaust gas. There are no waste collection or disposal issues.

The chemical reaction between ammonia and NOx may occur with the aid of a catalyst. This technology is called SCR. The same reaction may occur without the aid of a catalyst but at higher temperatures, and this technology is referred to as selective non-catalytic reduction (SNCR). The SNCR of NOx using carbon monoxide (CO) and hydrocarbons, as commonly is practiced in automotive or internal combustion engine emission control, requires carefully controlled and low excess-air conditions that are not always found in conventional boiler operations.

Technologies for controlling NOx emissions began wide development and practice in 1970s. The SCR technology, originally developed in Japan during the 1970s, defined the basic catalyst formulations and system process. Extended to Germany in the 1980s, the system was applied to coal-fired plants with multiple fuel and ash-related issues as well as system design variations. The system was deployed in the United States during the 1990s, with more ash and catalyst poison issues. Designs were simplified as more experience was obtained. The technology is considered to be mature, but it continues to evolve in order to address emerging needs and challenges. SCR has been applied to large utility boilers, smaller industrial boilers, gas turbines, and industrial processes. The SCR systems have been used on coal- and oil-fired utility boilers, waste- and sludge-fired incinerators, gas turbines, industrial heaters, and glass furnaces.

SCR CHEMISTRY

In an SCR system, ammonia vapor is blended with hot flue gas exiting the boiler unit. This ammonia must be mixed with the NOx-containing flue gas, which then is passed through one or more layers of catalyst, where a chemical reaction to form N_2 and water vapor takes place. The reactions between the NOx compound species and the reducing ammonia reagent vary slightly, depending on the individual NOx compound. For NO, which typically makes up 95% of total NOx emissions, the reaction is equimolar with ammonia:

$$4NO + 4NH_3 + O_2 \rightarrow 4N_2 + 6H_2O$$

Equation 5-3, Step 3

For the lesser amount of NO_2, the reaction with ammonia can follow several varying reactions:

$$2NO_2 + 4NH_3 + O_2 \rightarrow 3N_2 + 6H_2O$$

Equation 5-3, Step 4

$$6NO_2 + 8NH_3 \rightarrow 7N_2 + 12H_2O$$

Equation 5-3, Step 5

$$NO + NO_2 + 2NH_3 \rightarrow 2N_2 + 3H_2O$$

Equation 5-3, Step 6

In general, an equivalent molecular amount of ammonia is required to reduce a molecular amount of NOx, based on the typically high NO content and the reaction equations above. The flue gas, with a substantially lower NOx content, exits the SCR system and proceeds through the balance of the exhaust gas train to the stack.

SNCR CHEMISTRY

Treatment of NOx emissions by SNCR originally was developed in 1973 using ammonia vapor to react with NOx compounds. This process, also called Thermal DeNOx, has been applied on several boilers. A later development, based on urea, has been applied on numerous small to large utility boilers since the mid-1980s. In the SNCR system, either ammonia vapor, aqueous ammonia, or urea solution is injected into the hot flue gas at a location in the boiler where the temperature is sufficient to drive the following reactions:

$$4NO + 4NH_3 + O_2 \rightarrow 4N_2 + 6H_2O$$

Equation 5-3, Step 7

$$4NO + 2CO(NH_2)_2 + O_2 \rightarrow 4N_2 + 4H_2O + 2CO_2$$

Equation 5-3, Step 8

The remaining flue gas then passes through the rest of the boiler and the exhaust gas train to the stack.

SCR SYSTEMS

In the SCR process, the exhaust gas exits the boiler economizer or similar heat recovery section and proceeds to the SCR system. Near the entrance of the SCR system, a small amount of ammonia is distributed throughout the exhaust gas stream to achieve the proper molar ratio blend of ammonia and NOx. The ammonia and NOx-containing exhaust gas is introduced into the SCR reactor that contains the catalyst. The chemical reactions between the NOx and the ammonia occur as the exhaust gas passes through the catalyst layer(s). The exiting exhaust gas stream, now with a much lower content of NOx and ammonia, continues through the balance of the heat recovery equipment and other air emissions control equipment. The exhaust gas stream with the SCR end products finally exits through the stack.

In practice, most SCR systems can achieve NOx removal efficiencies of between 80 to 90%. Because of the relatively high cost of an SCR system, lower NOx emission levels usually can be obtained by less expensive, alternate technologies. In theory and laboratory experiments, SCR simulations can obtain very high levels of NOx removal. Practical SCR system design and operating limitations tend to influence the amount of NOx removal that may be obtained in an operating unit. The factors that determine the NOx removal capability include the operating environment, installed equipment costs (capital costs), catalyst life, and long-term system operating and maintenance costs.

SCR Process Variations

The catalysts used in SCR systems require specific operating temperatures and are sensitive to ash and other compounds in the flue gas. These process variations must be taken into consideration when designing an SCR system. These requirements have led to the development of three similar SCR systems.

HIGH-DUST SYSTEMS. In a high-dust configuration, the SCR catalyst bed is located immediately downstream of the boiler system, with no additional exhaust gas treatment systems located upstream of the SCR unit (see *Fig. 5-20*). The exhaust gas has a relatively high ash content. The SCR system may

be equipped with ash baffles (to knock out large ash particles) and ash hoppers upstream of the catalyst beds. Either soot blowers (using hot air or superheated steam) or sonic horns are located adjacent to the catalyst beds to keep ash deposits from forming on the catalyst surfaces and plugging the catalyst bodies. The catalyst itself often features larger openings or channels to help avoid plugging. Avoiding catalyst erosion requires moderate gas velocities, gas-straightening vanes (to provide gas flow parallel to the catalyst body orientation), and wear-resistant catalyst formulation. Advantages and disadvantages of high-dust SCR systems are outlined in *Table 5-3*.

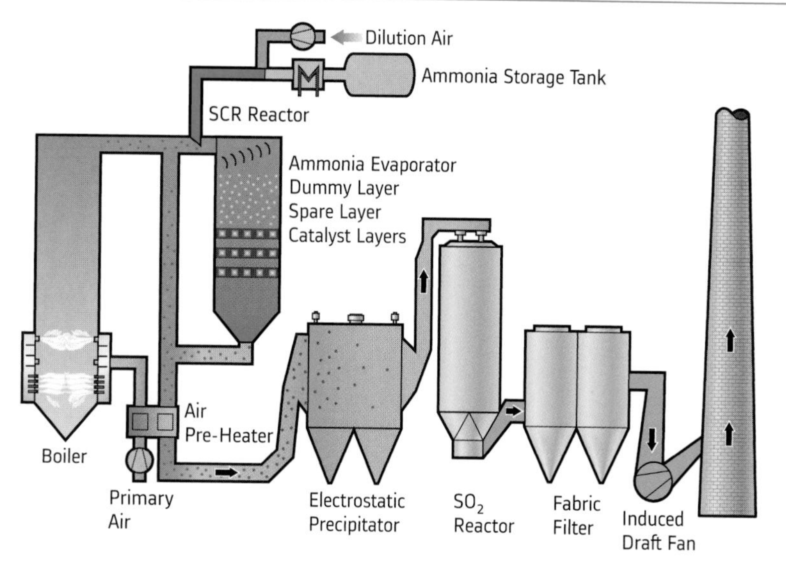

Figure 5-20 | High-dust selective catalytic reduction (SCR) location

TABLE 5-3 | ADVANTAGES AND DISADVANTAGES OF HIGH-DUST SELECTIVE CATALYTIC REDUCTION SYSTEMS

Advantages	Disadvantages
Convenient gas temperature	Shorter catalyst lifetime
Minimal impact on downstream equipment	Higher maintenance
	Retrofit design considerations
	Ash-handling requirements

LOW-DUST SYSTEMS. The low-dust configuration often is found on low ash fuel-fired boilers (e.g., natural gas or light fuel oils) or in applications where particulate removal equipment, operating at a high temperature, is upstream of the SCR system. Because the ash level is very low, special ash-handling equipment often is not required. Ash cleaning equipment may be needed for the catalyst if the ash has a tendency to collect on the catalyst surfaces. Advantages and disadvantages of low-dust SCR systems are outlined in *Table 5-4*.

TABLE 5-4 | ADVANTAGES AND DISADVANTAGES OF LOW-DUST SELECTIVE CATALYTIC REDUCTION SYSTEM

Advantages	Disadvantages
Less impact on catalyst lifetime	Not tolerant of high-ash fuels
Smaller reactor (than with high-dust systems)	Exhaust gas temperature may limit operation

TAIL-END DUST SYSTEMS. The tail-end SCR system is located downstream of several other gas cleaning devices, which are used to remove particulates, SOx, and heavy metal compounds from the exhaust gas stream. The exhaust gas coming to the SCR system is essentially free of catalyst-damaging compounds, so no special equipment is required to address these related issues. Because the other cleaning devices often operate at temperatures much lower than typical SCR systems do, exhaust gas reheating is required (see *Fig. 5-21*). The reheating can be done by directly or indirectly fired equipment or by steam heat exchangers. Gas-gas heat exchangers between the SCR incoming and exiting gas often are included to minimize the reheating demand of these systems. Advantages

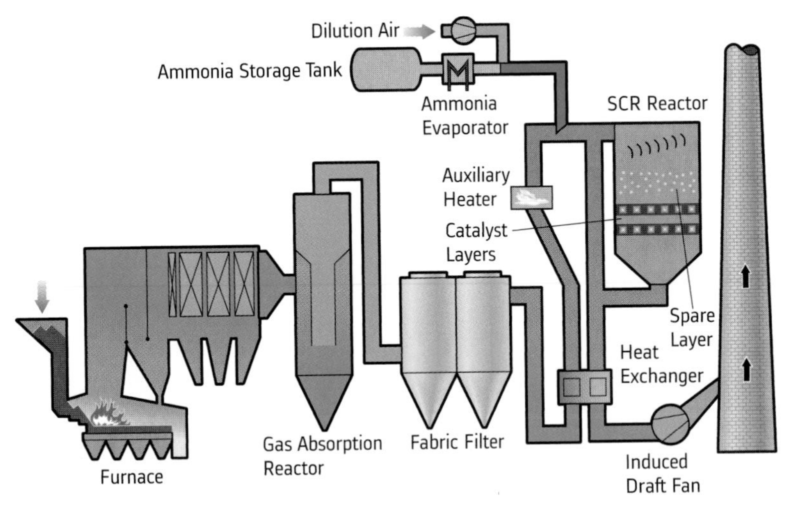

Figure 5-21 | Tail-end dust system (SCR, selective catalytic reduction)

and disadvantages of tail-end SCR systems are outlined in *Table* 5-5.

SCR Design Factors

The SCR processes use fixed beds of catalyst to reduce NOx emissions. The reactor that holds the catalyst beds may direct the exhaust gas flow in either a vertical-downward, a vertical-upward, or a horizontal direction. The reactor is designed to direct the entire exhaust gas flow through the catalyst beds. The reactor also must support and provide the proper arrangement of the catalyst beds.

In most SCR system designs, the amount of catalyst required is determined primarily by the amount of exhaust gas to be treated and by the degree of NOx removal that is required. The catalyst bed design is developed to provide an acceptable amount of pressure drop across the catalyst beds for the required amount of catalyst.

Catalyst beds often feature catalysts that are shaped as monolith structures, because these provide a large amount of surface while featuring a large open-area profile and relatively low flow resistance. The individual monoliths are bundled in steel containers for ease of handling and for protecting the monoliths from damage during shipping and handling.

REACTOR DESIGN. The exhaust gas enters an SCR system at a temperature suitable for the catalytic reactions to occur. If the exhaust gas temperature is too cool, then some form of gas heating is first performed. Heating can be accomplished using direct heating, such as fired burners or introducing hotter exhaust gas, or by indirect heating, such as heat exchangers. If a substantial amount of large ash is present, this ash may be directed to and removed by ash hoppers before continuing on to the balance of the SCR system.

Ammonia is introduced to the exhaust gas at a rate suitable for achieving the desired level of NOx level. It is necessary to avoid creating excessive ammonia slip farther downstream. The ammonia is distributed across the ducting containing the exhaust gas and is blended throughout the duct. Then, the exhaust gas is introduced to the catalyst reactor and passes through the catalyst bed(s), where the ammonia-NOx reactions occur. The resulting exhaust gas, now with a much lower content of NOx

TABLE 5-5 | ADVANTAGES AND DISADVANTAGES OF TAIL-END DUST SYSTEMS

Advantages	Disadvantages
Minimal impact on catalyst lifetime	Exhaust gas reheating costs (both capital and operating)
Flexible design options	Design influenced by upstream emissions control equipment

and ammonia, is directed to the remaining heat recovery and emission control equipment.

CATALYTIC REACTION CONCEPTS. The catalytic reactor can be simply described as a plug flow reactor. The following equation relates the amount of NOx reduced in the reactor with the ammonia reaction rate at the catalyst:

$$F_{\mathrm{NOx,i}} dx_{\mathrm{NOx}} = -r_{\mathrm{NOx}} dA$$

Equation 5-4

where

$F_{\mathrm{NOx,i}}$ = Molecular flow rate of NOx entering the reactor (inlet)
x_{NOx} = fraction of NOx reduced in the reactor
r_{NOx} = NOx reduction reaction rate in the catalyst
A = catalyst area where NOx reduction occurs

Multiplying both sides of Equation 5-4 with the inlet NOx concentration term ($C_{\mathrm{NOx,i}}$) and then rearranging the equations and integrating across the reactor unit yields

$$\int^{VA_\rho} \frac{C_{\mathrm{NOx,i}}}{F_{\mathrm{NOx,i}}} dA = \int^{x_{\mathrm{NOx}}} \frac{C_{\mathrm{NOx,i}}}{-r_{\mathrm{NOx}}} dx_{\mathrm{NOx}}$$

Equation 5-5

where the catalyst area can be defined using

V = volume of catalyst in reactor
A_ρ = area density of the catalyst, surface area per unit volume
x_{NOx} = fraction of NOx removed

The inlet molar flow of NOx ($F_{\mathrm{NOx,i}}$) also can be written as the product of the inlet NOx concentration and volumetric gas flow (Q). Integrating the left-hand side of Equation 5-5 yields

$$\frac{C_{\mathrm{NOx,i}}}{F_{\mathrm{NOx,i}}} VA_\rho = \frac{VA_\rho}{Q} = \frac{1}{A_v}$$

Equation 5-6

where the area velocity (A_v) is related to the space velocity (S_v) as shown:

$$\frac{Q}{A_\rho V} = \frac{S_v}{A_\rho} = A_v$$

Equation 5-7

The fraction of NOx reduced across the reactor also can be defined as

$$x_{\mathrm{NOx}} = \frac{\left(C_{\mathrm{NOx,i}} - C_{\mathrm{NOx,o}}\right)}{C_{\mathrm{NOx,i}}} = 1 - \left(C_{\mathrm{NOx,o}} / C_{\mathrm{NOx,i}}\right)$$

Equation 5-8

where

$C_{NOx,i}$ = concentration of NOx entering the reactor (inlet)
$C_{NOx,o}$ = concentration of NOx exiting the reactor (outlet)

The SCR reaction follows a first-order relationship with respect to NOx and can be stated as

$$-r_{NOx} = kC_{NOx} = kC_{NOx,i}\,(1 - x_{NOx})$$

Equation 5-9

where k is the reaction rate constant. Substituting the reaction rate expression above and integrating the right-hand side of Equation 5-5 yields

$$K = AV \ln\left(\frac{1}{1 - x_{NOx}}\right)$$

Equation 5-10

where K is the global reaction rate constant. The equation above is useful for conditions in which ammonia is not a limiting factor, but there are conditions when the amount of ammonia injected into the SCR system is restricted to minimize the amount of unreacted ammonia exiting the reactor. Using the definition for stoichiometric ratio (SR) between the inlet NOx and NH_3 concentrations entering the catalyst:

$$SR = \frac{C_{NH_3,i}}{C_{NOx,i}}$$

Equation 5-11

Cho[52] related the reaction rate of NOx to the reaction rate of ammonia across the catalyst by

$$-r_{NOx} = -r_{NH_3} = kC_{NH_3} = kC_{NH_3,i}\left(1 - \frac{x_{NOx}}{SR}\right)$$

Equation 5-12

and using this reaction rate equation, the reactor equation can be restated as

$$K = AV \ln\left(\frac{SR}{SR - x_{NOx}}\right)$$

Equation 5-13

This form is useful when the ratio between inlet NH_3 and NOx concentrations, SR, is less than 1.

The global reaction rate constant consists of rate constants for both the mass transfer rate of NOx and NH_3 reactants from the bulk exhaust gas to the catalyst

surface (k_m) and the rate of reaction between NOx and NH_3 on the catalyst surface (k_r):

$$K^{-1} = k_m^{-1} + k_r^{-1}$$

Equation 5-14

The term k_m mostly depends on the gas velocity in the catalyst cells, the catalyst cell geometry and dimensions, and the diffusivity of NOx in the exhaust gas. The term k_r primarily depends on the catalyst's chemical composition and internal pore structure as well as the exhaust gas temperature.

Catalyst activity tends to degrade over time because of a variety of factors, such as catalyst poisoning, fouling, and erosion. Deactivation of SCR catalysts can be commonly described as an exponential decay function over time:

$$K = K_0(1 - D)^t$$

Equation 5-15

where

- K = catalyst activity at time t
- K_0 = initial catalyst activity at time zero
- D = deactivation rate
- t = time

For a given catalyst configuration, the area density is the amount of catalyst surface per unit catalyst volume. For a square-channel configuration (see *Fig.* 5-22), the area density can be calculated using the expression

$$A_p = \frac{4b}{(a+b)^2} = \frac{4b}{\text{pitch}^2}$$

Equation 5-16

where

- a = catalyst wall thickness dimension
- b = catalyst channel opening dimension

and pitch is defined as the unit dimension of the catalyst cell or channel:

$$\text{pitch} = a + b$$

Equation 5-17

Pressure drop across the catalyst bed can be estimated using the Darcy equation:

$$\Delta p = 4f\frac{lv^2\rho}{2b}$$

Equation 5-18

where

- Δp = draft loss across the catalyst body
- f = friction factor
- l = catalyst body length
- v = gas velocity through the catalyst body
- ρ = gas density
- b = catalyst channel hydraulic diameter

and the friction factor for the catalyst can be determined using the Hawthorne correlation[53]:

$$4f = \frac{A}{N_{Re}}\sqrt{1+\frac{0.0445bN_{Re}}{l}}$$

Equation 5-19

where

- N_{Re} = Reynolds number
- A = 53 for triangular channels, 57 for square channel, and 96 for parallel plates (dimensionless)

SCR Process Chemistry

Before the catalytic reactions can occur between NOx and NH_3, these reactants must first move from the bulk fluid exhaust gas phase to the catalyst body surface, as shown in *Figure* 5-23. This involves film diffusion, or external

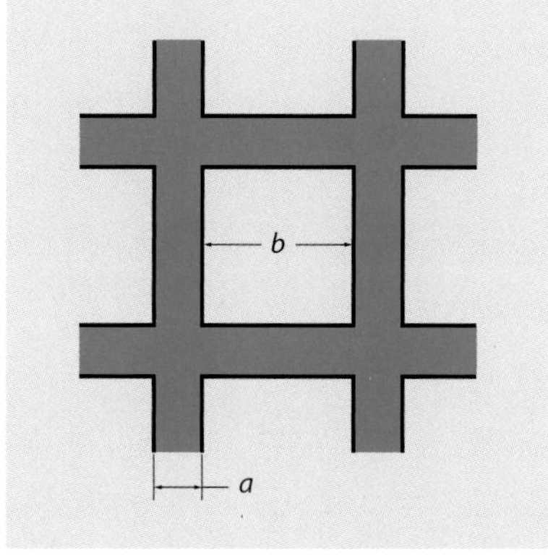

Figure 5-22 | Square-channel configuration

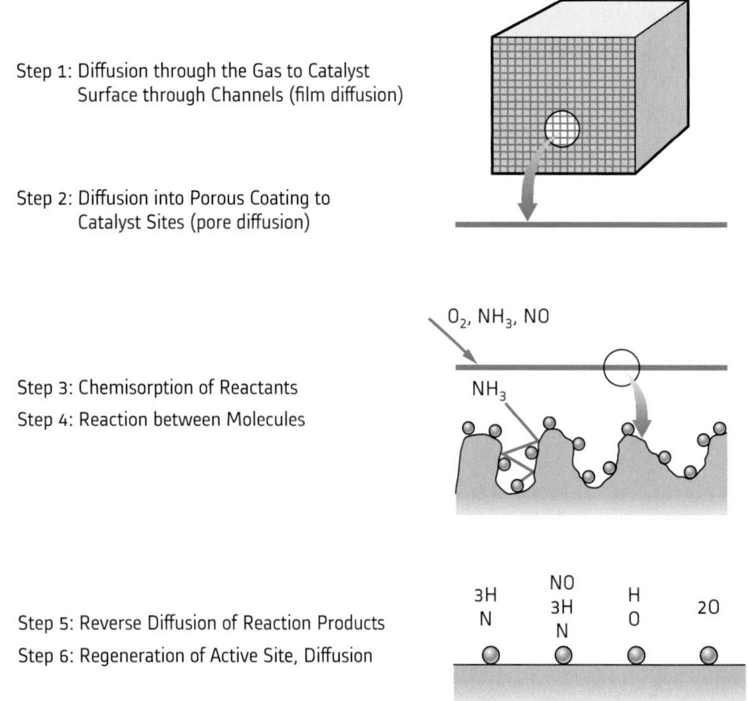

Figure 5-23 | Diffusion and chemisorption on catalyst

mass transfer, as denoted by k_m. At the catalyst surface, the reactant gas species must continue their journey through the small pores that exist on the catalyst body surface. The catalyst active sites, where the chemical reaction occurs, are found within these small pores. The internal reaction rate, k_r, accounts for both the diffusion of the reactants within the pores and the reaction on the catalyst active sites.

At the start of the catalytic reaction cycle, ammonia is adsorbed on a catalytic active reaction site (*Fig. 5-24, top portion of reaction schematic*). Then, NO (NOx) combines with the adsorbed ammonia to form an NOx-NH_3 complex (see *Fig. 5-24, right-hand side of the reaction schematic*). The NOx-NH_3 complex decomposes to form nitrogen and water vapor, which are quickly released from the catalyst reaction site (see *Fig. 5-24, bottom portion of the reaction schematic*). The end product from this reaction also is a reduced reaction site, which then must be oxidized with oxygen to convert the site into an active form and which produces more water vapor (see *Fig. 5-24, left-hand side of the reaction schematic*).

EFFECT OF NOx AND NH_3. As stated earlier, the NOx-NH_3 reaction is considered to be first order with respect to NOx. This means that the fraction of NOx reduced across a given catalyst body is independent of the inlet concentration of NOx when ammonia is not a limiting factor. When ammonia is a limiting factor, the fraction of NOx removed (x_{NO}) is directly proportional to inlet SR between NH_3 and NOx. As the SR exceeds unity, the relationship deviates because of greater inefficiencies, and x_{NO} never exceeds 100%. As the value for SR increases, the ammonia slip, or unreacted ammonia, exiting the catalyst beds also increases. For many practical operating environments, the amount of ammonia slip often is a limiting factor with regard to the amount of ammonia delivered to the SCR system. For this operating scenario, the amount of NOx removal is strongly dependent on the inlet NOx concentration. These relationships are shown in *Figure 5-25*.

EFFECT OF TEMPERATURE. The catalysts used in SCR systems have a strong dependence on operating temperature. Upper and lower temperature limits define the operating temperature window for a given catalyst and application design. At low temperatures, the SCR reaction is strongly kinetically limited by the reaction rate on

the catalyst surface. The influence of temperature variations on NOx removal efficiencies, relatively large catalyst sizes because of slow reaction rates, and increased poison effects are reasons to avoid operation below the appropriate temperature window. At high temperatures, thermal sintering that collapses the small catalyst pores may permanently damage the catalyst. Unwanted side reactions include ammonia oxidation reactions:

$$4NH_3 + 5O_2 \rightarrow 4NO + 6H_2O$$

Equation 5-20

$$4NH_3 + 3O_2 \rightarrow 2N_2 + 6H_2O$$

Equation 5-21

These unwanted side reactions can cause an apparent loss in ammonia efficiency. The behavior of the catalyst over the operating temperature range is shown in *Figure 5-26*.

EFFECT OF OXYGEN. In cases when the amount of excess combustion air is low enough such that the exhaust gas contains less than 1% oxygen by volume, the activity of the catalyst can be suppressed. In these cases, catalyst formulation and design must be specially considered for the application, or additional air may be delivered to the exhaust gas to provide a sufficient increase in catalyst activity. At exhaust gas oxygen concentrations of greater than 1% by volume, the influence on catalyst activity is not significant.

EFFECT OF SOx. The presence of SOx, SO_2, and SO_3 can have an effect on limiting the operating temperature range of the catalyst. The catalyst in the SCR system also will oxidize SO_2 present in the exhaust gas into SO_3 as it passes through the catalyst beds, as shown by the following reaction:

$$2SO_2 + O_2 \rightarrow 2SO_3$$

Equation 5-22

The formation of SO_3 is undesirable. Increased SO_3 concentrations raise the acid dew point of the exhaust gases, leading to corrosion of the downstream equipment. Additionally, SO_3 is considered to be a condensable particulate that can influence the amount of fine particulate matter in the gas stream (PM2.5). For combustion systems firing very low-sulfur natural gas, a higher degree of SO_2 oxidation and resulting SO_3 levels usually can be tolerated. For higher-sulfur fuels, such as many types of coal, a lower degree

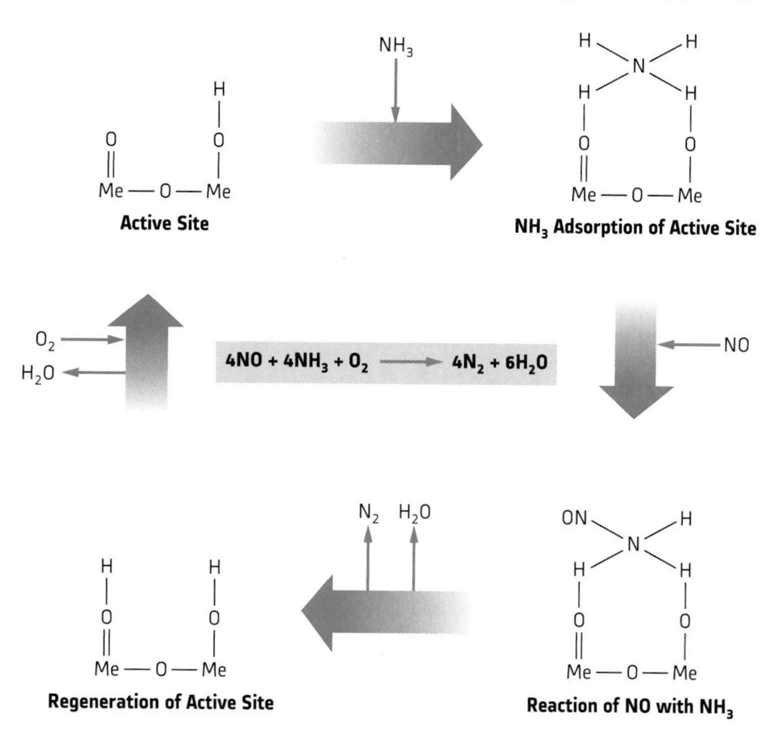

Figure 5-24 | Absorption of ammonia and NOx modified from Pritchard, et al, 1995

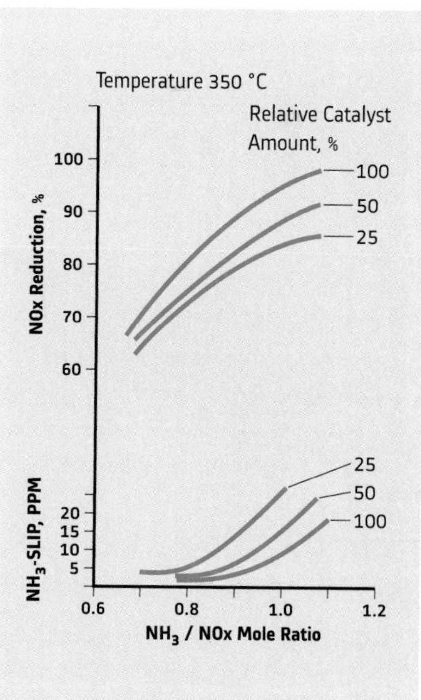

Figure 5-25 | NOx reduction and ammonia slip versus NH_3/NOx mole ratio

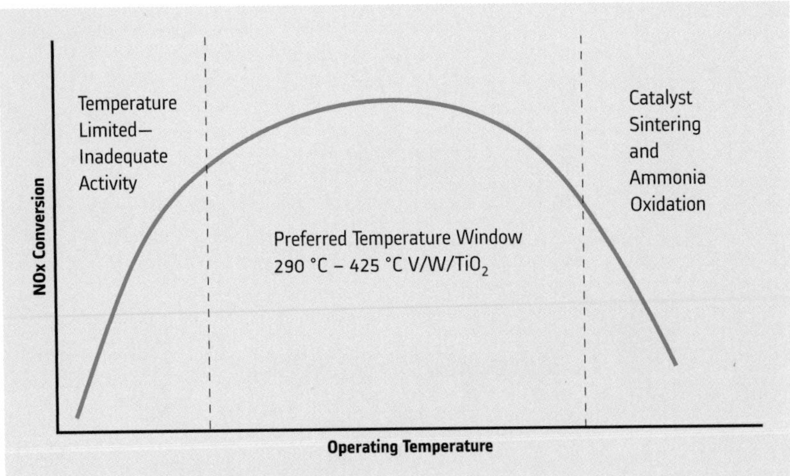

Figure 5-26 | NOx conversion versus operating temperature (TiO_2, titanium dioxide; V, vanadium; W, tungsten)

TABLE 5-6 | TYPICAL CONVERSION RATES OF SO_2 TO SO_3

Application	Typical Conversion Rate (%)
Gas firing	5–10
Oil firing	1–3
Coal firing	<1

of SO_2 oxidation normally is a design consideration. Typical levels of SO_2 oxidation are indicated in *Table 5-6*.

When the catalyst is operating at a relatively high temperature, the fraction of SO_2 oxidized increases with increasing operating temperature, as indicated in *Figure 5-27*. This side reaction needs to be factored into the design.

One of the key considerations with SO_3 emissions is the potential formation of ammonium bisulfate (ABS), or NH_4HSO_4, and ammonium sulfate, or $(NH_4)_2SO_4$, salts, as shown by the following reactions:

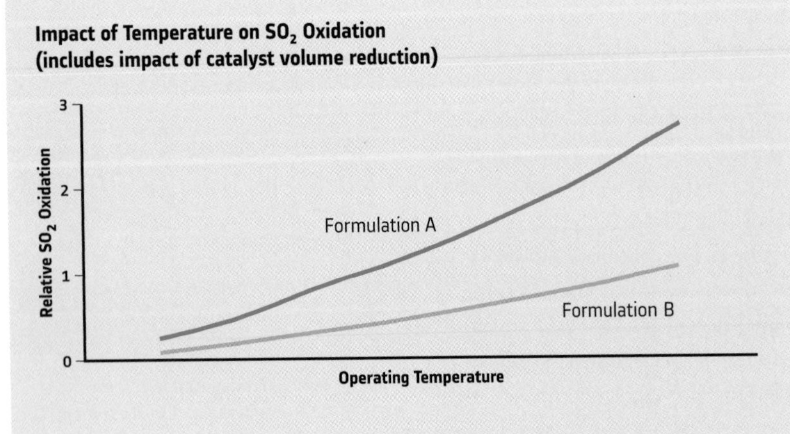

Figure 5-27 | Relative SO_2 oxidation

$$NH_3 + H_2O + SO_3 \rightarrow NH_4HSO_4$$

Equation 5-23

$$2NH_3 + H_2O + SO_3 \rightarrow (NH_4)_2SO_4$$

Equation 5-24

These solid salts can form when the flue gas temperature is cool enough and the concentrations of NH_3 and SO_3 are high enough, as illustrated in *Figure 5-28*. This potential effect should be considered for equipment located downstream of the SCR system, such as the gas-gas heat exchanger (GGH) or particulate collection equipment.

The formation of ABS also is a concern regarding the catalyst. The formation of this salt can occur at much higher temperatures, such that salts form in the small pores on the catalyst body. These salts can cause the catalyst to lose activity as the pores become blocked and the active sites become inaccessible to the NOx and NH_3 gases. It is best to avoid these low temperatures at which this phenomenon occurs. It may be possible to recover the catalyst activity, either by heating the catalyst at a higher temperature to drive off the salts or by special regeneration washing methods performed off-line.

EFFECT OF ASH. Ash can have a damaging effect on the catalyst by several different mechanisms. For exhaust gas streams that contain an appreciable amount of dust, there is a definite risk of the open channels in the catalyst body becoming plugged or blocked by ash deposits. During normal operation in a high-dust environment, small ash deposits are continually forming on the horizontal surfaces of the catalyst

face and adjacent equipment. These small deposits must be removed before they grow large enough to obstruct the gas flow paths through the catalyst channels. This can be done using conventional soot cleaning devices, such as hot, compressed air or steam-based soot blowers, or using acoustic or sonic horns. After being disturbed by the soot cleaner, the ash moves through the catalyst bed with the exhaust gas to the downstream equipment.

Large ash particles (a size equivalent to the catalyst channel openings) are a special plugging consideration. Because the soot cleaners do not address this special ash, other precautions must be taken if such ash is present. Special duct designs, baffles, and screens may be located upstream of the SCR reactor to direct this ash into a hopper system for removal. The catalyst module assembly also may have a fine screen on the upstream catalyst face to keep these particles from depositing in the catalyst channels.

Another concern for high-dust environments and high-gas-velocity conditions is the erosion of the catalyst body by the ash. To a degree, this erosion is accounted for in the catalyst and system design. The direction of the exhaust gas flow entering the catalyst should be parallel to the catalyst channel orientation to minimize erosive effects. The leading edge of the catalyst body also may be hardened to minimize erosion.

The last potential effect from the ash is known as "masking." Masking is the term used to describe ash deposits on the catalyst body surface and in the small pores on the catalyst body, which can block the NOx and NH_3 gases from reaching the active catalyst sites. This is best avoided by proper

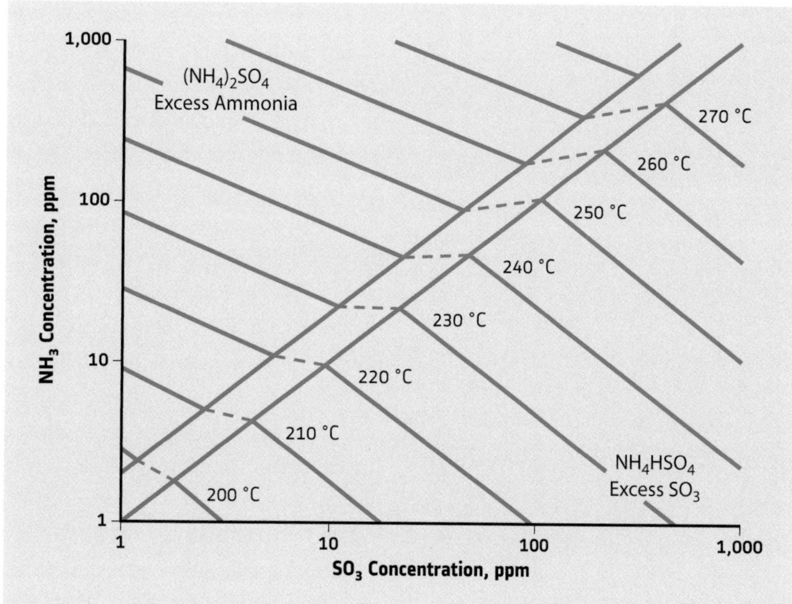

Figure 5-28 | Sodium bisulfate formation

SCR catalyst and system design, soot cleaning practices, and catalyst cleaning maintenance procedures.

EFFECT OF CATALYST POISONS. In many cases, the loss of catalyst activity also can be attributed to poisoning of the active catalyst sites by various compounds. These compounds chemically bind with the active sites and render them inactive for promoting the NOx-NH_3 reaction. Although several compounds may poison a given catalyst, some of the most commonly encountered are arsenic, phosphorus, and the alkalies sodium, potassium, and calcium.

The compounds containing arsenic and phosphorus may be found in the fuel source and are volatized into the hot exhaust gas during combustion. These slightly gaseous compounds will deactivate the catalyst as the exhaust gas passes through the catalyst layers. The catalyst design should consider the quantity of these two potential poisons that is present in the fuel sources. Because of the volatile nature of these compounds, such analysis should involve the fuel itself rather than the post-combustion ash. The poisoning effect of fuels with high levels of arsenic or with high arsenic and low calcium levels may be mitigated by adding additional calcium, often as limestone, to the fuel supply that is fed to the burners.

The alkali compounds also can bind with the catalyst active sites via another route. These compounds, often present as salts in the ash, can leach out and combine with the catalyst when excessive amounts of moisture form on the catalyst body. High-calcium fuels pose a pore-masking risk as well, because calcium may combine with SO_3 to form calcium sulfate when both of these are present in the catalyst pores. Poisoning by alkalies can best be avoided by careful ash deposit maintenance and by keeping the catalyst dry during off-line storage. The effect of catalyst poisoning may be permanent, but it can be addressed using careful washing treatments performed off-line.

REAGENT UTILIZATION. As noted in the reaction equations between NOx and NH_3, the reaction stoichiometry requires one molar amount of ammonia to react with one molar amount of NOx. Careful SCR system design can result in operation at a very high ammonia usage efficiency. Thus, the amount of ammonia required for a given system can be determined by the amount of exhaust gas to be treated, the amount of NOx to be removed, and the amount of ammonia slip (or unreacted ammonia) that can be tolerated:

$$C_{NH_3,i} = \left(C_{NOx,i} - C_{NOx,o}\right) + C_{NH_3,o} = C_{NOx,i} x_{NOx} + C_{NH_3,o}$$

Equation 5-25

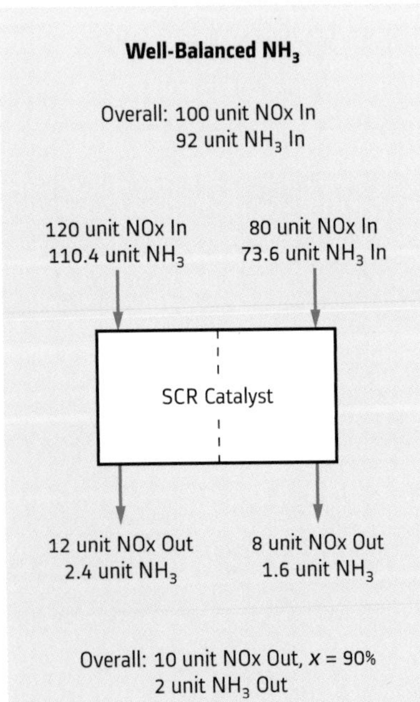

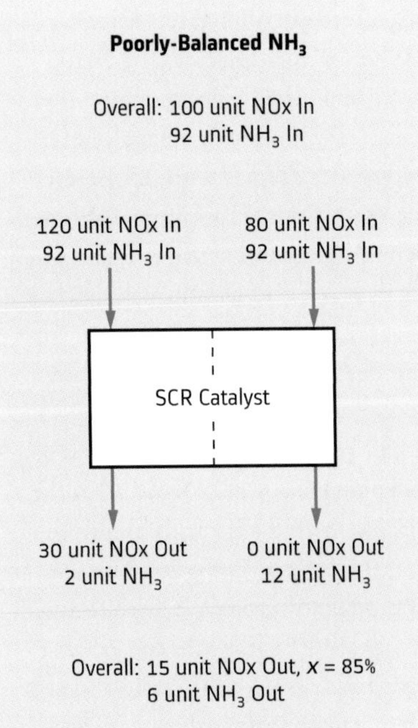

Figure 5-29 | Impact of poor ammonia distribution (SCR, selective catalytic reduction)

The challenge in achieving high ammonia utilization efficiency is blending the ammonia feed to the SCR system with the NOx in the exhaust gas. Poor blending results in low ammonia efficiency, poor NOx removal efficiency, and high ammonia slip levels, as shown in *Figure 5-29*. In almost all SCR applications, there are variations in NOx flow rates within the SCR system. Some imbalances between ammonia and NOx can partially be addressed by additional catalyst, but the ammonia to NOx distribution must be accomplished by the ammonia distribution and control system.

AMMONIA UTILIZATION. Effective utilization of ammonia in an SCR system typically occurs on two levels: overall ammonia flow delivery control and localized ammonia distribution. Both features are crucial for effective ammonia use and successful NOx removal within the SCR system. Each of these features involves unique and independent equipment in order to meet their respective objectives.

The overall control of ammonia fed to the SCR system is designed to meet the overall NOx removal efficiency and ammonia slip targets. Several strategies can be used to control the total ammonia fed to the SCR system. One feed-forward method relies on determining the inlet NOx load to the SCR system based on inlet NOx concentration and exhaust gas flow rate measurements. An appropriate amount of ammonia is fed to the SCR system based on the SR required to achieve an NOx removal efficiency target. The outlet NOx concentration measurement signal is used to trim the ammonia flow and avoid excessive ammonia injection.

Another control method relies on measuring NOx removal load on the SCR system based on both inlet and outlet NOx concentrations and the exhaust gas flow rate. The amount of ammonia is adjusted to achieve the desired NOx removal load or efficiency level. The outlet NOx concentration signal may be used to trim excessive ammonia flow. Inlet factors, such as boiler load and inlet NOx load, can be used as feed-forward signals to anticipate changes in the ammonia load demand.

Still another control method is based on maintaining a NOx emission level either as a concentration or as a load based on the outlet NOx concentration measurement and exhaust gas flow rate. Feed-forward signals can be taken from boiler load or inlet NOx concentration measurements. This simple approach works well for relatively low NOx removal efficiencies or for applications in which maintaining ammonia slip levels is not difficult to accomplish.

Supplemental measurements of O_2 or CO_2 may be used to account for changes in NOx concentration caused by air in-leakage. In general, reliable NH_3 slip measurements are difficult to make at ppm-level concentrations. Some in-duct analytical methods have shown promise as supplemental operating information. For applications in which ABS formation is a risk, the symptoms of salt deposits, such as heat exchanger draft loss or thermal efficiency, may be monitored for changes and an indication of excessive ammonia slip.

Very little mixing occurs within the SCR reactor. The treatment of NOx emissions with ammonia depends on creating an ammonia flow profile that matches the exhaust gas NOx profile. To accomplish this objective, distribution of ammonia throughout the exhaust gas duct is a critical objective. Carefully designed ammonia distribution equipment is located upstream of the SCR reactor to accomplish this task. An SCR system also may rely on ammonia slip exiting an SNCR system for some of the ammonia feed. For these systems, the ammonia control and distribution equipment must account for the ammonia slip profile exiting the SNCR system.

For a typical ammonia distribution system, the ammonia is introduced in relatively high concentrations at various locations across or around the duct. At this point in the SCR system, the exhaust duct contains a few small regions with feed gas that has a very high ammonia concentration and that is surrounded by exhaust gas that has zero ammonia content. This high-ammonia feed gas must diffuse and blend with the NOx-containing exhaust gas. Gas mixers often are located either upstream or downstream of the ammonia injection location in order to blend the ammonia throughout the exhaust gas stream.

A simple design assumption for the ammonia distribution equipment is that all of the individual ammonia injection points will require equal amounts of ammonia feed gas. For many real-world applications, however, this assumption is not true. A need exists to bias the amount of ammonia at each injection location to meet that location's corresponding NOx load. Most injection equipment also features some form of flow adjustment to modify the relative ammonia delivered to each injection location. Another strategy to obtain proper ammonia and NOx distribution is to rely on intensive mixing downstream of the ammonia injection location to smooth both NOx and ammonia distribution profiles. For cases with severe and variable NOx concentration profiles, it may be necessary to create multiple ammonia injection zones within a single SCR system. Each ammonia injection zone would be equipped with separate and complete control systems in order to control the amount of ammonia in each zone.

SCR Components

Any typical SCR system is composed of the following basic components: catalyst, reactor, and ammonia injection-distribution system. For high-dust applications, ash-handling equipment also must be provided. Although it is not typically considered as a component, the ductwork between the SCR system components will influence the exhaust gas behavior, consequently affecting the performance of the respective downstream components.

CATALYST. Most SCR catalysts are composed of a chemical blend of vanadium oxide (V_2O_5) and titanium dioxide (TiO_2). The vanadium oxide component provides the catalytically active sites for the SCR reaction, whereas the titanium dioxide component provides the support and the micropores for distributing the active sites. Other catalyst formulations may be based on zeolite materials, precious metals (e.g., platinum), or other base metals (e.g., iron), each with their own respective ranges of operating temperature.

The physical catalyst structure can exist as a homogeneous structure, in which the catalyst body is entirely catalyst material, or as a heterogeneous catalytic coating, supported by a mechanically strong but catalytically inert structure. The inert structure may be made into a mesh fabricated from metal or a ceramic material, such as fiberglass. Catalysts used in ash-free exhaust gas applications may consist of a thin coating of catalyst on a metal foil or rigid ceramic body, such as cordierite.

The catalyst body structure is designed to maximize both the surface area in a given catalyst volume and the frontal open area as well as to produce a low resistance to gas flow. Most catalyst bodies are monoliths composed of many small cells or channels with thin walls that are oriented parallel to the direction of gas flow. Some catalyst products are composed of packed beds of small, shaped pellets or beads.

Most homogeneous monolith catalyst bodies typically have face area dimensions of 5.9 × 5.9 inches (150 × 150 mm), with body lengths ranging from 1 inch (a few centimeters) to greater than 3 feet (1 m). The face area of supported, heterogeneous catalyst bodies may range from 1 inch (a few centimeters) to more than 20 inches (>50 cm) in side dimensions, with a similar range for the depth dimensions. Usually, the shallow monoliths are used in high-cell-density, dust-free, single-bed applications. The deeper monoliths are found in lower-cell-density, multiple-bed, dust- or poison-containing exhaust gas applications.

For most catalyst monolith bodies, the face side dimensions normally are fixed, regardless of the number of cells or channels in the monolith body. For example, a catalyst with a .16 inch (4.2 mm) pitch will have a 35 × 35 cell count. A catalyst with a .29 inch (7.4 mm) pitch will have a 20 × 20 cell count. For heterogeneous catalyst monoliths, the spacing between the plates also will vary with pitch or equivalent cell count.

The catalyst monoliths located in the SCR reactor are contained in steel structures. These are collectively referred to as "modules." These modules typically have nominal dimensions of 3.2 x 6.5 ft (1 × 2 m) in face area, with depth dimensions of between 1.6 and 4.9 ft (0.5–1.5 m). A typical assembly of homogeneous catalyst will hold 6 × 12 monoliths arranged in a single layer, whereas a typical assembly of heterogeneous catalyst will hold 2 × 4 monoliths arranged in either a single or double layers. For dust-free applications, the catalyst assemblies may have much larger face area dimensions.

The steel structure of the catalyst module typically features lifting components for handling and protective components to avoid damaging the catalyst monoliths during handling. It is important to have good sealing around the catalyst modules in order to avoid having untreated exhaust gas bypass the catalyst, resulting in high NOx emissions. In a downward exhaust gas flow arrangement, gasket material is placed between the metal edge on the bottom of the module and the surface that supports the module. Gas sealing devices also are placed between the catalyst modules to direct gas flow into the modules and to avoid forming ash deposits.

REACTOR. The primary roles of the SCR reactor structure is to arrange and support the catalyst modules and to distribute and direct the exhaust gas flow through the catalyst modules. A typical SCR reactor will have several layers for dirty or high-dust applications and, possibly, a single layer for clean or tail-end applications. Multiple layers are used when catalyst deactivation is a factor. When operating in a high-dust environment, the catalyst will continually and gradually lose its activity. This loss in activity will appear as an increase in either NOx or NH_3 slip emissions or an increase in ammonia consumption by the SCR system. Eventually, the activity loss will be great enough that the catalyst cannot simultaneously achieve the NOx removal and NH_3 slip requirements. At this time, fresh, fully active catalyst is installed. This behavior is shown in *Figure 5-30*.

Catalyst replacement is a considerable maintenance cost. The number of layers in a reactor design should be considered against lifetime catalyst

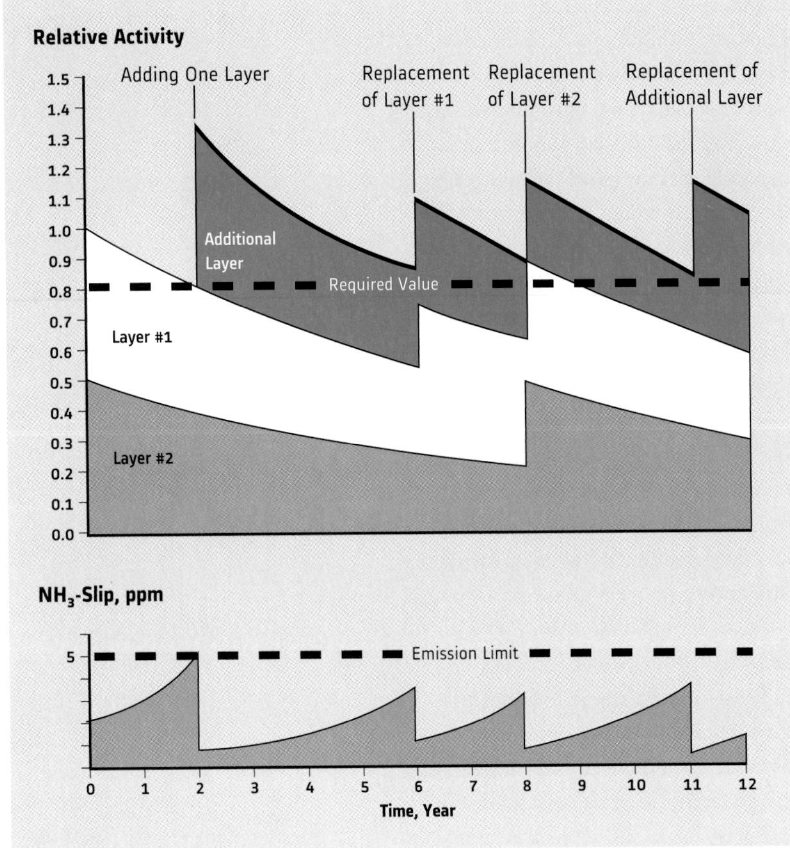

Figure 5-30 | Catalyst replacement cycles

management. For some applications, the cost of installing an additional spare, empty layer in the reactor is more than offset by cost savings in long-term catalyst replacement.

To help facilitate catalyst installation and removal, access provisions at the location of each catalyst layer in the reactor must be provided. Each layer should have access doors for moving the catalyst modules in and out of the reactor housing. In a vertically oriented reactor, the access typically is located along with access platforms. For these reactors, the catalysts usually are brought up to the access level via an elevator or a lifting winch. The catalyst modules are moved from the lifting location to the access door location using dolly carts. The modules are then lifted into the reactor using a beam winch and placed into the final position in the reactor using another dolly cart. Most horizontally oriented reactors have access doors along the roof of the reactor. The catalyst modules are installed with the use of a crane or similar lifting equipment.

Most conventional arrangements of catalyst modules in an SCR reactor provide a square shape for stand-alone reactors. If the reactor is incorporated into the boiler section, then the reactor dimensions typically follow those of the heat exchanger tube section. The gas velocity through the SCR reactor is approximately one-fourth the velocity through open ducts, or slightly less than the velocity through the boiler section leading to the reactor unit. Successful operation of the SCR catalyst often requires a fairly uniform gas velocity across the entire catalyst module layer. Flow devices may be required to evenly distribute the exhaust gas entering the SCR catalyst beds. This is especially true for most downward flow-oriented reactors or other SCR system designs with turns and expansions located upstream of the SCR reactor. These devices typically are turning vanes for the duct expansion and gas splitters or diffusion baffles at the duct turn. The design and placement of these devices usually is done with the aid of computational fluid dynamics software and/or cold flow, reduced-scale physical models.

The reactor design should provide a suitable operating environment for the SCR catalyst to achieve its optimal performance. The primary operating factors include the ammonia to NOx molar ratio (SR), the inlet NOx concentration ($C_{NOx,i}$), the exhaust gas velocity (v), and the exhaust gas temperature (T). The distribution for each of these parameters across the catalyst face should be relatively uniform. The distribution often is defined as the coefficient of variation (CV), which is the ratio of the standard deviation to the mean value for the respective parameter. The term CV is defined as

$$CV = \sqrt{\frac{\sum_{n=1}^{N}\left(u_n - \bar{u}\right)^2}{\left(N-1\right)\bar{u}^2}}$$

Equation 5-26

where

u_n = parameter value at location n
$\bar{u}$ = mean of all parameter values
N = total number of locations (across catalyst face)

Typical values for various parameter CVs are listed in *Table 5-7*.

ASH HANDLING. For systems fired by clean, ash-free fuel or tail-end systems, in which ash does not present a continual operating concern, no additional ash-handling equipment is required for successful SCR system operation. For other systems, such as high-dust applications, special SCR system design considerations and equipment provisions are necessary.

Soot cleaning equipment is required to avoid the formation of ash deposits on the catalyst that can plug the catalyst channels. Typical soot cleaning devices are either steam- or air-driven soot blowers or sonic horns. Soot blowers should be designed to use sufficiently hot media to avoid forming ammonia salts or condensation. If steam is used, there should be enough superheat of the steam to avoid any condensation. Water droplets will physically damage the catalyst elements because of the force at which they are delivered by a typical soot blower. For any soot blower, the blower nozzle rakes should be sufficiently far from the modules to avoid damaging the elements with the high-velocity media. Sonic horns should be located to provide complete sound energy coverage of each catalyst layer.

Large-particle ash, or popcorn ash, is another risk in terms of catalyst channel plugging. These ash particles typically have diameters on the order of the catalyst channel open dimension or greater. The presence of large-particle ash has been associated with coal types, combustion burner types and operation, ash slagging, and other circumstances that may lead to formation of large ash particles. On an existing (retrofit) application, an investigation is worthwhile to confirm the potential for large-particle ash. If large-particle ash is known or expected, then appropriate steps should be taken to avoid introducing this ash to the catalyst beds.

The first means of addressing this ash problem is to separate and direct the ash away from the exhaust gas. This can be done using several technologies. The largest, heaviest ash particles can settle out of the exhaust gas flow stream by use of horizontal and vertical, upward flow–oriented duct arrangements. Baffle plates, or other impinging devices, can be placed in a horizontal duct to remove the momentum of the large ash particles and direct them downward using gravity. Other technology involves collecting

TABLE 5-7 | TYPICAL COEFFICIENTS OF VARIATION (CVS) FOR VARIOUS PARAMETERS

Parameter*	Typical CV (%)
SR	Less than 5 to 10
$C_{NOx,i}$	Less than 10 to 20
V	Less than 10 to 20
T	Less than ±10°C from mean

*SR, stoichiometric ratio; $C_{NOx,i}$, inlet NOx concentration; V, volume of catalyst in reactor; T, temperature.

the large particles on screens or other similar devices that are periodically cleaned, driving the large ash downward. The second means of addressing the large-particle ash is removal of the ash from the SCR system. This generally is done using conventional ash hoppers, typically located upstream of the SCR reactor and adjacent to an upward flow-oriented duct. Hoppers should be designed to ensure that the ash introduced into the hopper does not re-entrain back into the exhaust gas flow.

AMMONIA INJECTION GRID. One of the primary components of any ammonia injection system is the injection nozzle, which is used to introduce the ammonia into the exhaust gas and distribute the ammonia across the exhaust gas duct. Nozzle designs can range from very simple (i.e., a hole in a pipe) to very complex, depending on the requirements of the application and the other components of the ammonia subsystem. Regardless of the design, the ammonia injection nozzle also must be able to perform effectively across a range of ammonia injection rates and, in high-sulfur or high-dust applications, to avoid plugging. The total number of nozzles, or the spacing between the nozzles for a given application, is influenced by the mixing distance between the injection location and the catalyst beds as well as by the design philosophy of the ammonia subsystem. The performance of a given ammonia injection nozzle arrangement often is validated using models, such as computational fluid dynamics or physical scale models, at the design stage. For ammonia-dilution air systems, the nozzles are based on single-fluid designs. For systems in which aqueous ammonia is injected directly into the exhaust gas duct, dual-fluid nozzles are used, where high-pressure air is supplied to atomize the ammonia solution into a fine spray for evaporation and distribution.

Although ammonia injection nozzle location and arrangement may take into account local NOx load variations, additional ammonia mixing may be required to achieve the proper ammonia to NOx ratio distribution across the catalyst inlet face. Some ammonia injection system designs utilize the mixing effects that the ammonia supply piping provides. Another approach to achieving good ammonia to NOx ratio distributions is to use static gas-mixing devices. Static mixers may be perforated plates or some variation of baffles. Baffle shapes may be elliptical, triangular, or rectangular, and they may be interconnected or freestanding. These devices may be placed upstream of the ammonia injection nozzle grid to address NOx load imbalances. Mixers also may be placed downstream of the nozzle grid location to achieve better diffusion of ammonia. To obtain a suitable ammonia to NOx ratio distribution in any given application, there usually is a design balance between injection nozzle spacing and the use of static mixers. A high nozzle density offers better tuning opportunities, but with more operating complexity. Aggressive gas mixing offers simplicity and robustness, but with a draft loss penalty. Additionally, the duct arrangement design often influences which mixing strategies are feasible.

The supply of ammonia to the injection nozzles is accomplished through a piping distribution system from a central ammonia vapor supply. This piping system is designed to maintain a reliable ammonia feed to each injection nozzle while considering variations in ammonia load and exhaust gas conditions with boiler load. To provide a means for biasing or adjusting the flow of ammonia to individual or sets of nozzles, each supply pipe, or header, often is equipped with flow adjustment valves and flow measurement capabilities. The amount of ammonia to each header typically is adjusted during the commissioning of the SCR system and then on a yearly basis as part of the SCR system maintenance program.

The control of the ammonia flow from the central ammonia vaporizer to the distribution header usually is done with ammonia gas-phase flow control equipment, suitable for ammonia service, for vaporized, anhydrous ammonia. For aqueous ammonia supplies, the flow control equipment often is placed on the liquid supply line leading to the vaporizer and also must be suitable for ammonia service. After vaporization and flow metering, the concentrated ammonia vapor stream typically is diluted with air, clean exhaust gas, or steam as a means to rapidly convey the ammonia to the nozzles and to reduce the ammonia level below its lower explosive level concentration limit.

The ammonia load demand is partially determined by the NOx levels at the inlet and the outlet of the SCR system. Systems for measuring NOx emissions sample one or more positions to obtain a representative sample of the average NOx concentration at each location. The sampling probes typically are located, for the inlet measurement, upstream of the ammonia injection nozzle grid to avoid any potential interference in the NOx analysis from ammonia. The outlet measurement sample typically is taken immediately downstream of the SCR reactor, or the continuous emissions monitoring system's NOx emission analyzer, located in the emission stack, may be used. The NOx concentration measurement often is performed using heated (dry)-extractive or dilution-extractive analyzer systems. Each system has its own merits and disadvantages. Whichever system is chosen, it must be able to effectively handle the ash, moisture, and acidic gases that exhaust gas normally contains. Recent advances for in-duct, laser-based sensors show promise for both NOx and NH_3 slip measurements.

Reducing Agent Systems

ANHYDROUS AMMONIA. Anhydrous ammonia systems commonly are used for many SCR and SNCR systems. This type of ammonia supply often offers the least expensive reagent cost as well as the lowest operating and capital costs of the three basic ammonia supply systems. Because of the nature of anhydrous ammonia, equipment suitable for ammonia service is required, and special considerations should be taken for the handling and storage of this form of ammonia. This type of system often poses special permitting concerns beyond those with the other two ammonia supply systems.

Anhydrous ammonia is pure ammonia provided as a liquefied gas under pressure. At ambient temperature, the liquid ammonia is at its boiling point, so the ammonia storage pressure can vary appreciably. To avoid damaging the ammonia service equipment, only technical-grade ammonia, with no additives, should be used.

For an anhydrous ammonia system, the ammonia is stored in pressure vessels at the site. Ammonia typically is delivered to the site by truck or rail. The liquid ammonia is transferred from the delivery vehicle to the storage tank by moving ammonia vapors from the storage vessel to the delivery car, while the ammonia liquid flows from the car to the vessel. The storage vessel and the delivery connection equipment usually are equipped with many special safety features.

The ammonia fed to the SNCR/SCR flow control system commonly is in the vapor phase, so energy is required to vaporize the liquid ammonia. The ammonia evaporator may be heated using commonly available sources, such as steam, hot water, or electricity. The evaporator may be located adjacent to the storage tank, where it is used to maintain a vapor pressure in the tank as ammonia vapor is directed to the SNCR/SCR reactor. The evaporator also may be located remotely from the tank, where the liquid ammonia used by the SNCR/SCR system is vaporized before entering the SNCR/SCR reactor. The advantages and disadvantages of these evaporator locations are summarized in *Table 5-8*.

The ammonia flow control equipment often is located between the ammonia vaporizer and the ammonia injection piping. A typical anhydrous ammonia storage and evaporation system is shown in *Figure 5-31*.

TABLE 5-8 | ADVANTAGES AND DISADVANTAGES OF AMMONIA EVAPORATOR LOCATIONS

Evaporator Location	Advantage	Disadvantage
Adjacent	Simple design	Tank maintenance
Close-coupled w/tank	Ease of operation Low NH_3 pressure	Larger vaporizer Larger piping
Remote	Minimal tank maintenance Smaller vaporizer Heating location	Pumps required Complex design Higher maintenance

AQUEOUS AMMONIA. Aqueous ammonia systems also commonly are used for many SCR and some SNCR systems. The reagent cost for aqueous ammonia typically is competitive with that for anhydrous ammonia, but with lower operating and higher capital costs. Aqueous ammonia has safety and handling concerns because of the ammonia content, but the lower pressure and water content provide lesser concerns with ammonia storage. This form of ammonia typically has less permitting concerns than an anhydrous ammonia system.

Aqueous ammonia is a concentrated solution of ammonia mixed with water. Various ammonia concentrations may be available, but the maximum concentration of 29% often is used. Technical-grade aqueous ammonia containing demineralized water should be used to avoid damaging the ammonia service equipment.

For an aqueous ammonia system, the ammonia solution is stored in conventional tanks at the site. Ammonia solution typically is delivered to the site by truck or rail. The ammonia solution is transferred from the delivery vehicle to the storage tank by pumping the solution from the delivery car into the tank, with the tank vapor being vented to the delivery car. The storage tanks and the delivery connection equipment usually are equipped with many special safety features.

For an SCR system, the ammonia ultimately is used in the vapor phase. Energy is required to vaporize the ammonia. Energy also is required to vaporize the substantial water fraction of the ammonia solution. The ammo-

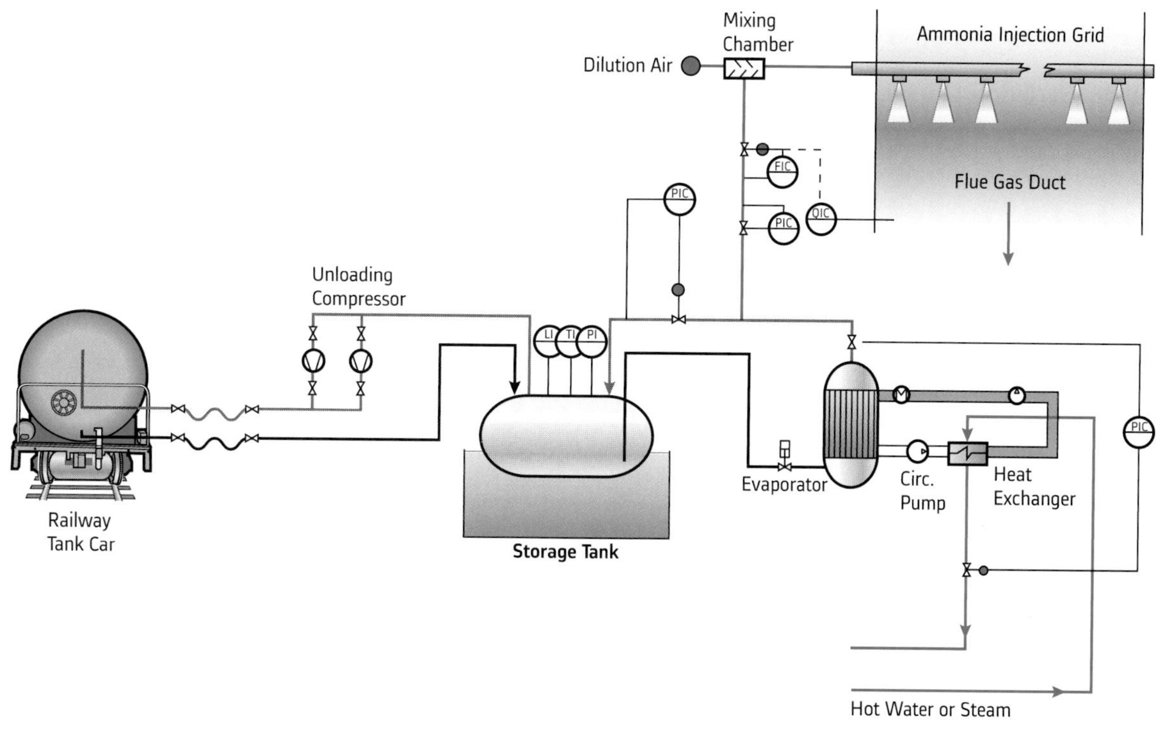

Figure 5-31 | Typical anhydrous ammonia storage and evaporation system

nia evaporator may be heated using commonly available sources, such as steam or electricity. Hot water usually lacks sufficient heat to evaporate both the ammonia and water in the ammonia solution. The evaporator often is located remotely from the tank, where the ammonia solution used by the SCR system is vaporized before entering the SCR reactor.

SNCR SYSTEMS

The process for SNCR occurs within the boiler unit, where the exhaust gas temperature is sufficient for the SNCR reactions to occur (see Equation 5-3, Steps 7 and 8). This location usually is found immediately downstream of the combustion zones. Ammonia or urea is introduced as a reducing agent into the exhaust gas through multiple injection points to react with the NOx. The resulting exhaust gas stream with lower NOx and ammonia concentrations continues through the balance of the boiler system. Similar to SCR, no liquid or solid wastes are generated in the SNCR process.

On a few demonstration projects, SNCR has been able to achieve NOx reduction efficiencies approaching 75%. In most commercial practice, however, the routine levels of NOx reduction are lower, and efficiencies of 30 to 50% are typical. The amount of NOx removal that can be obtained by SNCR on a given application is influenced by several factors, including the operating environment, the reducing reagent, and the system costs.

Process Variations

The two basic SNCR systems are differentiated by their reducing agent: ammonia, or urea. Although the design and operation basics are similar for both systems, each system has its own specific reagent handling and design issues. For ammonia-based systems, there are additional details for either anhydrous ammonia or aqueous ammonia solutions.

AMMONIA SYSTEMS. The first SNCR system was based on ammonia and originally developed in 1975. For anhydrous ammonia systems, vaporized ammonia is blended with either an air or steam carrier before it is injected into the exhaust gas stream in the boiler. For aqueous ammonia systems, the liquid ammonia solution may be injected directly into the exhaust gas boiler where it is vaporized. Advantages and disadvantages of anhydrous ammonia systems are given in *Table 5-9*. Advantages and disadvantages of aqueous ammonia systems are given in *Table 5-10*.

TABLE 5-9 | ADVANTAGES AND DISADVANTAGES OF ANHYDROUS AMMONIA SYSTEMS

Advantages	Disadvantages
Least expensive reagent	Vaporizer may be required
Least storage volume	Safety and permit concerns
	More injectors needed because of poor mixing

TABLE 5-10 | ADVANTAGES AND DISADVANTAGES OF AQUEOUS AMMONIA SYSTEMS

Advantages	Disadvantages
Easier handling	Water vaporization heat loss
Better mixing than with vapor	

TABLE 5-11 | ADVANTAGES AND DISADVANTAGES OF UREA SYSTEMS

Advantages	Disadvantages
Fewer safety risks	Reagent material costs
Best mixing technology	Reagent handling equipment

UREA SYSTEMS. The urea-based SNCR system was developed in 1980. The urea typically is used as a water solution. Dry urea supplies must be converted into a solution form. At a typical concentration of 50%, the solution freezing point is 64°F (18°C). Heating is required for most applications. The urea solution is injected directly into the exhaust gas of the boiler, where it is vaporized. The urea decomposes to form ammonia radicals that react with NOx. Advantages and disadvantages of urea systems are given in *Table 5-11*.

SNCR Design Factors

The SNCR process relies on injecting ammonia or urea reagents into very hot exhaust gas, where the reagent reacts with the NOx. The injection points are located where the exhaust gas meets the temperature and residence time required to achieve the desired NOx reduction. The physical location of the SNCR reactor is within the boiler unit. Because the boiler is designed primarily to meet steam generation requirements, the reactor often is not ideally designed to perform thermal NOx reduction. Boilers often need to change load, which changes the temperature profile of the exhaust gas. As a means to provide operating flexibility, multiple sets of injection points may be used to account for changes in the exhaust gas environment with boiler operating conditions.

REACTOR DESIGN. Hot exhaust gas containing NOx exits the combustion section and cools as it passes through the steam generation portion of the boiler. At a suitable temperature location, ammonia or urea is introduced as reducing agents into the flue gas through a series of injectors. The amount of reagent injected is suitable to reduce the NOx concentration and to avoid creating excessive ammonia slip at the reactor exit. The injectors are designed to distribute the reagent across the reaction zone and blend with the exhaust gas. Furnace modeling usually is required to optimize the injector location and mixing parameters. At this high-temperature location, the injected reagent vaporizes and decomposes into ammonia radicals. These radicals then react with and reduce the NOx into nitrogen, nitrous oxide, and water. The resulting exhaust gas, with lowered NOx and ammonia contents, is directed through the remaining steam generation sections of the boiler.

THERMAL SNCR REACTION CONCEPTS. The SNCR thermal reactor has to accomplish four basic tasks to successfully operate:

1. Mixing the injected reagent throughout the exhaust gas stream.
2. Evaporating the liquid reagent supply, if supplied as a solution.
3. Decomposing the ammonia or urea reagent into ammonia-free radicals.
4. Reacting the free radicals with the NOx compounds.

The design of the reagent injectors is one of the most critical aspects of the SNCR system. The placement of the injectors and their relation to the boiler arrangement is a primary consideration. The choice of the injector nozzle spray direction, the spray pattern, and the droplet size and velocity also are key design considerations. All of these factors must take into account the exhaust gas operating environment, composition, and flow. Certain boiler types have inherent mixing dynamics, such as circulating fluidized bed (CFB) boilers, which can assist the degree of mixing possible. Powerful modeling techniques, such as computational fluid dynamics, often are used to develop the optimal injector designs for the best mixing possible.

Upon entering the hot exhaust gas stream, the reagent droplet begins to evaporate and release NOx-reducing vapors as it travels across the SNCR reactor section in the boiler. The injector nozzle design and spray droplet characteristics must achieve suitable distribution and mixing while ensuring adequate droplet evaporation. Modeling methods often are used to help determine the best suitable reagent injection criteria. After evaporation is complete, the reducing reagent must continue to heat, up to the point where the reagent begins to decompose into ammonia radicals. These radicals then can react with the NOx in the hot exhaust gas.

SNCR PROCESS CHEMISTRY. As stated above, the NOx-reducing reagent must decompose to form radicals. For ammonia, the decomposition reactions are:

$$NH_3 + OH \leftrightarrow NH_2 + H_2O$$

Equation 5-27, Step 1

$$NH_3 + O \leftrightarrow NH_2 + OH$$

Equation 5-27, Step 2

$$H + NH_3 \leftrightarrow H_2 + NH_2$$

Equation 5-27, Step 3

For urea, the reactions are:

$$CO(NH_2)_2 \rightarrow NH_3 + HNCO$$

Equation 5-27, Step 4

$$HNCO + OH \leftrightarrow NCO + H_2O$$

Equation 5-27, Step 5

$$HNCO + H \leftrightarrow NH_2 + CO$$

Equation 5-27, Step 6

The contribution of hydrogen, oxygen, and hydroxyl radicals are proposed by reactions such as the following:

$$H + O_2 \leftrightarrow OH + O$$

Equation 5-27, Step 7

$$H_2 + OH \leftrightarrow H + H_2O$$

Equation 5-27, Step 8

$$H_2 + O \leftrightarrow H + OH$$

Equation 5-27, Step 9

The NOx reduction reactions are considered to be the following:

$$NH_2 + NO \rightarrow N_2 + H_2O$$

Equation 5-27, Step 10

$$NH_2 + NO \leftrightarrow HN_2 + OH$$

Equation 5-27, Step 11

$$HN_2 \rightarrow N_2 + H$$

Equation 5-27, Step 12

The termination reaction is considered to be the following:

$$NH_2 + O \leftrightarrow NO + 2H$$

Equation 5-27, Step 13

For cases in which urea is the reagent, the radical NCO from the reaction step (Equation 5-27, Step 5) is also involved in reducing NOx. These reaction mechanisms are illustrated in *Figure* 5-32.

As indicated above, there are many potential reaction pathways for the SNCR reactions to occur. Sophisticated chemical reaction kinetic models are used to predict the probable reaction pathways for the conditions of a given operating environment.

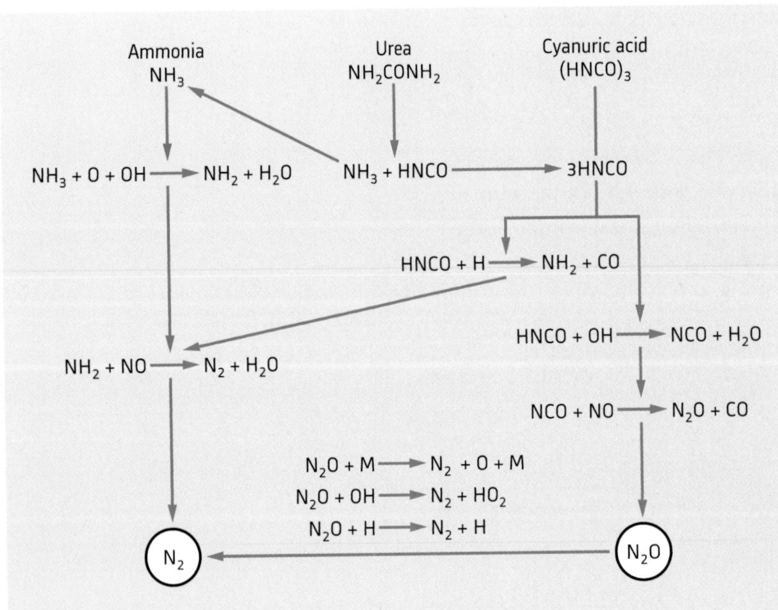

Figure 5-32 | Primary selective non-catalytic reduction reaction sequences

Process Effects in SNCR

The SNCR process has been able to demonstrate NOx removal efficiencies of over 75% under a few special cases, but the majority of applications find NOx reduction efficiencies in the range of 30 to 50%. The reason for the more common, lower efficiency is that each application has its own specific operating environment. This environment includes the following principal

factors: the exhaust gas temperature, the residence time in the boiler SNCR reactor, the amount of NOx that requires treatment, and the amount of reducing ammonia or urea agent used. The impact of these factors will be examined in the subsequent sections. There are other factors as well, such as exhaust gas composition, reagent mixing, exhaust gas temperature and flow profiles, supplementary additives, and a host of additional potential effects.

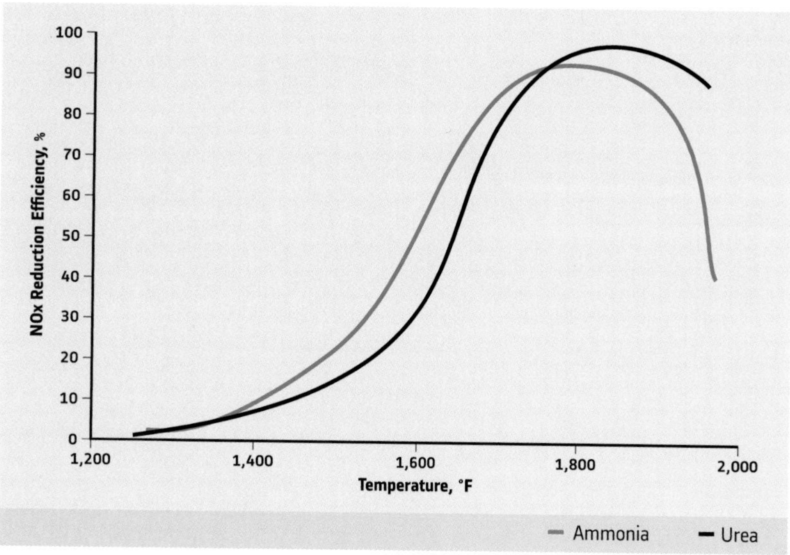

Figure 5-33 | Effect of temperature on NOx reduction

EFFECT OF TEMPERATURE. The reactions that make up the SNCR process are very dependent on temperature. Typically, the SNCR reactions best occur in the temperature range of 1,600 to 2,100°F (870 to 1,150°C), although this window is somewhat reagent dependent. Additives, often proprietary, may be used to modify the operating temperature range, and the degree of NOx reduction by SNCR at various temperatures is shown in *Figure 5-33*. When the exhaust gas temperature is too low (<1,600°F [<870°C]), then the reaction kinetic rate is very slow, and high levels of ammonia slip can occur. If the exhaust gas temperature is too high (>2,100°F [>1,150°C]), then the ammonia reagent can become oxidized and begins to form NOx, as indicated in Equation 5-27, Step 13.

EFFECT OF RESIDENCE TIME. The residence time of the SNCR reactor is the time during which the boiler exhaust gas and reducing reagent are at the effective operating temperature conditions together. The residence time classically is determined by the volumetric flow rate of the exhaust gas relative to the boiler gas path dimensions: The greater the residence time, the greater the degree of heat and mass transfer, and the longer the time for the NH_2-NOx reactions to occur. All of these conditions favor a higher degree of NOx reduction. In SNCR applications, the residence time may be as brief as 0.01 second or as long as several seconds. In general, SNCR applications may have residence times of approximately 0.3 second. Residence times much longer than 0.5 second do not normally provide much additional NOx reduction. The effect of residence time on the NOx reduction operating temperature window is shown in *Figure 5-34*.

EFFECT OF INLET NOx CONCENTRATION. The reaction rate for NOx reduction is directly dependent on the concentration of both NOx and ammonia (reducing) reagents. As the concentration of NOx increases, the rate of NOx reduction also increases, as shown in *Figure 5-35*. As the level of NOx decreases, the amount of NOx reduction as well as the optimal operating

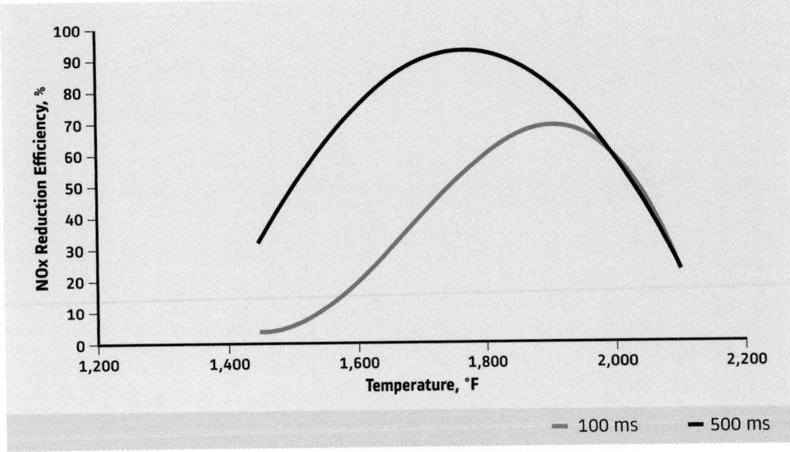

Figure 5-34 | Effect of residence time on NOx reduction

temperature decrease because of the reaction thermodynamics.

EFFECT OF REAGENT SR. The SR is the ratio of the amount of reducing reagent relative to the amount of NOx to be reduced. For the SNCR reaction, the SR is dependent on which reagent is used. When ammonia is the reducing agent, one molar amount of ammonia will reduce one molar amount of NOx. For cases in which urea is the reducing reagent, one molar amount of urea will reduce two molar amounts of NOx. For comparison, the term *normalized stoichiometric ratio* (NSR) often is used. This is defined as the ratio of equivalent molar amounts of ammonia relative to the amount of NOx to be reduced. Because one mole of urea will produce two moles of equivalent ammonia, a factor of two is used to convert between the actual SR and the NSR for urea.

As the reaction rate equation (Equation 5-12) indicates, increasing the amount of reducing agent, or the SR ratio, will increase the degree of NOx reduction. In practice, the amount of reducing agent required to achieve a degree of NOx reduction is much greater than the theoretical amount indicated by the reaction stoichiometry. This inefficiency may be attributed to many potential causes. One common cause is inefficiency resulting from poor mixing in a given application. For high-temperature applications, the ammonia reaction with NOx results in an observed poor efficiency. Another factor is that the SNCR reaction rate slows as the NOx and reagent concentrations decrease. In either case, operating the SNCR system at a NSR of greater than 2.0 does not provide much additional NOx reduction benefit, as shown in *Figure* 5-36.

Increasing the amount of reducing reagent does result in an increased level of ammonia slip exiting the SNCR reactor. The relationship between NOx removal and ammonia slip is depicted in *Figure* 5-37, which shows that the increasing ammonia slip rate does not equally match the gains in NOx reduction.

Some practical designs tend to favor operation at a relatively high operating temperature, even though this can result in lower NOx removal efficiencies. The design relies on this

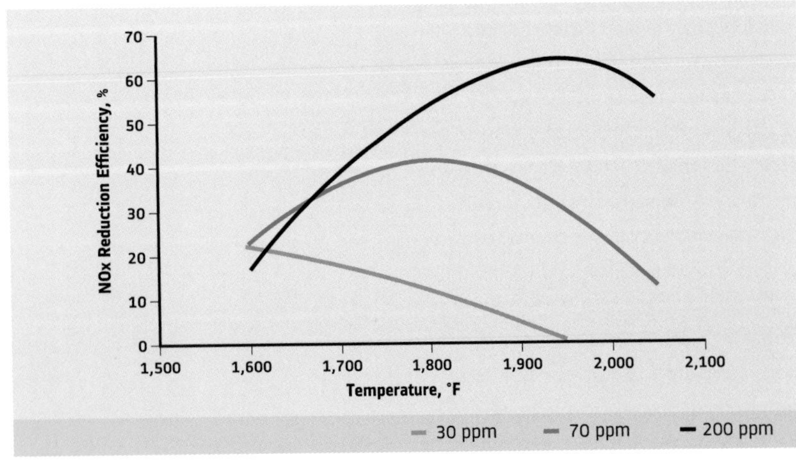

Figure 5-35 | Effect of inlet NOx concentration on NOx reduction

condition as a means to gain some reagent heating benefits and avoid creating excessive ammonia slip while incurring the relative cost of additional reagent consumption.

SNCR Components

A typical SNCR system is composed of reagent storage, reagent dosing, and reagent injection subsystems. (Descriptions of aqueous ammonia and aqueous urea solution systems are given under *SCR Components*.) An SNCR system often contains multiple locations of reagent injection subsystems. Both the placement and the number of locations are determined by boiler arrangement and by modeling programs during the system design phase. A centralized controller performs the operation of each injection location system based on NOx emission levels, boiler operation, and fuel qualities.

REAGENT METERING SYSTEM. Each injection location system contains a metering pump and flow control for reagent dosing. The reagent usually is supplied from a single, common source for all injection locations. The reagent flow is diluted and blended with pressurized, filtered water in order to maintain consistent pressure and flow qualities, regardless of varying reagent flow rates.

REAGENT INJECTION AND SNCR REACTOR. The diluted reagent flow to each injection location is distributed to each individual injection point based on flow metering equipment and control valves. Each injection point is equipped with an injector. Two types of injectors are used in SNCR systems: wall and lance. Wall injectors are mounted to the boiler wall and direct the reagent stream from the boiler wall toward the exhaust gas. A lance injector is a pipe that extends from the boiler wall into the exhaust gas stream; it may span the entire boiler dimension. A lance injector has one or multiple nozzles that spray the reagent stream into the exhaust gas flow. Wall injectors have shorter injection ranges than a lance injector's effective range. Lance injectors often have shorter service lifetimes, however, because of the direct exposure to the hot exhaust gas. An SNCR reactor may include both types of injectors to obtain more optimal distribution and mixing of reagent in the exhaust gas flow.

The nozzle on the injector is designed to spray the reagent stream with a specific direction, pattern, and droplet size. This is accomplished by using pressurized reagent flow and atomizers in each nozzle. Some nozzle designs are based on dual-fluid technology to develop the desired spray characteristics. These nozzles may rely on compressed air or steam to provide the required energy for atomization.

ECONOMIC CONSIDERATIONS

The decision of whether to use an SCR or an SNCR system for NOx emission control is based primarily on the NOx removal efficiencies that a given application requires. In almost all cases, an SNCR system is less costly to install than an SCR system. The SNCR system, however, does not offer the same high capability for NOx removal that an SCR system does.

The advantages of an SNCR system are relatively low capital equipment costs, simple operation, and minimal impact on boiler plant operation. The reagent consumption cost makes up

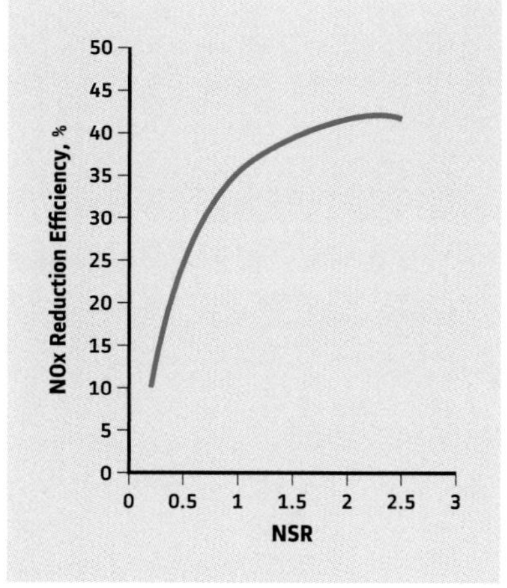

Figure 5-36 | Effect of normalized stoichiometric ratio on NOx reduction

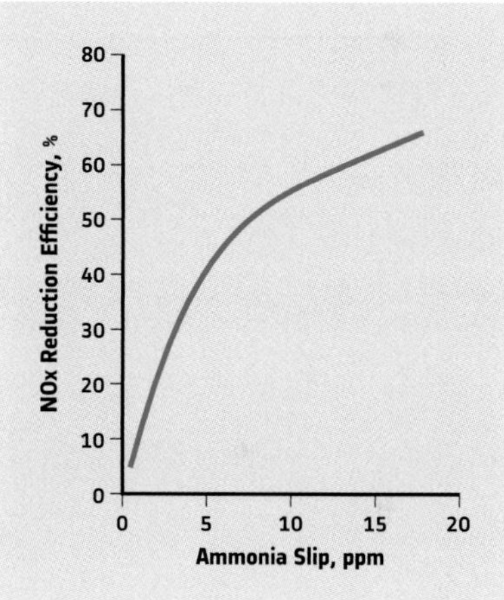

Figure 5-37 | Effect of ammonia slip on NOx reduction

The application of SCR or SNCR depends upon the type of fuel, the type of boiler, and the required level of NOx reductions.

the majority of the SNCR system operating costs. The disadvantages of the SNCR system are the aforementioned lower capability for NOx removal, the somewhat limited retrofit ability, and the operational problems with respect to changes with boiler load and other operating conditions.

The major advantage of the SCR system is the relatively high capability for NOx removal. Other advantages are that it is easier to retrofit (no pressure part disruption), tolerant of boiler load changes, and relatively simple to operate. The disadvantages are the relatively high capital equipment cost, sensitivity to fuel qualities, and greater impact on boiler plant operations. The SCR system operating costs mostly result from reagent consumption, catalyst replacement, and operating draft losses.

POST-SNCR AND POST-SCR EFFECTS

Ammonia Slip

Ammonia that is not consumed by the NOx-NH_3 reaction will exit the SNCR or SCR system as ammonia slip, and this ammonia can pose several risks. For low-dust exhaust gas applications, one potential risk is the emission of ammonia as ammonia species. For applications with emission scrubbers located downstream of the NOx treatment equipment, the ammonia can transfer from the exhaust gas into the scrubbing liquor. The choice of scrubber and associated liquor treatment equipment should consider the impacts of ammonia. Spent liquor discharge also will be a source of liquid-based ammonia emission.

Another potential concern regarding ammonia emission is its potential as a particulate emission. Ammonia can form condensable salts with sulfate and nitrate anions in the exhaust gas when they cool to ambient temperatures. Some emission permits and particulate emission testing methods specifically address these types of emissions. The potential presence of ammonia should be considered for these applications.

For high-dust applications, the ammonia slip exiting the SNCR or SCR system can deposit on the ash as the exhaust gas temperature cools. This ash is collected by the particulate collection equipment. In general, most particulate collection equipment will tolerate small amounts of ammonia on the ash. The concern is when the collected ash is disposed of or sold for use in construction products. If the ash is wetted or used in a water-based mixture with an alkaline pH, ammonia vapor can evolve from the wet ash. This can be a nuisance, or even a potential safety risk, if personnel are in close contact with the ammonia vapors. For most applications, the ammonia content in the ash does not affect the quality of the end product containing the ash.

AMMONIA SALTS. When high levels of ammonia are present with high levels of SO_3, a potential exists for the formation of ABS and ammonium sulfate salts:

$$NH_3 + H_2O + SO_3 \rightarrow NH_4HSO_4\,(ABS)$$

Equation 5-28

$$2NH_3 + H_2O + SO_3 \rightarrow (NH_4)_2\,SO_4$$

Equation 5-29

These solid salts can form when the temperature of the exhaust gas is cool enough and the concentrations of NH_3 and SO_3 are high enough. These salts are somewhat corrosive and can cause plugging problems because of their melting point behavior. The ABS salt has a very sticky nature and can bind with particulate emissions to create plugging concerns. This potential effect should be considered for equipment located downstream of the SCR system, such as the GGH or the particulate collection equipment. With respect to heat exchangers, special equipment designs and materials may be used in conjunction with SNCR and SCR systems to minimize the formation of the ash-ABS deposits and better facilitate equipment cleaning if they do form.

Because of the detrimental effects of ABS in high-ash systems, care must be taken to ensure that no localized high ammonia concentrations exist downstream of the SNCR or SCR system. Localized ABS deposits can cause problems even when the overall conditions do not favor ABS formation. A small region of high ammonia concentration can lead to very large areas of ABS formation if rotating heat exchangers are used or exhaust gas flow patterns shift because of plugging.

SO_3 Emissions

One of the detrimental side reactions of the SCR catalyst is the oxidation of SO_2 to SO_3:

$$2SO_2 + O_2 \rightarrow 2SO_3$$

Equation 5-30

In general, the concentration of SO_3 in the exhaust gas doubles as it passes across the SCR catalyst beds. As the catalyst ages, the amount of SO_3 formed tends to decrease. Any estimate of the lifetime potential for SO_3 formation in the SCR system also should consider the impact of additional, fresh catalyst layers that may be added in the later years of operation. One special risk is when the fuel contains appreciable amounts of vanadium metal (i.e., heavy oils). In these cases, the vanadium emissions from the oil combustion will deposit on the catalyst and increase the amount of SO_3 formation during the lifetime of the catalyst.

As stated above, SO_3 formation can contribute to ammonium salt formation. The SO_3 in the exhaust gas also can be considered as a potential source for condensable particulate emissions or may be regulated directly as an SO_3 emission concern. Equipment located downstream of the SCR system can face impacts from the elevated SO_3 level when the exhaust gas cools. The increase in SO_3 across the SCR system will result in a higher acid dew point temperature for the exhaust gas, which in turn may result in greater corrosion impacts. This often is observed at the GGH and the exhaust gas ductwork immediately following this device. Wet scrubbing systems may collect some of the SO_3 emissions; the design and operation of such equipment should take this into account. Lastly, any SO_3-specific emission control equipment will be impacted by the higher SO_3 levels.

CONTROL OF SO_2 EMISSIONS

Reduction of SO_2 emissions has been achieved through one or a combination of the following:

- Fuel switching (to lower-sulfur fuels)
- Coal cleaning (use of fuel desulfurization methods)
- FGD systems

The first two—low-sulfur fuel and coal cleaning—can be utilized in retrofit applications where appropriate emission regulations can be met. In many locations (particularly the European Union and the United States), air permits for new power plants require a percentage reduction in SO_2 emissions regardless of the sulfur content of the fuel.

Fuel desulfurization processes range from conventional coal washing to coal liquefaction and gasification. Coal washing is effective in reducing the pyritic sulfur in the coal. It generally does not remove the organic sulfur from the coal matrix, however, so it is limited to sulfur reduction of less than 50%. Coal liquefaction was developed in Germany and used in South Africa. The economics were not favorable at low oil prices, but there has been renewed interest with higher oil prices. Coal gasification has been developed as an alternative to PC or CFB technology. At present, only a small number of demonstration plants are in operation. The CFB technology captures the sulfur in the fluidized bed during the combustion process (see Chapter 3). Therefore, this chapter will focus on post-combustion FGD processes.

The FGD systems capture the primary acidic gas SO_2 and typically provide the additional benefit of also capturing the secondary gases, such as SO_3, HCl, and hydrogen fluoride (HF). Additionally, FGD systems provide capture of particulate matter, although particulate matter capture can be detrimental in wet FGD systems, either by causing chemistry problems or by fouling the gypsum by-product. Semi-dry FGD systems, such as spray dryer absorbers (SDAs) and flash dryer absorbers (FDAs), have particulate collection as an integral part of the environmental equipment and are less susceptible to particulate-based problems.

FGD SYSTEMS

The FGD technology was first tried in London, England, in 1935, when a local power station used the alkaline Thames River water in a wooden absorber for scrubbing flue gas. The visibility of the vapor plume caused abandonment of the process early in World War II, however, because it was an easily seen target. After the war, FGD technology remained dormant until the mid-1960s, when the United States and Japan began to institute environmental legislation. Since then, more than 50 FGD processes, differing in their chemical reagents and resultant end products, have been developed.

Initially, FGD processes were differentiated as either regenerable or non-regenerable and as either wet or dry. A non-regenerable, or "throwaway," system produced waste products of various sulfur compounds that were stored in ponds or treated for use as landfill. A regenerable system recovered the SO_2 in some commercially useful form, such as elemental sulfur or sulfuric acid. The original alkali was "regenerated" for repeated use in the absorption/regeneration cycles. A further differentiation was made between wet processes and dry processes: Wet processes saturate the flue gas with water vapor, and dry processes do not. The most dominant FGD process today is the limestone forced oxidation system, which is not a throwaway process, because the gypsum by-product

has value for gypsum wallboard or cement manufacturing. The process was developed from a throwaway process, however, and is still commonly categorized as a "non-regenerable" process.

Regenerable FGD

There has been minor interest in developing regenerable processes. Typically, the absorbed SO_2 is converted to a commercial product, such as sulfuric acid, sulfur, or ammonium sulfate fertilizer. The main problem for these processes is one of scale. Although the sulfur content of coal is relatively small (on the order of 2–3%), the consumption of coal for electric power generation is rather large. An average, 500-MW, coal-fired unit will consume approximately 200 tons/h (180 metric tonnes/h) of coal. In turn, this will generate a large quantity of sulfur by-products. This production rate will saturate the local markets for product for all except the largest industries (typically cement or construction). Consequently, only a handful of these technologies have been constructed, and these have met with varied success.

Non-Regenerable and Throwaway FGD Processes

The overwhelming majority of commercial FGD systems are limestone/gypsum wet-scrubbing or the lime dry-scrubbing systems. Lime-based FGD systems, some with magnesium as a performance enhancement and some with gypsum production, also are available. Finally, seawater FGD is preferred where applicable. The majority of this chapter will focus on the prevalent, limestone forced oxidation FGD systems with a gypsum by-product.

Seawater FGD

One of the most cost-effective desulfurization processes is the use of the alkalinity in seawater to absorb SO_2. Of course, the power plant needs to be located close to the sea in order to take advantage of this process. The process shown in *Figure 5-38* is composed of two steps:

1. An absorber with structured packing uses a portion of the seawater from the condensers to scrub SO_2 and then discharges to a water treatment plant.
2. A water treatment plant in which the sulfite is oxidized to sulfate, the pH and temperature are adjusted, and some fresh seawater is added before returning to the sea.

The change in seawater composition that results from the absorption of SO_2 typically is slight and within the normal variations of seawater. There is no liquid waste stream. Typically, an impact assessment is performed as the effluent is discharged back into the ocean.

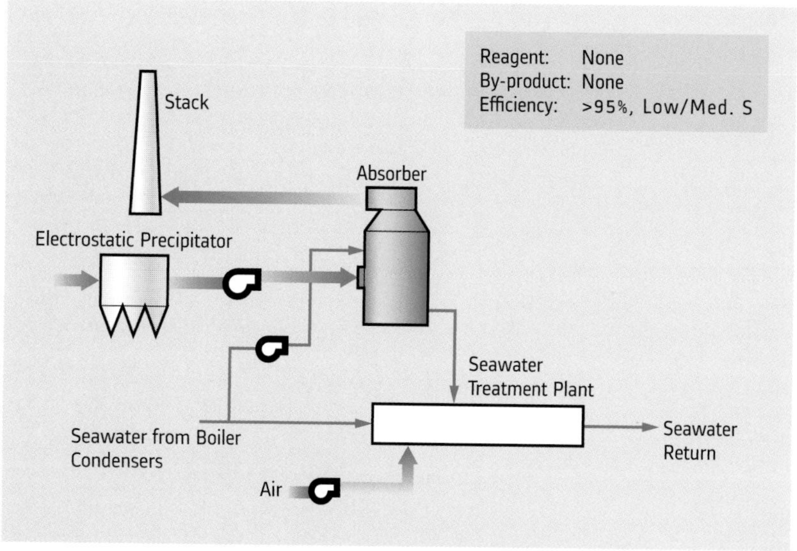

Figure 5-38 | Seawater flue gas desulfurization process flow diagram

Limestone Forced Oxidation Wet FGD Systems

The simplified flow diagram in *Figure 5-39* illustrates the generic forced oxidation limestone gypsum FGD. Typically, the forced oxidation FGD can be categorized into four major sub-systems:

1. **Gas Path.** The gas path is the ductwork, fans, heat exchangers, dampers, and stack, usually from the exit of the ESP or fabric filter to either the stack or, sometimes, other downstream equipment, such as a wet ESP or SCR.
2. **Absorber Island.** The absorber island is the absorber, recycle tank, mist eliminator, and supporting equipment, such as the oxidation blower and recycle pumps.
3. **Reagent Preparation.** The additive (usually limestone) is received, stored, crushed, and slurried.
4. **Dewatering.** Gypsum cake is produced in two steps. First, most of the water is removed in the primary dewatering (usually hydrocyclones), and then the remaining water is removed in the secondary dewatering (usually a vacuum belt filter).

An additional subsystem can be a wastewater treatment step if the system has a chloride purge.

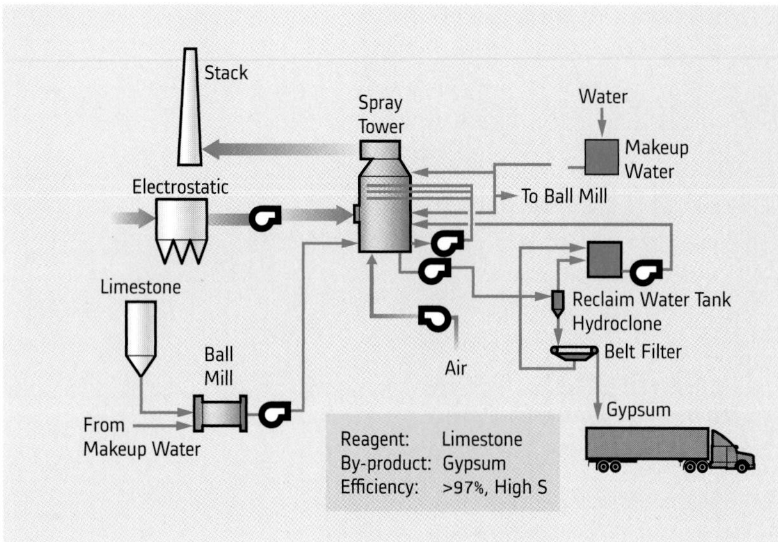

Figure 5-39 | Limestone forced oxidation flue gas desulfurization

TABLE 5-12 | COMPARISON OF DRY, SEAWATER, AND WET FLUE GAS DESULFURIZATION (FGD) SYSTEMS

Absorber	Spray or flash dryer	Packed tower	Spray or Flowpac® system
First installation	1980	1968	1968
Features	Low investment cost Dry by-product Small footprint No liquid waste	No reagent No by-product Low energy consumption	High-efficiency spray zone Low-cost reagent By-product flexibility
Reagent	Lime	Seawater	Limestone
By-product	Landfill	Seawater	Marketable gypsum or landfill
Sulfur	<2.5%	<1.5%	<6%
Removal efficiency	90–95%	>95%	>98%
Capital cost	0.7*X*	0.8*X*	*X*
Power consumption (including booster fans)	0.7%	0.7–1.0%	1.0–2.0%
Reagent cost	$60/ton	$0/ton	$15/ton
By-product cost	$5–10/ton	$0/ton	$5–10/ton (disposal) $5/ton (sale)

Gas Path

Typically, the gas path from a PC boiler includes an SCR before the air pre-heater, particulate control, desulfurization, and a wet stack. Additional options are SO_3 control with a wet ESP and gas reheating by means of heating the saturated gas from the wet FGD (gas reheater). *Figure 5-40* shows several common arrangements of air emissions control equipment after a PC boiler with both wet and dry FGD. *Table 5-12* lists the relative costs, applications, and benefits of the various FGD technologies.

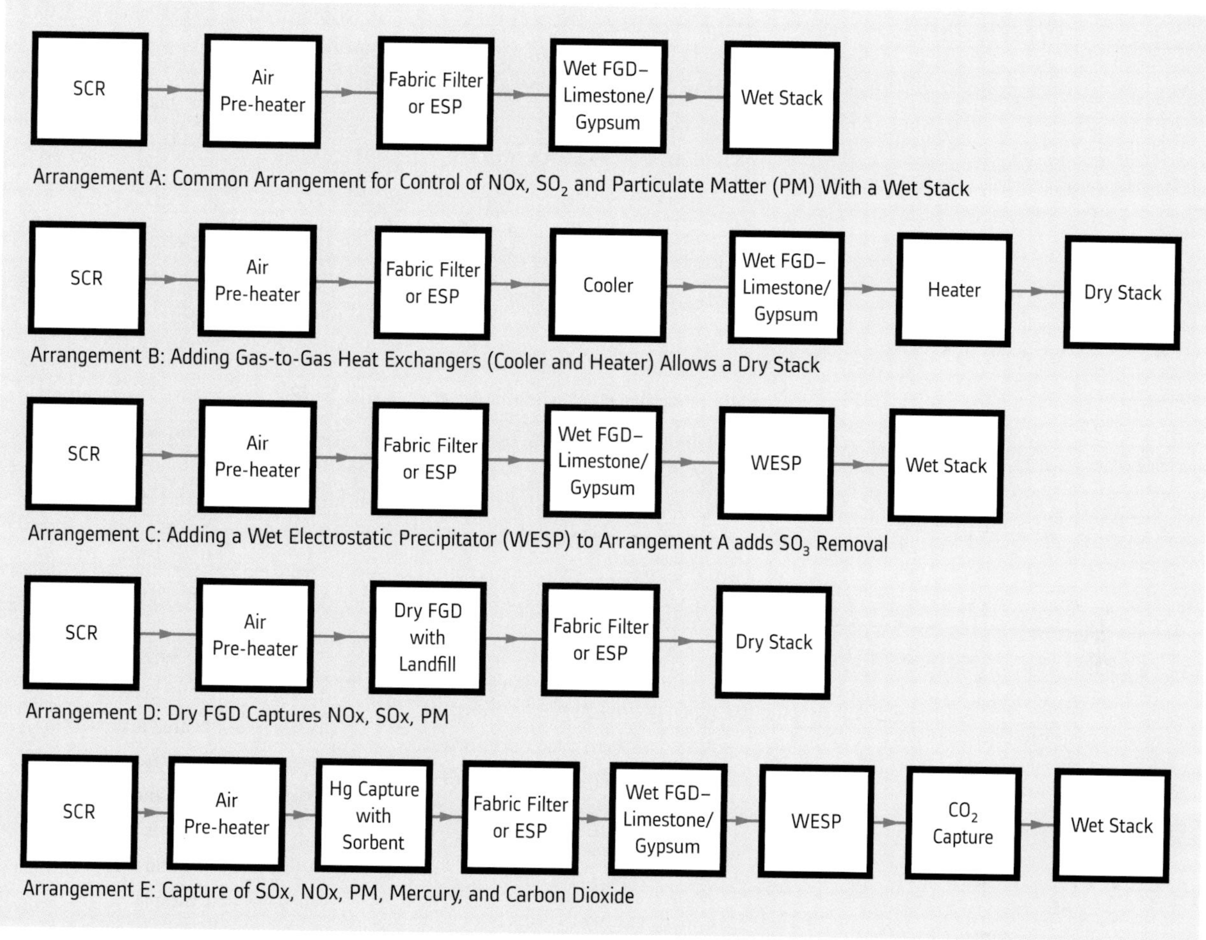

Figure 5-40 | Arrangements of emission control equipment after a PC boiler (ESP, electrostatic precipitator; FF, fabric filter; FGD, flue gas desulfurization; SCR, selective catalytic reduction; WESP, wet electrostatic precipitator)

SCR/FABRIC FILTER OR ESP/WET SCRUBBING/WET STACK. The most common flue gas cleaning system has an SCR for NOx control and uses an ESP for dust capture, followed by a forced oxidation limestone wet SO_2 scrubber with a wet stack. For certain types of fuels, the size of an ESP needed to meet current particulate emission standards becomes so large that fabric filters become a technical and economic alternative. The principal advantages of fabric filters (baghouses) are:

- Very high removal efficiency
- Ability to collect fine particles
- Insensitivity of collection efficiency to fuel characteristics

This last advantage is significant, because ESP performance is affected by the characteristics of the flue gas and fly ash particles. Fabric filter performance is less sensitive to such changes. Thus, fabric filters give the power generator the option of switching fuels without modifying the particulate collection system. The major disadvantages of fabric filters include gas pressure drops of 4 to 6″ WG (.75 to 1.1 cm Hg) and more maintenance compared with low-pressure-drop ESPs.

SCR/FABRIC FILTER OR ESP/WET SCRUBBING WITH REHEAT/DRY STACK. This arrangement is common in Asia and Europe.

A heat exchanger (see the section immediately following), typically a gas-gas, rotating, Ljungström®-type heat exchanger, extracts heat from the wet FGD inlet flue gas and then heats the saturated flue gas exiting the wet FGD absorber. Seals are used to minimize leakage, but a small amount of untreated flue gas can bypass the absorber. Another heat exchange system (called the "non-leak heat exchanger," because there is zero leakage) is available where the heat exchange is accomplished through gas-liquid coupling to finned tubes. This equipment is larger and higher in capital cost because of the costs involved with corrosion prevention and heat transfer (size); thus, these units are infrequently used.

SCR/FABRIC FILTER OR ESP/WET SCRUBBING/WET ESP/WET STACK. In a wet scrubber, SO_3 is difficult to control, because it condenses to very small droplet diameters and passes through the gas absorber as a particle. Adding a wet ESP after the wet FGD is very effective in capturing this submicron particle and in preventing the high opacity that SO_3 often causes in concentrations higher than approximately 4 to 5 ppm.

SCR/FABRIC FILTER OR ESP/SEMI-DRY FGD/DRY STACK. The use of a spray dry absorber or FDA with an ESP or fabric filter cools the flue gas, but not to saturation as a wet FGD absorber does. This allows use of a dry stack at the expense of slightly lower SO_2 removal. Use of a fabric filter for particulate control also will capture the fine SO_3 particles. The mixture of calcium/sulfur salts and fly ash may be used as roadbed material or simply landfilled.

SCR/FABRIC FILTER OR ESP WITH MERCURY CAPTURE/WET FGD/WET ESP/CO_2 CAPTURE/WET STACK. The state of the art in emission control includes potential mercury capture as well as CO_2 capture and sequestration. Subsequent sections will address these technologies in more detail.

Reheaters and Stacks

The wet stacks in some of the arrangements described above are common in North America. Japan and Europe typically eliminate the opaque water plume by heating the gas to temperatures well above the dew point. The decision to reheat the flue gas is almost always a local issue and is driven by the need to satisfy one or more of the following objectives:

- Eliminate or reduce the visible plume of condensed water vapor.
- Reduce corrosion in downstream ducts, dampers, fans, and stack liners.
- Enhance plume rise and dispersion of residual emissions.
- Meet government-mandated regulations for the exit temperature of stack gas.

The following reheat options are the most common:

- No reheat (wet stack operation)
- Bypass reheat
- Direct reheat with an in-duct heat exchanger or direct combustion burner
- Indirect reheat with hot air mixing
- Regenerative reheat with rotary regenerative or shell/tube-type heat exchangers
- Reheat with liquid-coupled heat exchangers

NO REHEAT/WET STACK. The "no reheat" option yields significant savings in

energy and has been dominant in the United States since 1980. High-efficiency mist elimination, resulting in minimal amounts of water entrained into the outlet duct and stack, have produced good wet stack operating results. Stack "rain-out" is minimized by using smooth stack liners and by operation at moderate velocities of 50 to 60 ft/s (15 to 18 m/s).

BYPASS REHEAT. Bypass reheat is a viable option for overall SO_2 removal requirements of less than 70 to 80%. In such cases, a fraction of the flue gas, usually 15 to 20%, is allowed to bypass the absorber and is mixed with flue gas that has been treated through the absorber. The bypassed gas warms the scrubbed gas by 20 to 40°F (10 to 20°C). Bypass reheat offers the advantages of low capital and operating investment as well as ease of operation. The maximum amount of reheat that can be obtained and the applicability of this mode of reheat, however, are limited by the constraints of emission standards.

DIRECT REHEAT. This type of reheat uses a heat exchanger directly in the wet flue gas ductwork downstream of the mist eliminators. The heat exchanger consists of multiple rows of tubes through which the heating fluid is circulated. The tubes typically are staggered. Bare-surface and finned-surface tubing have been used. The gas passes over the tubes and picks up thermal energy from the surfaces of the heating tubes. The initial rows of tubes must provide sufficient heat transfer to evaporate any residual mist leaving the mist eliminator. The subsequent rows of tubes serve to boost the gas temperature.

A direct combustion reheater eliminates the need for heat exchangers. Gas or oil is burned, and the combustion product gas (at 1,200–3,000°F [650–1,650°C]) is mixed with the flue gas to raise its temperature.

Direct firing requires some care in mixing the hot combustion gas with the cool, scrubbed gas. If mixing is not effective, hot spots can develop downstream from the heater, causing damage to the duct lining. Combustion chambers must be lined with refractory materials capable of withstanding the high temperatures. Also, maintenance of flame and flame stability are required for effective operation. The disadvantages of direct firing are the availability and cost of clean-burning gas and oil.

INDIRECT REHEAT. Indirect reheat consists of heating ambient air through an external heat exchanger and then mixing the hot air with the saturated flue gas to raise its temperature. The major components are a forced draft fan, heat exchanger, ducting, isolation damper, and air-gas mixing chamber.

The advantage of indirect hot air reheat over in-line reheat is that the heat exchanger is removed from the direct gas path. The potential for corrosion and plugging of the heat exchanger thereby is significantly reduced. The disadvantages include the need for an additional fan to convey hot air; the relatively large amount of space required for the reheat system (compared with other reheat methods); the increase in stack gas volume, which may be undesirable because of the limited capacities of induced draft (ID) fans and stacks; and the higher energy consumption, which is needed to heat air from the ambient temperature level.

Another variation of the indirect hot air reheat method involves use of

Stack gas reheat can reduce or eliminate, at the expense of additional energy costs, the white plume of water vapor that forms when the flue gas cools.

the air pre-heater associated with the boiler to provide hot air for stack gas reheat. In this case, the temperature of the combustion air entering the boiler would be lower than usual, because part of the heat content of the flue gas is used to provide the hot air for stack gas reheat. Also, the pre-heater is larger, because it is designed to heat a greater-than-normal amount of air (but to a lower-than-normal exit temperature).

REGENERATIVE REHEAT/LJUNGSTRÖM® GGH. In the GGH system, the sensible heat from the hot, unscrubbed, inlet flue gas is extracted and transferred to the desulfurized, moisture-saturated, outlet flue gas. The principal device used for this purpose is a close relative of the air pre-heater: the GGH of the rotary, regenerative, Ljungström® type. An alternative to the Ljungström® type is the shell-and-tube GGH. The shell-and-tube heat exchanger is sometimes referred to as a "no-leak" GGH. This designation is not strictly correct, however, because it is a liquid-gas exchange, not a gas-gas exchange, as implied with the term GGH.

The Ljungström® GGH transfers heat by rotating heating elements (typically called "baskets") at approximately 1 rpm between the hot and cold gas. Each element is heated by the hot (untreated) gas and then loses its heat to the cool (treated) gas. The flow of gas in the Ljungström® GGH is counter-current. The untreated and treated gases flow in opposing directions. Separate inlet and outlet ports are provided for the treated and untreated gas streams. A small amount of leakage (typically 0.5–1.5%) occurs between the two streams.

In the shell-and-tube GGH, the untreated flue gas (absorber inlet) flows vertically downward through the tubes. The gas tubes, typically with a diameter of 3.1 inches (80 mm) and a wall thickness of .04 inch (1 mm), are constructed of polytetrafluoroethylene (PTFE; Teflon® material). The treated flue gas (absorber outlet) flows across the outside of the tubes. The leakage of gas between the two streams in the shell-and-tube GGH is essentially zero (typically <0.01%). The leakage is attributable to the small diffusion of gases through the PTFE. The useful life of PTFE in this type of service is claimed to be from 10 to 14 years. The permeability of the PTFE will likely increase over its life. Water wash lances are used to wash the inside of the tubes.

The lower tubesheet of the heat exchanger is made of perfluoroalkoxy Teflon® material (PFA). This material is twice the cost of PTFE, but unlike PTFE, it can be welded. The tubesheet must allow for expansion of the PTFE tubes. Thermal expansion of PTFE is approximately tenfold greater than that of carbon steel. The upper tubesheet is an alloy construction. The casing is carbon steel, with a 0.6 inch (1.5 mm) PFA "foil" lining. The tubes must have an internal pressure that is greater than the external pressure; otherwise, the tubes would collapse. For this reason, a C-position fan is not acceptable.

REGENERATIVE REHEAT/LIQUID-COUPLED HEAT EXCHANGE. The basic equipment in this type of reheat system consists of two separate shell-and-tube heat exchangers mounted in the absorber inlet duct (untreated gas) and in the absorber outlet duct (treated gas).

Heat is transferred by water (or other heat-transfer fluid) that circulates between the two heat exchangers. The heat-transfer fluid flows on the inside of the tubes, and flue gas flows across the outside of the tubes. Teflon® (PTFE), Teflon®-coated, and enameled steel have been proposed for tube materials. Diffusion of acid gases, such as HCl or H_2SO_4, through PTFE tubes, resulting in acidification of the heat-transfer fluid, is a concern. Chemical dosing is required to prevent this problem.

Liquid-coupled reheat is an expensive alternative and is used only when leakage of SO_2 and fly ash cannot be tolerated because of requirements for low emissions. Both capital and operating costs for liquid-coupled exchangers are high.

Absorber Island

The widespread availability of lime or limestone alkali helped make the wet FGD scrubbing technology the oldest and most common method of FGD. Because calcium salts have very low solubility, however, these technologies require absorbers with high liquid/gas (L/G) ratios, crystallization holding tanks, and tolerance to corrosive and erosive slurries.

The first successful, closed-loop, lime/limestone process is credited to the English firm of J. Howden and Company.[54] From 1931 to 1933, pilot-plant tests were conducted in which the scrubber effluent was recycled to the absorber. Initially, scale formed in the absorber, but the critical breakthrough in system chemistry came during 1933, when the problem was identified as one of excessive gypsum ($CaSO_4{\cdot}2H_2O$) supersaturation in the scrubber. The solution was to add a crystallization tank and increase the L/G ratio. Adding a crystallization tank operating at a high solids concentration allows calcium/sulfur compounds to precipitate in the tank instead of fouling the interior of the absorber. Because of the precipitation reactions, the absorbent recycled to the scrubber has a lower concentration of scale-forming gypsum. A high L/G ratio minimizes the increase in supersaturation across the scrubber and, thereby, further diminishes the potential for scale formation. Finally, the recirculation of a slurry provides preferential sites for crystallization, reducing the likelihood of precipitation on the absorber surfaces.

Many subsequent attempts at countering scale and the other problems resulted in failure. Absorbers were chosen or designed to operate in an erosive, corrosive, scaling environment, and early adopters tried packed towers, marble beds, turbulent contact absorbers (TCAs), tray towers, and venturi spray towers. The U.S. EPA built a large test facility at the Tennessee Valley Authority's Shawnee station with a marble bed absorber, TCA, and venturi spray tower in parallel, 10-MW gas paths.[55] Support also was available from a small EPA pilot TCA glass absorber at its headquarters in Research Triangle Park, North Carolina.[56]

The TCA first used "ping pong"-like balls, which through constant motion prevented scale buildup, making it an early favorite. This absorber was only a short-term success, however, because the plastic balls failed quickly, became lodged in the support grids, and caused high pressure drop and, eventually, a shutdown for cleaning. Foam rubber

Limestone deposits are plentiful and widespread throughout the world, making calcium-based systems the most common for sulfur capture technologies.

was later substituted, at a higher cost, for plastic. With time, spray towers became the dominant solution. In the spray tower, scale was still a problem, but because the buildup was not catastrophic, the absorber could operate longer.

Borgwardt[56] and others[57,58] identified the mechanism for scale formation. The solid calcium sulfite crystals were actually a mixture of calcium sulfite hemihydrate and calcium sulfate—a co-precipitate. The upper limit of calcium sulfate in this co-precipitate is approximately 18%. Sulfite oxidation rates above this amount resulted in supersaturated slurries and, eventually, scale. Oxidation rates with these "natural oxidation" systems were not a controllable parameter; thus, scaling could not be controlled. Operation, however, was possible with either complete oxidation or no oxidation, and in both cases, scale-free operation was possible.

No oxidation operation was achieved by inhibiting oxidation with additives such as sodium thiosulfate.[59] Complete oxidation of the sulfite to sulfate could be obtained by simply injecting air into the recirculating slurry tank and converting the calcium sulfite to gypsum.[60] This latter process, also called "forced oxidation," had the added advantage of providing a potentially salable by-product, wallboard gypsum, instead of a calcium sulfite "sludge."

Of the two scale-free adaptations of limestone scrubbing, the forced oxidation, gypsum process quickly became prevalent. The cleaner operation also allowed certain cost savings. Scaling in the absorbers was so problematic that most utilities included spare modules that could be isolated and cleaned while the boiler continued operations. In fact, the U.S. EPA initially mandated spare modules in the United States. The scale-free operations of forced oxidation scrubbing, however, demonstrated that the spare modules were not required. A Dutch company built a single-module, forced oxidation, limestone, gypsum spray tower in the Netherlands and set the stage for similar designs globally.

Another breakthrough in wet FGD came from Rochelle and King,[61] who suggested using small concentrations of organic acids in the circulating fluid to enhance performance. Later, field tests proved the organic acids did, indeed, improve performance substantially, but the acids were lost at unanticipated quantities through not only material balance losses in the process water but also oxidative degradation losses,[62] especially in forced oxidation systems. Additionally, co-precipitation of the acids in calcium sulfite crystals provided another mechanism for loss.[63]

Even with these losses, organic acids proved to be cost-effective, especially adipic acid and a waste stream mix of organic acids (glutaric acid, succinic acid, and adipic acid),[64] commonly referred to by the DuPont trade name DBA (dibasic acid). Successful pilot testing,[65] full-scale testing,[66] plus strong U.S. EPA approval[67] led to commercial use in many installations.

In the late 1990s, Alstom supplemented the open spray tower technology with a high-efficiency, limestone, forced oxidation, pump-free, crossflow tray absorber called the Flowpac® system. The first installation of the Flowpac® system was at a power plant in Sweden.[68] Second-generation Flowpac®[69,70] absorbers are installed in several locations on oil, coal, and industrial smelter gases. The

Flowpac® system is unique in that it uses the energy of the oxidation air in an airlift to also move and agitate the slurry, eliminating the need for agitators and pumps (*Fig. 5-41*).

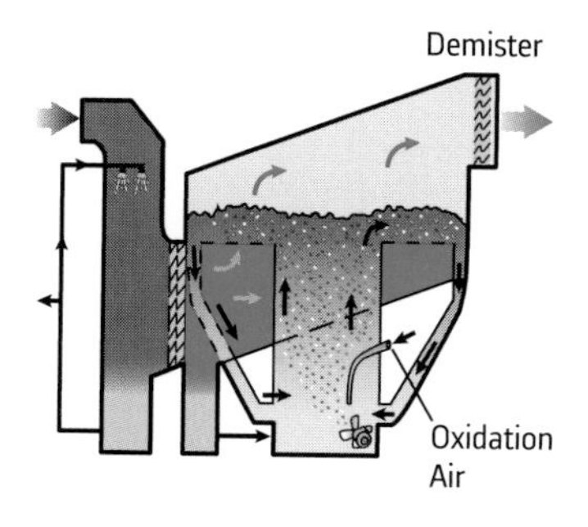

Figure 5-41 | Crossflow tray absorber

Chemistry of Calcium-Based Wet FGD Systems

In a wet limestone, forced oxidation, scrubbing system, a complex series of kinetic- and equilibrium-controlled reactions occur in the gas, liquid, and solid phases. The SO_2 gas is absorbed into an alkaline slurry in the absorber and then oxidized to gypsum in the recycle tank. Solid limestone particles are added to maintain a pH set point and slowly dissolve as SO_2 is absorbed and gypsum is crystallized.

SO_2 ABSORPTION. Lime and limestone slurry scrubbing involves mass transfer of SO_2, from gas to liquid, solid dissolution of $CaCO_3$ to the liquid, and subsequent crystallization of gypsum. Fundamentally, the principal steps are absorption, neutralization, regeneration, oxidation, and precipitation. The reactions may be stated in an overall expression as:

$CaCO_3$ +	SO_2	$+ 2H_2O +$	$½O_2 \rightarrow$	$CaSO_4 \cdot 2H_2O +$	CO_2
limestone +	sulfur dioxide +	water +	oxygen →	gypsum	+ carbon dioxide

Chemical reactions that occur in a wet limestone scrubbing system may be characterized as a series of steps. Although these steps are presented sequentially, they can occur simultaneously.

The absorption of SO_2 in the absorber tower involves the transfer of gaseous SO_2 to the liquid phase. To accomplish this, SO_2 must cross a gas/liquid interface, which can be modeled by classical two-film mass transfer theory. That is, the rate of transfer of SO_2 from the gas to the slurry is equal to the rate of transfer across a gas film boundary surrounding a droplet, which in turn is equal to the rate of transfer across a liquid film boundary at the surface of each droplet. The molar flux at which mass transfer of SO_2 from the gas to the liquid phase occurs is the same in the gas and liquid phase and is expressed as

$$N = k_l \phi (C^* - C)$$
$$N = k_g (y - y^*)$$

Equation 5-31

where

N = molar flux of SO_2
k_l = liquid side mass transfer coefficient
k_g = gas side mass transfer coefficient
y = component concentration in gas
y^* = component concentration in the gas/liquid interface
C = component concentration in liquid
C^* = component concentration in the gas/liquid interface
ϕ = non-dimensional concentration factor for the liquid

The rate of SO_2 absorption in the absorber can be written for a differential height as follows:

$$\frac{-GdSO_2}{P_t dz} = K_g a(y - y^*)$$

Equation 5-32

where

G = gas flow rate
$K_g a$ = Overall mass transfer coefficient in the gas phase
z = total height of the absorbing section
P_t = total pressure

and

$$K_g a = \left(\frac{1}{k_g a} + \frac{H}{\phi k_l}\right)^{-1}$$

Equation 5-33

where,

H = Henry's law constant
$k_g a$ = local mass transfer coefficient in the gas phase
k_l = local mass transfer coefficient in the liquid phase

For dominant liquid side resistance, as in limestone slurry scrubbing, $y^* \ll y$, and Equations 5-32 and 5-33 can be simplified to

$$\ln(1.0 - f) = \phi k_l az/HG$$

Equation 5-34

where f is the fraction SO_2 removal. The term $\ln(1.0 - f)$ often is expressed as the number of transfer units (NTU):

$$\text{NTU} = -\ln(1.0 - f) = \ln(y_{in}/y_{out})$$

Equation 5-35

where

y_{in} = absorber inlet gas concentration
y_{out} = absorber outlet gas concentration

and

$$\text{NTU} = \phi k_l az/HG$$

Equation 5-36

The difference between the bulk gas SO_2 concentration (y) and the gas/liquid interface SO_2 concentration (y^*) is a measure of the potential for SO_2 diffusion from the gas to the liquid. If the SO_2 concentration at the droplet interface (y^*) is lower than the SO_2 concentration in the bulk gas, there is a positive force for SO_2 mass transfer into the slurry droplets. Maintaining this differential is critical to effective SO_2 absorption.

As shown by the mass transfer rate equation (Equation 5-32), SO_2 absorption also is affected by the available absorbent surface area (a) and the resistance to mass transfer expressed by the overall mass transfer coefficient (K_g). Available surface area is a function of droplet size and the amount of liquid in contact with the gas stream at any one time. The resistance to SO_2 mass transfer (K_g) is dependent on many factors, including gas film thickness about a droplet, liquid mixing within a droplet, absolute gas pressure, gas/liquid temperature, and various parameters of the reactive slurry. Gas film thickness about a droplet and liquid mixing within a droplet are related directly to the spray-zone saturated gas velocity.

In addition to SO_2, the halogen acid gases, HF and HCl, typically are absorbed as well:

$$HCl + H_2O \rightarrow H^+ + Cl^- + H_2O$$
$$HF + H_2O \rightarrow H^+ + F^- + H_2O$$

Equation 5-37

The H^+ concentration (pH) is related to dissolved calcium by the following relationships[71]:

$$CaCO_3 + 2H^+ \rightarrow Ca^{2+} + CO_2 + H_2O$$

Equation 5-38

and

$$A_{Ca^{2+}} = \frac{KA_{H^+}^2}{P_{CO_2}}$$

Equation 5-39

where

$A_{Ca^{2+}}$ = activity of Ca^{2+}
$A_{H^+}^2$ = activity of H^+ squared
K = equilibrium constant (dimensionless)
P_{CO_2} = partial pressure of CO_2

Laslo et al.[72] theorized that dissolved magnesium and calcium have similar effects:

$$\left[A_{Ca^{2+}} \times A_{Mg^{2+}}\right] = \frac{KA_{H^+}^2}{P_{CO_2}}$$

Equation 5-40

Equations 5-37 and 5-38 are important when HCl is absorbed. Chloride ions build up in an FGD system, and as shown in Equation 5-38, the dissolved calcium ions concentrate as well. Then, referring to Equation 5-39, at a constant partial pressure of CO_2, the H^+ in equilibrium with Ca^{2+} increases with increasing dissolved calcium. In other words, the equilibrium (maximum) pH in the FGD decreases with increasing chloride concentration.

Figure 5-42 shows the decrease in equilibrium pH for both a natural oxidation and forced oxidation system (pilot data from Chang[73]). Although parallel, the difference between the two systems results from the forced oxidation air stripping the CO_2 and, thereby, slightly increasing the equilibrium pH.

GYPSUM PRECIPITATION. Precipitation is the process by which a substance separates from solution by a chemical change. Precipitation of gypsum will occur if the gypsum relative saturation (RS) of the solution is greater than 1.0. Gypsum RS is defined as the ratio of the ion activity product of calcium and sulfate over the solubility product constant of calcium sulfate dihydrate. Specifically,

$$\text{Gypsum RS} = \frac{A_{Ca^{2+}} \times A_{SO_4^{2-}}}{K_{sp}}$$

Equation 5-41

where

$A_{Ca^{2+}}$ = calcium ion activity
$A_{SO_4^{2-}}$ = sulfate ion activity
K_{sp} = gypsum solubility product

As discussed previously, the ionic activities for calcium and sulfate are a function of solution ionic strength and temperature. The RS of gypsum in the absorbing solution is important, because it is the driving force for gypsum crystallization. The solubility product constant, K_{sp}, is a function of solution temperature, increasing with increasing temperature. Gypsum RS values above 1.0 indicate that the solution is supersaturated and that gypsum precipitation, or crystal growth, will occur. If the gypsum RS falls below 1.0, the solution will be subsaturated, and dissolution of gypsum crystals can be expected.

Fine particles are generated by either primary or secondary nucleation. Secondary nucleation occurs from imparted energy or crystal collisions and

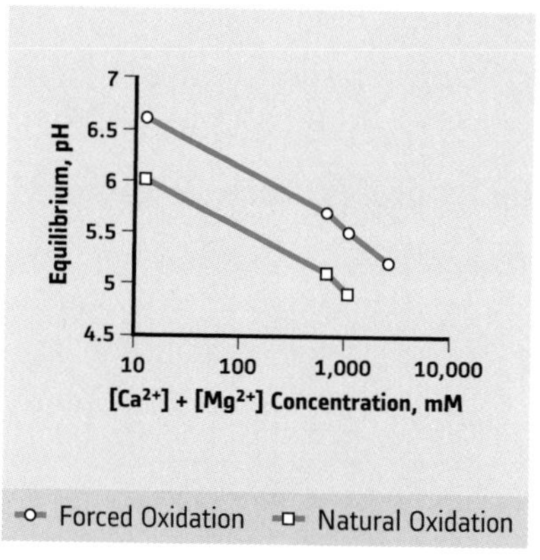

Figure 5-42 | Recycle tank equilibrium pH versus dissolved calcium and magnesium concentrations

A proper understanding of gypsum crystallization allows for control of scaling in wet FGD systems.

can be correlated with, for instance, pump impeller and agitator tip speed and with solids density. Primary nucleation is a function of saturation levels and crystal surface area (density and particle size).

At a gypsum RS of greater than 1.35, spontaneous nucleation of gypsum crystals can occur (primary nucleation). This can result in gypsum crystallization on foreign surfaces, such as pipes and walls, rather than the growth on existing recirculating crystals. The highest gypsum RS levels in the FGD process occur in the slurry inside, or leaving, the spray/gas contact zone. System design consideration must allow a sufficiently high L/G ratio and solids concentration in the slurry to maintain a gypsum RS below 1.35 for these streams. Gypsum RS values above 1.35 can result in heterogeneous formation of gypsum crystals on internal absorber surfaces.

The nucleation rate affects overall particle size distribution, because the formed particles are extremely small yet large in number. The population of "fines" will make the particle size distribution finer as the new nucleation sites overwhelm the overall particle size distribution. Conversely, if the fines are purged from the system in large quantity, the remaining larger particles are the precipitation surface, and a larger particle size distribution results. Separate purges (e.g., a wastewater treatment bleed or gypsum cake) are so small in volume that their effect can be ignored as a "double draw-off" fines disposal stream.

Gypsum crystals produced in a typical FGD process range in size up to 130 microns. The mass median particle size range is 48 to 64 microns, although the particle size may be smaller because of the classification effect of a hydrocyclone dewatering system. The size of gypsum crystals produced by an FGD process is a function of the relative amount of crystal handling (i.e., pump cycles), the degree of fractionation in the primary dewatering circuit, as well as other factors. The absorber reaction tank solids residence time must be adequate to allow full desaturation of the gypsum in the recycle slurry—that is, to allow the slurry to be maintained either at or near a gypsum RS of 1.0. It is expected that a minimum of 1 to 2 minutes will be necessary for forced oxidation systems.

Absorbers

There are many types of absorbers, including both co-current and countercurrent spray towers, tray towers, jet bubblers, packed towers, fountain sprays, and the high-performance Flowpac® system (a cross-flow tray design without recycle pumps). Because of the scaling history of the original limestone natural oxidation processes, the open spray tower was at times the default absorber because of its high reliability. The advent of the forced oxidation relaxed the requirements for FGD absorbers, and internals began to appear.

SPRAY TOWER ABSORBERS. The open spray tower is by far the most common absorber type. It is simple in design. Several banks of spray nozzles in a low-velocity, cylindrical tower provide high L/G ratios at a low gas pressure drop. The SO_2 removal efficiency is obtained by designing the tower with the proper L/G ratio. Some control can be obtained with slight variations in operating pH, but there is no fine control of the outlet SO_2

concentration. The sprayed slurry falls countercurrent to the gas flow and collects in an air-sparged, agitated tank at the bottom of the tower. The scrubbed gas travels upward, through a chevron mist eliminator, and out through a cone-shaped top.

SPRAY TOWER REACTION TANK. The reaction tank usually is an integral part of the absorber. (This tank is also called the "hold tank," or the "recycle tank"). The reaction tank performs several process duties:

- Providing adequate slurry and solids residence times to allow limestone dissolution and gypsum precipitation reactions
- Mixing fresh limestone slurry with spent absorber slurry
- Dispersing compressed air for forced oxidation of sulfite to sulfate
- Providing residence time for the gypsum crystals to grow
- Providing adequate NPSH for the absorber recycle pumps to operate properly

The reaction tank is sized to satisfy the kinetics of limestone dissolution and gypsum precipitation reactions. The former usually is the slowest, although at higher rates of sulfur removal, the latter may dominate. The agitators provide solids suspension, mixing, and air dispersion in the case of forced oxidized designs. The materials of construction must be resistant to both corrosion and erosion.

SPRAY TOWER SHELL. Velocity considerations dictate the tower cross-sectional area. Although higher gas velocities through the absorbing section improve SO_2 removal, the maximum allowable velocity through the close-coupled mist eliminator section sets a practical limit of 12 to 13 ft/s (3.7 to 3.9 m/s) through the absorbing section. A short transition piece with a gradually expanding area connects the mist eliminator section to the absorber section. The number of absorbing stages required to obtain the desired level of SO_2 removal governs the overall tower height.

The corrosive and erosive environment within the tower requires special materials. Type 318L and 317L stainless steels have been successfully applied in numerous instances. Under certain conditions of scrubber-slurry pH, temperature, and chloride concentration, the use of nickel-based alloys with higher molybdenum and chromium contents can provide superior corrosion protection.[74] The use of such high-grade alloys requires very careful fabrication. In general, failures of high-grade alloys incorporated in the tower shell and internal support members occur primarily because of faulty welding rather than corrosion.

In contrast to the spray tower shell, the gas ducts upstream and downstream of spray towers represent much more severely corrosive environments. Absorber inlet and outlet ducts as well as reheat mixing zones require special consideration with respect to material selection. Protective linings, such as inorganic cements or borosilicate glass blocks over carbon or stainless-steel plate, typically are used for the absorber inlet ducting.

SPRAY SECTION: PUMPS, PIPING, AND NOZZLES. There can be independent absorption stages, each consisting of a spray pump, piping, manifold, headers, and spray nozzles. If a spare pump is included, a complete spare absorption stage also is provided. This arrangement provides maximum flexibility and allows tailoring of the spray flow to system requirements by removing absorption stages from operation in steps.

Rubber-lined, centrifugal spray pumps provide erosion resistance and protection against unexpected process upsets in pH control. A tall reaction tank provides a large, net-positive suction head to prevent pump cavitation, which can damage the rubber pump liners. Fiberglass-reinforced plastic (FRP) spray piping, with an abrasion-resistant internal liner, provides both abrasion and erosion resistance. The FRP is an inert material used for its corrosion resistance. The FRP piping is easily fabricated and, unlike rubber-lined pipe, can be readily repaired in the field. The manifold and headers are built of FRP for the flow and geometry requirements of each application. Tapered manifolds and headers keep slurry velocities within allowable values (nominally 5–10 ft/s [1.5–3 m/s]). The spray nozzles at each absorption stage are arranged to provide full spray coverage over the tower cross section. The nozzles provide a full-cone, wide-angle spray pattern and typically are made of a wear-resistant, cast refractory containing silicon carbide.

MIST ELIMINATION. Mist elimination systems are installed in FGD absorbers either in the absorber itself (e.g., at the top of an open spray tower) or in the outlet ductwork (as with a Flowpac® absorber). Typically, a low-pressure-drop, two-stage, medium-efficiency, chevron mist eliminator is used. With proper design, washing, and good water quality, this system will have a long service life between manual maintenance cleanings. A high-efficiency mist eliminator, such as a mesh pad, would not be suitable with this service, because the solids in the slurry would plug the mesh rather quickly. With chevrons, higher velocities improve the collection efficiency. Each design, however, has a breakthrough velocity at which the liquid is no longer collected and, instead, is re-entrained into the gas stream. This limiting velocity must be avoided through conservative design practices. The average gas velocity may be quite acceptable, but variations across the cross section may contain areas that exceed the breakthrough velocity. Modern chevron mist eliminators increase this limiting velocity by slanting the blades in a design that looks like a roof.

The mist eliminator vanes must be washed often to remove solid deposits that collect on their surfaces. Observations and operating experience have shown the best approach for the wash system. Three main guidelines to follow include:

1. Use the best available washwater (low dissolved solids). Washwater will fall into the reaction tank and, therefore, become makeup water for control of the recycle tank level. The total amount of water will be regulated by intermittent operation of the wash system. Care must be taken, however, to follow the arrangement of the wash headers, nozzle type, spacing, and operating pressure. Evaluate the quality of the water based on the amount of dissolved solids present. If necessary, the washwater can be diluted with freshwater to keep

scale from forming on the vanes. (These are process design issues, which are covered in detail in the chemistry of calcium-based wet FGD systems.)

2. The design should allow no back side or downstream washing of the last mist eliminator vane. This results in too much washwater to carry over when there is gas flow.
3. There is very little penetration of the washwater in to the vanes. Only the visible surface of the vanes (relative to the washwater) will be cleaned.

If the wash system is to be supplied separately, the wash system design (nozzle pressure, angle, and layout) should be approved by the system supplier in order to maintain valid mist eliminator performance guarantees by that supplier.

The cleaned flue gas passes through a separation section with two stages: the bulk entrainment separator, and the mist eliminator. The bulk entrainment separator consists of 6-inch (15 cm) FRP vanes mounted at a 45° angle on 2-inch (5 cm) parallel spacing. It extends across the entire face area of the spray tower absorber. The mist eliminator located above the bulk entrainment separator is made from V-shaped FRP vanes arranged in a series of chevrons across the gas flow path. Two rows of chevrons ensure droplet impingement and minimize mist carryover. Wash nozzles are installed above and below the first stage mist eliminator and below the upper stage mist eliminator. The stages are washed a portion at a time such that the wash rate doesn't exceed the total makeup water required. The first stage is washed more often. Efficient cleaning prevents excessive droplet carryover, which would result from deposition on the vanes.

REACTION TANK. Usually located at the bottom of the spray tower, the reaction tank, or recycle tank, serves many purposes. It provides residence time primarily for the dissolution of solid limestone and for the various chemical reactions. It also provides residence time for gypsum crystallization and crystal growth. The tank is used to inject air for oxidation of sulfite to sulfate. Finally, the tank provides liquid head for the many recycle pumps.

The reaction tank performs several key functions including the dissolution of limestone, the crystallization of gypsum, the oxidation of sulfites, and the provision of liquid head for the recycle pumps.

A secondary absorption reaction, which occurs in the FGD process, involves the conversion of sulfite and bisulfite to sulfate:

$$HSO_3^- + \tfrac{1}{2}O_2\,(\text{aqueous}) \rightarrow SO_4^{2-} + H^+$$

Equation 5-42

$$SO_3^{2-} + \tfrac{1}{2}O_2\,(\text{aqueous}) \rightarrow SO_4^{2-}$$

Equation 5-43

This oxidation reaction will, to some extent, occur naturally because of oxygen in the flue gas, and it can be promoted, or forced, through the contact of sparged air with the absorber slurry. Several FGD system operating factors may influence the rate of natural oxidation, including the oxygen/sulfite SR, ionic strength of the absorbent slurry, absorbent slurry pH, gas/liquid temperature, gas pressure, and L/G ratio in the absorber.

As with the absorption of SO_2, oxidation of sulfite involves the mass transfer of a gas to the liquid phase. The rate of absorption can be expressed by two-film mass transfer theory as follows:

$$N = K_g A (y - y^*)$$

Equation 5-44

where

N = rate of oxygen mass transfer
K_g = overall mass transfer coefficient (resistance to mass transfer)
A = interfacial area for mass transfer
$y - y^*$ = driving force for mass transfer (concentration gradient)

In general, the rate of sulfite oxidation is nearly always faster than the rate of oxygen transfer from the gas phase. Thus, oxidation in an FGD system is usually mass transfer limited, and the rate of chemical reaction can be assumed to be instantaneous.

OXYGEN TRANSFER TO THE SLURRY FROM AIR BUBBLES. Borgwardt[60] used oxygen transfer data from Jackson et al.[75] to estimate FGD oxidation transfer rates. Jackson measured oxygen transfer using single bubbles rising through a tall tank with dissolved sulfite. As such, the mass transfer of oxygen was controlling. The dynamics of an FGD oxidizer will be more complex, however, because the slurry is agitated and has a flow field toward the tank exit. The bubble dynamics also are different (agglomeration and velocity vectors other than straight up)—all of which affect mass transfer. In the case of an agitated lance system, the bubbles can take a cyclonic route to the surface. Borgwardt's experiments, however, indicated excellent agreement with the data of Jackson et al. and, thus, became the basis for FGD oxidizer design. A brief summary of their findings follows:

Urza and Jackson[76] empirically determined the oxygen transfer efficiency of a bubble column to be

$$\frac{e}{3.0+0.791e}+\ln\frac{1.0+0.264e}{1-e}=\frac{70{,}000\times K_l a\times h\times\left(P+\frac{h_s}{2}\right)}{m_o H}$$

Equation 5-45

where

e = oxygen transfer efficiency (fraction)
$K_l a$ = overall liquid side mass transfer coefficient
H = Henry's law constant
P = barometric pressure (atm)
h = static sparger depth without aeration
h_s = sparger depth with aeration
m_o = air (oxygen) rate

Borgwardt then developed an empirical equation for $K_l a$ based on temperature and the data from Jackson et al.:

$$K_l a = 2.08\left(\frac{293}{T}\right)^{-0.666} 0.214\frac{m_o^{1.09}}{P+h_s/2.0}$$

Equation 5-46

where T is the slurry temperature (K).

Next, Borgwardt combined the two equations for 122°F (50°C) as follows:

$$\frac{e}{3.0+0.791e}+\ln\frac{1+0.264e}{1-e}=0.0474m_o^{0.09}h$$

Equation 5-47

The design oxygen transfer efficiency, *e*, is then determined by a trial-and-error solution of Equations 5-46 and 5-47. (Again, the equations are based on a static tank with a single bubble column and no slurry velocity.)

The air stoichiometry, SR_{ox}, is defined as

$$SR_{ox}=\frac{\text{gram atoms of } O_2 \text{ injected as air}}{\text{gram moles of } SO_2 \text{ absorbed in the scrubber}}=1/e$$

Equation 5-48

and the minimum SR_{ox} is 1.0.

FACTORS AFFECTING MASS TRANSFER IN SPRAY TOWERS

RECYCLE TANK PH. As SO_2 and other acidic gases are absorbed, the pH in the recycle tank falls. Alkaline reagent thus is added to control pH to a constant value. If the pH set point is too high, the resulting gypsum product will have too much unreacted calcium carbonate. A low pH, however, will result in backpressure of SO_2 and lower SO_2 removal in the absorber, plus increased susceptibility to corrosion. The efficiency of SO_2 removal increases with increasing pH, because the dissolved alkalinity increases and the SO_2 backpressure decreases. The pH will increase to the maximum equilibrium pH, after which adding additional limestone will have little effect. The pH also is increased by the oxidation air in the recycle tank as the acid gas CO_2 is stripped from the liquid by the injected air.

GAS VELOCITY. The design velocity usually is limited by the maximum velocity acceptable to the in-line mist eliminator and/or the gas side pressure drop, and it typically is in the range of 10 to 13 ft/s (3 to 4 m/s) for modern absorbers. In general, increasing gas velocity increases pressure drop, but it also increases mass transfer and, therefore, SO_2 removal efficiency. Higher gas velocity in the spray tower translates to smaller cross-sectional areas and, thereby, lower initial costs of the absorber tower.

L/G RATIO. Increasing the L/G ratio at a given gas velocity increases performance. As a power plant reduces load, at a constant liquid flow rate, the L/G ratio increases and the gas velocity decreases. These opposing effects are almost equivalent; thus, performance is maintained as load decreases.

INLET SO_2 CONCENTRATION. The concentration of SO_2 at the inlet to the absorber varies from a few hundred ppm or less with low-sulfur coal to over 5,000 ppm with some lignitic coals. At a given L/G ratio, higher inlet SO_2 concentrations will quickly deplete the dissolved alkalinity and decrease the interfacial pH, increasing

Nozzle coverage is critical so that flue gas does not bypass the scrubbing solution.

y^* and requiring higher L/G ratios for a given required performance. Lower inlet partial pressures of SO_2 do not deplete the dissolved alkalinity so quickly, leading to increased performance. For a given SO_2 removal performance requirement, lower L/G ratios are required.

HEADERS, SPRAY NOZZLES, NOZZLE LAYOUT, AND WALL RINGS. Typically, a spray tower has four to seven spray levels. Each level has a spray header with a dedicated recycle pump, allowing a spare spray header for pump, motor, or valve maintenance if necessary. Each spray header has a number of spray nozzles, with each typically approximately 300 gpm (80 lpm), spaced approximately equally across the tower, and operating at 8 psi (0.55 bar). Nozzles can be single-orifice nozzles or dual-orifice nozzles (nozzles that spray both up and down). The droplet size distribution is designed so there is not excessive drop migration upward to the mist eliminators at the design gas velocity.

If the nozzles are not arranged such that complete and even coverage of spray drops occurs across the cross-sectional area, then flue gas "sneakage" (raw flue gas bypassing the sprays and receiving virtually no scrubbing) can occur. This sneakage also occurs at the walls of the absorber, where it is difficult to place sprays without eroding the walls. For this reason, a baffle plate, or wall ring, is placed on the walls at several levels to disrupt the flow of unscrubbed gas and substantially improve performance.

LIMESTONE GRIND, STOICHIOMETRY. Dissolution of limestone in the absorber is the largest resistance to mass transfer. Decreasing limestone particle size or increasing excess limestone can increase performance by providing more surface area for limestone dissolution in the mass transfer zone. Finer-grind limestone also can produce lower excess $CaCO_3$ in the gypsum and, thus, a more pure product. Most installations today grind very fine (90–95% minus 325 mesh).

Limestone is the principal supplier of the alkaline species necessary for SO_2 absorption. The rate at which these alkaline species enter solution depends on the limestone dissolution rate, which is influenced primarily by particle surface area and the pH (hydrogen [H^+] ion concentration). In addition, other major factors that influence the limestone dissolution rate include the partial pressure of CO_2, fluid turbulence, dissolved solids concentration (e.g., chlorides), and temperature. Limestone dissolution decreases as temperature decreases and as chloride concentrations increase. Limestone dissolution increases with CO_2 stripping (forced oxidation), mixing, and higher temperatures.[77]

Minimizing the amount of alkaline additive required to obtain a desired SO_2 removal efficiency reduces the operating cost of an FGD system. To determine the factors influencing additive use, it is necessary to understand the additive dissolution process and the effect of system operating conditions, design, and additive properties on this process.

In a lime or limestone SO_2 scrubbing system, the addition of alkali is controlled to neutralize the SO_2 absorbed and precipitate the calcium-sulfur salts. Although in theory the amount of lime or limestone required is stoichiometrically equal to the amount of SO_2 removed, the kinetics of the limestone dissolution process dictates the use of excess additive to achieve the desired SO_2 removal efficiency. Additive stoichiometry usually is defined as the moles of additive fed (excluding impurities) to a scrubber per mole of SO_2 absorbed (although it can be, and sometimes is, defined as the moles of additive fed per mole of SO_2 entering the scrubber).

DISSOLVED SALTS. A brief discussion about the effect of chlorides and other dissolved salts is given here. For detailed discussions, please see the references cited.

CALCIUM CHLORIDE BUILDUP. The primary source of chloride ions in the FGD slurry is via absorption of HCl from the flue gas and subsequent neutralization by $CaCO_3$. The soluble $CaCl_2$ then concentrates to a steady-state level dictated by the material balance.

This salt buildup has a negative effect on system chemistry in several ways.[71] Mass transfer is suppressed by the lower alkalinity, but it is not dependent on absorber type.[78] The equilibrium pH also is suppressed—especially without forced oxidation air.[72] Chlorides can be purged to minimize these effects; otherwise, absorber L/G ratios must be raised to counter the effect. Note that other cations with chlorides, such as magnesium or sodium, do not have the same negative effect at the concentrations normally found in FGD systems.[72]

MAGNESIUM. Magnesium has a positive effect on mass transfer—even in forced oxidation systems. The effect is greatest when magnesium is not in equilibrium with Cl^- and, therefore, increases dissolved alkalinity (free sulfite). This is not common, however, because magnesium in the limestone usually is in a dolomitic form and insoluble. Magnesium ion buildup has an effect similar to that of calcium on pH suppression but does not suppress mass transfer as calcium does.[72]

ORGANIC ACIDS. Organic acids, commonly adipic acid, the waste stream DBA, and formic acid, increase SO_2 markedly in small concentrations (300 to 3,000 ppm).[67] The addition of these acids is an easy retrofit that may be added to existing units to enhance performance.

FACTORS AFFECTING MASS TRANSFER IN FLOWPAC® ABSORBERS. Similar to spray towers, Flowpac® absorbers also are affected by site-specific parameters, such as inlet SO_2 and HCl concentration. The Flowpac® design is unique in that the desired outlet SO_2 concentration can be controlled to a set point. The depth of the slurry bed above the cross-flow tray can be varied; thus, the mass transfer and pressure drop also are changed. Typically, this is the only process variable that is changed, because the pH and L/G ratio remain constant. Organic acids may be used with Flowpac® absorbers with a net result of lower pressure drop for the same performance or higher performance at the same pressure drop.

Reagent Preparation

Reagent preparation includes equipment for the delivery, storage, and grinding of the raw additive as well as the delivery of the reagent to the absorbers.

LIMESTONE DELIVERY AND STORAGE. For on-site grinding, limestone commonly is received as ¾ × 0 inch (20 × 0 mm) crushed rock. The handling properties of this material are similar to those of coal. Although rain shelters are common, limestone rock may be stockpiled outside in most climates. Conventional earth-moving equipment, such as front-end loaders and bulldozers, are used to push or move the rock into subgrade drop door bins. Foreign material, such as roots, wood, and iron, is separated from the rock at this stage. From the drop door bins, belt conveyors move the limestone to day bins located above the mills. The limestone is then gravity fed, using a control slide gate, onto a gravimetric feeder that discharges the rock into the feed end of the grinding apparatus.

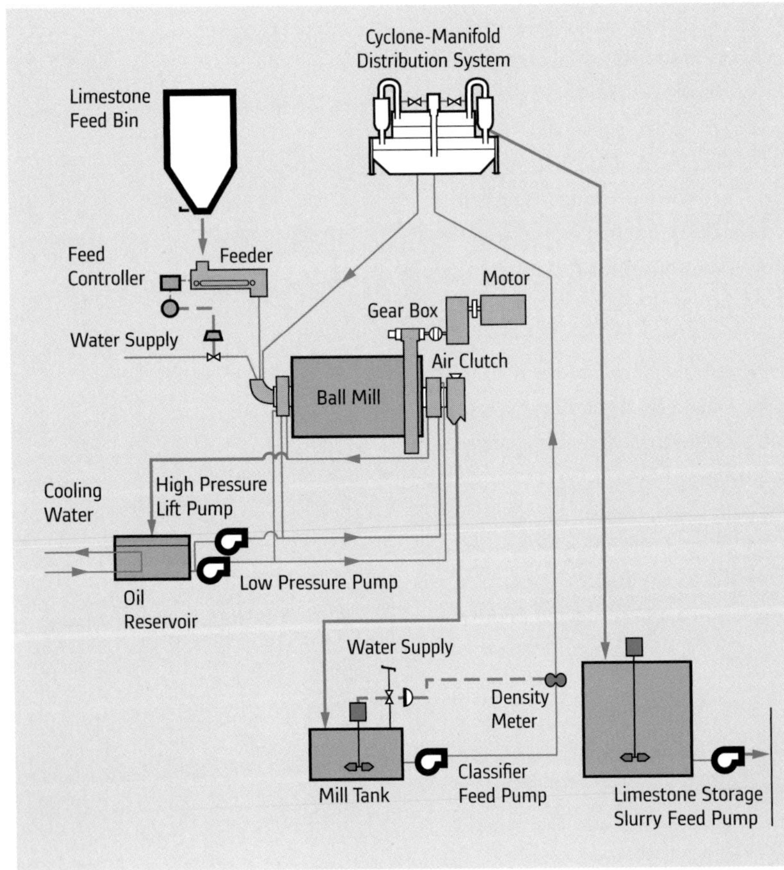

Figure 5-43 | Wet ball mill

LIMESTONE GRINDING. The limestone particle size required for proper SO_2 absorption/gypsum production is 95% by weight less than 44 microns (325 U.S. Standard Mesh). Grinding of the limestone rock can be performed at the site of the FGD system or at the quarry where the mineral is mined. In North America, on-site grinding using wet mills is the most common. In Europe and Asia, dry grinding at the quarry is common.

Three types of limestone grinding apparatus have been commercially used in FGD applications: horizontal ball mills, vertical tower mills, and roller mills. The first two types are used in wet grinding systems. Raw limestone is mixed with water or process liquor during the grinding operation, producing a slurry product of finely ground limestone particles. The third type, the roller mill, pulverizes the limestone without the addition of water, producing a dry powder.

WET BALL MILLS. Horizontal wet ball mills have been—and continue to be—the most common apparatus used for grinding limestone. As depicted in *Figure 5-43*, grinding is accomplished by tumbling the limestone in a cylindrical vessel that is partially filled with forged steel balls and water. The ball charge includes balls ranging from ¾ to 4 inches (20 to 100 mm) in diameter. Fresh or reclaimed process water is added in proportion to the rock to maintain constant slurry density. The resultant slurry output from the mill overflows into a mill product tank and is then pumped to a bank of hydrocyclones and classified.

Oversize particles are captured in the hydrocyclone underflow and returned to the mill. Fine particles exit in the hydrocyclone overflow and are sent to the limestone slurry storage tank. From the limestone slurry storage tank, pumps deliver the required flow (based on the amount of absorbed SO_2) to each operating absorber.

The grinding system operates as a closed circuit. That is, rock is recirculated until it has been ground small enough to be captured in the hydrocyclone overflow. In practice, however, it is not uncommon for the discharge end of the mill to produce a small stream of reject rocks. These usually are rocks containing higher-than-average amounts of silica and alumina compounds. These rejected hard rocks typically are less than 1% of the rock feed to the mill.

TOWER MILLS (ATTRITION MILL). An alternative to ball mills is a wet, vertically oriented, stirred, tower mill. The tower mill cannot be used when the rocks are larger than ⅜ inch (10 mm). Pre-crushing usually is required. In fine and ultrafine grinding applications, the tower mill can offer power savings over wet ball mills. The grinding medium generally is forged steel balls.

In the system depicted by *Figure 5-44*, the limestone entering the tower mill at the top moves down the vertical column of grinding charge in the grinding chamber. Grinding is by attrition, which occurs through collisions with the material to be ground, the grinding media, and the agitator for the grinding charge in the screw flight. The finely ground particles are carried upward through the grinding media by a rising column of liquid produced by the mill pump. As the finely ground material overflows the main body into the coarse classifier, the largest particles are removed and recycled to the bottom of the grinding chamber via a mill sump and the mill pump. The coarse classifier overflow reports to a collection sump. From the sump, it is further classified into final product by the external hydrocyclone classifiers.

LIMESTONE POWDER. For cases in which the limestone is ground at the quarry, it is delivered to the FGD site in bulk tank trucks or rail wagons as a ready-to-use, fine powder and then pneumatically conveyed to storage silos. Such silos may be sized for a 15- to 30-day supply. Volumetric screw

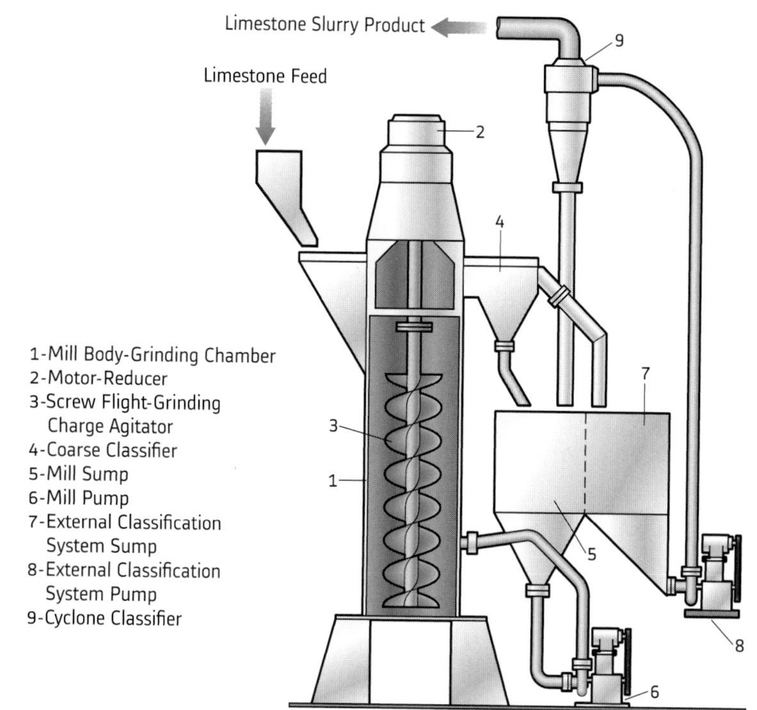

Figure 5-44 | Vertical tower mill

conveyers transfer the powder into the limestone day bins. The powder falls by gravity onto a covered conveyor weigh belt, which then dumps the powder into a wetting-and-mixing tank. Mixers to pre-wet the powder also are used at times. In the mixing tank, water is metered in to make the needed slurry. Typical slurries are prepared at 25 to 35% solids by weight.

MILL TYPE SELECTION. Ball mills are preferred when the limestone feedstock size is medium to large (0.8–1.0 inch [20–25 mm] top size), the rock has a high work index, and the required product grind is 80 to 95% less than 44 microns. Tower mills become competitive when ultrafine grinds are required, but the feed size to a tower mill generally is limited to ⅜ inch. A moderate work index favors a tower mill. Dry roller mill pulverizers are preferred when a source of heat and large rock sizes are available. No quantitative data are available regarding the comparative reliability of the various mill types. Anecdotal evidence, however, suggests that wet ball mills are the most reliable and that dry roller mill pulverizers are the least reliable.

MILL SIZING. Mill sizing is performed by the mill vendor. For approximations, detailed crushing and grind calculations, including horsepower, can be found in Bond.[79,80] The major factors influencing the mill size are:

- **Bond work index.** This is a measure of the limestone hardness and its resistance to grinding. Typical work index values range from 6 to 13. Soft stones have values of 6 to 8. Hard stones have values of 11 to 13.
- **Size of the feed rock.** This includes both the top (largest) size and the size distribution. The greater the top size, the greater the required energy input.
- **Size of the ground product.** The smaller the product size, the greater the required energy input.
- **Mill capacity.** The capacity in ton/h (kg/h) of the limestone grinding system is governed by the following factors:
  - **Steady-state limestone consumption rate.** This is determined by knowing the maximum SO_2 removal rate, the design stoichiometry, and the minimum $CaCO_3$ content (purity) of the limestone.
  - **Hours per day the mill will operate.** In most plants, grinding is performed during one or two shifts. Thus, if the mill is to operate for 8 hours in any 24-hour period, the capacity of the grinding system must be equal to three-fold the steady-state limestone consumption rate.

DEWATERING. Dewatering of the waste solids typically is performed in a primary and a secondary stage. Usually, in the case of gypsum, the primary dewatering concentrates the slurry from 15% solids to 50% solids, and the secondary dewatering further concentrates the gypsum to a moist cake of 10% moisture. Primary dewatering can be accomplished either with a thickener (highest flexibility but rarely used) or, more commonly, with a hydrocyclone.

Secondary dewatering is needed to get the product moisture that is desired for almost all of the final byproducts discussed in this section. The choices are:

- Rotary drum vacuum filter (up to 88% or more for forced oxidation solids)

- Horizontal belt vacuum filter (up to 90% or more for forced oxidation solids)
- Centrifuges (up to 95% or more for forced oxidation solids), typically vertical basket centrifuges

Other methods used to dewater and simultaneously store or dispose of the waste solids are ponding and gypsum stacking. The dewatered solids, like any other granular solids, may be transferred by belt conveyor, bucket elevators, front loaders, and so on to further processing steps, temporary storage, or disposal.

PRIMARY DEWATERING: HYDROCYCLONES. Hydrocyclones are used in a number of different types of applications for solids separation, solids washing, classification, dewatering, and so on. In wet FGD applications, hydrocyclones typically are used to separate, by centrifugal forces, the absorber bleed slurry into an overflow and an underflow. The overflow carries more of the liquid along with solid fines, and the underflow consists of a liquid with a major fraction of coarser solid particles. Depending on the configuration of the process flow, some of the overflow is discharged for reduction of dissolved salts and fine particulate matter.

The hydrocyclone classifies particles based on their size and density, which enables both physical and chemical separation. The potential for gypsum/limestone separation in the hydrocyclones depends on the particle size distribution of the limestone. Finer-grind limestone increases the potential to use hydrocyclones for limestone/gypsum separation. The typical particle size distribution for forced oxidation gypsum is shown in *Table 5-13*.

The basic operation of a hydrocyclone is as follows: The feed slurry, under pressure, enters tangentially into the cylindrical chamber of the hydrocyclone, where the fluid begins rotating and centrifugal forces act on the particles. Higher-density and larger particles receive larger centrifugal forces and tend to migrate to the cyclone wall, down the length of the cyclone, and out through the apex. This flow generally is called the "underflow." Lighter and smaller particles tend to follow the fluid flow and are forced into the vortex of the cyclone; this flow generally is called the "overflow." A certain amount of free fluid, including a bypass fraction of fine particles, is discharged with the larger particles in the underflow.

In summary, the underflow contains a higher concentration of solids, and the overflow a lower concentration of

TABLE 5-13 | TYPICAL PARTICLE SIZE DISTRIBUTION FOR FORCED OXIDATION GYPSUM

% Solids < Given Particle Size	Particle Size (microns)	Particle Size (microns)	% Solids < Given Particle Size
100	188	17.7	17.5
98.6	162	15.3	15.1
98.3	140	13.2	13.0
96.1	121	11.4	11.4
92.8	104	9.81	10.0
88.5	83.9	8.46	8.65
83.1	77.5	7.30	7.41
76.6	66.9	6.30	6.03
68.7	57.7	5.43	4.89
58.9	43.8	4.69	3.94
47.4	42.9	4.05	3.18
37.5	37.1	3.49	2.60
30.9	32.0	3.01	2.16
26.3	27.6	2.60	1.78
23.1	23.8	2.24	1.38
20.3	20.5	1.93	1.03

solids, than the feed. The degree of solids separation depends on the feed composition and characteristics as well as on the configuration, size, and operational parameters of the hydrocyclone equipment.

Quite a few equipment parameters can be selected or changed on a hydrocyclone setup. Hydrocyclones can be modified for different capacities and separation performances: type of inlet (involute vs. tangential), size of inlet, size of vortex finder, length of cylinder section, and cone angle. In general, long hydrocyclones help separation, whereas short hydrocyclones inhibit maximum recovery of solids. The inlet and the vortex finder fittings affect the capacity and the cut point. The effects of these changes are used to fine tune a particular cyclone for an application and do not have to be fixed for initial sizing.

Hydrocyclones are designed only for on/off operation. Variable flow operation is not recommended. The hydrocyclone underflow stream is routed either directly to the secondary dewatering device or to a filter feed tank via gravity feed. For a two-stage hydrocyclone arrangement, the overflow of the first stage is routed to a storage tank before entering the second stage.

SECONDARY DEWATERING. The secondary dewatering system makes a final reduction in the moisture content of the waste slurry. This system receives the underflow stream from the primary dewatering system and separates that stream into a filtrate stream and filter cake stream. The solids, concentrated as filter cake (65– 92% solids by weight), are transferred to the solids treatment subsystem. The liquor recovered as filtrate is returned for the plant's use.

Secondary dewatering is accomplished by vacuum filtration or centrifugation, using one of the following devices:

- Horizontal vacuum belt filter
- Rotary drum vacuum filter
- Centrifuge

The choice of device will depend on the degree to which the solids are oxidized and on the concentration of solids required in the filter cake.

ROTARY DRUM VACUUM FILTER. The main parts of a rotary drum vacuum filter are a rotating drum, slurry vat, vat agitator, vacuum pump, discharge blower, vacuum receiver, and filtrate pump (*Fig.* 5-45). The drum rotates through the slurry vat about a fixed internal assembly of piping. This piping radiates from the drum's axial centerline to the drum's surface in an arrangement that produces three operating zones: pick-up, drying, and blow discharge. Filter feed slurry is

Figure 5-45 | Rotary drum vacuum filter

discharged into the slurry vat. The vat agitator maintains suspension of the slurry solids. The pick-up zone is the portion of the drum that is submerged in the slurry vat.

The drum's surface (the cylinder walls) is the filter medium. It is a porous, canvas-like material through which the vacuum pump takes suction via the internal piping. In the pick-up zone, the suction draws the slurry into contact with the filter medium. The filter medium is selected based on the particle size of the slurry solids that the filter allows the maximum amount of liquor to pass through while holding virtually all of the solids on the surface. The suction is continued in the drying zone as the filter surface rotates out of the vat. Entrained moisture is drawn through the filter cake and filter media.

The blow discharge zone is the last zone before the rotation cycle repeats. Here, the suction is replaced with a positive pressure. Air is forced through the piping to the filter media by the discharge blower. This causes the filter cake to bellow out from the filter media. A horizontal knife, known as a "doctor blade," catches the dislodged filter cake and directs it onto the discharge conveyor. The filtrate removed from the filter cake is a mixture of slurry liquor, air, and suspended solids. The liquor and suspended solids are separated from the air by the vacuum receiver. The vacuum pump discharges the air stream to an outdoor location. The filtrate pump takes suction at the bottom of the vacuum receiver and delivers the filtrate slurry to a holding tank or the primary dewatering device.

The lower initial capital cost and a simpler method of operation make the rotary drum vacuum filter the preferred secondary dewatering device for all systems except forced oxidation, commercial-grade gypsum production. The rotary drum has not provided the degree of dewatering necessary for producing commercial-grade gypsum.

A rotary drum vacuum filter is sized based on the quantity and particle size of the solids to be processed. Because the particle size depends on the degree of solids oxidation, filter sizing is different for each of the three types of oxidation systems. Design guidelines for rotary drums used in natural, inhibited, and forced oxidation systems are presented in the following paragraphs. A more complete presentation is given for a natural oxidation system. Exceptions to the natural oxidation design are given for inhibited and forced oxidation systems rather than repeating the procedure in its entirety for each system.

Some systems require a surge tank, or a filter feed tank, upstream of the secondary dewatering devices. This is true of systems with batch operation of the secondary dewatering devices and for systems in which it is anticipated that the operation will either exceed or be significantly less than the design conditions. For surge protection, a retention time or storage capacity of two hours generally is acceptable. For batch operation, the retention time is equal to the number of hours that the dewatering devices will be inactive between periods of operation. Because of the suspended solids in the slurry, a filter feed tank requires an agitator. In general, the agitator blade centerline is located at a distance off the tank floor equal to one-third of the tank diameter. The agitator blade must remain submerged and operating at all times during plant operation. Continuous operation of an agitator requires a minimum level of submergence of the agitator's blade, which typically is two feet above the blade's centerline. This minimum level or volume of liquid (not active volume) should not be included when calculating the retention time of the tank.

Forced oxidation controls the degree of solids oxidation by introducing compressed air into the reaction tank slurry. The additional oxygen can produce a solids oxidation of 99% $CaSO_4 \cdot 2H_2O$ or greater. The particle size of forced oxidized solids is much larger than that in naturally oxidized or inhibited oxidized solids. Therefore, the slurry of a forced oxidation system is more easily dewatered.

A standard rotary drum for a forced oxidation system can be designed using the same guidelines given for a natural oxidation system, but with the following exceptions. For a filter feed slurry with a suspended solids concentration of 30 to 40%, a filtration rate of no greater than 250 $lb/h/ft^2$ (1,220 $kg/h/m^2$) should be used to produce a filter cake with a concentration of 75 to 80% solids. Design guidelines for a filter feed tank with a forced oxidation system are identical to those given for a natural oxidation system.

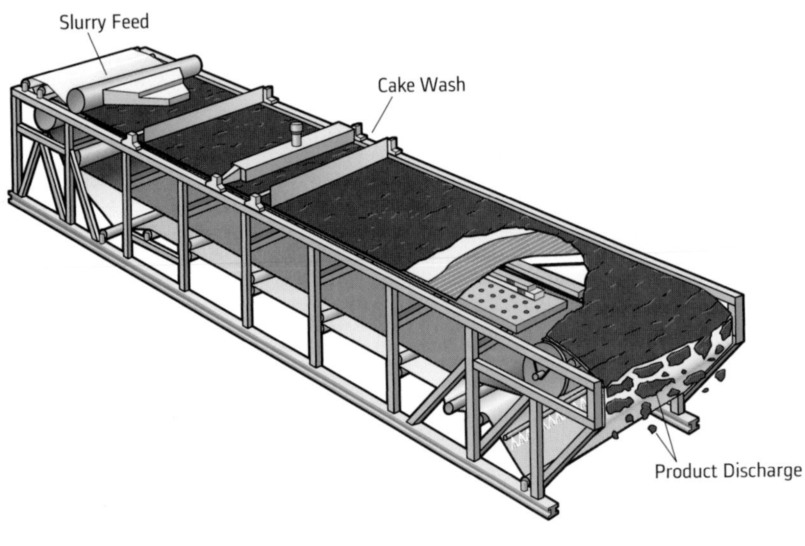

Figure 5-46 | Horizontal vacuum belt filter

HORIZONTAL VACUUM BELT FILTER. A horizontal vacuum belt filter uses a belt as the filtering medium. The filter feedbox assembly spreads the slurry uniformly across the entire width of the moving filter cloth. The slurry is dewatered by both gravity and vacuum as it travels on the filter media above the drainage/transport belt. The filtrate is collected in the vacuum pan assembly after being drawn from the slurry through the filter cloth and drainage belt. The washbox sprays the moving cake with washwater to rinse dissolved solids from the cake, and this liquid also is drained from the cake. A series of rollers separates the filter media from the drainage belt and breaks up the filter cake. The cake is discharged as the filter media travels around a small roller. The abrupt change in direction breaks the cake loose so that it falls away from the filter media. The filter media and drainage belt are then washed, tensioned, and guided in preparation for the next cycle. The filtrate removed from the filter cake is a mixture of slurry liquor, air, and suspended solids. The liquor and suspended solids are separated from the air by the vacuum receiver. The vacuum pump blows the air outdoors. The filtrate pump takes suction at the bottom of the vacuum receiver and delivers the filtrate slurry to a holding tank or the primary dewatering device (*Fig. 5-46*).

Horizontal vacuum belt filters can produce filter cakes with higher solids content than rotary drum filters—namely, 85 to 92% solids compared to 55 to 85% for drum filters. Typically, belt filters are favored over vertical bowl centrifuges, because they can operate continuously and require less capital cost. Because of these qualities, belt filters are the preferred secondary dewatering device for forced oxidation systems, especially if commercial-grade gypsum is required (typically, 90% solids minimum).

VERTICAL BOWL CENTRIFUGE. Vertical bowl centrifuges use centrifugal forces to remove the liquor from the cake. Simultaneously, the chlorides and other soluble salts are washed from the cake. Centrifuges are the best secondary dewatering device for forced oxidation systems producing wallboard-quality gypsum with a solids concentration of greater than 92%. Vertical bowl centrifuges operate in a batch-wise manner and, thus, need a centrifuge feed tank. A centrifuge feed tank can use the guidelines for a filter feed tank given in the discussion of the rotary drum natural oxidation.

Dry Scrubbing

The idea of using a spray dryer as a gas cleaning device dates back to at least 1958, when a Czech patent was issued covering use of a spray dryer and a dust collector in series. Dry scrubbing, or dry FGD, was pioneered in the United States as an enhancement to dry injection of nahcolite or trona ahead of a fabric filter. The intent was to develop a simple process with a dry product using one single-unit operation. The initial work was focusing on using soda ash solutions as the absorbent, but it was soon discovered that lime slurry produced very good results as well. Today, lime is exclusively used for power applications.

The most important chemical reaction in lime based dry FGD is the formation of calcium sulfite hemi hydrate [$CaSO_3 \cdot ½H_2O(s)$]. Its solubility is very low, thus being a chemical driver for the dry FGD process. As seen from *Table 5-14* below, calcium sulfite is much less soluble than gypsum.

In the dry FGD processes, lime [CaO] is first converted to hydrated lime [$Ca(OH)_2$] before the reagent is contacted with the flue gas. The hydrated lime may be injected into the flue gas either as slurry or as dry or moistened powder.

A prerequisite for the lime to react with SO_2 is that the humidity of the flue gas is high enough so that the particle surface picks up about one monolayer of water molecules. This has been shown to happen at a water concentration of the flue gas corresponding to a relative humidity of 40 to 50%.

The reaction is then believed to proceed predominantly according to

$$SO_2 + Ca(OH)_2(s) \rightarrow CaSO_3 \cdot ½H_2O(s) + ½H_2O$$

Equation 5-49

TABLE 5-14 | SOLUBILITY PRODUCTS OF CALCIUM SULFITE AND CALCIUM SULFATE

Compound	Formula	Solubility product (K_{sp}, 25°C [77°F])
Calcium sulfite	$CaSO_3 \cdot \frac{1}{2}H_2O$	6.8×10^{-8}
Calcium sulfate	$CaSO_4 \cdot 2H_2O$ (gypsum)	3.14×10^{-5}

A small portion of the sulfite, however, is further oxidized to calcium sulfate (gypsum):

$$CaSO_3 \cdot \frac{1}{2}H_2O(s) + O_2 + 1\frac{1}{2}H_2O \rightarrow CaSO_4 \cdot 2H_2O(s)$$

Equation 5-50

Other acid species react with lime in a dry FGD system. Hydrogen chloride (HCl) may form either calcium hydroxy chloride (CaOHCl) or $CaCl_2 \cdot 2H_2O$ according to

$$HCl(g) + Ca(OH)_2 \rightarrow CaOHCl(s) + H_2O$$

Equation 5-51

$$HCl(g) + CaOHCl + H_2O \rightarrow CaCl_2 \cdot 2H_2O(s)$$

Equation 5-52

The formation of calcium chloride is important for the process parameters. Because of its hygroscopic nature, it will influence the equilibrium water pressure over the absorbent. Dust handling properties and corrosion potential may be affected as well.

Furthermore, HF and sulfuric acid (H_2SO_4) react with lime:

$$Ca(OH)_2 + 2HF \rightarrow CaF_2 + 2H_2O$$

Equation 5-53

$$Ca(OH)_2 + H_2SO_4 \rightarrow CaSO_4 \cdot 2H_2O$$

Equation 5-54

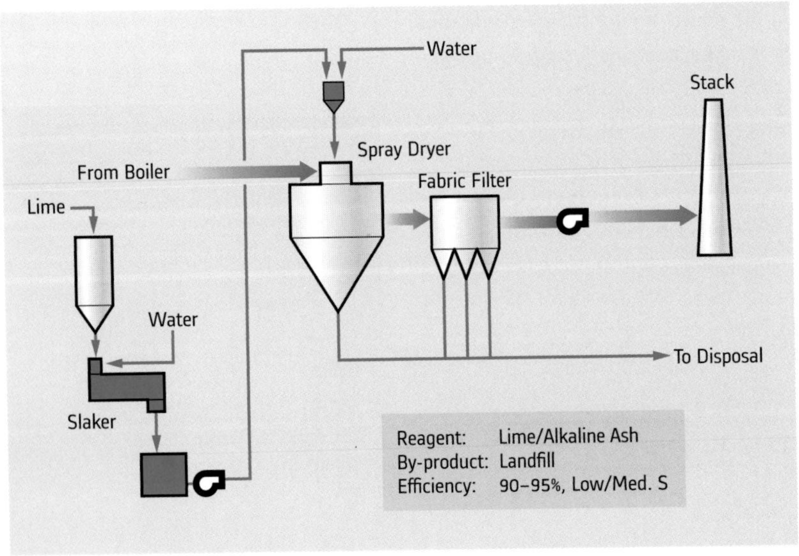

PROCESS DESIGN. Since its introduction in the late 1970s, the dry FGD process has been designed in a few different ways. The process versions can be differentiated with respect to method of adding reagent and reagent recycle rate. The simplest process version is termed the *single-pass system* (*Fig.* 5-47). In this case, the slurry of lime is injected into a reactor vessel, arranged as a spray dryer. The dryer commonly is termed an SDA. The slurry is atomized either by rotary atomizers or by dual-fluid nozzles driven by compressed air. The heat in the flue gas dries the slurry, and the dried particles plus fly ash are removed in a dust collector downstream of the SDA.

Figure 5-47 | Dry flue gas desulfurization system

Recycling of the dry product from the dust collector can be employed. This increases the utilization of the lime, because more active alkali is fed to the SDA. Moreover, the drying rate is increased, because the water required to cool the flue gas is spread out over a larger surface area than in the case of a single-pass system. The slurry feed to the atomizing device, however, must still be pumpable, which limits the amount of recycle that can be handled. This process version is thus defined as a *low-recycle system*.

A third version is defined as the *high-recycle system*. In this case, the feed of lime and recycle are dry. Water is added separately, either in a mixer immediately before the injection into the reactor vessel or directly into the reactor by pressure nozzles. Because the recycle rate is very high, the surface area available for the cooling water is much increased, yielding a very short gas residence time in the reactor. This means that the reactor vessel can be built significantly smaller than the SDA.

The dry solids content of slurry for a single-pass system typically varies between 2 and 15%. For a recycle system, the dry solids content is kept between 35 and 55%. The exact value is determined by the fly ash and SO_2 contents of the flue gas, its temperature, and the required removal rate of SO_2.

Two types of reactor vessel designs exist. The addition of water can take place inside or outside the reactor vessel. If injected inside the vessel, pressure nozzles spraying into a bed of recycle solids introduce water. This often is termed a CFB scrubber. The reactor residence time is reduced to about one-third of that for an SDA.

The final version, in which the drying time is an order of magnitude less than that of an SDA, is termed the FDA. This is enabled by adding water to the recycle in a dust mixer immediately before the injection into the reactor vessel. *Table 5-15* summarizes the dry FGD process designs.

SPRAY DRYER ABSORBER. When using an SDA the lime is hydrated according to

$$CaO + H_2O \rightarrow Ca(OH)_2 + \text{heat}$$

Equation 5-55

The hydration reaction is highly exothermic and takes place in the liquid phase. This process is commonly referred to as "slaking the lime." The temperature in the slaking reactor is controlled by the feed ratio between CaO and water.

The reactor usually is one of three types: a paste mixer or pug mill, a detention unit, or a ball mill. The mill may be arranged in a vertical or a horizontal position. The ball mill provides for slaking while simultaneously reducing the size of the impurities that always are present in the pebble lime. Both pug mill and detention slakers use a screen or settling unit to remove grit or rock-like impurities from the milk of lime. Pug mill slakers, which allow the highest ratios of pebble lime to water, can most reliably achieve the high slaking temperatures so important for the spray dryer scrubbing process.

TABLE 5-15 | DRY FLUE GAS DESULFURIZATION PROCESS DESIGNS

Process Version	Reagent Added As	Recycle Ratio	Reactor/Dryer	Reactor retention time (s)
Single pass	Lime slurry	—	Spray dryer absorber	10–15
Low recycle	Lime slurry	2–10	Spray dryer absorber	10–15
High recycle	Dry hydrated lime	50–100	Flash dryer absorber Circulating fluidized bed	0.5–5

The reagent slurry is prepared by mixing the milk of lime with additional process water as required to achieve a suitable degree of dryness in the solid effluent leaving the spray dryer. Reactant solids from the particulate collecting device also may be mixed into the reagent slurry. The practice of employing recycled solids in the reagent slurry tends to reduce the amount of fresh lime required for a given sulfur dioxide removal. Most often, the recycled solids are first premixed in a separate slurry tank and then pumped to the reagent preparation tank. The reagent preparation tank may be located at ground level, with pumps for supplying the slurry to the atomizers, or at a high elevation above the atomizers to facilitate gravity feed. A flow schematic is shown in *Figure 5-48*.

A very important unit operation in the spray dryer scrubbing system is atomization. Either air-assisted nozzles or rotary atomizers commonly are used. Rotary atomizers basically couple a high speed rotating atomizer wheel to a drive device. To protect the load-bearing components of the drive device, the coupling usually is designed to absorb vibrations induced by imbalanced operation. Generally, the drive device is a two- or four-pole, three-phase electric motor with a speed-increasing gearbox, although in some systems, a high-speed electric drive is used without a gearbox. The slurry leaves the atomizer through a number of nozzles at the periphery of the wheel. Because of the very high shear forces, the slurry is torn apart into very fine droplets. The nozzles often are manufactured of silicon carbide in order to protect the metallic wheel from wear and abrasion.

Air-assisted nozzles often are employing internal mixing of atomizing air and slurry. Like rotary atomizer nozzles, mouthpieces of the nozzles are, as a rule, manufactured of highly wear-resistant ceramics.

Almost as important as the quality of atomization is the mechanism for contacting the atomized slurry and flue gas in the SDA. Commercial systems can have as many as three rotary atomizers and gas inlets in one SDA. Using multiple-spray machines reduces the individual power requirements for each machine without appreciably affecting SDA performance.

When employing air-assisted nozzles in an SDA, the number of gas inlets often is greater than that for a rotary atomizer. The capacity of each nozzle is limited, but this capacity often is increased by arranging several mouthpieces in one nozzle assembly.

FDA AND FLUID BED SCRUBBER. As pointed out above, additional dry FGD process versions rely on massive recycling of solids with the aim of reducing equipment size and enhancing performance. In the CFB scrubber, the gas enters

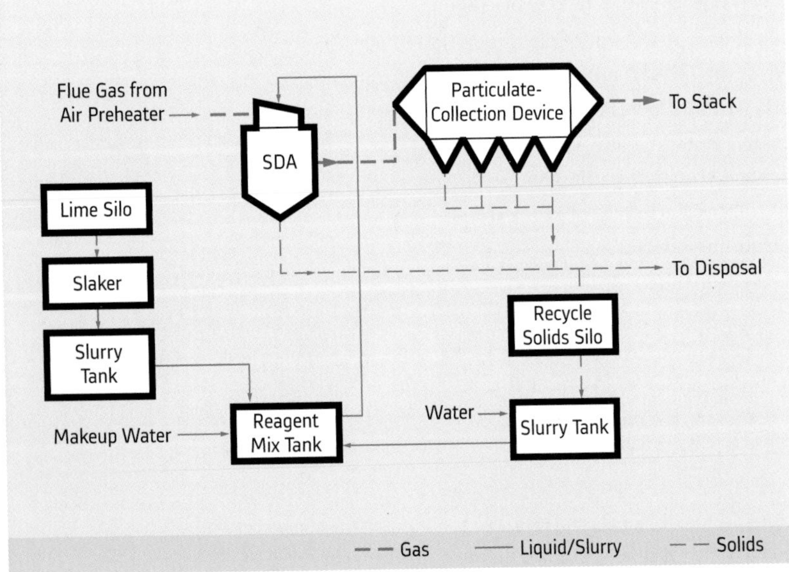

Figure 5-48 | Flow schematic of spray dryer scrubbing system (SDA, spray dryer absorber)

into a reactor vessel via one or several venturi-shaped inlet nozzles. Gas flow is vertically upward into a vessel, where the recycled dust from the end collector is introduced. Water is sprayed into the cloud of dust either at the level of the inlets or immediately above. High-pressure, spillback nozzles generally are used for this application. The dust-laden gas then passes upward through the reactor as it is being dried. The gas finally is discharged into the end collector. Air slides are used for the transport of recycle from the dust collector back to the reactor.

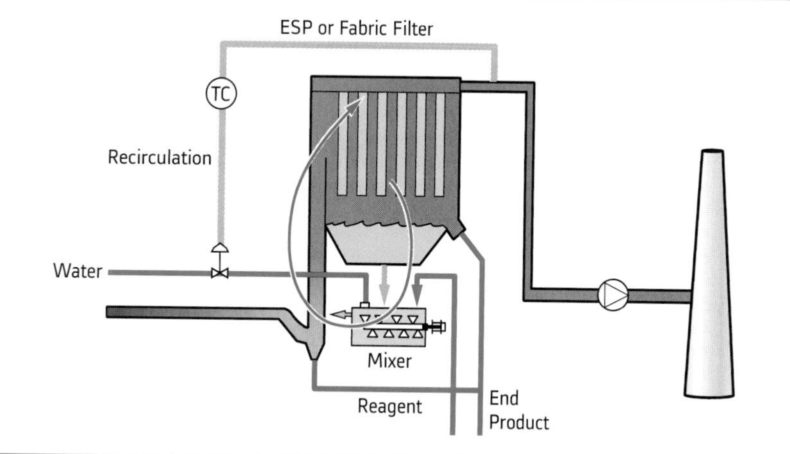

Figure 5-49 | The flash dryer absorber (ESP, electrostatic precipitator; TC, temperature control)

For lime hydration, a commercial dry lime hydrator is used. In this device, the dry lime is first contacted with water while being mixed in a pug mill. Then, additional reaction time is needed to allow the hydration reaction to proceed. During this process, coarse CaO is transformed into fine, powdery $Ca(OH)_2$. This product is stored in a separate silo. From there, it is transported to the recycle stream of solids.

In the FDA, the recycle is mixed with water just before being introduced into the reactor vessel. The mixing is done in a proprietary dust mixer that is able to handle large tonnages. The water is supplied via ordinary water nozzles. The dust recycle rate is controlled by means of rotary feeders. The process is schematically shown in *Figure 5-49.*

For the FDA, a lime hydration unit, integrated with the mixer, has been developed. Water needed for the hydration reaction plus CaO are supplied to a first stage. From there, the mix of lime and water overflows into a second stage, where the final conversion to $Ca(OH)_2$ takes place. Finally, the reacted lime overflows into the mixer. From there, recycle with freshly hydrated lime flows into the reactor via a mixing and dispersion device. Thus, no additional silo for $Ca(OH)_2$ is needed. *Figure 5-50* details the process in a lime hydration unit.

For both process versions, a continuous flow of recycle from the dust collector to the reactor is important. The pressure drop over the reactor is used as an indicator of the actual solids recycle rate. All of the dry FGD processes are controlled by keeping the outlet temperature constant, possibly after adjustments for the actual chloride and water contents in the flue gas. The addition of lime is controlled either by a control loop, adding more lime as required to keep a certain SO_2 emission rate, or in more advanced versions by feed forward controls, as well as accounting for the impact of chlorides in the flue gas.

In case the fly ash entering an FDA is alkaline, some of this alkalinity will absorb SO_2 from the flue gas. This phenomenon has been used at some plants where an FDA is installed after a CFB boiler (see Chapter 3). Limestone is added to the boiler to absorb SO_2 at high temperature. As

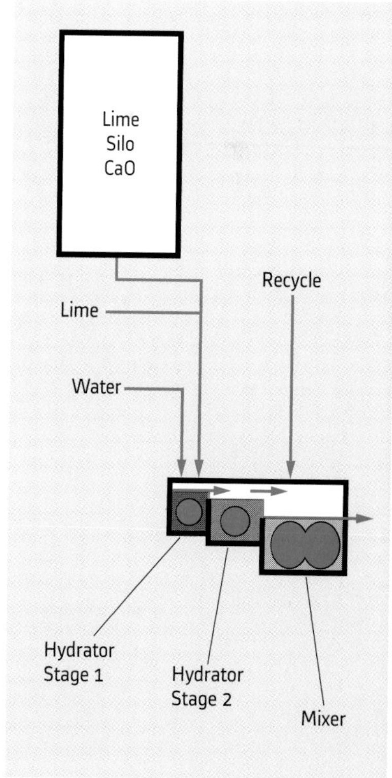

Figure 5-50 | A lime hydration unit

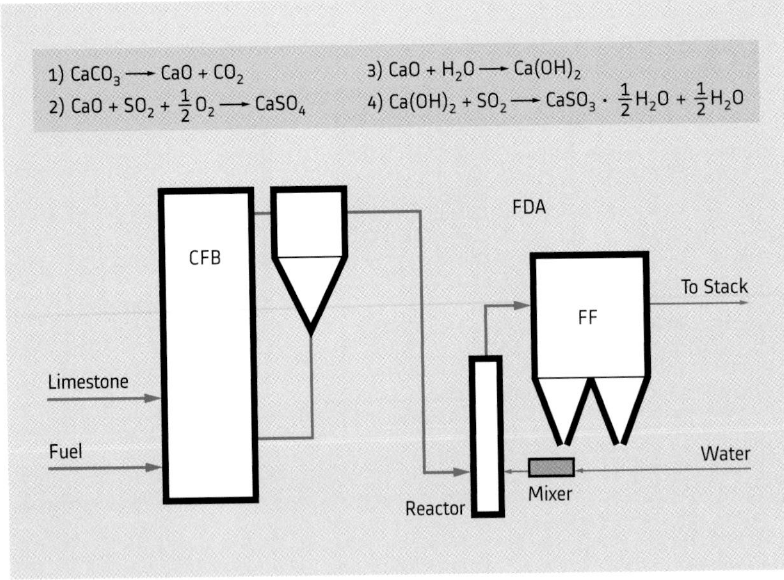

Figure 5-51 | Combination of a circulating fluidized bed (CFB) boiler and a flash dryer absorber (FDA) (FF, fabric filter)

limestone is added, however, some of it will be converted to CaO. The CaO entering the FDA is hydrated when adding water to the ash. The activated ash thus absorbs SO_2 in the FDA. The limestone added to the boiler is used both for primary desulfurization in the CFB boiler at high temperature and for polishing the emission of SO_2 in the downstream FDA. The FDA is particularly well suited to treat ashes with low alkalinity contents, which require that large tonnages of ashes be treated.

The combination of a CFB boiler and FDA is shown in *Figure 5-51*.

SDA DESIGN. The heart of the spray dry-scrubber process is the SDA. Vessels have been built with single inlets and single rotary atomizers as well as with three inlets and atomizers; from a process standpoint, the three-inlet units perform identically to the single-inlet designs.

The amount of flue gas to be processed dictates the choice of one or three inlets. Single-inlet designs generally are limited to no more than 300,000 ft^3/min (142 m^3/s) at the inlet conditions, whereas a three-inlet vessel can handle threefold as much flue gas. Another important factor is redundancy, even though the single-inlet designs have ready, spare machines that can be installed in 30 minutes or less after an unplanned spray-machine shutdown. When online redundancy is desired, the three machines usually are designed for handling one-half the rated load, thereby allowing one machine and inlet to be isolated if necessary. Three-inlet vessels can even be designed to operate with only one machine and inlet in service, amplifying the turndown capability.

The reasoning for SDAs with dual-fluid nozzles is somewhat different, because larger sizes require several gas inlets and nozzle assemblies. One nozzle generally can be taken out of service for maintenance without significantly affecting plant operation.

Inside the SDA, the slurry is introduced as a very finely divided spray, often with a mass median diameter below 35 microns and a largest droplet well below 150 microns. Each droplet, in effect, becomes a miniature reactor. Submicron particles of lime dissolve according to the reaction

$$Ca(OH)_2 \leftrightarrow Ca^{2+} + 2OH^-$$

Equation 5-56

thereby making OH^-, or hydroxyl ions, available in the liquid phase for neutralization of hydrogen ions (H^+). Hydrogen ions are produced as the sulfur dioxide molecules diffuse across the droplet surface, dissolve in the liquid, and dissociate according to the reaction

$$SO_2(g) + H_2O \leftrightarrow SO_2(l) + H_2O \leftrightarrow HSO_3^- + H^+ \leftrightarrow SO_3^{2-} + 2H^+$$

Equation 5-57

The dissolution of sulfur dioxide tends to lower the pH (or raise the hydrogen ion concentration) in the liquid phase, whereas the dissolution of lime tends to raise the pH. Slaked lime has an equilibrium pH of approximately 12.0; sulfur dioxide at 1,000 ppm by volume in the gas phase in equilibrium with pure water will lower the pH to approximately 2.5. Equations 5-56 and 5-57 characterize the acid-base neutralization that occurs in each droplet as it passes through the SDA.

Although it is clear how the OH^- ions in Equation 5-56 are removed through neutralization, it is not immediately apparent what happens to the Ca^{2+}. The calcium ions also must be purged from the solution in order to allow more lime to dissolve. The most important reaction is the precipitation of calcium and sulfite ions to form calcium sulfite crystals:

$$Ca^{2+} + SO_3^{2-} + \tfrac{1}{2}H_2O \rightarrow CaSO_3 \cdot \tfrac{1}{2}H_2O(s)$$

Equation 5-58

It has been observed, as expected, that some of the sulfite is oxidized to sulfate. The latter precipitates with the calcium ions to form gypsum ($CaSO_4 \cdot 2H_2O$) crystals.

The presence of chloride ions in the droplet affects not only the ionic activity of calcium but also the vapor pressure of water and of the dried reaction products. This means that chlorides affect both the drying time and the removal rate of SO_2.

MASS AND HEAT TRANSFER. The gas-phase heat transfer to the surface of the droplet and the mass transfer of water molecules away from the surface govern the rate of water evaporation. The rate of heat transfer is modeled, in the classical sense, by

$$dQ/dt = hA(T - T_s)$$

Equation 5-59

where

T = the gas-phase bulk temperature
T_s = the adiabatic saturation temperature of the gas/liquid system, generally assumed to be the temperature at the surface of the droplet
h = the heat-transfer coefficient
Q = quantity of heat transferred

The rate of water mass transfer is modeled by

$$dM/dt = D_{water}a(H_s - H)$$

Equation 5-60

where

$D_{water}a$ = the diffusivity of water in the gas phase
H = the absolute humidity of the gas
H_S = the saturation humidity of the gas/liquid system

For a pure water/air system, the heat and mass transfer driving forces are related by

$$H_S - H = Q_h/\lambda(T - T_S)$$

Equation 5-61

where

Q_h = the humid heat of moist air
λ = the latent heat of vaporization of water

This well-known relationship, upon which psychrometric charts are based, has prompted some practical designers to simplify or combine the heat and mass transfer Equations 5-60 and 5-61 to the form

$$dM/dt = KA(T - T_S)$$

Equation 5-62

where K is a pseudo or combined heat and mass transfer coefficient.

Studies have been made using computational fluid dynamics in which mass and heat transfer relations have been combined to model both drying and absorption. These studies reveal that initial conditions for the introduction of lime slurry and gas into an SDA are very important to the overall performance. The droplets introduced into an SDA must be thoroughly mixed with the flue gas. The inlet gas disperser must be designed to minimize "sneakage" in order to prevent gas from passing untreated, or essentially untreated, because of poor gas liquid contact. At the same time, no wet droplets are allowed to hit the walls of the reactor vessel.

The same principles are valid for a high-recirculation system. In a high-recirculation system, however, the drying time is greatly reduced, because the water is spread out over a very large surface area. The thin layer of water formed on the recycled dust dries very quickly. Requirements for efficient mixing remain. Sneakage is detrimental to performance for all dry FGD systems.

Process Effects in Dry FGD Systems

Various process parameters affect the efficiency and economics of the spray dryer scrubbing process. These include the type and quality of the additive used for the reactant, the degree of "dryness" achieved by the spray dryer, the amount of heat available for drying, the relative amount of solids product recycled to the atomizer, and a host of lesser process variables. The impact of these parameters is so important that it is nearly impossible to estimate the process performance and economics without a sophisticated model. Designers thus rely heavily on performance models derived from pilot-plant data. This section describes the major factors impacting the process performance.

ADDITIVE TYPE AND QUALITY. Lime is available in a variety of qualities, which are ranked according to the limestone source and/or grain size. The CaO may be purchased as "pebble lime" or as a ground, powdery matter. Dry hydrated lime likewise is available at a premium price. For dry FGD power

applications, it generally is advantageous to use CaO and hydrated lime at site. A further advantage of CaO is its higher reactivity. Pilot testing indicates that freshly slaked lime exhibits superior reactivity compared with powdered hydrate mixed in water.

Ideally, the lime should be a light-burned, high-reactivity lime. This ensures a high surface area of the hydrated lime when slaked and a high reactivity toward SO_2. Limes of lesser quality can be used, but additional lime may be needed for a given performance. This may require adjustments in slaking time and temperature.

STOICHIOMETRIC RATIO. Additive SR is an important parameter affecting the removal of SO_2. Its importance arises not because of the magnitude of its effect on process performance, which is substantial, but rather because of its effect on process economics. In general, control systems of dry FGD systems automatically adjust the additive feed rate (i.e., SR) to achieve a targeted level of SO_2 removal. The same dry FGD system requires little, if any, additional equipment to switch from low or high removal rates if boundary conditions permit.

APPROACH TO SATURATION. The closer that the dry FGD system operates to the saturation temperature at the outlet, the longer that "wet conditions" prevail in the system. The behavior of the gas is best understood by examining a conventional psychrometric chart. The flue gas enters the SDA at temperature T_{in} and humidity H_{in}. As the water from the evaporating droplets enters the gas phase, the gas temperature decreases and the humidity increases, following the adiabatic operating line. The gas leaves the SDA at temperature T_{out} and humidity H_{out}, with practically all of the water from the droplets evaporated. The maximum humidity that the gas could attain is H_S and the minimum temperature T_S (i.e., the saturation values). In practice, however, conventional SDAs cannot operate at saturation, because the droplets will not all be sufficiently dry. In fact, the drying efficiency is directly related to how closely an SDA can approach saturation at the outlet. More important, the SO_2 removal efficiency and the additive utilization are inversely related to how close the SDA can be operated to saturation conditions. This is also valid for CFB scrubbers and FDAs.

The impact of approach to saturation is dramatic. *Figure* 5-52 shows that at a lime SR of 1.4 moles of $Ca(OH)_2$ per 1 mole of SO_2 entering the SDA, the SO_2 removal will improve from an efficiency of 62% to an efficiency of 77% in the SDA simply by adding sufficient additional water in the slurry to reduce the outlet approach to saturation (ΔT_S) from 50 to 25°F (28 to 14°C). Note that the SR can be decreased from 1.4 to 1.0 at 65% SO_2 removal in the SDA.

Control of the approach to saturation temperature is, thus, as important as the lime feed (i.e., the SR). The actual approach to saturation temperature for operation is selected with respect to dust-handling characteristics as well as the need to operate under conditions that are corrosion free. Both factors are strong functions of the chloride content of the recycle ash.

SPRAY DOWN TEMPERATURE. The spray down temperature is the difference

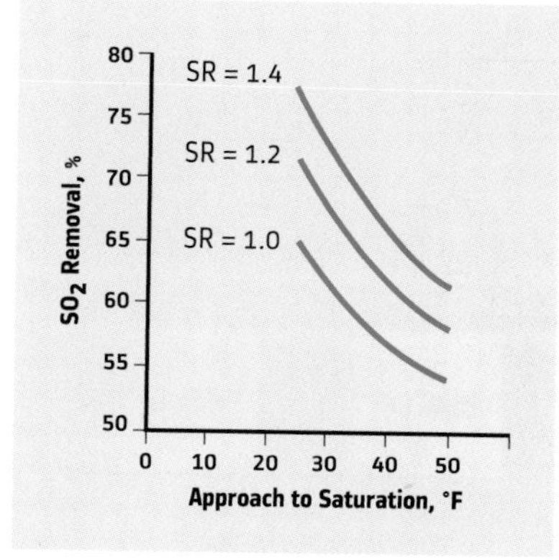

Figure 5-52 | Approach to saturation temperature (SR, stoichiometric ratio)

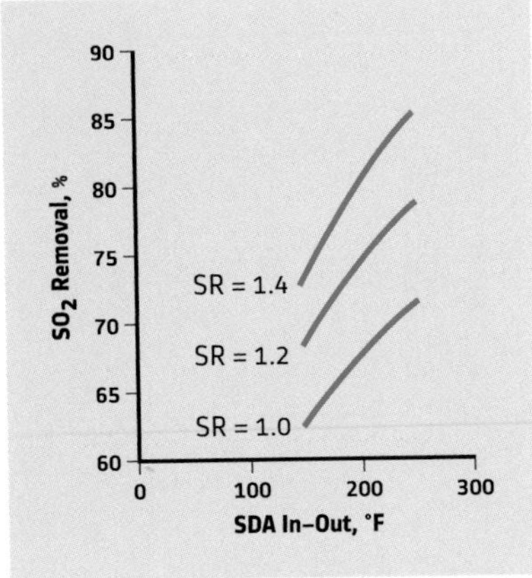

Figure 5-53 | Effect of spray down temperature (SDA, spray dryer absorber; SR, stoichiometric ratio)

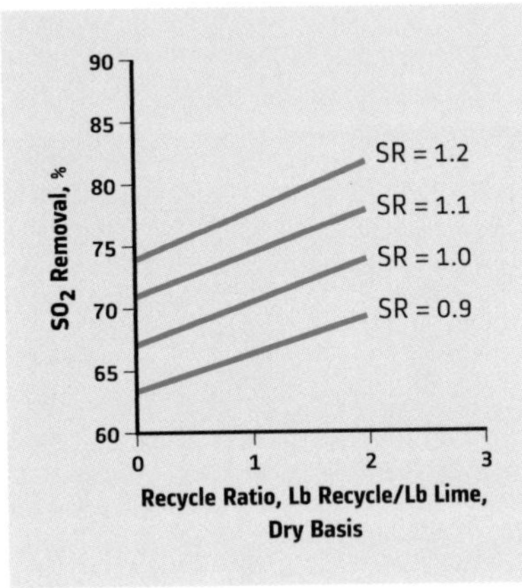

Figure 5-54 | Effect of recycling of collected solids (SR, stoichiometric ratio)

between the SDA inlet and outlet temperatures. It is directly related to the amount of water supplied to the atomizing system. It also is a key indicator of how much evaporative heat is available in the flue gas. Normally, the spray down temperature is not a controlled variable unless an air heater flue gas bypass is available for this purpose. Most often, spray down temperature is set by the requirements for maximizing boiler efficiency. A lower SDA inlet temperature typically is the result of a higher boiler efficiency. This also results in a lower spray down temperature.

Spray down temperature has a significant and direct effect on the efficiency of SO_2 removal. As shown in *Figure 5-53*, there are conditions in which an increase of 50°F (28°C) in spray down temperature can mean a decrease in SR from 1.4 to 1.2 at 75% SO_2 removal in the SDA if all other significant variables are held constant.

RECYCLE OF SOLIDS. The practice of mixing some of the fabric filter or ESP solids product with the fresh lime slurry has been shown to be beneficial for lime utilization. Several explanations for this are possible:

- Some of the unreacted lime in the recycled solids is available as it passes through the SDA again.
- The fly ash usually has some alkaline properties, which are made more effective when the fly ash is dissolved in the slurry.
- The silica in the fly ash reacts with the calcium in the lime to form a very reactive calcium silicate compound.
- The calcium sulfite in the reslurried solids product serves effectively as seed crystals in the droplets, which aid in the precipitation of fresh calcium sulfite (Equation 5-58).

All of these mechanisms probably play some part in the observed performance improvement seen with the use of recycle. The performance effect from using a ratio of up to 2 pounds (kg) of recycle solids for each 1 pound of fresh $Ca(OH)_2$ solids in the atomizer feed is shown in *Figure 5-54*. For a 2.5% sulfur coal, the SR decreases from 1.2 to 1.0% at 74% SO_2 removal in the SDA.

In the high-recycle systems (CFB scrubber, FDA), the stochiometric value that the reactor sees is significantly increased. A corresponding linear increase in performance is not realized. For the SDA, a limitation is set by the maximum solids content of the recycle slurry that is still pumpable. For high-recycle systems, however, this limit does not exist, and high recycle rates also can be realized for high-sulfur fuels.

ATOMIZATION QUALITY OF THE SDA. The quality of atomization affects SDA performance in two ways. The first and most significant is the impact on drying and dryer efficiency—that is, the minimum ΔT_S that can be achieved. The second is the impact on gas side mass transfer of SO_2 and water. Depending on the shape of the entrained spray cloud and the geometry of the SDA vessel, along with other operating parameters, an SDA will have a range of deposit-free operation. Computational fluid dynamics is used to investigate safe operating conditions for a given geometry of the dry FGD reactor (*Fig.* 5-55). For an SDA, the minimum achievable operating T_S depends on the trajectories of each droplet and on the drying process along this trajectory. Using

these studies, safe operating ranges can be established.

INLET SO_2 CONCENTRATION. Inlet SO_2 concentration has a surprisingly weak effect on overall system performance. Individual pilot test programs often produce conflicting data, usually because the range of testing is necessarily narrow for any single program. Analyzing data from a range of test programs, however, does show some trends. *Figure* 5-56 is a plot of additive utilization from several independent test programs with other effects factored out. This plot reveals a slight trend of increasing SO_2 removal efficiency in the SDA and in the combined SDA and fabric filter as the inlet concentration increases. This is not a large effect, considering that inlet SO_2 concentration varies by a factor of five.

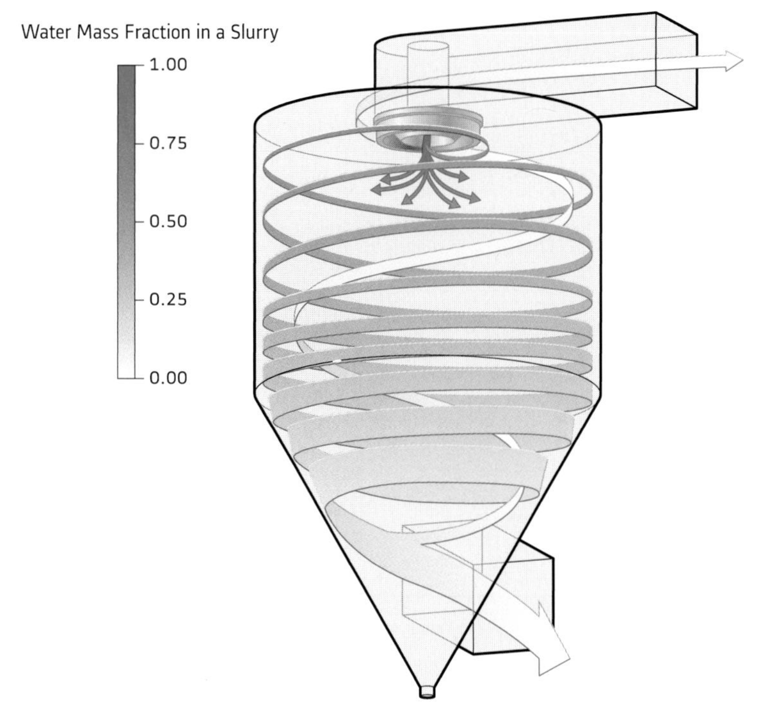

Figure 5-55 | Particle tracks determined by computation fluid dynamics

CHLORIDES. The presence of chloride ions in the spray slurry has a dramatic impact on SDA performance. Coals always contain some traces of chlorides. Typical western U.S. coals have a chloride content of 100 to 200 ppm, whereas some eastern U.S. coals are much richer in chlorides (700–800 ppm).

The effect of the chlorides on the performance of a dry FGD system is a function of chloride and sulfur contents as well as the amount of fly ash that enters the system. Thus, knowledge about the chloride content of the fuel is quite important for predicting performance and operating variables for dry FGD. Very high levels of chlorides, as seen at various waste incineration plants, require major adjustments to the approach to saturation temperature. For municipal solid waste, a common HCl concentration in the flue gas is 300 to 800 ppm by volume, although this figure may rise to more than 10,000 ppm for some hazardous waste applications. Often, both SO_2 and HCl are present together, with removal requirements established for both species. In other instances, chlorides are introduced through the use of high-chloride make-up water and are concentrated in the feed slurry when recycle of solids is employed.

Chlorides in the feed slurry impact operation in two important ways:

1. By changing the apparent saturation temperature of the gas leaving the system
2. By increasing the relative solubility of calcium ions in the slurry liquid or moistened feed

The dry FGD systems operating with chlorides present respond to a

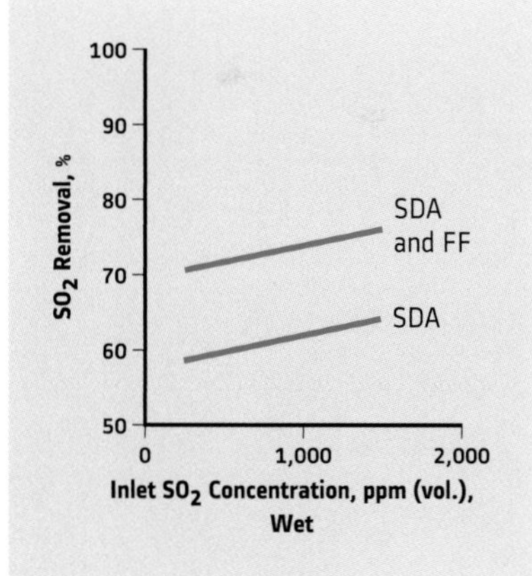

Figure 5-56 | Effect of inlet SO_2 concentrations (FF, fabric filter; SDA, spray dryer absorber)

different saturation line compared with systems containing only relatively insoluble salts. The deviation in saturation temperature from the pure water system can be substantial, because both calcium and chlorides are present. An unfortunate corollary to this situation is that the apparent saturation temperature, T_S, depends on the concentration of chloride ions in the recycled solids. Hence, the operating outlet temperature needed to ensure an appropriate approach to saturation temperature (and a corresponding SO_2 removal efficiency) varies with the concentration of chlorides. In turn, this concentration varies with the amount of HCl in the gas entering the dry FGD system relative to other acid gas components as well as with the use of recycle solids to improve efficiency.

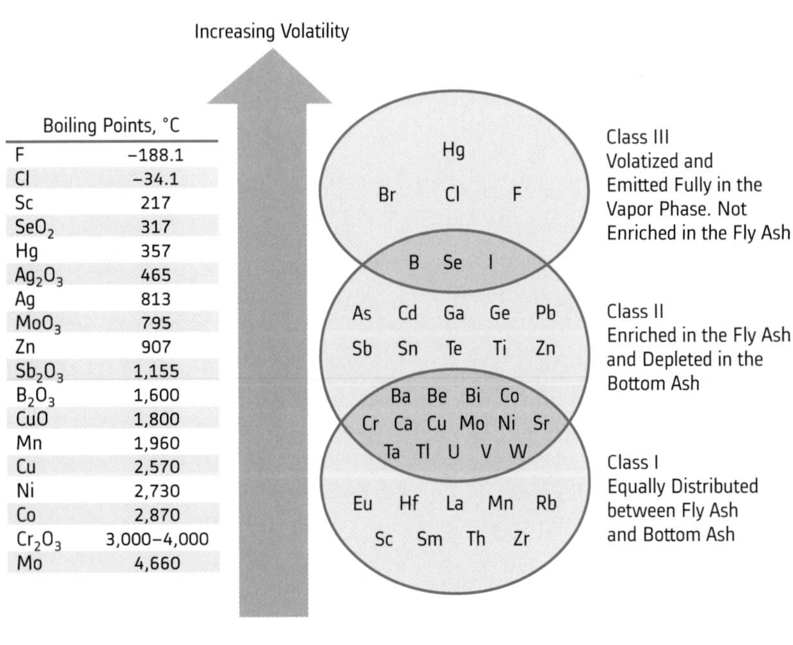

Boiling Points, °C	
F	−188.1
Cl	−34.1
Sc	217
SeO_2	317
Hg	357
Ag_2O_3	465
Ag	813
MoO_3	795
Zn	907
Sb_2O_3	1,155
B_2O_3	1,600
CuO	1,800
Mn	1,960
Cu	2,570
Ni	2,730
Co	2,870
Cr_2O_3	3,000–4,000
Mo	4,660

Figure 5-57 | Classification of trace elements (reprinted with permission from Frandsen[82])

REMOVAL OF MERCURY AND HEAVY METALS. Trace elements normally are classified with respect to their volatility during combustion. Meij[81] and others' many studies have shown that the trace elements can be categorized into three classes, as shown in *Figure 5-57*:

- **Class I** elements do not volatilize during combustion or gasification and distribute more or less equally between bottom ash and fly ash.
- **Class II** elements are vaporized and found mainly in the fly ash after condensation on particulates. A significant part of these fine particles are in the submicron-size class, where dust control systems are less effective.
- **Class III** elements are vaporized and condense only partly within the system.

The lime added to a dry FGD system works as a filter aid in the fabric filter and assists in removing very fine particulate matter. Furthermore, cooling of the flue gas makes some species that usually are present as vapor condense in the system. Hence, it is potentially possible to catch the particles belonging to all three classes in the fabric filter of a dry FGD system.

For some chloride-rich coals, the efficiency of mercury removal is very good in conventional dry FGD systems. For low-halogen coals (Cl < 100 ppm) with a very high fraction of Hg^0, however, the collection efficiency of the dry FGD system is poor. In these cases, the removal of mercury is then facilitated by the use of oxidizing additives and powdered activated carbon (PAC). The PAC also is regularly used as supplementary additive to remove dioxins and furans at dry FGD systems after waste incinerators.

SULFUR TRIOXIDE (SO_3). The same mechanisms as described above make dry FGD systems good collectors for sulfur trioxide (SO_3), or sulfuric acid mist. The SO_3 may be present as a gas or in the form of an aerosol. Tests using the controlled condensation procedure show that outlet emissions of SO_3 are close to the minimum detection limit. This is explained by the combination of good filtration and excess alkali for neutralization.

Process Effects in the Particulate Collector

The spray dryer process employs a particulate collecting device after the reactor to collect the dried reaction products and fly ash. Collection of SO_2 (and other acid species) as well as the drying process continue in the particulate collector. Two types of particulate collectors are applied as end collectors for dry FGD systems: the fabric filter, and the ESP.

FABRIC FILTER. The fabric filter can be expected to achieve, on average, from 10 to 30% removal of SO_2 (based on system inlet concentration) during normal operation, with wide variations depending on the operating history immediately before a particular measurement. The effect of the fabric filter is expected to be greater for dilute SO_2 gases, because the inventory of alkaline absorbent on the bags of the fabric filter remains essentially the same irrespective of SO_2 loading.

The longer the time between cleanings of fabric filter compartments, the greater the SO_2 removal will be. This is because more reactive cake is available for contact with the flue gas. A differential pressure signal initiates the cleaning cycle for most fabric filter installations. The value of this signal affects the average length of time between compartment cleanings at a specific plant load. The fabric filter is the preferred end collector for a dry FGD system, because it makes a significant contribution to the overall SO_2 removal.

ELECTROSTATIC PRECIPITATOR. The high humidity in an ESP downstream any type of dry FGD reactor makes dust collection an easy task, because dust resistivity is much reduced as a result of the high moisture content in the flue gas and the reduced temperature. The flue gas flow likewise is reduced as the flue gas is cooled, which increases the residence time for the dust in the precipitator. Precipitators also remove SO_2, although not as well as fabric filters. Typically, only 5 to 10% of the total SO_2 is absorbed.

Electrostatic precipitators have been applied for all types of dry FGD systems, but to a much lesser extent than fabric filters have been. With high-chloride coals, corrosion can occur if the precipitator is operated at too low an approach to saturation temperature. Raising the outlet temperature can minimize corrosion; however, performance and lime consumption are influenced negatively. At times, collection plates of an ESP have been manufactured of alloy steel to withstand chloride-rich environments.

Mercury can exist in the flue gas from coal-fired units at parts per billion levels in three different forms: elemental, oxidized, or particulate.

ECONOMIC CONSIDERATIONS

The economics of wet versus dry scrubbing involve a great many factors. The major ones include:

- Sulfur level in the fuel
- Waste disposal options
- Plant lifetime
- Cost of reagent
- Cost of labor

A dry FGD system has a lower investment cost than a conventional wet FGD system, but the cost for the reagent is relatively high. This means that a dry FGD is particularly well suited for low-sulfur applications. Smaller sizes, limited operating hours per year, and short remaining lifetime works in the same direction.

High-recirculation systems have no technical limitations for high-sulfur fuels. Thus, such systems are flexible and can cope with high- and low-sulfur fuels. This is an advantage for plants that are supplied with coals from varying sources, which often creates good potential for retrofitting older boilers with dry FGD systems.

The dry FGD system sometimes is limited in application because of a lack of waste disposal options for the end product. Unlike gypsum-producing wet FGD systems, the end product from dry FGD is not a well-defined product, which means that its reuse is somewhat limited. Potential uses for the dry FGD end product include concrete, lightweight aggregate, and fertilizer. In the fertilizer application, the product must be free from fly ash; this can be accomplished by installing a pre-collector for fly ash upstream of the dry FGD. The majority of plants, however, have used the end product for landfill.

The high capability of a dry FGD system with a fabric filter to remove secondary emissions (e.g., SO_3, HCl, HF, heavy metals, and especially mercury) makes dry FGD an interesting alternative for multi-emission control.

CONTROL OF MERCURY EMISSIONS

Mercury exists as a trace element, along with many other constituents, in coal. Most trace elements end up in the ash, which is collected with high efficiency as bottom ash or fly ash. Mercury, however, is different. During the combustion process, mercury becomes an elemental vapor that is of limited reactivity and that remains above its condensation temperature throughout the entire power system. Approximately 25% of the mercury entering the process with the coal remains in the vapor phase throughout the flue gas cleaning process.

The average mercury concentration in U.S. coals is 0.2 ppm, a figure that is close to the average mercury content in the earth's crust (0.1 ppm). The mercury content of U.S. coals ranges from an average of 27 lb/10^{12} BTU (12 kg/petajoule) for the Gulf Coast coals to 18 lb/10^{12} BTU (8 kg/petajoule) for the Northern Appalachian coals to 10 lb/10^{12} BTU (5 kg/petajoule) for the Powder River coals.[83]

BACKGROUND CHEMISTRY

To manage mercury emissions, the chemical form (speciation) of mercury as it enters the various control devices in a flue gas cleaning system must be known. Mercury is present in three forms:

1. Elemental mercury (Hg^0)
2. Oxidized components (Hg^{2+}) of the flue gas

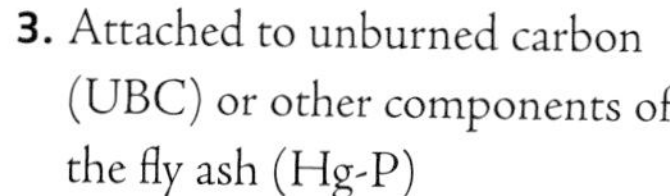

3. Attached to unburned carbon (UBC) or other components of the fly ash (Hg-P)

The speciation is critical, because Hg^{2+} is highly water soluble and, therefore, easily captured in FGD scrubber solutions. In contrast, Hg^{0} is insoluble. Both Hg^{0} and Hg^{2+} vapors may become attached to fly ash or sorbents to form Hg-P. Nearly any kind of particulate collection device (PCD) collects essentially all of the Hg-P. The proportions of Hg^{0}, Hg^{2+}, and Hg-P often change dramatically, however, with different fuels in the same cleaning configuration and even for different configurations with the same fuels.

The clearest perspective comes from recognizing mercury speciation as a marker for the various chemical reactions that transform the speciation through the gas cleaning system. The starting point for this chemistry is well defined: All the mercury fed into the furnace with the fuel will be present as Hg^{0} at the furnace exit. After the flue gas is cooled in the economizer, the Hg^{0} starts to oxidize into Hg^{2+} via various reactions in the flue gas—and at an even faster rate via reactions on suspended UBC particles. The Hg^{0} oxidizes even more quickly when exposed to a SCR catalyst. By the time, the flue gas leaves the air pre-heater, it is cool enough for Hg^{0} and Hg^{2+} to bind to UBC or any of the sorbents typically injected to recover it as Hg-P in a downstream PCD. The mixture of Hg^{0} and Hg^{2+} leaving the PCD will be stripped of almost all its Hg^{2+} in an FGD system. When an FGD system is present, most of the mercury that is emitted from the stack will be Hg^{0} vapor.

Like any set of chemical reactions, Hg chemistry is governed by how the temperature changes along the cleaning system path, by the residence time within the various components where reactions occur, and by the concentrations of the participating species. None of these important parameters is consistent among the different types of gas cleaning systems. These parameters also can change within a given system based on load, excess air, and fuel changes. Therefore, variations in the mercury speciation measurements are mostly a consequence of the different conditions for mercury chemistry that naturally arise among utility gas cleaning systems that are operated at the wide variety of conditions constituting normal utility practice.

Among the important coal properties, levels of coal chlorine (Cl), coal bromine (Br), and UBC in the fly ash are paramount. Chlorine and bromine are the species that actually oxidize Hg^{0} to Hg^{2+}. The UBC both accelerates mercury oxidation and acts as the most effective inherent mercury sorbent in fly ash. Generally, bituminous coals contain more chlorine and bromine and generate more UBC compared with low-rank coals. The difficulties in oxidizing the mercury from low-rank coals are well established in the test literature. It also has been observed that the chlorine and bromine levels in a given coal can fluctuate on a random basis by a factor of two or three, thus increasing the challenge of controlling mercury emissions.

Compounding the variable coal properties, the gas cleaning conditions also directly affect the underlying mercury chemistry and, therefore, directly determine the mercury emissions rates. Different flue gas quench rates imposed by different designs of economizers and air pre-heaters can affect mercury reaction rates. Longer ductwork sustains more chemistry compared with shorter connections. Utility SCRs are operated at space velocities from 1,700 to 5,000/h, which changes the residence time available for catalytic mercury oxidation by almost a factor of three. In addition, different SCR manufacturers use different flow passages and active ingredients, which also affect mercury oxidation rates. The operating temperature of PCDs also is crucial. Hot side ESPs collect much less mercury than cold side ESPs. The excellent contact between flue gas and fly ash in the filter cakes on fabric filters enhances Hg^0 oxidation and utilizes the full capacities of UBC or sorbent for capture of mercury. Spray dryer absorbers usually perform as well as or better than wet FGDs.

Mercury presents a special problem for the PCD compared to the other trace metals, which form compounds with low vapor pressures at the air pre-heater exit temperatures. Whereas the other trace metals can be successfully controlled using conventional particulate control technologies, the mercury compounds tend to be gaseous, because their partial pressure in the flue gas is well below their vapor pressures (roughly 1 million-fold less than the vapor pressure). The mercury flue gas content is equivalent to approximately 2 ppbv Hg. This extremely low concentration makes the problem of mercury control unusually challenging.

MERCURY CHEMISTRY IN THE FLUE GASES UPSTREAM OF THE AIR PRE-HEATER

As of this writing, the exact nature of the oxidized mercury compound in flue gases has yet to be precisely determined. It generally is believed to be a halogen compound, HgX_2 (frequently identified as $HgCl_2$). This denomination has the character of being an operative definition, because it is the result of an empirical determination. Consequently, it is interesting to examine the chemistry in the flue gases of the halogens in connection with mercury.

At the coal combustion temperature, the stable form of mercury is in the form of elemental gas (Hg^0), and the halogens are in the form of acidic gases (e.g., HCl and HBr). On cooling of the gases in the boiler, the thermodynamics of the halogen compounds change so that the halogen gas becomes stable in the Deacon reaction:

$$4HBr + O_2 \rightarrow 2Br_2 + 2H_2O$$
$$4HCl + O_2 \rightarrow 2Cl_2 + 2H_2O$$

On flue gas cooling, this reaction occurs first for bromine and then later, at a lower temperature, for chlorine. The kinetics of the chlorine reaction are slower.

High moisture contents tend to suppress the formation of elemental halogens. Moreover, at the same time, molecular chlorine is consumed by SO_2 in the Griffin reaction, shifting back the equilibrium of the chlorine species:

$$2Cl + SO_2 + H_2O \rightarrow SO_3 + 2HCl$$

Bromine, in contrast to chlorine, is not attacked by SO_2 in a Griffin

reaction. The net effect of this is that more molecular bromine will be present compared to molecular chlorine:

$$\frac{Cl}{Cl_{total}} << 1$$

$$\frac{Br}{Br_{total}} \approx 1$$

For practically all coals, the chloride content in the coal is far higher than the bromine content (Cl/Br = 50–500), but in the flue gas, the amount of molecular bromine may well be larger than the amount of molecular chlorine downstream of the combustion zone. Additionally, in practically all combustion processes, the chlorine exists as HCl at the boiler back end, whereas on combustion of high-bromine waste, a brown plume is sometimes observed—a clear sign of the elemental bromine gas.

When the gases have been cooled down below approximately 1,300°F (700°C), direct halogenation of the metallic mercury is becoming thermodynamically favorable:

$$Hg + Br_2 \rightarrow HgBr_2$$
$$Hg + Cl_2 \rightarrow HgCl_2$$

By the above reasoning, there will be only a limited supply of molecular chlorine in the flue gas. If the bromine content of the coal is high enough, there will be an ample supply of molecular bromine to brominate the typical amounts of mercury prevailing in flue gas.

In view of this, the relative abundance of chlorine and bromine in coals is of interest. Some data from the U.S. Geological Survey database COALQUAL are displayed in *Figures 5-58* and *5-59*. The database lists approximately 3,500 data points for bromine in coals from all over the United States. At least 50% of the coals have bromine contents of less than 10 ppm. There also is some correlation between the bromine and chlorine contents of the coal: With coal chlorine content of greater than 500 ppm, there is a high likelihood that the coal also contains bromine at greater than 10 ppm.

Full-scale experiments performed at a 790 MW boiler at a power plant near Lake Monticello, Texas, have confirmed the important role of the coal bromine contents for the oxidation of mercury in a coal-fired boiler.[84] During the testing, a mixture of Texas lignite and Powder River Basin coal was fired. Under baseline conditions, the mercury oxidation rate, Hg^{2+}/total Hg (Hg_{tot}; as determined by measurements at the air pre-heater outlet), was 10 to 40%. During the experiment,

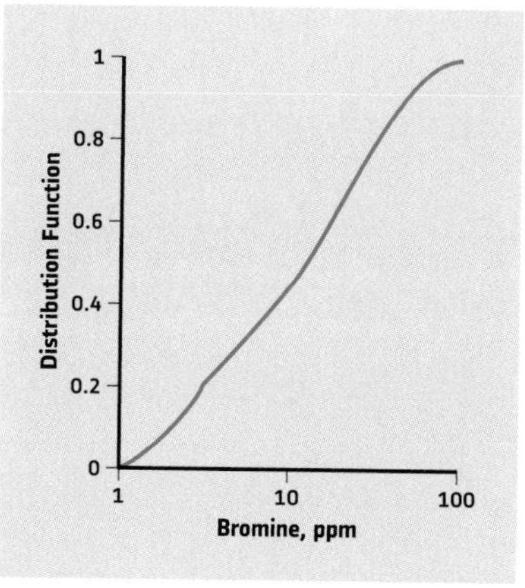

Figure 5-58 | Distribution of bromine content data in the U.S. Geological Survey COALQUAL database

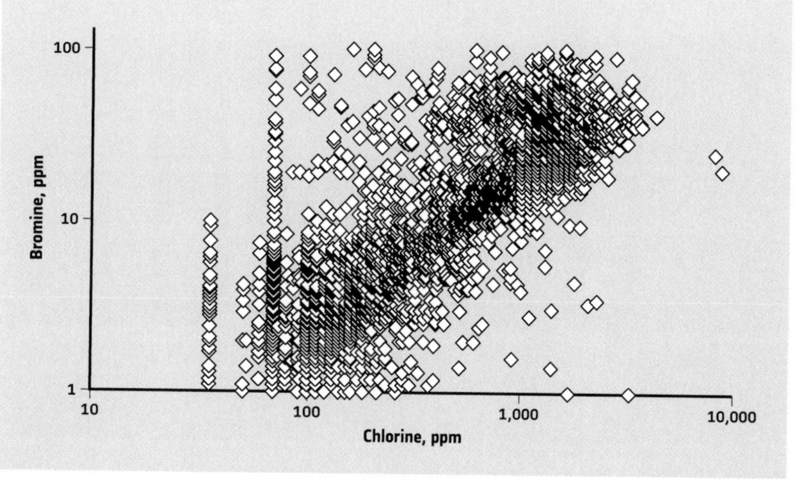

Figure 5-59 | Correlation between chlorine and bromine contents in the coals listed in the U.S. Geological Survey COALQUAL database

chloride and bromide were added to 40% of the burners, and the change in oxidation rate was determined. Adding up to the equivalent of 900 ppm of chlorine to the entire coal stream produced a marginal increase of oxidation from 35 to 40%. Addition of the equivalent of 100 ppm of bromine to the coal produced an increase in oxidation rate from 35 to 72%. This demonstrates in full scale the important role of bromine in the coal to control the oxidation of mercury in the flue gas in a boiler. The process to add bromine compounds to the coal for the purpose of controlling mercury chemistry was invented by Prof. Bernard Vosteen and is the subject of U.S. Patent 6,878,358. This process is licensed to and marketed by Alstom under the trade name KNX™.

The halogenation reaction is kinetically limited. Other factors, which also contribute to an increased ratio of Hg^{2+} to Hg_{tot} at the air pre-heater outlet, are the residence time in the system and the presence of UBC, which acts as a catalyst for the reaction. A high-dust SCR will provide additional residence time but also new reaction paths for the halogenation reactions. The effect of an SCR was investigated[85] by measuring the mercury species upstream of the SCR and downstream of the air heater at 10 different plants burning coals with chlorine levels ranging from 130 to 1,400 ppm (*Fig. 5-60*). The results clearly show that the halogenation of the mercury is augmented by the SCR. Other results show that when the catalyst ages, the effect becomes weaker. For low-halogen coals, the effect can be much less. A catalyst can only provide increased kinetics, not the halogen reactants.

MERCURY COLLECTION USING ACTIVATED CARBON

Some of the mercury can be caught with the fly ash in a conventional flue gas cleaning system. An early investigation of this[86] showed that this native collection in a conventional fly ash collection system is enhanced by a high UBC in the ash, a low ash filtration temperature, and use of a fabric filter rather than an ESP. Best results were obtained with high UBC, corresponding to a loss-on-ignition of 10 to 20% and a filter temperature below 210°F (99°C). Such values of operational parameters often conflict with other requirements for a modern PC boiler system.

The UBC fraction in the ash was surmised to have some similarity in structure to activated carbon, because both are of a carbonaceous nature and have a disproportionately high contribution to the fly ash specific surface area. Experiments with commercially

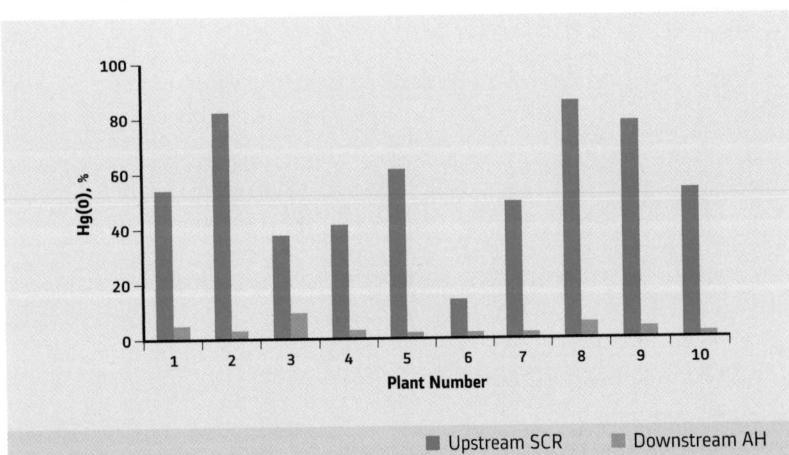

Figure 5-60 | Result of mercury testing at 10 different plants burning coals with chlorine contents of 130 to 1,400 ppm (AH, air heater; Hg(0), elemental mercury; SCR, selective catalytic reduction)

available PAC showed a consistent collection effect, which was used for the purpose of mercury and dioxin collection for waste-to-energy plants (these plants have mercury levels on the order of 10 to 20 fold that of coal combustion).

Commercially available PAC has a particle size distribution similar to that of the fly ash in a PC boiler. It can be injected into the ductwork and be transported by the flue gas flow. Injection rates for the purpose of mercury control are in the range 1 to 10 lb PAC/MMacf (millions actual feet) $\left(\frac{0.02-0.16\ \text{kg}}{1{,}000\ \text{m}^3}\right)$, which then will correspond to a PAC/Hg mass ratio of the order of 1,500 to 15,000 (and a PAC/fly ash mass ratio of 50 to 500). The mean particle-to-particle distance for the PAC in uniform distribution throughout the flue gas is then of the order of hundredths of an inch (millimeters). Compared to other gas absorption cases, the mercury/PAC situation is characterized by a very low mercury concentration with a large distance from the bulk of the gas to the nearest PAC particle sink, giving a comparatively weak gradient for transport from the bulk to the sorbent particle. This mass transfer limitation probably is one important reason why simple injection of conventional PAC upstream of an ESP does not appear to produce impressive mercury absorption results. To overcome this fundamental mass transfer problem, Alstom uses two different practical approaches: the Filsorption system and the Mer-Cure™ system.

The utilization of PC fly ash can be an attractive alternative to pond storage or landfill. One effective way to reuse ash is as an additive to concrete. In modern concrete technology, the use of an additive, which acts as an air entrainment agent, results in a controlled amount of small gas bubbles in the cast concrete. This gives a concrete with improved freeze and thaw resistance. Adding fly ash to the cement with even small amounts of PAC leads to the air entrainment agent being absorbed by the PAC and rendered less effective, resulting in poorer freeze and thaw resistance of the cast concrete.

Fly ash with a UBC content in excess of some 5% gives the same result. Again, the UBC has some similarities with PAC. If fly ash is to be utilized as a concrete additive, then it must be captured separately from the spent PAC.

The detailed chemistry of the complex sorption process of flue gas mercury compounds on the PAC surface in the multi-component coal combustion flue gas remains to be mapped and understood. At least two empirical discoveries, however, are of practical importance. First, impregnation of the PAC with limited amounts of bromine compounds leads to improvements in the sorption process. Second, if the flue gas content of SO_3 exceeds 5 to 10 ppm, this compound seems to be preferentially absorbed by the PAC, decreasing the PAC effectiveness for mercury sorption.

MERCURY CONTROL AND FGD

The dry FGD system utilizes an SDA with lime slurry injection, followed by a fabric filter. Here, the flue gas temperature after the SDA is low (150–180°F [66–82°C]), and the

A multi-faceted approach to mercury capture involving higher temperature oxidation and longer residence times with a modified activated carbon provides for a retrofit technology that uses considerably fewer additives.

bag filter cake provides excellent mass transfer between PAC and the flue gas. For bituminous, high-halogen, eastern U.S. coals, it was observed early on that most of the mercury exists as Hg^{2+} and that this system often gives a variable, but significant, native mercury collection efficiency. By adding controlled amounts of PAC, the mercury collection efficiency can be stabilized.

For western U.S., sub-bituminous, low-halogen, coals (Cl, <100 ppm) with a very high fraction of Hg^0, the native collection efficiency of the dry FGD system is close to zero. Adding conventional PAC to this system does little to improve mercury collection efficiency. This problem can be solved by using the Alstom KNX™ additive along with injection of ordinary PAC, which produces good mercury collection results.[87] Another solution is to use injection of the more expensive, bromine-impregnated PAC.

In the wet FGD system predominantly used today, with limestone-based forced oxidation producing gypsum, the metallic mercury entering the system is not collected at all because of the low aqueous solubility of the metallic vapor. The Hg^{2+} fraction is collected, because it has a high aqueous solubility and because the mercury halides also form complexes of the type $(HgCl_4)^{2-}$ and $(HgBr_4)^{2-}$, giving a low backpressure of Hg^{2+} from the solution. The dissolved mercury complexes, however, can be reduced by other dissolved ions in the solution. The amount of mercury in the solution is very small in comparison to several other species. The reduction occurs first to Hg_2^{2+}, which easily decomposes to Hg^{2+} and Hg^0. In such cases, the amount of emitted Hg^0 can be somewhat higher than the amount going into the FGD system. This phenomenon is called "re-emission of mercury," and it limits the total performance of the wet FGD as a collection system for Hg^{2+}. Various ways to modify the chemistry of the wet FGD system to stabilize the dissolved mercury without impairing the main function of the wet FGD system to collect SO_2 and to produce gypsum are being investigated.

ALSTOM MERCURY CONTROL TECHNOLOGIES

KNX™ Technology

The KNX™ Technology comprises adding a bromine additive compound to the coal in trace quantities to control mercury oxidation for all types of coal, irrespective of its composition. The process is under exclusive license from Vosteen Consulting of Germany.

The first application was in connection with low-halogen, western U.S. coal and dry FGD, in which the additive changes the mercury sorption process so that a high collection efficiency can be reached with the addition of regular PAC. The additive provides mercury bromination in the boiler backpass in order that inert Hg^0 is converted to the more reactive Hg^{2+} species. The additive also has shown good mercury control effects in other systems firing low-halogen coal, in which a typical amount of UBC can provide adequate absorption when the interaction between mercury and carbonaceous material is augmented by the effect of the additive. This process also integrates well with the wet FGD system, in which the upstream conversion of mercury to Hg^{2+} occurs regardless of coal quality, and this mercury species can then be absorbed in the aqueous phase of the scrubber liquid. It is a simple system, which is unique in that it does not employ PAC.

Mer-Cure™ Technology

The Mer-Cure™ technology is an advanced, PAC-based mercury control technology in which the mass transfer limitations of simple PAC injection to an ESP have been overcome by the application of several new and unique features:

- The PAC base sorbent is impregnated with an additive that accelerates the sorption process kinetics.
- The sorbent is mechanically processed before injection to provide a sorbent with maximal surface area and uniform dispersion in order to enhance mass transfer from the gas to the sorbent.
- The sorbent is injected upstream of the air pre-heater in order to prolong the flue gas contact time and take advantage of the catalytic effect of the sorbent on the oxidation reactions at the higher temperature.

By this multifaceted approach using the increased oxidation that results from the injection upstream of the air heater, the improved mass transfer from the processing of the PAC material just before injection, and the improved kinetics from sorbent chemical impregnation, the performance of this process is generally better than that of conventional PAC injection in an ESP. The PAC consumption is modest, and the system can be installed without any modifications to the existing ESP. Because the amount of PAC is approximately 0.2% of the typical flue gas fly ash content of PC boiler flue gas, it is within the normal tolerances of ash variability. The impact on ESP performance normally is negligible, and the existing ESP often can be used without modifications. To achieve a uniform distribution of the injected material throughout the flue gas in the short ducts that usually are available upstream of the air heater, a detailed fluid mechanics design is necessary.

Filsorption Technology

The Filsorption technology uses a combination of PAC addition and a bag filter (other than dry FGD). The PAC is added upstream of the bag filter by admixing to the flue gas. In suspension, some interaction between sorbent particles and flue gas occurs. The PAC material is then deposited on the bags. Here, the diffusion distance between PAC particles and the bulk gas is very short, leading to much improved, gas side mass transfer. The PAC particles reside in the gas stream for the duration of the cleaning interval of the bags, which is on the order of 10 minutes. This gives ample time for reaction between the gas and the PAC particles. The mass transfer limitations for the sorption of mercury are thus eliminated, and good mercury collection efficiency can be obtained using standard PAC. The fabric filter can be installed to perform fly ash collection as well. As in the ESP case, the injected PAC is then diluted by the ash. The dilution is so high that conventional fly ash discharge and handling technology can be used.

If the fly ash is used in cement production, a dedicated fly ash collection

The most cost effective means of reducing CO_2 emissions is efficiency improvement.

device can be located ahead of the fabric filter. The product from a fabric filter downstream of a dedicated ash collector will be high in PAC, which can be prone to auto-ignition if allowed to remain in large volumes for extended periods of time in non-ventilated areas. When the PAC resides on the bags, the heat produced by the slow oxidation of the PAC is readily dissipated by the passing flue gas. Only when the PAC is kept in a hopper for a long time can auto-ignition occur. The remedy is to design the filter with steep ash hopper angles and to have continuous ash discharge.

CONTROL OF CO_2 EMISSIONS

Concerns about CO_2 buildup in the atmosphere have led to the potential for CO_2 emission regulations covering steam generating and power plant equipment. Currently, there are a wide array of considerations, ranging from carbon taxes to cap-and-trade proposals to no control regimes. It is not the purpose of this text to debate the merits of such concerns; that is a topic for political, social, and scientific debate. Even the threat of controls, however, is of considerable consequence to a potential owner of plant equipment. Because Alstom supplies equipment throughout the world, development of CO_2 control technology is a critical research and development undertaking.

The most cost-effective means of reducing CO_2 emissions is efficiency improvement. As the cost of emitting CO_2 increases (by regulations, taxes, or allowance costs), the value of efficiency improvements increases. These improvements can occur throughout the range of economic activity. Indeed, the historical improvement in efficiency of the U.S. economy has averaged 1% per year (BTU/unit of GDP). Examples include more efficient appliances, fluorescent light bulbs, and improved auto mileage.

For power plant equipment manufacturers, efficiency improvements lead to the development of higher-temperature and -pressure steam conditions for steam turbines and boilers as well as lower power requirements for auxiliary equipment. The reduction of required auxiliary power leads to higher net output from power plants, improving overall efficiency. The development of "ultra-supercritical" steam technology is manifested in the world's first power plant with steam conditions at 1,300°F (700°C) at a plant in Wilhelmshaven, Germany. Such plants can lead to an improvement in efficiency from subcritical steam conditions of over 33%. (See Chapters 3 and 4 on supercritical boilers and supercritical steam turbines.)

Should longer-term stabilization of CO_2 in the atmosphere be required, larger reductions in CO_2 emissions will be required. Aside from abstinence regarding the use of fossil fuel altogether (requiring development of an economical substitute), emissions avoidance implies the capture and sequestration (or storage) of CO_2 from emitting sources. Capturing and effectively storing carbon dioxide (CO_2) produced by fossil-fueled power plants could, if done on a large enough scale and in enough countries, play a significant role in mitigating growth in global greenhouse gas emissions. It also could fundamentally alter the carbon footprint of conventional fossil fuels—particularly cheap, carbon-rich coal—and allow them to remain significant sources of energy for decades to come, without the potential CO_2 impact on the global climate.

The potential role that carbon capture and storage technology could have on the future of the global economy and energy mix is substantial. Oil, natural gas, and coal currently account for 70% of the world's primary energy supply and, collectively, produce 80% of man-made global CO_2 emissions. Although there may be some uses for the captured CO_2, the scale of the problem is enormous. The MIT Coal Report[88] points out that the underground storage for CO_2 would require a pipeline system three-fold the size of the existing natural gas pipeline system in the United States.

A number of technologies are being developed to address the issue of capture and sequestration of CO_2. In addition to the technology, both regulatory and liability issues need to be resolved. Ownership of the CO_2 after the storage site is filled also is a key issue. A number of demonstration projects are either planned or underway to explore these issues and demonstrate the feasibility of safe capture and storage of CO_2. It is not that CO_2 has never been captured before. The commercial process for producing sodium bicarbonate (a typical antacid) is to capture CO_2 from flue gas after natural gas combustion using naturally occurring sodium carbonate. The scale of the amount of capture now required, however, makes utilization for all but a fraction of the CO_2 nearly impossible. The United States consumes more than 1 billion tons (tonnes) of coal annually, which in turn produces more than 3 billion tons/yr (tonnes/yr) of CO_2. If all of this CO_2 were converted to sodium bicarbonate, the production level would be more than 6 billion tons (tonnes). That would mean that every living person in the United States would have to consume 20 tons/yr (tonnes) of sodium bicarbonate, or approximately 100 pounds (45 kg) of tablets per day. Of course, CO_2 also is produced through the use of other fuels as well—not to mention people and animals. It is the scale of the problem that makes the solution truly challenging.

One of the difficulties involved with the capture of CO_2 has to do with the fact that most combustion processes utilize air as the source of oxygen. Along with the air comes substantial amounts of nitrogen. Thus, the resulting product gases then contain substantial amounts of nitrogen, diluting the CO_2 and making it more difficult (and expensive) to separate (i.e., capture) from the rest of the gas. One means of avoiding this dilution problem is to use relatively pure oxygen as the reagent. There are two approaches to utilizing the oxygen. The first is direct combustion with oxygen (often referred to as oxy firing). The second is to use the oxygen to first gasify the fuel. This gasification process produces a reducing gas (mostly CO and hydrogen). The CO in this gas can be converted to CO_2 by use of the water gas shift reaction. Here, water vapor is reacted with the CO to produce CO_2 and hydrogen:

$$CO + H_2O = CO_2 + H_2$$

The CO_2 can be separated from this gas using processes developed in the refinery and petrochemical industries. The hydrogen subsequently is combusted with air for the purpose of generating heat and/or electricity. Because this fuel gas can be burned in a gas turbine, a combined cycle plant can be utilized for increased efficiency. (See Chapter 3 on heat recovery steam generators and the combined cycle). This process commonly is referred to as the "integrated gasification combined cycle" (IGCC) process. Because this process is not primarily a combustion process, the focus in this chapter will be the oxygen-fired combustion system.

OXYGEN FIRING

The combustion of fossil fuels with oxygen is not new in itself. Processes for making steel and glass have taken advantage of the higher gas temperatures that can be achieved through the use of relatively pure oxygen. The use of oxygen in boilers is still evolving, however, and designs will certainly change as studies are completed and understanding is increased.

A block diagram for a conventional PC unit is presented in *Figure 5-61*. The combustion air is heated in an air heater (see Chapter 6) and then split into two streams. Primary air is used to convey the coal from the pulverizer to the boiler. It provides the immediate air for combustion and can represent up to 25% of the total. Secondary air provides the remainder of the air needed for complete combustion. This air can be staged to reduce the formation of compounds such as NOx. The primary air passes to the coal mills to dry the coal, convey it to the burners, and provide the oxygen for initial combustion. The 21% by volume oxygen content of the air determines the peak flame temperature of approximately 3,600°F (2,000°C). The lower, or initial, region of the boiler (the furnace) is designed to cool the product gases to approximately 2,300°F (1,300°C) before encountering the convective heat-transfer surfaces. This temperature varies depending on the properties of the ash content of the fuel. The design goal is to bring the ash particles below their initial ash deformation temperature and prevent them from adhering to and fouling the convection pass tubes (see Chapter 3). As the product gases pass through the superheat, reheat, and economizer heat-transfer surfaces, they cool. The heat-transfer mechanism shifts from primarily radiation to a combination of radiation and convection and then to solely convection.

Although it is theoretically possible to burn fossil fuels in pure oxygen, the resulting increase in flame temperature would result in increasing NOx, ash slagging, and ash fouling problems. In order to moderate the flame temperature and reduce the NOx- and ash-related issues, a mixture of oxygen and recycled flue gas (RFG) can be deployed. The exact percentage of oxygen depends on whether the RFG has been dried or remains relatively wet. In

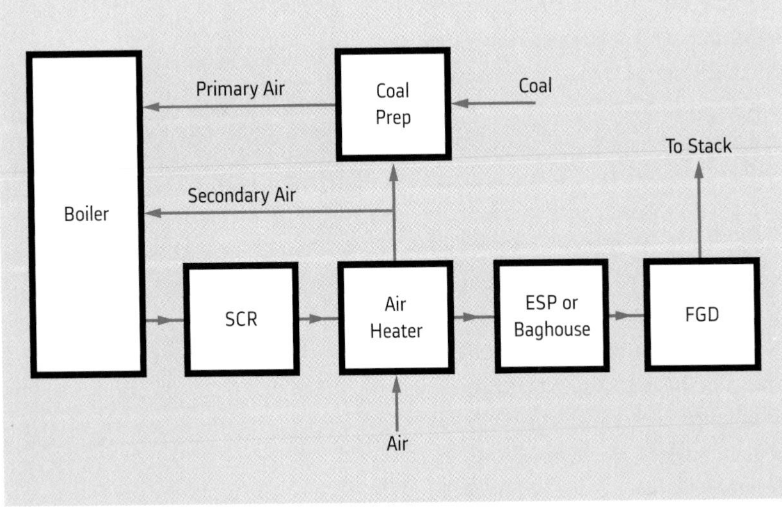

Figure 5-61 | Block diagram of an air-fired PC boiler (ESP, electrostatic precipitator; FGD, flue gas desulfurization; SCR, selective catalytic reduction)

either case, to avoid erosion damage to the forced draft fans needed to recycle the flue gas, the extraction point likely will be located after the particulate cleanup system. If a fabric filter (baghouse) is used for particulate removal, then the pulse gas used to clean the bags must be CO_2 in order to avoid introducing nitrogen into the flue gas stream and increasing the duty of the CO_2 cleanup and compression stages (see *Control of Particulate Emissions*).

A block flow diagram for an oxygen-fired PC unit is presented in *Figure 5-62*. The SCR unit is eliminated, because NOx emissions are greatly reduced in oxygen-fired combustion and are finally removed in the CO_2 purification stage. The diagram also shows the RFG as being taken after the FGD unit, which is appropriate for a high-sulfur coal. For a low-sulfur coal, the RFG could be taken before the FGD. It is possible that the FGD could be eliminated completely by removing the SO_2 in the CO_2 purification stage, but the practical and economic benefits of this approach remain to be established.

The RFG is split into primary and secondary flows. The primary RFG flow is used for coal drying duty and is cooled to remove moisture (and water-soluble acid gases [e.g., SO_3 and HCl], reducing the risk of acid corrosion) before passing to the flue gas heater (the equivalent of the air heater) and then to the mill system (for a coal-fired unit). To lower the potential for explosion, oxygen is not added until after the pulverizers. The secondary RFG flow can be either cooled or passed directly to the flue gas heater, after which oxygen is added.

The oxygen produced can range from 95 to 99.9% purity, with the balance being nitrogen and argon. Because nitrogen remains gaseous in the CO_2 compression stage, it increases the compression power requirement. Lowering the nitrogen in the oxygen helps lower the CO_2 compression costs but increases the cost of oxygen production. The benefits of increased oxygen purity can be negated if a large amount of air leaks into the furnace. Minimizing such leakage is important in reducing potential operating costs.

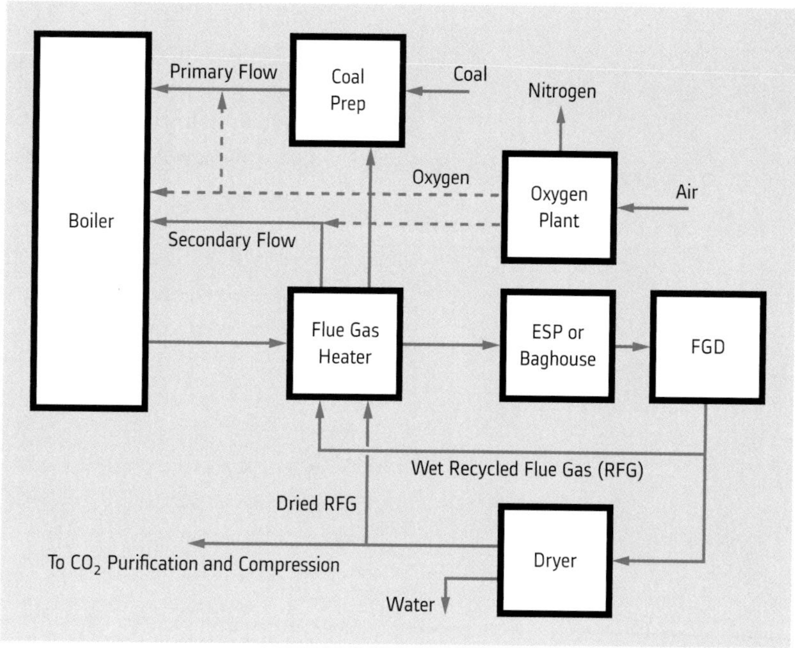

Figure 5-62 | Block diagram of oxygen-fueled PC boiler (ESP, electrostatic precipitator; FGD, flue gas desulfurization)

The RFG will contain SO_2, so its concentration in the boiler will be increased above that of an air-fired furnace. As a consequence, the potential for corrosion of the high-temperature, convection pass tubing increases. If the SO_2 is greater than approximately 3,000 ppmv (equivalent to burning a 3% sulfur coal), the RFG must first pass through an FGD unit (as shown in *Fig.* 5-62). Again, if a forced oxidation system is used in the FGD unit, then in order to avoid introducing nitrogen into the flue gas, the oxidant must be oxygen (possibly mixed with CO_2 to aid dispersion).

The flue gas that is not recycled is compressed before storage. In some instances, this storage might be at the site of the power plant, but more commonly, it will be located elsewhere. The compressed gas may be transported in a pipeline to a storage site or utilized for enhanced oil recovery. The raw flue gas leaving the FGD contains moisture, nitrogen, oxygen, and trace amounts of other species, such as SO_2 and NOx. These must be removed or reduced either before or during the compression process in order to satisfy certain pipeline criteria. For example, the oxygen must be reduced to below 100 ppmv, and the moisture to below 110 ppmv, to limit pipeline corrosion potential. If the gas is to be injected directly, however, less cleanup may be required, and essentially all of the gas can be sequestered. This situation represents the only true "zero emission" power plant.

Flames produced from coal burning in air are brighter than similar flames produced with an O_2/RFG mixture, even when the amount of oxygen present is the same. This results from the higher specific heat of CO_2, which lowers the adiabatic flame temperature. The flame also propagates less rapidly, resulting in increased release of volatiles and formation of soot. The additional soot that is formed can be seen as bright specks in the O_2/RFG flame. To obtain an adiabatic flame temperature similar to that of air, the percentage of oxygen in the combustion mixture must be increased from 21% by volume to between 25 and 30% by volume in wet RFG. For dry RFG, the oxygen content would have to be 37 to 40% by volume. The oxygen flow is fixed by stoichiometry, but the RFG flow decreases and the CO_2 content increases.

As with air, the RFG is split into primary and secondary flow streams into which the oxygen is introduced. Sufficient oxygen must be present in the primary RFG stream to achieve ignition and keep the flame close to the burner tip and so help to reduce NOx formation. The exact amount of oxygen required depends on the burner design. An important design safety consideration limits the oxygen concentration of any one stream to less than 40% by volume. Systems with oxygen purities of greater than 50% by volume flowing above a critical velocity can cause certain pipe materials to ignite. Carbon steel is one such material. The presence of oils and hydrocarbon-based greases exacerbate this tendency. Below an oxygen concentration of 40% by volume, the pipe work can be designed as for air, but it must be cleansed of oils and grease. Another approach is to limit the oxygen concentration to 23% by volume in the RFG flows to the burner and add the additional oxygen at the burner tip through a separate feed line. Such an approach may be required at low-load conditions to maintain flame stability and prevent ignition failure.

The greater density of CO_2 means that the volumetric flow of the RFG passing through the burner is less than that of the air in an air-fired unit. Because the coal carrying capacity of a gas

stream is determined by its volumetric flow rate, the volumetric flow rates of the primary RFG and the primary air should be the same. This requirement results in the volumetric flow of the secondary RFG stream being only 70% that of the secondary air flow in an air-fired unit. In an unmodified burner designed for use with air, this lower gas flow will result in reduced swirl and, possibly, an unstable, elongated flame. To avoid this condition, additional swirl must be introduced to the secondary flow. For tangentially fired units, a higher velocity may be required to generate the required swirl in the center of the furnace.

The RFG used to moderate the combustion temperature is high in CO_2 and moisture. The resulting higher specific heat of the gas will lower the mean furnace gas temperature for oxygen combustion with 21% oxygen by volume. This lower bulk temperature in turn lowers the radiation component, requiring an increase in heat-transfer area to achieve the same duty. Fortuitously, the CO_2 and water vapor also are strong radiators, having higher gas emissivities. This factor will help to compensate for the reduced gas temperature driving force. Testing has established that for oxygen-fired combustion to achieve similar furnace heat-transfer performance to that with air, the oxygen content must be increased. *Figure 5-63* presents data for a retrofit application using wet and dry RFG. For the wet RFG, the furnace heat transfer is similar to that of air when the oxygen content is 25% by volume. For the dry RFG, an oxygen content of 38% by volume is needed to provide the same heat-transfer performance. Additional data are presented in *Table 5-16.*

The following comments can be made with respect to heat transfer in the cases of air, wet RFG, and dry RFG:

- The air case has the highest furnace exit gas temperature and the lowest total emissivity. The wet RFG case has the lowest furnace exit gas temperature and the highest total emissivity. In combination, these two factors result in the furnace heat absorption being similar for all three cases.
- The heat transferred to the convection pass is similar for each case. Because of the higher CO_2 content, the specific heat and gas density are higher for the two RFG cases, and the gas velocity and gas mass flow

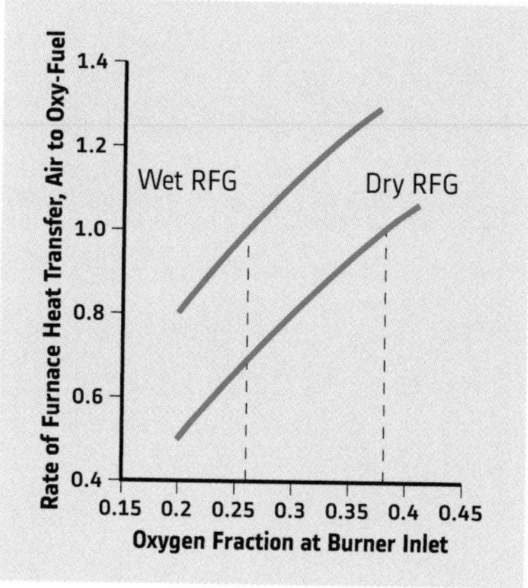

Figure 5-63 | Effect of oxygen fraction and recycled flue gas moisture on furnace heat transfer

TABLE 5-16 | FURNACE HEAT TRANSFER CHARACTERISTICS

		Recycled Flue Gas	
	Air	Wet	Dry
Recycle ratio (recycled flue gas/O_2 mass ratio)	—	2.55	1.36
Fraction of oxygen At burner inlet In flue gas	 0.21 0.033	 0.25 0.033	 0.38 0.033
Adiabatic flame temperature (°F [°C])	3,500 (1,930)	3,220 (1,770)	3,790 (2,090)
Gas temperatures (°F [°C]) Entering convection pass Exiting convection pass Convection pass temperature drop	 2,120 (1,160) 800 (430) 1,320 (730)	 1,980 (1,080) 720 (380) 1,260 (700)	 2,000 (1,090) 530 (270) 1,470 (820)
Gas emissivity	0.36	0.58	0.47
Total emissivity	0.50	0.70	0.65
Heat absorbed (BTU/ft^2-s [kWh/m^2])	8.36 (94.9)	8.42 (95.6)	8.43 (95.7)
Overall heat-transfer coefficient for convection pass (BTU/ft^2-h [W/m^2])	8.2 (46.4)	8.6 (48.6)	6.9 (39.4)
Gas velocity (ft/s [m/s])*	32 (9.8)	25 (7.5)	16 (5.0)
In-furnace gas residence time (s)	2.1	2.5	3.8

*Entering convection pass.

rate are lower. In combination, these factors influence the overall heat transfer coefficient relative to the air case but also result in opposite differences in the convection pass temperature drop. For example, the dry RFG case has the lowest overall heat-transfer coefficient but the highest convection pass temperature drop. This results in heat transfer to the convection pass being similar for all three cases.

- The convection pass exit temperature is lower for the two RFG cases. Thus, heat recovery in the economizer will be lower. This is the only difference in heat recovery for the three cases.
- The gas velocity is lowest for the dry RFG case. The in-furnace gas residence time is longer, resulting in higher carbon burnout. This case applies to retrofits. A new unit design could utilize a smaller furnace cross section to reduce capital cost.
- The dry RFG case offers certain other potential advantages: Less RFG is required, resulting in smaller ducting and furnace and a lower fan power requirement. These advantages are offset by the capital and operating costs of the cooling system. Additionally, the flame is shorter and more intense, and it may require a higher grade of burner materials.

TABLE 5-17 | NOx REDUCTION IN AIR-FIRED AND OXYGEN-FUEL TESTS

	Air (21% O2 by vol.)		Oxygen-Fuel (30% O2 by vol.)	
	Unstaged	Staged	Unstaged	Staged
Fuel NOx (relative)	100	63	47	29
Conversion ratio*	0.28	0.18	0.13	0.08
Unburned carbon	100	120	78	52

*Conversion of fuel nitrogen into NOx.

Emissions of NOx from oxygen-fired boilers are inherently low, without the need for deep staging of the combustion process. Compared to air-fired units, the emissions from oxygen-fired units are approximately 70% lower, with typical levels of approximately 100 ppmv (0.10 lb/MBTU [43 g/GJ]) being achieved. This amount can be reduced to near zero in the CO_2 purification stage. For this reason, the SCR can be eliminated, with associated reductions in capital and operating costs.

Because air is not used, the formation of thermal NOx from atmospheric nitrogen is eliminated in oxygen-fired combustion. This source contributes up to 50% of the total NOx formed. Fuel NOx will still be produced. In an air system, the conversion rate of fuel nitrogen to NOx averages 30 to 40%. In an oxygen-fuel system with 30% oxygen by volume, the conversion rate is approximately 8 to 10%, a reduction of more than 70%. Other results are presented in *Table 5-17*.

The reaction of NOx present in the RFG with adjacent burning particles is considered to inhibit the formation of additional NOx. The mechanisms involved are still under investigation.

Relative to operation in air, uncontrolled SO_2 emissions also can be reduced. This result was postulated to occur because of increased capture by the ash as a result of a change in chemistry. In air, the SO_2 can be captured by calcium in the ash through the following reactions:

$$CaCO_3 \rightarrow CaO + CO_2$$

Equation 5-63

$$CaO + SO_3 \rightarrow CaSO_4$$

Equation 5-64

$$SO_2 + \frac{1}{2}O_2 \rightarrow SO_3$$

Equation 5-65

At elevated temperatures, the equilibrium between SO_2 and SO_3 favors SO_2. Also, $CaSO_4$ dissociates at high temperatures. Thus, very little SO_2 is removed from the flue gas.

In the oxygen-fired environment, there is a high partial pressure of CO_2, which inhibits calcination (Equation 5-63). Under these conditions, SO_2 may be captured by direct displacement:

$$CaCO_3 + SO_2 + \frac{1}{2}O_2 \rightarrow CaSO_4 + CO_2$$

Equation 5-66

In this case, the partial pressure of CO_2 inhibits dissociation of the $CaSO_4$. To the extent that some calcium is present, the ash is able to lower the flue gas SO_2 content and, subsequently, the SO_2. The recycling flue gas also recycles more SO_3. This SO_3 exceeds the equilibrium level and reacts with the ash. Alternatively, SO_2 could react directly with the calcium, but some form of surface oxidation would be necessary to produce the more stable $CaSO_4$. In either case, these reductions are limited. As such, an FGD system is shown in *Figure 5-62*.

Initial testing has not revealed any significant differences in slagging and fouling characteristics. A wider range of coals needs to be investigated. The higher partial pressure of CO_2 results in ash with a higher carbonate content. Up to 40% of the flue gas passing to the compression stage can be composed of constituents other than CO_2 (*Table 5-18*).

The SO_2 and NOx concentrations will depend on the upstream processing equipment but are present in measurable quantities. If the gas is to be pipelined for any significant distance (either to an enhanced oil recovery [EOR] location or for geological storage), this stream must be cleaned up to meet pipeline specifications (*Table 5-19*).

First, the raw flue gas passes to a direct contact cooler, where circulating water removes most of the moisture, particulates, and soluble acid gases, such as SO_3 and HCl. Very little SO_2 and NOx are removed in this stage. The cooling water passes through an indirect

TABLE 5-18 | FLUE GAS COMPOSITION LEAVING AN OXYGEN-COMBUSTION BOILER

	Raw Gas	After Drying
Temperature (°F [°C])*	130 (54)	60 (15)
Composition (% by vol.)		
CO_2	60–70	75–88
H_2O	18–20	100 ppmv
N_2 + Ar	16–5.5	20–6.5
O_2	3.0–4.5	3.5–5.5
SO_2 (ppmv)†	500	500
NO_2 (ppmv)†	150	150

* After an SO_2 cleanup stage.
† Assumed values following direct cooling, compression, and desiccant drying.

TABLE 5-19 | TYPICAL CO_2 PURITY SPECIFICATION FOR PIPELINE TRANSPORTATION

	Specification	Reason
CO_2	Minimum of 95%	MMP*
N_2 + Ar	Maximum of 4%	MMP
Moisture†	Maximum 110 ppmv	Corrosion
O_2	Maximum of 100 ppmv	Corrosion
SO_2‡	Maximum of 25 ppmv	Corrosion
NOx‡	Maximum of 25 ppmv	Corrosion
CO	Maximum of 1,000 ppmv	Safety

* MMP, minimum miscibility pressure.
† Corresponding to a dew point of −40°F (−40°C).
‡ Assumed to be the same as H_2S specification, which is not based on corrosion concerns but, rather, on safety concerns following release to the atmosphere.

cooler and is sent to a water treatment plant, where the particulates and dissolved acid gases are removed before the water is recirculated. The cooled, impure CO_2 stream is compressed to approximately 440 psia (30 bar) using multiple compressors incorporating heat recovery, and the stream is then passed through temperature-swing desiccant dryers. The flow now contains approximately 80% CO_2 and 20% contaminants, and it still requires additional purification.

The minimum CO_2 purity required for EOR applications is 95%, with the majority of the balance being nitrogen. A lower purity level may be acceptable for CO_2 storage. The balance will still be mainly nitrogen, however, because the pipeline requirements for oxygen and moisture will remain at the ppm level. It is possible that there may be some relaxation in pipeline specifications, but this remains to be established. Although the increased nitrogen will lower purification costs, it will increase compression costs. A trade-off analysis is required to determine the optimum concentration. Because of this uncertainty, the remaining discussion is based on EOR applications.

Not all oil wells are suitable candidates for EOR, because certain criteria need to be satisfied:

- The reservoir depth should not be less than 2,500 feet (760 m).
- The oil viscosity should be less than 1 cP (.001 Pa sec), and the American Petroleum Institute gravity should be in the range 10 to 30.
- The recovery from a well is determined by the minimum miscibility pressure (MMP), which is a function of oil properties, reservoir pressure and temperature, and injected CO_2 purity. Operating below the MMP reduces oil recovery, and operating above the MMP increases costs with little or no additional oil recovery.
- Species decreasing the MMP include SO_2 and H_2S.
- Species increasing the MMP include O_2, N_2, argon, and NOx.
- For reasons of reservoir safety, oxygen concentration should be less than 10 ppmv.

In addition, there are pipeline criteria that need to be satisfied:

- Moisture levels must be reduced to a few ppmv to avoid corrosion issues and freezing across valves.
- Acidic corrosion occurs if moisture and SO_2 or H_2S are present.
- Electrochemical corrosion occurs if moisture and oxygen are present.
- High levels of impurities could form a second phase, resulting in mechanical damage through fluid hammering.

To achieve the level of purity presented in *Table 5-19*, several schemes have been proposed. One of the more commonly discussed schemes is presented here (*Fig. 5-64*). The flue gas leaving the desiccant dryers is cooled in two recuperators in series to −67°F and 440 psia (−55°C and 30 bar), close to the triple point of CO_2 (−69.5°F and 77 psia [−56.4°C and 5.3 bar]).

At the selected operating temperature, the majority of the CO_2 will condense as liquid and leave fixed gases in the gas phase. After each recuperation stage, the mixture is flashed to release the majority of the N_2, NO,

argon, O_2, and gaseous CO_2, but the majority of the SO_2 and NOx remain dissolved in the liquid CO_2. Some designs propose a single flash stage located after the second recuperator. The two-stage process is considered to remove more contaminants, and it results in lower CO_2 loss, thus increasing overall recovery and reducing the cost of CO_2. The 440 psia (30 bar) pressure is selected as a compromise between getting high recovery (favored by higher pressure) and high purity (favored by lower pressure). The CO_2 recovery also increases with the purity of the CO_2 feed, emphasizing the benefits of reducing air leakage and increasing oxygen purity. At lower temperatures, the CO_2 becomes a solid and will not flow through the equipment; at higher temperatures, less CO_2 condenses, reducing the percentage recovery.

The combined vent flow from the flash stages consists of approximately 25% CO_2, which based on the composition data presented in *Table 5-19* is approximately 5% of the total CO_2 flow. Hence, this loss limits the efficiency of CO_2 capture to approximately 95%.

The product stream now consists of approximately 95% CO_2 and 5% contaminants (down from 20% in the inlet stream). The contaminants, however, include significant O_2 (1% of total) and approximately 100 ppmv of SO_2.

To meet the pipeline specification, additional cleanup is required. Two approaches have been considered:

1. **Add a third flash stage.** This raises CO_2 purity to 98%, but the oxygen and SO_2 content remain above the pipeline specification values. This additional flash stage also increases the amount of CO_2 released, further lowering the percentage recovery of CO_2.
2. **Replace each flash stage with a distillation column.** The column after the first recuperator will remove SO_2 and NOx, and the one after the second recuperator will remove oxygen and nitrogen. This will raise the CO_2 purity to above 99% and satisfy the pipeline specification values, but it will also decreases the percentage recovery of CO_2.

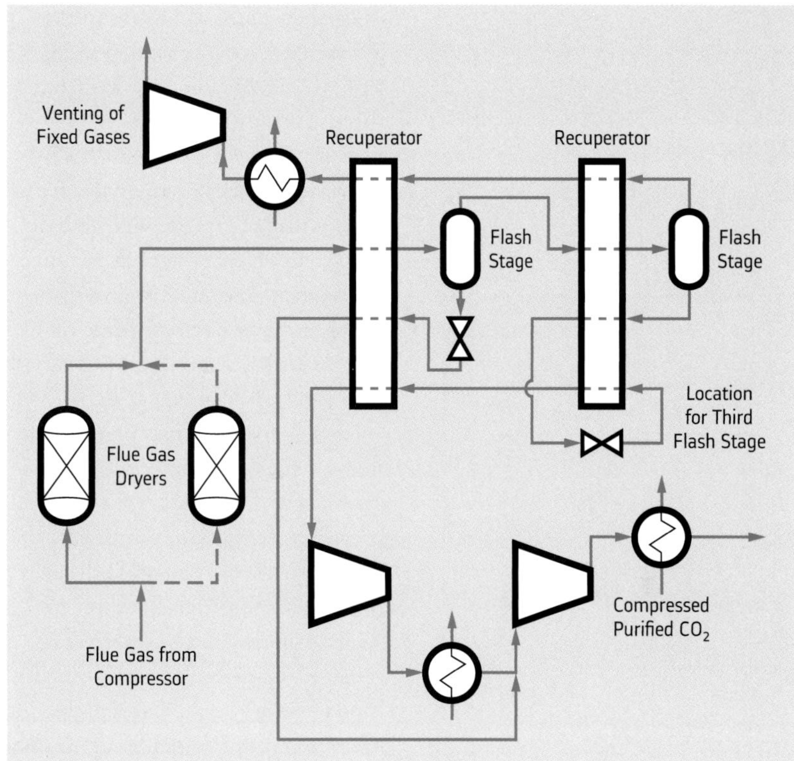

Figure 5-64 | Flow diagram for the CO_2 purification stage

For NOx separation by distillation, the NO has to be oxidized to NO_2. This occurs rapidly at approximately 220 psia (15 bar). The compression stages have to be designed to allow the reaction to proceed.

In all the designs, the vent stream requires treatment to remove the SO_2 and NOx. An SCR can be used, but this will be much smaller than that used on an air-fired PC unit. The SO_2 can be removed by passing the exit gas to an existing FGD unit or by building a compact unit especially for the vent stream. The remaining CO_2 and nitrogen can be discharged into the flue gas stream at a convenient location or passed to a dedicated stack.

Fireside corrosion may be increased in the immediate vicinity of the oxygen-fired burner because of the higher oxygen concentration. This threat can be offset by using coatings. If the heat fluxes are kept the same as those for air-fired units, standard materials of construction most likely can be used. If both the oxygen content and the heat fluxes are increased, some material upgrades probably will be required.

Startup considerations of the boiler and CO_2 purification plant are summarized in *Figure* 5-65. From cold-start conditions, the 60% minimum load condition is reached in 30 hours, which is slightly longer (by perhaps 5 hours) than that for an air-fired boiler. This longer time probably arises from the transition to oxygen-fired operation that is made after 20 hours with the plant at 30%. This requires bringing the air separation unit into service, starting the RFG flow, and adjusting the burners for the new combustion conditions. The CO_2 plant enters service after 35 hours with the output still at 60%. Up to that time, the flue gas has been passing to the stack. Full load is reached in a little over 40 hours, with the exact time depending on the operation of the CO_2 plant.

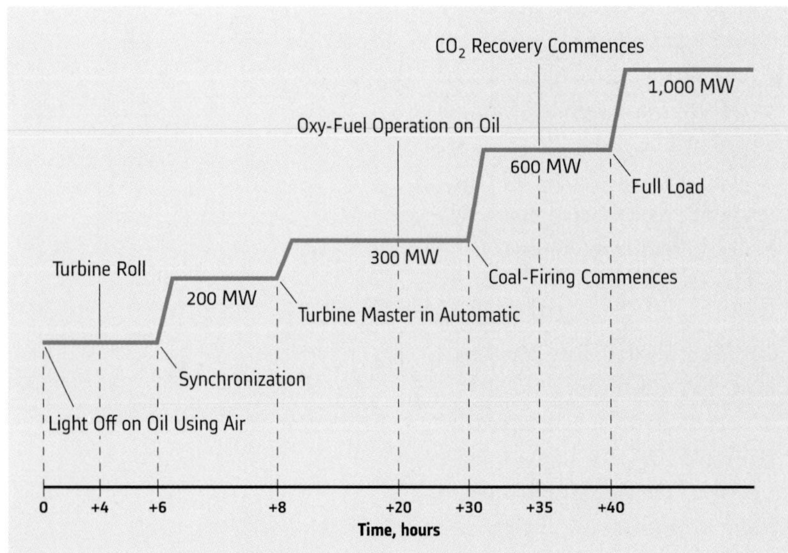

Figure 5-65 | Startup of an oxygen-fueled supercritical PC plant

POST-COMBUSTION CAPTURE

An alternative to oxygen firing is post-combustion capture of CO_2 using a solvent to chemically absorb the CO_2 from the flue gas. The higher the generating efficiency, the less CO_2 released per megawatt-hour. This lower release helps lower the cost of capture and storage. Thus, supercritical units are being considered as a starting point for post-combustion capture plants. One solvent currently in use for small-scale applications is monoethanolamine (MEA). Two early plants using Alstom CFB technology were installed with partial flue gas scrubbing of CO_2 for food-grade applications. Research is underway to identify solvents that are less costly for power industry applications.

For most scrubbing processes, the design consists of two stages. In the first, the flue gas is passed through an absorption column, where the solvent removes the majority of the CO_2 by chemical absorption. In the second, the solvent is sent to a stripping column, where heat is applied to release the CO_2 and regenerate the solvent. The flow sheet is similar to a standard generic gas treatment process (*Fig. 5-66*).

The flue gas and aqueous solvent solution are contacted countercurrently in an absorption column, with the flue gas entering at the bottom of the column and the CO_2-lean solvent at the top. To minimize solvent degradation, the inlet flue gas temperature should not exceed 150°F (65°C).

For an MEA system, the lean solvent typically enters the absorber at 110°F (45°C), and because the CO_2 absorption reaction is exothermic, the CO_2-rich solvent leaves the bottom of the absorber at 140°F (60°C). The rich solvent passes to a rich-lean solvent heat exchanger, where it is heated by the hot, lean solvent leaving the reboiler. The hot, rich solvent then enters at the top of the stripper column, with additional heat being provided by a steam-heated reboiler that raises the solvent temperature to approximately 250°F (120°C). This steam represents a parasitic loss to the power plant operation. To enhance desorption of the CO_2 and reduce the amount of heat required, the stripper operates close to atmospheric pressure. The hot, lean solvent is withdrawn from the reboiler inlet and then passed to the rich-lean solvent heat exchanger, where it is cooled ahead of re-entering the absorber.

Any MEA solvent carried over from the absorber by the CO_2-depleted flue gas is recovered by a water wash system and returned to the center of the absorber. The water added also helps maintain the solvent dilution at the required level. Solvent carried over from the stripper by CO_2 is recovered in a condenser and returned to the top of the stripper. A small portion of the lean solvent is extracted from

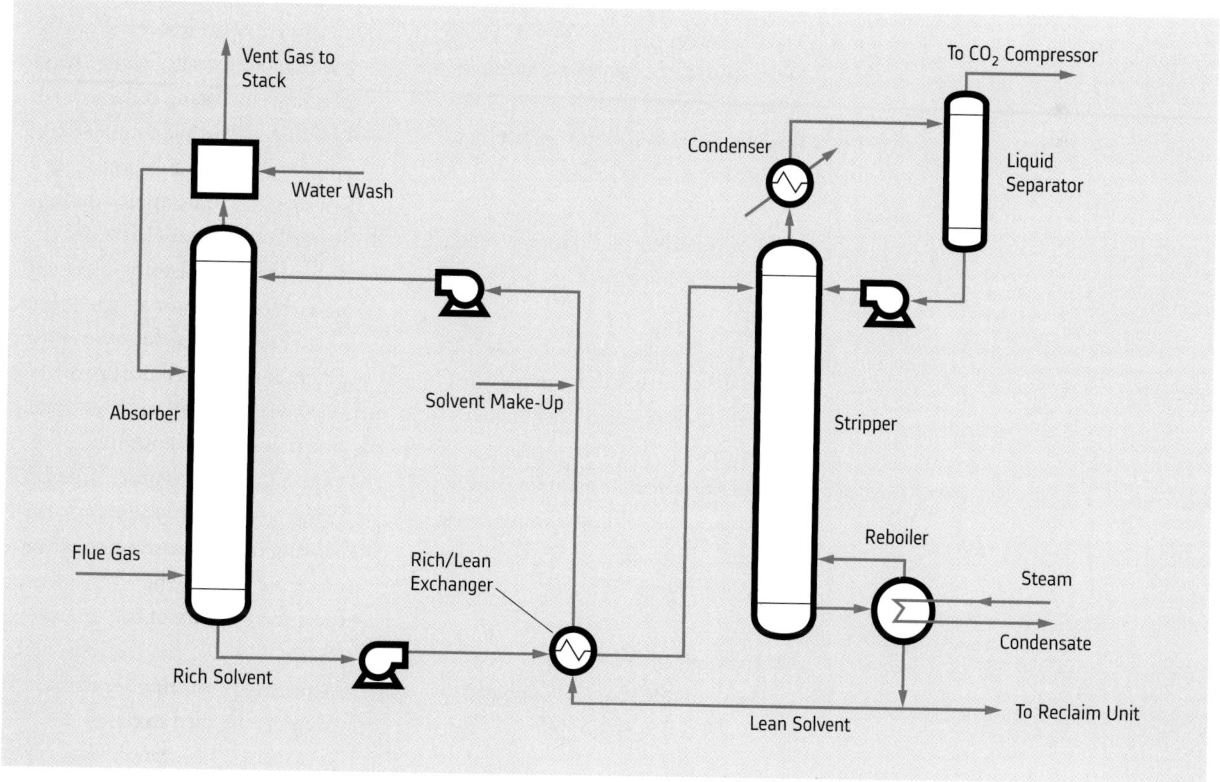

Figure 5-66 | General flow diagram for a CO_2 scrubbing process

the reboiler and then fed to a reclaim unit, where any degradation products are precipitated out following reaction with caustic soda. This small amount of material can be kept in suspension and injected into the boiler for disposal by incineration.

The MEA also reacts with the other acid gases in the flue gas, such as SO_2 and NO_2, forming heat-stable salts that must be removed from the process and replaced with make-up amine. To limit the increase in operating cost, it typically is recommended that the flue gas leaving the boiler be pre-treated to reduce both the SO_2 and the NO_2 to low levels. An economic trade-off study regarding the cost of acid gas scrubbing versus that of make-up MEA will determine the level of cleanup needed. Using low-NOx burners and SCR, NOx emissions can be reduced to below 20 ppmv. Because NO_2 usually represents only 5% of the total NOx, the NO_2 content is approximately 1 ppmv. The NO present in the NOx does not react with amines. A benefit of these reactions is that the flue gas discharged to the atmosphere contains virtually no SO_2.

Solvent improvements include a new formulation that has an increased CO_2 absorption rate. This decreases the required packing volume in the absorber, allowing a smaller, less expensive absorber to be used. The improved solvent also has a higher CO_2 carrying capacity, resulting in less solvent circulation and a corresponding reduction in reboiler steam demand. The reclaim stage has been improved as well, allowing degradation products to be removed with reduced solvent loss.

The desirable characteristics of a CO_2 solvent are as follows:

- Low heat demand (i.e., low heats of reaction [absorption and desorption] at a low temperature) lowers steam usage and the size of the reboiler. The lower the temperature of the heat supplied for a given duty, the lower the grade of heat that is required. The reduced steam demand improves the overall efficiency, which reduces the specific cost of CO_2 capture.
- High reaction rates (absorption and desorption) lower the size of the contactor required for a given capture rate.
- High CO_2 loading lowers the amount of solvent that has to be circulated. This lowers pumping duty and, as the absorber and regenerator operate at different temperatures, lowers the sensible heat duty.
- Low volatility lowers the amount of solvent carried over from the absorber and so lowers the heat consumed by evaporation.
- High stability lowers solvent decomposition and reduces make-up costs.
- Low corrosivity allows use of low-cost construction materials.
- Low toxicity reduces process hazards and environmental impact.
- Tolerance to impurities in the flue gas reduces solvent degradation.

Current research is focusing on achieving these properties by modifying the structure of amines. MEA is a primary amine, and recent studies suggest:

- Moving to secondary and tertiary hindered amines
- Increasing the size of the amino group
- Increasing the number and position of hydroxyl groups

In sterically hindered amines, the nitrogen atoms of the ammonia are substituted by a bulky molecule. By slowing down the rate of carbamate formation, the CO_2 capacity of the amine is increased. A primary hindered amine reacts as follows:

$$P\text{-}NH_2 + CO_2 + H_2O \leftrightarrow P\text{-}NH_3^+ + HCO_3^-$$

Equation 5-67

Because only one molecule of the hindered amine is used, compared to two molecules of MEA, the carrying capacity theoretically can be doubled.

Absorber inter-cooling can be used to limit the maximum temperature reached in the absorber. For a two-stage absorber, semi-rich solvent is extracted from the bottom of the upper section, cooled, and then returned to the top of the lower section. This process increases the CO_2 absorption rate, allowing a smaller and less expensive absorber to be used. The CO_2 loading in the rich solvent is increased, resulting in less solvent circulation and a corresponding reduction in reboiler steam demand.

A split flow configuration can be used to reduce steam demand. In this operation, CO_2 regeneration is achieved by combining the steam stripping with a flash stage. One portion of the rich solvent passes to the stripper, and as the flow is reduced, steam demand also is reduced. The other portion of the rich solvent is heated indirectly by the hot, lean solvent leaving the reboiler and is regenerated in a flash drum. This regeneration is achieved without any additional steam, the energy being provided by the heat contained within the hot, lean solvent. The semi-lean solvent leaving the flash drum contains more CO_2 than the lean solvent. When the two streams are combined, the solvent passing back to the absorber has a higher CO_2 loading. To achieve the same recovery, the solvent circulation rate must be increased. This increase is only marginal, however, being offset by the two previous improvements.

In order to decrease the partial pressure of CO_2 in the gas stream leaving the flash drum and, thereby, increase regeneration, live steam can be added. To avoid an increase in steam consumption, this steam is extracted by flashing the reboiler condensate down to the flash drum pressure. Increasing flash regeneration reduces the CO_2 loading of the solvent returning to the absorber, which decreases the solvent circulation rate and, in turn, the reboiler steam requirement.

Membrane gas absorption contactors are being investigated to replace the conventional packed-column designs. The membrane forms a gas-permeable barrier between the solvent and the gas. The gas diffuses through the pores to be absorbed in the liquid. The use of fine membrane material results in a high specific surface and very compact equipment. Operation is independent of gravity, and the process is not influenced by the L/G ratio. Thus, these flows can be adjusted independently. Because the gas and liquid flows are kept separate, solvent entrainment and foaming are eliminated. The design has no contact packing, so flooding and channeling are eliminated as well. The membrane minimizes contamination of the solvent with oxygen, SO_2, NOx, and dust and, therefore, reduces solvent degradation reactions. This eliminates the need for inhibitors and allows the solvent formulation to be

The chilled ammonia process attempts to capture CO_2 with less energy consumption by using a more favorable solvent (ammonia) and by regenerating the solvent at a higher pressure to reduce CO_2 compression costs.

optimized for CO_2 capture. By building the membrane gas absorption from cross-flow modules, a range of CO_2 removal rates can be satisfied. Units handling as much as 11,000 tons/day (10,000 tonnes/day) of CO_2 are thought to be feasible. These units will be much more compact and lighter than conventional absorbers.

As an alternative to amine-based scrubbing, Alstom is developing the chilled ammonia process. The chilled ammonia process uses ammonium carbonate as the solvent, capturing CO_2 as ammonium bicarbonate, which is then regenerated to release the CO_2 and reform the carbonate. The process equipment includes an absorber and stripping column similar to the amine process shown in *Figure 5-66*, but the operating temperature range is different. The chilled ammonia plant is shown in *Figure 5-67*.

The reversible chemical reaction is as follows:

$$CO_2 + (NH_4)_2CO_3 + H_2O \leftrightarrow 2NH_4HCO_3$$

Equation 5-68

The heat of reaction is lower than that of MEA, but ammonium carbonate can dissociate in solution, allowing ammonia to evaporate readily at typical absorber temperatures. This would increase the energy consumed by evaporation and produce a dilute ammonia solution in the water wash used to remove the ammonia from the flue gas. The energy required to concentrate this stream is high, thus impacting the economics. To overcome this limitation, the rate of

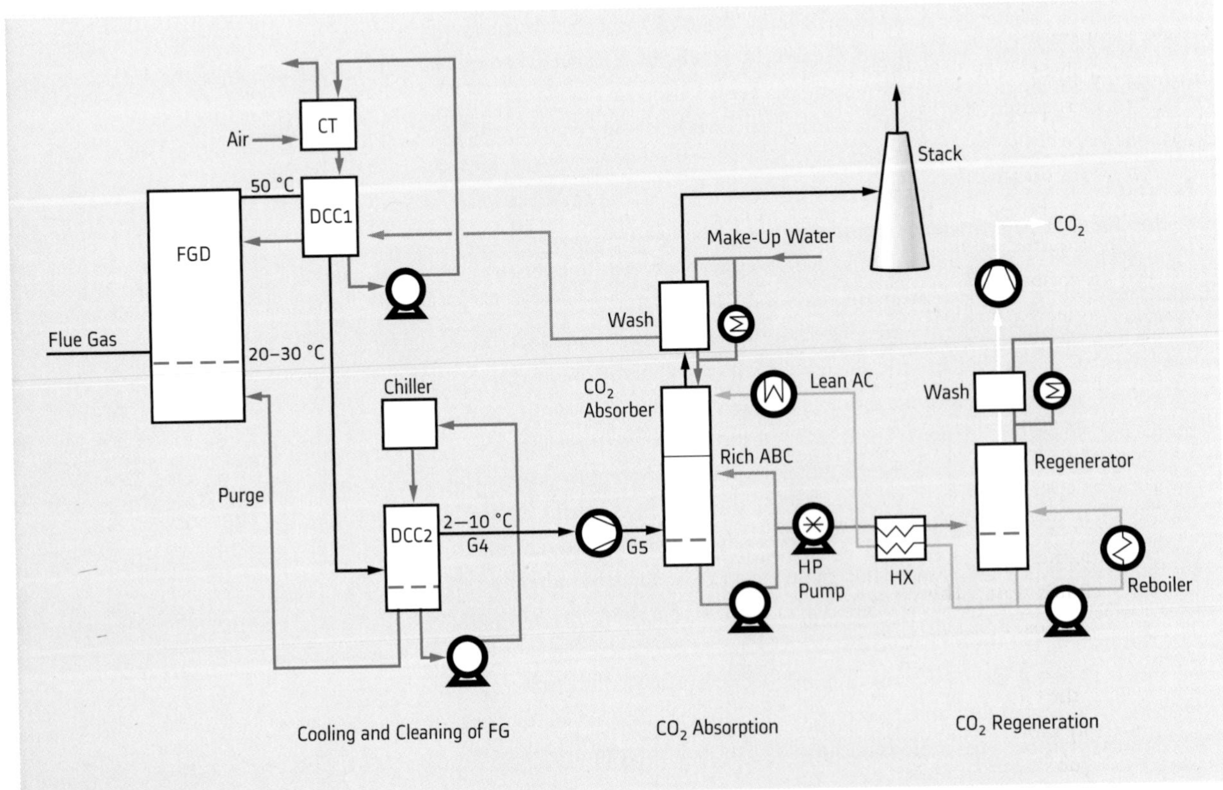

Figure 5-67 | Chilled ammonia system (ABC, ammonium bicarbonate; AC, ammonium carbonate; CT, cooling tower; DCC, direct contact cooler; FGD, flue gas desulfurization; G, gas; HP, high pressure; HX, heat exchanger)

evaporation is greatly reduced by operating the absorber at temperatures of 50°F (10°C) or below and by controlling the NH_3/CO_2 molar ratio to approximately 1.5. Furthermore, the low temperature enhances mass transfer of CO_2 into the solution, resulting in a smaller, lower-cost absorber.

A feature of ammonium bicarbonate is that it can be regenerated at elevated pressure, reducing the compression energy to raise the CO_2 to pipeline pressure. This reduced compression energy is significant in the overall process efficiency. Compression work accounts for half of the lost power in most scrubbing processes. A similar amount of energy is lost in both oxygen-firing and IGCC applications. In addition, the high pressure limits evaporation of ammonia and water, further reducing the energy consumed by heating and cooling. The higher pressure requires a higher stripper temperature than is used with MEA, but analysis shows that the overall energy requirement is reduced. Additionally, MEA could release the CO_2 at elevated pressure, but unlike ammonium bicarbonate, the higher temperature required would cause thermal degradation of the amine.

The flue gas leaves the FGD at approximately 130°F (55°C) and is cooled in a direct contact cooler using process water to approximately 80°F (25°C). The temperature is further reduced to the operating temperature of the absorber, approximately 50°F (10°C), in a second direct contact cooler using chilled water. This cooling stage condenses most of the moisture from the flue gas, reducing its volume and increasing the CO_2 concentration. This highly moist region has the potential to scrub out residual SO_2, SO_3, HCl, and particulate matter. As water is condensed from the flue gas, the overall water consumption of the plant is reduced.

The cooled flue gas flows through the absorber and contacts the circulated liquor containing ammonium carbonate and bicarbonate. To maintain the absorber at the required operating temperature, the chiller circuit removes the heat of reaction from the liquor. Any ammonia in the exiting decarbonated flue gas is removed in a water wash. Liquor is drawn from the base of the absorber, raised in pressure and passed to the regenerator to release the captured CO_2, and then returned to the absorber. Any ammonia in the CO_2 is condensed with the water and returned to the regenerator.

Preliminary evaluation shows that this technology has the potential to greatly reduce the effect of CO_2 capture on plant efficiency and cost of electricity. A 5-MW, integrated pilot plant at the Pleasant Prairie Power Plant of We Energies in Wisconsin has been started up, and several larger pilot and demonstration facilities are in progress.

ELECTRO-CATALYTIC OXIDATION

An alternative to the chilled ammonia process, but one that still uses ammonia, is the electro-catalytic oxidation process. Following particulate removal, the flue gas enters an electro-catalytic oxidation barrier discharge reactor, where water and oxygen dissociate to form hydroxyl radicals and atomic oxygen, which in turn oxidize the following flue gas substances:

- Hg to HgO and $HgCl_2$
- SO_2 to SO_3 and H_2SO_4
- NO to NO_2 and HNO_3

The flue gas then enters an ammonia scrubber that removes unconverted SO_2, acid gases, and $HgCl_2$. The NO_2 and SO_3 combine with the ammonia to form aqueous ammonium sulfate and nitrate. Mercury is removed from the liquor before it is crystallized. The cleaned flue gas passes through a wet ESP to remove aerosols and any residual fine particulate matter and is directed to the bottom of the ammonia scrubber. The CO_2 in the flue gas reacts with ammonia according to the following reaction:

$$CO_2 + (NH_4)_2CO_3 + H_2O \leftrightarrow 2NH_4HCO_3$$

Equation 5-69

Because ammonia is highly volatile, the flue gas leaving the absorber must pass through a water wash, creating a stream of dilute aqueous ammonia that is sent back to the barrier scrubber. This interdependence between the two control systems imposes a limitation on these systems, because they can only be used in conjunction with the electro-catalytic barrier systems. Without the barrier process, the dilute ammonia stream would have to be concentrated for reuse, and this requires significant energy, negating the thermal advantage gained.

BENEFIT OF USING A PC PLANT WITH ADVANCED ULTRA-SUPERCRITICAL STEAM CONDITIONS

Advanced boiler materials are being developed to accommodate higher steam temperatures and pressures and to raise generating efficiencies. The most ambitious program anticipates a double-reheat design operating at 5,000 psia/1,360°F/1,400°F/1,400°F (343 bar/740°C/760°C/760°C) with an efficiency of 48% (higher heating value [HHV]) for bituminous coal. By emitting less CO_2, these advanced PC plants will lower the cost of CO_2 capture.

The trends of the cost-of-electricity data for five PC plant designs investigated and for two coals, with and without CO_2 capture, are presented in *Figure* 5-68. There is only a slight effect of efficiency on cost of electricity for plants without CO_2 capture, which is a commonly observed trend. For plants with CO_2 capture, there is a clear reduction in cost of electricity with increased efficiency. The cost of electricity for the advanced ultra-supercritical PC plant with double reheat is approximately 10% lower than that of a subcritical plant for both Pittsburgh #8 and sub-bituminous coal.

The cost of electricity in *Figure* 5-68 shows that little financial incentive exists to go to higher steam conditions if CO_2 capture is not incorporated. If advanced PC technology is to be commercially available once CO_2 capture is required, however, it must be deployed now, so that it can evolve and improve through design and operational experience.

CHEMICAL LOOPING

Alstom is developing a longer-term concept that represents a new high-temperature process whereby calcium-based compounds are "looped" in a regenerative manner to extract oxygen from air for purposes of combustion (*Fig.* 5-69) or gasification and then to extract CO_2 from reformed syngas for purposes of hydrogen production (*Fig. 5-70*). Surplus heat from the exothermic oxidation reactions is transferred by the thermal loop of solids to satisfy the energy requirements for the endothermic reduction reaction. The thermal looping can employ either chemically inert solids (e.g., bauxite) or, more likely, excess calcium solids.

As shown in *Figure 5-69*, the exothermic oxidizer reactor oxidizes CaS to form $CaSO_4$ using preheated air:

$$CaS + 2O_2 \rightarrow CaSO_4$$

Equation 5-70

The hot, oxygen-rich $CaSO_4$ is then transported to the reducer reactor, where coal is introduced, and the oxygen is stripped from the $CaSO_4$ to form CaS (solid) plus pure CO_2 (gas). The CO_2 gas product is available for use or sequestration:

$$CaSO_4 + 2C \rightarrow CaS + 2CO_2$$

Equation 5-71

By decreasing the air/coal ratio, this system can produce a syngas of CO and H_2. The CaS is then transported back to the oxidizer to repeat the process (i.e., regenerate) and, thus, completes the "loop." Fresh $CaCO_3$ is added to the system to capture fuel-bound sulfur and form $CaSO_4$. The excess $CaSO_4$ must be drained from the reducer to maintain the mass balance. The continuous requirement to capture fuel-bound sulfur to form $CaSO_4$ regenerates calcium compounds in the loop to keep the chemical reactivity high. The heat balance between the exothermic oxidizer and the endothermic reducer can be satisfied independently of the chemically active solids by recirculation of solid particles between the reactors. This forms the "thermal loop."

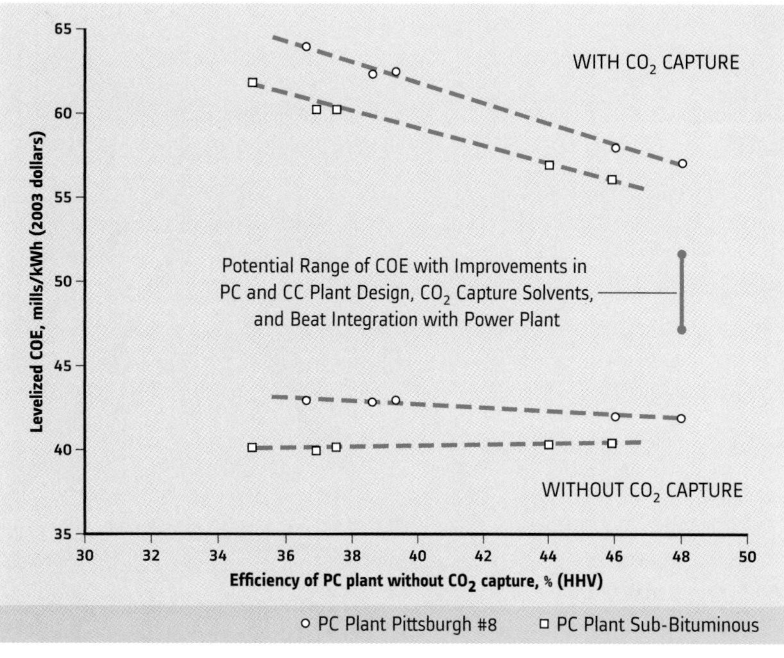

Figure 5-68 | Levelized cost of electricity (COE) versus efficiency (CC, combined cycle; HHV, higher heating value; PC, pulverized coal)

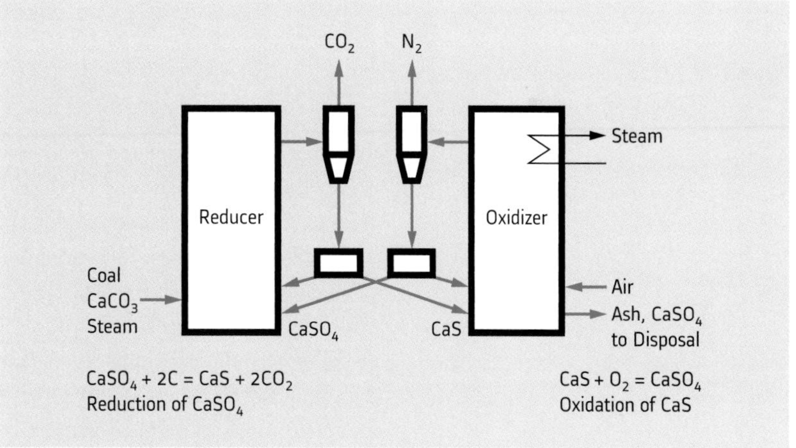

Figure 5-69 | Chemical looping combustion with CO_2 capture (Reprinted from Nsakala et al.[89])

The CaS/$CaSO_4$ loop can be configured in one of two freestanding chemical processes. When the amount of oxygen delivered is sufficiently high

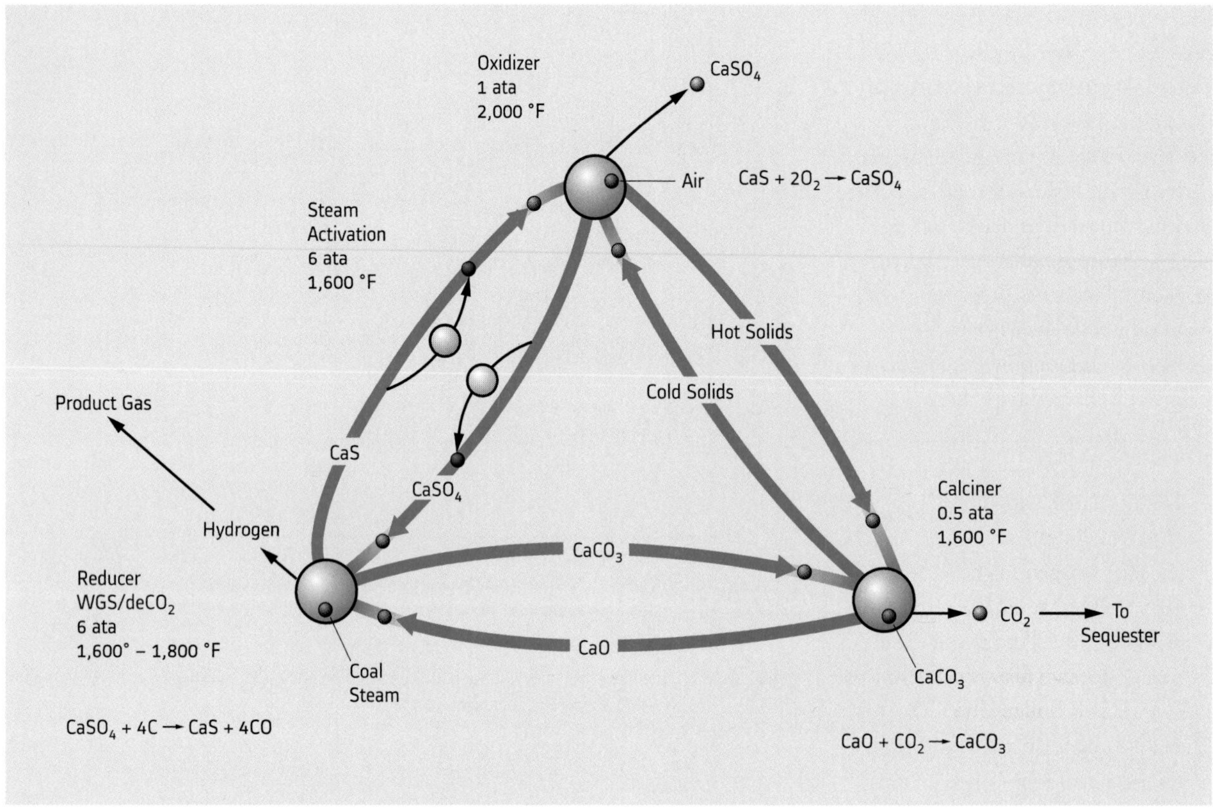

Figure 5-70 | Chemical looping with hydrogen production

to burn all the coal, the loop becomes a combustion system. The end products are pure CO_2 for sequestration and steam for electric power. The steam is generated by heat from the oxidizer (*Fig.* 5-69). Alstom considers this to be the early commercial application. If the amount of air delivered to the coal is only sufficient for partial oxidation, however, the end product is a sulfur-free syngas consisting mainly of CO and H_2 (~300 BTU/ft^3 [37 KJ/m^3], dry, HHV basis) suitable for a gas turbine combined cycle. Cold gas efficiency can exceed 85%. Thus, *Figure* 5-69 shows both the combustion and syngas production configurations.

Figure 5-70 shows the modification of the combustion loop to the syngas loop from *Figure* 5-69 with the addition of a calciner and the CaO/$CaCO_3$ loop. In this modification, the reducer uses steam to shift the CO-rich syngas to H_2 and CO_2. The CaO is added to the reducer to capture the CO_2 as $CaCO_3$, producing a hydrogen-rich stream (~300 BTU/ft^3 [37 KJ/m^3], dry, HHV basis) suitable for an advanced steam cycle, gas turbine combined cycle, fuel cell cycle, and so on. Cold gas efficiency can exceed 85%. The $CaCO_3$ is drained from the shift reactor and sent to the calciner, where it is mixed with hot solids from the oxidizer to drive off CO_2 gas and regenerate CaO. The CaO is then returned to the shift reactor to capture more CO_2, completing the loop. The CO_2 capture reaction is an exothermic reaction that drives the gasification reaction. The calciner is a high-temperature endothermic reactor that receives its heat in the form of hot solids from the oxidizer reactor in the first loop. Hot $CaSO_4$/CaO (or inert bauxite) from the oxidizer can be used for this purpose. The need to capture sulfur and dispose of spent $CaSO_4$ keeps both loops well stocked with chemically fresh "looping material."

The chemical looping process can be deployed in three options (*Figs. 5-71, 5-72, and 5-73*):

- **Option 1.** As shown in *Figure 5-71*, the limestone-based sorbent (CaS) is burned in the CFB oxidizer/boiler (at ~1,800–2,000°F [980–1,090°C]) to produce hot $CaSO_4$. Steam also is generated as in a CFB boiler. The $CaSO_4$ is used in the CFB reducer to combust the coal (at ~1,600–1,800°F [870–980°C]) to form CO_2 for use or sequestration. The CaS is formed when the limestone captures the sulfur in the coal. This option can be employed when CO_2 capture is required and with conventional steam cycles, both subcritical and supercritical steam conditions. This equipment will be smaller than a traditional CFB boiler for a given steam generation rate because of rapid reactions and higher gas velocities. The process requires approximately 85% of the materials of construction used in today's CFBs. This configuration separates CO_2 from the nitrogen flue gas. Such a plant could be deployed in the relatively near term at a capital cost close to that of a CFB. The use of modified, but essentially commercial, CFB technology provides equipment that is readily recognizable in the power industry, making commercial acceptance easier to achieve.

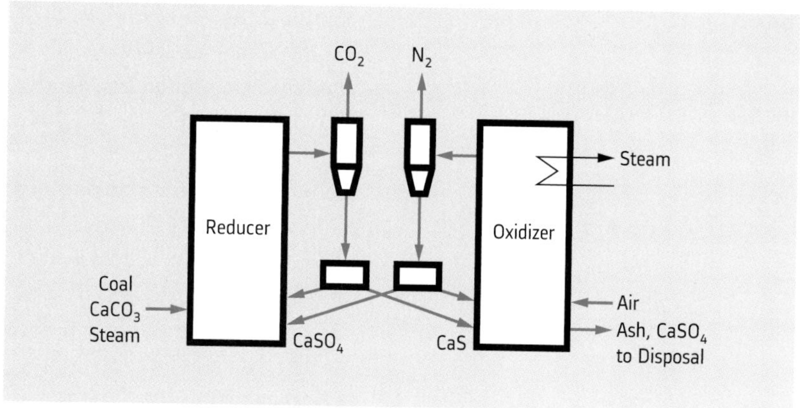

Figure 5-71 | Chemical looping combustion with CO_2 capture

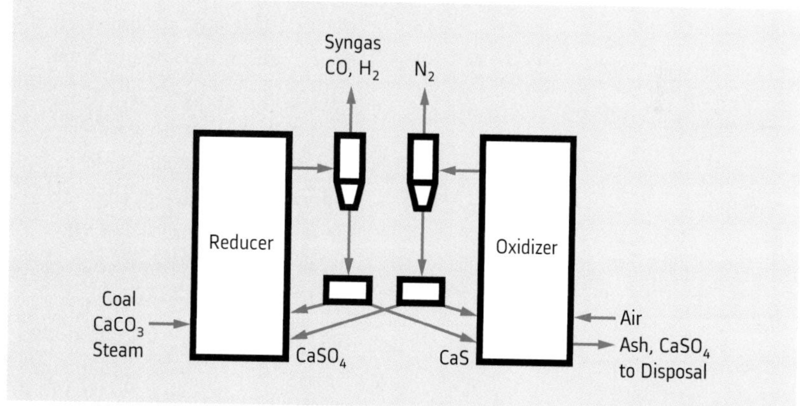

Figure 5-72 | Chemical looping gasification with syngas production and CO_2 capture

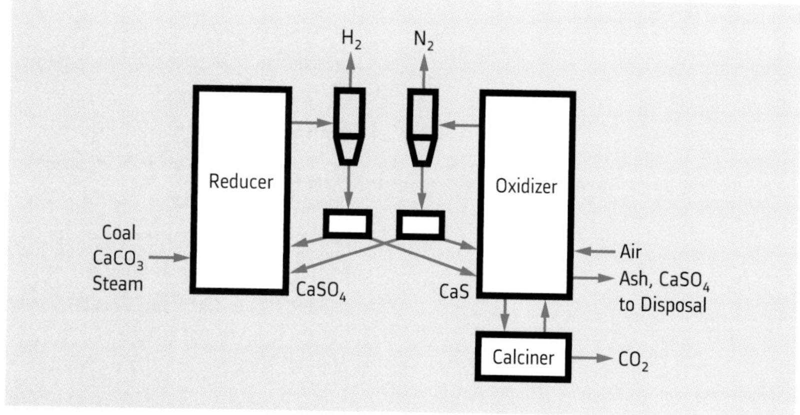

Figure 5-73 | Chemical looping gasification with CO_2 capture and H_2 production

- **Option 2.** As shown in *Figure 5-72*, the major difference between Option 1 and Option 2 is that the air/coal ratio for Option 2 is about one-fourth that of Option 1. Because of this lower air/coal ratio, medium-BTU syngas (CO and H_2) is produced instead of CO_2. Because less air is required, the equipment for this option is smaller than that for Option 1. Less than two-thirds of the typical CFB materials are required for this option, which is adaptable to more power cycles (e.g., advanced steam cycles, combined cycles, and fuel cell) compared with Option 1. Although CO_2 capture is not inherently accomplished with Option 2, it can be added downstream of the chemical looping system (as with conventional IGCC) by including water gas shift reactors to shift the CO via steam to CO_2 and H_2, with subsequent removal of the CO_2 via scrubbing (e.g., amine or ammonia). Compared with conventional IGCC using CO_2 capture, Option 2 avoids the cost and efficiency penalty of an oxygen plant.
- **Option 3.** As shown in *Figure 5-73*, this option operates at the same air/coal ratio as Option 2, but more steam is used in order to form mostly H_2 and CO_2 rather than syngas. The CO_2 is captured by the lime (CaO generated from the limestone) and liberated in the calciner using hot solids from the oxidizer to supply the heat of reaction. The pure CO_2 can be used or sequestered. This equipment is about the same size as that in Option 2, requiring about two-thirds of the typical CFB construction materials. Option 3 provides the highest net plant efficiency of all of the chemical looping options, and it can be used for clean, highly efficient, low-cost power plant applications or for hydrogen production. Because this concept requires the operation of more loops, which are interrelated, it will need additional development and can be considered to be a longer-term option.

Chemical looping has been under development since 1997. During this time, significant progress has been achieved in the development of the technology, and engineering/commercialization studies have helped to identify customer requirements and applications. In the course of this work, the application of chemical looping has been shown to be more flexible than originally envisioned.

Some of this flexibility is shown in *Table 5-20*, which summarizes the chemical looping product options described previously along with their associated product streams. Also shown are some of the specific uses (i.e., applications) of the particular product option. The wide range of application shows the flexibility of the chemical looping technology. Each product option is capable of capturing nearly all of the CO_2 from the coal (or any other carbonaceous fuel). Applications can serve nearly every major industrial market sector. The chemical looping concept provides the potential to be the lowest-cost option for capturing CO_2 from coal-fired power plants. Concerning power plant applications, *Table 5-20* shows that

chemical looping can be applied to advanced steam cycles, advanced gas turbine combined cycles, and in the future, fuel cell power cycles.

Table 5-20 also shows that product gas from chemical looping can be used in petrochemical/oil refinery applications to provide, for example, hydrogen for increasing refinery yields. The product gas also can be specifically tailored to provide a feedstock for producing Fischer-Tropsch or other liquid fuels from coal (or any other carbonaceous fuel [e.g., biomass, waste, or opportunity fuels]).

Table 5-21 shows potential performance and range of usage for some of the applications in *Table 5-20*. Referring to *Table 5-21*, Indices 1 and 4 represent the performance for conventional steam plants and IGCC,

TABLE 5-20 | CHEMICAL LOOPING PRODUCT OPTIONS

Option	Suboption	Products	CO_2 Capture	Applications
1	—	CO_2/Steam	Yes	Coal-fired advanced steam cycles
2	A	SynGas	No	Feedstock for transportation/liquid fuels Feedstock for chemical applications Industrial applications
2	B*	H_2/CO_2	Yes	Coal-fired advanced steam cycles Coal-fired advanced gas turbine combined cycles Coal-fired advanced cycles Industrial/oil refinery/petrochemical applications
3	—	H_2/CO_2	Yes	Coal-fired advanced steam cycles Coal-fired advanced gas turbine combined cycles Coal-fired advanced cycles Industrial/oil refinery/petrochemical applications

* Additional Water Gas Shift System and CO_2 Scrubber is required.

TABLE 5-21 | CHEMICAL LOOPING APPLICATIONS POTENTIAL

					Power Plant Efficiency (%, HHV basis)			
Index	Market	Chemical Looping Application*	Chemical Looping Option	Power Cycle	No. CO_2 Capture	95% CO_2 Capture	Plant Efficiency Ratio†	Basis
1	Coal power	Steam power plant	N/A	Subcritical steam‡	36			Reference 5
2	Coal power	Partial CO_2 capture	Option 1	Subcritical steam‡	36	31	0.86	Reference 5
3	Coal power	PC/CFB retrofit	Option 3	Supercritical steam‡	42	34	0.80	Preliminary
4	Coal power	IGCC	GE/Texaco (Quench)	Combined	35	27	0.79	Reference 5
5	Coal power	Turbo-charged boiler	Option 3	Ultra supercritical steam‡	45+	41+	0.91	Preliminary
6	Coal power	Chemical looping CC	Option 3	Combined	42	37	0.88	Reference 5
7	Coal power	Fuel cell	Option 3	Combined	60+	60+	0.91+	Preliminary
8	Industry	Syngas	Option 2	N/A				
9	Industry	Hydrogen	Option 3	N/A				

* CC, combined cycle; CFB, circulating fluidized bed; IGCC, integrated gasification combined cycle; PC, pulverized coal.[90]
† This column equals the plant efficiency with 95% CO_2 capture divided by the plant efficiency without CO_2 capture.
‡ Also applicable to other steam cycles.

respectively, from Nsakala et al.[89] and are included for comparative purposes.

The concept of partial CO_2 capture for power plants is shown in Index 2 of *Table 5-21*. The sixth column from the left shows the plant efficiency with no CO_2 compression/liquefaction, whereas the seventh column shows plant efficiency with nearly all of the CO_2 being compressed/liquefied. Partial CO_2 capture/sequestration would fall somewhere in between. For example, the efficiency at 50% CO_2 capture/sequestration would be approximately 33.5%. The value of this partial CO_2 capture approach might be that for some critical period of time, if allowed by the plant permit, more power could be made available for use by customers through reducing the CO_2 capture/sequestration rate. In this example, reducing the CO_2 capture rate from 95 to 50% would provide approximately 7% more power at full load coal flow. Of course, other partial capture scenarios are possible as well. This option is shown for a subcritical steam cycle, but it is applicable for a high-efficiency supercritical cycle. For example, with a supercritical cycle (e.g., steam conditions of 3,915 psi/ 1,085°F/1,148°F/2.5 inches Hg [27 mPa/585°C/620°C/64 mm Hg]),the efficiency would be approximately 42% (HHV basis) without CO_2 capture[90] and would be 86% of this value (i.e., 36%) with 95% CO_2 capture. These performance examples compete well against both conventional steam plants (Index 1) and IGCC (Index 4).

Index 3 of *Table 5-21* indicates how chemical looping Option 3 can provide a retrofit alternative for existing PC-fired and CFB steam power plants. Because this option produces a CO_2-free fuel (hydrogen), it can be used to provide boiler fuel for existing PC and CFB boilers. *Figure 5-74* shows how CO_2-free hydrogen from chemical looping Option 3 can be used to repower an existing boiler when CO_2 capture is required. For current PC-fired and CFB units, this concept could be implemented if sufficient space for Option 3 were available relatively near the PC boiler. When CO_2 capture is required, the Option 3 system can be added for approximately 20 to 25% of the original power plant cost. The 95% CO_2 captured by the chemical looping system can be used or sequestered. After conversion, the system would retain 80% of the original plant's net power. This same approach is compatible with future ultra-supercritical steam cycles (e.g., steam conditions of 5,075 psi/1,292°F/1,328°F/2.5 inches Hg [35 mPa/700°C/720°C/64 mm Hg]), with efficiencies of approximately 43.5% (HHV basis) without CO_2 capture[90] and approximately 35% with 95% CO_2 capture.

Table 5-21 also shows chemical looping applications for an advanced steam cycle concept (Index 5) and for a

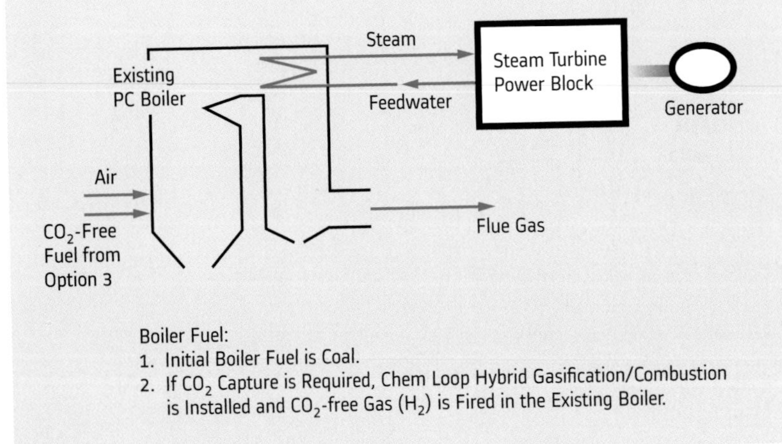
Steam
Existing
PC Boiler
Steam Turbine
Power Block
Feedwater
Generator
Air
CO_2-Free
Fuel from
Option 3
Flue Gas
Boiler Fuel:
1. Initial Boiler Fuel is Coal.
2. If CO_2 Capture is Required, Chem Loop Hybrid Gasification/Combustion is Installed and CO_2-free Gas (H_2) is Fired in the Existing Boiler.

Figure 5-74 | Retrofit CO_2-capture pulverized coal-fired power plant concept

combined cycle (Index 4). The ultra-supercritical turbocharged boiler concept (Index 5) is shown in *Figure 5-75*. In this concept, a pressurized ultra-supercritical boiler is integrated with chemical looping Option 3, which provides the source of pressurized CO_2-free fuel (hydrogen) and oxidant ($CaSO_4$). High-pressure steam is produced by the reaction of hot $CaSO_4$ and hydrogen. This high-pressure steam is used by the steam turbine to make additional power.

Index 6 of *Table 5-21* shows chemical looping Option 3 used in an IGCC system. This concept provides a coal-to-hydrogen chemical process that is more efficient than an oxygen-blown IGCC (*Table 5-21*, Index 4). The absence of parasitic power in the oxygen plant and heat losses because of water gas shift cooling and low-temperature sulfur recovery more than offset the power needed for the required syngas compressor in the chemical looping process. Dry solids will flow into and out of the reactor from both loops at a pressure close to atmospheric. The sensible heat in the gaseous N_2, CO_2, and H_2 streams is recovered by heating the air required by the oxidizer. Finally, particulate cleanup of all streams is done at cold conditions, without the need for high-temperature ceramic filters or the heat losses of a quench column.

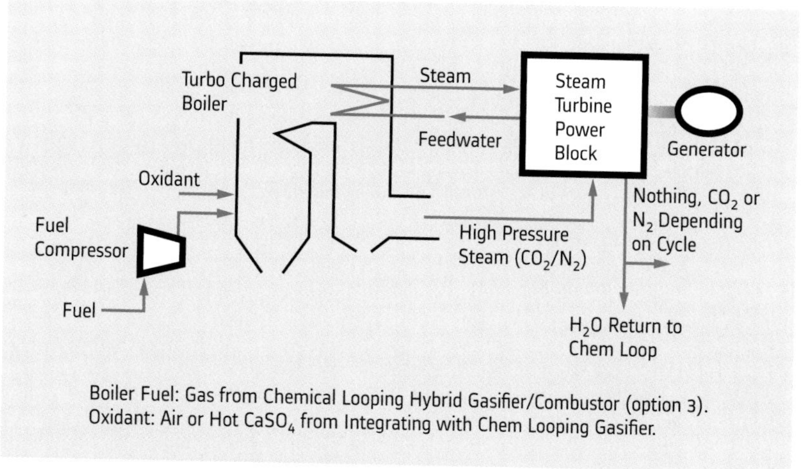

Figure 5-75 | Chemical looping turbocharged boiler concept

As a final comment, Index 7 of *Table 5-21* shows chemical looping potential performance when supplying hydrogen to future fuel cell cycles. Indices 8 and 9 show potential industrial markets for economical syngas and hydrogen for chemical looping Options 2 and 3, respectively.

ALAN FERGUSON
LEIF LINDAU
STEVE FRANCIS
KJELL PORLE
DENNIS LASLO
STEFAN AHMAN
LARS-ERIK JOHANSSON
MIKE RINI
LARRY CZARNECKI
JOHN WHEELDON
CARL BOZZUTO

REFERENCES

1. "Criteria for the Application of Dust Collectors to Coal-Fired Boilers: The Results of an ICCI/ABMA Joint Technical Committee Survey," *Proceedings of the American Power Conference*, 29: 572–580, 1967.

2. R. Srivastava et al., "Emission of SJ3," *JAWMA*, 54: 750, 2004.

3. Institute of Clean Air Companies, Inc., "Terminology for Electrostatic Precipitators," Publication EP-1. Washington, D.C.: Institute of Clean Air Companies, Inc., 2000.

4. Institute of Clean Air Companies, Inc., "Factors to Consider when Selecting Electrostatic Precipitators," Publication EP-5. Washington, D.C.: Institute of Clean Air Companies, Inc., 1982.

5. Institute of Clean Air Companies, Inc., "Gas Flow Model Studies," Publication EP-7. Washington, D.C.: Institute of Clean Air Companies, Inc., 2004.

6. Institute of Clean Air Companies, Inc., "Structural Design Criteria for Electrostatic Precipitator Casings," Publication EP-8. Washington, D.C.: Institute of Clean Air Companies, Inc., 1993.

7. Institute of Clean Air Companies, Inc., "Power Consumption Measurement for Electrostatic Precipitators," Publication EP-9. Washington, D.C.: Institute of Clean Air Companies, Inc., 1988.

8. Institute of Clean Air Companies, Inc., "Fundamentals of Fabric Collectors and Glossary of Terms," Publication F-2. Washington, D.C.: Institute of Clean Air Companies, Inc., 1972.

9. Institute of Clean Air Companies, Inc., "Operation and Maintenance of Fabric Collectors," Publication F-3. Washington, D.C.: Institute of Clean Air Companies, Inc., 2003.

10. Institute of Clean Air Companies, Inc., "Flue Gas Desulfurization Terminology," Publication FGD-1. Washington, D.C.: Institute of Clean Air Companies, Inc., 1982.

11. Institute of Clean Air Companies, Inc., "Gaseous Emissions Equipment: Product Definitions and Illustrations," Publication G-1. Washington, D.C.: Institute of Clean Air Companies, Inc., 1972.

12. Institute of Clean Air Companies, Inc., "Cyclonic Mechanical Dust Collector Criteria," Publication M-2. Washington, D.C.: Institute of Clean Air Companies, Inc., 1969.

13. Institute of Clean Air Companies, Inc., "Standardized Method of Particle Size Determination and Collection Efficiency," Publication M-5. Washington, D.C.: Institute of Clean Air Companies, Inc., 1975.

14. Institute of Clean Air Companies, Inc., "Wet Scrubber Terminology," Publication WS-1. Washington, D.C.: Institute of Clean Air Companies, Inc., 1975.

15. Institute of Clean Air Companies, Inc., "Basic Types of Wet Scrubbers," Publication WS-3. Washington, D.C.: Institute of Clean Air Companies, Inc., 1980.

16. Institute of Clean Air Companies, Inc., "Wet Scrubber System: Major Auxiliaries," Publication WS-4. Washington, D.C.: Institute of Clean Air Companies, Inc., 1975.

17. *Code of Federal Regulations*, Title CFR 40, Parts 53 to 80, "Protection of the Environment," revised as of August 26, 2005. Washington, D.C.: Office of the Federal Register, National Archives and Records Administration, U.S. Government Printing Office, 2005.

18. R. E. Bickelhaupt, "A Technique for Predicting Fly Ash Resistivity," U.S. Environmental Protection Agency Report EPA-600/7-79-204, Washington, D.C., 1979.

19. G. W. Driggers, A. A. Arstikaitis, and L.A. Hawkins, "Computer Model Use for Precipitators Sizing," Proceedings of Fourth Symposium on Transfer and Utilization of Particulate Control Technology, Houston, Texas, October 11–14, 1982.

20. D. O. Heinrich, moderator, "Panel Discussion on Wide Spacing Precipitators," Proceedings of the Second International Conference on Electrostatic Precipitation, November 1984, Kyoto, Japan.

21. D. O. Heinrich, "Are Non-Deutschian Phenomena Required to Explain Wide Spacing?" Proceedings of the Second International Conference on Electrostatic Precipitation, November 1984, Kyoto, Japan.

22. K. Porle and S. Maartmann, "On the Choice of Electrode Geometry and Voltage Waveforms for ESPs," Fourth International Conference on Electrostatic Precipitation, September 1990, Beijing, China.

23. L. Lillieblad, M. Thimanson, K. Porle, and H. Jacobsson, "On Dust Cake Removal in Electrostatic Precipitators," Eighth International Conference on Electrostatic Precipitation, May 2001, Birmingham, Alabama.

24. M. Kirsten, C. Mauritzson, M. Thimanson, and A. Karlsson, "Advance Switched Integrated Rectifiers for ESP Energization," Eighth International Conference on Electrostatic Precipitation, May 2001, Birmingham, Alabama.

25. H. Jacobsson, M. Thimanson, K. Porle, and M. Kirsten, "Back-Corona Control with Help of Advanced Microprocessor Enhances Performances," Sixth International Conference on Electrostatic Precipitation, June 1996, Budapest, Hungary.

26. J. G. Singer, "Design for Better ESP/Fabric-Filter Hopper Operation and Maintenance," Presented at Air Pollution Control Association '83, 76th Annual Meeting and Exhibition, Atlanta, Georgia, June 19–24,1983.

27. S. Matts and P.-O. Ohnfeldt, "Efficient Gas Cleaning with the SF Electrostatic Precipitator," *Fläkt Review*, 6(7): 105–122, 1963.

28. C. W. Penney, "Weaknesses in Conventional Theory of Electrostatic Precipitation," ASME Paper 67-WA/APC-1. New York: American Society of Mechanical Engineers, 1967.

29. H. J. White, "Effect of Fly Ash Characteristics on Collector Performance?" ASME Paper 54-A-259. New York: American Society of Mechanical Engineers, 1954.

30. H. J. White, *Industrial Electrostatic Precipitation*. Reading, MA: Addison-Wesley, 1963.

31. S. Oglesby, Jr., and G. B. Nichols, "A Manual of Electrostatic Precipitator Technology. Part 1—Fundamentals," Report PB-196 380 (AVT'D-O610). Springfield, VA: National Technical Information Service, 1970.

32. S. Oglesby, Jr., and G. B. Nichols. "A Manual of Electrostatic Precipitator Technology. Part II—Application Areas," Report PB-196 381 (APTD-0611). Springfield, VA: National Technical Information Service, 1970.

33. J. P. Cooch and G. H. Marchant, Jr., "Electrostatic Precipitator Rapping Re-entrainment and Computer Model Studies," Report FP-792, Vol. 3. Palo Alto, CA: Electric Power Research Institute, 1978.

34. G. W. Driggers, L.A. Hawkins, and R. W. Gray, "Applying Performance Results of C-E Rigid Frame Precipitators over a Wide Range of Coal Characteristics," Presented at the ASME-IEEE Joint Power Generation Conference, Indianapolis, Indiana, September 25–29, 1983.

35. Kermeth J. McLean, "Survey of Australian Experience in Collecting High-Resistivity Fly Ash with Electrostatic Precipitators, Final Report," Report PB-221 139 (EPAR2-73-258). Springfield, VA: National Technical Information Service, 1972.

36. Kenneth J. McLean, "Some Effects of High-Resistivity Fly Ash on Electrostatic Precipitator Operation," Presented at Electrostatic Precipitator Symposium, Birmingham, Alabama, 1971.

37. Z. Herceg and K. J. McLean, "Efficiency of Electrostatic Precipitators and Relationship to Corona Voltage-Current Characteristics," Presented at the 64th Annual Meeting of the Air Pollution Control Association, Atlantic City, New Jersey, June 27–July 1, 1971.

38. L. A. Hawkins and H. L. Wheeler, "Characterization of Discharge Electrode Performance: Results of Laboratory and Pilot Plant Experiments," Presented at the Sixth Joint EPA/EPRI Symposium on Transfer and Utilization of Particulate Control Technology, New Orleans, Louisiana, February 25–28, 1986.

39. K. Wark and C. F. Warner, *Air Pollution: Its Origin and Control*. New York: IEP, 1976.

40. H. J. White, "Electrostatic Precipitation of Fly Ash: Part II, Section 3—Fly Ash and Furnace Gas Characteristics," *Journal of the Air Pollution Control Association*, 27(2): 114–120, 1977.

41. C. C. Shale, J. H. Holden, and G. E. Fasching, "Electrical Resistivity of Fly Ash at Temperatures to 1,500°F.," U.S. Bureau of Mines Report of Investigations 7041. Washington, D.C.: U.S. Government Printing Office, 1968.

42. A. B. Walker, "Operating Experience with Hot Precipitators on Western Low-Sulfur Coals," *Proceedings of the American Power Conference*, 39: 582–594, 1977.

43. W. F. Frazier and W. Borowy, "Evaluation of Utility Cold-Side Electrostatic Precipitators," Presented at the ASME-IEEE Joint Power Generator Conference, Milwaukee, Wisconsin, October 20–24, 1985.

44. R. M. Kotan, E. G. Drdla, P. Yosick, and K. Hognefelt, "Omaha Public Power District Nebraska City Unit No. 1 Electrostatic Precipitator Upgrade," Presented at the Ninth Particulate Control Symposium, Williamsburg, Virginia, October 1991.

45. R. E. Bickelhaupt, "An Interpretation of the Deteriorative Performance of Hot Side Precipitators," *Journal of the Air Pollution Control Association*, 30: 812, 1980.

46. H. J. White, "Resistivity Problems in Electrostatic Precipitation," *Journal of the Air Pollution Control Association*, 24(4): 313–338, 1974.

47. G. C. Schneider et al., "Selecting and Specifying Electrostatic Precipitators," *Chemical Engineering*, 82(11): 94–108, 1975.

48. Y. Goland, "Mechanical and Structural Design Consideration for Internals in Electrostatic Precipitators," ASME Paper 76-WA/Pwr-7. New York: American Society of Mechanical Engineers, 1976.

49. J. Makansi, "Particulate Control: Optimizing Precipitators and Fabric Filters for Today's Power Plants;" Power Special Report, December 1986. New York: McGraw-Hill, 1986.

50. Joint Technical Committee of the American Boiler Manufacturers Association and Industrial Gas Cleaning Institute, Inc., "Design and Operation of Reliable Central Station Fly Ash Hopper Evacuation Systems," *Proceedings of the American Power Conference*, 42: 74–85, 1980.

51. J. A. Hudson et al., "Design Considerations and Initial Startup of Shawnee Baghouses," *Proceedings of the American Power Conference*, 42, 1990.

52. S. M. Cho, "Properly Apply SCR for NOx Removal," *Chemical Engineering Progress*, 90: 35–45, 1994.

53. R. D. Hawthorne, "Afterburner Catalysis—Effects of Heat and Mass Transfer Between Gas and Catalyst Surface," *AIChE Symposium Series*, 70: 428–438, 1974.

54. J. L. Pearson, G. Nonhebel, and P. H. N. Ulander, "The Removal of Smoke and Acid Constituents from Flue Gases by a Non-Effluent Water Process," *Journal of the Institute of Fuel*, 8: 119–156, 1935.

55. M. Epstein, EPA Alkali Scrubbing Test Facility: Advanced Program," PB 245 279. Springfield, VA: National Technical Information Service, 1975.

56. R. H. Borgwardt, "EPA/RTP Pilot Studies related to Unsaturated Operation of Lime and Limestone Scrubbers," *Combustion*, 47: 37–42, 1975.

57. B. F. Jones, P. S. Lowell, and F. S. Meserole, "Experimental and Theoretical Studies of Solid Solution Formation in Lime and Limestone Scrubbers," Vols. 1 and 11. Final Report. PB-264 953 (EPAJ600/2-76/273a) and PB-264 954 (EPA/600/2-76/273b). Springfield, VA: National Technical Information Service, 1976.

58. P. C. Rader, M. R. Gogineni, and K. Poglitsch, "Co-Precipitation: A Method for Gypsum Scale Prevention in Lime/Limestone Flue Gas Desulfurization Systems," Presented at the 72nd Annual Meeting of the American Institute of Chemical Engineers, San Francisco, California, November 25–29, 1979.

59. G. T. Rochelle, D. R. Owens, J. C. S. Chang, and T. G. Brna, "Thiosulfate as an Oxidation Inhibitor in Flue Gas Desulfurization Processes: A Review of R&D Results," Presented at the Ninth Symposium on Flue Gas Desulfurization, Cincinnati, Ohio, June 4–7, 1985.

60. R. H. Borgwardt, "Sludge Oxidation in Limestone FGD Scrubbers," EPA-600/7-77-061. Washington, D.C.: U.S. Environmental Protection Agency, 1977.

61. G. T. Rochelle and C. J. King, "The Effect of Additives on Mass Transfer in $CaCO_3$ or CaO Slurry Scrubbing of SO_2 from Waste Gases," *Industrial & Engineering Chemistry Fundamentals*, 16: 67–75, 1977.

62. Y. J. Lee and G. T. Rochelle, "Oxidative Degradation of Organic Additives for FGD: Products, Kinetics, and Mechanism," *Environmental Science and Technology*, 21: 266–272, 1987.

63. R. Ruiz-Alsop and G. T. Rochelle, "Co-precipitation of Organic Acids with $CaSO_3$ Solids," *Industrial & Engineering Chemistry Response*, 27: 2123–2126, 1988.

64. J. H. Lester and D. Danley, "Buffered Flue Gas Scrubbing System Using Adipic Acid By-Product Stream," U.S. Patent 4423018, December 1983.

65. S. Wang and D. Burbank, "Adipic Acid Enhanced Lime and Limestone Testing at the EPA Alkali Scrubbing Test Facility," PB 82 230 624. Springfield, VA: National Technical Information Service, 1982.

66. O. W. Hargrove, J. D. Colley, R. L. Glover, and M. L. Owen, "Full-Scale Utility FGD (Flue Gas Desulfurization) System Adipic Acid Demonstration Program. Volume 1. Process Results," PB 83 238 683. Springfield VA: National Technical Information Service, 1983.

67. J. D. Mobley and J. C. S. Chang, "The Adipic Acid Enhanced Limestone Flue Gas Desulfurization Process: An Assessment," PB83131219. Springfield, VA: National Technical Information Service, 1981.

68. K. Nolin, "Newly Developed FGD Plant for the Oil-Fired Condensing Power Station in Karlshamn, Sweden," VGB PowerTech, p. 37, 2000.

69. K. Nolin and D. Schreyer. "Flowpac®—Major WFGD Advance in Flue Gas Contact," Presented at the EPA/EPRI Mega Symposium, Washington, D.C., September 2004.

70. M. Maripuu et al., "Design of the Flowpac® WFGD System for the Amager Power Plant," Presented at Power-Gen, Orlando, Florida, November 2006.

71. J. Chang and D. Laslo, "Chloride Effects on Limestone FGD System Performance," Presented at the EPA/EPRI FGD Symposium, Hollywood, Florida, 1982.

72. D. Laslo, J. Chang, and J. Mobley, "Pilot Plant Tests on the Effect of Dissolved Salts on Lime/Limestone FGD Systems," Presented at the EPA/EPRI FGD Symposium, New Orleans, Louisiana, 1983.

73. J. C. S. Chang and N. Kaplan, "SO_2 Removal by Limestone Dual Alkali," *Environmental Progress* (3), 267–274, New York, November, 1984.

74. W. H. D. Plant and W. L. Mathay, "Nickel-Containing Materials in Flue Gas Desulfurization Equipment," Technical Paper 10072. Toronto: Nickel Institute, 1999.

75. M. L. Jackson et al., "Oxygen Transfer in a 23-Meter Bubble Column," *AIChE Symposium Series*, 71(151): , 1976.

76. I. J. Urza and M. L. Jackson, "Pressure Aeration in a 55-ft Bubble columns," *Industrial & Engineering Chemistry Process Design and Development*, 15: 106–113, 1975.

77. A. J. Toprac and G. T. Rochelle, "Limestone Dissolution in Stack Gas Desulfurization Processes—Effect of Type and Grind Modeled by Mass Transfer," Presented at the Annual AIChE Meeting, New Orleans, Louisiana, November 8–12, 1981.

78. D. Laslo and E. Bakke, "The Effect of Dissolved Solids on Limestone FGD Scrubbing Chemistry," Presented at the ASME 1983 Joint Power Generation Conference, Indianapolis, Indiana, 1983.

79. F. C. Bond, "Crushing and Grinding Calculations: Part I," *British Chemical Engineering*, 6: 378–385, 1961.

80. F. C. Bond, "Crushing and Grinding Calculations: Part II," *British Chemical Engineering*, 6: 543–548, 1961.

81. R. Meij, "The Fate of Trace Elements at Coal-Fired Power Plants," Proceedings of the Second International Conference on Managing Hazardous Air Pollutants, Washington, D.C., 1993.

82. F. Frandsen, "Trace Elements from Coal Combustion," Ph.D. Thesis, Department of Chemical Engineering, Technical University of Denmark, 1995.

83. U.S. Geological Survey, Fact Sheet 095-01.

84. K. Dombrowski et al., "Mercury Control Evaluation of Furnace Halogen Injection at TUX's Monticello Unit 3," Presented at the International Conference on Air Quality, Arlington, Virginia, September 19–21, 2005.

85. J. A. Withum, "Mercury Emissions from Coal Fired Facilities with SCR-FGD Systems," DOE/NETL Mercury Control Technology Conference, Pittsburg, PA, December 12, 2006.

86. L. Lindau, "Mercury Sorption to Coal Fly Ash," Staub-Reinhaltung der Luft, 43, pp. 166–167, 1983.

87. S. Sjostrom, "Evaluation of Sorbent Injection for Mercury Control," U.S. Department of Energy Cooperative Agreement DE-FC26-03NT41986, Topical Report 41986R07.

88. "MIT Study on the Future of Coal." Cambridge, MA: MIT, 2007.

89. N. Y. Nsakala et al., "Greenhouse Gas Emissions Control by Oxygen Firing in Circulating Fluid Bed Boilers," Alstom Power–U.S. Department of Energy (DOE) Report, PPL Report PPL-03-CT-09, U.S. DOE Project Manager: Suresh C. Jain, May 15, 2003.

90. H. E. Andrus, Jr., et al., "Hybrid Combustion-Gasification Chemical Looping Coal Power Technology Development, Phase 1 Report," Alstom Power–U.S. Department of Energy (DOE) Contract DE-FC26-03NT41866, U.S. DOE Project Manager: Suresh C. Jain, December 2004.

SUGGESTED READINGS

F. A. Ayer, ed., *Proceedings: Symposium on Flue Gas Desulfurization, Hollywood, Florida, 1977.* Report EPA-600/7-7 8/058. Springfield, VA: National Technical Information Service, 1978.

G. P. Behrens et al., "The Evaluation and Status of Flue Gas Desulfurization Systems." EPRI Report CS-3322, Project 982-28. Prepared by Radian Corporation, January, 1984.

D. C. Borio et al., "Design of Spray Tower Absorbers for Lime/Limestone Wet Scrubbers," ASME Paper 79-WA/Fu-9. New York: American Society of Mechanical Engineers, 1979.

D. Burbank and S. C. Wang, "EPA Alkali Scrubbing Test Facility: Advanced Program — Final Report," PB 8O 204 241. Springfield VA: National Technical Information Service, 1980.

"Evaluation of Advanced Coal Technologies with CO_2 Capture: Canadian CPC Phase 1 Studies of Coal Technologies with CO_2 Capture," Report 1004880. Palo Alto, CA: Electric Power Research Institute, 2004.

D. Frahotta and P. C. Rader. "Lime/Limestone Air Quality Control Systems: Effect of Magnesium on System Performance," ASME Paper 76-WA/APC-10. New York: American Society of Mechanical Engineers, 1976.

H. N. Head, "EPA Alkali Scrubbing Test Facility: Advanced Program. Third Progress Report," PB 274 544 Springfield, VA: National Technical Information Service, 1977.

K. A. Hoff et al., "The Kvaerner–Gore Membrane Process for CO_2 Removal: Mathematic Model and Experimental Verification," Presented at the AIChE Annual Meeting, Los Angeles, California, November 2000.

"Just Catch™ Development Project for CO_2 Capture from Gas Power Launched by Aker Kvaerner," Available at http://www.akerkvaerner.com/Internet/MediaCentre/PressReleases/Group/2006/AKPressRelease_1025215.htm

Krebs Engineers, "The Use of Hydrocyclones in Classification and Separation," Presented at the Sixth Annual Meeting of the Association for Crystallization Technology, Charlottesville, VA, 1995

C. C. Leivo, "Flue Gas Desulfurization Systems; Design and Operating Considerations. Vol. II," Technical Report PB-280 254 (EPk600/7-78/O3oB). Springfield, VA: National Technical Information Service, 1978.

E. C. Lewis, G. W. Driggers, and K. W. Malki, "Laboratory Evaluation of Several Alloys in High Chloride FGD Environment—Progress Report," Presented at Solving Corrosion Problems in Air Pollution Control Equipment, Denver, Colorado, August 11–13, 1981.

F. W. Linkand and W. H. Ponder, "Status Report on the Weilman Lord/Allied Chemical Flue Gas Desulfurization Plant at Northern Indiana Public Service Company's Dean H. Mitchell Plant," PB-282 091, Springfield, VA: National Technical Information Service, 1978.

T. Ohishi, "Mitsubishi CO_2 Recovery Technology from Flue Gas: Experience and R&D Facilities," Presented at the Ninth International CO_2 Capture Network Meeting, Copenhagen, June 16, 2006.

C. Rader et al., "The Role of Crystallization in the Design of Lime/Limestone Wet Scrubbing Systems for Flue Gas Desulfurization," Presented at the Symposium on Crystallization and Energy Systems, 83rd National Meeting of the American Institute of Chemical Engineers, Houston, Texas, March 20–24, 1977.

S. Reddy et al, "Fluor's Econamine FG Plus^{SM} Technology: An Enhanced Amine-Based CO_2 Capture Process," Presented at the U.S. Department of Energy's Second National Conference on Carbon Sequestration, Alexandria, Virginia, May 5–8, 2003.

Y. Yagi et al, "Improvement of CO_2-Capture Technology from Flue Gas," Presented at the Seventh International Conference on Greenhouse Gas Control Technologies, Vancouver, Canada, September 5–9, 2004.

Auxiliary Equipment

Chapter Six

Although most of the attention is given to the main plant components, no plant can operate properly without adequately designed auxiliary equipment. This equipment includes pulverizers, air preheaters, ash-handling equipment, pumps, fans, feedwater heaters, and condensers. This chapter provides an overview of this type of equipment.

PULVERIZERS AND PULVERIZED COAL SYSTEMS

Suspension firing of coal as a fine powder has been the predominant method of coal combustion in utility scale steam generators since the 1950s. Suspension firing has dominated over lump-coal combustion techniques for a number of reasons. Pulverized coal is easily ignited and controlled with characteristics similar to those of natural gas. Pulverized coal is easily transported with air, allowing multiple fuel injection points, which makes furnace design and size essentially unlimited. Virtually all coal types can be reduced to a fine powder, making suspension firing technology universally applicable in all geographic regions.

HISTORICAL PERSPECTIVE

"A change of coal upsets the operation of a pulverized-coal plant to a much smaller degree than it does a stoker fired plant. Pulverized-coal furnaces can be readily adapted to burn other fuels that burn like gas, and in that respect are capable of burning almost any fuel which is used for making steam." Henry Kreisinger, former Director of Research at Combustion Engineering, made this statement at a 1937 meeting of the American Society of Mechanical Engineers in Windsor, Canada.[1]

One of the most significant engineering achievements in the 20th century was the commercial development of methods for firing coal in pulverized form. This development made possible extremely large, technologically advanced, steam-generating units operating with minimized emissions, high thermal efficiency, high reliability, and increased safety.

Worldwide, practically every type of coal mined is now being burned successfully in pulverized form. Similarly, many other types of low-grade, waste, and by-product solid fuels also may be fired economically and efficiently in this manner. Pulverized fuel firing has contributed to the reduction of labor costs in steam power plants, increased operational flexibility, and allowed the practical use of an extremely wide range of fuels.

Since the first information attributed to the Niepce brothers was published in France in the early 1800s, there have been many examples of engineers whose visions of future developments in pulverized coal technology have far outreached the materials and technical understanding of their time. In his 1824 engineering classic, *Reflections on the Motive Power of Fire*,[2] Sadi Carnot and his colleagues provided a critical thermodynamic analysis of the pyreolophore, an engine fired by powdered coal. During the 1890s, Rudolf Diesel conducted his first experiments on the internal combustion engine bearing his name using pulverized coal as the primary fuel. At this time pulverized coal firing was achieving its first real commercial success in the cement industry.[3,4] In the early 1900s, Thomas A. Edison made improvements in the firing of pulverized coal in cement kilns, greatly increasing their efficiency and output.[5,6]

Largely developed as an empirical art, pulverized coal firing progress has been marked by the efforts of devoted engineers whose success may be attributed to persistence in the face of many discouraging obstacles. In general, theoretical understanding has followed rather than preceded practical accomplishment in the field of pulverized coal firing.

In the U.S., the rapid increase in oil prices in the 1890s provided the principal incentive to develop the use of pulverized coal for firing cement kilns, the first industrial application to achieve commercial success. E. H. Hurry and H. J. Seaman of the Atlas Portland Cement Company began a series of experiments relating to the use of pulverized coal in 1894, and in the following year, pulverized coal was successfully used in a rotary cement kiln. Since that time, pulverized coal has been the dominant fuel in the cement industry. By the time of World War I, powdered coal, the term then generally used for what is now designated "pulverized coal," had gained sufficient acceptance for the American Society of Mechanical Engineers (ASME) to sponsor a symposium bringing together the accumulated experience in several fields of application.[7–11]

By the end of World War II, pulverized coal still had not achieved its full potential, despite an increasing number of applications, ranging from the cement industry to the metallurgical industry, to the steam locomotive, and to several stationary boilers. Although all of the elements for success appeared to be present, integration of the many ideas to adequately demonstrate pulverized coal firing in the central station power industry was needed. John Anderson, then chief engineer of power plants of what is now WE Energy, provided the necessary leadership. He effectively enlisted the support and active participation of exceptionally able engineers from his own organization, the public utility industry, equipment suppliers, and the U.S. Bureau of Mines. Anderson's pioneering efforts resulted in the construction of pulverized coal installations in the Oneida Street Station and at Lakeside.[12–19] Two outstanding test reports stand as engineering classics. Based on experimental work at the Oneida Street and Lakeside Stations, these reports contain important basic information on pulverized coal firing and establish a pattern for subsequent research, including many of the activities of the ASME Furnace Performance Factors Committee.[20–25]

Studies on velocities and characteristics of pulverized coal particles were reported by E. Audibert[26] and John Blizard[27] who a few years earlier had published a comprehensive study of the state of the art of pulverized coal.[28] Research linking studies of inflammability of coal mine dust to desired combustion properties appears in an article by Henri Verdinne.[29] W. Nusselt published results of research on the ignition times of coal particles in 1924,[30] and P. Rosin reported on studies of thermodynamic data based on heat liberation in 1925.[31] The first of a series of papers on the study of heat transfer in boilers at Yale University by W. J. Wohlenberg and his colleagues was also published in 1925.[32] Despite the extensive theoretical studies that were made in the 1920s, much of the progress was achieved on an empirical basis with boiler installations of ever-increasing size. This was particularly true in the development of pulverizers, for which the theory of the underlying principles had not advanced very rapidly. Even today, the laws for crushing materials are subject to much dispute.

Rittinger's law of crushing dates back to a book published in Germany in 1867, which states that the work required to produce material of a given size from a larger size is proportional to the new surface produced. This expression finds more general acceptance than Kick's law, which was first published in 1885 and states that the energy required to effect crushing or pulverizing is proportional to the volume reduction of the particle. While Rittinger's law is a closer approximation, neither of these laws can be used for comparing efficiencies of different size or design coal pulverizers. The energy required for pulverization is dissipated in a number of ways and affected by several process variables. It cannot be accounted for in the specific manner that is applicable to a boiler or power plant heat balance. For this reason, both the design and the application of pulverizers have retained many of the elements of an engineering art, as the demands on pulverizer performance have continually increased.

PULVERIZING PROPERTIES OF COAL

To predict pulverizer performance on a specific coal with some degree of accuracy, the ease with which the coal can be pulverized must be estimated.

Grindability

A grindability index has been developed to measure the ease of pulverization. Unlike moisture, ash, or heating value, this index is not an inherent property of coal. Rather, it represents the relative ease of grinding coal when tested in a particular type of apparatus. The consistency of grindability test results permits the pulverizer manufacturer to apply the findings to a particular size and, to a lesser degree, type of pulverizer.

Grindability should not be confused with the hardness of coal (See also *Tables* 6-4 and 6-5 and related text.) The same coal may have a range of grindabilities, depending on other constituents in the coal. For example, anthracites and some lignites have at least one point at which their grindabilities are very close. Anthracite, however, is a very hard coal whereas lignite is soft, yet both are difficult to grind. *Figure 6-1* gives typical curves for North Dakota lignites and shows the variation in Hardgrove grindability as the moisture content changes.

Pulverizing a small, air-dried sample of properly sized coal in a miniature mill determines its grindability. Results may then be converted into a grindability index factor that, with appropriate correction curves, can be used to predict, or interpret, mill capacity.

The Hardgrove method was developed to measure the quantity of new material that will pass through a 200-mesh sieve after a standard grinding duration. The apparatus for this method, shown in *Figure 6-2*, is extremely simple.

A 50-g (1.76 oz) sample of air-dried coal, sized to less than 16 and greater than 30 mesh, is placed in the mortar of the test machine along with eight, 2.54-cm (1-inch)-diameter steel balls. A weighted upper race is placed on the ball and coal charge, and is turned 60 revolutions. The sample then is removed and screened. The quantity

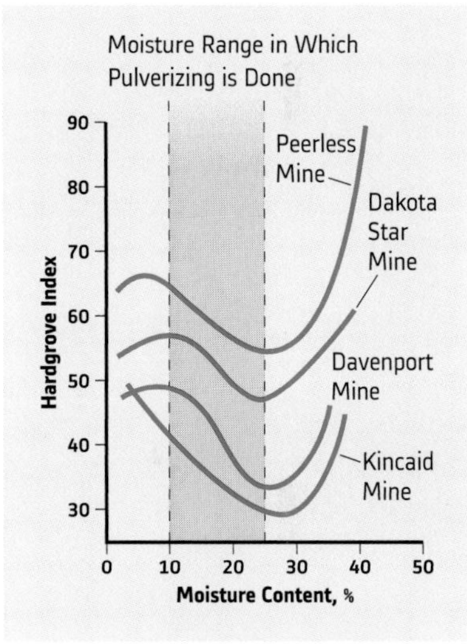

Figure 6-1 | Variation of grindability index with moisture content, North Dakota lignites (average of standard and corrected values)

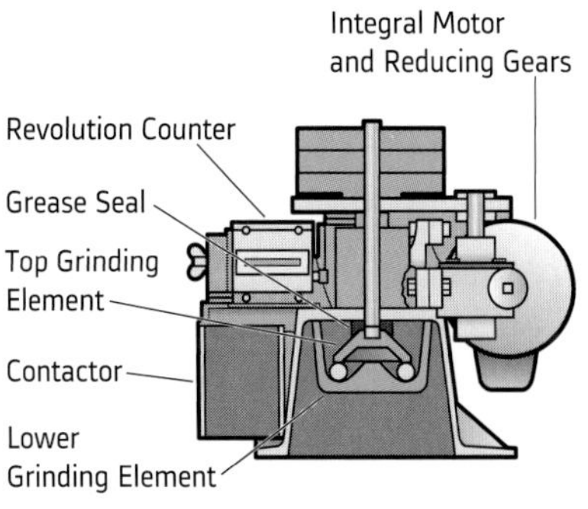

Figure 6-2 | Hardgrove grindability machine

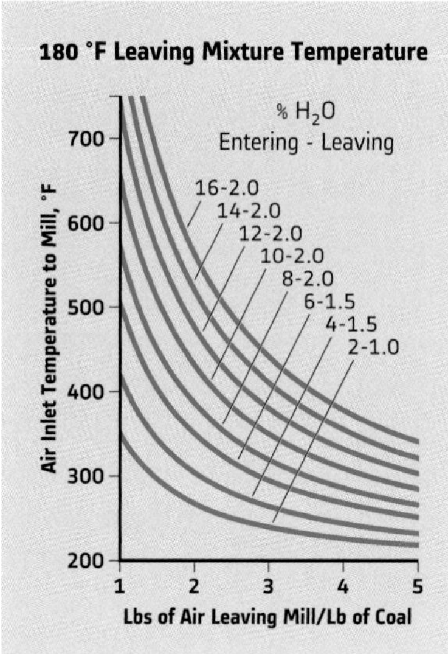

Figure 6-3 | Temperature of air to mill, Eastern U.S. coals

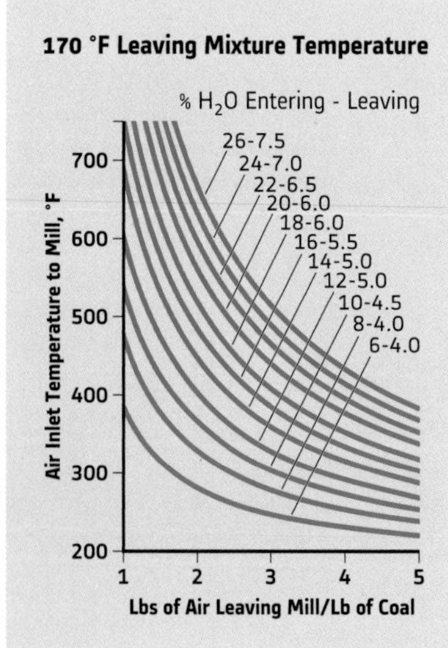

Figure 6-4 | Temperature of air to mill, Midwest-U.S. coals

passing through the 200-mesh sieve is used in the preparation of a calibration chart, from which the grindability of the coal sample is determined in accordance with ASTM Standards D 409, Grindability of Coal by the Hardgrove-Machine Method. Four coal samples, obtained from ASTM, standardized especially for this purpose and representing grindability indices of 40, 60, 80, and 100, are used to calibrate each grindability machine and associated apparatus, before the equipment is used to test coals.

Often, too much emphasis is placed on grindability while other factors affecting mill capacity, such as moisture, are almost entirely overlooked. Pulverizer capacity is proportional to the grindability index of the coal within a range of 40 to 60 HGI (Hardgrove Grindability Index). Outside this range, varying correction factors apply, depending on machine design and manufacturer. Corrections must also be made for fineness of product and moisture of the raw feed.

Moisture

Usually, a reference to moisture in coal pertains to the total moisture content, which comprises what is commonly termed "equilibrium moisture" and surface or free moisture. Equilibrium moisture varies with coal type or rank and mine location, and would be more accurately called "bed" or "seam" moisture. In reality, surface moisture is the difference between total moisture and bed moisture. Surface moisture adversely affects both pulverizer performance and the combustion process. The surface moisture produces agglomeration of the fines in the pulverizing zone, and reduces pulverizer grinding capacity because of the inability to remove the fines efficiently and as quickly as they are produced. Agglomeration of fines has the same effect as coarse coal during the combustion process, because the surface available for the chemical reaction is reduced. Since in-mill drying is the accepted method of preparing coal for pulverized fuel burning, air with a sufficient mass flow and temperature is necessary in the milling system transport air. The process of flash drying coal contributes to the recirculating load in an operating pulverizer. If high levels of moisture are present in bituminous coals, a reduction in the grinding capacity of the pulverizer will occur. Curves such as those shown in *Figures 6-3* and *6-4* indicate the air temperature required to dry coal of various total moistures and coal-air mixtures.

Achieving rated pulverizer capacity depends on having sufficient heat input to dry the coal. If there is a deficiency of hot air, the mill output will be limited to the "drying capacity" and not the "grinding capacity" of the mill. Thus, it may be possible to obtain more capacity with a relatively dry coal with a lower grindability index than with a high-moisture coal with a higher grindability index. Predicting pulverizer capacity for a given fuel-rank grindability and moisture content involves independent analysis of the machine's grinding and thermal capacities, as well as the impact of the moisture content on grinding capacity.

Relation of Pulverizer Capacity to Grindability

As stated previously, mill capacity is not directly proportional to grindability for any given fineness distribution. This is in part due to the differences between a commercial pulverizer and a grindability test machine. The test apparatus and procedure have no provision for continuous removal of fines or recirculation of partially ground coal, as is the case in an operating pulverizer. The crushing pressure of the test equipment is also considerably lower. As a result, some of its energy is dissipated in deforming the coal particles without breaking them. Because the work required to produce more surface area increases as a finer product is made, the product fineness grindability index and coal moisture content must be considered together to develop reasonable expectations for pulverizer throughput. The effects of a finer product and a wider range for the coal grindability index have become predominant considerations since the early 1990s, as commercial pulverizing equipment is required to support reduced emission combustion with a wide range of globally sourced coals. Although the test equipment does not indicate a direct proportion of capability between hard and soft materials, the value of these tests remains a key input used for performance assessment. Correction factors developed by pulverizer manufacturers on commercial equipment provide for overcoming these discrepancies. *Figure 6-5* gives correction curves for variations in fineness, grindability, and moisture. As a rule of thumb, for every point the grindability index changes within the range of 40 to 60 HGI, there will be a corresponding change of about 1.5% in pulverizer capacity. Changes in fineness have a similar impact on pulverizer throughput, although depending on the fineness range, the corresponding capacity change will be between 1 and 5% per %-200 mesh fineness.

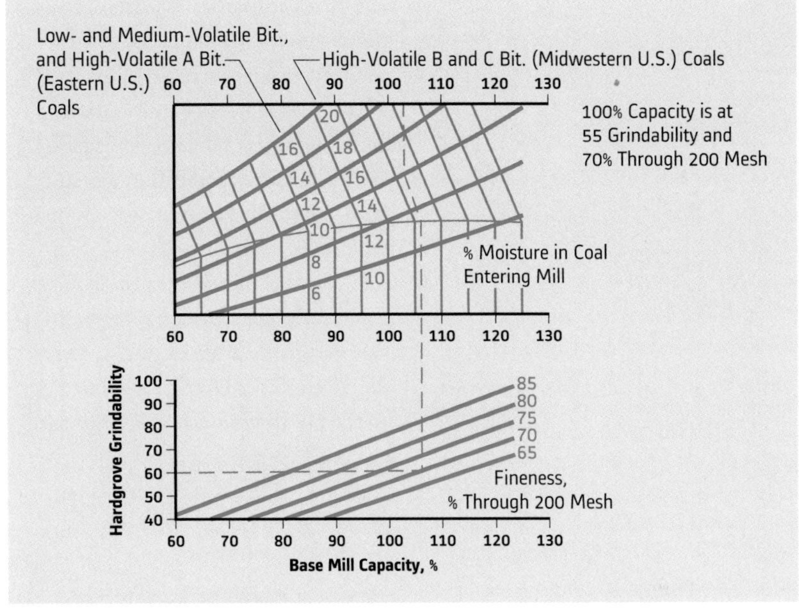

Figure 6-5 | Mill correction factors for grindability, fineness, coal type, and moisture—bituminous coals with preheated air and static classifier

Variation of Lignite Grindability with Moisture

The U.S. Bureau of Mines at Grand Forks, North Dakota, and others have reported the grindability of lignites at various moistures. The results show a wide variation, as in *Figure 6-1*. Some think that such curves are of little value because it seems impossible to select the proper index from them. Others think that these curves do have significance. With the increased use of lignites, the solution to this problem is important.

In setting up the present ASTM code for grindability, the test specifies the use of an air-dried sample. In the Alstom bowl mill, all of the surface moisture and some of the equilibrium moisture are evaporated during pulverization with a hot air sweep. The moisture content of the pulverized product leaving the mill is thought to be the moisture level that exists in the grinding zone. Thus, grindability versus moisture indices above the equilibrium level is of little interest. Hardgrove indices, therefore, have meaning to the pulverizer designer only below the equilibrium moisture level and in the general range of moisture contents between 10 and 25%. The actual choice of the grindability index for pulverizer design capacity requires consideration of total moisture, equilibrium (bed) moisture, heat input to the pulverizer, and experience with the coal's drying and grinding behavior.

Relationship of Coal Rank to Required Fineness

Successful pulverized coal firing depends on recognizing differences in coal constituents and the impact they have on efficient combustion. Experience over the years has established that a relationship exists between the rank of bituminous coals and the degree of fineness required for successful operation. To ensure complete combustion within the furnace confines for minimal carbon loss, high-rank coals must be pulverized to a finer size than coals of lower rank. Since the 1990s, in furnace air staging technologies have been widely applied as an effective means to reduce thermal NOx production. These systems create a lower stoichiometric region at the point of initial combustion, which calls for a finer coal product to support complete burnout. When firing certain coals in the low-volatile content group in small pulverized coal furnaces, the fineness may be increased to as high as 80% to ensure adequate burnout of the carbon content. *Table 6-1* lists the specifications set by ASTM for classifying coal by rank. Rank classifications are based on varying combinations of volatile-matter content, heating value, and agglomerating properties.

After the predrying step is accomplished in the pulverizing operation, the low-rank sub-bituminous coals and lignites manifest a higher degree of reactivity than do the higher-rank bituminous coals. Recent investigations confirm that this increased reactivity results primarily from the lack of agglomerating properties and increased O_2 content of the fuel.[33] A comparison of flammability indices with volatile matter and heating value suggests that factors other than these have a great influence on ignition temperature and particle burnout. Because lower flammability temperatures are experienced primarily with lignitic and sub-bituminous coals, it is reasonable to ask what property is common to lower-rank coals. Exclusive of heating value, the most obvious difference between the two groups is the property known as "agglomerating character." Sub-bituminous coals and lignites do not agglomerate. As applied to coals, agglomeration is the property of coal particles to fuse into a coke-like mass or bond together into a firm cake when the particles are heated to temperatures of 1,000°F (540°C) or above.

While the determinations of both volatile matter and heating value are well defined, tests for establishing the agglomerating character of coals are less commonly known. ASTM Standards D 388, Specifications for Classification of Coals by Rank, describes agglomerating character as follows:

The test is carried out by the examination of the residue in the platinum crucible incidental to the volatile matter determination. Coals which in the volatile-matter determination produce either an agglomerate button that will support a 500-g weight without pulverizing, or a button showing swelling of cell structure, shall be considered agglomerating from the standpoint of classification.

TABLE 6-1 | CLASSIFICATION OF COALS BY RANK[*]

Class and Group	Fixed Carbon Limits, % (Dry, Mineral-Matter-Free Basis)		Volatile Matter Limits, % (Dry, Mineral-Matter-Free Basis)		Calorific Value Limits, BTU/lb (Moist,[†] Mineral-Matter-Free Basis)		Agglomerating Character
	Equal or Greater Than	Less Than	Equal or Greater Than	Less Than	Equal or Greater Than	Less Than	
I. ANTHRACITIC							
1. Meta-anthracite	98	—	—	2	—	—	Non-agglomerating
2. Anthracite	92	98	2	8	—	—	Non-agglomerating
3. Semianthracite[‡]	86	92	8	14	—	—	Non-agglomerating
II. BITUMINOUS							
1. Low-volatile bituminous coal	78	86	14	22	—	—	Commonly agglomerating[‖]
2. Medium-volatile bituminous coal	69	78	22	31	—	—	Commonly agglomerating[‖]
3. High-volatile A bituminous coal	—	69	31	—	14,000[§] BTU/lb (32,600 KJ/kg)	—	Commonly agglomerating[‖]
4. High-volatile B bituminous coal	—	—	—	—	13,000[§] BTU/lb (30,000 KJ/kg)	14,000 (32,600 KJ/kg)	Commonly agglomerating[‖]
5. High-volatile C bituminous coal	—	—	—	—	11,500 BTU/lb (26,700 KJ/kg)	13,000 (30,000 KJ/kg)	Commonly agglomerating[‖]
					10,500 BTU/lb (24,400 KJ/kg)	11,500 (26,700 KJ/kg)	Agglomerating
III. SUB-BITUMINOUS							
1. Sub-bituminous A coal	—	—	—	—	10,500 BTU/lb (24,400 KJ/kg)	11,500 (26,700 KJ/kg)	Non-agglomerating
2. Sub-bituminous B coal	—	—	—	—	9,500 BTU/lb (22,100 KJ/kg)	10,500 (24,400 KJ/kg)	Non-agglomerating
3. Sub-bituminous C coal	—	—	—	—	8,300 BTU/lb (19,300 KJ/kg)	9,500 (22,100 KJ/kg)	Non-agglomerating
IV. LIGNITIC							
1. Lignite A	—	—	—	—	6,300 BTU/lb (14,700 KJ/kg)	8,300 (19,300 KJ/kg)	Non-agglomerating
2. Lignite B	—	—	—	—	—	6,300 (14,700 KJ/kg)	Non-agglomerating

[*] This classification does not include a few coals, principally nonbanded varieties, which have unusual physical and chemical properties and which come within the limits of fixed carbon or calorific value of the high-volatile bituminous and sub-bituminous ranks. All of these coals either contain less than 48% dry, mineral-matter-free fixed carbon or have more than 15,500 moist, mineral-matter-free British thermal units per pound.

[†] Moist refers to coal containing its natural inherent moisture but not including visible water on the surface of the coal.

[‡] If agglomerating, classify in low-volatile group of the bituminous class.

[§] Coals having 69% or more fixed carbon on the dry, mineral-matter-free basis shall be classified according to fixed carbon, regardless of calorific value.

[‖] It is recognized that there may be nonagglomerating varieties in these groups of the bituminous class, and there are notable exceptions in high-volatile C bituminous group.

Reprinted from *ASTM Standards* D 388, Classification of Coals by Rank.

Since the agglomerating property of coals is the result of particles transforming into a plastic or semi-liquid state when heated, it reflects a change in the surface area of the particle. This surface change is manifested by a transformation of the particle from an angular, irregular shape into a spherical particle. Also, the surface character of the particle changes from a porous, irregular, absorptive surface to a glass-like, nonporous surface. Thus, with the application of heat, agglomerating coals tend to develop a nonporous surface, while that of non-agglomerating coals becomes even more porous with pyrolysis. This explanation indicates why agglomerating coals require a correspondingly finer particle size to maintain an equivalent surface area for efficient, rapid ignition and burnout.

In addition to the correlation of agglomerating properties with coal reactivity, an equally strong correlation exists between the ultimate analysis oxygen level of coals and their response to reactivity as reflected in the flammability temperatures. Data in *Table 6-2* show ranges in oxygen from 4.8 to 14.8% for agglomerating coals, moisture and ash free (MAF), and from 18.7 to 26.6% MAF for the lower-rank coals that are non-agglomerating. Seemingly, the higher the inherent or organically bound oxygen content of the coal, the more reactive it is. These data do not conflict with the observed correlation with agglomerating character. In fact, deliberately varying degrees of oxidation temper can destroy the agglomerating properties of caking coals. Apparently, the breaking point between agglomerating and non-agglomerating coals is a 14 to 15% oxygen level.[34,35]

Standards for Measuring Fineness

When burning solid fuels in suspension, it is essential that the fuel–air mixture contain an appreciable quantity of extremely fine particles to ensure rapid ignition. Conversely, to obtain maximum combustion efficiency, a minimum amount of coarse particles in this same fuel-air mixture is desirable. The former condition is usually expressed as percentage through a 200-mesh screen (74 microns), while the latter is designated as percentage retained on a 50-mesh screen (297 microns). The number of openings

TABLE 6-2 | COAL PROPERTIES*

	Bituminous					Sub-bituminous			Lignite
	Low Volatile	Medium Volatile	High Volatile						
			A	B	C	A	B	C	A
Agglomerating character	Agg.	Agg.	Agg.	Agg.	†	Non-Agg.	Non-Agg.	Non-Agg.	Non-Agg.
Proximate, %									
Moisture (seam)	2.0	2.0	4.0	7.0	10.0	14.0	19.0	25.0	40.0
Volatile matter, VM	21.1	32.3	38.4	33.8	35.9	35.3	34.5	25.8	25.9
Fixed carbon, FC	68.6	55.8	51.5	47.3	43.3	41.2	37.5	40.9	27.4
Ash	8.3	9.9	6.1	11.9	10.8	9.5	9.0	8.3	6.7
HHV, BTU/lb, As-fired	13,150	13,210	13,410	11,610	10,590	9,840	8,560	7,500	5,940
Flammability index, F	1,010	1,030	950	1,030	990	970	970	990	890
Ultimate (MAF), %									
Hydrogen	5.0	5.5	5.6	4.6	5.5	5.4	5.1	5.6	4.3
Carbon	88.5	84.1	82.5	81.0	74.3	74.2	69.8	66.4	67.0
Sulfur	0.4	1.1	2.5	0.9	4.0	0.5	0.8	0.6	0.9
Nitrogen	1.3	1.7	1.5	1.3	1.4	1.2	1.1	1.3	1.2
Oxygen	4.8	7.6	7.9	12.2	14.8	18.7	23.2	26.1	26.6

* Agg., agglomerating; HHV, higher heating value; MAF, moisture ash free; Non-Agg., non-agglomerating
† Agglomerating but non-caking.

per linear inch designates the mesh of a screen. Thus, a 200-mesh screen has 200 openings to the inch, or 40,000 per square inch. The diameter of the wire used in making the screen governs the size of the openings. The U.S. Standard and W. S. Tyler are the most common screen sieves. The mesh and opening of these and other international screens are shown in *Table 6-3* and *Figure 6-6*.

CLASSIFICATION AND SIZE CONSIST

In the combustion of pulverized coal, it is important to have a proper percentage of fine particles yielding a large surface area. It is equally necessary to reduce or eliminate the oversize on the coarser screen. Despite the small percentage of less than 200 mesh (−200 mesh), as little as 3 to 5% greater than 50 mesh (+50 mesh) may produce furnace slagging and increased combustible loss, even though combustion conditions are excellent for the finer coal. The small amount of oversize represents very little additional surface if it is pulverized to all −50 mesh and all +200 mesh. As an illustration, assume a typical screen analysis of a high-volatile bituminous coal sample, pulverized to 80% −200 mesh:

99.5% −50 mesh
96.5% −100 mesh
80.0% −200 mesh

This represents a surface area of approximately 1,500 cm^2/g, with over 97% of the surface in the −200 mesh portion. By overgrinding and poor classification it would be possible, on

TABLE 6-3 | COMPARISON OF SIEVE OPENINGS

U.S. Standard Sieve		
Mesh	Inches	Millimeters
20	0.0331	0.840
30	0.0234	0.595
40	0.0165	0.420
50*	0.0117	0.297
60	0.0098	0.250
100*	0.0059	0.149
140	0.0041	0.105
200*	0.0029	0.074
325	0.0017	0.044
400	0.0015	0.037
W. S. Tyler Sieve		
Mesh	Inches	Millimeters
20	0.0328	0.833
28	0.0232	0.589
35	0.0164	0.417
48*	0.0116	0.295
60	0.0097	0.246
100*	0.0058	0.147
150	0.0041	0.104
200*	0.0029	0.074
325	0.0017	0.043
400	0.0015	0.037

* Commonly used screens in pulverized-coal practice for combustion purposes.

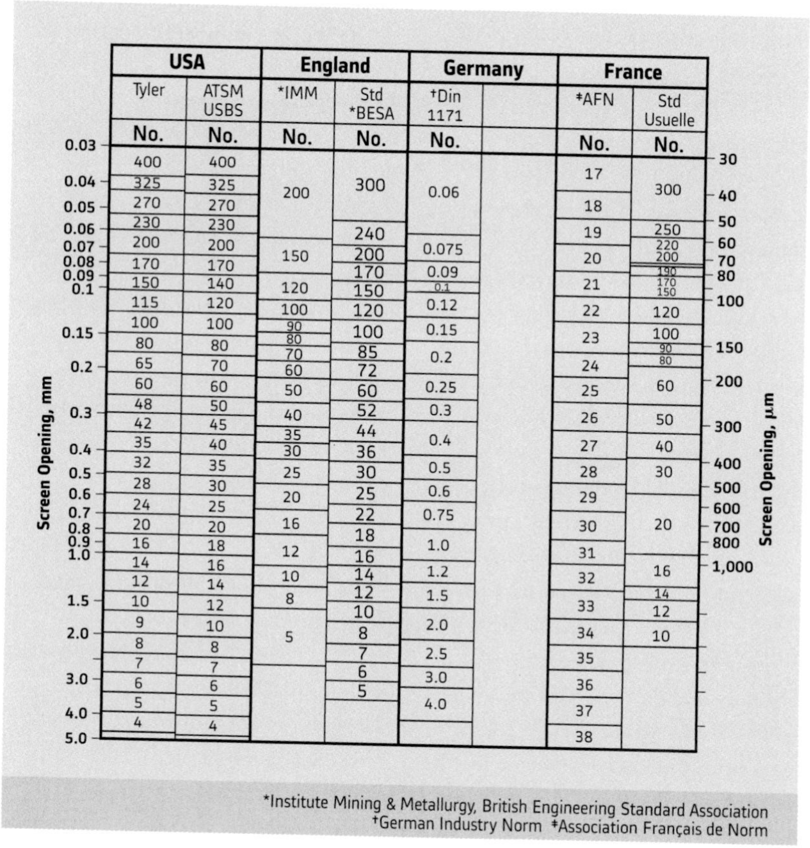

Screen Opening, mm: 0.03, 0.04, 0.05, 0.06, 0.07, 0.08, 0.09, 0.1, 0.15, 0.2, 0.3, 0.4, 0.5, 0.6, 0.7, 0.8, 0.9, 1.0, 1.5, 2.0, 3.0, 4.0, 5.0

Screen Opening, µm: 30, 40, 50, 60, 70, 80, 100, 150, 200, 300, 400, 500, 600, 700, 800, 1,000

USA Tyler No.	USA ATSM USBS No.	England *IMM No.	England Std *BESA No.	Germany †Din 1171 No.	France ‡AFN No.	France Std Usuelle No.
400	400	200	300	0.06	17	300
325	325	150	240	0.075	18	250
270	270	120	200	0.09	19	220
230	230	100	170	0.1	20	200
200	200	90	150	0.12	21	190
170	170	80	120	0.15	22	170
150	140	70	100	0.2	23	150
115	120	60	85	0.25	24	120
100	100	50	72	0.3	25	100
80	80	40	60	0.4	26	90
65	70	35	52	0.5	27	80
60	60	30	44	0.6	28	60
48	50	25	36	0.75	29	50
42	45	20	30	1.0	30	40
35	40	16	25	1.2	31	30
32	35	12	22	1.5	32	20
28	30	10	18	2.0	33	16
24	25	8	16	2.5	34	14
20	20	5	14	3.0	35	12
16	18		12	4.0	36	10
14	16		10		37	
12	14		8		38	
10	12		7			
9	10		6			
8	8		5			
7	7					
6	6					
5	5					
4	4					

*Institute Mining & Metallurgy, British Engineering Standard Association
†German Industry Norm ‡Association Français de Norm

Figure 6-6 | International Screen Opening Comparisons

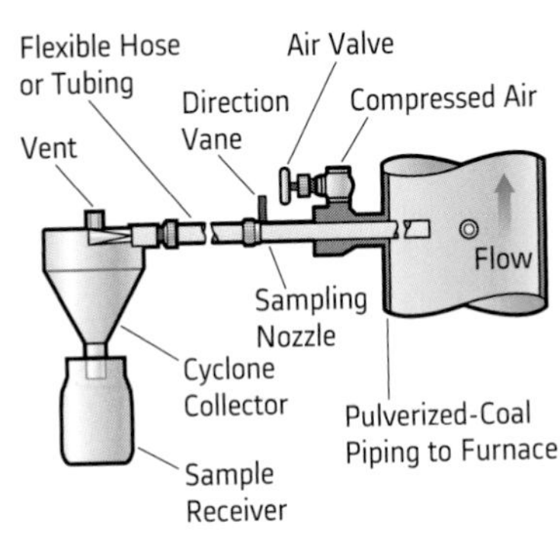

Figure 6-7 | Pulverized-coal sampling device and aspirating fittings

a commercial-sized mill, to have a sample of the following analysis:

95%	–50 mesh
90%	–100 mesh
80%	–200 mesh

This is not a satisfactory grind, because of the high percentage retained on the 50 mesh, even though the surface area is still 1,500 cm^2/g.

In the pulverizing process, then, classification plays a major role in matching the particle size to the reactivity of the fuel. This factor is of greater importance when low-NOx, in-furnace combustion systems are used. Both fine and coarse particles must be controlled within limits by the use of mechanical classification techniques. Careful attention must be paid to both the design and the operation of the classification system.

SAMPLING PULVERIZED COAL

It is apparent that product fineness has a considerable bearing on pulverizer performance. Fineness samples should, therefore, be analyzed periodically. Samples should be analyzed on a monthly basis or any time combustion performance indicates that a change has occurred. On a direct fired system, the sample must be taken from a flowing coal–air stream. Fineness analysis is a relative measure of pulverizer performance. The sampling routine is most beneficial when it is easily accomplished, repeatable, and yields results that are comparable from one measurement to the next. ASTM Standard D 197, Sampling and Fineness Test of Pulverized Coal and ASME PTC 4.2, Coal Pulverizers, gives information on recommended sampling techniques that meet these criteria. A sampling device, consisting of a small cyclone collector, sample jar, and sampling nozzle with connecting hose, may be used. See *Figure 6-7*. The results of the percentages of coal passing through the individual screens are considered a representative sample if they result in a straight line plot on a Rosin-Rammler graph.

Depending on the sampling location and mill loading results, the accuracy may be improved by taking measures to ensure that the sampling process is isokinetic. In this refinement, the pipe traverse with the coal-sampling device is timed to obtain an isokinetic coal sample. The method uses the proportion of coal pipe area to the sample probe opening area in conjunction with the pulverized fuel loading in the individual transport pipe. Because pulverized fuel in a transport pipe is not a homogeneous mixture, another sample taken at the same time at a different location in the same pipe may yield different results.

More elaborate fineness sampling techniques, such as ISO 9931 using the "rotoprobe" sampler or the SMG-10 sampling apparatus, can also be deployed. The techniques and tools are specialized to measure the total amount of pulverized coal being carried in a given fuel line. While these methods can also be used as the basis of routine fineness checks, their results may vary as compared with standard cyclone methods.

GRINDING

When a large piece of coal is reduced to a number of smaller ones by any method, a great number of fine particles will be produced simultaneously. Therefore, it is not possible for a pulverizer to produce a product that will pass a 50-mesh screen without also obtaining a large percentage of material finer than 200 mesh. Thus, if a quantity of coal at one stage of pulverization contains 50% material that will pass through a 50-mesh sieve, and, if this −50-mesh material is removed from the grinding zone, it will contain a smaller percentage of −200-mesh material than if it had been permitted to remain in the grinding zone until the total quantity had been reduced to pass a 50-mesh sieve.

As already noted, an abundance of fine particles is necessary to ensure prompt ignition of coal in suspension burning. Substantial energy consumption is required in the production of this fine material. However, when grinding finer than necessary, power is wasted. The pulverizing equipment must then be larger than actually required. Removal of the fines from the pulverizing zone as rapidly as they are produced and return of the oversize for regrinding eliminates unnecessary production of fines and reduces energy requirements. Better product sizing and increased capacity result from the continuous removal of the fines. This process is called "closed circuit grinding." The pulverizing system component that accomplishes this size control is known as the "classifier." The fineness requirements for utility boilers were satisfied by static double-cone classifiers through the late 1980s. By the early 1990s, many countries had implemented stationary boiler emission regulations, which drove the need for in-furnace emissions reduction technologies. These technologies require finer coal to support complete combustion and avoid excessive carbon loss. The need for a higher level of product fineness has been met through the implementation of integral rotating classifiers.

Abrasion

Pulverizing results in an eventual loss of grinding-element material. Balls, rolls, rings, races, and liners gradually erode and wear out as a result of abrasion and metal displacement in the grinding process. The power for grinding, and the maintenance of the grinding elements make up the major costs of the pulverizing operation. In itself, "pure coal" is relatively nonabrasive. However, silica and quartz commonly found in the coal ash are quite abrasive. Foreign materials such as slate, sand, and pyrites, commonly found in coal as mined, are also quite abrasive. These are the undesirable constituents that produce rapid and sometimes excessive wear in pulverizing apparatus. The economics of coal cleaning to remove such abrasive foreign materials depends on many variables and must be determined for each individual application.

The resistance of a smooth planar surface to abrasion is called its hardness. It is commonly recorded in terms of 10 minerals according to the Mohs scale of hardness (*Table 6-4*). There is no quantitative relation between these materials. The diamond is much greater in hardness above sapphire than sapphire is above talc. Hardness of selected common materials is shown in *Table 6-5*. The relatively low hardness of pure coal is compared to the abrasive impurities usually found in the commercial product.

Coal Preparation

Coal should be prepared and delivered properly for safe, economical, and efficient use in a pulverizing system. Controllable continuity of flow to the pulverizer must be maintained. Organic foreign materials such as wood, cloth, and straw should be removed. Such materials may collect in the milling system and become a fire hazard. They may also impair material or airflow patterns in the mill.

TABLE 6-4 | MOHS SCALE OF HARDNESS

Hardness	Mineral
1	Talc
2	Gypsum
3	Calcspar
4	Fluorspar
5	Apatite
6	Feldspar
7	Quartz
8	Topaz
9	Sapphire
10	Diamond

TABLE 6-5 | COMMON MATERIALS AND THEIR MOHS HARDNESS

Material	Hardness
Coal	0.5–2.5
Slate	0.50–6.0
Mica	2.0–6.0
Pyrite	6.0–6.5
Granite	6.5
Marble	3.0
Soapstone	1.0–4.0
Kaolin clay	2.0–2.5
Iron ore	0.50–6.5
Carborundum	9.5

Although many mills are designed to reject, or are not adversely affected by, small inorganic or metallic materials, a magnetic separator should be installed in the raw-coal conveyor system to remove larger metallic objects. If this is not done, these objects may damage the pulverizer coal feeder or obstruct the coal flow.

The raw coal should be crushed to a size that will promote a uniform flow rate to the mill by the feeder. Favorable size consist will minimize segregation of coarse and fine fractions in the bunker, and result in a more uniform rate of feed to various pulverizers being supplied from a given bunker. When mixed with relatively dry lump coal, fine coal with high surface moisture accentuates the segregation problem in bunkers. Crushing by size reduction of the dry lumps exposes additional dry surfaces for the adsorption of moisture from the wet fines, thereby producing a more uniform size and moisture distribution in the raw-coal mass.

The most commonly used method for steam generation is direct firing of pulverized coal. In this application, an uninterrupted and uniformly controllable supply of pulverized coal to the furnace is essential. A steady and continuous flow of raw coal to the pulverizer will ensure this supply. An ideal feed is one that is closely sized and double-screened (e.g., ¾ inch by ¼ inch [19 mm × 6.4 mm]). Coal of this size will permit excess water to drain off; it will flow freely from bunkers and can be fed uniformly. However, such favorable sizing can be obtained only at a considerable price, and this usually precludes its use. In most cases, power plants will receive coals classified as "run-of-mine" or "screenings with lumps." Therefore, crushing equipment must be installed to provide uniform, raw feed sizing. Generally, coal feed sizing up to 2 inches (51 mm), as sieved through a round screen, is permissible with large pulverizers.

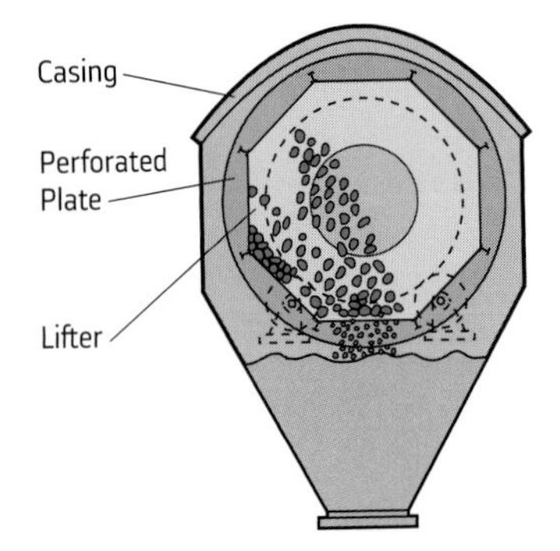

Figure 6-8 | Bradford breaker

Coal Crushers

Although there are numerous types of crushers commercially available, the type generally used for smaller capacities is the swing-hammer type. This crusher has proved satisfactory for overall use and has demonstrated reliability and economy. The swing-hammer crusher consists of a casing enclosing a rotor to which are attached pivoted hammers or rings. Coal is fed through a suitable opening in the top of the casing. Crushing is effected by impact of the revolving hammers or rings directly on, or by throwing the coal against, the liners or spaced grate bars in the bottom of the casing. The degree of size reduction depends on hammer type, speed, wear, and bar spacing. The latter is usually somewhat greater than the desired coal size. These crushers produce a uniform coal sizing and break up pieces of wood and foreign material, with the exception of metallic objects. Foreign material that is too hard to crush is caught in pockets.

Roll crushers have been used but are not entirely satisfactory because of their inability to deliver a uniformly sized product. Probably the most satisfactory crusher for large capacities is the Bradford breaker. This design, *Figure* 6-8, consists of a large-diameter, slowly revolving (approximately 20 rpm) cylinder of perforated steel plates, the size of the perforations determining the final coal sizing. In diameter, these openings are usually 1.25 to 1.5 inches in diameter (31.8 mm to 38.1 mm).

The breaking action on the coal is accomplished as follows: the coal is fed in at one end of the cylinder and carried upward on projecting vanes or shelves. As the cylinder rotates, the coal cascades off these shelves and breaks as it strikes the perforated plate. As the coal drops a relatively short distance, crushing occurs, with the production of very few fines. Coal broken to the screen size passes through the perforations to a hopper below. Rocks, wood, slate, tramp iron, and other foreign material are rejected. This breaker produces a relatively uniform product and uses very little power.

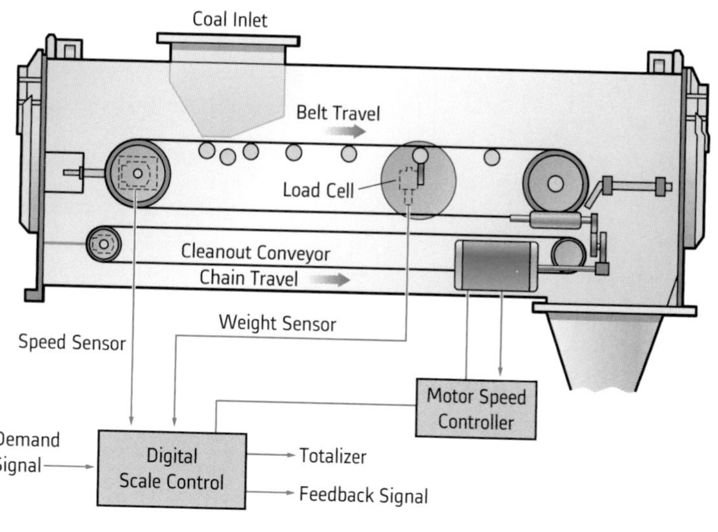

Figure 6-9 | Schematic of belt-type gravimetric coal feeder

Coal Feeders

A coal feeder supplies the pulverizer with a regulated uninterrupted flow of raw coal to meet system requirements. This is important for safe operation of any pulverizer and especially important in a direct-fired system for smooth boiler operation. There are several types, including the belt feeder and the overshot roll feeder.

THE BELT FEEDER. The belt feeder uses an endless belt running on two separated rollers receiving coal from above at one end and discharging it at the other. Varying the speed of the driving roll controls the feed rate. A leveling plate fixes the depth of the coal bed on the belt. The belt feeder can be used in either a volumetric or gravimetric type of application (see *Figure 6-9*).

The gravimetric type has gained wide popularity in the industry for accurately measuring the quantity of coal delivered to an individual pulverizer. Generally, this type is applied to steam generators with combustion-control systems requiring individual coal metering to the fuel burners. The most common method of continuously weighing the coal on the feeder belt is a solid-state load cell across a weigh span on the belt. This same belt-feeder design can also be used for volumetric measurement. Another acceptable method of continuously weighing the coal feed rate uses a series of levers and balance weights.

THE OVERSHOT FEEDER. The overshot roll feeder (*Figure 6-10*) has a multi-bladed rotor that turns about a fixed, hollow, cylindrical core. This core has an opening to the feeder discharge and is provided with heated air to minimize wet-coal accumulation on surfaces and to aid in coal drying. A hinged, spring-loaded leveling gate mounted over the rotor limits the discharge from the rotor pockets. This gate permits the passage of oversize foreign material. Feeders of this type may be separately mounted, or they may be integrally attached to the side of a pulverizer. The roll feeder and the belt feeder, by virtue of their designs may be considered highly efficient volumetric feeding devices.

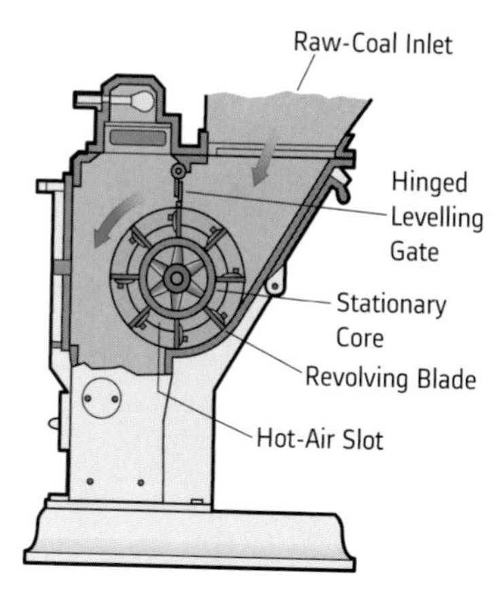

Figure 6-10 | Overshot roll feeder

METHODS OF PULVERIZING AND CONVEYING COAL

Early coal-pulverizing installations received undried coal and used ambient air in the mill system. Because no heat was added to the system, the coal feed was limited to that of very low moisture content. Therefore, maximum pulverizer capabilities were not realized. Subsequently, external coal dryers were added to the system. Because of the lack of cleanliness, high initial cost, fire hazard, and space requirements, these dryers were replaced with the now universally accepted in-mill drying. Three methods of supplying and firing pulverized coal have been developed: the storage or indirect system (*Figure 6-11*), the direct-fired system, and the semi-direct system. These methods differ on the basis of their drying, feeding, and transport characteristics. Because of advantages in capital cost, safety, reliability and operational efficiency the direct-fired systems have become the standard for any large thermal plant supplied today.

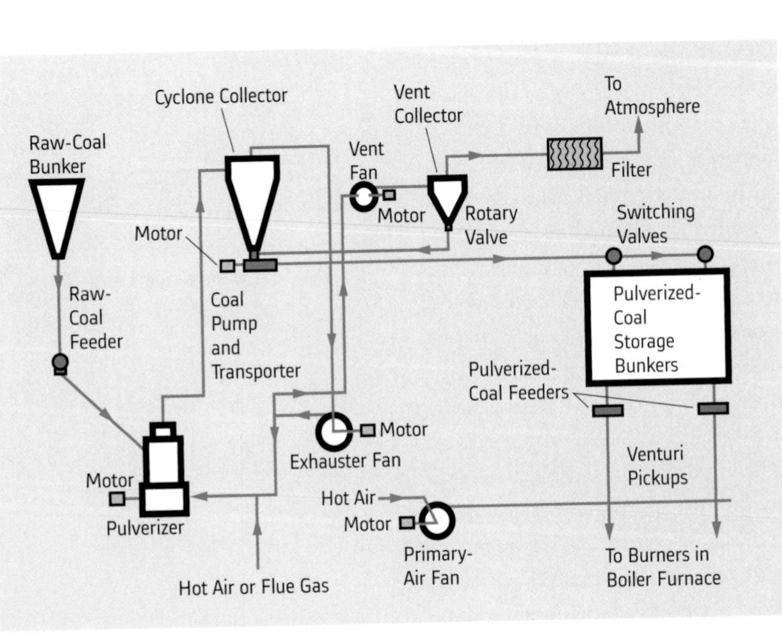

Figure 6-11 | Storage (indirect) pulverizing system

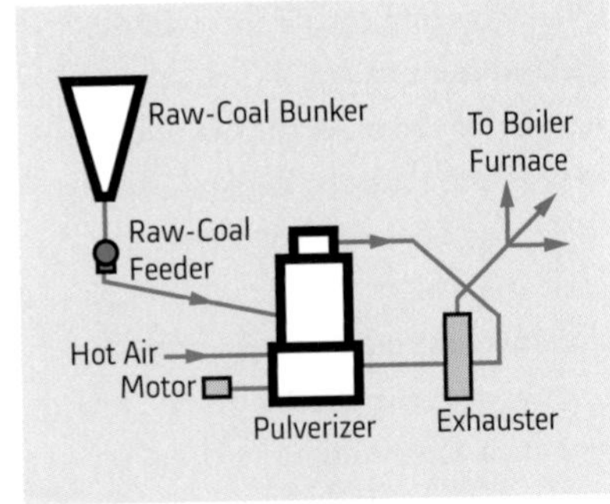

Figure 6-12 | Direct-fired pulverizing system

The Direct-Fired System

In a direct-fired system (*Figure 6-12*), coal is pulverized and transported with air, or air slightly diluted with gas, directly to the furnace, where the fuel is consumed. Hot air, or diluted furnace gas, supplied to the pulverizer furnishes the heat for drying the coal and transporting the pulverized fuel to the furnace. Known as primary air, this air is a portion of the combustion air. Because a reduction in oxygen concentration in this primary air stream affects the rapidity and stability of ignition, it is necessary, when using hot gas, to draw it from a point of low CO_2 concentration and high temperature. This prevents the use of flue gas for drying in a direct-fired system.

Figure 6-13 illustrates a schematic arrangement of the primary-air system for a pulverizer using a Ljungström® trisector air heater. As the name implies, this air heater has three sections: flue gas, primary air (the air that dries and conveys the coal to the furnace), and secondary air (the balance of the air that goes to the furnace). The primary air section is located between the openings for the secondary air and the flue gas. With this design, a higher primary air temperature can be obtained. If there is a large variation in primary airflow, there is relatively little effect on heat recovery, because the heat not recovered in the primary section will be picked up subsequently in the secondary section.

Source of Heated Air

The best source of hot air for mill drying is either a regenerative or a recuperative air heater using combustion gas as the source of heat. Those used in connection with large boiler installations usually provide sufficiently high temperature for almost any fuel moisture condition. On small installations, where the moisture in the coal is not high, steam air heaters may dry the coal. For higher moisture conditions a furnace gas supplement may be necessary. Direct-fired air heaters, properly interlocked and protected, may also be used to supplement air-heating requirements.

All the moisture present on the surface of the feed coal and all that is exposed via pulverization must be evaporated before rapid ignition can take place. This same drying process facilitates pulverization. The rank of coal and its total moisture govern mill drying requirements. The drying capability of a given pulverizer design depends on the extent of the circulating load within the mill, the ability to rapidly mix the dry classifier returns with incoming, wet, coal feed, and the primary air heat input the design will tolerate. Alstom pulverizers are designed to operate satisfactorily with inlet air temperatures up to 750°F (400°C).

High-rank, bituminous coals have a relatively dense structure and appear dry only when they contain less than 2 or 3% total moisture. The inherent moisture of these fuels varies from 1 to 2%. Extremely low-rank fuels, such as lignite, are of a relatively porous or cellular structure and contain inherent

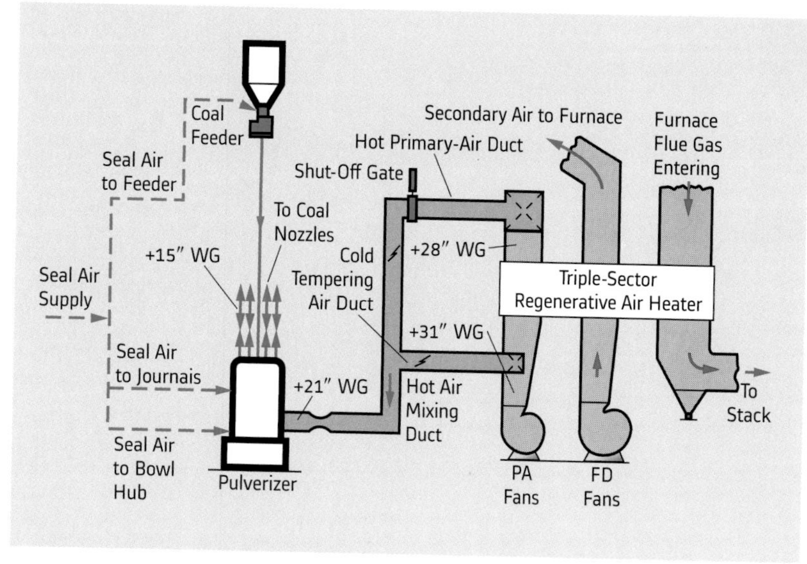

Figure 6-13 | Primary-air system of balanced-draft furnace. Air pressures shown are illustrative only

moisture of from 15 to 35%. These same fuels with 3% surface moisture (18 to 38% total moisture) still appear dry. For both the pulverizing and ignition processes, it is necessary to reduce the total moisture contained in the fuel to the inherent moisture level.

If a particular pulverizer type is designed for low, air-to-coal ratio operation, wet coal cannot be used without a considerable reduction in mill capacity. The pulverizer design should permit high-temperature incoming air in sufficient volume to maintain a condition of relative humidity below saturation at the mill output temperature. A pulverizer designed for a larger volume of low-temperature inlet air for normal moisture fuel will require the admission of large quantities of cold tempering air when grinding dry coals. Safe limits for pulverizer exit temperatures are determined based on the rank of coal as shown in *Table 6-6*.

Mill-capacity selections are based on coal-rank drying characteristics within a range of total moisture. Operation with feed-coal moistures significantly

TABLE 6-6 | ALLOWABLE MILL OUTLET TEMPERATURES, °F

System	Storage	Direct	Semidirect
High-rank, high-volatile bituminous	130* (54°C)	170 (77°C)	170 (77°C)
Low-rank, high-volatile bituminous	130* (54°C)	150 (66°C)	150 (66°C)
High-rank. low-volatile bituminous	135* (57°C)	180 (82°C)	180 (82°C)
Lignite	110 (43°C)	150 (66°C)	150 (66°C)
Anthracite	200 (93°C)		
Petroleum coke (delayed)	135 (57°C)	180–200 (82–93°C)	180–200 (82–93°C)
Petroleum coke (fluid)	200 (93°C)	200 (93°C)	200 (93°C)

* 160°F permissible with inert atmosphere blanketing of storage bin and low-oxygen-concentration conveying medium.

higher or lower than the original design values will affect the mill's capacity. Significantly higher moisture content can cause the milling system to reach a thermal limit below the desired coal flow. Conversely, much lower raw fuel moisture content can result in mill operation with excessive cold tempering air and high air-to-coal ratios.

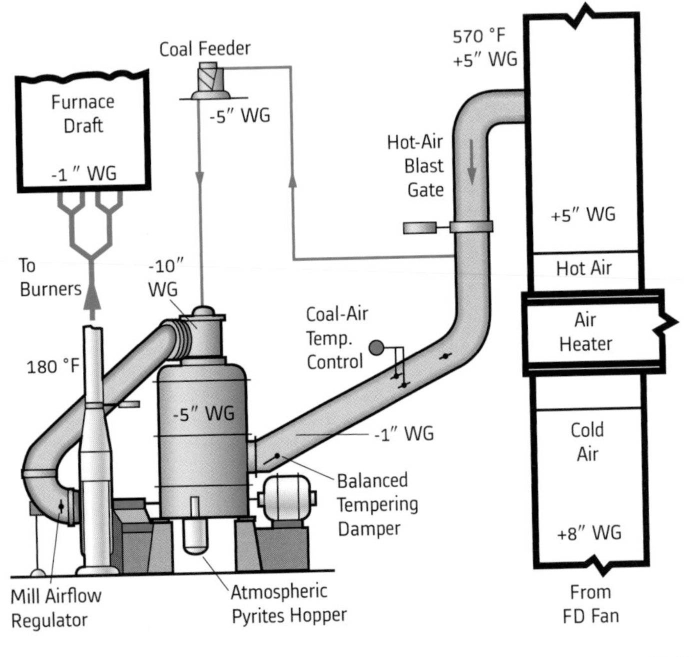

Figure 6-14 | Balanced-draft furnace with suction mill. Air pressures shown are illustrative only.

Pulverizing Air Systems

All coal pulverizing systems use air or gas for drying, classification, and transport purposes. Two methods are used for supplying the air requirements and overcoming system resistance. In a direct-fired system, one method uses a fan behind the pulverizer, while the other has a fan ahead of it. The former is a suction system, with the downstream fan handling coal-dust laden air. The latter is a pressure system with the upstream fan handling relatively clean air. With direct firing, the exhauster, or blower, volume requirement depends on the pulverizer size and is usually set by the base capacity of that pulverizer. The pressure or total head requirement is a function of the combined pulverizer and classifier resistance, the fuel distributing system resistance, and the burner resistance. These resistances are, in turn, affected by the system design, the required fuel-line velocities, and density of the mixture being conveyed.

DIRECT FIRING ARRANGEMENTS

Most direct-fired pulverized coal systems are for furnaces operated under suction (balanced draft). *Figure 6-14* shows an arrangement of equipment for a suction-type mill when applied to a furnace of this design; *Figure 6-13* shows a pressure-type mill for a similar furnace.

With a suction mill, the coal feeder discharges against a negative pressure, whereas in the pressurized mill, the feeder discharges against a positive pressure of 18 (3.4 cm Hg) to 21 (3.9 cm Hg) inches water gage (WG). No coal feeder can act as a seal. Thus, the head of coal above the feeder inlet must be used to prevent backflow of the primary air. As a rule of thumb, the height of the coal column above the feeder should be about 1 foot (0.3 m) for every 3 inches of primary air, mill inlet pressure. If the primary air fan outlet pressure is 30 inches, then the coal column height will have to be at least 10 feet (3.0 m).

Three basic air conveyance systems have been used for direct firing:

- the suction system, in which an exhauster induces airflow through the pulverizer and discharges the coal–air mixture under pressure to the furnace.
- the pressurized-exhauster system, in which the pulverizer is pressurized by the forced draft fan with both hot and ambient air and discharges the coal–air mixture through an exhauster, acting as a booster fan, to the furnace (this system is used only in conjunction with pressurized furnaces).
- the cold primary-air system, in which a primary-air fan forces air through the air heater, ductwork, and pulverizer and then forces the coal–air mixture into the furnace.

Systems for use on pressurized furnaces were common through the early 1970s. For practical operations reasons, many of these boilers have been upgraded to balance draft furnace operation.

Suction System

The suction system has a number of advantages. It is quite easy to keep the area around the pulverizer clean. To control the airflow through the pulverizer, a damper is placed in the constant-temperature coal–air mixture just in front of the exhauster entrance. Control of the coal–air mixture temperature is by a single, hot air damper and a barometric damper through which a flow of ambient air is induced by the suction in the pulverizer. With this control, the fan is designed for a constant, low-temperature mixture and has low power consumption, even though such material handling fans have a relatively low efficiency of 55 to 60%.

The main disadvantage of the suction system is the maintenance required on the exhauster. On the other hand, by using proper design techniques and wear-resistant materials, the maintenance on an exhauster can be minimized. Exhauster maintenance costs are more than offset by the power and capital cost savings of the system. This justifies the continued use of the suction system on smaller units.

Cold Primary Air System

In this system, the primary air fan handles only ambient air. The fan is located ahead of the air preheater, and supplies tempering air and heated air via a separate primary air section of the air heater. Although not as simple as the other two systems, its chief advantage is in fan power and maintenance. Because the fan handles cold air, it can be smaller, run at higher speeds, and use highly efficient airfoil blade shapes without concern for wear. Inlet vanes can control airflow and further add to fan efficiency.

Some other advantages of this system are that, with high efficiency fans handling ambient air, design for higher pressure differentials is possible and larger mills with longer fuel pipe runs are practical. Thus, mills may be located farther from the boiler. Because individual fans for each pulverizer are not necessary, the space requirements for the pulverizer bays can be reduced. Moreover, experience has demonstrated that metering airflow on the inlet air side of the pulverizer is most desirable. With the higher fan head available, the airflow can be quite easily measured by installing a Venturi or other metering device. Even with fewer pulverizer fans, controlling airflow to the various pulverizers is still relatively simple. The total primary air required is a function of the number of pulverizers in operation. This permits the use of a simple control for the airflow requirements. Because of possible variations of load and coal moisture content between pulverizers, it is necessary to control not only the total airflow but the temperature of the air to individual pulverizers. This is accomplished with a system similar to that outlined under the pressurized exhauster system, which uses a hot, primary air duct and a cold primary air duct with a damper in each for each mill. The airflow requirement for a pulverizer is met by operating both dampers, while controlling temperature by properly proportioning the flow between the hot and cold air ducts.

When very wet coals are pulverized in the suction systems described, a capacity limit is reached due to the fixed volumetric limit of the exhauster fan. The exhauster supplies less air at the very time when maximum airflow is required for maximum drying. In the suction systems with the exhauster located between the pulverizer and the furnace, the high level of evaporated water vapor content in the coal–air mixture will reduce the exhauster's air-handling capacity. Conversely, the cold primary air system may produce a higher capacity any time it is needed. The cold primary air system offers numerous advantages. As compared with the other systems, the total savings with this system, from elimination of exhauster maintenance and reduction in fan power, may be 35 to 40% of the cost per unit of coal pulverized. These savings are partially offset by the capital cost of additional ductwork, dampers, and controls. With larger units and pulverizers, the use of the cold primary air system becomes economically favorable.

AIR HEATING FOR THE COLD PRIMARY AIR SYSTEM. By definition, the cold primary air system requires independent primary air heating that had been accomplished in the past by several different methods. Several systems have been installed using a separate, primary, tubular air heater with Ljungström® air heaters for secondary air, while some have been installed using separate primary Ljungström® air heaters. These systems are expensive and become rather complicated in ductwork design. With the cold primary air system, the trisector Ljungström® air heater, shown schematically in *Figure 6-15*, is now being used as a standard design.

As the name implies, the flow channels of this heater have been divided into three sections, with the primary air section being located between the secondary air and the flue gas sections. With this arrangement, primary air temperatures higher than that of the secondary air can be obtained. Further, the efficiency of heat recovery is not significantly affected by variations in pulverizer hot-air requirements, because the secondary air recovers the heat that is not recovered by the primary air sections.

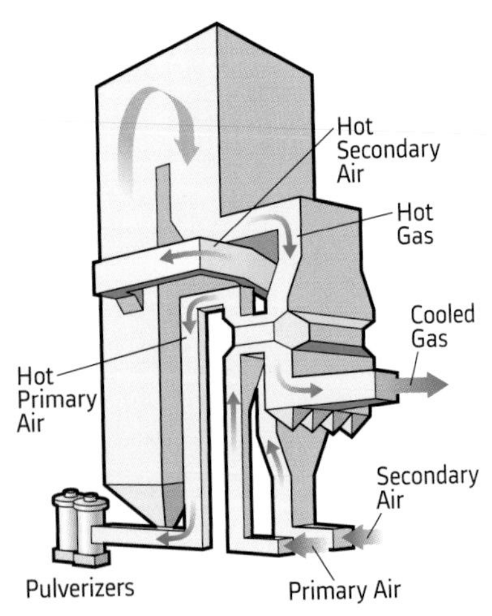

Figure 6-15 | Ljungström® trisector air heater

PRINCIPAL TYPES OF PULVERIZERS

The particle size reduction needed for proper combustion in pulverized coal firing, has been accomplished with many different machine designs over

the years. All grinding mill types use either one, two, or all three of the basic principles of particle size reduction, namely, impact, attrition, and crushing. The speed of these machines may be classified as low, medium, and high. The four most commonly used pulverizers are the ball tube, the ring-roll or ball-race, the impact or hammer mill, and the attrition mill. Their respective speed characteristics are shown in *Table 6-7*.

TABLE 6-7 | TYPES OF PULVERIZERS

Speed:	Low	Medium	High
Type:	Ball-tube mill	Ring-roll or ball-race mill	Impact or hammer mill Attrition mill

Ball-Tube Mills

A ball-tube mill (*Figure 6-16*) is a hollow horizontal cylinder, rotated on its axis. Heavy-cast, wear-resistant liners fit the inside of the cylindrical shell, which is filled less than halfway with forged steel or cast alloy balls varying from 1 to 4 inches (25 cm to 100 cm) in diameter. Rotating between 18 to 35 rpm, depending on diameter, the balls are carried two thirds of the way up the periphery and continually cascade toward the center of the cylinder. Coal is fed into the cylinder through hollow trunnions and mixes with the ball charge. Pulverization is accomplished by the impact of the falling balls on the coal, attrition as particles slide over each other and over the liners, and crushing as balls roll over each other and over the liners with coal particles between them. Larger pieces of coal are broken by impact. Fine grinding is done by attrition and crushing, as the balls roll and slide within the charge.

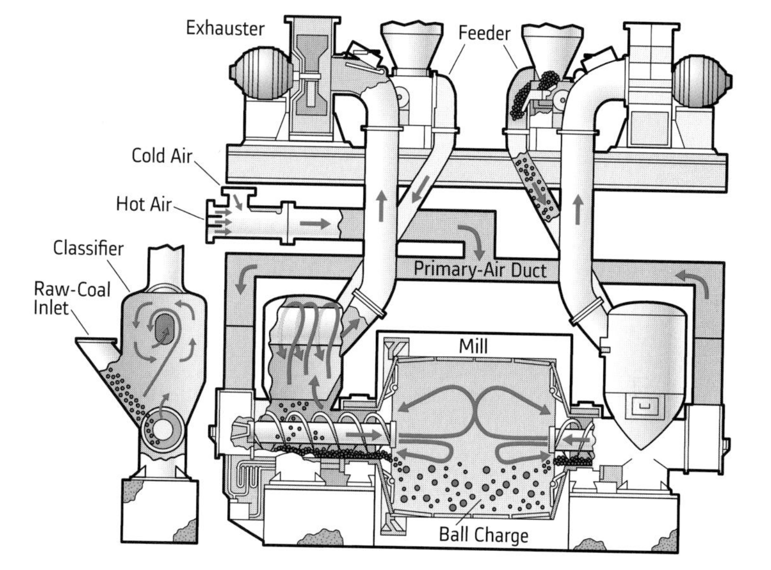

Figure 6-16 | Arrangement of ball-tube mill

Hot airflow is passed through the mill to dry the coal and remove the fines from the pulverizing zone. In most designs used for firing boilers or industrial furnaces, an external classifier regulates the size or degree of fineness of the finished product. The oversize or rejects from the classifier, sometimes called "tailings," already dried in the pulverizing and classifying process, are returned to the grinding zone with the raw coal. This type of pulverizer is particularly susceptible to reductions in capacity from the surface moisture of the coal. Reducing the average moisture content of the mixture is very important in maintaining a continuous flow of coal through the feed end. The recirculation of dried tailings, then, reduces the tendency for wet coal to plug the feed end.

During operation, the relatively large quantity of pulverized coal in the grinding zone of a ball-tube mill acts as a storage reservoir from which sudden increases in fuel demand are supplied. The power consumption of ball-tube mills, kilowatts per unit of coal pulverized, is very high, particularly at partial loads.

Physically large per unit of capacity, these mills require considerable floor space. Because of their size and weight, the initial capital cost is also quite high. The presence of a high circulating load within the mill results in an overproduction of fines within the mill charge. Using an adequate external classifier permits the removal of the fine product from the grinding zone and reduces the production of extreme fines. The comparatively poor mixing of heated air with the partially pulverized material reduces the drying efficiency of this type of mill. High-moisture coals produce a large reduction in mill capacity.

Ball-tube mills are not well suited to intermittent operation, as the large amount of heat stored in the coal and ball charge may produce overheating and fires when the mill is idle. The mass of this mill type makes it necessary to use high-power, high-starting-torque motors. In addition, these mills emit excessive levels of sound. Most installations require that insulated enclosures be erected over each mill for noise attenuation.

Maintenance in the grinding zone of ball-tube mills is relatively easy to perform. Periodically, a ball charge is added to the mill to make up for metal lost in the grinding process. It may take years to wear out the cast liners, but considerable downtime is necessary for their replacement. Over the long run, maintenance costs per unit of coal ground are about the same as for ring-roll type pulverizers. Because of limited operational flexibility and comparatively high capital and operating costs, ball-tube mills are not usually supplied on modern thermal plants. Extremely high-ash or low-grindability fuels are applications that may warrant consideration of tube mills.

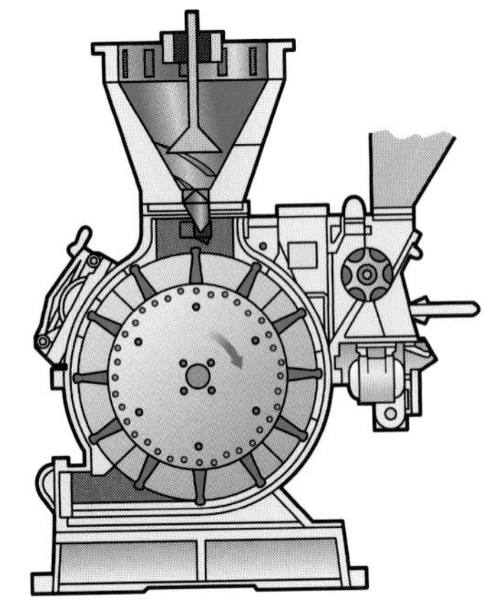

Figure 6-17 | Impact mill with external classifier and exhauster integrally mounted

Impact Mills

An impact mill consists primarily of a series of hinged or fixed hammers revolving in an enclosed chamber lined with heavy-cast wear-resistant plates. Grinding results from a combination of hammer impact on the larger particles and attrition of the smaller particles on each other and across the grinding surfaces. An air system with the fan mounted either internally or externally on the main shaft induces a flow through the mill. An internal or external type of classifier may be used. (See *Figures 6-17* and *6-18*.)

This class of mill is simple and compact, low in cost, and may be built in very small sizes. Its ability to handle high inlet-air temperatures, plus the return of dried classified rejects to the incoming raw feed, makes it an excellent dryer. The high-speed design results in high maintenance and high power consumption when suitable

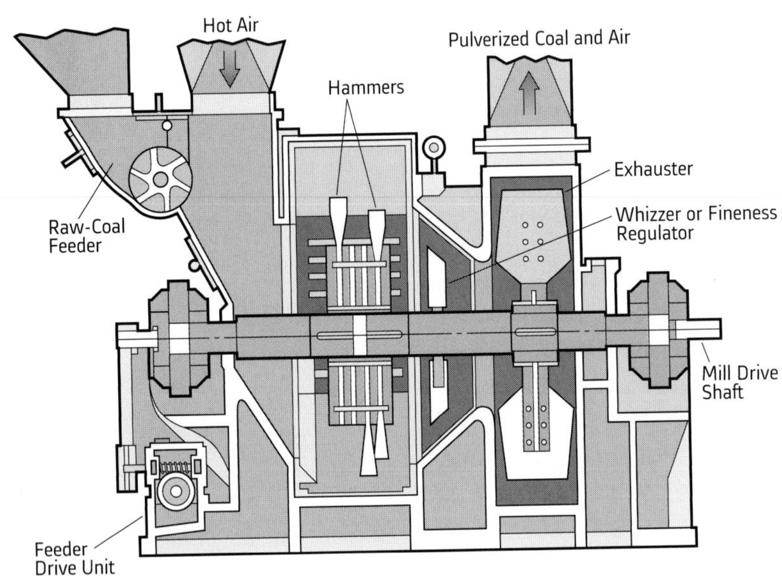

Figure 6-18 | Impact mill with hammers, classifier, and fan on common shaft

fineness for combustion is produced. Progressive wear on the grinding elements produces a rapid drop-off in product fineness. It is difficult, if not impossible, to maintain fineness over the life of the wearing parts. Using an external classifier permits maintenance of fineness, but only at the expense of a considerable reduction in capacity as parts wear. Because the maximum capacity attainable from impact mills is lower than that of most other types and product fineness is generally low, these machines are not supplied for large or modern steam plants.

Attrition Mills

No true attrition mill is used for coal pulverizing because of the high rate of wear on parts. However, a high-speed mill, which uses considerable attrition grinding along with impact grinding, is used for direct firing of pulverized coal. In this mill, the grinding elements consist of pegs and lugs mounted on a disk rotating in a chamber. The periphery of the chamber is lined with wear-resistant plates, and its walls contain fixed rows of lugs within which the rotating lugs mesh. The fan rotor is mounted on the pulverizer shaft. Instead of an external classifier, a simple, shaft mounted rejector type is used. This design uses wear-resistant alloy lug and peg facings and casing linings to reduce the wear effect on fineness and to extend the periods between part replacements. This mill type exhibits the unfavorable wear life and performance characteristics of the impact mills and is, therefore, found primarily on older, low-capacity installations.

Ring-Roll and Ball-Race Mills

Ring-roll and ball-race mills comprise the largest number of pulverizers used for coal grinding. They are of medium speed and use primarily crushing and attrition of particles, plus a very small amount of impact, to obtain size reduction of the coal. The grinding action takes place between two surfaces, one rolling over the other. The rolling element may be either a ball or a roll, while the member over which it rolls may be either a race or a ring. The ball diameter is generally from 20 to 35% of the race diameter, which can be as large as 100 inches (254 cm). If the element is a roll, its diameter may be from 50 to 60% of the ring diameter, which can be as much as 130 inches (330 cm). Its face width, depending on mill size, will vary from 15 to 20% of ring diameter.

When the rolling elements are balls (*Figure 6-19*), they are confined between races. In the majority of designs, the lower race is the driven rotary member, while the upper race is stationary.

Some older designs also use a rotating upper race. The required grinding pressure is obtained by forcing the races together with either heavy springs or pneumatic or hydraulic cylinders. Some additional grinding pressure is obtained from the centrifugal force of the rotating balls.

There are two general classes of mill that use rollers as the rolling elements. In one (*Figure 6-20*), the roller assemblies are driven and the ring is stationary, while in another (*Figure 6-21*), the roller assembly is fixed and the ring rotates.

Perhaps the most frequently used application of the first class is the Raymond® roller mill, used in storage systems. Grinding pressure is obtained from centrifugal force resulting from the rotation of these rolling elements. The other classification of ring-roll mills, commonly known as bowl mills, are those in which the ring rotates. These constitute the largest number

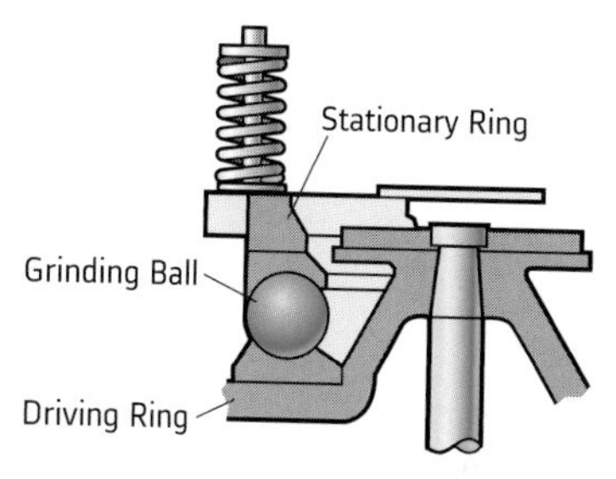

Figure 6-19 | Diagram of ball-race mill

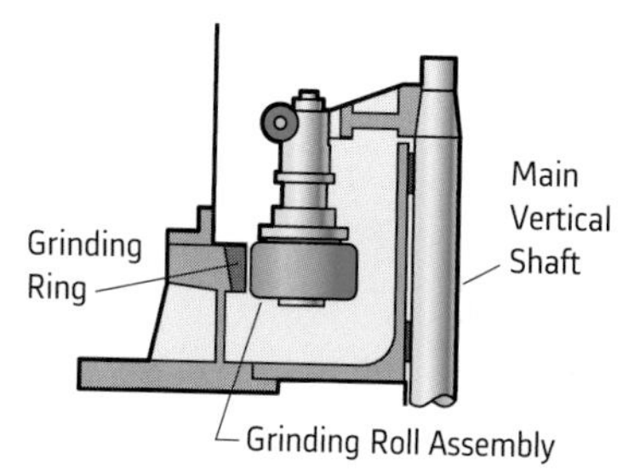

Figure 6-20 | Diagram of roller-type ring-roll mill journal assembly

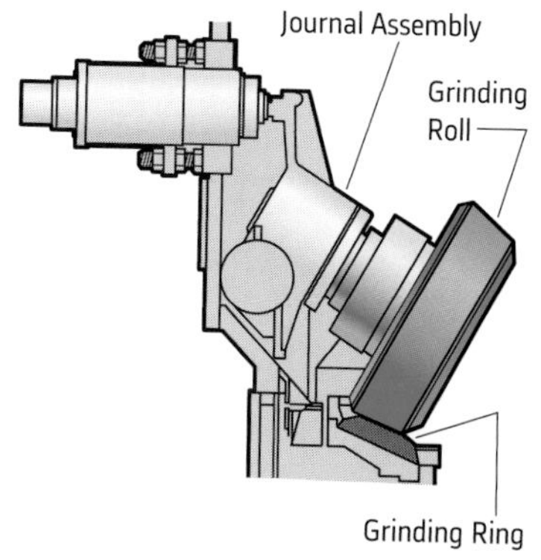

Figure 6-21 | Diagram of bowl-type ring-roll pulverizer journal assembly

of mills used for grinding coal. Bowl mills are manufactured by most major boiler companies and have become the standard for modern power stations. The rotating bowls of these mills operate between 20 and 70 rpm, with larger mills running at the slower speeds.

Generally, bowl mills are equipped with self-contained or integral classifiers to regulate the fineness of the finished product. The classifiers can be of the fixed-vane or rotating type. In some cases, this device may be external to the mill itself and is then termed an "in-stream classifier." Primary air fans or exhausters create a flow of heated air through the mills. This heated air dries the coal, removes it from the grinding zone, carries it through the classifying zone, and conveys it to the burner in a direct-fired system.

When this type of mill is provided with sufficient air at a temperature to produce a satisfactory mill outlet temperature, it can handle very wet coals with only a small reduction in capacity. The high ratio of circulating load (classifier rejects returning to the grinding zone for further size reduction) to output, with the resulting rapid reduction of average moisture content, facilitates the grinding process. These mills require less power than other types on a specific energy-consumption basis, kilowatt hours per ton, giving a significant advantage in operating cost. Physically, these mills are compact and occupy a relatively small amount of floor space per unit of capacity. Some designs of ring-roll mills are extremely quiet in operation. Fineness of the product is relatively uniform throughout the life of the grinding elements and easily controlled by classifier adjustment.

Several references have been made to the ability of the various types of pulverizing equipment to grind different coals economically and efficiently. This capability is a reflection of the grinding pressures available, the method of application of this force, the speed of the moving elements, abrasion, and power and size limitations of the particular units. A list of materials capable of being commercially pulverized by the mill types described could be extended indefinitely. Therefore, the scope of *Table 6-8* covers combustible materials of primary concern in power generation.

ALSTOM PULVERIZER DESIGN

The positive-pressure-type, Alstom HP ring-roll, bowl mill is shown with Dynamic™ classifier in *Figure 6-22*. When fitted with an exhauster (such that the pulverizer operates below atmospheric pressure), it is designated an HPS or HPPS mill, a cross-sectional view of which is given in *Figure 6-23* with static classifier. *Table 6-9* shows the type of mill used with different furnaces and air systems, for the two pressure regimes in which these mills can operate.

Operation of the HP Pulverizer

Raw coal enters the center of the pulverizer through a center feed pipe. It falls onto a rotating bowl. Centrifugal force causes the coal to move outward from the center and under the three journal assemblies, where it is crushed by large rolls. To prevent physical contact of the rolls and bowl liners when the mill is run without coal, a stop limits the downward movement of the journal assembly. The force to pulverize the coal is applied to the journal assembly by an external spring. As the journal rotates about its trunnion in response to increasing coal feed, the spring is compressed and the force for grinding is increased. The partially

TABLE 6-8 | TYPES OF PULVERIZERS FOR VARIOUS MATERIALS

Type of Material	Ball-tube	Impact and Attrition	Ball race	Ring roll
Low-volatile anthracite	x	—	—	—
High-volatile anthracite	x	—	x	x
Coke breeze	x	—	—	—
Petroleum coke (fluid)	x	—	x	x
Petroleum coke (delayed)	x	x	x	x
Graphite	x	—	x	x
Low-volatile bituminous coal	x	x	x	x
Med-volatile bituminous coal	x	x	x	x
High-volatile A bituminous coal	x	x	x	x
High-volatile B bituminous coal	x	x	x	x
High-volatile C bituminous coal	x	—	x	x
Sub-bituminous A coal	x	—	x	x
Sub-bituminous B coal	x	—	x	x
Sub-bituminous C coal	—	—	x	x
Lignite	—	—	x	x
Lignite and coal char	x	—	x	x
Brown coal	—	x	—	—
Furfural residue	—	x	—	x
Sulfur	—	x	—	x
Gypsum	—	x	x	x
Phosphate rock	x	—	x	x
Limestone	x	—	—	x
Rice hulls	—	x	—	—
Grains	—	x	—	—
Ores—hard	x	—	—	—
Ores—soft	x	—	x	x

pulverized coal passes over the rim of the bowl and is entrained by the rising hot air stream and is flash dried. The pyrites and tramp iron that enter the mill with the coal follow the same path as the coal until they pass over the rim of the bowl. Being denser than coal, they cannot be carried upward by the air stream and fall into the under-bowl plenum. Once there, rejected materials are swept around by a set of pivoted scrapers until they reach the tramp iron opening. Reject materials fall into a hopper external to the mill, which can be emptied with the mill in service.

Initial classification of the partially ground coal takes place in the air patterns created by the vane wheel just above the bowl grinding zone. Here the heavy, or more moisture-laden particles, are returned to the bowl, while lighter particles are carried upward. The balance of the coal and air stream passes up through the separator body until it reaches the classifier. When a double-cone static classifier is used, the coal–air mixture begins to spin in a cyclonic path. Externally adjusted vanes control the amount of spin. Because of the differing mass of the particles and the amount of spin, the oversize particles fall into the cone and slide downward until they mix with the incoming raw coal. In this way, only the desired size of coal particles leaves the pulverizer. In pressurized applications, the flow is split into four equal streams before exiting through the discharge valves. With an exhauster mill, there is only one discharge pipe, which conducts the pulverized product to the exhauster.

The fineness of the pulverized product leaving this type of pulverizer is affected by the grindability of the coal, the coal and airflow rate, as well as the mechanical setup and condition of the mill internals. Fineness can be increased by either changing the static classifier blade position or increasing the rotating classifier's speed.

Pulverizer Shell Design Requirements

All pulverizing equipment containing coal-dust laden air is designed and built according to the recommendations of the National Fire Protection Association (NFPA) (Standard NFPA 85 chapter 9, "Pulverized Fuel Systems"). The pressure-containing

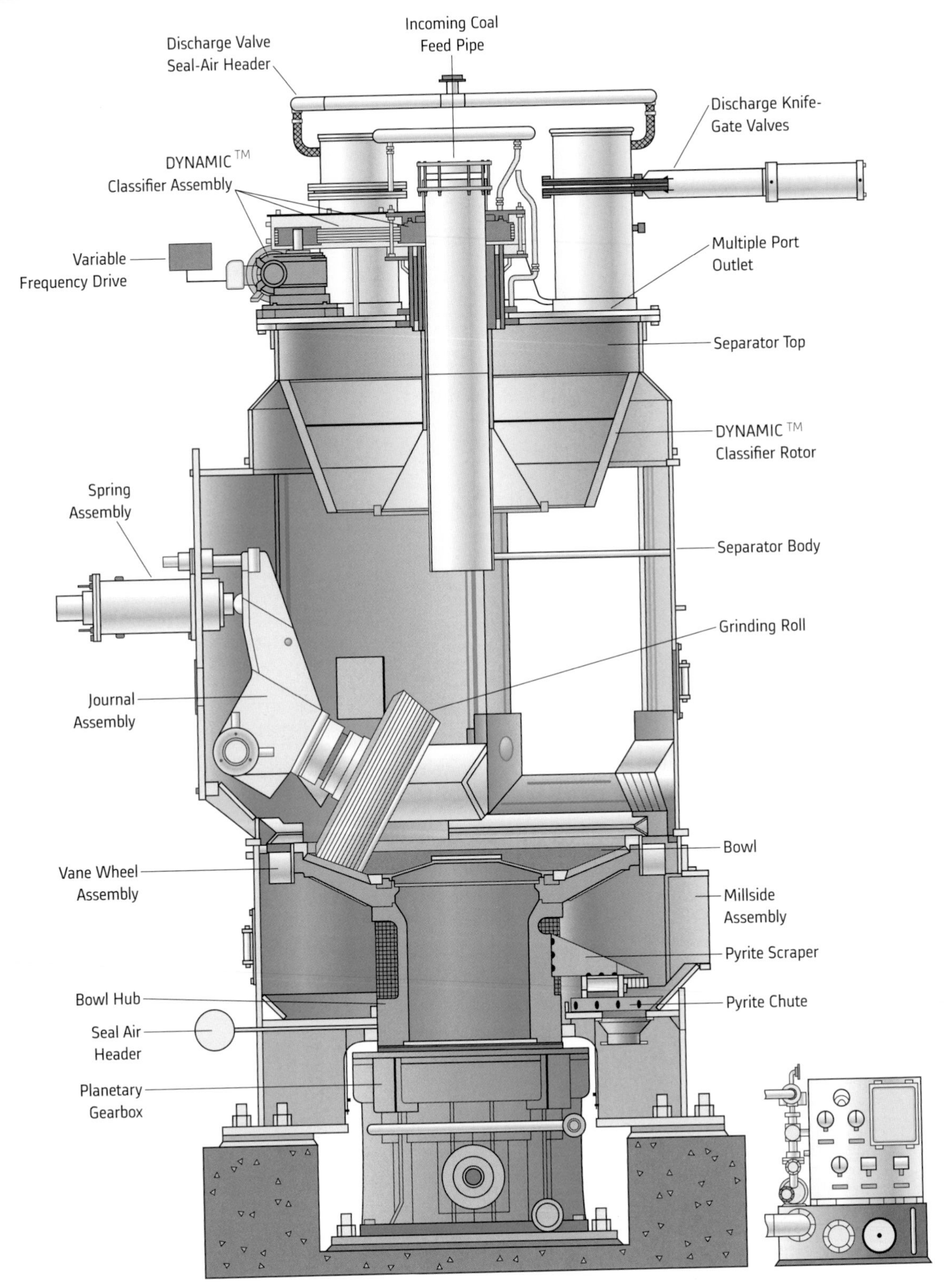

Figure 6-22 | Alstom HP ring-roll bowl mill for positive-pressure operation (shown with Dyamic™ classifier)

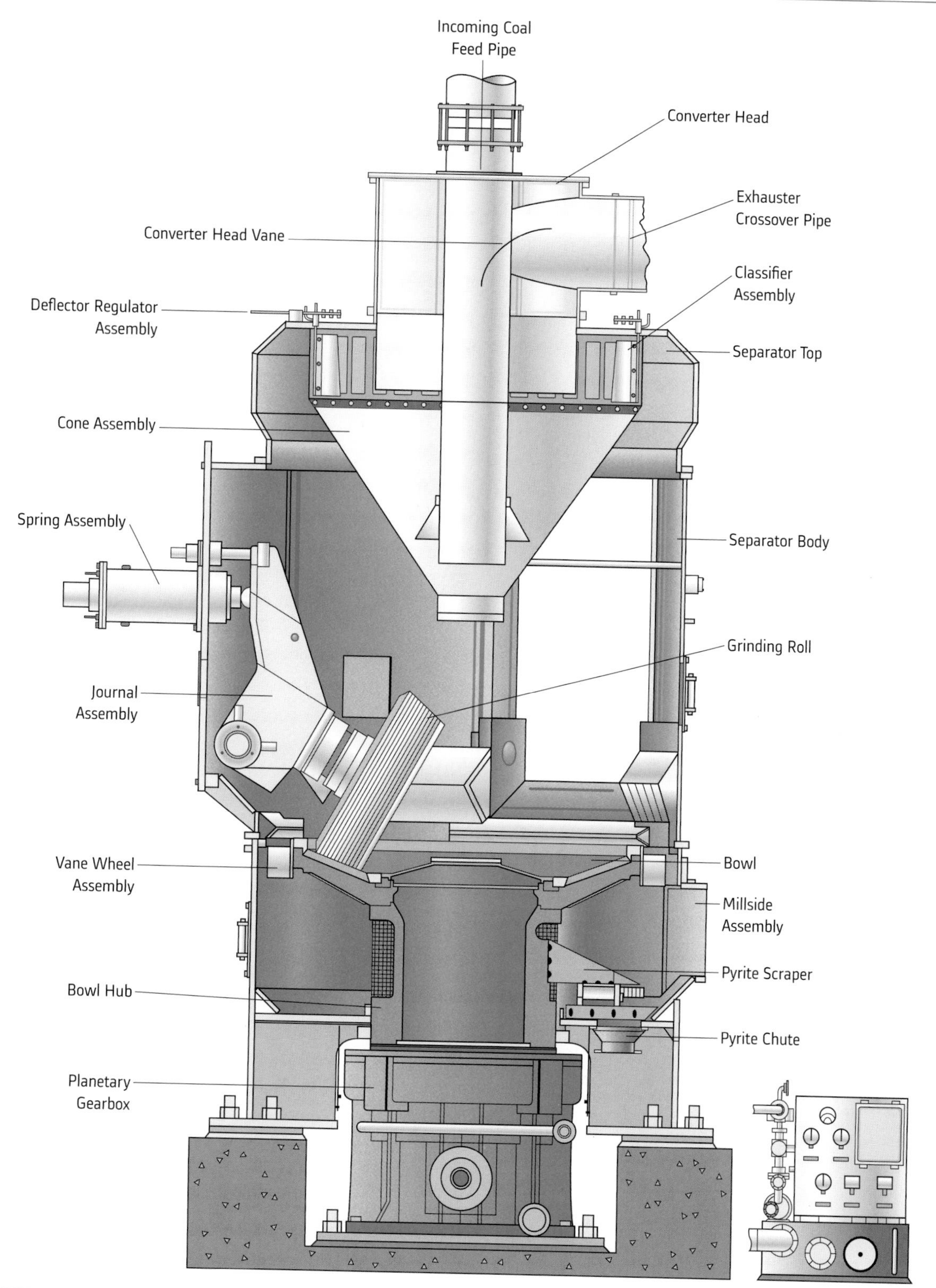

Figure 6-23 | Alstom HPS or HPPS ring-roll bowl mill for use with exhauster (shown with static classifier)

TABLE 6-9 | ALSTOM HP PULVERIZER APPLICATIONS

Mill Type	Furnace Type	Mill Pressure	Air System	Capacity†
HP	Balanced draft	Positive	Primary air fan	36,600–238,000 lb/h‡
HP	Pressurized	Positive	Primary air fan	36,600–238,000 lb/h‡
HPS	Balanced draft	Negative	Exhauster fan	36,600–87,200 lb/h
HPPS	Pressurized	Positive	Exhauster fan	36,600–87,200 lb/h

†Pulverizer capacities are based on a 55-grindability coal pulverized to 70% through a 200-mesh sieve, having a moisture content of 12% with low-rank bituminous coals or 8% with high-rank bituminous coals.
‡Design levels for HP mill capacities are now up to 291,800 lb/h.

shell of the pulverizer, exhauster, and rejects hopper are designed to contain the forces associated with a 50-psig (3.5 bar gage) operating pressure. This requirement is independent of any lower design or operating pressure in the equipment.

Pulverizer Foundation Design

The HP pulverizer exerts three types of loads on its concrete foundation: the static weight of the machine itself, the dynamic loads that are the result of the grinding process, and the thermal loads from the heating of the pulverizer by the hot primary air, which results in expansion forces on the foundation. The foundation design must take these loads into account in both anchor-bolt and concrete reinforcement sizing and placement. The mill and its drive motor are mounted on the same foundation, so there is no relative vibration or settling between the two, which could affect component alignment.

Removable Gear Drive

The HP pulverizer uses a removable planetary-gear drive (*Figure 6-24*). This drive is lighter in weight yet stronger than similar capacity worm-gear or triple-reduction, spiral-bevel, helical gear drives. The HP gear unit is independent of the mill housing structure and can be removed for inspection or maintenance. Its size and weight make it practical to move it to a maintenance area away from the pulverizer bay. Mill outage time will be minimal if a spare gear unit is available at the site.

Since the gear unit does not penetrate the mill housing, it is not exposed to the pulverized coal entrained in the primary air. The input-shaft and output-table seals are of the non-contacting labyrinth type operating at local ambient pressure. The mill housing penetration seal is on the grinding bowl support hub, above the gear unit. Any heat load on the gearing is substantially reduced by its physical separation from the hot-air inlet, allowing the gears and bearings to run cooler. Internally, the gear unit consists of a right angle, spiral-bevel, reduction-input stage and a planetary-reduction output stage. The sun gear is connected to the bevel-gear shaft by a crowned gear-type coupling to allow both axial and radial movement. Floating sun and planet gears ensure equalized loads on the meshing teeth. This acts to

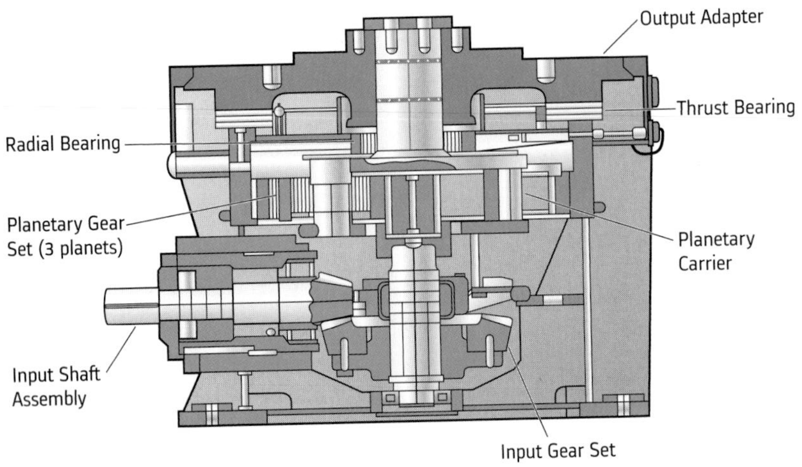

Figure 6-24 | Removable planetary-gear drive of HP pulverizer

distribute the total horsepower equally among the three planets. Input-gear, bevel-gear, and planet-gear shaft bearings are all designed for Anti-Friction Bearing Manufacturers Association (AFBMA) B-10 life of 100,000 hours minimum.

Mill grinding forces are carried by a hydrodynamic tilting-pad, thrust-bearing assembly located above the planetary stage. There are multiple bearing pads, four of which have dual-element sensors to measure pad temperature. The pad temperature is interlocked with mill operation to prevent damage to the thrust bearing. The thrust-bearing pad pitch-circle diameter is the same as the gear housing outer structural wall, to maximize thrust-bearing support and to transfer grinding forces directly to the foundation without affecting gear meshes.

Lubrication System

An external lubrication system supplies cooled and filtered oil to the roller bearings, the gear meshes, and the hydrodynamic thrust-bearing pads. All major components of the system are shop-mounted on a self-contained skid. An isolation device allows maintenance of the system skid assembly without draining the gear unit hydrodynamic bearing reservoir, which is at a higher elevation. A duplex filter assembly provides for maintenance of a standby filter while the pulverizer is operating. After filtering, the oil passes through an oil-to-water, shell-and-tube heat exchanger. Electrical temperature and pressure sensors monitor the lubrication system. Mill starting, operation, and stopping are all interlocked to prevent running the gear unit without proper lubrication. Low-wattage oil heaters, installed in thermowells in the reservoir, bring the oil up to minimum operating temperature before the mill may be placed in service.

Mill Side and Air Inlet Assembly

The mill side and air inlet assembly (*Figures 6-22* and *6-23*) is a weldment that supports the upper section of the pulverizer and receives the hot primary air from the air preheater. It is mounted on sole plates and is secured to the foundation by anchor bolts. The mill side is designed to handle the thermal stresses created by the hot primary air without the use of a complicated internal insulation system. An oversized, tramp-iron spout in the floor of the mill side conducts rejected material to the external rejects hopper and conveying system. Doors in the mill side give access to the underside of the bowl and provide for a ventilating airflow when maintenance is being done.

Bowl, Bowl Hub, and Vane Wheel Assembly

Figures 6-22 and *6-23* show these components, located above the gearbox. The rotating bowl and bowl hub carry the two scrapers, the vane wheel segments, and the bowl wear plates, called "bull ring segments." The bull ring is subject to abrasive wear as a result of the grinding that takes place. Replacement is necessary when the wear becomes excessive. Alstom furnishes segmented bull rings for ease of handling, and uses high-chrome, white iron for the segments in most applications. The rotating vane wheel segments are made from heat-treated, abrasion-resistant, steel plate allowing easy weld repair, if necessary. The vane wheel opening shapes are optimized to achieve aerodynamic flow patterns that simultaneously promote mixing and primary classification, while coal spillage, pressure loss, and localized wear rates are minimized. The pyrites (mill-rejects) hopper can be arranged opposite the mill drive motor, 90 degrees on either side. This flexibility of arrangement allows the HP mill to fit the maintenance requirements of any plant. The standard HP mill setting height permits mounting of the hopper and the pyrite-handling system without pits or entrenchment.

Separator Body and Vane Wheel Assembly

As described above, initial coal-particle classification is done in the grinding zone by the bowl-mounted, rotating, vane wheel and the housing-mounted, stationary, coal–air deflectors. The vane wheel as the primary classifier on HP mills, promotes uniform distribution of the coal and primary air, while it also lessens erosion of mill internals by the coal–air stream. Large coal particles return immediately to the bowl for regrinding before entering the main classifier above. The rotating part of the vane wheel is constructed of an abrasion-resistant plate, segmented for convenience in assembly and maintenance. Removable liners protect the wear surface of the stationary vane wheel deflectors, which direct the upward airflow past the bowl rim.

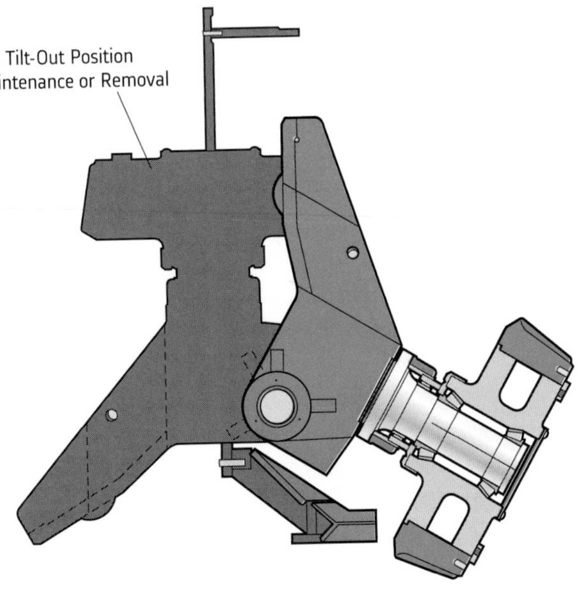

HP Pulverizer Journal Assembly

The roll-assembly bearing system consists of two identical tapered roller bearings in an opposed arrangement (*Figure* 6-25). The system is designed for an AFBMA B-10 life of 100,000 hours minimum, under a severe duty cycle.

A self contained oil bath lubricates the grinding-roll bearings. To prevent contamination of the oil, seal air flows through the trunnion ends, then outward through a roll air seal. No parts of the seal-air supply system are exposed to the coal–primary air stream. HP mills have a unique grinding-roll, tilt-out feature, as depicted in *Figure* 6-25. Each roll assembly can be rotated out of the mill on its trunnion mounting shaft, using a tilting fixture and an overhead mill hoist or crane. With the roll locked in this vertical service access position, several inspection and maintenance tasks can be performed without removing the assemblies from the mill: worn grinding rolls can be removed and new ones installed, roll bearing end play can be inspected and adjusted, oil seals can be inspected or replaced, oil can be changed, and the entire roll stem assembly can be removed and taken to another area for bearing maintenance.[36]

Maximum roll life is a primary goal of the HP pulverizer design. It is accomplished by incorporating large

Journal Tilt-Out Position for Maintenance or Removal

Figure 6-25 | HP pulverizer journal assembly with tilt-out feature

rolls to increase the total volume of wear material available, and by using roll material with high wear resistance. Combustalloy™ wear material, an Alstom proprietary weld overlay, provides effective wear life five times greater than standard NiHard and can be easily rewelded when worn.

The externally mounted spring assembly (*Figures* 6-22 and 6-23) has a major advantage in that maintenance personnel do not have to enter the pulverizer to inspect or adjust the springs. Since the assembly is located away from the coal flow, erosion is eliminated. Spring travel can be maximized with an external mechanism, to allow large ungrindable material to pass under the rolls until it is rejected from the mill. A positive spring-preload locking device prevents any change in spring setting during operation. The entire spring assembly is a cartridge type to reduce change-out time, to allow for stocking of spare assemblies, and to allow convenient inspection and refurbishing. The spring assembly, as well as the journal assembly and the main bowl–hub air seal, have labyrinth-type seals that use air for sealing between stationary and moving parts. The pressure of the filtered seal air is 8 to 16 inches WG above the mill-inlet pressure, with the flow rate a function of mill size.

Static Classifier and Discharge Valve Assemblies

The top of the mill is made larger than the main body to reduce coal–air stream velocity and mill aerodynamic pressure drop and to optimize classifier efficiency. Plant personnel can adjust the position of the classifier vanes when the pulverizer is operating, by using two manually operated levers on the mill top; each lever operates half of the vanes. Particle separation is accomplished in a stationary-cone, cyclone classifier. As described previously, oversized coal particles are returned to the grinding zone through the return spout at the bottom of the cone, where they mix with the incoming raw coal feed to increase drying efficiency. The classifier and outlet configuration has been designed to minimize areas of localized wear and reduce the number of components exposed to erosive wear. For very abrasive coal applications the static classifier and outlet assembly can be lined with 90%-alumina tile for extended wear life. Knife gate valves, at the outlet of a positive-pressure HP pulverizer, isolate it from the fuel piping leading to the furnace, as recommended by the NFPA. Each valve has a set of replaceable valve seats, coated to minimize wear. Pneumatic cylinders operating in unison open and close the valves. They are actuated by a single solenoid valve, which also controls the supply of purge-seal air to the fuel piping. *Figure* 6-22 shows the seal-air header for this purpose, located downstream of the discharge valves. HP pulverizers are available with manually adjustable coal deflectors at the mill outlet to adjust pipe-to-pipe coal distribution.

Dynamic™ Classifier

Alstom has been supplying rotating classifiers since the 1960s. By the late 1980s, emission regulations and the competitive economic pressure of the power industry required staged firing conditions and the use of lower-cost fuels. These factors increased the need for increased mill capacity and finer pulverized coal for new boilers, as well as retrofits to existing

Dynamic™ classifiers provide improved fineness that allow for combustion modifications to reduce NOx emissions.

units. The Dynamic™ classifier has been optimized to meet these needs. The Dynamic™ classifier must be a reliable piece of processing equipment. Use of simple, reliable, off-the-shelf components has proven an effective approach to meet this goal. The Dynamic™ classifier uses two oversized, spherical, roller bearings in a simple grease-lubricated arrangement, with lip-type grease seals and clearance-type air seals to prevent leakage and contamination. The drive system has proven to be very reliable and compact. A single, small, horizontally mounted, variable speed motor driving an integral, self-contained, bath-lubricated gearbox provides the initial reduction. Final speed reduction is handled by a single-set, multi-strand V-belt. Speed control is managed by a variable-frequency drive typically mounted in the plant's motor control center away from the mill bay.

The heart of the Dynamic™ classifier is the rotor assembly located inside the mill upper housing. The rotational speed of the classifier rotor controls the product fineness leaving the mill. For a utility-sized mill, rotor speeds are in the range of 50 to 80 rpm to produce fineness levels in the range of 70 to 85% passing a 200-mesh sieve. Alstom uses a single rotating stage for all HP pulverizers for effective fineness control. Because of the uniform flow field set-up within the HP mill internals, there is no need for stationary preconditioning vanes. Because the rotor speeds are low, pressure loss and wear rates are minimized. Classifier speed is typically ramped as a function of feed rate and is easily adjusted if needed for significant changes in fuel or firing conditions. Because the fineness control is automated, classifier speed can easily be biased to trade between high fineness and high coal throughput with no other adjustments required.

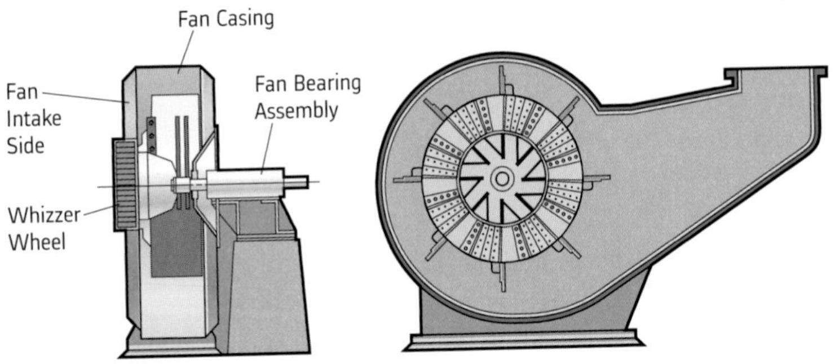

Figure 6-26 | Centrifugal material-handling exhauster for Alstom suction-type pulverizer

Coal–Air Exhauster Fans

For suction-type HP pulverizers, Alstom supplies material handling fans to match the mill and fuel-piping system requirements. These exhausters are horizontal-shaft, straight-bladed, centrifugal fans, (*Figure 6-26*) operating at constant speed and at temperatures between 150 and 180°F (65 and 80°C).

They are designed in accordance with NFPA standards. There are replaceable liners on the housing scroll and sides. The fan spider is removable to make replacing fan blades easy. The fan wheel is supported by anti-friction bearings mounted in an external bearing housing located between the exhauster and its driving motor. Exhausters used with HP pulverizers are driven by separate motors. The pulverizer and exhauster motors are interlocked logically to ensure coal transport out of the mill. Fan bearing lubrication is independent of the mill lubrication system.

Safety and Controls

The production and handling of pulverized fuels can be hazardous. Because fine particles in suspension or deposition are readily volatilized and become combustible, under certain conditions explosions may take place. Notwithstanding these dangers, the industry has achieved a remarkable safety record since the inception of pulverized coal firing. To protect property and life, all pulverizing equipment and related auxiliaries, including strength of equipment, valving, and inerting, are designed in accordance with NFPA 85 as detailed in Chapter 9, "Pulverized Fuel Systems."

Various controls and safety devices are used for the correct and proper operation of the equipment. Pulverizer output is controlled by the regulation of feed rate in response to a load signal. Airflow and air temperature are proportioned to feed rate by automatic control. Also included are permissive interlocks for the proper sequential operation of equipment, flow alarms to indicate cessation of coal flow to and from feeders, and load-limiting devices to prevent overfeeding the mills. Anticipating actions and more responsive feedback may often be included with the above in pulverizer control systems. Control systems and instrumentation are covered in detail in Chapter 7.

Pulverizer Inerting and Fire Extinguishing

To supplement the above operational controls, current practice is to install systems to detect and extinguish mill fires and to reduce the possibility of destructive positive pressures. An ideal inerting system continuously purges any combustible volatiles from the pulverizer to the furnace and avoids "bottling up" of the pulverizer. The system allows a mill to be returned to normal service quickly after the inerting takes place. Alstom's pulverizer inerting and firefighting system is designed to provide an early warning of a potentially hazardous situation. It uses readily available plant steam as the inerting medium because steam is less damaging to equipment than other inerting media and makes for easier restart of the pulverizer. Plant water is used as the fire-extinguishing agent. It is hard-piped to fixed water spray nozzles installed in the pulverizer. The purposes of such a system are:

- to dilute the oxygen content of the mill when there is risk of explosion;
- to clear the pulverizer of fuel by means of an inert medium when transport by air may be hazardous; and
- to extinguish fires in the pulverized-fuel system.

System Design Features

The Alstom pulverizer inerting and firefighting system includes the following features:

- The pulverizer is automatically inerted when conditions exist for a fire or potential explosion.
- Steam is used as the primary inerting medium, with CO_2, water mist or other cold inert gas used to cool the pulverizer.
- The inerting system is capable of supplying steam in sufficient quantities to transport the combustible contents of the pulverizer to the furnace, while maintaining an inert atmosphere within the mill. As an alternative, a water-flushing system can be used to clear the mill of coal via the pyrite system while the mill remains inerted.

- Multiple water-spray nozzles are strategically installed in the pulverizer to provide complete internal fire-extinguishing coverage,
- The system monitors the entire pulverized fuel system from the feeders through the fuel piping.
- Audible and visual alarms are activated in all critical areas and in the control room upon detection of a hazardous condition.
- Provision is made for interfacing with existing plant control systems.

In Chapter 10 on power plant operation, further information is given on the efficient and proper operation of pulverizer inerting and fire-extinguishing systems.

AIR PREHEATERS

The functions of combustion air preheaters have been described in Chapters 2 and 3. Although justified by the increased efficiency resulting from lower exit-gas temperatures, air preheaters also make pulverized coal firing practical by providing the drying and transporting medium.

Two principal types of air preheaters are in use: the rotary regenerative (Ljungström® air preheater) and the tubular recuperative air preheater. The choice of the size and type of air preheater depends on economic and engineering factors. The economic factors include the original equipment cost, the fuel cost, and the fan power cost resulting from air-heater draft losses. The engineering factors include the air temperature required for combustion and/or pulverized coal drying, as well as unit reliability and installation space requirements.

REGENERATIVE AIR PREHEATERS

The Ljungström® air preheater transfers to the combustion air sensible heat in the flue gas leaving the boiler; it does this through a regenerative heat transfer surface in a rotor that turns continuously through the gas and air streams at from 1 to 3 rpm (depending on diameter). The principle is illustrated in *Figure 6-27*.

Figure 6-27 also illustrates the major components of a large, vertical-shaft, Ljungström® air preheater designed for gas flow downward and airflow upward. The rotor, packed with an efficient heat-transfer surface, is supported through a lower bearing at the cold end of the air preheater and guided through a guide-bearing assembly located at the top or hot end.

Depending on its size, the rotor has between 12 and 48 radial members, which are attached to a center post. The rotor compartments are closed with seal plates, as shown in *Figure 6-28*. The rotor sealing system contains simple leaf-type labyrinth seals bolted to the

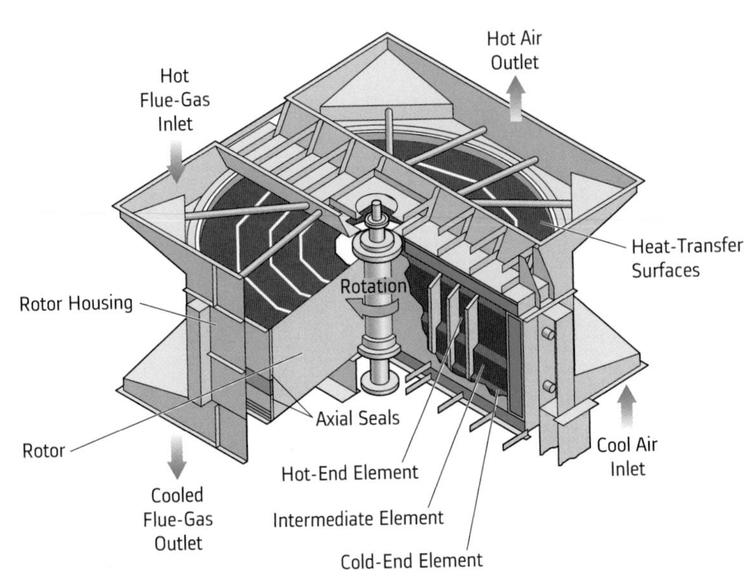

Figure 6-27 | Ljungström® air preheater, bisector vertical design

rotor radial members at both the hot end and the cold end. The radial seals sweep across radial plates, again located at both the hot end and the cold end of the rotor. To complete the system, axial seals are positioned at the peripheral end of the radial members of the rotor. These are also leaf-type labyrinth seals used with axial sealing plates. This system effectively separates the air stream from the flue gas stream.

An electric motor provides drive action through a speed-reducer, pinion gear, which engages a pin rack attached to the periphery of the rotor.

Ljungström® air preheaters are designed with rotor diameters from 7 to 67 feet (2.1 m to 20 m). The smaller units are completely assembled in the shop, while the larger utility-size units are arranged for convenient field assembly. The size designation of a Ljungström® air preheater has no direct relationship to the rotor diameter or radius. The difference between each air preheater size designation is related to a percentage increase in the rotor area.

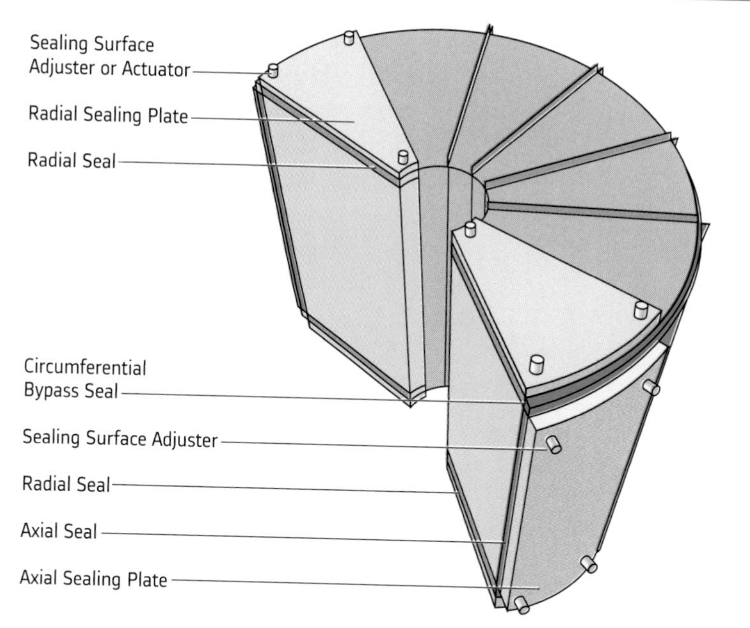

Figure 6-28 | The Ljungström® air preheater rotor sealing system

Air Preheater Types

The air preheater design can accommodate any steam generator duct arrangement. The ducts and heating surface can be positioned for either vertical or horizontal flow; the most common design is vertical, with the rotor mounted on a vertical shaft and the air and gas flow passing vertically through the preheater. Designs are available where the gas flows upward or downward through the preheater, with downward flowing arrangements being the most common type, as gravity aids in clearing any ash or particulate from the rotor.

Horizontal air preheaters are less common and have a horizontal shaft, with the gas and air flow passing horizontally through the preheater. They can be arranged for gas-over-air or air-over-gas at the option of the plant designer. These designs are not as common or as preferred as the vertical design because of their inherent cyclic stresses, which can accelerate element loosening and limit the expected life of the rotating equipment.

Air Preheater Arrangements

The majority of Ljungström® air preheaters supplied to date are the bisector design, which have only two separate flow streams, one of flue gas and one of air. (See *Fig. 6-27.*)

Pulverized coal boiler systems included the necessity to preheat air for coal pulverization. Ordinarily, hot air supplied to the pulverizers furnishes both the heat to dry the coal and the medium to transport the pulverized fuel to the furnace. This portion of the

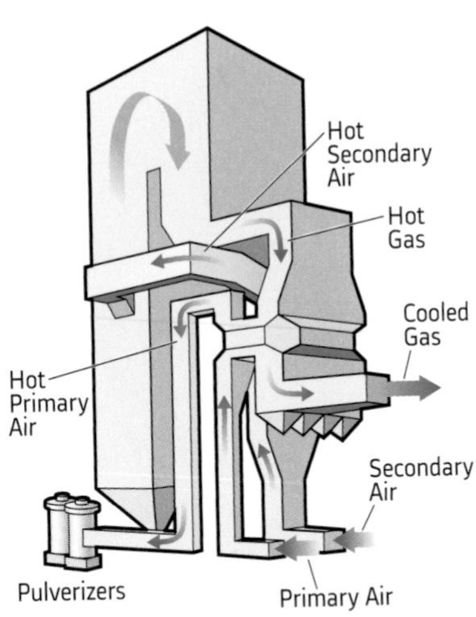

Figure 6-29 | Trisector Ljungström® air preheater with primary and secondary air system on a pulverized coal boiler

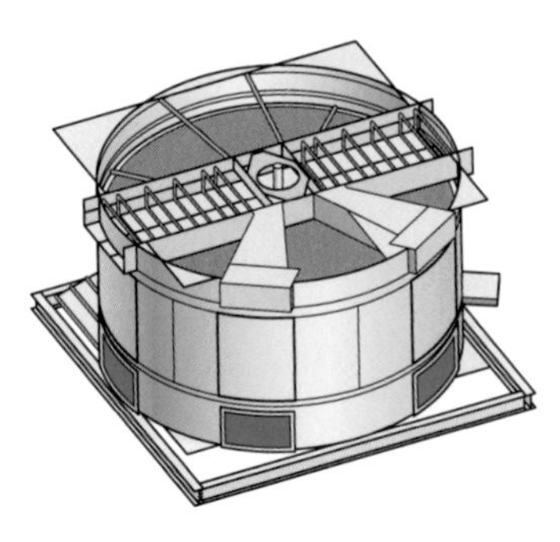

Figure 6-30 | The quadsector Ljungström® air preheater

total air for combustion is called the "primary air."

Historically, separate air preheaters were used for the combustion air (secondary air) and the primary air. The trisector air preheater is now widely used to provide the higher-pressure primary air and the lower-pressure secondary air, but heated by a single air preheater (*Fig.* 6-29). The trisector is equipped with an additional radial sealing plate at both the hot end and cold end and an axial sealing plate separating the primary and secondary air streams. The heater is readily adaptable to coal types and moisture contents, by varying the size of the primary air opening, with a 35-, 50-, or 72-degree primary air opening normally furnished.

Some advantages of the trisector over a separate primary and secondary air preheater system include:

- No gas-biasing dampers and controls.
- Because only one gas duct is required, the need for ductwork, expansion joints, and insulation is greatly reduced when compared with a separate air heating system.
- Since the average cold-end temperatures can be maintained using only secondary air, the requirement for air steam is eliminated.
- Equipment layout is simplified. Less structural steel is needed to install the system and less cleaning equipment is required.
- Fewer soot blowers and water-washing devices are required with one heater in lieu of two.
- Even with a large variation in primary airflow, there is relatively little effect on overall heat recovery, because heat not recovered in the primary section will be picked up in the secondary section.

The quadsector air preheater is designed with four flow streams through the air preheater rotor, which consist of one gas and one primary air flow as in the trisector, but two separate secondary air flows (*Figure* 6-30). The design has the primary air sector "flanked" on either side by secondary air; the aim is to reduce the total air-to-gas leakage of the unit. This method of leakage reduction is ideal for applications in which the pressure differential between the air and gas sides is high, such as in CFB applications. (See Chapter 3.)

Heating Surface Design

The heating surface of the Ljungström® air preheater uses combinations of flat, or formed, pressed-steel sheets with corrugated, notched, or undulated ribbing. When used in combination, these form longitudinal passages of the most desirable contour for the predetermined spacing. Although the gas and airflow are turbulent, the smooth path for their travel through the rotor offers low resistance. As an approximate rule, 1 inch (2.54 cm) of height of this highly efficient heating surface recovers about as much heat as 2 feet (0.6 m) of surface in a tubular heater, with equivalent resistance to gas and air flow. The compact arrangement of light metal sheets permits a large amount of effective heating surface to be placed in a relatively small rotor. The metal sheets, commonly called "heating elements," are typically packed in containers at the factory.

Normally, the heating surface is divided into two or more layers. Advantages resulting from layering include the ability to vary the configuration of surface profiles throughout the preheater depth (to satisfy different flow conditions) and to vary the material selection of sheets in each layer (to accommodate the temperature and other conditions particular to each zone).

There are a number of materials commonly used for the heating surface, with mild steel surfaces being widely used for hotter parts of the rotor and low-alloy corrosion-resistant steel used for colder sections that are exposed to corrosion. In addition, porcelain enamel-coated heating surfaces are the industry standard for cold-end sections in more severe applications or when prolonged element life is required.

Rotors

Large rotors have between 24 and 48 compartments extending axially along the full radius of the rotor. Each compartment consists of two side plates connected by a series of circumferential stay plates and/or grating. Horizontal rotor designs have the rotor mounted between two spherical roller bearings, while the vertical rotors have the rotor shaft supported by a spherical roller, or tilting pad, thrust-bearing. Various rotor designs are available, ranging from fully welded arrangements to modular designs that use a pinned connection to the shaft to reduce or eliminate field welding.

Designing for Operation after an SCR

Environmental regulations designed to reduce NOx emissions have resulted in fuel changes, burner upgrades, and new equipment and chemical process installations, including selective catalytic reduction (SCR) and selective non-catalytic reduction (SNCR) systems (Chapter 5). The operation of these systems generally results in some ammonium bisulfate (ABS) deposits, as excess ammonia combines with sulfur trioxide and water. The ABS deposits collect within the air preheater on metal surfaces within a temperature range generally between 300 and 375°F. ABS, in combination with fly ash, forms a sticky deposit that is difficult to remove with conventional soot blowers. Frequent outages for water washing may be required. In addition, during water washing, ABS becomes very corrosive, which can shorten the operational life of the heating element and the cold-end rotor structure. Experience has shown that if the ABS collects in a region that bridges two layers of heating elements, the rate of accumulation and subsequent consequences are accelerated. Significant cleaning energy is lost when the cleaning medium for the soot blower has to cross an opening between element layers. Any remaining cleaning energy will have little effect on deposits in the adjacent layer.

For maximum cleaning effectiveness, the ABS deposit should be trapped in the single deep layer of heating element profile that is designed to aid the cleaning of the layer (preferably a "closed channel" design) (*Figure 6-31*). In addition, the use of a corrosion-resistant, smooth, enamel-coated surface in the ABS deposition zone inhibits deposit adhesion and improves the cleaning effectiveness. The use of specially designed cleaning devices is also typically investigated to provide the most cleanable solution.

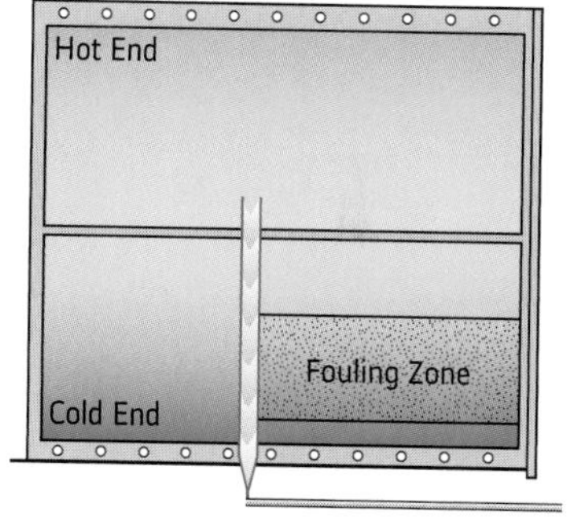

Figure 6-31 | Preferred rotor arrangement for operation after an SCR

Air Preheater Leakage

The air-to-gas leakage in an air preheater must be taken into account in the design and selection of associated fans. The leakage is composed of two main components:

- "Direct" leakage is the air that passes into the gas stream between the radial and axial seals and sealing surfaces as a result of the static pressure differential between the air and gas streams. The leakage across the sealing

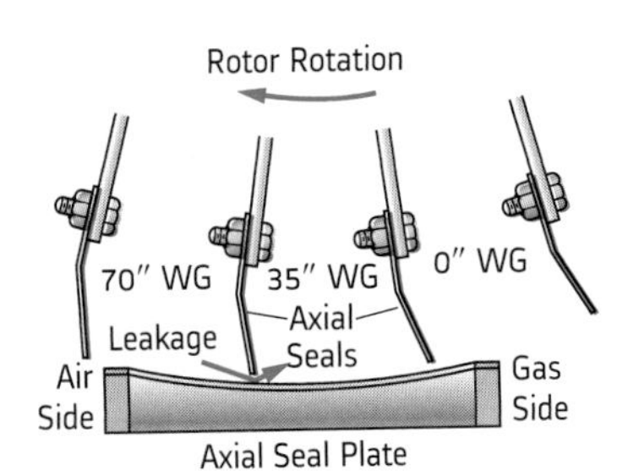

Figure 6-32 | Double sealing of rotor seals

system is directly proportional to the square root of the pressure differential, but also depends on the air density.

- "Entrained" leakage is the air contained in the rotor as it passes from the air side to the gas side. The quantity of entrained leakage depends on the rotor depth, rotor diameter, and rotor speed.

Whether direct or entrained, the leakage has no effect on the heat-transfer efficiency of the Ljungström® air preheater. There is no difference in the heat transferred to the air stream from the gas stream because of leakage. However, the gas temperature leaving the preheater can typically be decreased by 10 to 20°F (5 to 11°C) by the mixture of the cooler air with the hotter gas stream.

Rotor Sealing Arrangements

The continuous process of heat exchange between cold air and hot gas results in a significant metal temperature gradient through the air preheater, which in turn leads to a predictable deformation in the shape of the cylindrical rotor. The hot end (where the gas enters and air exits) expands radially, becoming larger in diameter and convex, while the cold end (where the air enters and gas exits) remains smaller in diameter and becomes concave.

To compensate for this thermal distortion, the radial and axial seals are set, in the cold condition, a prespecified distance from their respective sealing plates. During normal operation, in the hot condition, these preset gaps are reduced to a "near-zero" condition.

Almost every new Ljungström® air preheater larger than a size 24½ now comes standard with a system of double sealing (*Figure* 6-32). The nature of this design is to ensure that there are two seals interfacing with the sealing surface at all times during the cycle of the rotor, which together create a moving plenum across the sealing surface. This is analogous to a double orifice. There is a double restriction to flow crossing from one side of the Ljungström® air preheater to the other.

The formation of this intermediate-pressure plenum between the air and gas streams serves to reduce the air-to-gas pressure differential by a factor of nearly 2. This decrease in pressure differential can reduce direct leakage by as much as 30%. Double sealing is normally applied to the radial and axial seals together, but can be applied to either one separately.

Leakage Reduction and Control Systems

On larger air preheaters, a system to reduce or control the leakage may be furnished. These systems act to minimize the air-to-gas leakage, which occurs when the hot end radial seal clearance increases as the rotor approaches its operating temperature and the seals move away from the sealing plate. Controlling the hot-end radial seal clearance during operation requires the installation of a drive system (*Figure* 6-33). The sector plate drive assembly is typically composed of an electric motor, speed reducer, and two mechanical screw actuators mounted to a welded steel base. The electric motor is operated by the appropriate control system.

A leakage "control" system (LCS) is a self-adjusting system that minimizes the direct air-to-gas leakage by using sensors to detect the position of the rotor. The hot-end sector plates are moved to follow the thermal deformation of the rotor during operation. In operation, the LCS periodically moves the hot-end sector plates toward or away from the rotor, to maintain the radial seal clearance at a constant, minimal value. During periods of stable operation a timer may periodically retract and reposition the sector plate to maintain functional mobility. This system provides maximum leakage control at any operating point.

A leakage "reduction" (LRS) system moves the hot-end sector plates a predetermined set distance toward or away from the rotor, when a signal from the power plant control room indicates that a specified load point has been passed. This system benefits from a simplified control scheme, as it does not require a rotor position sensor, but instead is designed to provide leakage reduction at full load. Typically, the system is designed so that the sector plates will extend (or retract) when the boiler unit reaches 75% of full load megawatts (MW), either during start-up or shut-down.

Air Preheater Fouling Mechanisms

Cold-end deposition occurs when the boiler flue gas reaches the sulfuric acid condensation temperature, or acid dew point. The fly ash in the flue gas can combine with moisture and sulfur derivatives to form a fine-grained deposit or scale on the cold-end heating surface. Soot blowing can generally remove and control regenerative air heater cold-end deposits, provided those deposits are not subjected to moisture. Moisture can be introduced as drainage from water-cooled gas analysis probes, economizer or boiler tube leaks, and unprotected forced draft (FD) fan inlets, through

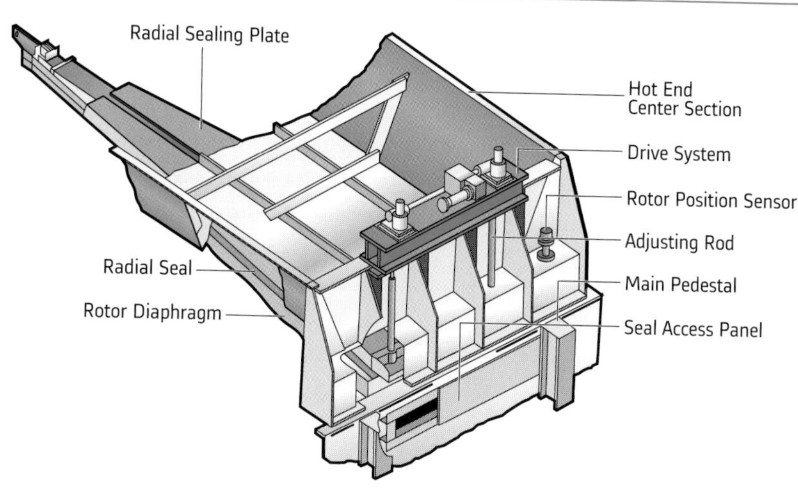

Figure 6-33 | A typical sector plate drive arrangement

which rain can enter the air preheater. Leaking steam soot blowers and water-washing shutoff valves can also add to the problem. The most frequent source of external moisture is the soot-blowing medium itself. Care must be taken to use a suitable medium source that has controlled pressure and temperature to provide a dry medium to the soot blowers at all times.

Air-heater element fouling also can result from the carryover of material from the economizer and the subsequent lodging of the larger particles in the heating surface, particularly at the air-heater hot end.

Online Soot Blowing

Various arrangements and styles of soot-blowing equipment can be furnished on Ljungström® air preheaters. Power-driven soot blowers, which have nozzles mounted on a swinging arm, or stationary multi-nozzle types are widely used on smaller air preheaters. Retractable blowers, similar to those used in boiler convection passes, are installed on larger air preheaters. These are most often located at the gas-outlet side to prevent fly ash from being carried into the wind boxes. They are installed either as an integral part of the air preheater duct or in the gas-outlet ductwork immediately adjacent to the unit.

Additional combined "multimedia" cleaning devices are also available. These devices operate as normal retractable soot blowers during boiler operation. They have the capability to quickly switch to operate with medium- or high-pressure water during boiler outages to provide water washing capability.

Superheated steam (approximately 300°F [150°C] superheat) or dry compressed air is the recommended cleaning medium. Although compressed air is considered to be the premium cleaning medium, its merits do not stem from any inherent cleaning ability, but from its dryness as compared with steam. A steam source must be selected to have pressure and temperature conditions that, by proper control measures, may be used to provide dry steam to the air preheater soot blower.

Soot-blowing pressures are set by the equipment suppliers for each type of heat-transfer surface (typically in the range of 100 to 250 psig [6.8 bar to 17 bar]). A steam soot blower piping system should include an automatic drain valve, thermocouples, and an automatic admission valve to the blowers. The automatic drain valve is open to free drain discharge until the temperature-sensing thermocouple indicates steam of adequate quality. When using air, care should be taken to install a proper line of traps and separators to remove moisture from the blowing medium.

Water Washing

In cases in which soot blowing cannot readily remove residual deposits, it sometimes becomes necessary to water wash the heating surface to maintain acceptable draft losses through the air preheater. In some instances if the air preheater is subjected to factors that create serious fouling problems, this may be required more frequently than during the scheduled boiler outages. Most deposits forming on the air preheater heat-transfer surface are highly soluble in water, and can be easily removed by washing with a sufficient quantity of it. A high-penetration, low-pressure, stationary, multi-nozzle device is the standard washing apparatus and is available for all air preheater types and sizes. Adequate drainage is necessary before planning to wash an air preheater. Washing can be on either the air or the gas side, depending on which has the best drainage.

Washing is generally performed during out-of-service periods, when the boiler has been shut down. During shutdown is the best time to control the washing operation and to make a thorough inspection of the heating surface, both during and after washing.

The speed of the air-preheater rotor is typically reduced by means of an auxiliary drive before admitting water to the washing devices. The slower speed permits the wash water to drain from the rotor and heating surface before the wash water enters the other stream. To ensure coverage of all heating surfaces when using stationary, multi-nozzle devices, the washing cycle must consist of at least one revolution of the preheater rotor.

An intermediate- or high-pressure, low-volume wash is sometimes necessary to remove particles of insoluble material that are carried from the boiler by the gas stream. The larger particles can become wedged in the flow passages of the hot-end, heating surface. These obstructed passages then fill up with fly ash, which restricts flow. This type of deposit accumulation is difficult to remove with low-pressure, multi-nozzle devices.

Special mobile equipment, using one high-energy jet or more, has been developed for this application. Some newer designs of soot-blowing devices have a high-pressure washing function built in to provide water washing to the plant at all times, and shorten the required setup time. The procedure with these devices is similar to that followed in a regular out-of-service washing using multi-nozzle washing devices, except that the water nozzles are moved radially across the surface, allowing sufficient time for the rotor to complete at least one revolution between each movement of the nozzle of the cleaning device. Heat-transfer surfaces should be examined frequently during any washing process. After the deposits are removed, the unit should be allowed to dry completely before being returned to service.

Air Preheater Fires and Detection Systems

While not a common event, fires do pose a significant threat to air preheaters installed on fossil fuel fired boilers and furnaces. The origin of an air preheater fire can generally be traced to combustible deposits on the heat-transfer surface. In its initial stage, the fire is limited to the combustion of these deposits and often confined to a relatively small area. With time, however, this fire will progress to a metal fire, with an associated rise in temperature into the 4,000 to 5,000°F (2,200 to 2,800°C) range. At this point, the fire becomes far more damaging to the equipment and becomes significantly challenging to extinguish.

Appropriate unit operation, coupled with routine maintenance, can minimize but not eliminate this risk. Early warning is key to minimizing the damage. Reliable indication of a fire is complicated by several process variables. First, localized hot spots in the heat-transfer surface are moving targets as the air preheater rotates. Second, the detection system must be capable of indicating trouble during various boiler load conditions, from transient start-up to full-load, steady-state conditions.

Various designs and configurations of detection systems are available. The most common systems use either thermocouple- or infrared-based monitoring. The systems are typically not intended to automatically initiate fire-fighting. Rather, they are designed to signal an alarm to the plant operators, which allows further investigation and necessary corrective action in advance of a major problem.

Air Preheater Temperature Terminology

Table 6-10 lists the most common terms used when discussing the thermal performance of Ljungström® air preheaters.

Factors Affecting Air Preheater Performance

There are many factors that combine to influence the operating performance of an air preheater as shown in *Table 6-11*.

Designing for Low Exit Gas Temperature

Combustion of the sulfur in the coal results in the formation of sulfur dioxide. About 1 to 4% of this sulfur is further oxidized to sulfur trioxide, depending on the flue-gas constituents, temperature and catalytic activity within the boiler, and the presence of an SCR. The SO_2 and SO_3 may then combine with moisture in the flue gas

The air heater not only heats the air, but cools the flue gas, which improves efficiency and reduces emissions.

TABLE 6-10 | COMMON TERMS USED FOR AIR PREHEATER PERFORMANCE

Term	Definition
Exit-gas temperature with leakage (also termed "corrected")	This is the observed or measured average exit-gas temperature and includes the dilution effect of leakage.
Exit-gas temperature with no leakage (also termed "uncorrected")	This is the average temperature at which the gas would leave the preheater if there were no leakage. This temperature cannot be measured directly, but it can be arrived at by a simple calculation accounting for the cooling effect of the leakage.
Gas drop	Difference between the gas entering temperature and the uncorrected exit gas temperature.
Air rise	Difference between the average air leaving temperature and the air entering temperature.
Temperature head	Difference between the gas entering temperature and the air entering temperature.
Gas side effectiveness, %	$\frac{\text{Gas Drop}}{\text{Temperature Head}} \times 100$

TABLE 6-11 | FACTORS AFFECTING AIR HEATER PERFORMANCE

Factor	Effect
Entering Gas Temperature	Changes in entering gas or air temperatures result in a change in the temperature head, which directly affects the drop in gas temperature, resulting in the exit-gas temperature changing in the same direction.
Gas Flow	An increase in gas mass flow rate to the heater will result in a higher exit-gas temperature, while conversely a lower exit-gas temperature results from a lower gas mass flow entering the unit.
Heat-Capacity Ratio (HCR)	Also called the "X" ratio, the heat-capacity ratio (HCR) = $\frac{\text{mass flow of air} \times \text{avg. specific heat of air}}{\text{mass flow of gas} \times \text{avg. specific heat of gas}}$ A decrease in the HCR results in an increase in the exit-gas temperature. A 10 to 12% change in this ratio may alter exit-gas temperature by as much as 30 to 35°F (15 to 20°C). Factors that affect the HCR include tempering air, overall boiler-system infiltration, and air preheater bypass for cold-end protection.
Pressure Drop	The air and gas side pressure drops will change approximately in proportion to the square of the air and gas weights through the heater. If excess air is greater than anticipated, the air preheater pressure drop will be greater than expected. A buildup of heating-element deposits will result in higher air preheater resistances, with the consequence of an increase in pressure drop. Pressure drop will also vary directly with the mean absolute temperatures of the fluids passing through the heater as a result of changes in flow density.
Air Preheater Leakage	A change in the temperature of the fluid leaking past the seals will, by reason of density change, have a slight effect on the amount of leakage. Variations in pressure levels between the high- and low-pressure sides of the heater will, likewise, alter the air preheater leakage. An increase in the pressure differential will increase the leakage, while a decrease in pressure differential will reduce the leakage. Improper settings of the heater radial and circumferential seals will also result in an increase in leakage.

to form sulfurous and sulfuric acids. Sulfurous acid will not form above the water dew-point temperature and is seldom a problem. However, sulfur trioxide is hygroscopic, and will absorb moisture at temperatures well above the water dew point, resulting in the formation of sulfuric acid vapor. The temperature at which this acid vapor condenses to form liquid sulfuric acid is called the "acid dew point."

While boiler efficiency can be improved by adding surface to reduce the air preheater exit-gas temperature, this practice lowers the cold-end metal temperatures, possibly below the acid dew point. Consequently, steel construction materials are subject to corrosion from the sulfuric acid in the flue gas.

The acid dew point varies with the concentration of sulfur trioxide in the flue gas. High-sulfur coals result in the existence of a dew point at a higher temperature, thus exposing more of the air heater surface to corrosion and fouling. Typical acid dew points for coal firing are between 280 and 320°F (135 and 160°C).

For coal firing, the fouling potential increases as the exit temperature of the gas decreases. Water condensation causes a marked increase in dew-point meter response at 140°F (60°C) or below. While operating at temperatures below the water dew point would likely lead to corrosion issues for unprotected steels, the major concern is the rapid fouling that would likely take place. With low-sulfur coal, the corrosion and fouling potential is reduced and restricted to the extreme cold end of the air preheater.

A number of means have been developed to minimize the rate of corrosion, as well as to provide for replacement of corroded surface. Because corrosion occurs on the lowest-temperature surface, air-heater designs have been developed that incorporate replaceable cold-end sections. Other means to minimize corrosion are aimed at increasing the metal temperature. One such arrangement directs a portion of the preheated air to the inlet of the forced draft fan and recirculates it through the air preheater. Thus, the temperature of air leaving the fan and entering the air preheater is increased, correspondingly increasing the cold-end metal temperature.

Air bypass around the air preheater is used to a limited extent. With reduced airflow, metal temperatures within the air preheater are higher because of the influence of the higher gas-to-air ratio. Also, because the overall heat recovery is less as a result of the reduced airflow, gas-outlet temperature rises, causing a rise in the cold-end metal temperature.

The most common means of increasing the cold-end metal temperature is the use of steam air preheated coils located in the cold-air duct between the FD fan and the air preheater. These coils increase the temperature of the air entering the heater, correspondingly causing an increase in the metal temperature. Steam bled from the turbine is used as the heating medium in the steam-coil air preheater. In supplying heat to the cold air, steam is condensed and the condensate returned to the appropriate stage of the feedwater heating system.

To assist designers and operators in arriving at reasonable cold-end temperatures, average cold-end temperature (ACET) recommendations are prepared by the equipment suppliers, considering variables such as fuel type, sulfur content, excess air level, and material selection.

GAS–GAS HEATER FOR FGD REHEAT APPLICATIONS

The Ljungström® gas–gas heater (GGH) is used in applications in which heat can be recovered from the flue gas in front of the flue-gas desulfurization equipment and then used to reheat the flue gas. The GGH's main purpose is to lower the flue-gas temperature to a level at which the flue-gas scrubbing equipment can function and then provide buoyancy to the flue gas for its path up the stack. The GGH is a regenerative heater with many of the same design features and principles as the Ljungström® air preheater.

One major difference of the FGD GGH is a sealing system that is capable of lowering the leakage to as little as 0.5%. The position of the induced draft, forced draft, and booster fans determines the type of sealing system required and the achievable level of undesirable untreated-to-treated gas leakage, as a result of the pressure differential. Leakage of untreated gas reduces the overall collection efficiency of the FGD system.

Various fan-assisted sealing systems are available to minimize the entrained-leakage and the direct-leakage components. Entrained leakage is minimized by blowing treated, clean gas into the rotor as it passes from the untreated to the treated side. Direct, radial leakage is minimized by pressurizing the plenum between the sector plates and the rotor with similar treated clean gas.

The FGD GGH design raises significant concerns as a result of the very low exit gas temperatures. Corrosion is a major consideration. The material selection throughout the heater is tailored to suit the operating conditions. For example, special design attention is given to the use of a suitable corrosion-resistant lining on the interior of the housing. Special seal materials such as stainless steel and lined sealing plates are used. Substantial corrosion allowances on the rotor plate work and enamel-coated heating elements are all evaluated.

GAS–GAS HEATER FOR SCR REHEAT APPLICATIONS

The SCR GGH is used in "tail-end," or "low-dust," flue gas sulfurization (SCR) systems to assist in raising the flue-gas temperature up to the SCR reaction temperature. The position of these SCR systems minimizes the effect that flue-gas contaminants have on the catalyst design and operation, with the SCR and heater operating in a low-dust environment.

The SCR GGH is designed with special features to reduce the negative impacts from the SCR related to SO_2 oxidation, acid condensation, ammonia slip, and formation of ammonia salts. The potential for ABS fouling, together with the lower flue-gas ash concentration, means that there is a reduced surface area of ash to adsorb the ABS and transport it through the GGH. To minimize the effects of ABS-enhanced fouling, the GGH typically incorporates many of the design features of an air heater operating after an SCR. Similarly to the FGD GGH, the sealing arrangement of the SCR GGH can incorporate fan-assisted sealing systems to minimize the leakage of untreated to treated gas.

TUBULAR AIR PREHEATERS

A typical application of a tubular air heater might be an industrial boiler for which perhaps the tubular heater would generally provide lower leakage rates than a regenerative air preheater when considering higher system pressures. The heater would typically be arranged for vertical gas flow through the tubes and horizontal air flow across the outside of the tubes usually 2 to 3 inches (5 cm to 7.6 cm) in diameter. The tubes are in a staggered relationship for optimal heat transfer. The air passes over all the sections of the air preheater in sequence, the effect of which is to provide counterflow heat transfer. Tube sheets at the top and bottom support and guide the tubes. Most frequently, the bottom tube sheet or sheets form the structural support. The upper tube sheet is welded to the outside casing, and the tubes pass through slightly oversized holes in the upper sheet, which allows for expansion when the equipment is brought up to temperature. Many designs for use with sulfur-bearing fuels have separated cold-end sections, to reduce the cost of tube replacement in the event of excessive corrosion.

In contrast to regenerative designs, tubular, or recuperative, air preheaters have more severe cold-end corrosion problems. With variations in cleanliness of the tube wall, entering air temperature, and flow intensities on the gas and air sides, very low metal temperatures and correspondingly severe corrosion can occur. Although the tube metal temperature may be considered to be the arithmetic average of the air temperature entering the air preheater and the gas temperature leaving, actual field measurements have shown metal temperatures as low as 120°F (49°C) below the mean of the air and gas temperatures. Such conditions can result in deposits that reduce heat transfer and increase draft loss until they are removed, usually by water washing.

ASH-HANDLING SYSTEMS

Other chapters presented both the physical and chemical properties of coal ash and the effects that ash in its various forms can have on the operation of a boiler. This section describes some of the equipment being used for the collection and transport of ash, particularly from pulverized coal-fired steam generators. Heat losses, power consumption, and water use in operating this equipment also are considered. Only through complete understanding of the design and operation of ash-handling equipment, as well as the comparative features of the many available types, can the large systems currently being installed be made both more reliable and more economical to operate.

There are essentially two types of ash produced in a suspension fired furnace: bottom ash and fly ash. Bottom ash is the heavier material, possibly slag, that builds up on the heat-absorbing surfaces of the furnace, superheater, and reheater that eventually falls either by its own weight or as a result of load changes or soot blowing. With low ash fusion temperatures, a large amount of molten slag can adhere to these surfaces and subsequently fall through the opening in the furnace bottom (*Fig. 6-34*).

Other, lighter, ash becomes entrained with, and carried away by, the flue gas stream. A small percentage is collected in hoppers under the economizer, selective catalytic reduction (SCR), air heater, or in other hoppers in the ductwork. The bulk of the lighter material moves through to the emissions control system, where it is collected in the electrostatic precipitator or baghouse. This is called "fly ash."

The amount of airborne ash passing through the furnace depends on the dust-bearing capacity of the combustion gases, on the size and shape of the particles, and on the density of the ash relative to that of the upward flowing gas. *Figure 6-35* shows the effects of particle size on terminal velocity,[37,38] which is the rate at which particles of various diameters settle in still air.

Coarser particles fall more rapidly than fine. Thus, for a given upward velocity, fine particles will leave the furnace and coarse particles either will drop to the bottom or be thrown from the center of the furnace toward the bounding furnace walls. For example, according to the curve, particles larger than 0.011 inch (0.28 mm) in diameter (not passing through a 50-mesh screen) can be expected to fall to the bottom when the

Figure 6-34 | A large pulverized coal furnace viewed from above. Ash and slag falling from the walls pass through the bottom opening into a bottom ash hopper or submerged scraper conveyor

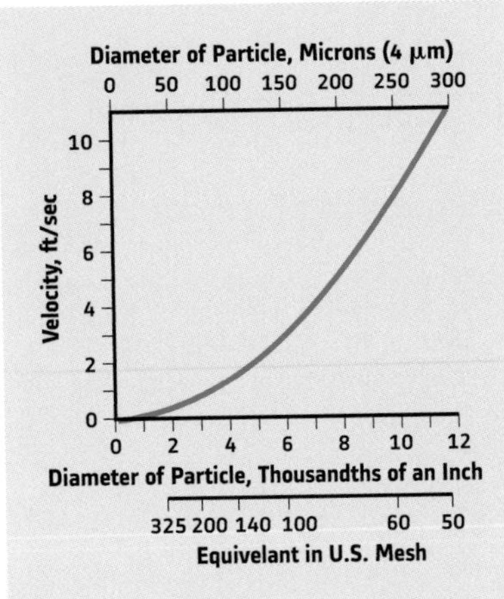

Figure 6-35 | Velocity of airborne particles (specific gravity 1.2) falling through still air at 70°F (21°C)

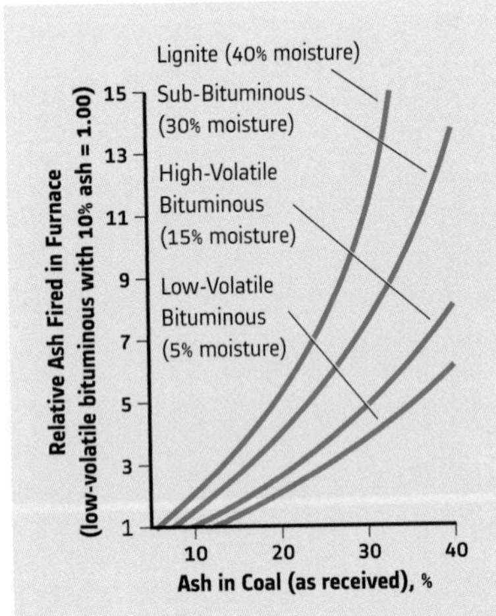

Figure 6-36 | Relative ash amounts with various types of coals, compared to Eastern bituminous coal with 10% ash as a base (corrected for boiler efficiency). Figures in parentheses are as-received moisture contents (by weight) in the coal

vertical velocity of the gases in a furnace is 10 ft/sec (3 m/sec) or less.

In this regard, a situation occurs in the design and operation of large, pulverized fuel furnaces that is of interest. As furnace plan areas increase for a given quantity of net heat input to accommodate a very poor fuel for example, the upward gas velocities correspondingly decrease. At the same time, the furnace wall area becomes greater, leading to the possibility of larger accumulations of slag or ash on the walls for a given heat input. The greater ash deposits (and lesser upward velocities that result) mean that more ash will fall to the furnace bottom. Typically, the ratio of bottom ash to fly ash increases with these poorer fuels, which impacts the cost of the resultant ash-handling systems.

FACTORS IN SYSTEM SELECTION

Many factors determine the method of handling and storing ash from coal-fired power plants, including:

- Fuel source and ash content
- Plant siting (land availability, presence of aquifers, adjacent residential areas)
- Environmental regulations
- Steam generator size
- Auxiliary power cost
- Local market for ash
- Cementitious character of the ash

Ash quantities and properties, both physical and chemical, determine the type and size of an ash-handling system, from storage and transport to on-site disposal. They also provide an indication of the environmental impact associated with ash disposal, establish overall system constraints, and influence disposal site design.

Peak ash production rates (based on 100% capacity factor) are used to size ash-handling and transport systems. On the other hand, the average rate of ash production, which considers the projected plant capacity factor over the operating life of the plant, is used to size disposal sites.

Fuel Source and Ash Content

A major factor affecting the choice of an ash-handling system is the type of fuel to be fired. *Figure* 6-36 illustrates the wide variation in ash "fired" into a furnace as a function of fuel ash content and moisture. For example, a boiler firing 15% ash sub-bituminous coal generates almost three times the total ash as the same-size unit burning 10% ash, high-calorific value, medium-volatility coal.

It is usually more meaningful to define ash content as it relates to energy input rather than on the basis of a weight percentage of the coal alone. The pounds of ash per million BTUs fired is arrived at by the formula:

$$\frac{\text{Ash \%}}{\text{HHV (BTU/lb)}} \times 10{,}000 = \frac{\text{lbs ash}}{10^6\,\text{BTU fired}}$$

Equation 6-1

Relating the ash to be handled directly to the required heat input gives a realistic relationship to the amount that must be handled as bottom ash as well as that handled as economizer, SCR, air heater, and fly ash. It also gives an insight to the potential rate of ash that has to be handled in the furnace and on convective surfaces.

PLANT SITING. The available water supply and locations of an ash disposal site, relative to the power plant, can greatly affect the design and cost of ash disposal. An ample water supply and a great deal of land were prerequisites of many older ash-handling systems. More modern designs greatly reduce the amount of water and land needed. If land for a plant is limited, ash storage bins can be used for temporary on-site storage. Trucks or rail cars then are used to carry the ash away. If there is insufficient water, the fly ash must be collected by one of the available dry systems, while bottom ash is collected in a submerged scraper conveyor or recirculated water system.

ENVIRONMENTAL REGULATIONS. Federal, state, and local effluent regulations probably have the greatest impact on installations today and will continue to do so in the future. For example, *Table 6-12* lists typical limitations for bottom ash and fly ash transport water. The total suspended solids (TSS) limitations usually are the most difficult to meet, resulting in the trend toward dry fly ash systems.[39] But this consideration does not preclude storage ponds to which fly ash can be trucked or conveyed pneumatically. Dust is controlled with water sprays and no net effluent is created.

Ash Collection Points

After the combustion process in a suspension-fired solid-fuel furnace, the ash collects or is collected in several areas (*Fig. 6-37*).

Hoppers or conveyors in troughs are used under the furnace bottom to collect the material falling from the furnace heat-absorbing surfaces. This material can be in either a dry or a molten state. If dry, it can be collected in water-impounded or dry receivers. If molten (from wet bottom furnaces) it must be directed into a water impoundment.

Hoppers are also used under the pulverizer rejects discharge spout. These collect high-density, pulverizer rejects, pyrites, and tramp iron separated from the coal during pulverization. In recent times, pulverizer inerting systems also require the full fuel contents of the mill, including coal and debris, to be conveyed away from these hoppers.

Hoppers under the rear convection pass and air heater(s) of the steam generator are commonly called "economizer hoppers" and "air heater hoppers." It is here that coarser particles drop from

TABLE 6-12 | TYPICAL EFFLUENT LIMITATIONS

Bottom ash Transport water	Oil and grease	1 mg/l × Flow (Max) 0.75 mg/l × Flow (Average)
	pH	6–9
	TSS	5 mg/l × Flow (Max) 1.5 mg/l × Flow (Average)
Fly ash Transport water	Oil and grease	0
	pH	6–9
	TSS	0

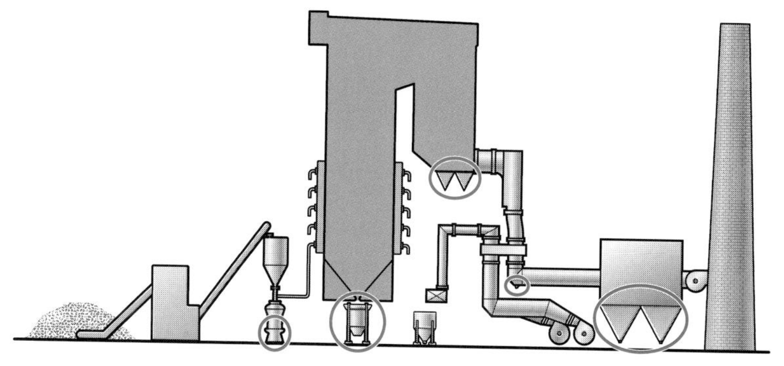

Figure 6-37 | Ash must be collected and transported from at least the five points shown. In each location, the physical and chemical characteristics of the ash vary.

the gas stream with directional changes in the gas flow. The recent addition of SCR systems for the removal of NOx has added another set of hoppers in this area, generally just downstream of the economizer hoppers. The catalyst itself must be kept clear of ash. The design of the ash-handling systems ahead of the SCR have become more critical and the use of continuous-removal systems more common. Fly ash hoppers included under the precipitators or baghouses collect the material extracted from the flue gas stream by these particulate removal devices.

Quantities of Ash

Most pulverized coal-fired steam generators are dry-bottom units in which 20 to 40% of the ash from the coal falls to the furnace bottom. Sixty to 80% of the ash leaves the furnace as fly ash. Some ash is collected in the economizer/SCR/air heater hoppers and the rest in one of several available dust-collection systems.

However, with some fuels less than 20% bottom ash has been measured, while with certain lignites, more than 45% bottom ash has been reported. As a guide to establishing the size of the equipment in the total ash-handling system, typical collection quantities (mass basis) are used in the early, budgetary phases of the design. A true ash analysis of the proposed fuel is preferred before final system selection. For example, the 20 to 40% figure can vary according to experience with the type of fuel burned. With low- and medium-volatility bituminous coals, 15 to 20% bottom ash is appropriate. With a high-volatility bituminous coal, 20 to 30% bottom ash is used. Systems for sub-bituminous coal and lignite are sized using 30 to 50% bottom ash.

The economizer, SCR, and air heater ash hoppers each are sized to collect about 5% of the ash, while a precipitator, fabric filter, or other collection device would be sized to extract 80 to nearly 100% of the fly ash from the flue gas.

Note that the sum of all the assumed collection-point values can exceed the total ash in the coal by 50% or more because of the lack of precision of the individual factors. Variations in fuel quality must also be considered.

Ash Density

Fly ash density depends primarily on particle size, particle structure, and carbon content. In general, the relatively large, coarse particles containing a high percentage of carbon have a low density. These particles commonly have a porous, or lace-like, structure and result from the partial combustion of the pulverized coal. It appears that the volatile portion burns out, leaving black coke-like particles. These particles have densities of about 35 to 65 lb/ft^3 (560 to 1,040 kg/m^3) (true density). The finer ash particles, which tend to be low in carbon content, have much higher densities, usually ranging from 90 to 180 lb/ft^3(1,440 to 2,880 kg/m^3) (true density).

In the hot state, freshly collected ash is normally very fluid, with a lower density than cold ash—generally between 30 and 50 lb/ft^3 (480 to 800 kg/m^3) bulk density. The fresh ash is aerated as the individual particles are exposed to the gas. With standing and cooling, deaeration occurs and the ash compacts. It becomes less fluid and can approach bulk densities as high as 90 lb/ft^3 (1,440 kg/m^3). When cold, sub-bituminous coal ash, which is very fine, will usually have loosely packed bulk densities between 65 and 85 lb/ft^3 (960 and 1,360 kg/m^3).

Bituminous coal ash, on the same basis, will have a density between 60 and 70 lb/ft^3 (960 and 1,120 kg/m^3).

The bulk density of dry bottom ash, as initially dropped into an ash receiver, can be as low as 40 to 45 lb/ft^3 (640 to 720 kg/m^3), but it can compact to above 75 lb/ft^3 (1,200 kg/m^3). A value of 45 to 55 lb/ft^3 (720 and 880 kg/m^3) bulk density can be used for establishing bottom-ash hopper or conveyor storage capacity. Pulverizer rejects, when principally iron pyrites (iron disulfide, FeS_2), will have a bulk density of at least 135 lb/ft^3 (2,160 kg/m^3).

TYPES OF SYSTEMS

The three principal methods of moving ash from the collection points to the on-site disposal or storage location are hydraulic, pneumatic, and mechanical. In a hydraulic system, a stream of water conveys the ash in a closed pipeline or open sluiceway. Commonly, a jet or centrifugal pump provides the motive force. A pneumatic system transports the ash in a stream of air or flue gas induced by either an upstream pressure or a downstream vacuum. The oldest technique for ash removal is the mechanical method, the most rudimentary form being a shovel or hoe to rake ash out of the boiler, with the more sophisticated type being submerged or dry scraper conveyors using chain and flight bars.

Two basic philosophies have evolved throughout the world for removing ash from pulverized coal-fired steam generators:

- Collection, storage, and periodic removal, usually called "intermittent" or "batch removal systems"
- Collection and continuous removal, commonly termed "continuous-removal systems"

Ash-handling systems are further differentiated by their conveying frequency and conveying medium. The major systems are:

1. Bottom ash
   - **a.** Water-impounded hopper with wet pipeline or sluiceway, to a pond or closed recirculation system—intermittent, hydraulic
   - **b.** Dry hopper, dry pipeline—intermittent, pneumatic
   - **c.** Submerged scraper conveyor—continuous, mechanical
2. Pyrites (pulverizer rejects)
   - **a.** Hoppers with wet sluicing (pipeline or open trough)—intermittent, hydraulic
   - **b.** Hoppers with manual removal—intermittent, mechanical
   - **c.** Hoppers with dry vacuum removal (infrequently used)—intermittent, pneumatic
   - **d.** Hoppers with drag conveyor removal—continuous, mechanical (rare but possible)
3. Economizer ash
   - **a.** Dry pipeline—intermittent, pneumatic
   - **b.** Dry drag or screw conveyor—continuous, mechanical
   - **c.** Wet pipeline using receiving tanks below economizer hoppers—continuous/batch, hydraulic
   - **d.** Dry pipeline using receiving tanks below economizer hoppers—continuous/batch, pneumatic
4. Fly ash
   - **a.** Dry pipeline, vacuum—intermittent, pneumatic
   - **b.** Dry pipeline, pressure—intermittent, pneumatic
   - **c.** Dry pipeline, vacuum-pressure combination systems—intermittent, pneumatic

d. Dry/wet pipeline, vacuum—intermittent, pneumatic/hydraulic (using water jet exhausters)
e. Dry, screw or drag conveyor—continuous, mechanical (not common because of the high volume of fly ash)

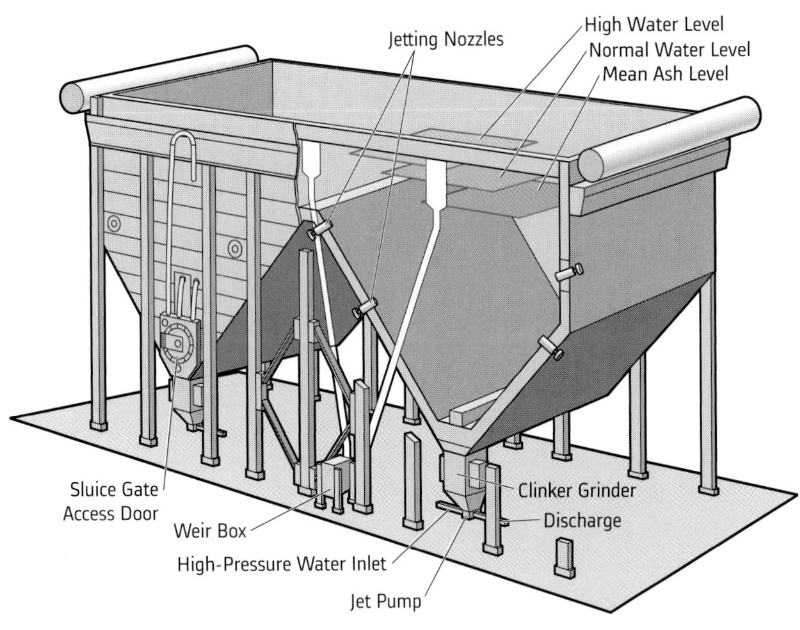

Figure 6-38 | Water-filled intermittent removal ash hopper for large pulverized coal boiler

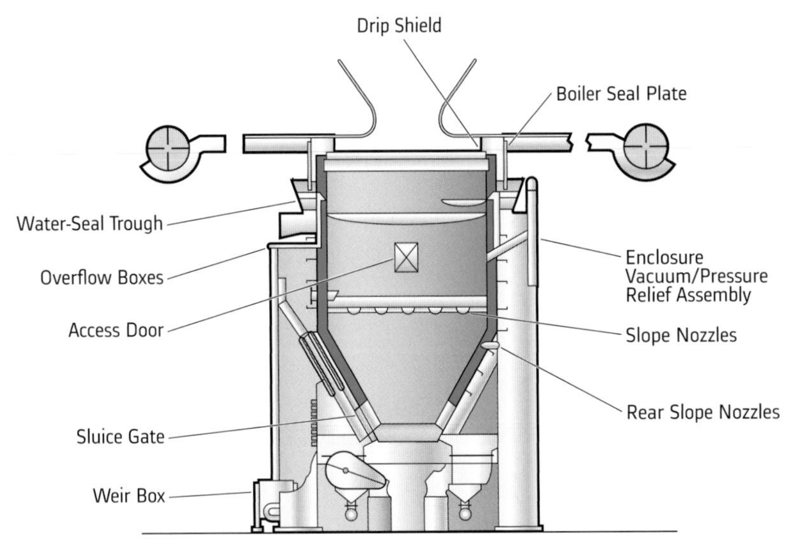

Figure 6-39 | Cross section of water-filled ash hopper under a large pulverized coal boiler

Bottom-Ash Systems

A wet-bottom-ash system collects and hydraulically or mechanically removes ash falling from the furnace heat-transfer surfaces. One type, a water-impounded hopper (*Figs. 6-38* and 6-39), receives, quenches, and stores ash from the furnace. In this system the ash is intermittently drained by discharging the water–ash mixture through an outlet gate to clinker grinders that reduce the size of the materials to facilitate transport to disposal by jet or centrifugal pumps.

The principal reasons for using a water-impounded hopper/trough initially include the following:

- To break up large pieces of slag by thermal shock as they fall into the pool of approximately 140°F (60°C) water. This is an approximately 10:1 change in temperature for the 1,500°F (815°C) ash that falls from the 2,400°F (1,315°C) boiler combustion zone.
- To keep the ash and slag submerged so that they do not fuse into the large unmanageable masses that would result if they were exposed to furnace heat. The lower temperature in the water also reduces the malleability of the ash so that it can be further crushed by grinders and not merely reshaped.
- To provide a resilient medium to decelerate the large pieces of slag and protect the walls of the ash hopper and the key components in the ash removal system.
- To lower the ash temperature for the downstream conveying system for cost-effective equipment selection and the safety of plant personnel.

INTERMITTENT REMOVAL BOTTOM-ASH HOPPER. On most pulverized coal-fired units above 400,000 lb (180,000 kg) of steam/hr, intermittent-removal bottom-ash hoppers use the V-, W-, or triple-V-shaped "pant leg" design. This design has hopper floors sloping at angles of 35 to 55 degrees, allowing gravity to help remove ash from the hopper. During ash removal the high-pressure water to the jet pump is turned on and the clinker grinder is started. The control system opens the hydraulic-cylinder-controlled sluice gate, and the ash flows from the hopper through the sluice gate and grinder into the jet pump, then to a transfer tank, dewatering system, or settling pond. Alternatively, a centrifugal materials-handling pump evacuates the hopper and transports the ash to the disposal system.

Operating experience with water-filled hoppers has shown that most of the ash will flow toward and through the sluice gates by gravity. However, large slabs of fused ash do occur that will not move by gravity alone. Their removal requires the assistance of high-pressure (125 psig [8.6 bar]) water-jetting nozzles located on the sloping floors of the hopper. In addition, jetting nozzles in the wall opposite each sluice gate break up the arching and packing of the ash that may occur at the gate.

Whenever practical, the hopper should have a volume corresponding to the ash produced during 12 hours of operation at full boiler load while firing the fuel with the lowest heating value and highest ash content for which the boiler is designed. This guideline is based on the normal practice in the United States of emptying ash hoppers once each 8-hour shift. The extra 4 hours allows time to deal with any problem encountered when first starting up the system each shift.

Depending on the fuel ash content and the boiler load, the usual time required to evacuate a bottom-ash hopper is 1 to 3 hours. The hopper volumetric capacity is measured below a mean ash level, which is usually 12 to 24 inches (30 to 60 cm) below the normal water level, depending on the bottom-ash hopper width (*Table 6-13* and *Fig. 6-40*).

It is important to realize that the ash falling from the furnace walls does not pass through the furnace bottom "coutant" opening in equal increments along the length of that opening. *Figure 6-41* shows that, for a large "open" furnace (one without a center wall), all of the ash from each sidewall falls through the first 3 or 4 feet (0.9 or 1.2 m) of the bottom opening. The ash falling from the front and rear walls can be assumed to distribute fairly equally along the furnace width. Thus, as shown by the figure, about 25% of the total ash to the furnace bottom will go through the 3- to 4-foot portion near the sidewall, and less than 2% of the bottom ash will go through each remaining foot of the bottom "slot." It is of utmost importance to take this distribution into account when designing equipment that receives bottom ash. The normal water level should be at least 30 inches (76 cm) below the horizontal plane of the furnace tubes forming the furnace throat opening ("A" in *Figs. 6-40* and *6-42*). This dimension is with the boiler pressure parts in the hot (expanded) condition. This distance minimizes the amount of water that may splash on the furnace tubing. The hopper is designed with 5 to 10 foot (1.5 to 3 m) end-wall submergence to provide a deep pool of water at this critical portion of the hopper.

Depending on the boiler width and headroom available, the hopper configuration should adequately provide

TABLE 6-13 | FREEBOARD WATER LEVELS*

Hopper Width Inside Refractory	Effective Ash Level (EAL) Below NWL, ft
7´ 0˝	0.8
8´ 0˝	1.0
9´ 0˝	1.2
10´ 0˝	1.4
11´ 0˝	1.6
12´ 0˝	1.8
13´ 0˝	2.0
14´ 0˝	2.2

* An interpolation can be made for other hopper widths.

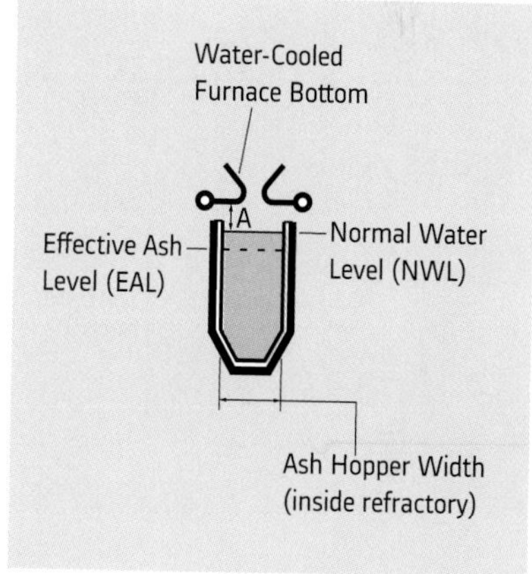

Figure 6-40 | Effective ash level below normal water level varies as a function of ash hopper width (see Table 6-13)

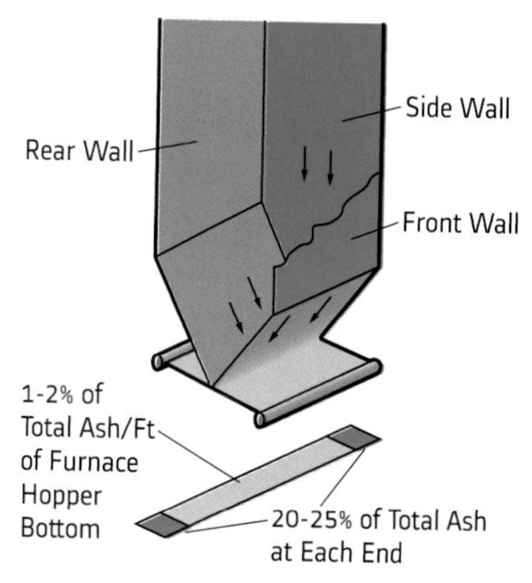

Figure 6-41 | Approximate distribution of pulverized coal bottom ash along the furnace hopper opening

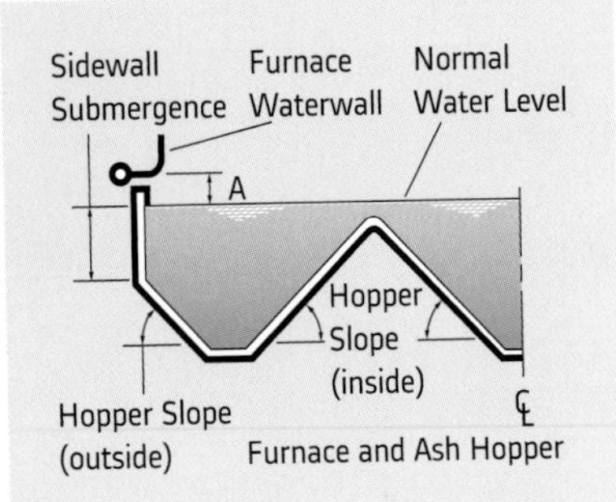

Figure 6-42 | Schematic arrangement of half of a triple-V water-impounded bottom-ash hopper. Dimension A is defined with the boiler in hot/expanded condition

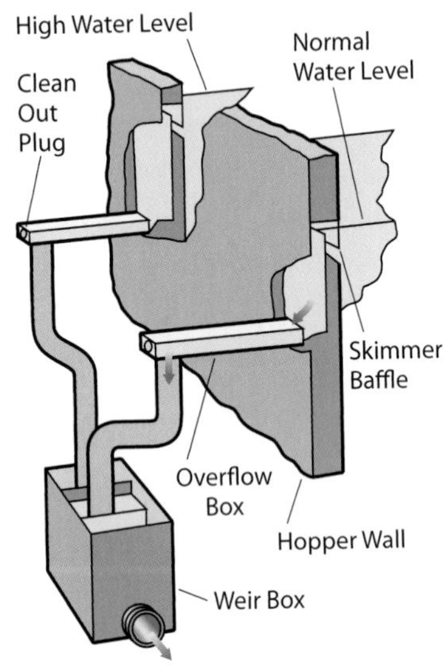

Figure 6-43 | Arrangement of bottom ash hopper overflow weirs and piping

the needed storage capacity. Centerwall boilers must have an odd number of sections. This places the center of a hopper section underneath the center wall so that there is maximum submergence to collect the ash properly from both sides of the wall.

For ease of maintenance, the ash hopper should be designed so that the entire hopper and its discharge equipment are located above grade. Pits should be avoided. If they are used to put the sluice piping below the level of the basement floor, their depth should be limited to a maximum of 3 feet (0.9 m). These pits should have adequate drains and sump pumps to avoid flooding and submerging the grinders.

OVERFLOW WEIRS. To maintain the normal water level (NWL) in the hopper, an NWL overflow should be provided. The bottom opening of the weir is at the normal water level (*Fig.* 6-43). To protect from overfilling the hopper and possibly wetting the boiler tubes, there is a second, independent "high-water-level" overflow. The opening at the bottom of this weir is a minimum of 6 inches (15 cm) above the NWL weir. A conductivity device in the outlet box from the high-level overflow provides an alarm when high overflow occurs.

ASH HOPPER CONSTRUCTION. Ash hoppers are constructed of carbon steel plate with structural framing similar to that of the furnace walls. A high-temperature, water-resistant, gunnite or cast refractory, supported by stainless steel anchors, lines the sides and bottom slopes. Alternatively, on the sloped bottom portions of the hopper, acid-resistant bricks backed by concrete can be used.

A separate water seal-trough around the upper periphery of the ash hopper, together with the seal plates hung from the boiler tubes, provides a seal against furnace pressure fluctuations and accommodates the downward expansion of the furnace. Nozzles located throughout the seal-trough periodically flush accumulated sludge and sediment from the trough bottom.

REFRACTORY COOLING. At the top of the hopper is a water distribution assembly for cooling the hopper refractory that extends above the normal water level (*Fig.* 6-44). The curtain of water flowing over the refractory face also retards refractory deterioration during extended periods when the hopper is drained of water during boiler operation.

The water-distribution pipe must be equipped with a deflection shield to prevent water from being sprayed on the furnace tubes. Periodic flushing of this pipe with a high-volume water flow through a drain connection in each section ensures that pieces of ash do not clog the holes.

Figure 6-45, a flow diagram for a single-V bottom-ash hopper, shows all of the water flows entering and leaving this hopper. Optimal operation of a water-impounded hopper can be achieved by maintaining the water level at all times, except for short periods while discharging the ash from each section. In this way, the design makes use of all the advantages of water impounding. The only other time the water level has to be lowered with this arrangement is when it is necessary to visually inspect the hopper interior or to remove oversized pieces manually. Each end of the hopper should be equipped with access doors for maintenance.

HOPPER SLUICE GATES. Bottom-ash hopper sluice gates (*Fig.* 6-46) (usually a minimum of 24 inches (61 cm) wide by 24 inches high) allow for periodic removal of bottom ash from the hopper. Around the discharge gates are watertight steel enclosures, commonly called "gate housings," or "doghouses," which flood when ash is being discharged.

These enclosures are equipped with access doors, observation ports, and floodlights, and are designed to withstand negative and positive pressures. A large vent pipe equipped with a pressure relief valve provides vacuum/pressure protection. Positive-pressure protection is achieved by allowing the water in the enclosures to enter the vent pipe to discharge water through a drain line. Air-check valves located at the top of the vent pipe loop provide vacuum protection. A large-bore diameter cylinder designed for water service hydraulically lifts the gate. Limit switches or telltale rods indicate a fully open or fully closed position. This cylinder should be extended away from the gate housing for longer cylinder life. High wear areas in the sluice gate enclosure are often made of abrasion-resistant steel, tungsten-carbide tiles, ceramics, or stainless steel.

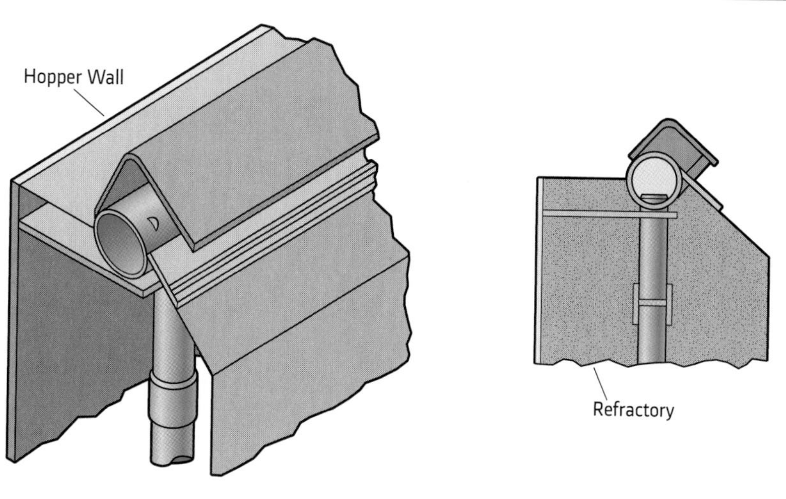

Figure 6-44 | Distribution pipe for refractory cooling water

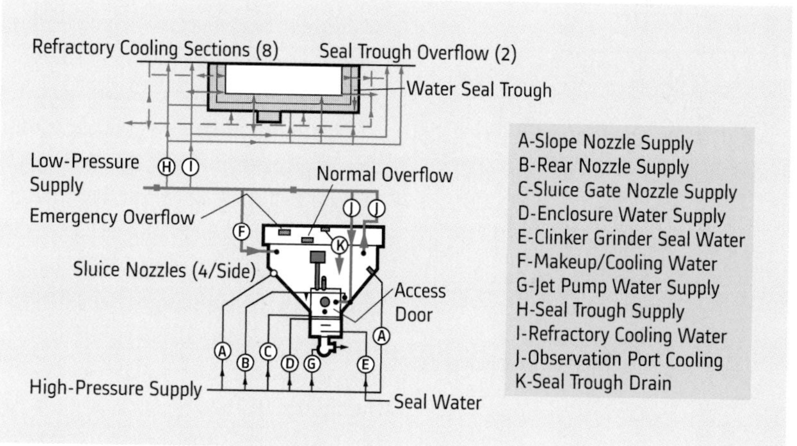

Figure 6-45 | Flow diagram for a single-V bottom-ash hopper

CLINKER GRINDERS. Single- or double-roll clinker grinders are provided at the outlet of each sluice gate. The grinding elements are made from heavy-duty, abrasion-resistant materials, such as Ni Hard, work-hardened manganese steel, or high-chrome alloy steel. Ash is ground by a shearing, splitting, or crushing action to facilitate hydraulic or pneumatic transport (*Figs.* 6-47 and 6-48). Typical particle sizes for crushed ash are approximately 2 to 3 inches (5.1 to 7.6 cm) in diameter.

Because of the severe duty, relatively frequent replacement is required for the wear-prone internal parts of these crushing machines. It is important to provide easy access for their removal while the steam generator is operating. The designs shown in *Figures* 6-47 and 6-48 provide an easily removed front panel for such access, allowing maintenance personnel to replace worn grinding elements without entering the enclosure. Shaft bearings are of the spherical roller type, with provisions for forced grease lubrication. They should be positioned away from the grinder housing and packing gland areas.

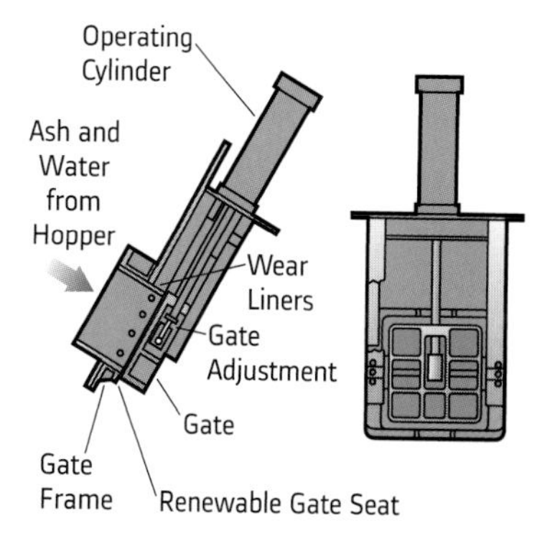

Figure 6-46 | Bottom ash hopper sluice gates

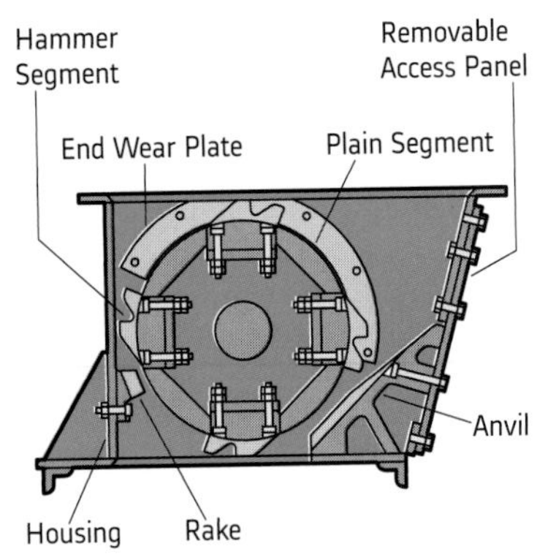

Figure 6-47 | Single-roll clinker grinder for reducing size of bottom-ash; hammers and anvils are replaceable through removable access panel

Figure 6-48 | Advanced design of single-roll clinker grinder showing extended bearing supports for better access to packing gland area

Shaft seals have continuous grease or seal-water flow requirements during periods of both grinder operation and shutdown. The selection of the proper wear rings, lantern rings, and packing materials for optimal shaft sealing is an ever-changing science based on hydraulic head and water quality.

JET PUMPS. A jet pump is a Venturi-type solids/fluids transport device with no moving parts (*Figs.* 6-49 and 6-50). The pump has an inherently low efficiency, but its non-overloading characteristic, ease of maintenance, and lack of rotating parts offset this drawback. For these reasons, the majority of hydraulic bottom-ash and especially pulverizer-rejects systems use jet pumps instead of centrifugal pumps when water is readily available.

To minimize the effects of abrasion, the jet pump is made of abrasion-resistant alloys. The combining tube (diffuser) can be provided in high-hardness, cast, chrome–nickel alloy material with a minimum Brinell hardness number (BHN) of 550, or an even higher chrome alloy with a minimum BHN of 700.

A jet pump is supplied at the outlet of each clinker grinder. Alternatively, a mechanical, centrifugal pump can be used. The advantages of each are listed in the box on the next page.

As more high-ash coal is used for steam-generator fuel, producing greater ash loading on bottom-ash systems, a duplicate, backup, sluice gate, grinder, and pump for each hopper section should be considered (or the alternate use of a submerged scraper conveyor). The purpose of this redundant equipment is twofold: first, to increase the overall system reliability and, second, to increase the rate of ash removal when quicker-than-design evacuation is desired.

PIPING, FITTING, AND VALVES. Ash slurry piping is supplied in several materials, including:

- Centrifugally cast chrome–iron alloy with a hardness range of 280 to 340 BHN in a standard alloy and a range of 475 to 550 BHN in a harder available alloy.
- Internal surface-hardened carbon-steel piping, referred to as induction-hardened pipe (especially good for short pyrites lines or fly ash)
- Basalt-lined steel pipe
- Ceramic lined steel pipe

Ash in a water slurry usually travels along the bottom portion of pipes in saltation flow. That is, it alternately "rests" (settles out) and "jumps" (becomes re-entrained in suspended flow). Thus, most wear on slurry piping is on the bottom third (the lower 120-degree arc) of the pipe. Directly downstream of elbows, piping wear is higher than in straight runs because of the turbulence and impact created at the elbow. This calls for more frequent replacement of downstream runs.

Whenever there is a change in direction in the slurry piping, the fitting located at the change of direction will undergo accelerated wear as a result of turbulence and solids-impact erosion. Thus, fittings, such as 45- and 90-degree

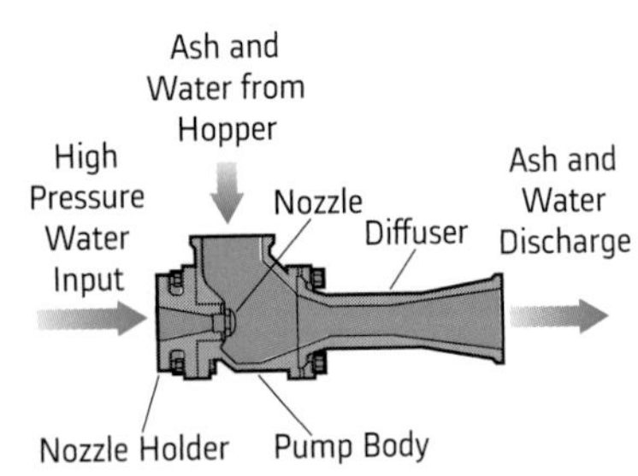

Figure 6-49 | Schematic arrangement of a jet pump for handling abrasive solids

Figure 6-50 | Jet pump for bottom-ash transport

elbows and laterals, are normally constructed from alloy castings that range from 400 to 550 BHN (*Fig. 6-51*).

White irons (high chrome) and Ni-Hard casting materials are used with the cast pipe above, while matching basalt and ceramic fittings are used with their respective pipeline material. Material hardness alone cannot provide long life at points of change in direction. To add additional life to the fitting, the impact area has a thicker cross section than the normal conveying pipeline. This thicker section is commonly termed an "integral wearback."

Fittings can have connections that have either a plain or a beveled end. Plain-end fittings are connected to the pipelines using sleeve couplings with two gaskets held in place by friction. When plain-end sections are used, piping harnesses and supports prevent the fitting from dislodging because of the reactive loads of the conveying medium. Beveled-end fittings do not require friction-type couplings to secure the fitting to the pipe, but supports should still be used at all fittings for the reactive loads.

In conveying water-ash slurries, it may be necessary to divert flow or isolate branch lines when multiple sluice lines exist. Industry practice is to provide heavy-duty knife-gate valves for this service because of their profile characteristics. When the knife-gate valve is open, its orifice matches the diameter of the sluice pipe in which it is installed. Minimizing the turbulence through the valve reduces erosion. In addition, the insertion of the narrow valve in the line requires no special fittings. Also, knife-gate valves can have bonnets to prevent leakage from the packing and flushing ports for cleaning the seat and the gate before closing. Manual hand wheels or pneumatic operators are commonly used to open and close knife gates. Automatic knife-gate systems can have limit switches to provide feedback to the control system.

Any slurry piping system must be designed with minimum and maximum velocities in mind. The minimum velocity is that required to convey the particle in the pipeline without settling. This velocity is a function of the specific gravity of the material being conveyed, the pipeline size, and the

COMPARISON OF JET PUMPS VS. CENTRIFUGAL PUMPS

ADVANTAGES OF JET PUMPS

- A jet pump is a simple device. There are no moving parts; it is made up of only three principal components: nozzle, body, and diffuser. This makes maintenance and replacement easier and less expensive than for a centrifugal pump.
- A jet pump can handle air without any deleterious effects; lack of suction head is never a problem.
- A jet pump is self-regulating. The amount of suction material depends on the discharge head. The higher the discharge head, the less suction material will be taken—when there is no suction flow, the only flow through the pump is the motive (clear water) flow. This makes for a self-cleaning action. If the discharge line becomes clogged, the flow of more material into the pump is limited so that the motive flow can flush the line.
- There are no rotating parts subject to erosive ash.

ADVANTAGES OF A CENTRIFUGAL PUMP

- A centrifugal pump can obtain much higher volumetric capacities than a jet pump. A typical jet pump has a practical limit of about 3,500 gpm discharge flow. Centrifugal pumps can produce flows of 35,000 gpm and higher. Larger MW plants with higher ash generation and conveying rates and with more distant disposal areas will tend to use centrifugal pumps.
- A centrifugal pump has a higher efficiency than a jet pump. Stated in another way, the power required for a centrifugal pump to convey a given flow at a given head is considerably less than the power required to give the jet-pump motive fluid the required head and flow to convey the given mixed water slurry head and flow. Often, a jet pump will require an increase in line size over a centrifugal pump (8-inch (20 cm) instead of 6-inch (15 cm) diameter, for example) thus increasing the power differential.
- No separate motive-water pump is required. This is a major horsepower savings in most cases.
- In areas where water is limited and in short supply, a centrifugal pump can handle a given tonnage rate of bottom ash with recirculated water and in many cases a smaller line size than a jet pump, thus minimizing the water requirements.

Figure 6-51 | Chrome–nickel alloy 90-degree elbow with integral wearback helps reduce wear from solids-impact erosion and turbulence experienced with changes in flow direction

slurry concentration. Typical ash-slurry pipeline velocities are:

- Bottom ash—7.5 to 8 ft/sec (2.3 to 2.4 m/sec) in horizontal lines with 9 to 10 ft/sec (2.7 to 3.0 m/sec) in vertical risers (higher for slag)
- Economizer ash—7.5 to 8 ft/sec (2.3 to 2.4 m/sec) in horizontal lines with 9 to 10 ft/sec (2.7 to 3.0 m/sec) in vertical risers
- Pyrites—10 ft/sec (3.0 m/sec) in horizontal lines with 12 ft/sec (3.7 m/sec) in vertical risers
- Fly ash—4.5 to 5 ft/sec(1.4 to 1.5 m/sec)

DISPOSAL OF BOTTOM ASH FROM HYDRAULIC SYSTEMS. Hydraulic ash systems dispose of the ash and water slurry in various ways, depending on the overall plant layout, ecological considerations, and available disposal areas.[40] As previously mentioned, the ecological considerations are presently a major influence on decisions made about the means of disposal of ash and slurry. The following methods explain how ash products are removed from the associated water. Bottom ash is either removed from the site for other use or remains on site in a permanent impoundment (landfill).

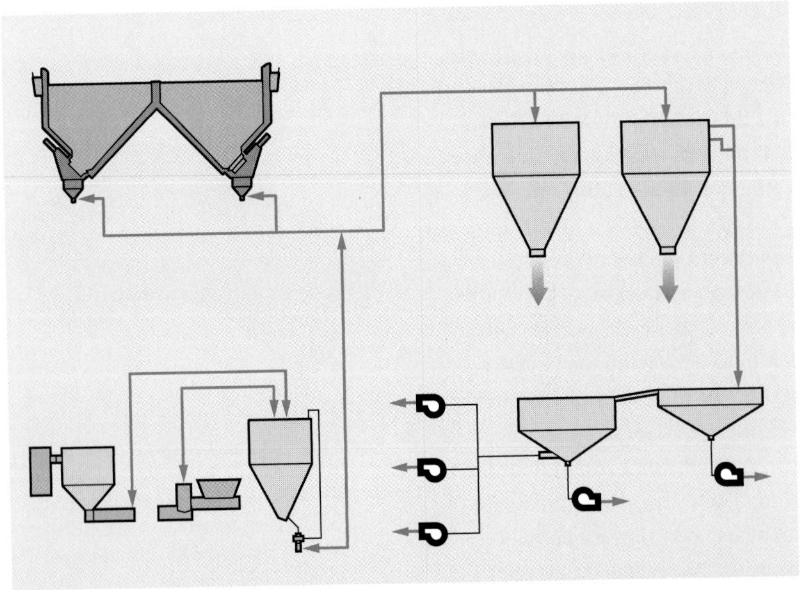

Figure 6-52 | A complete water-recirculation system with jet pumps, two dewatering bins, a settling tank, a surge tank, and recirculation pumps; pyrite hoppers and transfer tank shown also

DEWATERING SYSTEMS. Ash from a conveying sluice line can be deposited into one of two dewatering bins. As the ash enters the bin and settles, it displaces water, which overflows into a trough extending around the circumference of the bin top. The overflow water then drains by gravity to the settling tank, recirculation basin, or waste drain (*Fig. 6-52*).

A series of baffle plates, concentric with the outer shell of the bin, minimizes ash carryover and undesirable turbulence in the overflow trough. Submerged beneath the water level at the ash inlet location in the center of the bin, the inner baffle inhibits the finer material from reaching the overflow by targeting the larger particles to the outer walls. The second baffle, extending above the water level of the overflow trough, creates a barrier to retain the floating material before it reaches the overflow trough. Eventually, floating material settles and is released through the discharge gate after the bin is dewatered. Any particulate that can flow under the inner baffles and over to the overflow trough is still met with either a serrated weir edge on the trough or mesh screens to limit carryover of fines to the water-recirculation system.

Dewatering bins are installed in pairs. When one bin is filled, the input flow is diverted to the empty bin. After a short period of natural settling, a level of surface water will exist. This surface water is quickly drained off through vertical decanting pipes or floating decanters.

After the surface water is drained, the lower drain valves in the decanting pipes or screens are automatically partially opened, resulting in a slow, controlled draining of water from the ash in the bin. Depending on the composition of the ash and the desired moisture content (about 20% water by weight for the final ash discharge is considered nominal), this process generally takes less than 8 hours. With proper filtration, settling, and chemical treatment, the overflow water can be recycled to the bottom-ash system in what is essentially a closed loop. Make-up water does need to be added to account for the 20% lost with the disposed ash. It is important to protect dewatering bins from freezing by providing heaters at the bottom. Also, the lower cone section of the bin normally has vibrators to aid in removing the dewatered ash.

SETTLING AND STORAGE TANK. The discharge water from the dewatering bins normally is routed into a settling basin or tank. To separate the ash fines, low velocities are maintained throughout the basin or tank, which are designed for maximum retention time. Any agitation is confined to a small area. Water and ash fines are deposited into the center of the settling tank. As the ash fines settle into the tank, the displaced water overflows into a trough that extends around the circumference of the top of the tank. The overflow water drains into the ash water storage or surge tank. As in the case of the dewatering bins, it is important to protect the settling tanks from freezing.

STORAGE OR SURGE TANK. In a recirculating system, an ash water storage tank provides sufficient volume to absorb the volumetric fluctuations of the hydraulic ash removal system. In addition, this tank provides further separation of fines by maintaining a low velocity. Again, protection against freezing must be provided. Centrifugal pumps recirculate the discharge water from the surge tank to supply the jet pumps and other requirements for water in the system. Typically, several sets of pumps need to be considered: high pressure (for the jet pumps), intermediate pressure (for 100 psig [6.9 bar] flushing service in the ash hopper area), and low pressure (for make-up and hopper fill applications).

PONDS OR FILL AREAS. Where geological and siting conditions permit, ash can be pumped to ponds or fill areas. Any ash-receiving pond needs a large capacity to permit the ash to settle by gravity. The design of such ponds can include recovery and reuse of the water in the ash removal system.

Dry Bottom-Ash Hopper System

Dry bottom-ash hopper systems for intermittent removal are used when there is no need to provide for water impoundment, and less automation is acceptable. A rule of thumb is that dry bottom-ash hoppers are generally practical on units rated below 400,000 lb/hr (180,000 kg/hr) of steam. (For example, most stoker-fired, industrial boilers have dry bottom-ash hoppers, often with side discharges.)

Customarily constructed of carbon-steel plate, these hoppers, like the hoppers used in a wet system, have a water-seal trough, complete with flushing nozzles. Unlike water-impounded hoppers, dry hopper slopes must be steep to ensure that the dry ash flows to the discharge openings.

The inside of the steel-plated hopper is lined with several inches of insulation. Anchors, normally of stainless steel and welded to the hopper plate, are used to hold 4 to 6 inches (10 to 15 cm) of gunned refractory lining forming the inside of the ash hopper. Ash is periodically removed from the hopper through a series of water-cooled discharge gates. Each gate has a sealed enclosure, a pneumatic operator, an access door, an observation port, and a floodlight.

At the discharge of the ash gates, grinders may be provided to reduce any large clinkers to a size that can be handled by a pneumatic (typically, 1 inch [2.54 cm] diameter or less) or hydraulic (typically, 2 to 3 inch [5.1 to 7.6 cm] diameter or less) conveying system. The grinders are similar in construction but normally smaller than the grinders under the wet bottom-ash hoppers. Instead of grinders, sizing grids for manual handling may be placed at the discharge gate outlet.

The Submerged Scraper Conveyor for Continuous Removal

Another method of bottom-ash removal uses a drag chain and flight conveyor of heavy construction submerged in a water trough below the furnace. With the submerged scraper conveyor (SSC), ash is evacuated mechanically on a continuous basis so there is no long-time storage in the water impoundment beneath the furnace. After discharge from the SSC in a dewatered condition, ash is dumped on the ground in a bunker or transported further by belt conveyors. The major advantages of the SSC are:

- Continuous and reliable removal of bottom ash—reduces the removal rate to approximate the ash generation rate with a sizable safety margin, and does not allow larger ash formations to block removal
- Less operator involvement and maintenance—continuous operation requires mere monitoring of ash levels for adjustments to the chain speed
- Reduced water usage and consumption—no water needed for transport, only make-up
- Reduced power consumption—by eliminating the high-pressure sluicing water required by the jet pumps
- Lower boiler setting height than with traditional ash hopper although several hours storage still provided

The SSC concept has been proven over many years for pulverized-coal units.[41–47] It serves the same functions as the intermittently emptied refractory-lined ash hopper; that is, it seals the furnace bottom, quenches the falling ash, and removes it from under the furnace. The most widely accepted SSC configuration has two separated compartments in which the flights and chains move (*Fig.* 6-53).

The upper (wet) chamber, containing a minimum of 5 feet (1.5 m) of water, receives the ash falling from the furnace and conveys it up the dewatering slope. At the top of the dewatering slope, the flights reverse direction, dumping the conveyed ash. They return through the dry chamber below. This has open sides to facilitate inspection while the equipment is operating (*Fig.* 6-54).

Generally, the maximum speed of the scraper conveyor chain ranges from approximately 2 to 10 ft/min (0.6 to 3.0 m/min), with an infinitely variable speed-controlling device. Normal operation at lower speeds, typically 2 to 3 ft/min (0.6 to 0.9 m/min), reduces abrasive wear on both flights and supporting wear surfaces. Travel wheels, when furnished, support the entire conveyor. They ride on rails located in or on the power plant floor. The dewatering slope on the ash removal conveyor leads to a transfer chute. In many instances, the ash is dropped into a three-sided bunker just outside the boiler plant wall for intermittent removal by truck. In other instances, the ash is directed into a transfer chute or hopper, in which a conventional clinker grinder reduces the size of the ash to allow for use of a series of belt conveyors for more remote disposal.

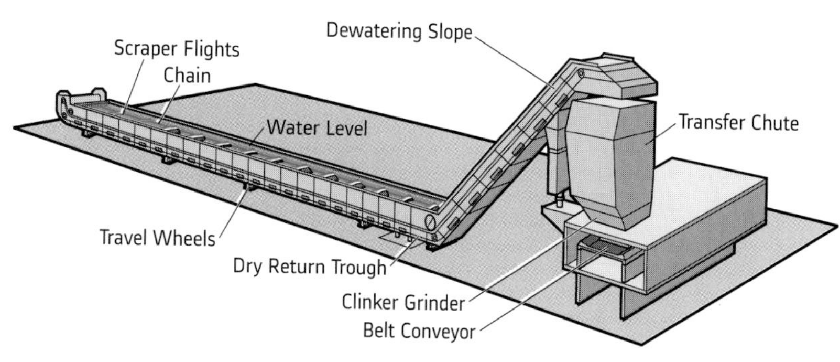

Figure 6-53 | Submerged scraper conveyor for bottom-ash removal

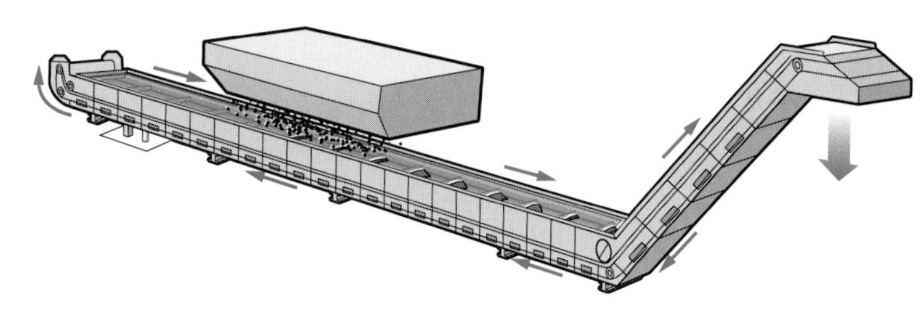

Figure 6-54 | A typical flow diagram for a submerged scraper conveyor with upper submerged trough, dewatering incline, drive section, return trough, and rear take-up section

CONVEYOR CHAIN DESIGN. The most common SSC chain is the double-stranded round link or ship-type chain made from alloy steel, case hardened to have a minimum surface hardness of 800 HV (63 HRC). Chain coupling links are made of the same material as the chain. The chain is supplied in matched sets and undergoes stringent quality control and testing to ensure a long service life. Useful life is a function of chain speed and tension, which affects the wear of the inner portion of the links. This inner link wear increases the effective chain pitch, resulting in a mismatch of the chain to the driving sprocket. It is also important to maintain the proper tension on the chain using an automatic, hydraulically operated circuit with hydraulic cylinders. It is not unusual for the chain to last 5 years or more when recommended maintenance and operating procedures are followed.

OTHER DESIGN FEATURES. The flights are made of commercially available structural angles or tubing attached to the chains using chain attachments provided by the chain manufacturer. Wear plates are added to the sliding surfaces of the flights that contact the trough wear plates. The upper trough of the conveyor has overflow boxes to regulate the height of the water above the flights. Cooling water is added to maintain a normal 140°F (60°C) (maximum, 160°F [71°C]) temperature for quenching, cooling, and equipment protection, just like in a traditional ash hopper. In this respect, the submerged scraper conveyor uses approximately the same amount of cooling water as a water-impounded hopper, as the heat presented to the equipment is the same. Additional make-up water is needed in the SSC to replace the nominal 20% water by weight that the disposed ash takes with it out of the SSC. This number is consistent with the dewatering bin discharge in a traditional intermittent system discussed above. The only significant difference in water usage between the intermittent systems and the SSC system is the large amount of water used for actual conveying in the jet pump or centrifugal pump systems.

Dewatering slopes are at an angle between 25 and 45 degrees, with a nominal 30 degrees used most often. The actual physical configuration depends on the unobstructed space available, the boiler-house structural-steel design considerations, and the method of handling the ash after it leaves the conveyor.

SETTING HEIGHT OF STEAM GENERATORS AS AFFECTED BY THE BOTTOM-ASH SYSTEM. The operation and maintenance of bottom-ash hoppers and associated auxiliary equipment are easier and better when no equipment is located in sub-basement floor pits. But, by eliminating such pits it is sometimes necessary to have boiler setting heights up to 35 feet (10.7 m) to accommodate the intermittent-removal, water-impounded bottom hopper. (*Setting height* is the vertical distance from the basement-floor level to the centerline of the horizontal furnace-wall tubing directly above the ash removal equipment; this dimension is measured with the steam generator in the "cold" condition, before expansion has taken place.)

Such generous setting heights are not necessary with the submerged scraper conveyor. When SSCs are specified before the boiler is purchased, the setting height can be adjusted to save substantial amounts in the cost of boiler structural steel, piping, and ductwork.

In most new boiler installations, the boiler is being set "low" in anticipation of an SSC. There is still the need to seal the boiler using a modification of the traditional seal plate. While the continued use of separate water seal-troughs is still possible, many new boiler designs eliminate the high maintenance water seal-trough and integrate the boiler seal with a suspended transition chute that extends down into the water level of the SSC. That leads to ongoing discussions about where the "boiler" scope ends and the "ash handling" scope begins. It appears that the boiler manufacturers are handling any bars or plates welded to the boiler tubes/pressure parts and then the ash-handling supplier is bolting to that bar or plate. An example is shown in *Figure 6-55*.

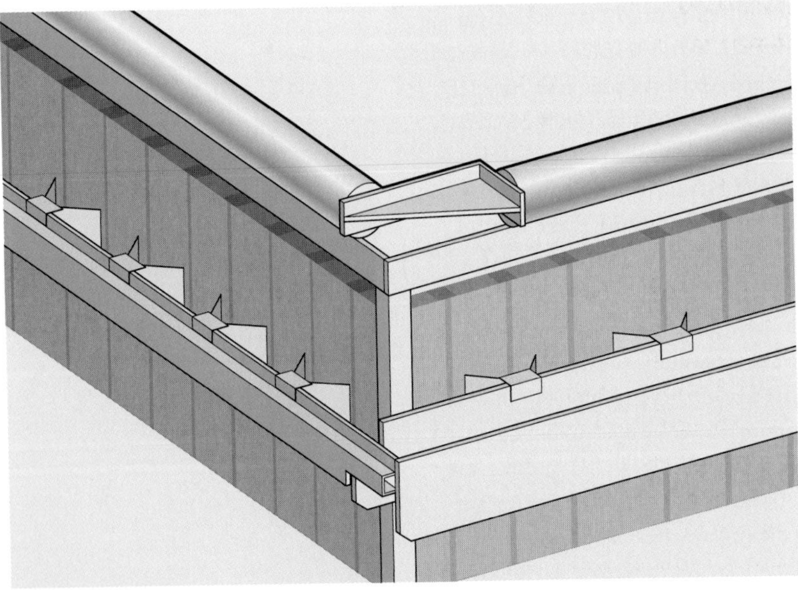

Figure 6-55 | Three-dimensional model of typical suspended transition chute showing buckstay support

COMPARISON OF CONTINUOUS- AND INTERMITTENT-REMOVAL BOTTOM-ASH EQUIPMENT. Continuous mechanical removal offers reduced power consumption compared to hydraulic evacuation and eliminates the need for conveying water. It is also possible to observe the ash removal process without drawing down the water level. Continuous removal provides "auto-dewatering" without the use of dewatering vessels. Maintenance is also much less with continuous-removal systems.

In addition, operational control systems for continuous removal are simpler than those on an intermittent-removal system. Moreover, the reduced height of the boiler above the basement floor has a savings potential in fuel piping, ductwork, structural steel, and building costs. There is also an advantage in being able to move the conveyor to the side at times when the boiler is out of operation. This feature facilitates access to the interior of the furnace through the furnace's bottom opening. The high-pressure pumps and water piping of the intermittent hopper (*Figs. 6-45* and *6-52*) are not required with an SSC. Because the SSC is designed for continuous removal, provision must be made for continuous receiving of the ash dropping from the top of the dewatering slope into a bunker or onto belt conveyors or other similar mechanical devices. The usual intermittent-removal hopper system in the U.S. is operated only 20 to 30% of the time. There is thus a period during which the equipment is not in operation and is available for inspection and maintenance.

Redundancy of mechanical conveying equipment downstream of the scraper conveyor should be considered to ensure continuous ash removal. However, several hours of ash storage is usually considered in designing an SSC, so it can be shut down for short periods to repair downstream equipment.

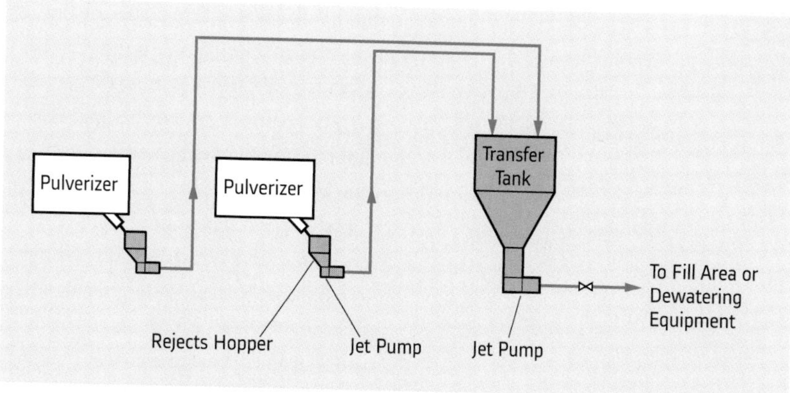

Figure 6-56 | A mill-rejects (pyrites) hydraulic transport system uses individual pipelines from each pulverizer to the transfer tank

Pulverizer-Rejects Systems

The pulverizer-rejects system collects and transports pulverizer rejects (principally pyrites and tramp iron) hydraulically from the pulverizers (also called "mills"). A typical system (*Fig. 6-56*) uses an enclosed pyrites-reject hopper located next to each pulverizer to receive and store the pulverizer rejects for intermittent removal.

Removal and transport from the pyrite hopper is by a jet pump similar to the jet pumps used in bottom-ash sluicing, but smaller in size and conveying capacity (*Fig. 6-57*).

Although the mill rejects may be pumped directly to a dewatering bin or pond, it is more common to have all the pyrites-removal jet pumps discharge to a local collection or transfer tank (*Fig. 6-56*). This arrangement permits emptying more than one hopper at a time. (In cases in which an SSC exists, this same design concept is used, but the small jet pumps discharge directly into the SSC.)

From this central collection tank, jet or centrifugal pumps remove the pyrites rejects to the dewatering equipment. Discharging mill rejects into bottom-ash hopper equipment is not acceptable unless a method can be provided to prevent splashing of ash-hopper water onto the boiler tubes above the pyrites injection point. This splashing has caused stress-cracking failure of these tubes. With an SSC, it is practical to introduce mill rejects

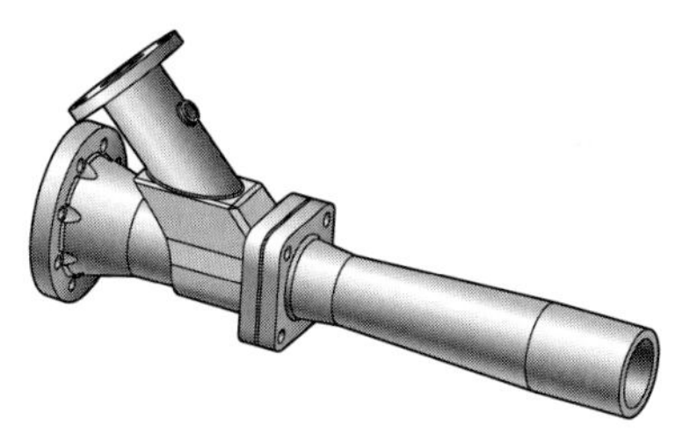

Figure 6-57 | Small jet pump used for pulverizer-rejects systems at each mill hopper

outside the water-seal plates, obviating the problem. Plant maintenance and operating flexibility demands that the pulverizer-reject system be operable simultaneously with the main bottom-ash system. This needs to be kept in mind when developing the plant service-water balance diagrams.

When pressurized pulverizers are used, it is a requirement of the National Fire Prevention Association (NFPA) to design the rejects hoppers to withstand 50 psig (3.5 bar) (*Fig. 6-58*). To seal out pulverizer pressure during normal operation, a water-seal overflow box is used. This seal box is sized for 120% of the static pressure specified for the primary air fan.

Each rejects hopper must be equipped with a:

- High-level indicator
- Steel grate with approximately 1- to 1½-inch (2.5- to 3.8-cm) square openings to capture large particles for manual removal
- Floodlight
- Inspection port/window
- Hinged or bolted access panel
- Discharge chute to connect the reject outlet on each pulverizer to the hopper. A pneumatically operated knife-gate valve is located in the discharge chute for isolation of the hopper. The pyrites slurry piping and fittings are similar to those provided for the bottom-ash systems.

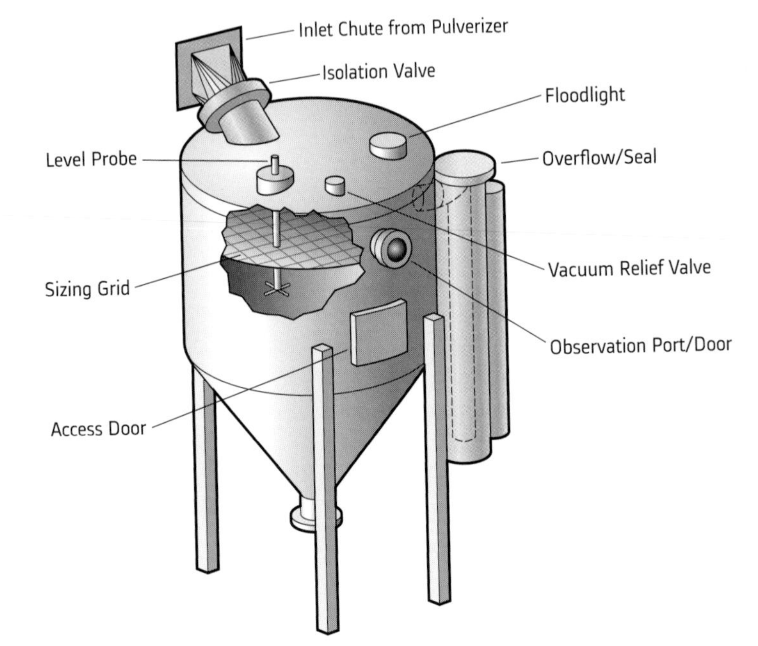

Figure 6-58 | Mill rejects hopper for pressurized pulverizers, in accordance with NFPA 85F

With suction-type mills, the pyrites hopper is an open tank to store and collect the rejects (*Fig. 6-59*).

On open hoppers, accessories such as floodlights and inspection ports are eliminated. On small steam generators equipped with suction mills from which there will not be a large amount of pulverizer rejects, a simple wheelbarrow may substitute for hoppers. The amount of rejects from a pulverizer varies greatly as a function of the type of coal, the type of firing system, the pulverizer, and the way the pulverizer is operated.

Removal of Economizer Hopper Ash

Economizer ash is usually over 700°F (370°C), and frequently coarse. Its size and shape lead to its often-used nickname: "popcorn ash." It sometimes contains combustible material. This ash can have the physical characteristics of furnace-wall ash and the chemical characteristics of hygroscopic fly ash. It is collected in a row of pyramidal hoppers beneath the boiler economizer section, usually at the point of the 90-degree turn in the combustion gas flow.

Years ago, economizer ash was most often handled dry, as an extension of the dry precipitator fly ash system. However, exposed to in-leaking, oxygen-laden air, it could combust and form clinkers, making it impossible for the ash to flow through the hopper outlets, which usually were only 6 inches (15 cm) in diameter. In today's marketplace, the higher carbon content of the economizer ash makes it a contaminant to the fly ash that can be sold. This ash is now kept separate.

Economizer ash should be removed continuously, in a method analogous to the continuous removal of bottom ash from a hot furnace. Continuous removal gets the ash out of the hot environment of the hopper and prevents further combustion of any carbon it may contain. For low-calcium content bituminous coals, water-filled tanks beneath each economizer-hopper outlet (*Fig. 6-60*) were used. The ash fell continuously into these tanks and was stored for intermittent removal.

Unfortunately, wet holding is not feasible with economizer-hopper ash produced by certain high-calcium lignite or sub-bituminous coals. Powder River Basin (PRB) coal, in particular, produces a high-calcium ash. Some of this ash shows pozzolanic and cementitious properties when dropped into or mixed with water, and may require very frequent evacuation from wet tanks to obviate the possibility of plugging. Some utilities burning such "concrete-making," high-calcium coals have used dry transfer tanks below the economizer hoppers to achieve continuous removal without tank- or line-plugging problems. However, the temperature of the ash still presents some problems with downstream equipment selection such as bag filters.

It is important, then, to recognize that such economizer ash has the potential of producing synthetic silicate rocks that cannot be redissolved and flushed out of tanks or transport lines. The ash is in the category of a pozzolan/siliceous or alumino/siliceous material, which in itself possesses little or no cementitious value but which will, in finely divided form and in the presence of moisture, chemically react with calcium hydroxide to form compounds having cementitious properties. Therefore, the best solution to the handling of economizer ash having these characteristics is to remove it continuously from the hoppers under the high-temperature gas zone into a mechanical dry drag conveyor.

A dry drag chain conveyor will continuously remove economizer ash from all economizer hoppers on one row simultaneously in a two-level horizontal chamber that can extend outside the existing boiler-building wall to allow a straight downcomer to a storage tank or bin for intermittent disposal. The conveyor itself is sealed against escape of any flue gases so at some point in the disposal path a seal transfer device needs to be installed. This can be a double-dump tipping valve in the downcomer, or the storage tank itself can be sealed using a material-handling valve or airlock at its outlet. The basic economizer dry drag chain conveyor itself includes only a drive section, one or more horizontal sections and a tensioning section (*Fig. 6-61*).

The dry drag chain conveyor uses a single chain of the forked-link, drop forged, design. The ash is conveyed along the bottom trough of the conveyor with the return path being over the top. The ash entering the conveyor falls through the return flights onto the bottom trough liner. A catenary idler and shaft in the drive section allows for automatic chain tension adjustment necessitated by thermal changes. When SSCs are used for the main bottom-ash system, all economizer ash, from any coal, should be collected in dry drag conveyors and directed to the SSC.

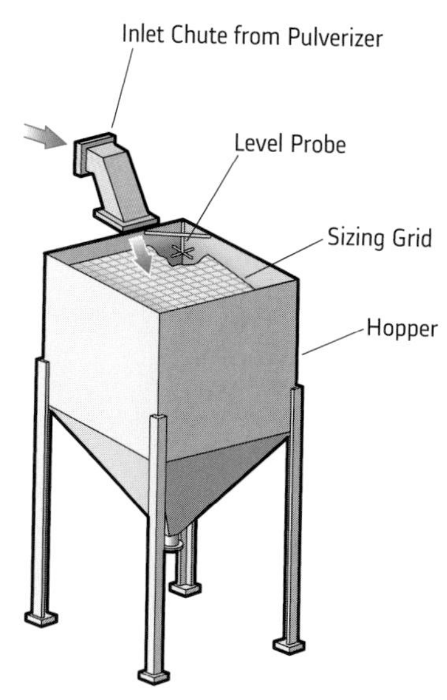

Figure 6-59 | Open top rejects hopper for suction pulverizers

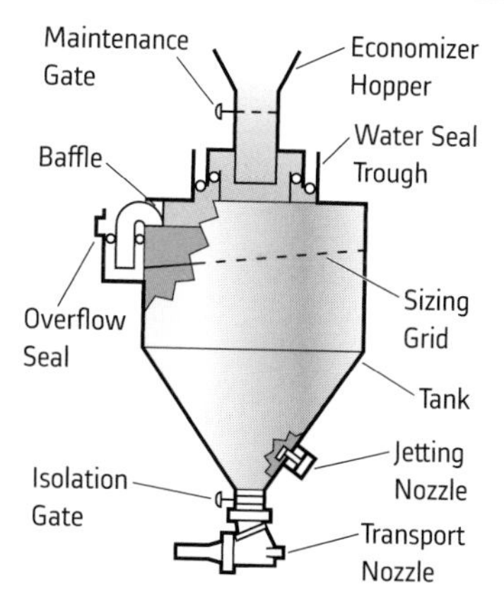

Figure 6-60 | Water-filled tank beneath economizer hopper receives low-calcium-content ash for cooling and intermittent flushing

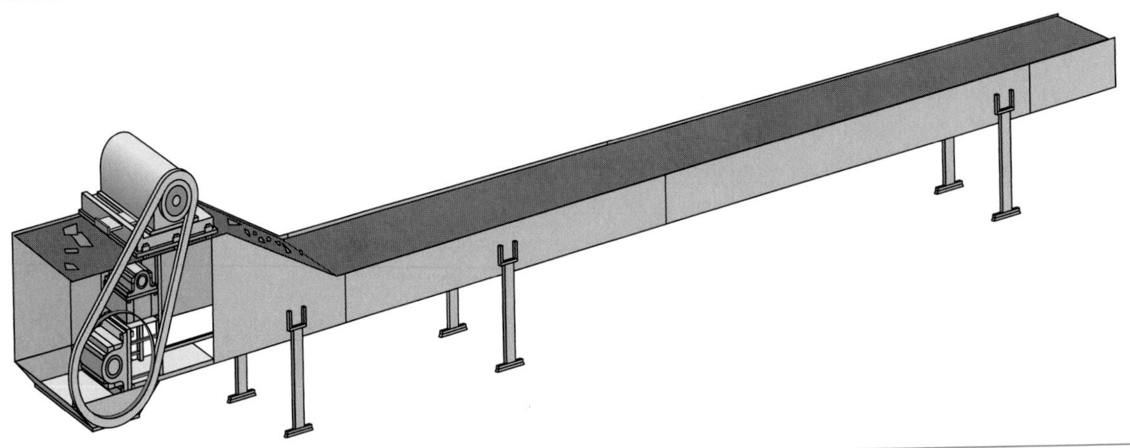

Figure 6-61 | Dry drag conveyor with catenary shaft in drive section

Fly Ash Removal Systems

Fly ash from the hoppers serving air heaters, electrostatic precipitators (ESPs), and baghouses is removed intermittently by either vacuum (negative-pressure) or pressure (positive-pressure) pneumatic type systems, or combinations of the two.

VACUUM SYSTEMS. A vacuum system (*Fig. 6-62*) uses a mechanical blower, water exhauster, or a steam exhauster to create a vacuum that removes the fly ash from the hoppers. A fly ash intake valve located at each hopper regulates the flow of the fly ash.

Fly ash intakes have carbon-steel or cast-iron bodies and a swing disk, which seals against a hardened seat. For maintenance, the outlet of each hopper has a manual isolation gate. Each fly ash intake is actuated automatically by the system logic that controls both the flow rate and quantity of fly ash leaving the hopper to avoid plugging the discharge line. Because the system operates on a vacuum, only one fly ash intake and one conveyor branch line operate at any given time. As each hopper is emptied of fly ash, the system will step to the next hopper in the same branch line. When all hoppers in a branch line have been emptied, the system will step to the next branch line. The system logic ensures the proper sequence of events and positioning of valves. The intake valve, shown in *Figure 6-63*, has the moving parts and multiple access areas needed to work with today's varied fuels, including high-calcium ash from coals such as Powder River Basin (PRB).

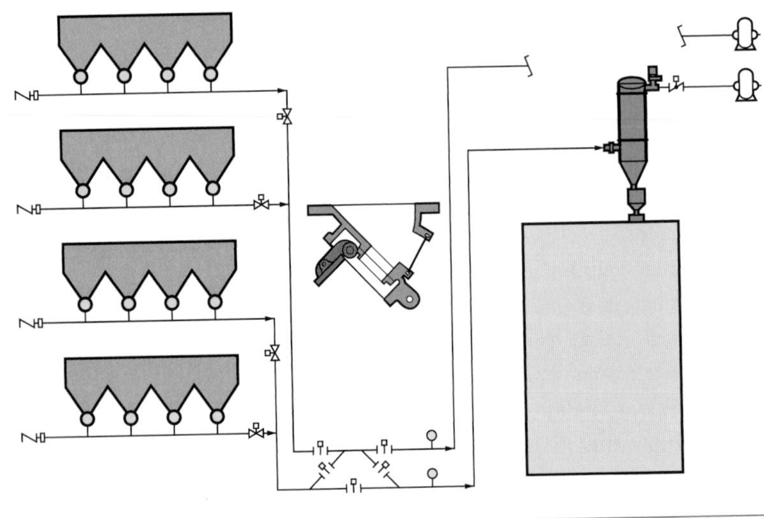

Figure 6-62 | Typical pneumatic vacuum system serving an assortment of collection hoppers using a swing-gate-type material intake valve at each hopper

When a mechanical blower produces the necessary vacuum, fly ash is transported to a silo, where a combination filter–receiver separates the air–ash mixture[53,55] (*Fig. 6-64*). To protect the blower, it is important to collect practically all of the ash in the receiver vessel. Thus, the bag filters are typically 99% efficient. The ash collected in the receiver is discharged into the silo through the airlock valves, and, in turn, is then emptied from the silos into enclosed trucks or railcars.

The water exhauster (*Fig. 6-65*) is another, older, method of transporting fly ash through the conveying line. High-pressure water supplied to the water-exhauster inlet nozzles creates the transport vacuum; fly ash, air, and water are mixed in the Venturi exhauster. Water exhausters normally have hardened ductile iron bodies, wear-resistant liners, and stainless steel nozzles. Diffusers are made of hardened ductile iron, Ni-Hard, or high-chrome alloys, or they can be ceramic-lined.

Following the water exhausters, an air separator tank is provided to separate and vent the air from the fly ash–water–air mixture (*Fig. 6-66*). Air separator tanks are made of cast iron or carbon steel with an abrasion-resistant basalt or ceramic liner. The separator discharge is elevated sufficiently to allow the ash–water slurry to flow by gravity to a pond or disposal area. Fly ash slurry is never discharged to a dewatering bin because it is very difficult to settle out the fine fly ash particles in the dewatering bin. Most fine particles would pass over the overflow weir.

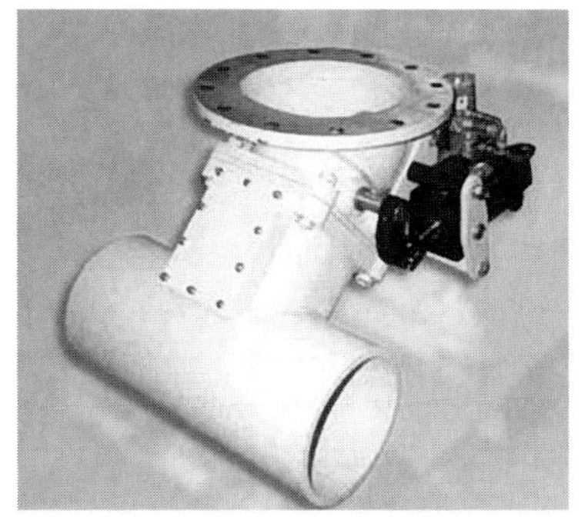

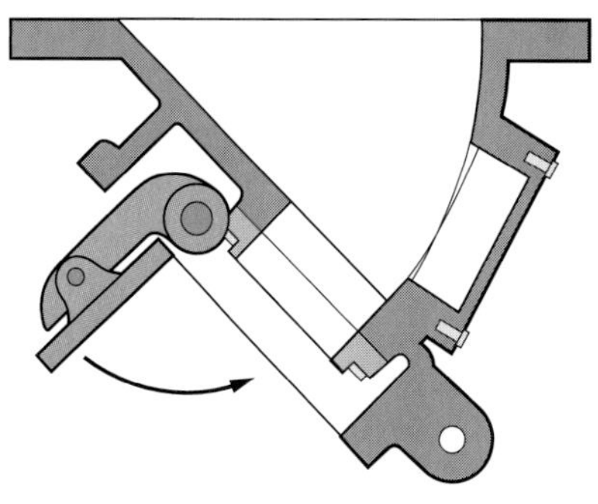

Figure 6-63 | Typical swing-gate-type fly ash intake valve for vacuum system service

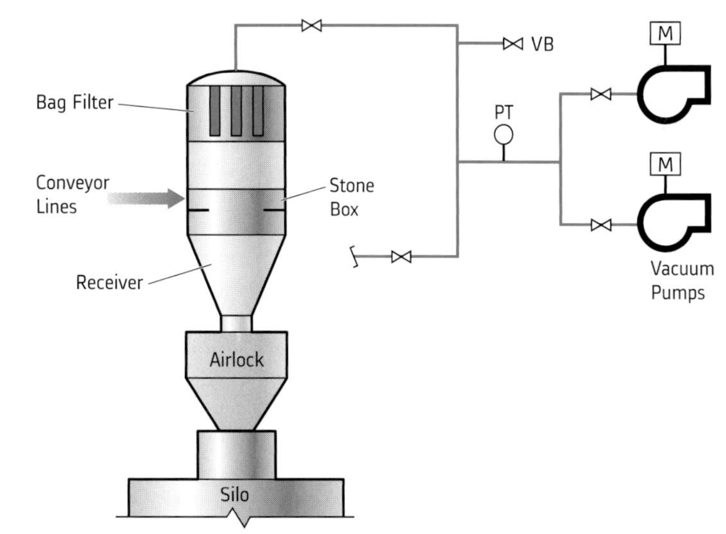

Figure 6-64 | Typical filter–receiver arrangement for collection of ash

PRESSURE SYSTEMS. In a pressure system (*Fig. 6-67*), an airlock feeder transfers fly ash from a hopper, typically under a slightly negative pressure to a pipeline conveyor at a higher pressure. Compressors or blowers provide the airflow and pressure to convey the fly ash.

These airlock feeders are designed with a storage capacity based on the desired conveying rate, ash density, and number of hoppers to be conveyed in a given unloading sequence. The volumetric feeders are controlled to empty each selected group of hoppers on a staggered cycle, thus providing uniform loading into the conveyor system. Fluidizing air at the inlet and outlet of each feeder

Figure 6-65 | Water exhauster for vacuum removal of fly ash (ash and water are combined in exhauster for transport as a slurry to disposal; upper flange is high-pressure water inlet; dry ash enters at left end)

ensures ash flow, especially for denser and high-calcium ashes.

Vacuum transport systems usually move fly ash in a quite "airy" mixture (i.e., very dilute phase), but the consistency of the mixture can vary with a positive-pressure system. For example, the mixture might be in a dilute phase, a dense phase (in which there is much more ash than air), or the mixture may begin as a dense phase and gradually change to a dilute phase at the discharge end. Many low-velocity, dilute-phase systems operate at some time in a dense phase because dense phase occurs whenever saltation takes place in a pipeline.

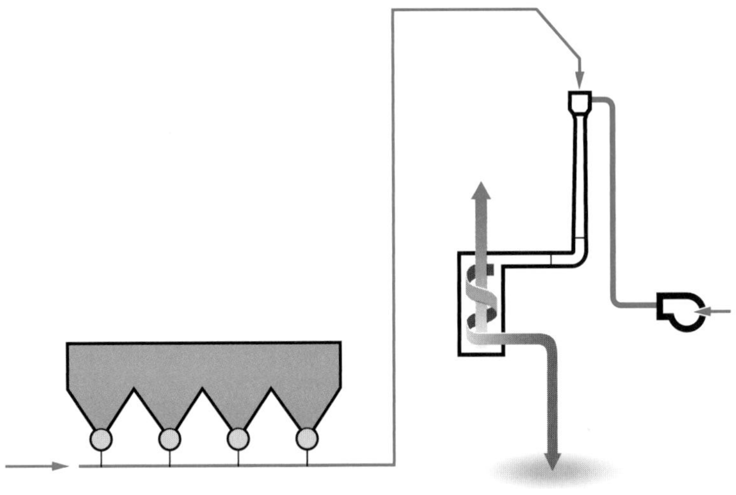

AIRLOCK FEEDER OPERATION. It is customary in dilute-phase fly ash transport to use the collecting hoppers for storage. The airlock tank is used only during the actual ash-moving process. Thus, the inlet valve to the pressure tank is kept closed until the transport cycle begins. This exposes the ash to the unheated tank metal for the shortest possible time, but keeps the ash in the collecting hoppers for the longest possible time.

In dense-phase transport, the inlet valves of the pressure tanks are kept open whenever the tanks are not full. The ash, then, leaves the area that is heated by flue gas and drops into the tanks, normally unheated, until the tank level indicator causes the inlet valve to close. The filled tank remains at essentially atmospheric pressure until its turn in the transport "queue" is signaled. The time that the ash remains in the tank before fluidization and transport will depend on the filling/emptying status of any other tanks on the same conveying line.

EQUALIZING VALVES. It should be noted that airlocks can be used in both vacuum systems, under the filter-receivers, and in pressure systems, under the main ash-collection hoppers. In both systems, the airlock needs to move the ash from one pressure zone to another using an intermediate chamber while not allowing back flow of higher-pressure air. This "double dumping" action is accomplished by using one or two equalizing valves to equalize the

Figure 6-66 | Typical water jet exhauster–based vacuum system with drain to a pond

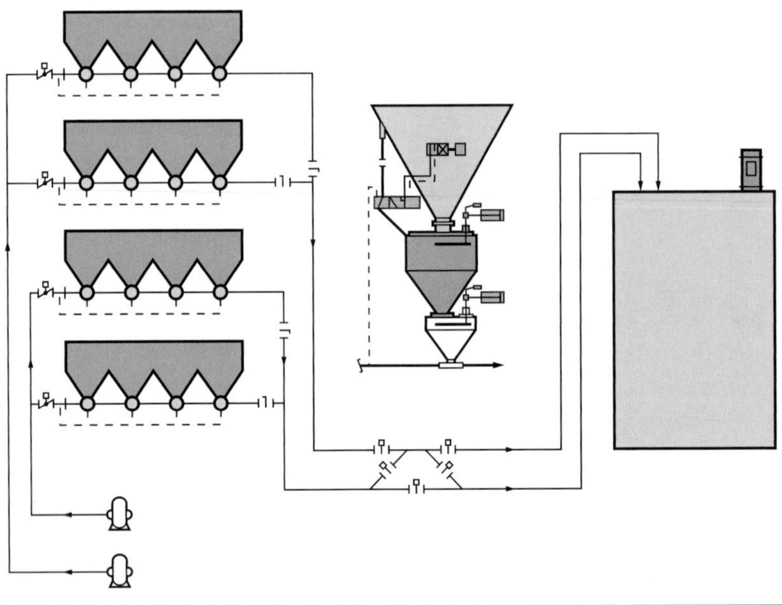

Figure 6-67 | Typical pneumatic pressure system serving an assortment of collection hoppers using an airlock-type valve at each hopper

pressure between any two zones before the appropriate airlock gate opens and allows gravity or gravity-assisted flow down through the airlock. The equalizing valves are exposed to ash-laden air traveling at very high velocities. Their design is as critical as the airlock.

Either two 2-way (open–closed) equalizing valves can be used or one 3-way equalizing valve with each airlock. In a 3-way equalizing valve installation for a pressure system (*Fig. 6-68*), the 3-way equalizing valve is first opened to vent the upper chamber of the airlock and allow it to be at the same pressure level as the hopper above.

The top gate of the airlock is then opened to allow ash to fall by gravity down into the upper chamber. On a timed cycle, the upper gate of the airlock closes and the 3-way equalizing valve switches position to allow the same blower pressure from below the airlock to fill the upper chamber. An orifice before the airlock intake tee is used to ensure slightly higher pressure through the equalizing valve. The lower gate of the airlock is then opened to allow gravity-assisted flow down into the conveying line. After the volume of ash in the airlock is discharged, the 3-way equalizing valve returns to the first position to vent the upper chamber and start the continuous cycle over again.

COMPARISON OF VACUUM AND PRESSURE SYSTEM. Selecting a vacuum or pressure fly ash removal system for a given unit depends on an evaluation of:

- Conveying rate
- Altitude
- Number of hoppers to be evacuated
- Distance to be conveyed
- Number of disposal options desired

A vacuum conveying system features less equipment and less headroom required under each hopper: one fly ash intake valve versus two sets of airlock deck plate valves, an airlock upper chamber, and an equalizer valve required for a pressure system. Also, a vacuum system uses the more positive means of suction to evacuate the fly ash from the hoppers, whereas a pressure system uses gravity alone to move the ash from the hopper to the feeders. Of course, fluidization and rappers are available, but to be effective, they must be used properly. Vacuum systems are more dependent on ambient air, which can be moist, for conveying, while pressure systems have the warmed air coming from the blowers to aid in dealing with any sluggish ash. A vacuum system also has the advantage of being able to indicate, from the conveying-line vacuum switches, whether a given hopper is full, empty, plugged, or rat holed. This is not always possible with a pressure system, as multiple hoppers are being evacuated simultaneously on quicker time cycles.

However, the practicality of a vacuum system is limited by the amount of pressure differential that is available for conveying. The actual pressure drop increases as the conveying rate increases. Thus, if all else is constant, higher conveying rates may require a pressure system. When plants are at high elevations, the available pressure decreases (at 7,000 feet [2,100 m], approximately 5 inches Hg [12.7 cm/Hg] are lost over that of sea level), further limiting the application of vacuum systems. In addition, the pressure will drop as conveying distance increases, making a pressure system more feasible for longer conveying distances.

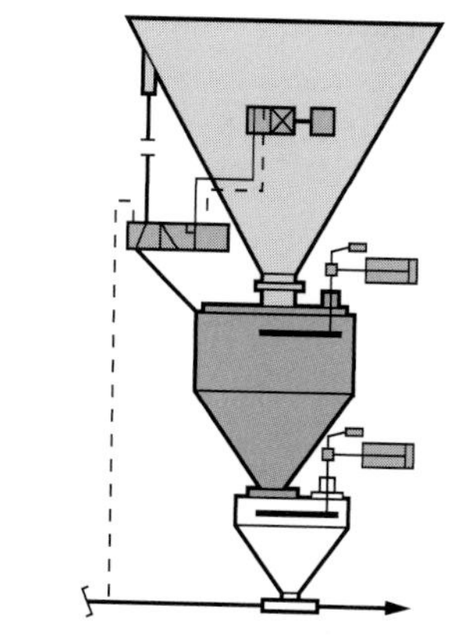

Figure 6-68 | Equaling flow paths using a 3-way equalizing valve with an airlock

With the increase in options for the sale of fly ash depending on the texture and carbon content of the ash, more and more plants need and want separate fly ash silos to receive and store "saleable" and "non-saleable" ash. Re-injection of high loss on ignition (LOI) ash also comes into play as a possible option. These multiple disposal points are more easily handled by pressure systems, where the blowers are located back where the ash is first collected and need only additional pipeline and valves to send the ash in any direction desired.

To understand a pneumatic transport system, it is important to realize that conveying distance is the total developed length of the pipeline. In pneumatics, the pressure drop through an elbow can easily be the equivalent of 50 feet (150 m) of pipe. Therefore, the optimal system would have a minimum number of elbows.

VACUUM/PRESSURE SYSTEMS. When the number of precipitator or baghouse collection hoppers is relatively high (say, 20 to 40, or more) and the conveying distance dictates a pressure system, it is usually economical to provide a vacuum-pressure system (*Fig. 6-69*). In this system, a transfer station is located close to the precipitator, or baghouse, and the fly ash is transported by vacuum from the hoppers to the transfer station. At the discharge of the station, a set of airlock feeders starts the pressure system to convey the fly ash by pressure to the main ash-storage silos. The capital and maintenance cost is reduced because there is less equipment and more headroom under the hoppers. This reduction in equipment under the hoppers can more than offset additional costs associated with the transfer station and the positive-pressure blowers. On the other hand, a vacuum-pressure system uses more power than a straight pressure system.

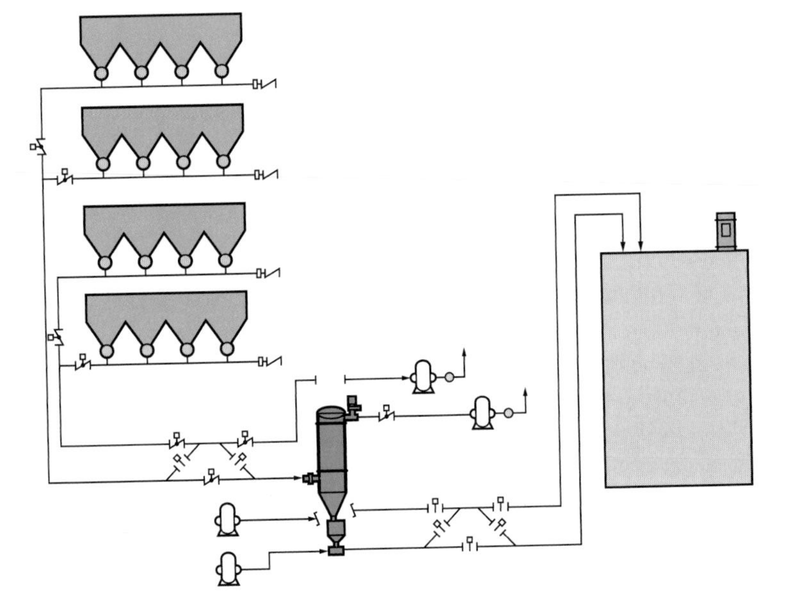

Figure 6-69 | Typical vacuum-pneumatic pressure system with transfer station

FLY ASH HOPPER DESIGN. Problems have been experienced in the removal of powdery fly ash from hoppers, particularly with large precipitators on utility steam generators. Because of the very high ash content found in many coals, and increasingly stringent particulate-collection regulations, precipitators on a large pulverized coal/fired unit commonly have more than 40 hoppers (sometimes as many as 128). Research has shown that the incidence of hopper operational and maintenance problems is directly related to the number of hoppers on a precipitator.[48,49]

Pneumatic ash removal systems are not designed to handle wet material. Thus, it is critical in the design and operation of hopper systems to maintain collected material at a temperature sufficiently above the water or acid dew point to keep it absolutely dry, so that it will be as free-flowing as possible.

Dry dust in hoppers ordinarily will flow freely by gravity and be transported pneumatically without difficulty. In order to do so, it:

- Must be kept essentially at the temperature at which it was collected
- Must not be exposed to any moisture
- Must not compact from its own weight to cause bridging above the hopper outlet
- Must have no clinkers formed as the result of oxidation of any combustibles in the ash

In power plant operation, it is frequently difficult to keep the ash flowing freely. With the steam generator at full load, temperatures as low as 90°F (32°C) have been reported in hoppers of cold precipitators (those that follow the boiler air heaters). Similarly, temperatures 20 to 40°F (–7 to 4°C) above ambient have been recorded in the hoppers of "hot" precipitators (those located ahead of the boiler air heater).

The problem in the industry is even more severe with the high-calcium ash associated with certain sub-bituminous coals and various lignites. In addition to being highly hygroscopic, such ash shows pozzolanic and cementitious properties when exposed to moisture. With the increased use of low-sulfur, PRB coal to lower or avoid the high cost of scrubbing equipment, this issue is more common than ever before.

HOPPER SIZING. Hoppers under precipitators and baghouses should be considered only as funnels. Because of difficulties with removing fly ash that has been stored for a long time while exposed to flue gas containing moisture and sulfur, recommendations state that there should be no specified storage time in collecting-equipment hoppers. Minimum hopper-outlet size should be 12 inches (30 cm) (diameter or square). In any case, 6- or 8-inch (15 or 20 cm) outlets should be avoided wherever possible, unless such sizes have proven successful with identical fuels.

HOPPER FLUIDIZING DEVICES. A fly ash fluidizer, as it is used in a conical or pyramidal hopper, is a porous membrane that allows pressurized airflow through it to be uniformly distributed to the material above, filling the voids between the particles at a slight pressure and changing the effective angle of repose of the material to promote gravity flow. Properly located fluidizing devices can help evacuate hoppers (particularly precipitators), if these devices are well maintained and reliably supplied with dry air preheated above dew-point temperatures. If not, fluidizers will only aggravate evacuation by caking the ash, and provide unwanted surface areas for ash accumulation and bridging. Where significant percentages of combustibles are present in the collected fly ash, the fluidizing-medium supply must be non-oxidizing to prevent destructive hopper fires.

HOPPER VIBRATORS. When their operation is properly controlled and timed, hopper vibrators can help prevent bridging and rat holing. In the automatic operation of vacuum pneumatic systems, vibrators should be regulated by ash evacuation controls to ensure operation only when an "empty hopper" signal is generated and the evacuation cycle is completed. Routine use of the vibrators during evacuation of damp ash will further compact the ash and make evacuation difficult.[50] It should be possible to manually operate the vibrators from each hopper to assist maintenance personnel during emergency evacuation.

Moving the ash before it compacts or sets up is key to trouble-free operation.

WEATHERPROOF ENCLOSURES FOR HOPPERS. Many owners add skirts to precipitators or baghouses to keep wind and weather from reducing the hopper metal temperatures. Such enclosures are recommended, although reducing the heat loss from the hoppers can be accomplished equally well by the judicious use of insulation and lagging. Skirts are also instrumental in reducing hopper plugging.[49]

CONTINUOUS REMOVAL OF FLY ASH. The ideal fly ash removal system is one that takes ash from the receiving hoppers at the same rate as it enters. The hoppers then effectively become chutes, and there is no time for cooling, de-aeration, or compaction to occur. There are virtually no such systems in U.S. utility power plants, and only a few in certain industrial boiler or process applications. The majority of multiple-dust-outlet precipitators and baghouses have their removal systems intentionally designed for intermittent removal to minimize the power consumed by the ash transport system. Such an approach ignores the harmful impact on the reliability of collection equipment when hoppers are used for storage.

Utility plants in Europe report good experience with continuous removal, as have some industrial installations in the United States. In these systems, fly ash is transported by either mechanical or air fluidized conveyors, instead of by pneumatic conveying equipment. It appears that a principal feature of such continuous removal devices is that, with proper valving, they do not allow any substantial amount of air to leak into the precipitator or baghouse hoppers. This feature maintains the gas temperatures in those hoppers above the dew point.[48]

Air fluidized conveyors can be used only if the fly ash remains fluid under all conditions of startup, normal load, and shutdown. Although these conveyors are a form of continuous removal, there have been numerous problems in keeping the ash completely dry during startup. Also, if ash clinkers form, they are impossible to fluidize and transport.

Two types of mechanical conveyors have been used for conveying fly ash: screw conveyors and flight conveyors. Often prone to wear, screw conveyors are usually used for ash transport only when conveying a relatively small quantity of material. Flight conveyors, like those previously discussed for economizer ash, transport the ash in a dust-tight casing using elements linked by a single or double strand of chain. The units are sized either on a volumetric basis or on an en masse basis, in which the material is conveyed in bulk, without agitation. Flight conveyors have been successfully operated for many decades on coal-fired units, both in North America and Europe. When properly designed, they are relatively insensitive to problems such as moisture in the fly ash and fly ash clinkers (which may force outages in other types of systems).[51]

With continuous-conveying devices, the system can combine the mechanical conveyor with a pneumatic pipeline. Mechanical devices have the ability to move the ash "uphill," to the top of a storage silo. Perhaps in the future more fly ash systems will incorporate more of the continuous-removal arrangements.

FLY ASH RECEIVING AND STORING EQUIPMENT. Fly ash storage silos and their related accessories form an integral part of the ash-handling equipment. Silos are made of concrete or steel, depending on size, seismic condition, and plant economics. For vacuum systems, equipment is required on top of the silo to separate the fly ash from the conveying air stream before it can be discharged into the silo. Pressure systems require only a target box or an entry elbow on the silo roof.

AIR/FLY ASH SEPARATION EQUIPMENT. As stated in the discussion of vacuum systems, filter–receivers are the primary mechanism to separate the fly ash from the conveying air. The stone box entry in the receiver tank (*Fig. 6-64*) allows capture of most of the heavier ash particles. By using an airlock and equalizing valves at the base of the receiver tank, the storage silo is never under vacuum and the system can function continuously. The bag filter on top of the receiver tank acts to precipitate the remaining fly ash from the conveying air stream. These multiple levels of separation protect the vacuum pump from unnecessary particulate carryover. The bag filter usually features pulse jet air cleaning with a good air-to-cloth ratio. The vacuum-producing device (blower, vacuum pump, exhauster), which has pulled the fly ash–air mixture down the pipeline and through the discharge equipment, is located at the side or underneath the silo. Sound enclosures can ensure proper noise abatement. A small, bin vent, bag filter is also needed on a silo with a vacuum system to vent the displaced air, aeration air, and unloading system air.

On a pressure system, somewhat simpler filtration equipment is used. The conveying air enters the silo directly to join the displaced air, aeration air, and unloading-system air. All of this air needs to be vented to keep the silo near ambient pressure. Large, bin vent, bag filters are the least expensive passive form of venting. Alternatively, fans and motor drives can be mounted on top of the storage silo. The vent fan should be designed to handle the static head required to transport all the air back to the precipitator inlet duct. The vent fan places the silo under a slight negative pressure, eliminating the possibility of blowing dust out of the silo. Vent-fan operation can be synchronized with that of the conveying blowers.

SILO FLUIDIZATION. Fly ash, when not allowed to agglomerate and when fluidized with heated air, takes on the flow properties of a fluid. To expedite fly ash removal, troughs with fluidizing air are provided at the bottom of the silos. The fluidizing elements are normally constructed of canvas or porous stone. Some plants have been using porous laminates of sintered, stainless steel wire. This provides a microporous filter that allows controlled amounts of heated air to pass and fluidize the fly ash. The possibility of stress cracking that is common with fluidizing stones is eliminated by using this metallic material. Because of the microporous construction, the metallic cloth is highly resistant to blinding. In addition, water will not penetrate into the porous openings. This will allow washing of equipment with water without having to remove the fluidizing element. Fluidizing-air blowers and associated heaters provide the required air and temperature level to the fluidizing-air troughs. Care must be taken to properly size the blowers to account for a full head of fly ash in the silo (*Fig. 6-70*).

Silo discharge equipment is designed so that fly ash can be removed dry into enclosed vehicles, or so that it can be moistened (to 12–20% moisture by weight) for transport in open vehicles. It is increasingly common for fly ash to be sold for use in landfills, roads, and the cement industry.

Telescoping ash discharge chutes convey fly ash dry from the storage silo to an enclosed removal vehicle stationed below. Normally, each chute is capable of extending a full 18 feet (5.4 m) using a motor-driven, winch retract system. A vent fan and piping in each chute, vent back into the silo any fugitive dust released during the unloading process, which involves displacing the air volume in the receiving vehicle. An air-operated gate controls the inlet flow to the chute and is placed just below a manual maintenance gate. A clean-out compartment should be included between the maintenance gate and the control gate.

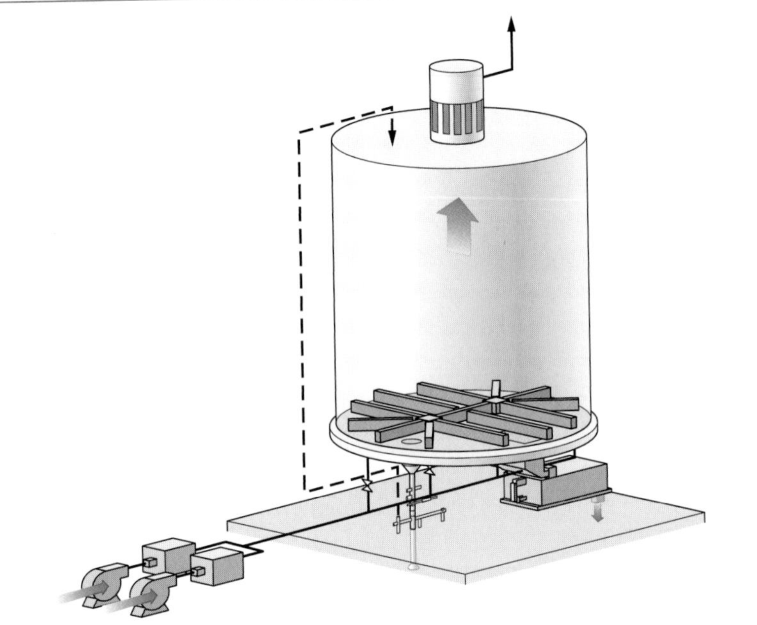

Figure 6-70 | Typical silo layout showing arrangement of fluidizing elements on the silo floor with fluidizing blowers and heaters. Several unloaders and a bin-vent filter are also shown

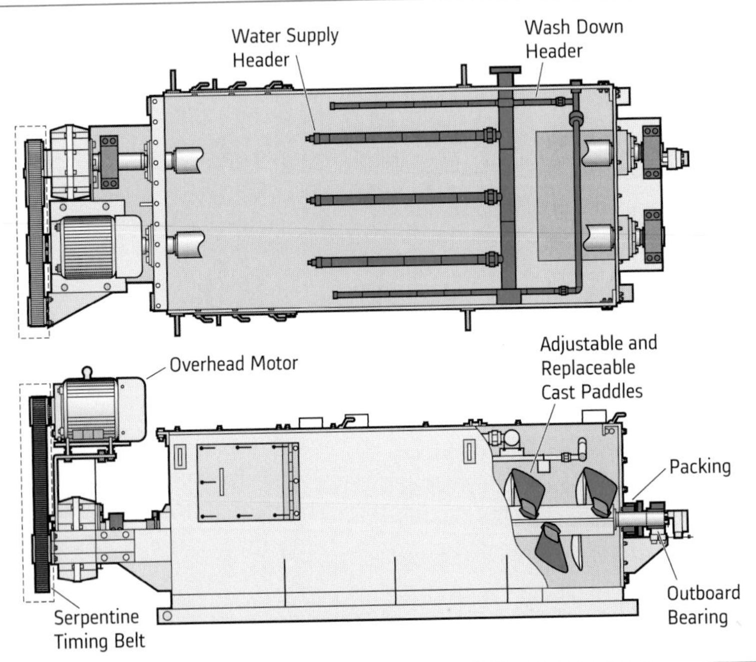

Figure 6-71 | Typical pugmill unloader for conditioning fly ash from storage silos before discharge into open-top disposal trucks

FLY ASH CONDITIONERS. Pugmill ash conditioners (*Fig. 6-71*), add moisture to the fly ash discharged from the storage silo into open-top vehicles. These replace the high-maintenance rotary ash conditioners/drum unloaders used for decades in this service.

The conditioning and moisture prevent any nuisance from fugitive dust. An ash-control valve manages the rate at which the dry material moves from the silo into the inlet of the pugmill. A series of atomizing nozzles spray the material with water as paddles move the ash through the pugmill. Paddles are mounted on two parallel shafts that counter-rotate to mix the ash and water, and move the wetted material to the discharge opening. The shafts are externally driven by an electric motor connected to a serpentine belt arrangement that provides quiet, low-maintenance performance. Ultra-high molecular weight (UHMW) abrasion-resistant materials are used with the paddles (or pins) and shafts when dealing with ashes with higher calcium content, such as those from burning PRB coal.

OPERATIONAL CONTROLS

Ash-handling controls range from completely manual to completely automatic systems of either the relay or programmable logic controller (PLC) type. Often the control logic is merely added into a plant-wide distributed control system (DCS). Many factors should be considered when selecting the type of control system and the degree of automation that should be used. First, the more automated the plant, the less attention paid by the plant operators. If little attention is paid to ash systems, breakdowns are inevitable. When breakdowns occur, the operators may lack sufficient knowledge of the system to take corrective action. For intermittent-removal bottom ash and pyrites systems, many utilities select a push-button automatic system, in which the operator, at a local panel, performs the ash-removal sequence. The operator can judge by the crushing sound of the grinder whether each hopper section has been emptied. If a problem arises, the operator is on hand to analyze it and take action.

Similarly, on a vacuum pneumatic system, the operator can make a check by examining the strip chart that records the vacuum in the pneumatic pipeline. Because the vacuum level can be related to the ash flow, the operator can easily determine the removal rate and time required to empty each hopper. Inconsistencies in removal time and/or removal rate per hopper are signs of a problem.

On multi-field precipitators, PLCs can be used to advantage. Because the front fields will collect ash at a much faster rate than the rear fields, the operator may choose to alter the sequence in which hoppers are "visited" by the ash-removal system. Such adjustments accommodate unequal distribution across the fields, or compensate for fields being removed from service.

Continuous-removal systems obviously require the least-sophisticated controls, but on/off switches, indicating lights, and alarms should be provided. Programmable controllers are rarely justified with such systems.[41,42] The plant-wide DCS can easily handle these few control signals and alarms.

MATERIAL- AND ENERGY-BALANCE CONSIDERATIONS

Water-impounded, ash-receiving equipment beneath a furnace, as previously stated, helps to quench the ash as it falls from the furnace and to transport it to a disposal point. The thermal shock to the hot ash as it enters the low-temperature water helps to break up the large pieces, while submerging the ash prevents sintering during the time that it may be stored (longer time with intermittent-removal systems, shorter time with an SSC).

Part of the heat released in the furnace is transmitted to the ash hopper by radiation from the burning fuel. However, most of the heat input is from the sensible heat given up to the water by the hot bottom ash falling from the furnace. The ash systems engineer must perform a heat-balance analysis to determine the flow of cooling water required to absorb the incoming heat and maintain the water temperature at a predetermined level.

Field experience indicates that the optimal temperature of the impounded water is about 140°F (60°C), and it should not be higher than 160°F (71°C). Temperatures at this level are effective in rapidly cooling and fracturing the falling ash. Lower temperatures require more cooling water. Higher temperature may prove uncomfortable or unsafe in the area around the bottom-ash receiver.

Bottom-Ash Cooling System Design

Heat is removed from bottom-ash hoppers or submerged scraper conveyors by:

- Evaporation of water from the surface of the water pool
- The heat removed in the water going out the overflow or leakage points

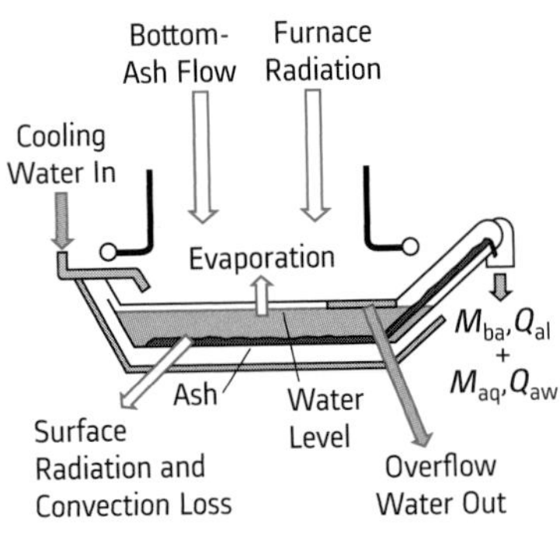

Figure 6-72 | Simplified heat-balance diagram for furnace bottom-ash receiver

- The heat removed with the accumulated bottom ash as it is discharged
- The heat loss by radiation and convection from the outside metal surfaces

The last loss is small and is usually neglected in view of the unknown accuracy of some of the other assumed factors. *Figure 6-72* is a simplified heat-balance diagram around a bottom-ash receiver, in this case, a submerged scraper conveyor with continuous ash removal.

The heat balance forms the basis for the calculation of the cooling-water flow needed to maintain a temperature of about 140°F (60°C):

$$Q_{in} = Q_{out}$$

Equation 6-2

where:

Q_{in} = Q ash entering + Q furnace radiation + Q inlet water = $Qae + Qfr + Qiw$

Q_{out} = Q overflow water + Q ash leaving + Q evaporation + Q external radiation loss + Q water in ash leaving = $Qow + Qal + Qe + Qer + Qaw$

MASS AND ENERGY TERMS. Before equating and simplifying the above inputs and outputs so that they can be mathematically manipulated, it is necessary to define and discuss them further.

HEAT IN THE BOTTOM ASH. The mass of bottom ash, M_{ba}, is the collection rate—lb/hr or kg/hr:

$$Qae = M_{ba} \times C_{ash_1} \times (T_{hot\ ash} - T_r)$$

Equation 6-3

where:

C_{ash_1} = specific heat of the ash at the mean temperature between $T_{hot\ ash}$ and T_r

$T_{hot\ ash}$ = the temperature of the falling ash or slag as it enters the water pool

T_r = reference temperature for defining heat contents

The temperature of ash leaving the bottom of a furnace depends on the thickness of the pieces dislodged from the walls, the face-metal temperature of the furnace walls, the temperature of the soot-blowing medium, the distance of fall, and the average gas temperature surrounding the material during its fall. For pulverized coal fired in suspension (without the use of furnace-bottom grates), the temperature is estimated to be between 1,200 (650°C) and 1,800°F (980°C), averaging 1,500°F (820°C). Obviously, the validity of the heat-balance calculation depends on this temperature to a great extent.

The heat of the cooled bottom ash exiting the collection device is:

$$Qal = M_{ba} \times C_{ash_2} \times (t_{out} - T_r)$$

Equation 6-4

where:

C_{ash_2} = specific heat of the ash at the mean temperature between t_{out} and T_r

t_{out} = the temperature of the water and ash leaving

FURNACE RADIATION TO THE IMPOUNDED WATER. Furnace radiation passing through an opening in the hopper bottom varies with firing rate, furnace and firing system configuration, and

the effective center of the fuel-admission nozzles or burners in operation (measured vertically above the furnace bottom opening). The heat transfer is

$$Q_{fr} = A_{fa} \times R_f \times F_{tr}$$

Equation 6-5

where:

A_{fa} = furnace hopper bottom aperture above the ash receiver
R_f = radiation rate through the furnace aperture, BTU/hr-sq ft
F_{tr} = fraction of the radiation transmitted to the water surface through the space between the furnace bottom and the water (*Fig.* 6-73).

A typical value for R_f, the heat radiated through the bottom aperture to the space above the impounded water, is 20,000 BTU/hr-sq ft (6,300 w/m^2). *Figure* 6-73 shows that the radiation reaching the water surface decreases as that surface is located farther away from the aperture, as would be expected.

HEAT IN COOLING WATER. The mass of incoming cooling water, from all sources (including any refractory cooling water or SSC bearing-flush water), is designated M_{iw}:

$$Q_{iw} = M_{iw} \times C_{iw} \times (t_{iw} - T_r)$$

Equation 6-6

where:

t_{iw} = incoming water temperature
C_{iw} = incoming water specific heat

The mass of cooling water leaving, M_{ow}, includes any outward leakage, but not the water entrained by the exiting bottom ash; the latter is shown as M_{aw}, the mass of heated water leaving with the ash.

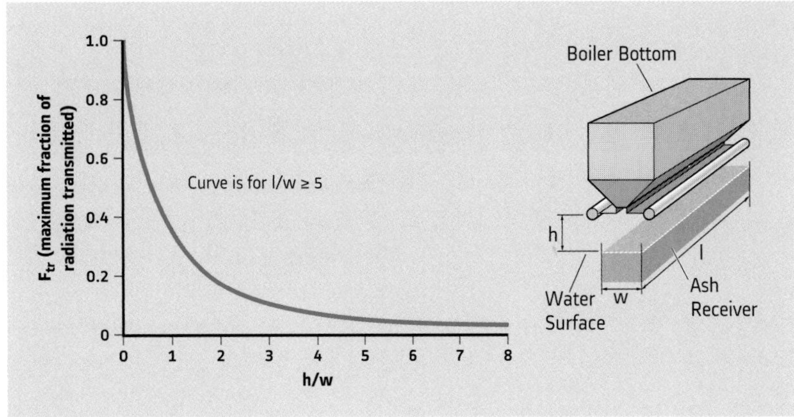

Figure 6-73 | Curve to determine fraction of radiation transmitted to ash-receiver water surface

$$Q_{ow} = M_{ow} \times C_{ow} \times (t_{ow} - T_r)$$
and
$$Q_{aw} = M_{aw} \times C_{ow} \times (t_{ow} - T_r)$$

Equation 6-7

where:

C_{ow} = specific heat of water leaving
t_{ow} = temperature of the impounded water

HEAT LEAVING IN EVAPORATED WATER. The rate of evaporation from a water pool below a large coal-fired furnace is a complex function of the water temperature, the temperature of the radiating gas, and the other factors involved in the determination of the radiation rate. In general, rates between 4 and 10 U.S. gallons/day sq ft (0.15 and 0.32 l^3/day-sq m) are to be expected. Large pieces of slag falling into the water can result in additional localized evaporation, which is neither calculable nor separable from the overall effect. It is calculated by:

$$Q_e = A_w \times R_e \times h_{fg}$$

Equation 6-8

where:

A_w = total area of ash-receiver water surface

R_e = evaporation rate per unit of surface area

h_{fg} = latent heat of vaporization of the water at T_{ow}

SIMPLIFICATION OF THE HEAT-BALANCE EQUATION. If T_r, the reference temperature, is equal to t_{ow}, the water temperature in the water pool, Q_{al}, Q_{ow}, and Q_{aw} go to zero, then:

$$Q_{ae} + Q_{fr} + Q_{iw} = Q_e$$

or

$$Q_{ae} + Q_{fr} = Q_e + [M_{iw} \times C_{iw} \times (t_{ow} - t_{iw})]$$

Equation 6-9

Note that the mass of the water leaving, M_{ow}, must not be less than zero; that is:

$$M_{ow} = (M_{iw} - M_{aw} - M_e) \geq 0$$

Equation 6-10

where:

M_e = mass rate of evaporated water

In a closed-loop cooling-water system, M_{ow} is the amount of water that must be cooled and recirculated. The extent of physical cleanup and chemical treatment applied to this recirculated water is principally a function of what the system heat-transfer and pumping equipment can tolerate. Generally, the cleanup required for the low-pressure cooling stream of an SSC is much less than that for an intermittent-removal hopper with slope jetting nozzles, which use water at high pressure.

Recirculation equipment size and cost are sensitive to the ash temperature and quantity, the furnace radiation absorbed, and the evaporation rate, as shown above. It is important that economic comparisons of such loops be based on equivalent boundary conditions, which include, in addition, the inlet water and impounded water temperatures. It is fairly accurate, for these heat-balance calculations, to use 0.25 BTU/lb°F (1.05 kJ/Kg°C) for the specific heat of ash, 1.0 BTU/lb°F (4.2 kJ/Kg°C) as the specific heat of water, and 1,014 BTU/lb (2.36 MJ/Kg) as h_{fg} at 140°F (60°C).

COOLING-WATER FLOW VARIATION. Two inputs to the equation can vary widely, greatly affecting the cooling water flow. First, the bottom ash collection is a function of:

- Quantity of fuel burned (boiler load and heating value of the coal)
- Percentage of ash in the fuel
- Percentage of the total ash that falls to the furnace bottom

Second, the cooling water temperature can vary substantially from summer to winter, and with geographical area.

The designer is faced with the problem of deciding what should be used for ash-collecting rates and the water temperature to the hopper. The common design approach requires excess water because the designer uses *maximum* values for all calculations. Systems so designed will pump and treat excessive quantities of water when the unit is burning a good fuel in winter when the cooling water is cold.

The potential difference in cooling-water usage is illustrated in *Table 6-14*. These data consider only the water necessary to cool the incoming ash (not taking into account the radiation and evaporation heat exchange), to point out how great is the difference between the two postulated conditions.

If the ash system were designed to provide the maximum cooling water at all times, the pumping power consumption would be considerably greater than needed. Because the purpose of the cooling water is to maintain the ash hopper water at a temperature such as 140°F (60°C), it is logical to regulate the flow on a demand basis. This is done by monitoring the overflow water temperature and using an automatically controlled cooling-water supply valve, which can also be opened when a low-level signal is received in the SSC. The system design has to provide for the worst case (maximum cooling water), but the actual water use will only be as required, thereby saving pumping power and the cost of cleanup of the ash-receiver overflow water under many load conditions.

TABLE 6-14 | COOLING WATER USAGE*

	High Use	Low Use
Coal burned (lb/hr)	750,000	200,000
Ash content (percent)	25	10
Cooling water temperature (°F)	90	50
Ash down (percent)	50	30
Bottom ash collection (lb/hr)	93,750	6,000
Cooling water flow (U.S. gpm)	1,275	45

* Approximate, based on absorbing heat from incoming ash at 1,500°F only; no radiation or evaporation considered. Ash receiver water temperature, 140°F.

PROPER INSTALLATION

It is important to state that any ash-removal system must be installed, set up, checked out, and deemed ready for use by a plant startup crew. There have been many reports of damage to boiler pressure parts and precipitator elements, with consequent unit shutdowns caused by well-designed, ash removal systems that were not ready for use.[52]

Also, ash, by nature, is a very abrasive material, and wear and replacement of worn components are inevitable. Plant personnel must perform regular inspections of these wear components and make replacements as necessary. The use of ceramics and tungsten carbide materials has extended the life of many replacement parts, which is very important to plants that are trying to extend the time between scheduled outages.[54] Increased use of rebuilding services (such as for grinders) has also provided cost-effective solutions for life extension practices.

AUXILIARY EQUIPMENT

PUMPS

Pumps are used to transfer fluid, generally water, from a low-pressure system or component to a higher-pressure system or component. Pumps are designed to provide optimal performance for their intended service. The varying requirements require different types of pumps. The pumps can be categorized in the following general categories: reciprocating, rotary, jet, and centrifugal. Key variables related to hydraulic design and pump selection are velocity head, static head, pressure head, total dynamic head, net-positive-suction head, developed head, and pump horsepower (both hydraulic and shaft).

Centrifugal Pumps

Centrifugal pumps have two categories, horizontal and vertical, with many variations within the categories to best address a specific application. They are the pumps most commonly used in power plants. Centrifugal pumps provide a large capacity, and with multistage pumps can provide a significantly high pressure for power-plant allocations. The centrifugal pump moves fluid by rotating an impeller. The power used to rotate the impeller imparts a velocity and pressure to the fluid. The design of the impeller results in certain flow and discharge-pressure characteristics of the individual pump. Generally, the design intent is to have a single value of discharge pressure for a specific flow and a relatively significant (approximately 25%

or more) increase in discharge pressure at the pump shutoff as compared with pump design flows.

HORIZONTAL CENTRIFUGAL PUMPS. The more commonly used centrifugal pump is the horizontal centrifugal pump. This style consists of a horizontal shaft generally driven by an electric motor. Other drivers, such as turbines, may be used in power-plant applications. Horizontal centrifugal pumps are driven by a shaft extending from the pump casing. The fluid inside the pump casing is contained by a stuffing box, which contains packing material held in place by the packing gland. The horizontal pumps are supported by bearings on both sides of the impeller casing. Thrust bearings are also used to compensate for the imbalances in pressures within the pump and the resulting reaction forces on the shaft. Some horizontal pumps use a double-suction design, which helps reduce the hydraulic imbalance on the pumps.

Figure 6-74 | Vertical single-stage centrifugal pump for boiler-water circulation

VERTICAL CENTRIFUGAL PUMPS. Vertical centrifugal pumps are used in applications for which the available pump suction pressure (net positive suction pressure available) is not sufficient to prevent cavitation at the pump impeller inlet. The pump impeller is supported by the shaft. The inlet to the impeller may be open, as is the case when water is drawn from a basin, pond, or large body of water; or the inlet to the impeller may be closed, as is the case when water is drawn from a source above or below atmospheric pressure. Examples of the latter design would include condenser hot-well pumps.

The most important vertical centrifugal pumps are those used for boiler-water circulation (*Fig.* 6-74).

Pumping water at or near saturated temperature and high pressure requires pumps of special design because of the possibility that shaft seal leakage water may flash rapidly into steam. For this type of service, three types of boiler circulating pumps have been used. The zero-leakage pump is driven by a wet motor. The motor is cooled and lubricated by recirculated water at system pressure. The stator windings are immersed in the high-pressure water. This unit is also known as a glandless submerged motor pump (*Fig.* 6-75).

The canned-motor boiler circulating pump is a zero-leakage pump designed to circulate boiler water at high temperature and high pressure. No shaft seals are required. The motor and pump components are designed as an integral pressurized unit, sealed by a gasket and studs. The impeller is rotated by an AC polyphase, squirrel cage, induction motor. The spaces between the stator and the rotor and around the bearings are filled with cooled system water. A heat barrier limits the conduction of heat from the high-pressure hot water being pumped to the high-pressure internal motor water. The dry stator winding is completely isolated from the high-pressure water by a corrosion-resistant can lining the stator bore.

The injection-seal pump is a controlled-leakage design that is mounted vertically with a rigid shaft designed to carry its own thrust. No thrust load is carried to the motor, which is entirely supported by the pump. The internal pump materials are selected to accommodate the expansion encountered at high temperatures and to provide corrosion resistance. The suction pressure and temperature at the pump are virtually the same as the boiler operating conditions. The injection seal reduces the pressure and temperature at the stuffing box packing by injecting high-pressure cool water into the annulus formed by the shaft running clearance. The injection water serves as a thermal barrier against conducted heat and as a means of keeping the boiler water from entering the close tolerances of the throttling sleeve and floating seals. The floating seals and the packing control the leakage at the stuffing box. The injection water, free and clear of foreign particles, can be supplied from the discharge of the boiler-feed pump or any other source that can supply a pressure differential of 50 to 100 psi (3.5 bar to 6.9 bar) over the discharge of the boiler circulating-water pump.

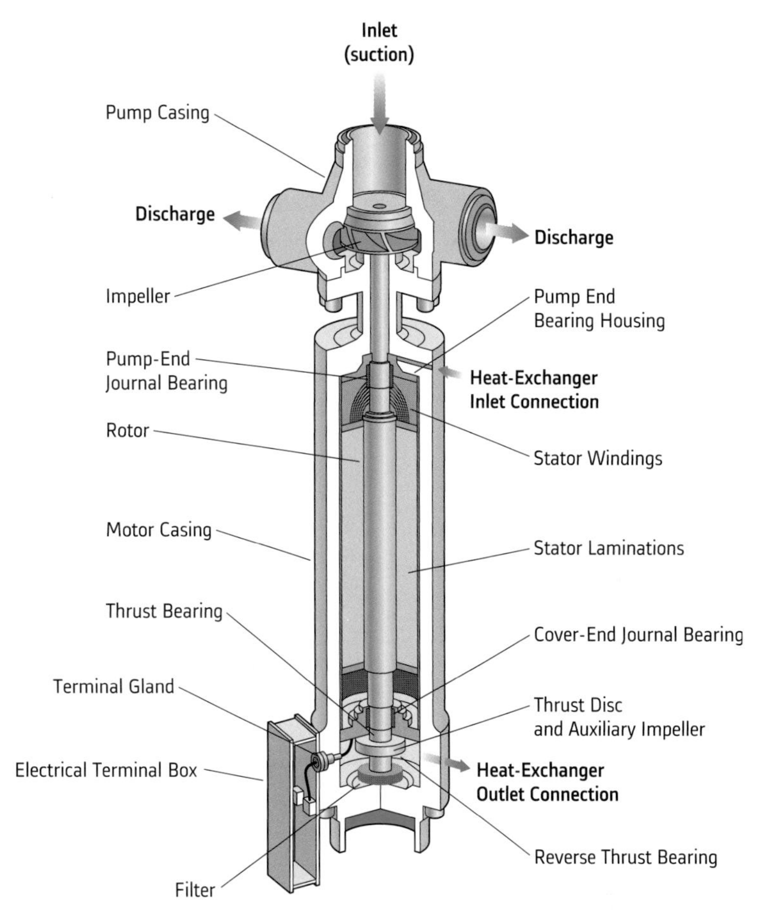

Figure 6-75 | Schematic of a typical glandless, wet-motor, boiler-water circulating pump

CIRCULATING-WATER PUMPS. In an open cooling system, the function of the circulating-water pump is to supply the main condenser with cooling water to remove waste heat from the closed steam system. The circulating-water pump is generally a single open-impeller, vertical, wet-pit pump. The pump is supported in the vertical position. The pump driver is mounted on the motor support head and is coupled to the upper shaft. The driver supports the weight of the pump motor plus any up or down thrust forces created within the pump. Expansion joints are provided on the pump discharge to allow for pump vibration and to minimize stresses on the discharge nozzle. The major components of the pump include suction casing, shroud, casing, impeller, bearings, and shaft.

The suction casing directs the flow of water from the suction-pit impeller. The suction casing may have features such as a cage or vanes to minimize the creation of vortices. The shroud encloses the impeller. Close running clearance between the ends of the impeller vanes and the interior surface of the shroud prevents the leakage of water past the impeller vanes from the higher-pressure section to the lower-pressure section, improving pumping efficiency. The casing contains bearings, which maintain the pump shaft in alignment. The casing directs the flow of water through the shaft column to the discharge head. The impeller is mounted on the pump shaft and is enclosed by the shroud and casing. The pump shaft and impeller are held in place by lower guide bearings near the pump impeller and upper guide bearings near the connection to the motor. These bearings are usually lubricated by a clean pressurized water source, which can also act to keep particles and silt away from the bearings. The shaft is connected to the impeller and extends the length of the casing, exiting at the top. The shaft packing prevents leakage of the pump discharge fluid through this casing penetration. The shaft is connected to the motor and is generally supported by the motor bearings. The motor is generally a large-horsepower, low-speed motor. Because the motor is usually heavier than the pump shaft, the motor is supported by the structure and the shaft is supported by the motor's thrust bearing.

Compressors

Compressors are used to provide compressed air at higher pressures than is commonly done with fans. Compressed air is used for plant or station air, instrument air, and soot blowers, if the soot blowers use compressed air rather than steam. Plant air is used for general services and is usually supplied throughout the plant at a pressure range of 80 to 110 psig (5.5 bar to 7.5 bar). The plant air is relatively free of oil. Instrument air is provided throughout the plant for specific services used by pneumatic instruments and valves or other specific uses requiring filtered, moisture-free, and oil-free air. The instrument air-supply pressure is similar to the plant air, and the pressure is reduced at the specific device to the pressure required by that device. Compressed air for soot blowers and other filter cleaning is provided at a higher pressure than plant or instrument air. Compressors are usually positive-displacement pumps. Multistage reciprocating compressors are commonly used. The newer technology with rotary screw compressors makes these types of compressors a useful alternative.

FANS

The most significant fans in a fossil-fueled power plant are those serving the boiler and the flue-gas treatment systems; they include forced draft fans, induced draft fans, and recirculation fans. Fans are used for applications throughout a power plant. Ventilation fans are necessary to maintain a particular temperature in many areas in the boiler and turbine areas of the plant. While insulation is used to minimize the loss of heat from the process, ventilation fans are needed to maintain temperature in an area below the maximum allowable operating temperature of the equipment. High temperatures will result in accelerated aging of the plant equipment and could result in equipment malfunctions. Rooms containing plant operations personnel and electronic equipment will be ventilated, and heated or cooled as necessary, to provide a comfortable operating environment for personnel and a controlled environment for equipment.

Forced Draft Fans

Forced draft (FD) fans supply the air that is necessary for fuel combustion. The fans must be sized to handle the

stoichiometric air and the excess air needed to properly burn the intended fuel for the unit. In addition, they provide air to make up for the leakage across the air preheater and for some sealing air requirements. Forced draft fans supply the total airflow except when an atmospheric suction, primary air fan is used. Most FD fan installations have inlet silencers for noise reduction and screens to protect the fans from any entrained particles in the incoming air (*Fig. 6-76*).

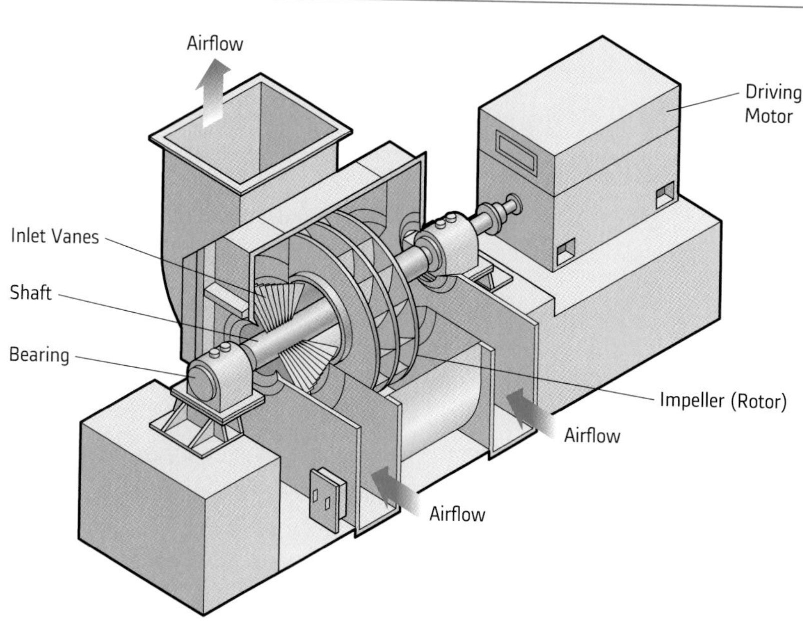

Figure 6-76 | Schematic of a centrifugal FD fan

Primary Air Fans

Large high-pressure fans supply the air needed to dry and transport coal either directly from the pulverizing equipment to the furnace or to an intermediate storage bunker. Primary air fans may be located before or after the milling equipment. The most common applications are either pulverizer exhauster fans or cold (ambient temperature) primary air fans. The mill exhauster fan draws hot air from the secondary air duct and through the pulverizer. The coal–air mixture from the pulverizer then passes through the fan and discharges into the fuel pipes, which carry the mixture to the furnace for ignition. One fan is usually supplied for each pulverizer. Cold primary air fans draw air from the atmosphere and supply the energy to force the air through the ducts, air heater, pulverizer, and fuel piping. Usually two fans are supplied for each steam generator.

Induced Draft Fans

Induced draft (ID) fans exhaust combustion products from a boiler. In doing so, they create a sufficient negative pressure to establish a slight suction with the furnace (usually from 0.2–0.5 inches WG [0.04–0.09 cm Hg gage]). This condition gives rise to the terms *suction firing* and *balanced draft* operation. These fans must have enough capacity to accommodate any infiltration caused by the negative pressure in the equipment downstream of the furnace and by any seal leakage in the air preheater.

Fans are used to control the pressure in various areas of the power plant to contain hazardous areas within the plant. Areas such as the tripper floor, where combustible dust may be present are maintained at a slightly negative pressure relative to adjacent rooms to minimize hazardous areas and improve plant safety. Other rooms requiring a clean environment, such as the control room, are maintained at a slightly positive pressure relative to the surrounding rooms. This positive pressure helps to minimize in-leakage of dust and gases to potentially sensitive equipment.

Mechanical draft cooling towers have large fans to assist in the cooling tower's performance. The cooling tower fans can be as large as 250 horsepower (186 kW). The fans sometimes have

Feedwater heaters recover energy from the steam before it goes to the condenser, improving cycle efficiency. Improved efficiency reduces air emissions. By routing heat around the condenser, less heat is rejected to the environment as well.

multiple speeds to adjust for changes in the ambient conditions. Generally, two-speed fans are installed in the larger mechanical draft cooling towers. Variable-speed fans are also used to optimize the performance of cooling towers. Smaller cooling towers may have multiple-speed fans or single-speed fans. The selection is established by the system needs and an economic evaluation of the operating needs of the cooling system.

HEAT EXCHANGERS

Most of the heat exchangers used in the balance of power-plant systems are contact heat exchangers used to improve the plant cycle efficiency, to remove heat from the steam cycle, or to provide a heat sink for equipment cooling.

Feedwater Heaters

Feedwater heaters preheat the water that is going from the condenser to the boiler. Preheating the feedwater reduces irreversibilities in the cycle, leading to improved efficiency. The preheating is normally accomplished by extracting some steam from the steam turbine and using it to heat the feedwater. The steam is condensed in the process. By routing the steam around the condenser, less energy is rejected to the surroundings, where it is essentially lost. This energy is recovered by the feedwater, raising its temperature prior to entering the boiler. This process reduces the amount of energy that must be supplied by the boiler.

There are generally two types of feedwater heaters: open and closed. An open feedwater heater is a direct contact heater, in which the steam is directly contacted and mixes with the water. This type of heater will need a pump at the inlet and one at the outlet, as the pressure inside the heater is between the boiler pressure and the condenser pressure. A de-aerator is a specially designed, open feedwater heater that removes non-condensable gases from the feedwater. This step is important because a buildup of non condensable gases in the steam cycle will lead to an increase in the backpressure on the steam turbine. Because the recoverable work from the steam turbine is proportional to the log of the pressure ratio, the amount of work is reduced when the backpressure is increased, thus degrading the efficiency of the plant.

Closed feedwater heaters are typically shell-and-tube heat exchangers. The water passes through the tubes and is heated by the extraction steam. The steam passes over the tubes and is condensed, giving up its latent heat to the feedwater. The condensed water from the steam is sent to the next lower pressure feedwater heater to be mixed with the feedwater going to the boiler. The advantage of this approach is that only one pump is needed between the condenser and the boiler.

CONDENSERS. The largest contact heat exchanger in the plant is the condenser. This is a cross-flow heat exchanger used to condense the turbine exhaust steam so it can be pumped back to the boiler. For the larger power plants, the condenser is located beneath the low-pressure turbine. The turbine exhaust flow enters the condenser and is condensed by removal of heat to the circulating water system. The condensed steam, or condensate, is collected at the bottom of the condenser in the hot well, routed by pipeline to the condensate pumps, and pumped through several condensate heaters to the deaerator. The condensate may also be pumped through other equipment for other services before it enters the deaerator. The condenser is generally of the shell-and-tube design. The exhaust steam enters the condenser shell at a sub-atmospheric pressure. The steam is condensed by the circulating water.

COOLING TOWERS. Cooling towers are frequently used to exhaust process heat into the atmosphere. Cooling towers are deployed where water usage is restricted. They are used to avoid using rivers, lakes, or other bodies of water for cooling. Cooling towers can also be installed as a supplemental heat sink to limit the release of process heat into rivers, lakes, or other bodies of water.

Cooling towers can be classified as wet or dry. Wet cooling towers are designed to have the cooling water in direct contact with the atmosphere. Dry cooling towers do not have the cooling water in contact with the atmosphere. Wet cooling towers lose some cooling water to evaporation as a normal part of the process. Dry cooling towers do not lose water to evaporation. Because dry cooling towers do not lose water to evaporation, they are sometimes used where water resources are restricted.

Cooling towers are also classified as either natural draft or mechanical draft. Natural draft cooling towers circulate air by the natural draft created from heating the air. The design of the natural draft cooling tower shape is intended to take advantage of this draft to improve the performance. Large hyperbolic cooling towers are examples of an efficient design to optimize the performance of a natural draft cooling tower. Mechanical draft cooling towers use circulating fans to move air through the tower to improve heat transfer to the air. While the mechanical draft cooling towers need energy to operate the fans, their design is smaller than natural draft cooling towers. Dry cooling towers are mechanical draft cooling towers, effectively being a steam-to-air or a water-to-air heat exchanger.

AIR-COOLED CONDENSERS. Air-cooled condensers condense exhaust steam from the steam turbine and return the condensate to the boiler. They are used in electrical power plants and waste-to-energy plants when cooling water is in short supply (i.e., dry regions) or when environmental concerns over water usage, visibility, etc., are paramount. An air-cooled condenser is made of modules arranged in parallel rows. Each module contains a number of fin-tube bundles. An axial flow, forced draft fan located in each module forces the cooling air across the heat exchange area of the fin tubes. Fin tubes are critical to the technology; they are necessary because of the low thermal conductivity, low density, and low heat capacity of air. This larger surface area required to obtain a given heat-removal rate, the area increasing with the design ambient air temperature. This fact also means that the footprint of air-cooled condensers is larger than that of their water-cooled equivalents. Noise created by the large number of fans may introduce its own environmental problem. Finally, an air-cooled condenser is more expensive than its water-cooled equivalent.

RORY EASTMAN
GUS SHEARER
GARY MOONEY
DENNIS PIONTEK
PHIL LAFAVE
DOUG MARTIN
ROGER MARTINSEN
PETER KELLY
CARL BOZZUTO

The cooling system provides the heat sink that is required by the second law of thermodynamics. The lower the cooling temperature, the higher the plant efficiency.

REFERENCES

1. H. Kreisinger, "Combustion of Pulverized Coal," *Transactions of the ASME*, 60 (Paper No. FSP-60-8): 289–296, 1938.

2. N. L. Sadi Carnot, E. Clayperon, and R. Clausius, *Reflections on the Motive Power of Fire; and other Papers on the Second Law of Thermodynamics*; edited with an introduction by E. Mendoza. New York: Dover, 1962.

3. R. Diesel, *Theory and Construction of a Rational Heat Motor*, trans. by Bryan Donkin. London: Spon, 1894.

4. F. Klemm, *A History of Western Technology*. Cambridge, MA: MIT Press, 1964, pp. 342–347.

5. C. F. Herington, Powdered Coal as a Fuel. New York: Van Nostrand, 1918, pp. 68–72.

6. F. L. Dyer and T. C. Martin, *Edison—His Life and Inventions*, with collaboration of W. H. Meadowcraft. Vol. II. New York: Harper and Bros., 1929.

7. "Symposium on Powdered Fuel," Spring Meeting, American Society of Mechanical Engineers, St. Paul-Minneapolis. *Transactions of the ASME*, 36: 85–169, 1914.

8. R. C. Carpenter, "Pulverized Coal Burning in the Cement Industry," *Transactions of the ASME*, 36: 85–107, 1914.

9. W. Dalton and W. S. Quigley, "An Installation for Powdered Coal Fuel in Industrial Furnaces," *Transactions of the ASME*, 36: 109–121, 1914.

10. F. R. Low, "Pulverized Coal for Steam Making," *Transactions of the ASME*, 36: 123–136, 1914.

11. "Topical Discussion on Powdered Fuel," *Transactions of the ASME*, 36: 137–169, 1914.

12. J. Anderson, "Pulverized Coal Under Central-Station Boilers," *Power*, 51(9): 336–339, 1920.

13. P. W. Thompson, "Pulverized Fuel at Oneida Street Plant," *Power*, 51(9): 339–340, 1920.

14. "Four-Day Test on Five Oneida Street Boilers Burning Pulverized Coal," *Power*, 51(9): 354–357, 1920.

15. "Pulverized Coal at Milwaukee," Power, 51(9): 341–342, 1920.

16. "The New Lakeside Pulverized-Coal Plant, Milwaukee," *Power*, 52(10): 358–360, 1920.

17. "Largest Station Using Pulverized Coal," *Power*, 55(16): 604–610, 1922.

18. H. Kreisinger and J. Blizard, "Milwaukee's Contribution to Pulverized Coal Development," *Mechanical Engineering*, 61: 723–726, 737.

19. F. L. Dornbrook, "Developments in Burning Pulverized Coal–Thirty Year Review of Experience in Milwaukee Plants," *Mechanical Engineering*, 70: 967–974, 1948.

20. H. Kreisinger, F. K. Ovitz, and C. E. Augustine, "Combustion in the Fuel Bed of Hand-Fired Furnaces," U.S. Bureau of Mines Technical Paper 137. Washington: U.S. Bureau of Mines, 1916.

21. W. T. Ray and H. Kreisinger, "The Flow of Heat Through Furnace Walls," U.S. Bureau of Mines Bulletin 8. Washington: U.S. Bureau of Mines, 1911.

22. H. Kreisinger and W. T. Ray, "The Transmission of Heat into Steam Boilers," U.S. Bureau of Mines Bulletin 18. Washington: U.S. Bureau of Mines, 1912.

23. H. Kreisinger and J. F. Borkley, "Heat Transmission Through Boiler Tubes," U.S. Bureau of Mines Technical Paper 114. Washington: U.S. Bureau of Mines, 1915.

24. H. Kreisinger, J. Blizard, C. E. Augustine, and B. J. Cross, "An Investigation of Powdered Coal as Fuel for Power-Plant Boilers-Tests at Oneida Street Power Station, Milwaukee, Wisconsin," U.S. Bureau of Mines Bulletin 223. Washington: U.S. Bureau of Mines, 1923.

25. H. Kreisinger, J. Blizard, C. E. Augustine, and B. J. Cross, "Tests of a Large Boiler Fired with Powdered Coal at the Lakeside Station, Milwaukee," U.S. Bureau of Mines Bulletin 237. Washington: U.S. Bureau of Mines, 1925.

26. E. Audibert, "Etude de l'Entrainement du Poussier de Houille par I'Air," *Annales de Mines*, 1(3): 153–191, 1922.

27. J. Blizard, "The Terminal Velocity of Particles of Powdered Coal Falling in Air or Other Viscous Fluid," *Journal of the Franklin Institute*, 197(2): 199–208, 1924.

28. J. Blizard, "Transportation and Combustion of Powdered Coal," U.S. Bureau of Mines Bulletin 217. Washington: Government Printing Office, 1923.

29. H. Verdinne, "The Technique of Powdered Fuel Firing," *Fuel in Science and Practice*, 2: 146–151, 1923.

30. W. Nusselt, "Der Verbrennungsvorgang in der Kohlenstaubfeuerung (The Combustion Process in Pulverized Coal Furnaces)," *VDI Zeitschrift*, 68(6): 124–128, 1924.

31. P. Rosin, "Die Thermodynamischen und Wirtschafthichen Grundlagen der Kohlenstaubfeuerung (Thermodynamic and Economic Bases of Pulverized Coal Firing)," Braunkohle, 24(11): 241–259, 1925.

32. W. J. Wohlenberg and D. G. Morrow, "Radiation in the Pulverized-Fuel Furnace," *Transactions of the ASME*, 47: 127–176, 1925.

33. R. P. Hensel, "Coal Combustion," presented at the Engineering Foundation Conference on Coal Preparation for Coal conversion, 1st, Franklin Pierce College, Rindge, N.H., 1975. Paper updated in 1978. Combustion Engineering publication TIS-4599.

34. R. P. Hensel, "The Effects of Agglomerating Characteristics of Coals on Combustion in Pulverized Fuel Boilers," Symposium on Coal Agglomeration and Conversion, Morgantown, W.V., 1975. Sponsored by the West Virginia Geological and Economic Survey in Cooperation With the Coal Research Bureau. Combustion Engineering publication TIS-4353.

35. V. F. Parry, "Production, Classification and Utilization of Western United States Coals," Economic Geology, 45(6): 515–532, September-October, 1950.

36. D. Magnum and P. L. Stanwicks, "HP Series Pulverizer Design, Testing, Maintenance Cost," Proceedings of POWERGEN '89 Conference, Book 2, POWER-GEN '89, New Orleans, LA, December 5–7, 1989.

37. E. H. Tenney, "Pulverization and Boiler Performance," FSP-54-7, Proceedings of the Fourth National Fuels Meeting, Feb 11 to 13, 1931, pp. 55–65. Chicago: The American Society of Mechanical Engineers. 1931.

38. E.G. Bailey, "Present Status of Furnace and Burner Design for Pulverized Fuel," *Transactions of the American Society of Mechanical Engineers, September to December 1928*, p. 177. New York: The American Society of Mechanical Engineers.

39. W. E. Loftus, "Ash Handling, Storage and Utilization." *Proceedings of the American Power Conference*, 38: 707–717. Chicago: Illinois Institute of Technology, 1976.

40. J. C. Singer and A. J. Cozza, "Material and Energy Balances of Ash-Handling Systems," Presented at the Joint Power Generation Conference. Dallas, Sept. 10–13, 1978.ASME, N.Y., N.Y.; also. Alstom Power publication TIS-5822, Windsor, CT.

41. J. C. Singer and A. J. Cozza, "Design for Continuous Ash Removal: Alternative Concepts in Ash Handling," *Proceedings of the American Power Conference*, 41: 544–553, 1979. Chicago: Illinois Institute of Technology. 1979; also, Alstom publication TIS-6211.5.

42. J. E. Horne and A. Bosso, "Southwestern Public Service Company Pioneering in Continuous Bottom Ash Removal," Presented at Frontiers of Power Conference, October 11 and 12, 1982, Stillwater, OK; also, Alstom publication TIS-7261.

43. C. R. Gretz and G. D. Mooney, "Bottom Ash Methods: A Look at Drag Conveyors for U.S. Applications," Presented at Coal Technology Conference , Houston, Tx, Nov 13-15, 1979. PenWell Corporation, Tulsa, OK 1979.

44. J. M. Chapman and D. S. Piontek, "A Modern Ash Handling System for a Large Multi-fuel Boiler Installation," Presented at TAPPI Conference, 1985. TAPPI Jour., Vol 69, No. 7, pp55-60, 1979.

45. J. F. Bender, D. S. Piontek, and R. G. Walsh, "Case Study—Retrofit Submerged Scraper Conveyor for Bottom Ash—5 Years Later-Ray Nixon Unit 1," Presented at Power-Gen International Conference, Orlando, FL, Nov 30- Dec 2, 2004. PennWell Corporation, Tulsa, OK, 2004.

46. R. G. Walsh and D. S. Piontek, "Financial/Cost Benefit Considerations and Analysis for Replacement of Conventional Bottom Ash Systems with a Submerged Scraper Conveyor," Presented at Power-Gen International Conference, Orlando, FL, Nov 28 – 30, 2006. PennWell Corporation, Tulsa, OK, 1979; also, Alstom Power publication TIS-8708.

47. G. D. Mooney and J. J. Murphy, "Ash Handling Systems for Coal Fired Boilers," *Coal Technology*, volume 2: *Storage and Handling*. Houston, TX. Dec., 1982.

48. Joint Technical Committee of the American Boiler Manufacturers Association and Industrial Gas Cleaning Institute, Inc., "Design and Operation of Reliable Central Station Fly Ash Hopper Evacuation Systems." *Proceedings of the American Power Conference*, 42:74–85. Chicago: Illinois Institute of Technology, 1980.

49. J. C. Singer, "Design for Better ESP/Fabric Filter Hopper Operation and Maintenance," Presented at Air Pollution Control Association 76th Annual Meeting and Exhibition, Atlanta, June 19–24, 1983. AWMA, Pittsburgh, PA.; also, Alstom Power publication TIS-7402, Windsor, CT.

50. J. C. Singer and A. J. Cozza, "Ash-Handling Options on Retrofitted and Converted Steam Generators," Presented at ASMEIEEE-ASCE Joint Power Generation Conference, St. Louis, October 4–8, 1981. ASME, New York, NY; also, Alstom Power publication TIS-6869.Windsor CT.

51. J. C. Fleming and D. M. Rode, "Ash Removal from Industrial Boilers—The Changing Scene," *Power*, 126(9), 1982.

52. M. B. Caron, A. J. Cozza, J. C. Singer, and J. R. Young Jr., "Steam-Generator Availability as Affected by Ash-Handling Equipment," *Proceedings of the American Power Conference*, 44:214–225. Chicago: Illinois Institute of Technology, 1982; also, Alstom Power publication TIS-7118, Windsor, CT.

53. G. D. Mooney, R. J. Kowalik, and C. D. Hicks, "Dry Fly Ash System Conversion for an Existing 480 MW Power Plant—Justification, Design and Construction." Power-Gen International Conference, Dallas, TX, Dec 9-11, 1997. PennWell Corporation, Tulsa, OK.

54. G. D. Mooney and R. G. Walsh, "Upgrades and Rebuilds in the Aftermarket for Ash Handling," Presented at Coal-Gen Conference, Las Vegas, NV, Dec. 6-8, 2005,PennWell Corporation, Tulsa, OK.; also Alstom Power publication TIS-8703, Windsor, CT.

55. G. D. Mooney and R. G. Walsh, "Matching Ash Systems to Fluidized Bed Boilers and Fuels," Presented at Council of Industrial Boiler Owners (CIBO) Conference, Lexington, KY, May 8-10, , 2007.CIBO, Burke, VA.; also Alstom Power publication TIS-8710, Windsor, CT.

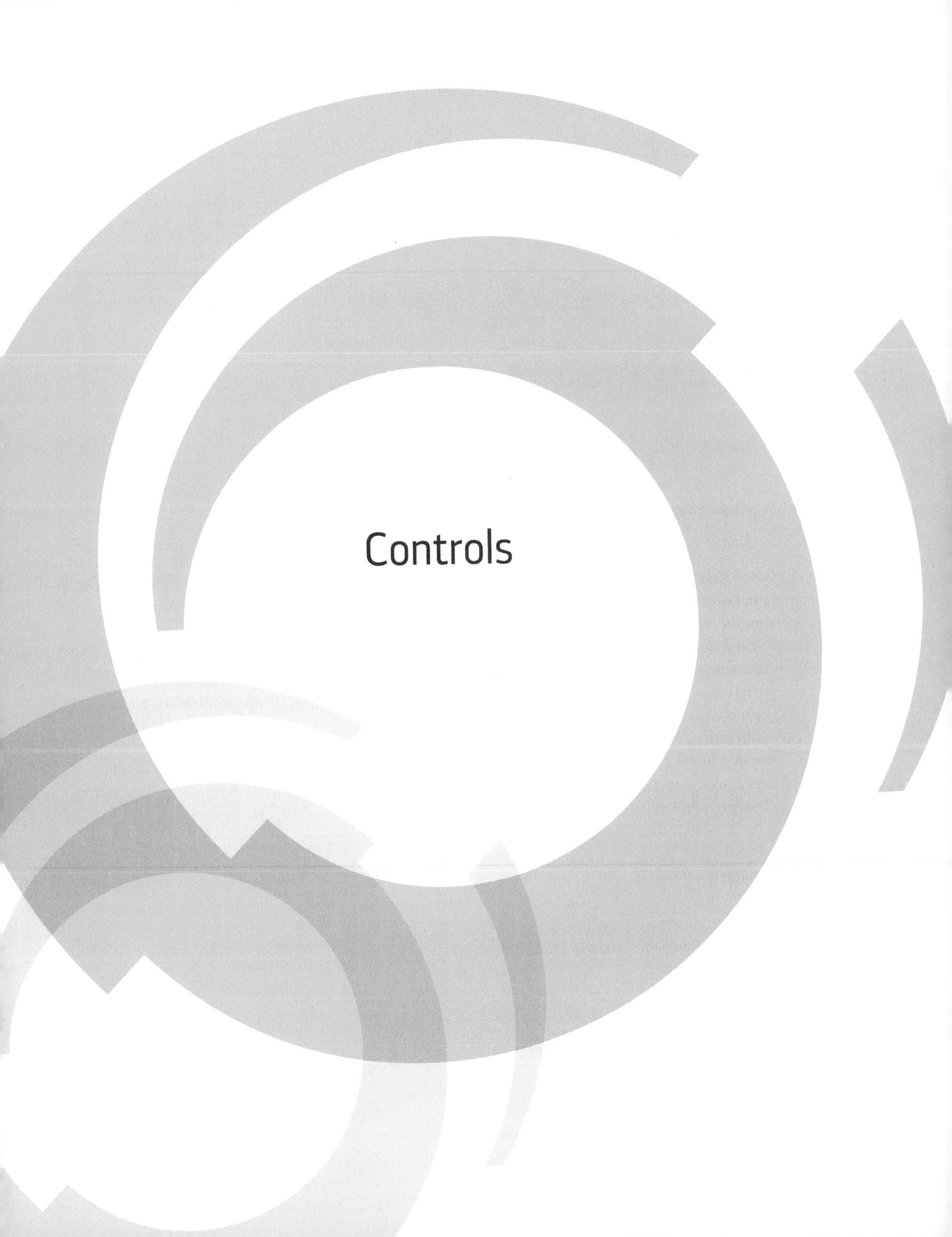

Controls

Chapter **Seven**

In today's markets, customers are moving from the business of simply operating the plant to the business of selling electricity. Their primary aim is to achieve faster payback and higher returns on investment. Control systems are expected to meet the need for different solutions and capabilities. In addition to state-of-the-art equipment and systems, the control system technology is a key feature of any clean and efficient power plant. Historically, meters, gages, and lights displayed equipment status to the operator, while recorders made a permanent record of plant performance. Remotely operated air cylinders and electric motors gave plant operators the capability of responding quickly and efficiently to changing plant requirements. More recently, liquid crystal displays (LCDs) have replaced the panel board instrumentation, to link the operator with past and present process information through sophisticated microprocessor-based distributed control hardware.

A TOTAL CONTROL SOLUTION

The plant automation system in a flexible market covers both the traditional distributed control system (DCS) functions and advanced plant management functions. This contributes to reduce operation and maintenance (O&M) costs. Installation costs can be optimized by close integration within the overall electrical engineering. A fieldbus-based distributed architecture, integrating widely available hardware elements keeps the architecture open and flexible. This feature means that the system can be optimized for all types of projects: new plants or retrofits, overall plant automation, all power plants (thermal, hydro, nuclear, diesel, and associated substations), and machine control (turbine governing and generator control).

The range of control stations and controllers provided allows for the choice of the best technical and economical solution. Three major parts constitute the system:

- The operator control interface and control room environment with high availability and high performance
- The automation cells that execute the control and protection functions of the machines and connect to the process (the use of fieldbuses allows geographical distribution of the equipment)
- The engineering station that provides a set of advanced engineering tools both for the design office and the on-site high quality documentation.

The advanced control system provides many features and benefits for the plant owner and operator including

- Advanced technologies (object-oriented engineering, Internet, fieldbus)
- Intuitive, user friendly operator interface (based on modular design concept, adaptable multifunction controllers, distributed control architecture, and open system architecture based on international standards)
- Deterministic/high-performance communication networks
- High reliability and availability, with tolerance to data spikes during transient operations
- Galvanic isolation on input/output (I/O) and communication networks
- Integrated comprehensive plant management system (*Fig. 7-1*).

RELIABLE AND VERSATILE OPEN COMMUNICATION NETWORKS

Open, flexible, and reliable communications are a fundamental requirement for the efficient operation of any plant automation system. The distributed elements of the ALSPA™ Digital Control System are linked together by standardized networks. Deterministic protocols ensure predictable and repeatable performance of the networks even during heavy loading and data flood situations. Redundancy implemented at all levels in the communications systems, together with automatic fault diagnosis, provides for high levels of system reliability. The digital control system uses three networks, each of which is designed to ensure optimum performance at its own level and of the complete DCS.

The plant network passes data and commands between the operator workstations and the data servers. It is based on standard Ethernet IEEE 802.3, arranged on a dual redundant architecture and operates on Transmission

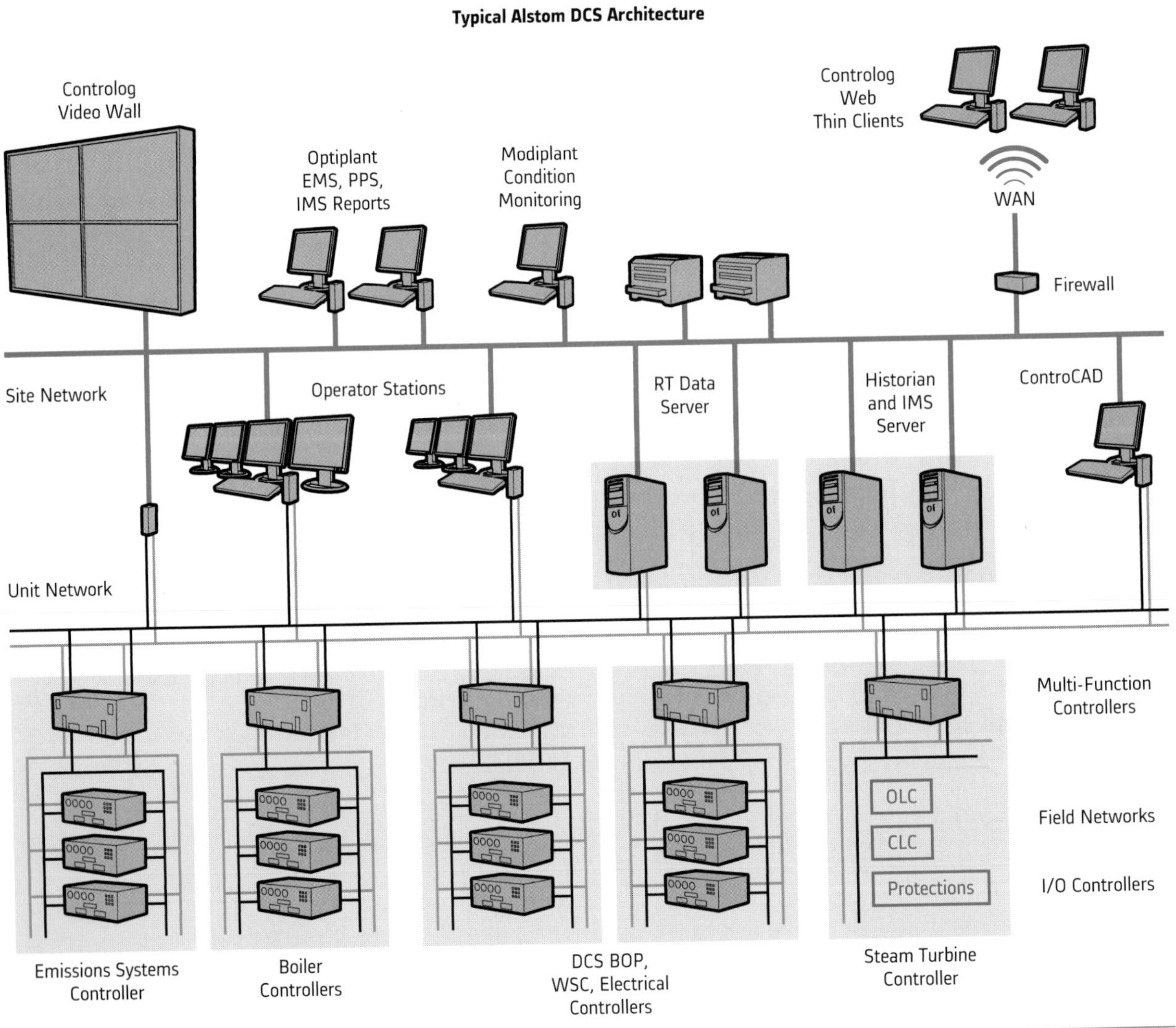

Figure 7-1 | Typical Alstom DCS architecture

Control Protocol/Internet Protocol (TCP/IP). It is an open system with communications to integrate the plant management system and asset management.

The unit network passes data and operator commands between the automation cells and to/from the control room stations. It is a fast deterministic network or fast Ethernet arranged on a dual redundant architecture, with copper and fiber optics with optimized distance.

The fieldbus network links the automation cell controllers to their associated smart I/O or instrument resources. Based on WorldFIP standard to EN50170, it is a fast deterministic network, arranged on a dual redundant architecture, with copper or fiber optics implementation (*Fig. 7-2*).

A RANGE OF CONTROLLERS

The distribution of the multifunction controllers and the field controllers gives the digital control system some advantages over a non-fieldbus-based DCS. These include reduced field cabling, tolerance to failures of part of the system, and a unified approach to plant interfacing (a single control system for the whole plant). Thanks to its scalable and modular design concept, the digital control system can easily be integrated into various applications from stand-alone turbine and excitation controllers to global power plant automation systems for both new and retrofit projects. An automation cell is a cell comprising one multifunction controller (MFC), field controllers, and distributed I/Os dedicated to a functional area interconnected by field

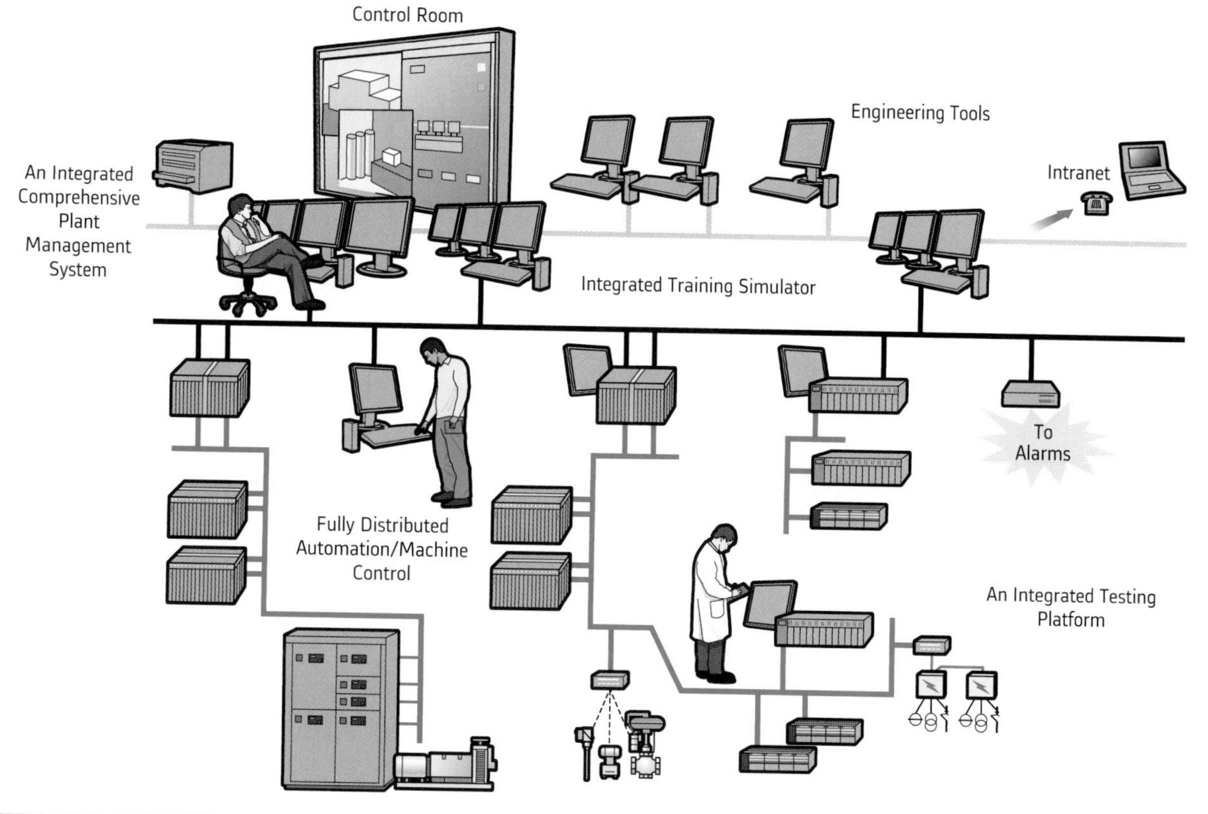

Figure 7-2 | Typical network architecture

networks. The field networks enable the controllers and the distributed I/Os to be installed in one or more physical enclosures (*Fig.* 7-3).

The MFC provides the computational power within the automation cells. Any controller is capable of executing any of the possible control functions, i.e., digital control, sequencing, and analog control. The MFC is connected to a number of field controllers; these controllers hold the I/O cards that interface to the process and manage local processing. I/O cards are available for all standard interfaces. The MFC executes the process control functions of the automation cell I/O controllers within deterministic and multiple cycles and communicates with the automation cell I/O devices via the field networks. It manages open communications with smart devices and systems and synchronizes the field devices so as to enable time-stamping of events at the source. It also communicates with the other automation cells and with the operator interface through the unit network.

The MFC allows a high availability based on full hot standby redundancy structure (central processing unit [CPU], communication networks, and power supply) (*Fig.* 7-4).

Figure 7-5 illustrates redundancy features in a single rack.

OPERATOR CONTROL FACILITIES

The DCS control room architecture provides the control, supervision, communication, and expertise for the plant. It allows wide flexibility to control single or multiple distributed

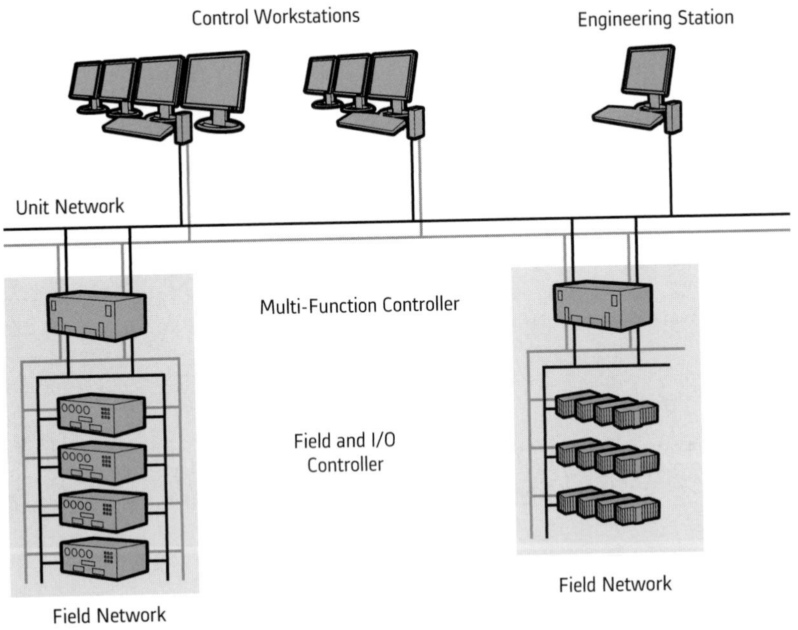

Figure 7-3 | Typical controller arrangement

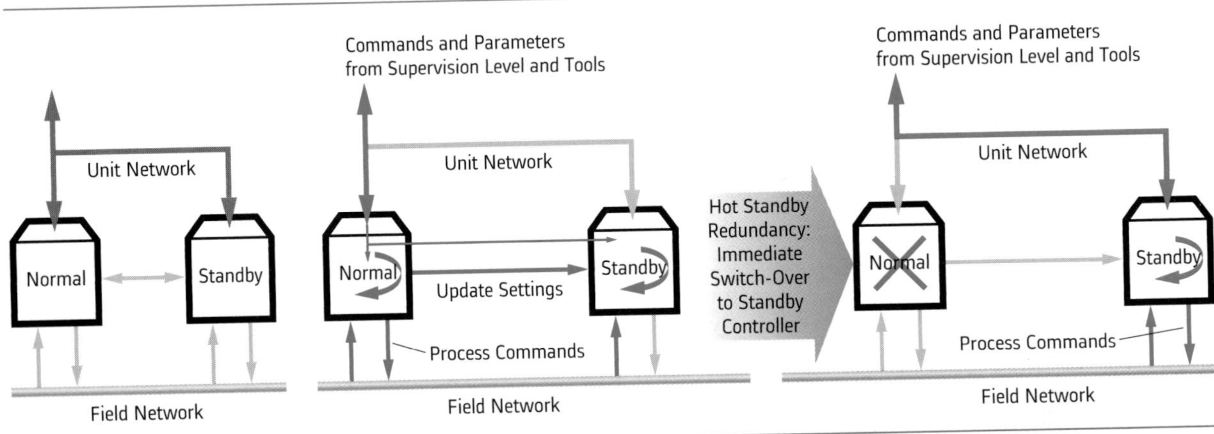

Figure 7-4 | Hot standby redundancy structure

units, elementary systems, and human interfaces with the equipment. The centralized station includes advanced functions, Web thin clients, local interfaces, and a multiscreen station that is managed like one screen with continuous mouse access. It includes all necessary features to access the plant through the Internet technology for maintenance and operation needs.

From the proper interface, the operator can operate the plant through a large range of functions. The hierarchical objects organization enables the operator to understand and analyze the situation as quickly as possible, particularly during an operational incident. Workspace, explorer, and viewers are the main dynamic graphical objects associated with the latest tools including groups, zoom, panning, drag and drop, drawing, analysis rulers on curves, tool tips, flashing, and hide/show. These allow intuitive and direct access to complex objects from real-time, historical, engineering, and diagnostic data servers. Advanced operations are managed from *specialized viewers* such as alarms, sequence monitoring, operating schedule, animated mimics, and diagrams. The explorer function provides a direct access to the functional diagrams of the engineering tools to analyze and tune the process objects inside the controllers (*Fig. 7-6*).

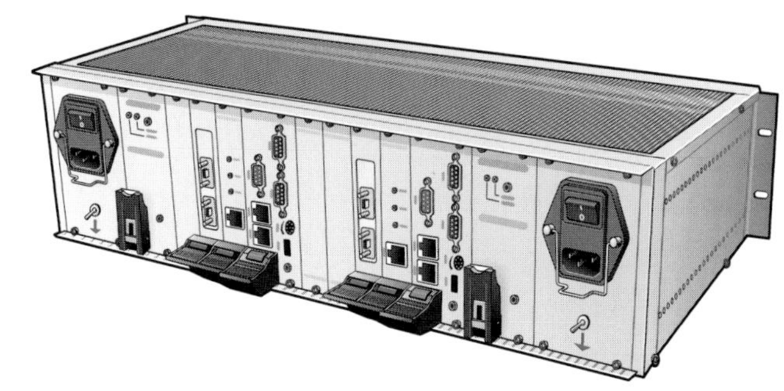

Figure 7-5 | Redundancy in a single rack

Figure 7-6 | Advanced control room with master screen

OPERATOR MIMIC VIEWER

The mimic viewer displays dynamic animated pictures to monitor and control the values and states of various process objects. The different mimic views are organized in groups. The groups can be customized in order to navigate in functional hierarchy. Associated symbols and animations are available as a library. The device states may be represented using different colors and shapes (outline color, frame etc.). Extended mimics may represent a fraction of the full mimic. With panning/zooming layers, the decluttering function enables the display of graphic objects with several degrees of zoom. The mimics pop-up may represent a detail of a full mimic opened on the parent mimics in a floating window.

By pinpointing on mimic, different faceplates can be opened. They contain dynamic data associated with different command modes, allowing commands and instructions intended for the process. Depending on the

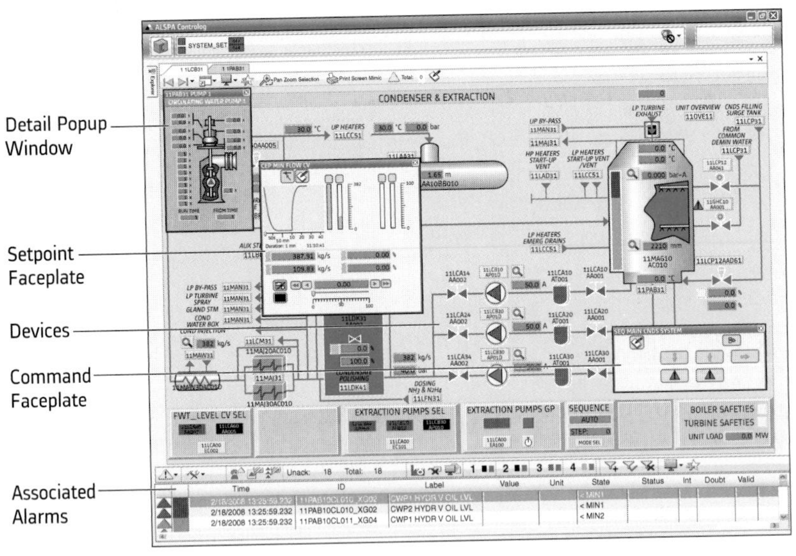

Figure 7-7 | Control mimic and faceplates (The "screen data" in *Figures 7-7* to *7-14* are for illustrative purposes only.)

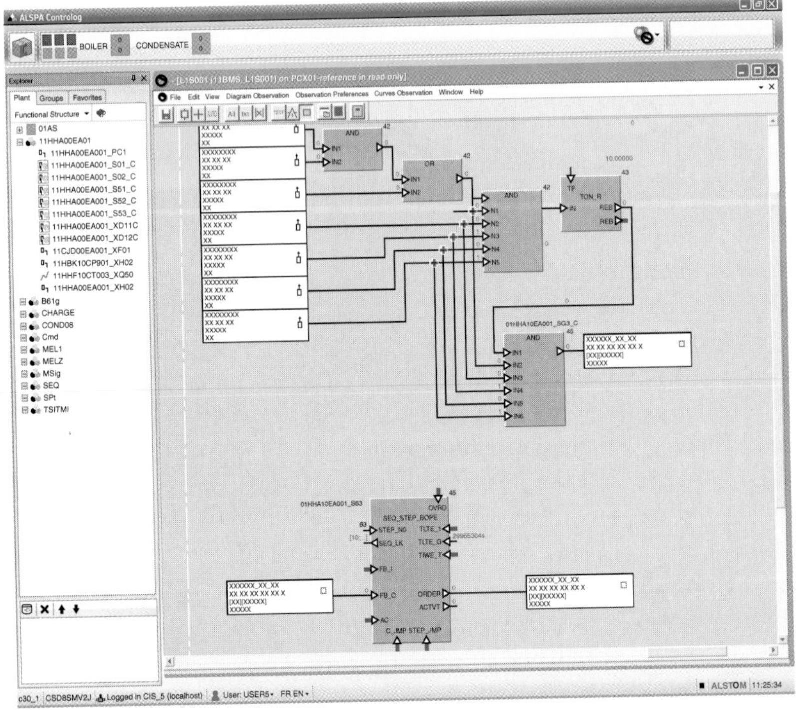

Figure 7-8 | Functional diagram viewer

authorization rights, the command is accepted or refused. In addition, a variable known as an execution check variable can be associated with the command. The operator can also lock, test, or unlock faceplates. A locked block cannot be controlled (*Fig. 7-7*).

FUNCTIONAL DIAGRAM VIEWER

The functional diagram viewer allows the display of the dynamic animated applications diagrams generated for every controller from the control log. These views are displayed from the explorer. The functional structure of the plant application studies is accessible directly by the operator in the control room. The operator can follow and check the status of the open and closed loops. Depending on the operator rights, the application parameters and the forced variables can be tuned and modified (*Fig. 7-8*).

$y = f(t)$ CURVES AND $y = f(x)$ CURVES VIEWER

The $y = f(t)$ curves function enables the operator to quickly analyze a group of process variables by providing their graphical trend as a function of time. The curves viewer displays the curves from a single variable or from a public or a private group. The curves viewer plots the curves with the real-time or the historian mode. The curves are displayed in different customizable colors (*Fig. 7-9*).

The $y = f(x)$ curves function provides a graphic display of plotted points of changes occurring over time in an analog process variable relative to another analog variable. The $y = f(x)$ curves viewer displays pairs of variables grouped in public or private $y = f(x)$ groups. The

curves viewer plots the curves with the real-time or the historian mode. For $y = f(t)$ curves and $y = f(x)$ curves, the group management provides tools like «Add», «Delete» (a variable of a viewer), and «Save» the viewer configuration into a group (*Fig. 7-10*).

ALARMS AND EVENTS MANAGEMENT

An alarm is an event representing an operational anomaly in the process or in the system. It is triggered by a state change in a logical variable that is acquired, calculated, or produced by the system or by the violation of thresholds or limits of analog variables.

Alarms generated by acquired logic states are time-tagged at the source. Alarms generated by analog variables are time-tagged with a one-second resolution. The time tagging is managed in universal time coordinates (UTC) and can be presented to the operator in local time. A degree of urgency is associated with each alarm. Sixteen degrees of urgency are available and each degree of urgency is allocated to a different alarm color code. The system can be configured to include an audible warning signal activated on the appearance and/or disappearance of an alarm.

An alarms and events viewer enables the operator to get information about operational malfunctions immediately and monitor whether corrective actions are being taken automatically by the system. The multiple possible presentations of the alarms (full screen, last alarms, etc.) and the navigation in the alarms' views allow the operator to identify malfunctions easily. Events and alarms can be sorted and filtered. Pre-filtered alarm pages can be displayed directly from the explorer.

When a process alarm appears, the operator is guided through a set of

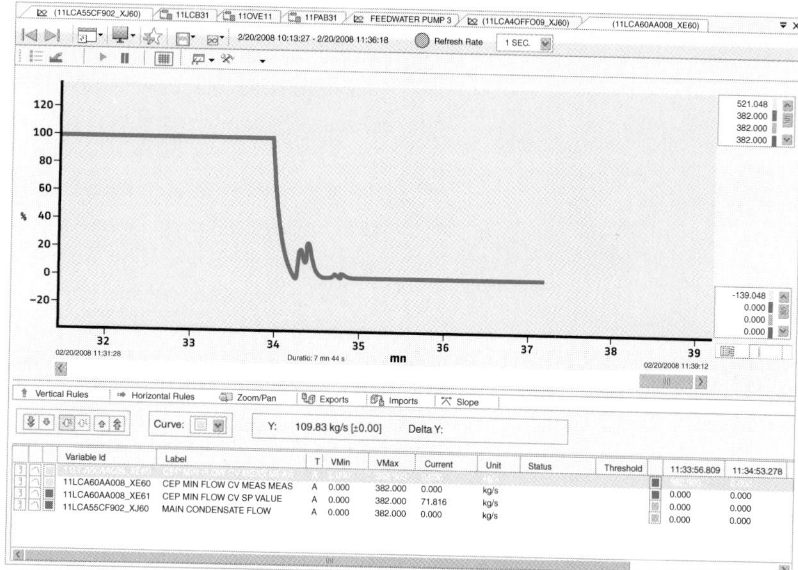

Figure 7-9 | $Y = f(t)$ curves viewer

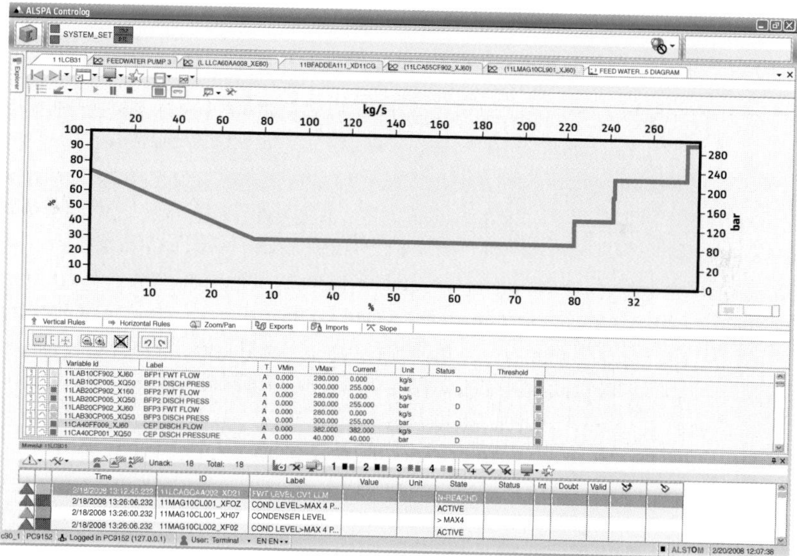

Figure 7-10 | $y = f(x)$ curves viewer

views accessed hierarchically according to the situation while analyzing the malfunction. Mimic views display the state of the different functional subsets. The process alarm analysis views include overall alarm view, alarm by degree of urgency views, mimic alarm views, alarm by functional subset views. The views associated with alarms are associated mimics, alarm sheets, synthesized alarm views, and variable property views (settings, etc.) (*Fig. 7-11*).

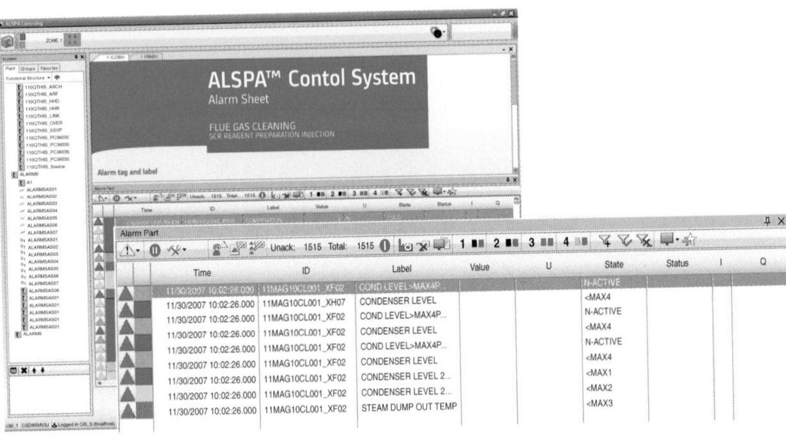

Figure 7-11 | Alarms and events viewer

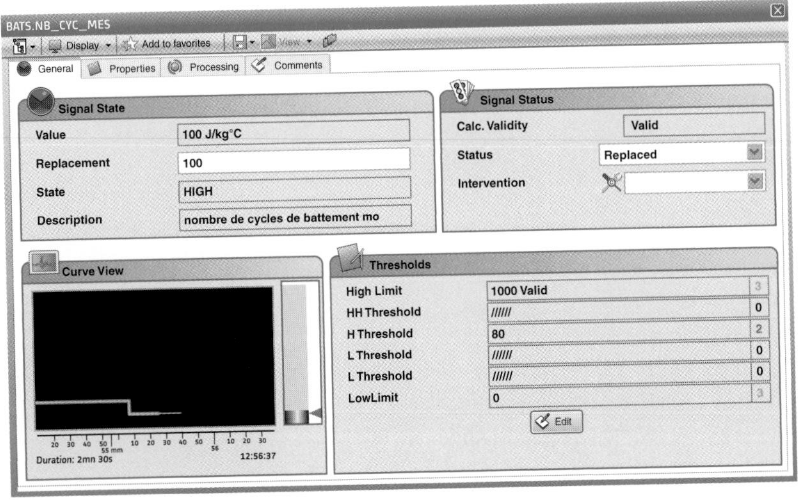

Figure 7-12 | Data properties display

DATA PROPERTIES DISPLAY

Data properties displays the static and dynamic attributes of the variables used in the application or system software. The operator can use the data properties display to modify the status of variables and faceplates, to inhibit or replace a variable, to set a variable "on" or "off monitoring," to modify an analog variable threshold, to assign a value to an analysis variable, or to lock or test a variable (*Fig. 7-12*).

BAR-GRAPH VIEWER

The bar-graph viewer displays the changes in the values of process analog/logic/multistate variables in the form of dynamic vertical/horizontal bars. The bar-graph viewer displays bar graphs for a single variable or a group of variables belonging to public or private groups. The view contains bar graphs in the top part and the data grid in the bottom part. Bar graphs and data grids are animated in real time (*Fig. 7-13*).

VARIABLES TREND VIEWER

The variables trend viewer shows the changes in the values at any time for a set of variables in the form of a table. This table gets updated according to the sampling period associated with the view. The sampling period can be modified by the operator. The permissible sampling periods are 1 sec, 5 sec, 10 sec, 15 sec, 20 sec, 30 sec, 1 min, 5 min. The operator can add or delete variables from the table.

Trend view also incorporates $y = f(t)$ curve for the selected variables. The upper half of the viewer shows the curves and the lower half of the viewer shows the variables table (*Fig. 7-14*).

STEAM GENERATOR OPERATIONAL CONTROL SYSTEMS

The concept of a centralized control room was a big step forward in power plant control. Nevertheless, as first conceived and executed, remote-manual systems relied entirely on operator judgment and response. The number of operating steps required for safely and properly admitting fuel to a furnace (or removing incompletely burned fuel from a furnace) leaves considerable latitude for operator error, if left solely to her or his judgment. Determining the adequacy of ignition energy levels is another area that should not be left to operator discretion. A major furnace explosion can result from the ignition of unburned fuel accumulated in only one to two seconds. It is apparent that human reaction time is inadequate, to say nothing of the need for an instantaneous decision making capability. The recognition of these limitations to a completely operator-dependent operating mode led to the development of automatic protection systems designed to minimize the risk of furnace explosions.

Instrumentation and controls permit the operation of major power plant systems from a central location. Control room screens, meters, gages, and lights display equipment status. DCS permanently chronicle plant performance and diagnostic systems monitor and evaluate both status and performance.

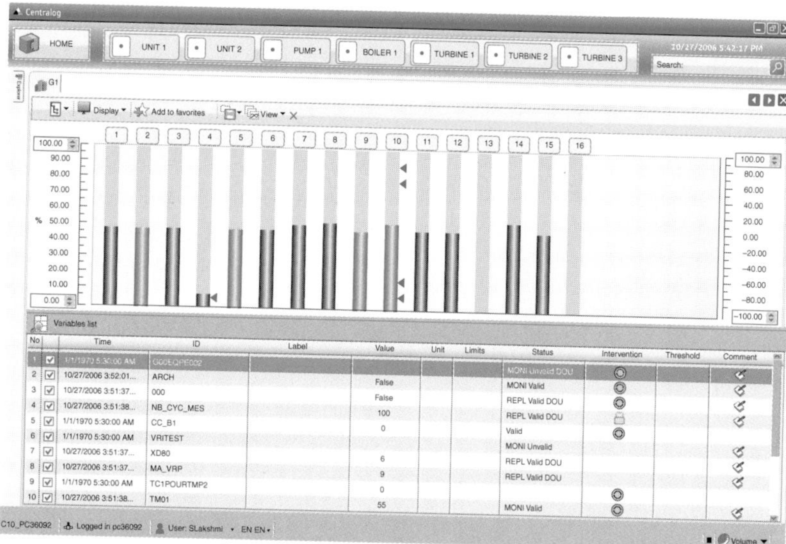

Figure 7-13 | Bar-graph viewer

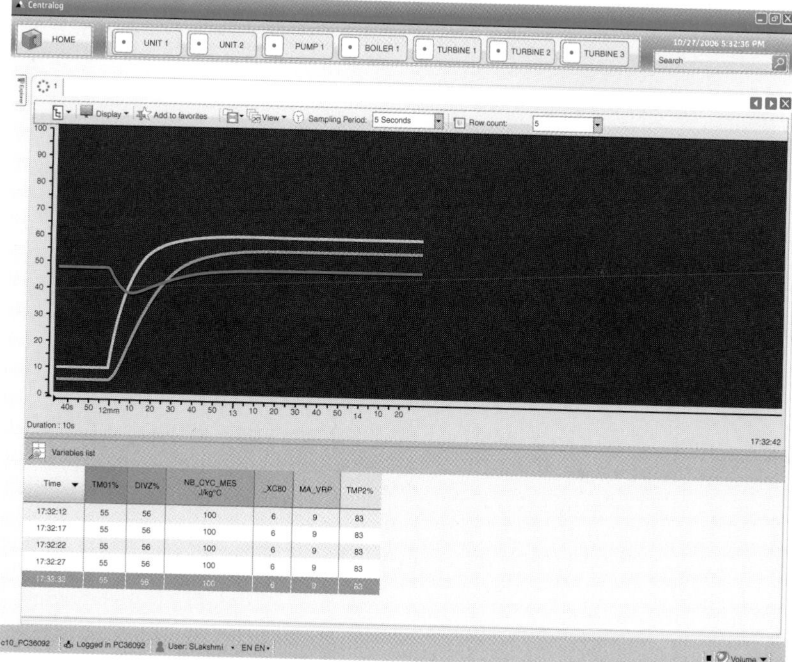

Figure 7-14 | Variables trend viewer

FURNACE EXPLOSIONS

Furnace explosions are rare and unlikely. When compared with the total number of unit operating hours, the hours lost because of explosions are minimal. This desirable situation exists because (1) furnaces are supplied with an explosive accumulation only

A well designed operator interface provides the operator with all of the information needed to maintain safe operation of the boiler and power plant system.

during a small percentage of their operating lives and (2) just a minute part of those explosive charges receive sufficient ignition energy to actually cause an explosion.

In suspension burning, the combustion process is primarily controlled by the admission rate of fuel and air to a furnace, independently of each other. The dynamic response of the combustion reaction, however, depends on the diffusion of the fuel and air to a flammable limit and the elevation of this diffused mixture to its kindling temperature. The aerodynamic diffusion of fuel and air results from both the rate and method of admission. This admission flow pattern produces diffusion mechanically by intermixing the fuel and air masses. Molecular diffusion is also present as a result of the elevated temperature level at which combustion takes place. Furnace explosions result from a rapid rate of volume increase of the gaseous combustion products when too great a quantity of fuel and air reacts almost simultaneously in an enclosure with limited volume and strength. Avoiding furnace pressures in excess of furnace enclosure design pressure is, therefore, necessary to prevent furnace rupture.

The basis for any explosion prevention system must be to limit the quantity of flammable fuel/air mixture that can exist in the furnace at any given instant. The rate of maximum pressure rise possible during the reaction is a function also of the available oxygen (O_2) per unit volume of reactants. The effect of any O_2 diluent (nitrogen, increased temperature, decreased pressure, excess fuel, or inert gases) reduces the possible explosion pressure.

Furnace explosion prevention should be aimed at limiting the quantity of diffused flammable fuel/air mixture that can be accumulated in a furnace in proportion to the total volume and the mechanical strength of the furnace. While fuel and air are being admitted to a furnace, there are only three possible methods of preventing excessive flammable diffused accumulations:

1. Igniting all flammable mixtures as they are formed, before their excessive accumulation
2. Diffusing all flammable mixtures with sufficient additional air, prior to ignition, to a point beyond the diffused flammable-mixture ratio; and accomplishing this with a sufficient degree of diffusion before a critical percentage of the furnace volume becomes occupied by the flammable mixture
3. Supplying an inert gas to diffuse simultaneously with the fuel and air, thereby diluting the O_2 content of the mixture below the flammable limit

Implementation of these preventive methods requires operator action beyond the response, memory, and judgment capabilities of the normal operator controlling a plant in the manual mode. A fireside safeguard system must supervise the flow and processing of fuel, air, ignition energy, and the products of combustion. Satisfactory boiler operation requires that these four ingredients be properly prepared, ratioed, directed, and sequenced so that the furnace is not supplied with an explosive mixture. At the same time, the combustion process

must be supervised to check the results. Combustion must be kept efficient or the unconverted chemical energy may accumulate and subsequently become explosive.

The following factors influence the effective composition change of an explosive charge:

- The facility for mixing
- The inert material in the fuel
- The fuel/air ratio (a near-stoichiometric ratio develops the highest explosion pressure)
- The kind of fuel

Satisfactory boiler operation requires that the flow and processing of fuel, air, ignition energy, and products of combustion be properly prepared, ratioed, directed, and sequenced to prevent the possibility of an explosive mixture in the furnace.

A furnace explosion requires both sufficient explosive accumulation within the furnace and sufficient energy for ignition. The ignition requirements for an explosive charge are very small, making it impossible to protect against all possible sources of ignition, such as static electricity discharges, hot slag, and hot furnace surfaces. Therefore, the practical means of avoiding a furnace explosion is the prevention of an explosive accumulation. The factors determining the magnitude of a furnace explosion (mass, change in composition, and reaction time) are related in the explosion factor.

$$\text{Explosion Factor} = (\text{Mass}/\text{Furnace Volume}) \times (\text{Composition Change}/\text{Elapsed Time})$$

Equation 7-1

Each furnace has a limiting explosion factor. If the conditions create an explosion factor exceeding this limit, a catastrophic explosion can result. Any lesser reaction will produce a furnace "puff" (a nondestructive explosion) or a temporary upset.

To protect a furnace from an explosion, a safety system must ensure a minimum reactive mass accumulation with a minimum available composition change and with a maximum reaction time required. Only control of the composition of the furnace atmosphere offers complete coverage in minimizing the explosion factor. After firing has begun, furnaces always contain sufficient mass to have an explosion and control of the time factor is impossible. Therefore, the composition change must be controlled to prevent furnace explosions.

The mechanics of furnace explosions, although defining the actual process, do not describe the furnace operations that provide the explosive accumulations. Ideal furnace operation continuously converts reactive furnace inputs into unreactive products as fast as the inputs enter the furnace. This precludes furnace explosions. However, in practical furnace firing, unfavorable operations that create explosive situations are difficult to avoid completely.

Several correctly timed events precede a damaging furnace explosion. The furnace explosion event itself is the rapid change in composition of the furnace atmosphere (not the furnace inputs). The change in furnace composition is not spontaneous, and suitable ignition energy, which can be substantially less than that required for continuous furnace input ignition, must be supplied after the explosive composition is attained.

The potentially reactive furnace accumulation must be formed from an earlier buildup process that introduces reactive inputs not converted by oxidation to nonreactive or inert products. This buildup process must continue long enough to create a damaging accumulation. The accumulation composition, which must be within the limits of flammability for that particular fuel, is formed in one or more basic ways.

- A flammable input into any furnace atmosphere (loss of ignition)
- A fuel-rich input into an air-rich atmosphere (fuel interruption)
- An air-rich input into a fuel-rich atmosphere (air interruption)

Furnace firing systems are designed to start-up air rich by introducing fuel into an air-filled furnace. Main fuel is introduced after the integral ignition system has satisfied permit main-fuel interlocks that it can provide more ignition energy than the main fuel requires to be ignited or to remain ignited. Additional air is introduced around the primary air/fuel mixture to take it beyond flammable limits, if it has not been ignited and reacted to inert combustion products. This is done to avoid a critical portion of the total furnace volume being occupied by a flammable mixture.

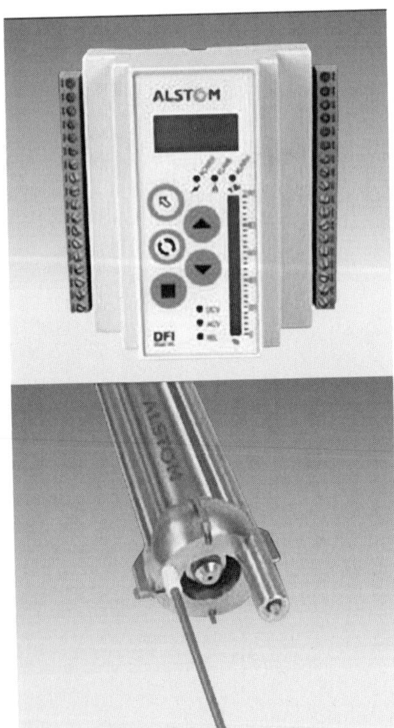

Figure 7-15 | Ionic flame rod detector

Flame Detection

In the prevention of furnace explosions, the detection of the absence of flame while fuel is being admitted is the only proper criterion for any control action initiated by a flame-monitoring system. The burning process exhibits many characteristics that can be sensed as indicators of existing flame. Heat sensors, for example in the form of thermocouples and bimetallic strips, have been used successfully for many years in small space-heating systems, though the application of these devices to larger suspension-fired installations is not practical.

Another characteristic of the burning process used for flame detection is the electrical conduction capabilities of the ionized gases of a flame. An electrical conduction path is established by a flame rod that extends into the flame envelope. The ionized gases themselves and the boiler tubes serve as the ground return of the system. This flame rod concept is also used on smaller burners or ignitors fueled by oil or gas, (*Fig. 7-15*) but the erosive nature of suspension fired, pulverized coal (PC) makes this type of flame detection impractical for that fuel.

Especially in large, suspension fired, burner/furnace installations, the most practical characteristic to sense for proof of flame has proven to be the light emitted by the burning process. The light emission covers a very broad spectrum and it is a continuous, rather than a line, spectrum. The shape of the emission versus wavelength plot for fossil furnace flames generally resembles the black body curve, with peak emissions characteristic of the fuel being fired.

The light emitted by these furnace flames is further characterized by a fluctuating intensity, commonly called flicker frequency, which depends on the area of the flame being viewed, as well as physical conditions at the fuel nozzle. Fuel/air ratio, fuel velocity, air velocity, and the location and effectiveness of turbulence producing diffusers all influence the frequency of the pulsating intensity.

Flame Detector Hardware Arrangement

Flame monitoring hardware must be reliable, must be sensitive enough to discern the minimum flame envelope, and must have fail-safe characteristics to avoid unnecessary trips or firing in an unsafe condition. There are several hardware arrangements for a flame detector. Typically, a flame detector consists of a detector head that is mounted on the burner or adjacent to the fuel nozzle. The detector head contains a light collecting lens that is mounted in a location where it can collect light from the flame. The geometry of the burner and the flame shape produced by the burner will determine the optimum viewing location for the detector. Tilting tangential burners and some wall mounted burners will require that the lens be mounted close to the flame front inside the burner windbox. In most modern flame detectors, a fiber optic cable is used to transmit the light from the lens to the detector head.

The detector head collects the light from the flame and converts the light energy to an electrical signal (*Fig. 7-16*). The electrical signal from the flame detector is processed by the flame analyzing circuit to determine the presence of a flame.

The flame analysis circuit can be mounted local to the burner front inside the detector head or can be mounted remotely in a less hostile environment (*Figs. 7-17* and *7-18*). The flame detector electronics then transmit a contact signal to the BMS/BPS indicating if flame is present. Other signals can include detector fault, indicating instrument failure, and an analog signal indicating flame signal strength.

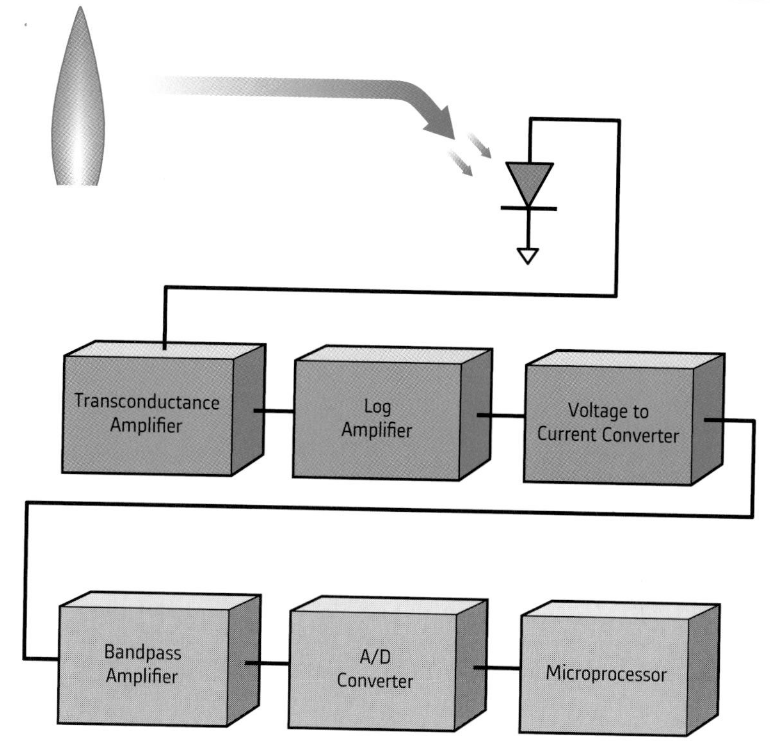

Figure 7-16 | Photodiode schematic

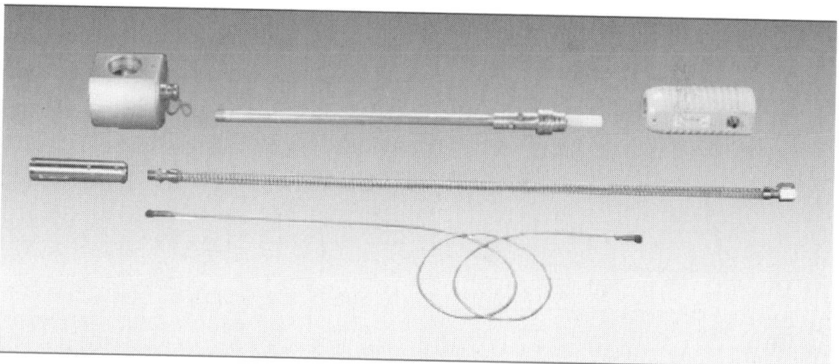

Figure 7-17 | Spectrometer flame detector

Flame Properties

Flame characteristics from fossil fuel combustion can take several different forms depending on fuel type, burner design, furnace geometry, and other factors (*Figs. 7-19* and *7-20*).

The light emissions can range from ultraviolet (UV) to infrared (IR)

Figure 7-18 | Hardware for flame detector

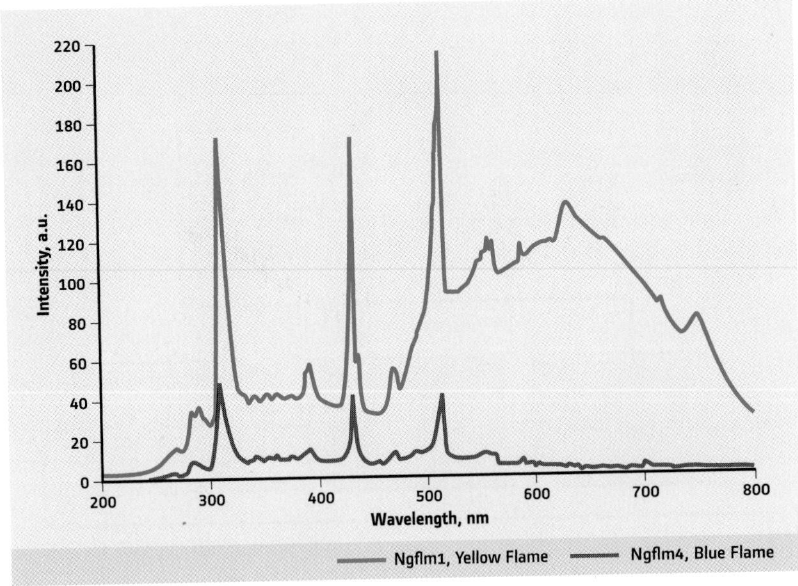

Figure 7-19 | Gas fired curve

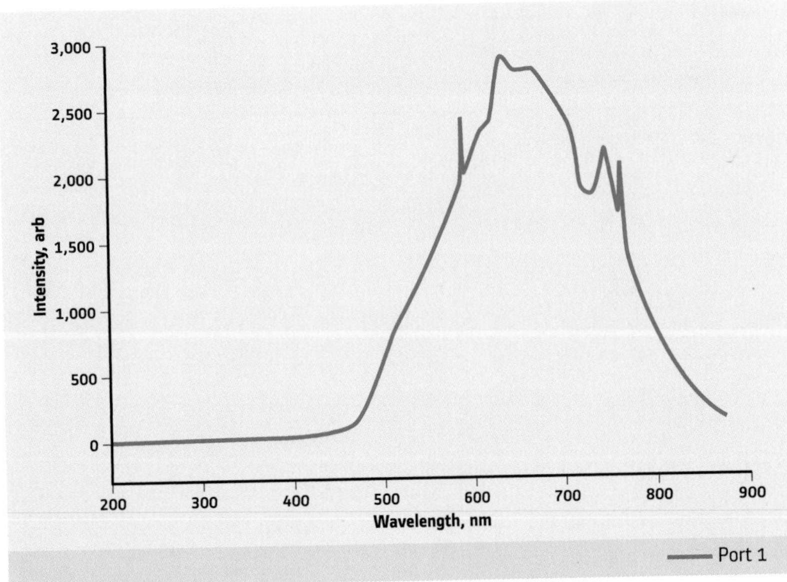

Figure 7-20 | Coal fired curve

frequencies that are invisible to the human eye (<400 nm or >750 nm), as well as the bright blue, orange, yellow, or red flames that are produced in the visible light range (400–750 nm). In addition to the light frequency, the intensity of the flame, measured in direct current (DC), and the flicker frequency of the flame is important.

Frequency flicker is produced by the varying intensity of the light within the flame envelope caused by the turbulence inherent in the combustion process. Peak to peak variations are measured to verify the chaotic nature of the flame and differentiate the signal from background light levels.

Flame Spectral Analysis

Early flame detectors using lead sulfide cells were effective at detecting broad light intensity and frequency. The peak response was produced in the IR frequency spectrum, which can indicate that a flame is present. However, IR is also produced by non-flame heat sources such as refractory or boiler tubes and these early detectors were unable to adequately differentiate flame from other sources of radiation reliably enough for safety purposes.

UV sensing tubes made from tungsten in a helium atmosphere were highly effective at detecting flames produced by gas and oil fossil fuels without being fooled by other heat sources. Electrical shorts were common in UV tube technology, which helped institute fault detection in flame monitors. A mechanical shutter would be placed in front of the detector to block the light from the flame. A self-check circuit was designed to verify that the flame detector did not sense flame when the shutter is closed (light is blocked from the detector). Poor response to coal flames and overall lack of reliability led to the use of visible light technology for flame monitoring.

The use of visible light frequencies occurred almost simultaneously with the use of solid state electronics to replace tube type technology. Silicon carbide photodiodes convert light from the flame to an electrical signal that can be amplified, filtered, and analyzed to verify that flame is present. Visible light in the range of 400–750 nm is highly effective as it is able to match the observations of trained operators. Improvements in sensitivity to coal flames extended the operating range of coal burners without the need for support fuel. The equipment reliability was also improved with solid state electronics and the ability to perform fault detection electronically rather than mechanically. Visible light flame detectors are provided as a stand-alone technology or as part of a new broad range spectral analysis covering UV, visible light, and IR (*Fig. 7-21*).

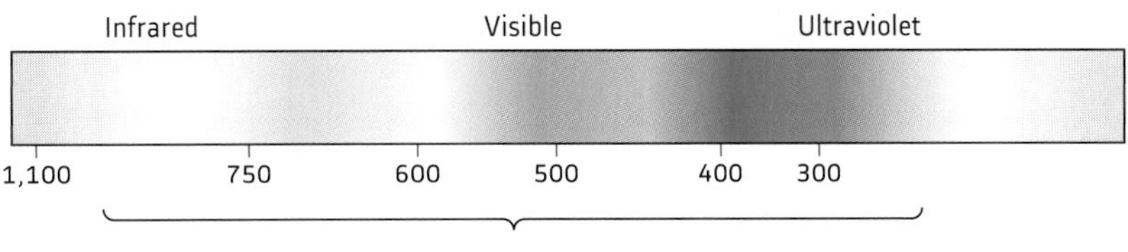

Figure 7-21 | Flame spectral range

Digital Signal Processing (DSP)

The age of semiconductors and microprocessors ushered in a new era of flame detection technology. Regardless of the light spectrum being used, the speed and precision of digital signal processing brought improvements to plant safety and operation. Measuring multiple flame characteristics at speeds of 2,000 times/second allows precise flame measurements in real time to avoid delay in detecting unsafe firing conditions. In addition to electronic self-checking to prevent false flame detection, software code was written to perform backup checks on the health of the equipment. Safety is still the primary mission of the flame detectors and reliability continues to improve. Once the use of microprocessors in the power plant environment was proven to be effective, additional enhancements were on the way. Communication to plant control systems and personal computer networks allowed information to be spread to a number of users beyond the safety system. More communication led to more information (*Fig. 7-22*).

Multi-Spectrum Analysis

With the power of microprocessors increasing rapidly, more detailed information from the flame can be captured and analyzed. Flame detectors can use multiple sensors to measure light frequencies in the UV, visible light, and IR range simultaneously. The light signal is distributed to the multiple sensors for analysis, both individually and in relation to each other, to provide a rich detail of the light emitted from the furnace. In addition to verifying the presence of flame, analyzing narrow bands of light frequencies allows users to determine the color of the flame and the shape of the flame curve. Algorithms for determining flame temperature resulting from localized fuel/air ratios have also been developed.

Each type of fuel fired emits a color spectrum. In addition, the color spectrum can change with the fuel firing rate. As the overall furnace conditions

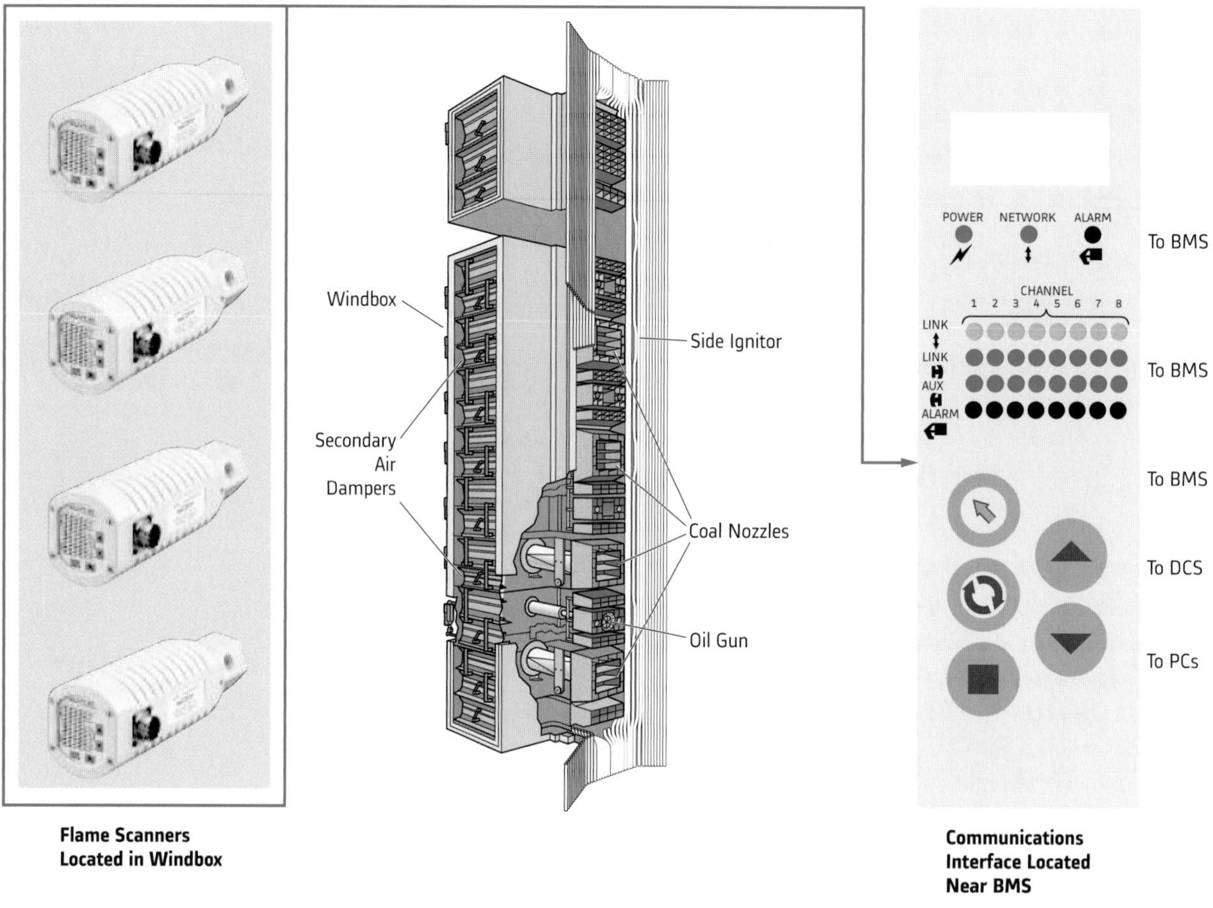

Figure 7-22 | Spectrometer communication to BMS/BPS, DCS, and PCs

change, i.e., temperature, fuel fired and excess air levels, the flame temperatures may also change to shift the light and color spectrum.

As an example of flame color analysis, the color spectrum for an oil flame typically demonstrates a more brilliant flame pattern over a coal flame as well as differences in flicker frequency. In the first graph shown in *Figure 7-23*, the data illustrates a change in the color spectrum as an oil gun was placed in service when firing coal. The significance of this information is such that the operator has the ability to obtain real-time data from the scanner that will identify the change in fuel or flame quality remotely. The first half of the graph shows signals resulting from a coal only flame, the second half shows an oil flame with coal flame in the background. The light spectrum is shown in the upper right hand corner of the figure. On the graph, the relative percentage of each color is presented. The relative percentage of green light to total light rises when the oil gun is fired in conjunction with coal, indicative of the higher temperature flame from oil firing. These color ratios tend to be stable with load and the flame scanner can be set to differentiate between oil and coal flame based on this change. Similarly, in the second graph there is a large change in intensity of the light when the oil gun is fired. This is a less reliable method of differentiating oil flame from coal flame on its own because the difference may be a load change or a coal elevation taken out of service. However, if a rapid change in intensity has not occurred, this can be used as a positive indication that an oil gun has not ignited.

BOILER PROTECTIVE SYSTEMS

One of the major control systems furnished on all modern fossil fuel fired steam generators is a protective system, commonly identified as either a boiler protective system (BPS) or a burner management system (BMS). The main function of such a system is to prevent the formation of an explosive mixture of fuel and air in any portion of a boiler during any phase of operation, including start-up and shutdown. Preventing damage to the steam generator and/or the firing system components requires simultaneous, continuous monitoring of a substantial number of parameters and, at times, instantaneous reaction to a hazardous situation. This task can be performed adequately only by a dedicated protective system.

The manner in which this protective system is provided is largely based on the requirements and country of origin of the end user. Regardless of the "designation of the system," its function is to provide protection for the steam generator and interface with the associated firing system equipment.

Boiler Protection System Architecture

To meet international codes, the functions required to protect the boiler are provided in a standalone system that partitions protection functions from control functions. This protective portion of the overall boiler control system is designated as the boiler protection system (BPS) and is physically and functionally separated from the remainder of the boiler control systems. The system is based on usage of specific safety controllers holding the furnace critical functions such as flue gas path protection, furnace purge, ignition time monitoring, ignition trials release, evaporator protection, oil burners trip, and coal mills and associated feeders trip.

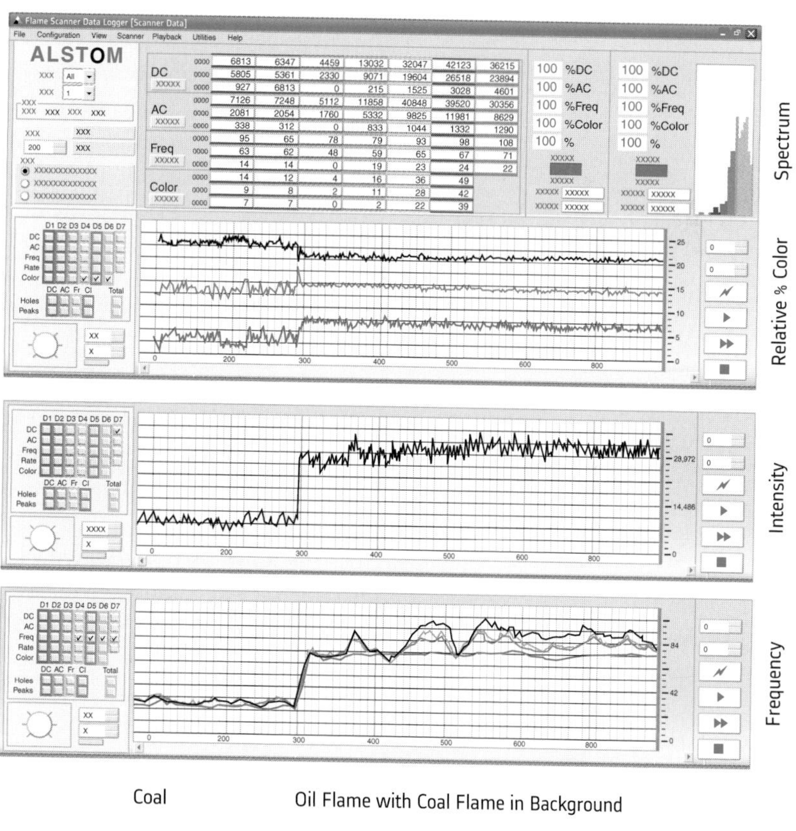

Figure 7-23 | Flame spectral analysis

To implement this strategy, the normal starting and stopping functions provided for the fuel firing equipment are provided in a separate control system commonly identified as a burner control system (BCS). This is implemented in this manner due to the extensive control system redundancy requirements needed to meet international codes for the BPS.

The aim of the BPS is to prevent the fuel firing equipment from starting if secure conditions are not met and to trip the boiler if emergency conditions arise. A boiler trip is carried out by stopping all fuel inputs to the furnace.

BPS Logic System Architecture

The BPS logic system is implemented in a fail-safe and triplicate modular redundant system. In case of a failure, the system continues to operate in a safe operational state because the critical circuits are redundant and perform identical functions simultaneously and independently. The data output from each of the three circuits is voted in a majority-voting circuit, before affecting the system's output. If one of the redundant circuits fails, its data output is ignored and the system continues to output to the process the value that agrees with the majority of the functional circuits. If for any reason the failed module is not replaced before a second failure in a parallel circuit occurs, the second failure will cause the BPS to shut down to a fail-safe state.

BPS Operator Interface

The human-machine interface is a part of the overall digital control system that provides a direct means of communication between the operator, at the central control room level, and the plant equipment, using one or more operator display stations. The human-machine interface is customized according to the nature of the process to which the control and supervision is applied. This is particularly true for the BPS due to the critical nature of the parameters to transmit to the operator's level. Regarding the BPS monitoring and control, several facilities are provided to allow the operator to analyze the status of the boiler safeties: a boiler safeties set of dedicated mimics, an alarm monitoring, a sequence monitoring, a sequence of events log, and a historical data storage and retrieval function.

All critical status and commands are concentrated in a single mimic allowing the operator to launch and manage the furnace purge operation, the setting of boiler safeties, the flame detection monitoring, and all critical parameters that require a boiler trip. Notably, from this mimic, the operator can follow the furnace purge sequence progress, the leak test sequence progress, and the correct setting of boiler safeties. Along with the physical process data, the interface also displays the status of the logic protection system itself. All warnings for the operator about required maintenance action in order to avoid any inconvenient boiler tripping are displayed. In the BPS control mimic, the detailed list of the data involved in the boiler safety monitoring (permit conditions as well as trip conditions) is displayed. This allows the operator to identify the missing conditions that prevent the furnace purge from being carried out and the boiler safeties to be set. It is also the means to identify, on a boiler trip occurrence, which is the faulty condition (first out criteria) and which are the induced protection faults that may have happened after the boiler trip, if any.

Burner Management System Architecture

To meet applicable U.S.-based NFPA codes, the functions required to protect the boiler and operate the fuel firing equipment are provided in a stand-alone system that partitions boiler protection and firing system control functions from other boiler control system functions, (i.e., feedwater control). This protective boiler control system is designated as the burner management system (BMS) and is physically and functionally separated from the remainder of the boiler control systems. The system performs critical functions like flue gas path protection, furnace purge, ignition time monitoring, ignition trials release, evaporator protection, oil burners trip, and coal mills and associated feeders trip as well as supervision of placing fuel firing equipment into service.

Unlike the BPS system architecture described above, the normal starting and stopping functions provided for the boiler firing equipment are an integral part of the burner management system. Like the BPS system, the BMS prevents the fuel firing equipment from starting if secure conditions are not met and trips the boiler if emergency conditions arise. A boiler trip is carried out by stopping all fuel inputs to the furnace.

Experience has shown that the burner management system cannot be treated as an auxiliary function of the steam generator process (e.g., combustion, feedwater, and steam temperature) control systems. Rather, the BMS is a separate and distinct system, more closely allied to the firing-system digital actions than to the process controls. The most important design criterion of a fuel-firing protective system is that it be tailored specifically to the requirements and operating characteristics of the firing system.

BMS/BCS Logic Implementation

The logic portion of the BMS may be implemented with computer-based programmable logic controllers (PLCs) or (DCS), electromagnetic relays, or solid state electronics. All of these installations must be able to tolerate the dust, temperature variations, and electrical noise encountered in a power plant. The normal method of powering the BMS logic system is via an un-interruptible power source (UPS).

The BMS may be designed in two basic ways: "energize-to-trip" and "de-energize-to-trip." A "de-energize-to-trip" system closes or trips the fuel-firing equipment on a loss of power, i.e., a fail-safe design. An "energize-to-trip" system requires the presence of power to close or trip fuel-firing equipment. Supply of an "energize-to-trip" system generally increases the steam generator's availability, is less prone to nuisance trips, and has been most commonly used in the utility boiler industry. The type of system to be provided is determined by the needs/requirements of the end user. Where an "energize-to-trip" system is provided, DC power from the plant battery system is also provided to the BMS to ensure the capability of shutting off the fuel input in the event of a loss of the AC power source. Systems based on electromagnetic relays and solid state electronics, which had been the traditional building blocks of burner management system logic in the past, are now rarely built.

With modern microprocessor capability, redundant architecture, and two-out-of-two or two-out-of-three logic, the failure of a single controller will not jeopardize the safety of the steam generator.

Microprocessor-Based Systems

Currently, the predominant technique for implementing BPS/BMS/BCS logic is with microprocessor-based DCS or PLC hardware. These devices make it possible to program the system directly from logic diagrams. They are also configured to be strong in logic capability and can be packaged ruggedly enough for the power plant environment.

When microprocessor-based systems were first introduced into the power industry in the early 1980s, the architecture commonly used in BMS was quite complex. This was in part due to the technology available at the time including limited processor size and capability and self-diagnostics. As a result, the logic for a large steam generator was commonly distributed to multiple controllers arranged in a fault tolerant configuration. This fault tolerant configuration provided redundancy from a safety as well as availability standpoint. As the reliability and capability of microprocessors advanced, alternate configurations were developed where logic controllers were typically arranged in a hot standby configuration. This hot standby configuration is arranged where two controllers simultaneously execute logic instructions. In the event that the primary controller fails, control to the I/O and communication system is automatically transferred to the redundant (backup) controller.

To improve overall safety and reliability of microprocessor-based systems, and dependent on applicable safety codes, additional fault tolerant configurations are in use that are arranged in a two out of two or in a two out of three redundant architecture. In these configurations, each microprocessor is independently "connected" to its respective I/O system, which connects to the BMS field equipment and instrumentation. The basic design criterion of this fault-tolerant architecture is that failure of a single controller, with all its logic capability, or an I/O module, will not jeopardize the steam generator safety or availability.

Process Controls

Plant operators retain the ultimate responsibility for the operation and protection of both utility and industrial steam generators. But as discussed, automatic safety systems are customarily installed to relieve operators of the task of instantaneously analyzing and reacting to a rapidly developing hazardous condition. Safety systems improve unit availability by preventing improper operating sequences and by automatically shutting down equipment before damage can occur. But acceptable availability can only be achieved by installing process control systems to prevent the plant-controlled variables from reaching the deviation from normal values that result in safety system action. The continuous, automatic regulation of controlled variables is the function of these process control systems.

Although it is still common to divide the process controls for a large steam generator into subsystems (such as combustion control, feedwater control, and steam temperature), a coordinated approach to process control has proven to be the most effective technique to achieve optimum boiler performance.

BPS/BMS Organization

- The operator interface of the BPS/BMS is mainly located in the central control room. It is composed of a set of mimic displays from which the operator can pass all necessary commands and monitor the status of firing conditions from a safety point of view (*Fig. 7-7*).
- The driven devices are primarily those by which fuel and air are admitted to the steam generator. Typical examples are valve operators (oil and gas firing), feeders and pulverizer motor starters (pulverized-coal firing), air damper drives, and fan motor starters (*Fig. 7-24*).
- Sensing devices include not only position information on the driven devices, but also such items as fuel pressures, temperatures and flow, boiler drum level, and flame presence or temperature.
- The logic system constitutes the heart of the BPS/BMS. All operator initiated commands are routed to the logic system. The status of the sensing elements is monitored continuously by the logic system. Operator commands are passed on to the driven devices only if its logic verifies that the proper safety permits have been satisfied. On the other hand, the logic system will shut down equipment automatically whenever continued operation would endanger the furnace.

BMS/BPS FOR TANGENTIALLY FIRED UTILITY BOILERS

This section describes the primary functions and interlocks associated with a tangentially fired steam generator.

The typical conditions that would cause an emergency shutdown (trip) of a tangentially fired steam generator are as follows:

- Low airflow
- Loss of all FD fans
- Loss of all ID fans
- Loss of all primary-air fans (PC fired)
- Turbine trip
- Inadequate waterwall circulation
- High furnace-gas-side pressure
- Low furnace-gas-side pressure
- Low drum level (drum units)
- High waterwall outlet temperature (once-through units)
- High separator level (once-through units)
- High superheater-outlet pressure (once-through units)
- Flame failure
- Loss of logic power to BPS/BMS
- Loss of primary and redundant BPS/BMS processors (if applicable)
- Operator's emergency-trip push buttons depressed

Burner Management/Burner Control–Degrees of Automation

The BMS/BCS arrangement discussed so far is commonly called a remote-manual system. With this type of system, the operator initiates the start-up and shutdown of each individual piece of equipment from a remote operating panel. The system logic ensures that the operator commands are performed in the correct sequence and intervenes only when required to prevent a hazardous condition. Higher levels of automation commonly specified are "automatic" and "automatic with load programming." An automatic

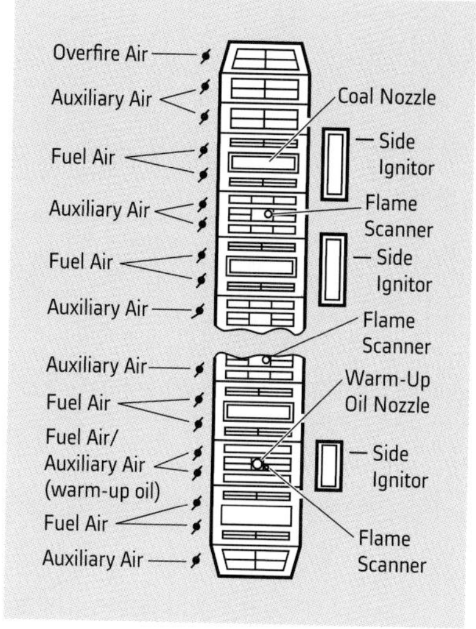

Figure 7-24 | Typical air and fuel nozzle arrangements within a windbox

system allows an operator to place in service or remove from service a related group of firing equipment (a sub-loop) in the proper sequence by initiating a single command. A typical example of a sub-loop would be the feeder, air dampers, and other equipment associated with a single coal pulverizer.

In the automatic mode, a single operator command to start a pulverizer would initiate the following appropriately timed sequence of events (provided all of the required permit conditions are established):

- Associated ignition system placed in service
- Pulverizer motor started
- Hot-air gate opened
- Pulverizer airflow and temperature controls released for automatic operation
- Feeder started
- Feeder speed control released for automatic operation
- Associated windbox dampers released for automatic operation

As the required load on the steam generator is varied over a wide range, firing system sub-loops are placed in, or removed from, service to maintain the most stable flame conditions and make the most efficient use of the firing-system components. With the inclusion of the load-programming feature, the BMS/BCS will take care of this function automatically as steam-generator load demand changes.

Basic Safety Functions

Although the BPS/BMS/BCS does not regulate the fuel and airflow quantities and does not, in most cases, initiate the start-up or normal shutdown of firing-system components, it does exercise authority over both the operator and the process controls through its safety interlocking features.

If, for example, the combustion control should drop the airflow below the minimum value (typically 25%), the BPS/BMS would trip the fuel automatically. Similarly, it will not permit the operator to start equipment out of prescribed safe sequences and will shut down equipment if prescribed operating practices are not followed. Removing ignitors too early, for example, would result in the shutdown of the associated main fuel.

The specific safety interlocking included in the BPS/BMS depends on the physical characteristics of the firing system and type of fuel or fuels being fired. All safety systems of this type, however, are concerned with the following functions:

- A pre-firing purge of the furnace
- Establishment of the appropriate permits for firing the ignition fuel (i.e., purge complete, fuel pressure within limits)
- Establishment of the appropriate permits, including ignition permits, for the main (load-carrying) fuel
- Continuous monitoring of firing conditions and other key operating parameters
- Emergency shutdown of portions or all of the firing equipment when required
- A post-firing purge of the steam generator

The purpose of the pre-firing purge is to be sure that any unburned fuel that may have accumulated in the furnace is completely removed prior to initiation of firing. To complete this function, a flow of air is passed through the steam generator at a minimum rating (usually 30% of that required for rated steam-generator capacity) for a minimum of 5 minutes. At the same time, windbox dampers are maintained in a particular configuration, the fuel-admission devices are proven closed (or off), and the flame-monitoring devices indicate "no-flame." This combination of conditions will provide the proper velocities and number of air changes through the furnace and convection pass to ensure the removal of any fuel accumulations. These purge-permit requirements also provide a check on the proper operation of the air damper, fuel-admission, and flame monitoring sensing devices just prior to firing.

On completion of the purge, the steam generator is ready to be fired. The 30% minimum airflow requirement is maintained throughout the operating range of the steam generator including low-load operation in order to ensure an air-rich furnace mixture. Initial firing is accomplished with a group of ignitors that have the capability of lighting the ignition fuel with an electric spark. A flame detector must be provided with each ignitor to determine the presence or absence of a stable flame. In the case of the Alstom ignitor, the flame detector is an integral part of the ignitor, and a fuel-flow measurement is included to ensure the proper quantity of ignition energy.

Depending on the type of load-carrying fuel and the firing-system arrangement, the load-carrying fuel may obtain its ignition energy directly from the ignitors or an elevation of ignition fuel guns may be used as an intermediate step. On coal-fired units, for example, ignition fuel is normally kept in service until two adjacent coal elevations are being fired at 50% of their rated capability, thereby assuring sufficient ignition energy to maintain stable firing conditions during the steam-generator start-up phase of operation.

Flame Monitoring

The Alstom tangential firing configuration (*Fig. 7-25*) operates during start-up with a separate, independent flame emanating from each operating fuel admission point (nozzle). Each flame is monitored independently by the use of continuous, self-flame-proving ignitors or with oil guns provided with discriminating flame detectors.

As soon as any main fuel elevation is fired at a rate exceeding 30% of its design rating, the characteristics of this firing configuration change dramatically (*Fig. 7-26*).

Front-fired (horizontal-burner) systems exhibit, at all firing rates, the individual burner characteristics that the tangential configuration exhibits at low firing rates: that is, the flame produced at one firing location does not provide ignition energy for fuel admitted at the other locations. The flame monitoring system for such burners must be designed accordingly. In general, it is not appropriate to use front-fired flame monitoring techniques on tangential firing configurations and vice versa.

CONTROL OF UTILITY STEAM GENERATORS

This section describes the major control loops required to operate a utility steam generator.

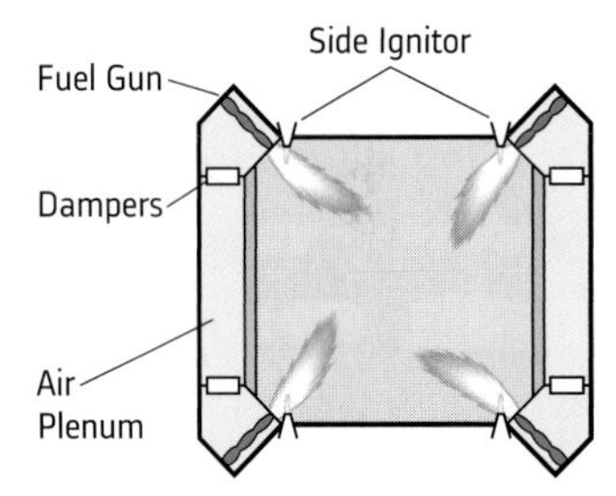

Figure 7-25 | Tangential firing pattern at low firing rates

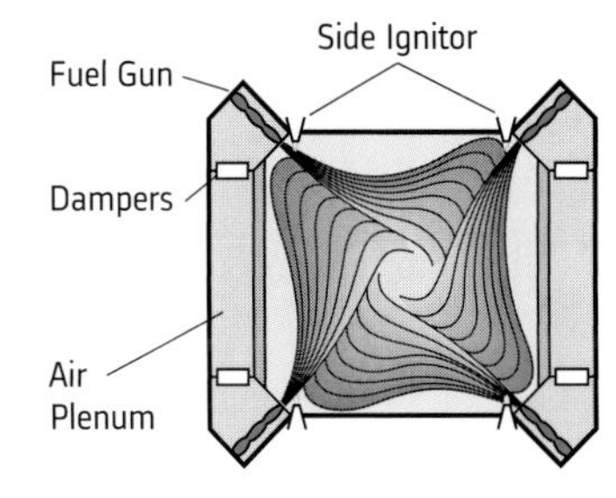

Figure 7-26 | Tangential firing pattern: fireball condition

BOILER FOLLOW SYSTEMS

For many years, the most common process control system employed on subcritical, drum-type units was the "boiler-follow" system that relies heavily on feedback control principles. With a boiler-follow system on a subcritical pressure, drum-type unit, a change in required electrical generation results in the following events:

1. The turbine control valves are repositioned to establish the new generation level, at the expense of a change in steam generator energy storage level.
2. Changes in steam flow initiate changes in the flow of feedwater, fuel, and air on a feed-forward basis. Fuel and air are further modified by the feedback of throttle pressure deviation from set point, which is an indication of the energy balance between the steam generator and the turbine. Feedwater is adjusted by drum level deviation, which is a measure of the feedwater-flow/steam-flow balance. The large energy storage of drum type units allows boiler-follow systems to be very effective as long as generation level (load) changes are small or are accomplished slowly.

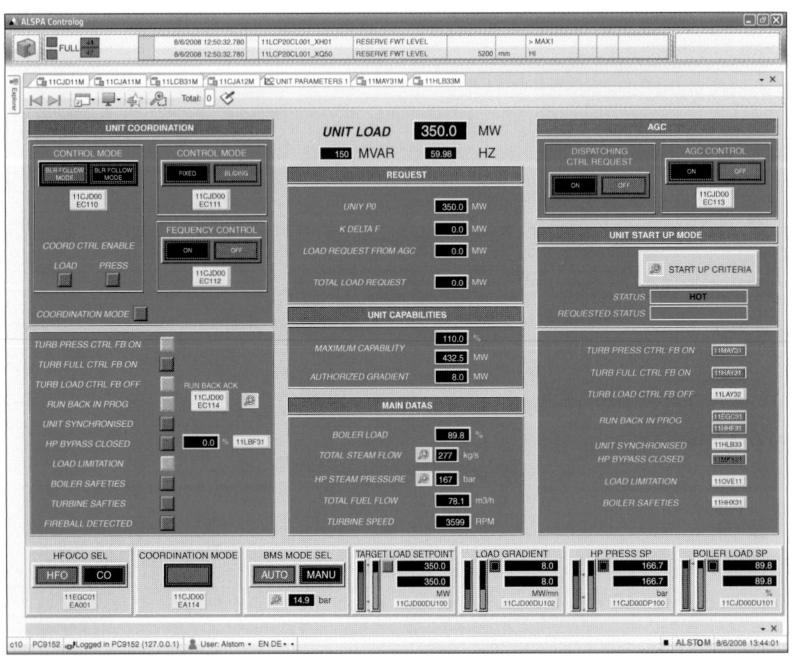

Figure 7-27 | Typical operator interface for the unit load control of a CCS

COORDINATED CONTROL SYSTEMS

The advent of the Combined Circulation® supercritical unit in the 1960s, with its relatively small energy storage, quickly demonstrated the limitations of the boiler-follow system. The solution to this problem was the development of the coordinated control system (CCS).

Ideal for Combined Circulation® supercritical units, the CCS is well suited for subcritical, drum-type units, as well as sliding pressure supercritical units. Its fundamental objective is to operate the steam generator and turbine generator as an integrated unit in order to maintain the process control variables (unit generation, steam pressure, flue gas O_2, furnace draft, and steam temperatures) within acceptable limits. The system operates the unit in an integrated (coordinated) manner by developing a unit load demand (ULD) signal in the unit load control (ULC), and transmitting the ULD signal simultaneously to both the steam generator master (fuel, air, and feedwater control) and the turbine governor valve control. *Figure 7-27* shows a typical control room operator interface for the unit load control in a coordinated-control system.

Figure 7-28 shows the functional design arrangement of a CCS. This design illustrates that the ULD signal, which represents generation demand, goes directly to the steam-generator input variable as well as to the turbine governor. This parallel control arrangement is based on the principle that the only way to permanently change unit generation is to change the energy output of the steam generator.

The presence of any error between required output and actual generation will bias the steam generator and turbine demand signals in order to recalibrate the system for cycle changes. Similarly, throttle pressure error is used to recalibrate the balance between steam production and steam use. Both of these error signals operate on a transient basis to compensate for the difference in response time of the boiler and turbine, allowing the faster responding turbine to minimize generation errors by modifying boiler energy storage levels.

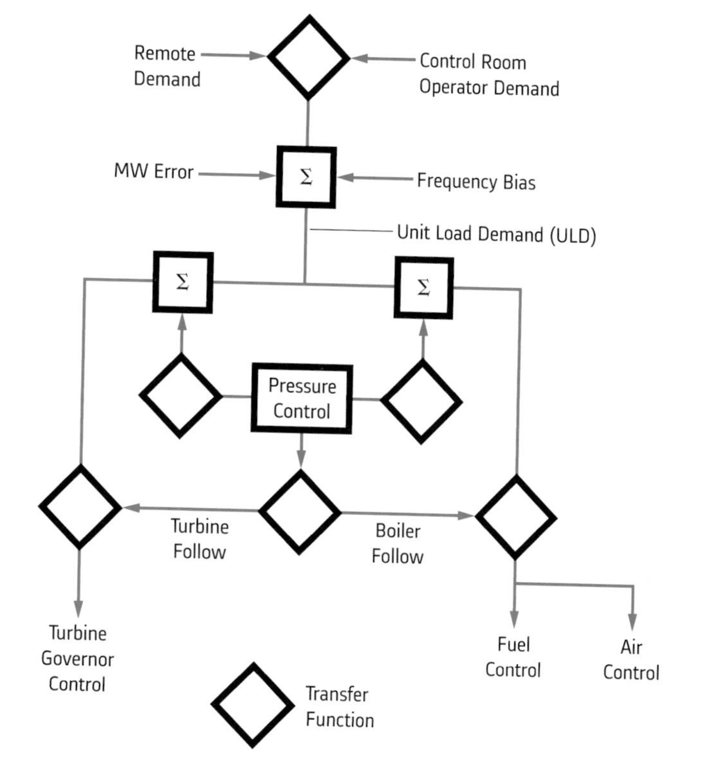

Figure 7-28 | CCS signal flow diagram

Today's modern CCS are designed to accommodate both fixed-pressure type of operation and also sliding-pressure type of operation. Sliding-pressure operation has long been popular in Europe because of Europe's smaller grid systems and the resulting need for cycling and two-shift units. As a result of a requirement to cycle units in the United States, sliding-pressure operation has become more common.

In fixed-pressure operation, the CCS regulates throttle pressure to a fixed set point for the entire range of unit load after start-up. The turbine governor valving strokes open as unit load increases. Fixed pressure provides for boiler storage and thus the capability of the unit to more effectively respond during transient load changes without suffering excessive process-variable deviations.

In sliding-pressure operation, throttle pressure set point is ramped over most of the unit load range. The turbine governor valving is fixed at a near-open position (normally 90% open) throughout the ramp. The 10% position reserve allows for moderate unit load change accommodation. The fixed position of the turbine governor valving is temporarily influenced during a unit load change by the rate of change of ULD.

Limit circuits prevent the system from trying to operate beyond the current capability of the plant, thus maintaining safe operation.

The preceding discussion summarizes the basic differences between boiler-follow and coordinated control type systems. The Alstom CCS contains a number of additional features designed to provide several layers of defense between the direct regulation of the variables and the automatic shutdown actions of the burner management system.

Each major subsystem, such as fuel, air, or feedwater, contains a flow tie-back loop to ensure the process variable will quickly match required output. Typically, triple or dual redundant transmitters are provided for critical process measurements. Control algorithms contained within the control system monitor the transmitters for failure or excessive deviation and transfer the control loop automatically to manual if a transmitter malfunction occurs. When triple redundant transmitters are provided, the control algorithms are designed to allow failure of a single transmitter within the control loop while maintaining automatic operation. When all process loops are well tuned and calibrated, and are functioning properly on automatic, the controlled variables will be maintained well within acceptable limits. Various limit circuits are provided to take care of the times when this desirable condition does not exist.

Referring again to *Figure 7-28*, note that the "output adjustment signal" (the desired generation value established by the operator or the load-dispatch system) must pass through several conditioning devices before emerging as unit load demand.

The first such device is the operator-set, rate-of-change limiter. This device prevents the unit from accepting a load demand change at a rate that would create instability and a resulting unit trip. Turbine governors automatically change unit steam flow in response to an electrical-grid frequency disturbance. To prevent the CCS from fighting the governor, and to match the boiler demand to the turbine action, the frequency bias conditioner is required. This circuit simply adjusts required output to match the governor action.

Limit actions occur when the CCS detects that one or more process variables cannot follow the output adjustment demand signal. If, for example, a feedwater pump were out of service, the limit circuit would not allow required output to exceed the capability of the pumps in service. Without this limit, firing rate would be allowed to exceed feedwater flow, resulting in loss of drum level (drum units) or high waterwall outlet temperature (once-through units). The limit circuits also act whenever such process variables as generation and throttle pressure deviate from their required values by a preset amount. These deviations are indications that the steam generator or turbine, or both, are unable to follow the desired output.

An extension of the limit circuits, which is not shown on *Figure 7-28*, is the run-up and run-down circuits. These circuits act to return the required output within the capability of the unit when a change in boiler unit conditions occurs. For example, if all coal feeders are operating near maximum output and one feeder trips, the unit cannot maintain its existing load. The run-down circuit would automatically reduce load to a value within the capability of the existing operating feeders.

The run-back actions shown next are simply a more dramatic version of a run-down. The loss of a major piece of auxiliary equipment such as a feed pump or forced draft (FD) fan may reduce the load-carrying capability of the unit to 50–60% of maximum continuous rating. When such an equipment loss is detected, the run-back circuit very rapidly reduces the required output signal to a value within the capability of the remaining equipment. Without such a circuit, a unit trip would almost certainly result.

One final protection circuit, which is the last line of defense designed to act before the safety system limits are reached, is the deviation-limit system. This system continuously monitors the fuel/air ratio. *Figure 7-29* illustrates the fuel/air ratio monitoring concepts. If the fuel/air ratio exceeds allowable limits, the deviation-limit system directly operates the control loops to restore a permissible ratio. This system, which overrides manual control, would normally activate only when the operator has made a serious mistake or an automatic-control computational element has failed.

COMBUSTION CONTROL SYSTEM

The combustion control system is a full metered, cross-limiting type where the boiler master demand serves as a demand for both fuel and air with cross-limiting features being implemented to ensure that a safe fuel/air ratio is maintained under all circumstances. This system is designed to provide the following:

1. Fuel demand can never exceed measured airflow.
2. On a load increase, fuel demand will follow the lower of either fuel demand or measured airflow. This is to ensure that fuel demand cannot be increased until an airflow increase is proven through the airflow measurement loop.
3. Air demand can never be less than measured fuel flow. On a load decrease, air demand will follow the greater of either air demand or measured fuel flow. This is to ensure that air demand cannot be decreased until a fuel flow decrease is proven through the fuel flow measurement loop.

Oxygen Correction

Above the minimum required unit airflow, the total unit air/fuel ratio is optimized by the oxygen (O_2) correction controller. The O_2 controller acts on the error between measured flue gas O_2 and the O_2 set point programmed as a function of unit steam flow (modified by an operator adjustable bias). The controller output adjusts the unit airflow demand within a limited range as required to maintain the desired O_2. The deviation-limit system is a protection circuit that continuously monitors fuel/air ratio and, if needed, directly takes action to restore a permissible ratio (*Fig. 7-29*).

Furnace Pressure and Unit Airflow Control—General

Furnace pressure is controlled by the induced draft (ID) fans, while unit airflow is controlled by the FD fans. ID/FD fan control can be accomplished with variable inlet vanes, control dampers, blade

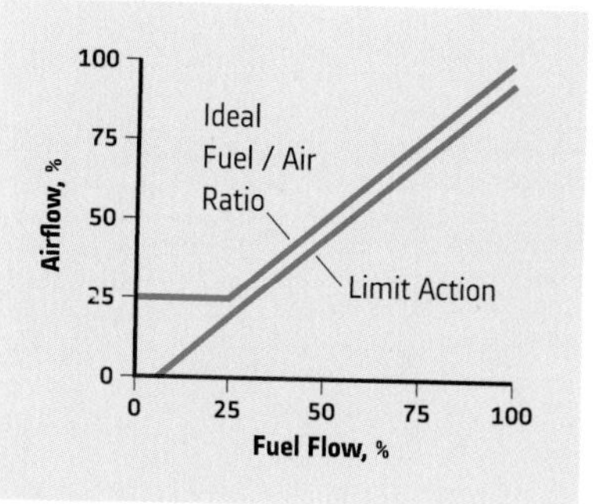

Figure 7-29 | The deviation limit system's protection limits

pitch, or control of fan speed. Furnace pressure control is accomplished by manipulation of the ID fan(s). The furnace pressure control loop maintains furnace pressure to approximately a –0.5″ WG (–0.9 mm Hg). A feed forward from FD fan demand is provided to position the ID fan control device.

Three pressure transmitters are used to monitor furnace pressure and are arranged in a median select function block to ensure the pressure signal integrity to the furnace pressure controller. The furnace pressure controller compares measured furnace pressure to the furnace pressure set point and generates a demand that is summed with the secondary air feed-forward signal. This ID fan demand is subject to overriding action as described in the next section.

Furnace Pressure Directional Blocking

To protect the furnace from potential damage due to excessive positive or negative pressures, directional blocking of the FD and ID fans is provided.

If furnace pressure goes excessively low, the control system responds as follows:

- Further increases in demand to the ID fan control devices are blocked.
- Further decreases in demand to the FD fan control devices are blocked.

If furnace pressure goes excessively high, the control system responds as follows:

- Further decreases in demand to the ID fan control devices are blocked.
- Further increases in demand to the FD fan control devices are blocked.

For unit airflow control, refer to the specific section associated with control loops that are unique to tangentially fired or fluidized bed steam generators.

Feedwater/Steam Drum Water Level Control (Drum Boilers)

In a drum type steam generator, it is critical to maintain proper drum level at the desired level set point. To achieve this objective, typically, three independent drum level and pressure measurements processed through median select circuits provide the process inputs for the calculation of drum level. Steam drum pressure is used to compensate the raw drum level measurement. The measured differential pressure of the transmitters is adjusted for the differences in specific gravity of the water and steam in the steam drum and the reference leg subcooled water.

From start-up to approximately 25% unit steam flow, steam drum water level is controlled with a single element control scheme. The demand for feedwater is developed in response to the deviation in drum level from drum level set point.

Above approximately 25% unit steam flow, drum level control is transferred to three-element control. In three-element control, the feed-forward signal from unit steam flow provides the primary index of required feedwater flow. This feed-forward signal, summed with drum level error, provides a feedwater set point. A second controller compares this set point to the total measured feedwater flow to develop a demand for feedwater.

CONTROL OF TANGENTIALLY FIRED STEAM GENERATORS

This section describes the major control loops that are required for control of a tangentially fired boiler.

UNIT AIRFLOW CONTROL

As described above, unit airflow control is accomplished through manipulation of the FD fan(s). The boiler master demand provides the uncorrected demand for both fuel and air. This demand signal to the unit airflow controller is cross-limited by measured fuel flow, as described in the combustion control section, minimum unit airflow demand, and the output of the O_2 trim controller. The output of the airflow controller provides a trimming function to the FD fan demand based on the error between unit airflow demand and total measured unit airflow. The FD fan demand is derived from a strong feed-forward signal from unit airflow demand and is trimmed by the output of the airflow controller. This FD fan demand is subject to overriding action as described under Furnace Pressure Directional Blocking above.

SECONDARY AIR DAMPER CONTROL—IN-FURNACE NOx REDUCTION

As described in Chapter 2-Combustion Technology the distribution of combustion air into the furnace is accomplished by control of secondary air dampers located in the windbox. Secondary air dampers are provided to distribute fuel air, auxiliary air, close coupled overfire air, and separated overfire air. The secondary air damper control system is commonly integrated into the overall boiler control system and regulates the distribution of secondary air within the furnace based on unit firing conditions. The secondary air damper control loops are designed to provide several operating advantages:

- Increased boiler turndown capability through the improvements of individual fuel combustion characteristics
- Improved air distribution within the furnace
- Increased unit efficiency through the reduction of excess air requirements
- Improved NOx emissions control

Fuel Air Damper Control

Fuel air dampers are typically ramped as a function of the fuel being fired. For coal-fired units, fuel air dampers are ramped as a function of the associated coal feeder speed.

Auxiliary Air Damper Control

Auxiliary air dampers are used to control the overall windbox to furnace differential pressure. The set point for the auxiliary air damper controller is a function of unit steam flow.

Close-Coupled Overfire Air Control

Close-coupled overfire air (CC-OFA) dampers are controlled as a function of unit airflow. Typically, as unit airflow increases, each level of overfire dampers are ramped open individually and provide a means of staging the overall combustion air delivered to the furnace.

Separated Overfire Air Control

Separated overfire air (SOFA) air dampers are controlled in the same manner as CC-OFA dampers. As unit airflow increases, each level of SOFA air dampers is ramped open.

TFS 2000™ Firing System

The TFS 2000™ firing system provides multiple zone, controlled global staging of the combustion air, via use of the CC-OFA, L-SOFA and H-SOFA (L, low; H, high) air compartments—over the boiler operating envelope (*Fig. 7-30*). The TFS 2000™ firing system relies on controlled stoichiometric conditions to reduce in-furnace NOx formation levels.

The OFA control strategy uses cascade arranged, elevation based, CC-OFA, L-SOFA and H-SOFA damper position ramps. The elevations of CC-OFA dampers are stagger ramped with total measured unit airflow. The L-SOFA elevations and H-SOFA elevations are stagger ramped with total L-SOFA demand and total H-SOFA demand, respectively.

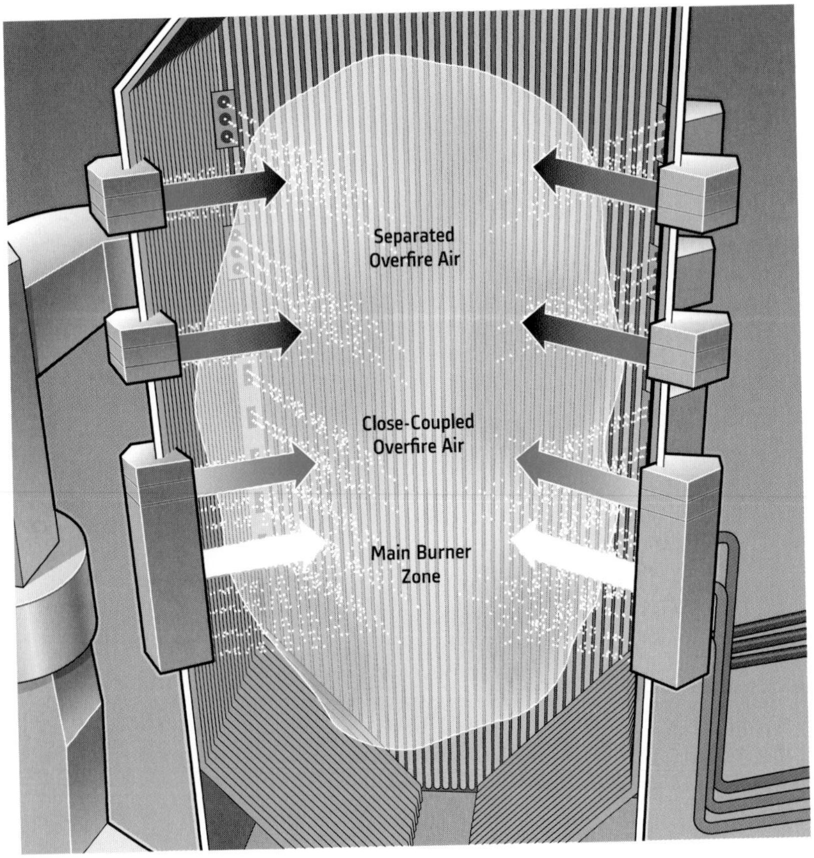

Figure 7-30 | TFS 2000™ Low NOx firing system

The control scheme relies on stoichiometry-based function curves—defining the L-SOFA and H-SOFA flow requirements as a function of total measured unit airflow. These stoichiometry-based curves in combination with SOFA flow measurement are used for modulating the L-SOFA and H-SOFA damper demands and resultant flows to maintain the required stoichiometry profile.

These stoichiometry-based function curves control the main burner zone stoichiometry demand, L-SOFA stoichiometry demand, and H-SOFA demand as a function of total measured unit airflow. For a given total measured unit airflow, the L-SOFA stoichiometry control function curve defines the L-SOFA flow contribution to the total measured unit airflow. The cascaded L-SOFA damper ramp curves establish the individual L-SOFA damper positions or demand, for a given total measured unit airflow. The L-SOFA flow measurement feedback trims and adjusts the overall L-SOFA demand, maintaining the desired L-SOFA contribution to the furnace stoichiometry.

The H-SOFA flow demand for a given operating mode and airflow is determined by subtracting the sum of the L-SOFA stoichiometry contribution plus the main burner zone stoichiometry contribution from the furnace exit stoichiometry or equivalence ratio (i.e., 1.20 at 20% excess air). The resultant required airflow flows through the H-SOFA compartments to maintain the correct final excess air. As described for the L-SOFA above, the cascaded H-SOFA damper ramp curves establish the individual H-SOFA damper positions or demand, for a given total measured unit airflow. The H-SOFA flow measurement feedback trims and adjusts the overall H-SOFA demand, to maintain the desired H-SOFA contribution to the furnace stoichiometry, and final exit O_2 concentration.

FEEDWATER/SEPARATOR STORAGE TANK LEVEL CONTROL (ONCE-THROUGH STEAM GENERATORS)

In a once-through type steam generator, at start-up and at low loads, the control of feedwater is similar to a drum type steam generator, where feedwater demand is controlled in response to the deviation between measured separator storage tank level and separator storage tank level set point.

To achieve this control objective, typically, independent storage tank level and pressure measurements provide the process inputs for the calculation of separator storage tank level. Separator pressure is used to compensate the raw level measurement. The measured differential pressure of the transmitters is adjusted for the differences in specific gravity of the water and steam in the separator storage tank and the reference leg subcooled water.

WET TO DRY TRANSFER

On an Alstom once-through type steam generator, during low load operation, a minimum waterwall flow is established to ensure adequate cooling of the waterwall tubing. This minimum waterwall flow is provided via a boiler circulation pump or through the use of drain valves that recirculate boiler water to a flash tank and return it to the condenser.

A minimum once-through load point is established where the transition from wet to dry operation occurs. Below this load point, waterwall flow is kept constant. In order to achieve once-through operation, feedwater flow, as determined from the separator storage tank level demand, is limited from increasing by the minimum waterwall flow set point. As boiler demand increases above the minimum once-through load point, the increase in firing rate, without a corresponding increase in feedwater flow, forces the boiler into once-through operation. During this transfer, feedwater demand is held from increasing until the separator outlet temperature reaches the desired set point.

ONCE-THROUGH OPERATION

As described above, on a drum type steam generator, the control of feedwater flow is a separate, independent, control loop with no influence or effect on the control of final superheat (SH) steam temperature. On a once-through type of steam generator, the feedwater and steam temperature control loops are interdependent with one another. A change in feedwater flow has a direct effect on steam temperature and a change in SH spray flow indirectly affects the feedwater supply to the boiler's economizer and waterwalls.

Above approximately 30–40% steam flow, the demand for feedwater is established predominately by a feed-forward signal derived from the boiler master demand. This boiler master feed-forward is modified with feedback correction from two controllers in a cascade arrangement. The first controller acts on a load dependent (indexed from boiler master demand) average primary SH spray differential temperature. Its output represents the required adjustment to waterwall heat transfer/steam generation to maintain both the steam conditions and flue gas temperatures entering the superheat section so as to ensure adequate spray water control range. A second controller acts on a load dependent (indexed from boiler master demand) separator outlet temperature set point corrected by the SH spray differential temperature controllers output. This controller acts to adjust feedwater in response to firing system disturbances and the relatively fast effect they have on separator outlet steam temperatures. The overall combined feedwater feedback control action is such that feedwater demand is responsive to changes in the overall unit heat transfer profile.

The combined feed-forward/feedback demand signal is subject to a minimum economizer inlet flow set point (wet mode) activated if the boiler circulation pump is not in service and the unit is being fired. This ensures the minimum economizer inlet cooling flow is maintained by the feedwater supply system in the event the start-up system is not available. The feed-forward/feedback demand signal is subject to a second "wet mode" feedwater demand developed to support separator storage tank level control. The resulting demand provides the set point to a feedwater master controller. The feedback to this controller is the lower of total feedwater flow (as measured before the start-up/recirculation system) or economizer inlet flow. With the start-up system in service (wet mode), economizer inlet flow is greater than feedwater flow due to recirculation. Therefore, feedwater flow is the selected feedback. Three measurements are provided for each of these flows, with each measurement individually temperature compensated. The actual value used for control is the median of three temperature compensated signals.

STEAM TEMPERATURE CONTROL (GENERAL)

On an Alstom tangentially fired steam generator, superheat and reheat steam temperature are controlled by a combination of fuel nozzle tilt positioning, gas recirculation, gas proportioning dampers, desuperheating spray water, adjustment of feedwater to firing rate ratio, and control of excess air. The method of control used is dependant on the type of unit provided and the fuel being fired. Superheat spray water control can be accomplished with either one or two stages of spray water injection (*Figs. 7-31A* and *7-31B*). Reheat spray water control is accomplished with a single stage of spray water with the desuperheater generally located at the cold reheat (RH) inlet (*Figs. 7-31C*).

SH/RH Spray Water Control

Where a single stage desuperheater is provided for either SH or RH control, the control objective of the desuperheater is to control the final steam outlet temperature. Desuperheating spray control is a cascade type control. A master controller associated with final steam outlet temperature develops the set point for a slave controller. The slave controller positions the final spray valve in response to the master output as compared to the associated spray station outlet temperature. *Figures 7-31B* and *7-31C* show typical SH/RH steam temperature control schemes with a single stage desuperheater.

Where two stages of desuperheat are provided for superheat control (*Fig. 7-31A*), the primary objective in control of the primary superheat spray water control valves is to keep the final superheat spray water control valves in their desired operating range. The control structure is a cascade arrangement where the master controller acts on the differential temperature measured across the corresponding final spray station as compared to a load dependent differential temperature set point. The output of this controller represents the required temperature entering the primary superheat section to achieve the desired temperature at the primary SH outlet (i.e., corresponding final spray station inlet). The resulting master output provides the set point to a slave controller. This controller acts on this set point as compared to steam temperature measured at the spray station outlet (i.e., inlet to primary superheat section). The slave controller output provides the spray valve position demand.

The control concept/structure for final superheat spray water control is the same as that provided for a single stage desuperheater.

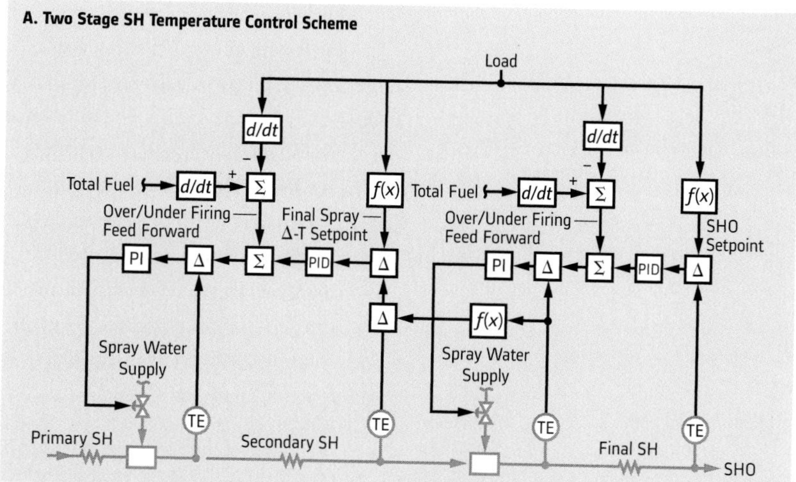

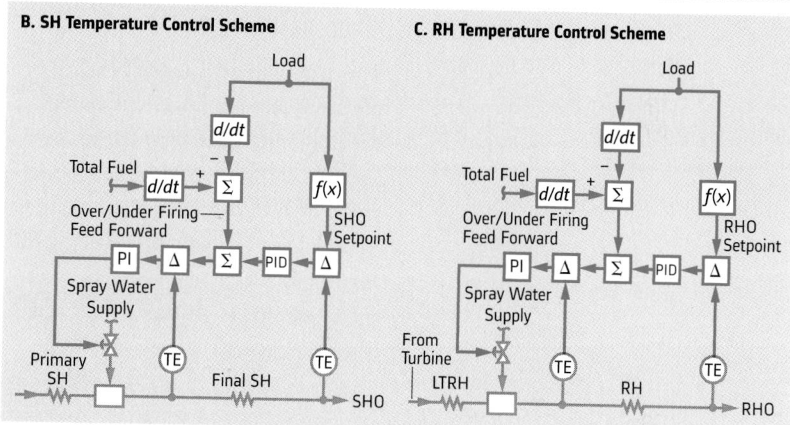

Figure 7-31 | Typical steam temperature control system

SH STEAM TEMPERATURE CONTROL—(DRUM UNITS)

On an Alstom subcritical, drum type, tangentially fired steam generator, steam temperature control is accomplished by a combination of fuel nozzle tilt positioning and superheater and reheater desuperheating sprays. Steam temperature is maintained by allowing fuel nozzle tilts to respond to the lower of either SH or RH outlet temperatures, with sprays responding to the higher. Under normal operating conditions, the fuel nozzle tilts will respond to control RH temperatures.

STEAM TEMPERATURE CONTROL—(ONCE-THROUGH UNITS)

On an Alstom sliding pressure, supercritical, PC unit, SH steam temperature control is accomplished by a combination of adjustment of the feedwater to firing rate ratio and SH desuperheating spray water. Reheat steam temperature control is controlled by a combination of fuel nozzle tilt positioning and reheater desuperheating sprays.

The control of SH spray water is similar to the general spray water control description provided above (*Figs. 7-31A* and *7-31B*). The difference is the interaction between control of spray water and its effect on adjustment of the feedwater to firing rate ratio. As SH spray water flow is controlled to control SH steam temperature, the feedwater to firing rate ratio is adjusted to account for deviations in desired versus actual spray water flow.

BOILER PROTECTION AND BURNER MANAGEMENT SYSTEMS FOR FLUID BED UNITS

This section describes the primary functions and interlocks associated with a fluidized bed steam generator and is in accordance with the requirements of NFPA 85 for a circulating fluidized bed (CFB) boiler. The typical conditions that would cause an emergency shutdown (trip) of a fluidized bed steam generator are as follows:

- Low airflow
- Loss of all secondary air fans
- Loss of all ID fans
- Loss of all primary air fans
- Turbine trip
- Low drum level
- Low combustor temperature
- Loss of fluidizing air
- High furnace-gas-side pressure
- Low furnace-gas-side pressure
- Loss of logic power to BMS
- Loss of primary and redundant BMS processors (if applicable)
- Operator's emergency-trip push buttons depressed

FLUIDIZED BED STEAM GENERATORS—DEGREES OF AUTOMATION

The BMS/BCS arrangement discussed above is commonly called a remote-manual system. With this type of system, the operator initiates the start-up and shutdown of each individual piece of equipment from a remote operating panel. The system logic ensures that the operator commands are performed in the correct sequence and intervenes only when required to prevent a hazardous condition.

An automatic system allows an operator to place in service, or remove from service, a related group of firing equipment (a sub-loop) in the proper sequence by initiating a single command. A typical example of a sub-loop would be the feeder, conveyors, and other equipment associated with a single coal feed point. In the automatic mode of operation, a single operator command to start a coal feeder would initiate the following appropriately timed sequence of events (provided all of the required permit conditions are established):

- Coal isolation valve opened
- Coal conveyor(s) started (if provided)
- Coal feeders started
- Associated secondary air dampers placed into operation

Higher levels of automation are generally not provided as coal feeders are placed into service manually and are regulated via the boiler load demand. Unlike coal feeders on PC fired steam generators where feeders/pulverizers are placed in and out of service to follow boiler load demand, coal feeders on fluidized bed steam generators are operated in unison throughout the load range to ensure proper distribution of solids within the combustor.

BASIC SAFETY FUNCTIONS

Although the BPS/BMS does not regulate the fuel and airflow quantities and does not, in most cases, initiate the start-up or normal shutdown of firing-system components, it does exercise authority over both the operator and the process controls through its safety interlocking features.

If, for example, the combustion control should drop the airflow below the minimum value (typically 25%), the BPS/BMS would trip the fuel automatically. Similarly, it will not permit the operator to start equipment out of prescribed safe sequences and will shut down equipment if prescribed operating practices are not followed. Removing start-up burners before the combustor temperature reaches the minimum set point for firing main fuel, for example, would result in the shutdown of the associated main fuel.

The specific safety interlocking included in the BPS/BMS depends on the physical characteristics of the firing system and type of fuel or fuels being fired. All safety systems of this type, however, are concerned with the following key safety functions:

- A pre-firing purge of the furnace
- Establishment of the appropriate permits for firing the start-up burners
- Establishment of the appropriate permits for firing the main fuel
- Continuous monitoring of firing conditions and other key operating parameters
- Emergency shutdown of portions or all of the firing equipment when required
- A post-firing purge of the steam generator

In a fluid bed steam generator, unlike a PC steam generator, a portion of the bed material is made up of solid fuel that cannot be removed from the furnace during a furnace purge. Therefore, the purpose of the pre-firing purge is to be sure that any unburned gaseous fuel that may have accumulated in the furnace is completely removed prior to initial firing. To do this, a flow of air is passed through the steam generator at a minimum rating (usually 30% of that required for rated steam-generator capacity) for a minimum of 5 minutes. At the same time, secondary air dampers are maintained in a suitable position and the fuel-admission devices are proven closed (or off). This combination of conditions will provide the proper velocities and number of air changes through the furnace and convection pass to ensure the removal of any gaseous fuel accumulations. These purge-permit requirements also provide a check on the proper operation of the air-damper and fuel-admission devices just prior to firing.

On completion of the purge, the steam generator is ready to be fired. The 30% minimum airflow requirement is maintained throughout the operating range of the steam generator including low load operation in order to ensure an air-rich furnace mixture. Initial firing is accomplished with a group of start-up burners that have the capability of lighting the warm-up fuel with an electric spark. A flame detector must be provided with each start-up burner to determine the presence or absence of a stable flame.

Depending on the type of load-carrying fuel and the firing system arrangement, the load-carrying fuel may be placed into service when the combustor temperature reaches the auto ignition temperature of the fuel being fired. Start-up burners remain in service until the combustor temperature reaches the point where the main fuel is self-sustaining.

Start-up of fluid bed combustors requires raising the bed temperature to the level where the main fuel combustion is self sustaining using start-up burners while continuously maintaining safe operating conditions.

COMBUSTOR TEMPERATURE MONITORING

As described above, in a fluidized bed steam generator, due to the absence of a flame characteristic, combustor temperature is continuously monitored. This is accomplished with a series of thermocouples placed in the bed zone of the combustor. These thermocouples ensure that a stable operating condition exists in order to operate the main fuel equipment. In the event that the bed temperature should fall below the minimum temperature set point, a main fuel trip is generated.

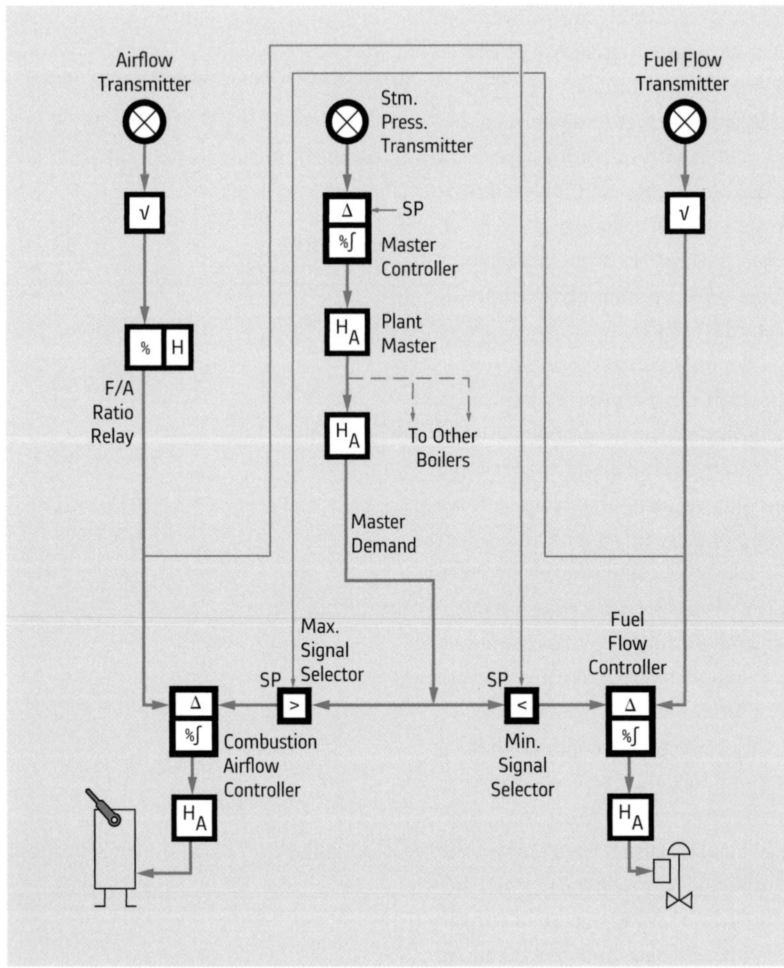

Figure 7-32 | Typical cross-limited metering control system

CONTROL OF CFB BOILERS

CFB boilers, which are described in detail in Chapter 3, include many significant features of operation that the control system designer must consider. In its basic elements, the combustion-control system for a CFB unit is a cross-limited metering system similar to that shown in *Figure 7-32*. Primary air and secondary air are individually controlled combustion-air streams that are staged as a function of firing rate for effective distribution. Seal pot and fluidized bed heat exchanger (FBHE) fluidizing air streams provide additional combustion air and are measured but not modulated. O_2 in the flue gas is measured and automatically adjusts fuel feed rate for fuel/air ratio trim. It is important to maintain the combustor temperature within a narrow band to ensure optimal capture of sulfur dioxide within the combustor. The combustor temperature is controlled by regulating the flow of ash to the FBHE, thereby affecting the distribution of heat absorption in the unit. Sulfur dioxide in the flue gas is measured and is controlled by adjusting the rate of sorbent feed to the combustor. The combustor differential pressure is measured and controlled by varying the rate at which ash is drained from the combustor.

Oil or gas fired start-up burners operate to increase the combustor temperature gradually and at a low rate in order to protect the refractory during start-up. The start-up burners are horizontal burners that are operated with flame monitoring and safety interlocks similar to those required for horizontal burners in conventional boilers. The start-up burners are required to raise the combustor temperature to a level exceeding the auto-ignition temperature of the main fuel. This is a key firing permit for the main fuel interlock in the fluidized bed BPS/BMS.

The CFB combustor may include oil- or gas-fired burner lances designed to provide a fuel input to the combustor in the event of problems with the solid-fuel feed system. The combustor temperature must exceed the auto-ignition temperature of the boiler lance fuel as a permit to fire the burner lances.

FLUID BED STEAM GENERATOR CCS

The control loops in this section describe the primary control loops specifically required to control a fluidized bed steam generator.

AIRFLOW CONTROL

The overall airflow control concept is designed to maintain proper combustor fluidizing air and secondary air to the combustor over the steam generator operating range through an air master station. The boiler master demand serves as the input to an air master control station. The output of the air master control is provided to two independent function curves that determine the required primary and secondary airflows and forms the basis of the primary air/secondary air (PA/SA) ratio.

PRIMARY AIR CONTROL

In a fluidized bed steam generator, primary airflow is used as the means to fluidize the material in the combustor. The demand for primary air is based on primary airflow demand as derived from the airflow PA/SA ratio. The primary airflow controller responds to the error between primary airflow demand and measured primary airflow. The output of the primary air airflow controller provides the demand to the primary air fan inlet vanes. Additional interlocks are provided as described under Furnace Pressure Directional Blocking.

SECONDARY AIR CONTROL

The overall control concept is designed to maintain proper air admission over the furnace profile in addition to total required secondary airflow.

Secondary airflow is controlled by modulation of the secondary air fan inlet vanes. The demand for secondary air is based on secondary airflow demand as derived from the airflow PA/SA ratio. The secondary airflow controller responds to the error between secondary airflow demand and measured secondary airflow. Additional interlocks are provided as described under Furnace Pressure Directional Blocking.

The distribution of the secondary air to the furnace is controlled by furnace front and rear wall secondary air dampers and through the start-up burner combustion air dampers. The secondary air dampers are sequentially opened and closed automatically based on unit steam flow and location of the introduction of solid fuel.

FURNACE TEMPERATURE CONTROL

The CFB furnace temperature is kept as constant as possible for optimum sulfur capture. At steady state load, the rate of energy withdrawal (consumer demand) is balanced with a defined rate of energy supply (fuel feed rate) and the furnace temperature is maintained

The ability to capture sulfur compounds within the combustion process is one of the salient features of fluidized bed combustion technology.

at a constant temperature for optimum performance. During a load change, the energy demand and supply become temporarily unbalanced. This can create variations in furnace temperature. The furnace temperature control loop minimizes these temperature deviations. It does so by varying the flow of solids returning to the furnace via the finishing superheat FBHE.

The finishing superheat FBHE ash control valve provides the means for varying the flow of solids to the finishing superheat fluid bed heat exchanger. The primary demand to this ash control valve is a load dependent feed-forward signal with corrective feedback action from the furnace temperature controller and the superheater outlet temperature controller. The furnace temperature controller receives process feedback from the average of a predetermined number of flue gas temperature measurements with a fixed furnace temperature set point providing the reference value. A measured temperature in excess of the set point will open the ash control valve. This control action will reduce the amount of hot solids returned directly to the furnace. It will also increase the amount of cooled solids returned to the furnace from the SH fluid bed heat exchanger. The heat removed from the hot solids diverted to the fluid bed heat exchanger equals the increase in heat transferred to the finishing superheat steam.

FURNACE DIFFERENTIAL PRESSURE CONTROL

The furnace differential set point can be derived as a function of unit steam flow or can be entered by the operator during start-up. The furnace differential pressure controller responds to control the inventory of solids recirculating within the boiler. The amount of recirculating solids correlates to heat transfer. The differential pressure measured between the furnace air plenum and the furnace outlet compared to the set point provides the basis for regulating material inventory. To maintain the proper combustor differential pressure set point, material is removed from the bottom of the combustor. This can be accomplished with ash control valves that discharge material into a fluid bed ash cooler or with ash screw coolers that discharge material directly into an ash handling system. In either case, the demand is modulated to control the level of solids circulating within the boiler.

SO_2 EMISSIONS CONTROL

Sorbent flow to the furnace controls flue gas SO_2 emissions leaving the steam generator. The required sorbent feed rate is related to coal feed rate. The basic demand for sorbent is established from total measured coal flow multiplied by an operator-entered coal/sorbent ratio. Measured flue gas SO_2 concentration from the SO_2 analyzer system, located at the steam generator outlet or stack, provides the process feedback to an SO_2 controller. The operator manually adjusts this controller set point. The SO_2 controller output acts as a trim to the basic sorbent demand. A sorbent master controller responds to the error between the sorbent demand and the total measured sorbent feed rate. The sorbent master output provides the demand for sorbent feed rate.

STEAM TEMPERATURE CONTROL—GENERAL

The methods used to control steam temperature in a fluid bed steam generator vary to some degree. In general, superheat steam temperature is controlled by a combination of superheat spray water flow and either solids flow through an external FBHE or control of flue gas distribution using dampers located in the backpass. Reheat temperature is controlled by the control of solids through a FBHE, control of flue gas distribution with backpass dampers, or control of reheat bypass steam flow. RH spray water flow is used as a backup to the above for unit operation during abnormal operating conditions. For a general understanding of steam temperature control, the section below describes control of steam temperature using FBHEs.

SUPERHEAT TEMPERATURE CONTROL

The heat transfer surfaces associated with superheat steam are split between the finishing superheat FBHE, the SH vertical panels, and the furnace backpass. Superheat outlet temperature is maintained by a combination of solids flow through the finishing superheat FBHE and the superheater desuperheater spray water station. Superheat outlet temperature set point is derived as a function of boiler steam flow or can be entered manually by the operator.

The position of the superheat FBHE ash control valve determines the distribution of solids returned directly to the furnace and solids flowing through the superheat FBHE. The amount of solids flowing through the FBHE directly affects the heat transfer to the finishing superheat steam.

As mentioned above, the primary demand to the SH FBHE ash control valve is a load dependent feed-forward signal with corrective feedback action from the furnace temperature controller and from the SH outlet temperature controller. When the furnace temperature is within established limits, the demand to the ash control valve is trimmed by the superheat temperature controller. This SH outlet controller responds to the error between superheat outlet temperature set point and superheat outlet temperature. This same superheat temperature set point (plus an offset bias) and final superheat outlet temperature serve as the inputs to the superheater desuperheater spray valve master controller. The addition of the offset bias ensures the superheater desuperheater spray control valve will only respond to excessive superheat temperatures avoiding undesirable interaction between the superheater desuperheater and finishing superheat FBHE solids flow control.

Desuperheating spray water control is a cascade type control. A master controller associated with final steam outlet temperature develops the set point for a slave controller. The slave controller positions the desuperheat spray valve in response to the master output as compared to the associated spray station outlet temperature.

REHEAT STEAM TEMPERATURE CONTROL

The heat transfer surfaces associated with reheat steam are split between the reheat FBHE and the

The use of a fluid bed heat exchanger allows for independent control of superheat and reheat steam temperatures, which is a unique feature of CFB technology.

furnace backpass. Reheat steam outlet temperature is maintained by a combination of solids flow through the reheat FBHE and the reheat desuperheater spray water flow.

The position of the reheat FBHE ash control valve determines the distribution of solids returned directly to the furnace and solids flowing through the reheat FBHE. The amount of solids flowing through this FBHE directly affects the heat transfer to the reheat steam.

The primary demand to the RH FBHE ash control valve is a load dependent feed-forward signal with corrective feedback action from the reheat outlet temperature controller. Reheat outlet temperature set point can be derived as a function of unit steam flow or can be manually entered by the operator. The reheat outlet temperature set point (plus an offset bias) and final reheat outlet temperature serve as the inputs to the reheat desuperheater spray valve master controller. The addition of the offset bias ensures the reheat spray valve will only respond to excessive reheat temperatures, avoiding undesirable interaction between the reheat desuperheater and reheat FBHE solids flow control.

The reheat desuperheater spray control loop employs a cascade configuration similar to that described above for SH spray water control.

FURNACE IMPLOSIONS

Earlier in this chapter, techniques to prevent furnace explosions were discussed. In the mid-1970s, a new problem, which came to be known as a furnace implosion, appeared. Before discussing the impact of the implosion phenomenon on steam generator control systems, the fundamental nature of the problem should be examined.

THE IMPLOSION PHENOMENON

Two basic mechanisms can cause a negative pressure excursion of sufficient magnitude to cause structural damage. The first of these mechanisms is well understood and is applicable to multiple burner, tangentially fired, steam generators as well as fluid bed steam generators. The second mechanism is not applicable to fluid bed steam generators as the temperature of the flue gas in the combustor does not change rapidly as a result of a master fuel trip. This is due to the large inventory of solids resident in a fluid bed steam generator.

The first mechanism is well understood. Simply attach to a boiler an ID fan that is capable of producing more suction head than the boiler structure is capable of withstanding. Next, through control malfunction and/or operator error, establish circumstances that result in this pressure capability being applied to the structure. An example is opening the dampers on an operating ID fan with the FD fan dampers closed, which can result in a destructive negative pressure with the boiler not being fired. The second mechanism, the so-called flame collapse or flameout effect, is not generally understood. As a matter of fact, the use of such terms as flame collapse has led to many distorted conceptions of the physical reality.

It is important to understand negative pressure excursion following a fuel trip and loss of furnace flame, in order to realistically evaluate pitfalls and preventive techniques. The physical state of the gases in a furnace or other subsystem at any instant in time can be described by the Perfect Gas Law as follows:

$$PV = MRT$$

Equation 7-2

where:

P = absolute pressure
V = volume of system under consideration
M = resident mass (not mass flow)
R = the universal gas constant
T = absolute temperature, all in consistent units

Because V is fixed and R is approximately constant, P is directly proportional to the product MT. Thus, for two different conditions of pressure and temperature in a given boiler system, this approximate relationship holds:

$$\frac{P_2}{P_1} = \frac{M_2T_2}{M_1T_1}$$

Equation 7-3

During steady state operation, P is held constant at approximately atmospheric pressure by balancing the resident mass M and the existing temperature T. Furnace temperature in a steam generator is not directly controlled and depends on the thermal balance between the heat in (in the burning fuel and heated air) and the heat out (in the flue gas and heat transferred to the pressure parts). The resident mass is automatically balanced by controlling the flue gas flow out of the boiler to maintain a given furnace pressure.

When the fuel input is terminated, this balance no longer exists. The flue gas being pulled out of the furnace by the ID fan is now being replaced only by preheated air rather than by the products of combustion in the firing zone. As a result, the average temperature of the gases resident in the furnace (or other subsystem) at any given time following the fuel trip will decrease rapidly. Because of the temperature drop, the pressure in the furnace starts to decrease (*Fig. 7-33*).

If the resident mass were to remain constant in quantity, the absolute pressure in the furnace would drop in direct proportion to the absolute temperature drop. A gage pressure of −1.0″ WG (−0.2 cm Hg) is equivalent to 406″ WG absolute (75.9 cm Hg absolute). Thus, with a constant resident mass, a 10% change in absolute temperature would cause a 10% change in furnace pressure; that is, 40.6″ WG (7.6 cm Hg absolute). Fortunately, the natural characteristics of FD and ID fans and their control devices are such that a constant resident mass situation is virtually impossible to achieve.

Assume, for the moment, that all FD and ID fan dampers are fixed

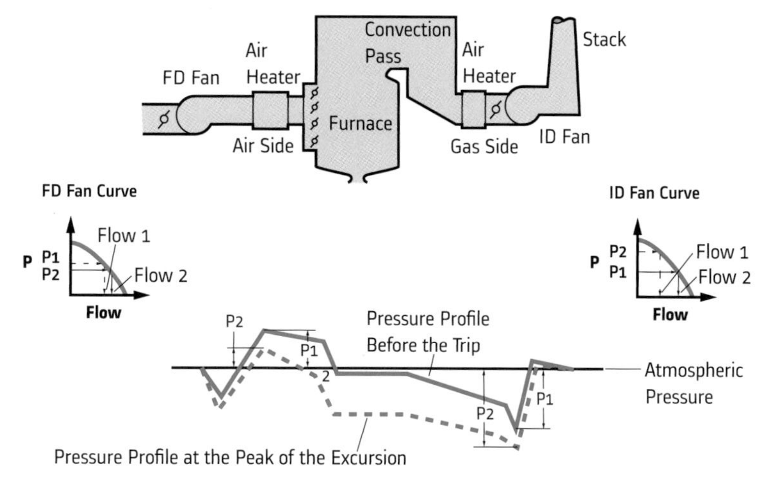

Figure 7-33 | Pressure profile in a balanced-draft unit

in position. As the furnace pressure begins to decay because of the temperature decay, the fans will move to different operating points on their respective performance curves. The FD fan will move in the direction of increasing volume, the ID fan in the direction of decreasing volume (*Fig. 7-34*).

- The airflow through the windbox will increase because the lower furnace pressure appears to the FD fan to be a reduced system resistance.
- The flue gas flow will decrease because the lower furnace pressure appears to the ID fan to be an increased system resistance.

The net effect of this increase in airflow and reduction in gas flow is to increase the resident mass in the furnace, which tends to compensate for the temperature decay. This natural corrective action taken by the FD and ID fans is a key ingredient in the ability to contain furnace pressure excursions to values that are within tolerable limits. It should be apparent that the Perfect Gas Law does not recognize the difference between:

- Types of firing systems (corner, front and rear, dry-bottom, or slagging bottom)
- Coal firing, oil firing, or gas firing
- Balanced-draft or pressurized operation

To understand, then, why the most serious implosion problems have been experienced with oil fired, balanced-draft boilers, it is necessary to keep in mind that the key to holding furnace pressure constant is to maintain the product of resident mass and temperature constant. On a pressurized boiler, the action of the FD fan during normal operation pushes the flue gases out of the furnace.

When the combustion process in such a pressurized unit is terminated, the resulting temperature decay causes the furnace pressure to drop rapidly. As soon as the furnace pressure drops below atmospheric pressure (ignoring stack effect), the flue gas will no longer leave the furnace but the airflow will continue to enter. Moreover, any additional decrease in furnace pressure will cause a reverse flow down the stack, back into the furnace.

When firing is terminated on a balanced-draft unit, flue gas (with its mass at furnace temperature) will be pulled out of the furnace until the pressure there reaches a negative value that is directly related to the cutoff pressure of the ID fan corresponding to the temperature entering the fan. The higher the head capability of the ID fan, the larger the pressure excursions that may be experienced.

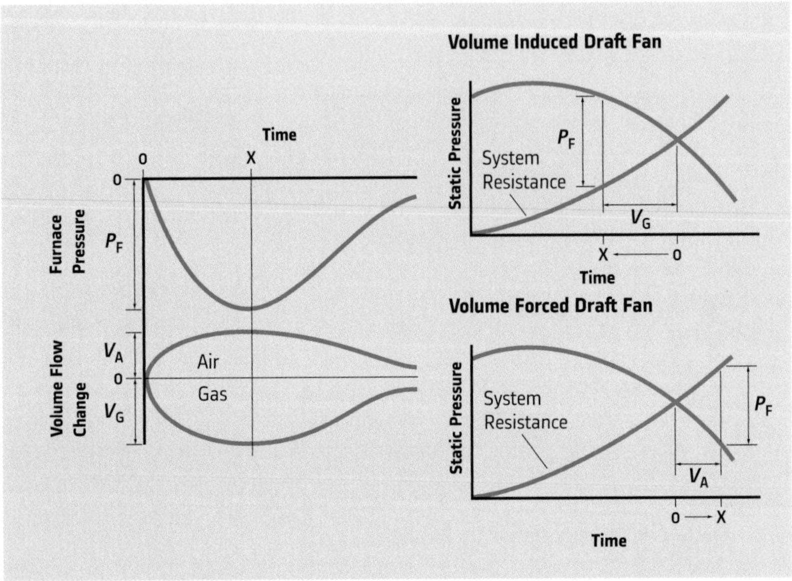

Figure 7-34 | Destructive negative pressure (DNP) with constant speed, centrifugal fans and dampers locked

Thus, although some authors have attempted to treat the ID fan characteristics and the fuel cutoff as two independent effects, they are actually inseparable.

With respect to PC and oil firing, the difference is one of the rate of temperature change. This rate depends on how fast a given percentage of the furnace volume undergoes a replacement of combustion products with preheated air. Coal-fired units have the following characteristics that produce a slower temperature decay:

1. The fuel cutoff is generally more gradual than with oil firing, because of the pulverized fuel residual in the pulverizer and fuel piping.
2. The ratio of resident mass to mass flow rate is higher than for an oil-fired boiler, because coal-fired furnaces are significantly larger in size than oil-fired only furnaces.

THE ID FAN

In connection with the implosion phenomenon, it is most important that engineers responsible for draft-system and furnace-framing-system design understand how an ID fan operates, how it is controlled, and how it responds to changes in the inlet pressure that it "sees."

ID fans are used singly, or in multiples of two, three, or four, to evacuate the products of combustion from a boiler furnace while maintaining the pressure at the top of such a furnace about 0.5″ WG (0.9 mm Hg) below atmospheric pressure. Centrifugal-type ID fans customarily are equipped with inlet vanes or inlet louver dampers for control of the volumetric flow of gas through them. These devices have similar control characteristics (as compared to outlet dampers or variable-speed drives), but can have widely varying time constants, depending on the type of actuator used to move them.

Figure 7-35 shows the effect on the pressure/volume curve of such a fan when either vanes or dampers are closed to reduce the gas through-flow. On this curve, fan static-pressure capability is plotted against rated volume, and a system-pressure curve is shown, a simple square relationship of static pressure to volume (static pressure is proportional to volume squared).

The control device is regulated so that the required static pressure to satisfy the resistance of the physical system is developed at any given volumetric flow rate. But, at the same time, for the particular vane position, a fan characteristic curve is established such that the fan is capable of an infinite number of discrete static-pressure values versus any given volumetric flow.

Consider an operating mode in which the ID fan control vanes or dampers are capable of infinitely fast response. Any change in the furnace pressure of a balanced-draft unit that

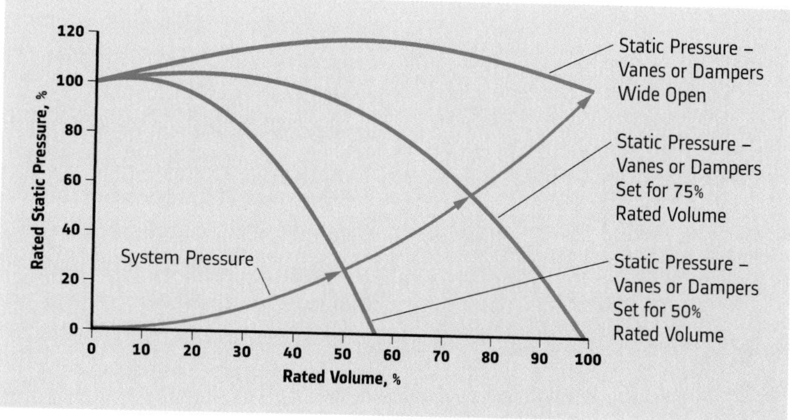

Figure 7-35 | The effect on a centrifugal-type ID-fan pressure/volume curve when either vanes or dampers are positioned to reduce the gas through-flow

is sensed by the system will cause the vanes to change position to maintain the required system static pressure exactly, and along the system-pressure curve. For instance, if there should be a reduction in furnace pressure (caused, say, by a decrease in the fuel fired and the corresponding combustion airflow), the vanes will immediately close to reduce the gas flow handled by the fan before the furnace pressure drops any further. With such infinitely fast vane control assumed, even with an instantaneous very large drop in furnace pressure level (such as there could be if there were a master fuel trip or if the FD fan dampers were to accidentally close), the system curve will always be followed and the ID fan will make instantaneous corrections to maintain furnace pressure at the level preset (below atmospheric).

Another condition can be postulated, in which the control vanes or dampers are maintained in a fixed position as boiler load varies. This is equivalent to a zero rate of damper response. When boiler load decreases (and fuel flow, airflow, and gas flow decrease correspondingly), the developed fan static pressure increases following a static-pressure versus volume curve sloping upward to the left; furnace suction (pressure below atmospheric) increases rapidly. The obvious limit to the furnace suction that can be developed is the highest static-pressure value on the curve, which for damper settings below 50%, appears to be at or about the fan no-load cutoff value (the static head developed by a fan when its volumetric delivery is zero).

Under normal load-changing conditions, if fan vanes are maintained at a given position, either accidentally or purposely, furnace suction will vary, with the maximum static-pressure capability of the fan being the limit. Under these conditions, of course, FD airflow continues, but is automatically varied with boiler firing rate.

Assume that a master fuel trip occurs under this condition of vanes-maintained-in-position. Assume further that the FD fan dampers close quickly, so that there is a rapid decrease in the gas available to the ID fan. The ID fan will immediately ride up along the characteristic curve to the cutoff point; after reaching the cutoff point, reverse flow of gas down the stack will occur (at some indeterminable flow rate) until the furnace suction that has been established by the decrease in the average gas temperature is satisfied. If the rate of reverse flow is not high enough, the furnace will fail structurally if the framing system is not capable of withstanding the low absolute pressure that results from the fuel trip.

Of course, what happens during a master fuel trip, in which equipment is on automatic control, is somewhere between the above two postulated situations. Fan dampers or vanes close in an effort to reduce the gas flow leaving the furnace, restricting the magnitude of the furnace pressure level reduction. With good mechanical response to the control signal (particularly if an "early" signal has been received through the use of a feed-forward arrangement), fan static-pressure capability will match the furnace suction being developed as a result of the reduction in furnace gas temperature, all while the volumetric gas flow through the fan is being reduced to zero. Ultimately, this frustrates any implosion tendency.

The above analysis applies to constant-speed, centrifugal-type, or vane-controlled axial-flow fans. A similar approach can be used in assessing the implosion potential of variable-speed centrifugal, or variable-pitch axial-flow fans.

CONTROL IMPLICATIONS

Implosion concerns have resulted in many control system developments. The NFPA has issued the NFPA 85 code, which provides specific requirements to minimize the occurrences of implosions. Each steam generator manufacturer has established specific recommendations to meet these requirements. Space does not permit going into the specifics of the control system designs that are outlined in such recommendations. However, the following must be provided in any furnace-draft and combustion-control system:

1. The airflow to a furnace must be maintained at its pre-trip value and must not be prevented from increasing by following natural fan curves. Positive control action to increase airflow is not allowed by NFPA.
2. The flow of combustion products from a furnace must be reduced as quickly as possible following a unit trip.
3. If the removal of fuel from the furnace can be over a 5–10 s period (rather than instantaneously), there will be a reduction in the magnitude of the furnace pressure excursion that follows a unit trip.

Obviously, even the most carefully designed control system will be of limited value if all its components are not completely installed, if it has not been properly checked out or is in "poor tune," or if it has been inadequately maintained. It is essential, therefore, that protective control systems for large, high draft-loss boilers be properly designed, installed, tested, and maintained, and that plant operators consider these control systems to be vital.

JACK O'ROURKE
MARC THOMAS
JEAN-PAUL DROUIN
MARK WAGNER
RICH DONAIS

Materials for Fossil-Fueled Steam Generators

Chapter **Eight**

A wide variety of materials are used in the construction of fossil-fueled steam generators, ranging from structural steel support members to refractory ceramic insulation to wear-resistant tungsten carbide composites in coal pulverizers to low- and high-alloy steels for high-temperature pressure parts. The latter materials are the focus of this chapter, both because the capabilities of alloys for pressure parts in the furnace and backpass set limits on the maximum steam pressure and temperature (and, hence, efficiency) of the unit and because these components tend to be the most prone to failure in service as a result of the demanding environment in which they operate. This chapter presents an introductory description of the metallurgy, processing, properties, and applications of alloys used for pressure parts in fossil-fueled boilers, and common failure modes observed. The chapter concludes with an overview of recent developments in alloys for advanced supercritical steam plants with high efficiency.

FUNCTIONAL REQUIREMENTS FOR PRESSURE PART MATERIALS

Pressure parts in steam generators are subject to highly demanding operating conditions. The key functional requirements for these components are to contain water or steam at high pressure and temperature and, for waterwall, superheater, and reheater tubes, to absorb heat released during the combustion process, whether directly by radiation from the fireball or from hot, flowing combustion gases. These fundamental requirements translate into the following set of specific material requirements:

1. **Strength at low and high temperatures to resist stresses induced by high-pressure water and steam.** For steam piping, headers, manifolds, and superheater and reheater tubing, the resistance to long-term creep deformation and rupture is a critical property.
2. **Compatibility with the expected service environment.** This includes resistance to oxidation and corrosion by high-temperature water or steam on the inside of tubes and pipes as well as resistance to high-temperature, fireside corrosion on the outside of tubes exposed to the combustion environment.
3. **Ease of fabrication, including bending, forging, and welding.** Good fabricability usually is a trade-off with increased strength: High-strength alloys tend to be more difficult to fabricate, requiring greater care and precision.
4. **Appropriate thermal and physical properties for efficient heat transfer and reduced stresses associated with thermal transients.** Efficient heat transfer requires high thermal conductivity, whereas transient thermal stresses are reduced by both high thermal conductivity and low coefficient of thermal expansion.
5. **Overall cost, including raw material costs, costs of fabrication, and costs of any heat treatment required.** A more expensive (per unit of weight),

higher-strength alloy may have lower overall cost because of the reduced component weight that is permitted by higher allowable stresses.

The aim of the designer of a large steam generating unit is to use materials and fabricating methods in the most economical way to produce a unit that will perform properly throughout its planned useful life. Achieving these objectives requires a fundamental knowledge of material properties and behavior under a wide range of manufacturing and service conditions.

BASIC METALLURGY OF STEEL

Steels are alloys of iron and carbon that have carbon contents of less than approximately 2% by weight (all compositions referred to in this chapter are by weight). Iron–carbon alloys with carbon contents of greater than 2% typically are used in cast form only and are termed *cast irons*. In addition to carbon, steels may contain a wide range of additional alloying elements, including manganese, silicon, chromium, molybdenum, nickel, vanadium, and others. The function of some of these alloying additions in different classes of steels is described later in the chapter.

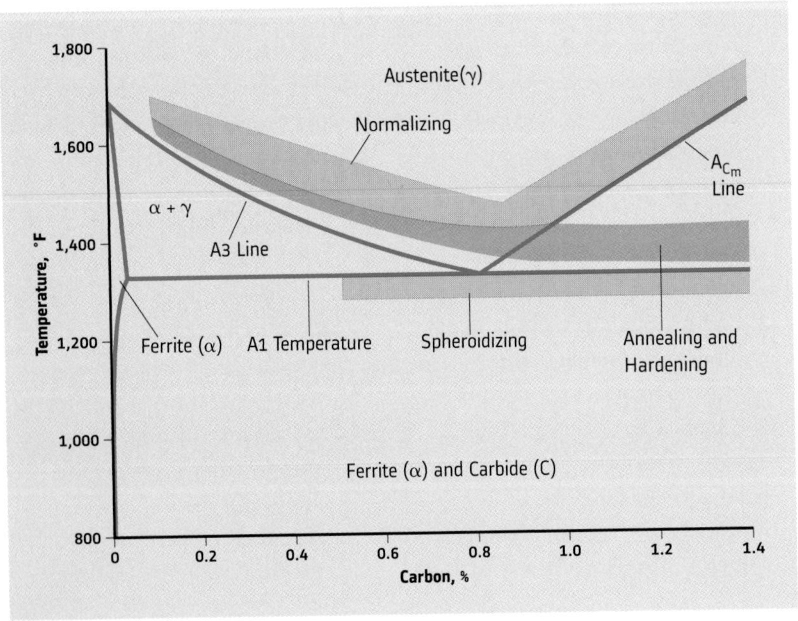

Figure 8-1 | Iron-rich section of the iron–carbon phase diagram

IRON–CARBON PHASE DIAGRAM

Figure 8-1 shows the iron–carbon phase diagram, which is the foundation for describing the structure and heat treatment of steel. A *phase* is a body of matter with a specific, uniform physical form (e.g., liquid, gas, or solid). A particular lattice structure (fixed physical arrangement of atoms) in a crystalline solid, such as a metal, constitutes a unique phase. Pure iron exists in three solid phases, depending on the temperature:

1. At low temperatures (<1,670°F [910°C]), iron has a body-centered cubic (BCC) crystal structure, which is termed *ferrite* or α phase (and sometimes *α-ferrite*).
2. Between 1,670 and 2,535°F (910–1,391°C), the face-centered cubic (FCC) crystal structure, which is termed austenite or γ *phase*, is stable.
3. From 2,535°F (1,391°C) to the melting point of 2,795°F (1,535°C), another BCC phase, which is termed *δ-ferrite*, is stable.

An alloy may contain one or more phases, depending on the composition and temperature. The phase diagram in *Figure 8-1* depicts the phases that are thermodynamically stable at a defined temperature and carbon content in a simple iron–carbon steel. At low temperatures and carbon content above approximately 0.025% (the solubility limit of carbon in ferrite), steel consists of a mixture of two solid phases, ferrite and cementite. *Cementite* is the mineral name of the iron carbide, Fe_3C. Depending on the specific heat treatment of the steel, the cementite may be present as either discrete spherical particles, as shown in *Figure 8-2*, or as a lamellar mixture of cementite and ferrite, which is a microconstituent termed *pearlite*, as shown in *Figure 8-3*.

The physical shape and arrangement of different phases in an alloy, as seen in an optical microscope at magnifications of up to ×1,000, is termed the *microstructure*. *Figures 8-2* and *8-3* represent two different microstructures observed in low-carbon steels. The microstructure has a critical influence on the properties of an alloy—manipulation of the microstructure to obtain desirable properties is one of the prime objectives in metallurgical engineering.

At higher temperatures, between approximately 1,300 and 2,400°F (700–1,300°C), the austenite phase is stable. Because carbon has a greater solubility in the FCC structure of austenite, cementite present at low temperature dissolves, and only a single phase is present. The difference in carbon solubility between ferrite and austenite is the fundamental basis for the strengthening of steels by heat treatment. Carbide phases are taken into solution during high-temperature heat treatments, such as annealing and normalizing (*Table 8-1*), then reprecipitated in a controlled manner during cooling and subsequent tempering.

The ferrite and austenite stability regions are separated by a small area in which both phases are present. The A_1 temperature is the lower boundary of the two-phase region and is frequently termed the *lower critical temperature*. The A_1 temperature for a simple Fe-C

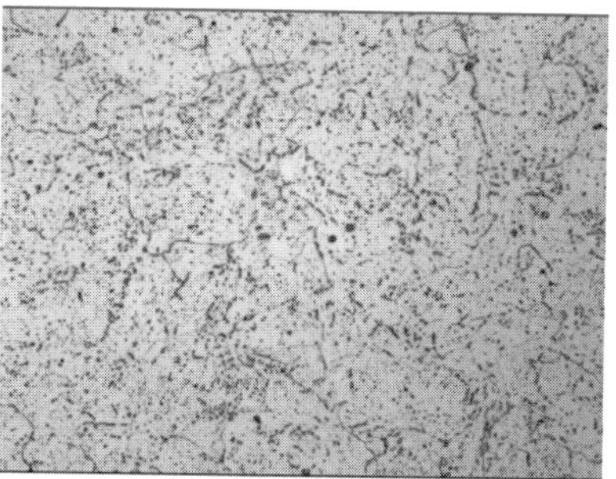

20 microns

Figure 8-2 | Typical microstructure of spheroidized cementite in a ferrite matrix. Cementite is observed as fine black particles; the light background phase is ferrite

20 microns

Figure 8-3 | Typical microstructure of pearlite in a ferrite matrix. Pearlite, a lamellar mixture of cementite and ferrite, comprises the darker patches; the white background phase is ferrite

TABLE 8-1 | PROCESSES FOR HEAT TREATMENT

Process	Example	Purpose	Procedure
Annealing	Cold-worked metals	To remove work-hardening and increase ductility	Heat above the recrystallization temperature.
Annealing	Steel	To soften	Heat into the austenitic range, and then slow cool, usually by furnace cooling.
Normalizing	Steel	To homogenize, relieve strains, and refine grain size; also to form martensite in 9–12% Cr steels	Heat into the austenitic range, and then air cool.
Process annealing and stress-relieving	Steel	To soften and toughen	Heat close to, but below, the lower critical temperature (A_1).
Spheroidizing	Steel	To soften and toughen	Heat for a sufficiently long time close to, but below, the lower critical temperature (A_1).
Quenching	Steel	To harden	Rapidly cool by immersion into water or oil.
Tempering	Steel	To toughen	Heat at temperatures below the lower critical temperature (A_1).
Solution treating	Stainless steel	To soften and produce a single-phase alloy; to dissolve carbides and other precipitates	Heat to a suitable temperature for sufficient time to bring one or more constituents into solution and then rapidly cool to room temperature.
Age-hardening	Ni-base alloys	To harden	Solution treat first, and then reheat to intermediate temperature to cause precipitation of hardening phases.

steel is 1,333°F (723°C); this temperature will vary with other alloying additions. The upper boundary is the A_3 temperature, also termed the *upper critical temperature*. The A_1 temperature is more important in practice, because it defines the upper limits of heat treatments such as tempering or subcritical annealing.

Additional elements in the steel will alter the phases that are present and the regions of phase stability, although for low-alloy steels, the basic shape of the iron–carbon phase diagram still holds. For very highly alloyed steels, such as stainless steels with chromium contents of greater than 18% and nickel contents of greater than 8%, the austenite phase is stable at room temperature, and the steel is referred to as an "austenitic stainless steel."

TRANSFORMATION DIAGRAMS

Phase diagrams describe the phases that are present at thermodynamic equilibrium (e.g., those present after a long holding time at temperature or those formed by extremely slow heating and cooling). At lower temperatures, true equilibrium phases may not be achieved in practical time frames because of the slow movement rates of atoms. Transformation diagrams depict the phase changes that occur on cooling a steel from the austenite phase field at different rates or after various holding times at constant temperature. These diagrams account for the kinetics of transformation—that is, the time needed for atoms to rearrange themselves from the structure stable at one temperature (e.g., austenite) to structures stable at a new, lower temperature (e.g., ferrite and cementite).

Two types of transformation diagrams are used in metallurgical practice: the continuous-cooling-transformation (CCT) diagram, and the time-temperature-transformation (TTT) diagram. The CCT diagram depicts phase changes that occur on cooling from the austenite field at different rates; the TTT diagram depicts the kinetics of transformations that occur after rapid cooling to a particular temperature and then holding at that temperature.

An example CCT diagram for an advanced 2¼Cr steel (Grade T24) is shown in *Figure 8-4*. The starting point is the upper left corner of the graph. Lines depicting various cooling rates emanate from this point. The intersection of cooling rate lines with areas of phase formation depict which phases are formed on cooling at a particular rate.

Two microconstituents found on the CCT diagram that are not present

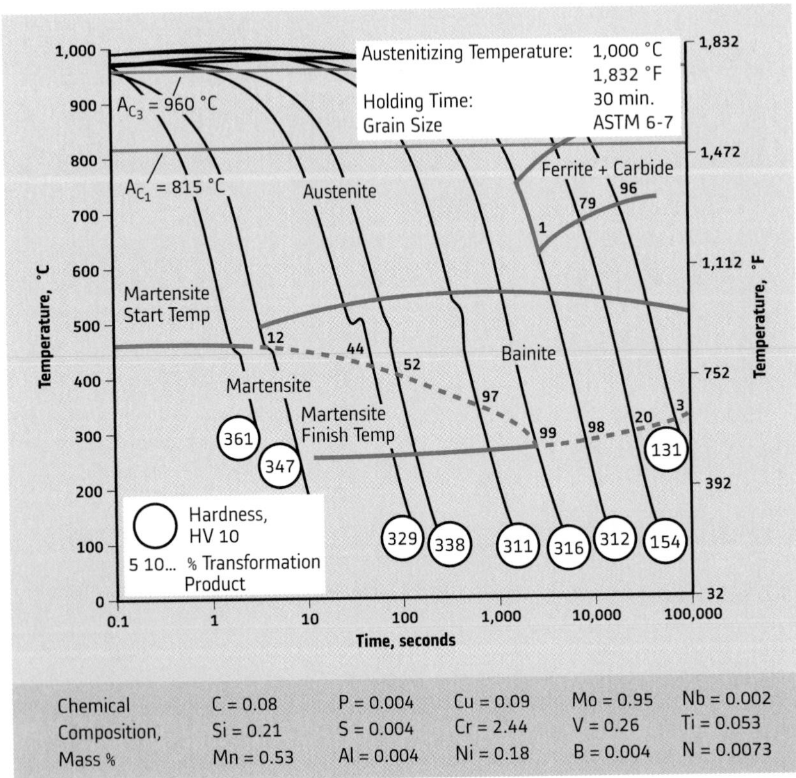

Figure 8-4 | Continuous-cooling-transformation diagram for an advanced 2¼ Cr steel (Grade T24)

on the equilibrium phase diagram for this steel are martensite and bainite. These non-equilibrium structures form on rapid cooling of some steels from the austenite phase field. Martensite is an actual phase with a body centered tetragonal crystal structure and is very hard and brittle. Low carbon martensites have a characteristic lath-like structure, as shown in *Figure 8-5*. Bainite is ferrite with a fine dispersion of carbides and the ferrite can take on a lath-like or plate-like structure depending on the temperature at which the bainite forms. Bainite is not as hard and forms at slower cooling rates than martensite does. If formed as part of a heat treatment operation, both of these phases are subsequently tempered (i.e., heat treated below the A_1 temperature) to reduce hardness and increase ductility. Much slower cooling from the austenite phase field will produce the equilibrium structure of ferrite and cementite, which has a much lower hardness.

With this knowledge, it sometimes is possible to use the structure observed in post-mortem metallurgical examination of a pressure part to estimate the temperature that the component has experienced in service, which can be useful in failure mechanism diagnosis.

GRAIN STRUCTURE

A grain is a single crystal within a solid composed of many similar crystals. Within any particular grain, all of the atoms are arranged onto a single crystal lattice, but, at the boundary between two adjacent grains, a transition zone exists that is not directly aligned with either grain. The grain boundary transition zone represents a crystal lattice defect, which frequently is a point of weakness. When a metal is observed under a microscope, although the individual atoms cannot be seen, the grain boundaries can be readily located if the metal has been polished to a mirror-like surface and etched with an acid. The grain boundaries are attacked differently from the body of the grain (because of the local atomic disorder) and become visible. Different phases also may become visible.

Figure 8-6 shows the microstructure of an austenitic stainless steel with fine and coarse grains. The grain size in an alloy may be controlled by combinations of mechanical processing and heat treatment. The ideal grain size for an alloy will depend on the specific properties required; for example, a fine grain size may give good low-temperature tensile strength but reduced elevated-temperature creep strength.

FABRICATION PROCESSES

A number of fabrication processes are used to create boiler components, such as waterwalls, steam drums, headers, and superheater assemblies, from stock tubing, piping, and plate received from steel manufacturers. These processes include bending, rolling, forging, and welding, and depending on the alloy, they may enhance or degrade the properties. Heat treatment may be performed either before or after fabrication to enhance or restore the structure and properties.

BENDING, FORGING, AND ROLLING

Fabrication processes such as bending and forging of tube and pipe and rolling of plate are collectively referred to as either "cold working" or "hot working," depending on whether the operation is carried out near room

Figure 8-5 | Typical lath-like tempered martensite structure observed in an advanced 9Cr steel (Grade 91)

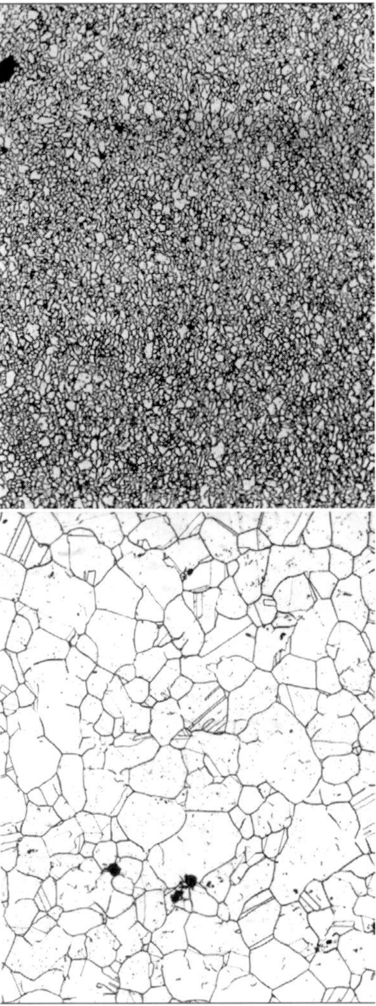

Figure 8-6 | Comparison of fine (top) and coarse (bottom) grain structures in an austenitic stainless steel 100× magnification

temperature (cold working) or at high temperatures (hot working). Working (deforming) metals at low temperatures usually increases the hardness (resistance to further deformation) and reduces ductility. Because of the work-hardening phenomenon, only limited deformation can be performed at low temperature without reannealing the alloy to restore its ductility. Typical cold-working operations include tube bending and roll-expanding tubes into header sockets.

Much greater deformation can be imparted, using lower forces, if the alloy is worked at high temperature. For steels, this typically is in the austenite phase field, above approximately 1,600°F (870°C). The ductility is much greater, and continual annealing and recrystallization occur during the forming operation. Typical hot-working operations include rolling of plate into cylindrical sections and induction bending of pipe.

WELDING

Pressure parts usually are joined by fusion welding, a process in which two metal pieces are joined by locally melting the contacting surfaces, which then cool to a continuous solid. A filler metal usually is added to the joint to fill in the gap between the pieces. Variations of fusion welding processes include the heat source used for melting, the nature of the filler metal used (if any), and the shielding gases used to protect the molten weld metal from oxidation.

A full discussion of welding processes and metallurgy is outside the scope of this book. The key idea to remember in terms of pressure parts in steam generating equipment, however, is that welds have unique microstructures and properties because of the cast nature of the weld metal (as opposed to heavily worked, "wrought" base metals) and the high heat input of welding, which can greatly alter the structure of the base metal adjacent to the weld (the so-called "heat-affected zone"). High stresses also exist in the vicinity of weld joints in the as-welded condition because of the constrained shrinkage of the weld metal and the surrounding heat-affected zone. Even in the absence of defects, the weld thus represents a metallurgical (and, frequently, geometric) discontinuity in the structure of the component and is a common location for cracking. Attention to quality-control procedures during welding processes is critical.

HEAT TREATMENT

Heat treatment is used to alter the structure and, hence, properties of metals and can be used to strengthen, soften, or improve ductility. *Table 8-1* presents a list of common heat treatment procedures used on steels for steam generator pressure parts. The specific times and temperatures for each treatment type will depend on the alloy being treated. As with welding, attention to quality-control procedures during heat treatment are critical, because some alloys are very sensitive to small variations in heat treatment conditions.

STEELS FOR FOSSIL-FUELED STEAM GENERATOR PRESSURE PARTS

A wide range of steels is utilized in the construction of fossil-fueled steam generator pressure parts, ranging from low-carbon steels used in the economizers and waterwalls to austenitic stainless steels used in high-temperature superheat and reheat sections. These steels may be roughly grouped into different classes based on alloy content. *Table 8-2* lists the common steels used for steam

TABLE 8-2 | STEELS USED IN FOSSIL-FUELED STEAM GENERATOR PRESSURE PARTS*

Nominal Composition	Product Form	ASME		EN Designation	Min UTS	Min YS	Chemical Composition Limits, % by weight									
		Specification	Grade		ksi (MPa)		C	Mn	P	S	Si	Ni	Cr	Mo	V	Other
LOW-CARBON STEEL																
Low Strength	Seamless tube	SA-192			47 (325)	26 (180)	0.06–0.18	0.27–0.63	0.035	0.035	0.25					
	Welded tube	SA-178	A		47 (325)	26 (180)	0.06–0.18	0.27–0.63	0.035	0.035						
Medium Strength	Seamless tube	SA-210	A-1		37 (255)	60 (415)	0.27	0.93	0.035	0.035	0.10 min					
	Welded tube	SA-178	C		37 (255)	60 (415)	0.35	0.80	0.035	0.035						
	Pipe	SA-106	B		35 (240)	60 (415)	0.30	0.29–1.06	0.035	0.035	0.10 min	0.40	0.40	0.15	0.08	Cu: 0.40 max
High Strength	Pipe	SA-106	C		40 (275)	70 (485)	0.35	0.29–1.06	0.035	0.035	0.10 min	0.40	0.40	0.15	0.08	Cu: 0.40 max
	Plate	SA-299	A		40 (275)	75 (515)	0.28	0.84–1.62	0.035	0.035	0.13–0.45					
	Plate	SA-515	70		38 (260)	70 (485)	0.35	1.30	0.035	0.035	0.13–0.45					
LOW-ALLOY FERRITIC STEEL																
C-0.5Mo	Seamless tube	SA-209	T1		30 (205)	55 (380)	0.10–0.20	0.30–0.80	0.025	0.025	0.10–0.50			0.44–0.65		
1Cr-0.5Mo	Seamless tube, pipe	SA-213 SA-335	T12 P12	13CrMo4-5	30 (205)	60 (415)	0.05–0.15	0.30–0.61	0.025	0.025	0.50		0.80–1.25	0.44–0.65		
1.25Cr-0.5Mo	Seamless tube, pipe	SA-213 SA-335	T11 P11	10CrMo5-5	30 (205)	60 (415)	0.05–0.15	0.30–0.60	0.025	0.025	0.50–1.00		1.00–1.50	0.44–0.65		
2.25Cr-1Mo	Seamless tube, pipe	SA-213 SA-335	T22 P22	10CrMo9-10	30 (205)	60 (415)	0.05–0.15	0.30–0.60	0.025	0.025	0.50		1.90–2.60	0.87–1.13		
ADVANCED FERRITIC STEEL																
2.25Cr-1.5W-Mo-V-Nb	Seamless tube, pipe	SA-213 SA-335	T23 P23	7CrWVMoNb9-6	58 (400)	74 (510)	0.04–0.10	0.10–0.60	0.030	0.010	0.50		1.90–2.60	0.05–0.30	0.20–0.30	W: 1.45–1.75 Nb: 0.02-0.08 N: 0.030 max Al: 0.030 max B: 0.0005–0.006
9Cr-1Mo-V-Nb	Seamless tube, pipe	SA-213 SA-335	T91 P91	X10CrMoVNb9-1	60 (415)	85 (585)	0.07–0.14	0.30–0.60	0.020	0.010	0.20–0.50	0.40	8.0–9.5	0.85–1.05	0.18–0.25	Nb: 0.06-0.1 N: 0.030–0.070 Al: 0.040 max
9Cr-1.75W-Mo-V-Nb	Seamless tube, pipe	SA-213 SA-335	T92 P92	X10CrMoWVNb9-2	64 (440)	90 (620)	0.07–0.13	0.30–0.60	0.020	0.010	0.50	0.40	8.5–9.5	0.30–0.60	0.15–0.25	W: 1.5–2.00 Nb: 0.04–0.09 N: 0.030–0.070 Al: 0.040 max B: 0.001–0.006
AUSTENITIC STAINLESS STEEL																
18Cr-8Ni	Seamless tube	SA-213	TP304H	X6CrNi18-10	30 (205)	75 (515)	0.04–0.10	2.00	0.045	0.030	1.00	8.0–11.0	18.0–20.0			
18Cr-8Ni-3Cu-Nb	Seamless tube	SA-213	Super304H S30432		34 (235)	86 (590)	0.07–0.13	1.00	0.040	0.010	0.30	7.5–10.5	17.0–19.0			Cu: 2.5–3.5 Nb: 0.30–0.60 N: 0.05–0.12 Al: 0.003–0.030 B: 0.001–0.010
18Cr-10Ni-Nb	Seamless tube	SA-213	TP347H	X7CrNiNb18-10	30 (205)	75 (515)	0.04–0.10	2.00	0.045	0.030	1.00	9.0–12.0	17.0–19.0			Nb: 8xC–1.10
25Cr-20Ni	Seamless tube	SA-213	TP310H		30 (205)	75 (515)	0.04–0.10	2.00	0.045	0.030	1.00	19.0–22.0	24.0–26.0			
25Cr-20Ni-Nb-N	Seamless tube	SA-213	TP310HCbN		43 (295)	95 (655)	0.04–0.10	2.00	0.045	0.030	1.00	19.0–22.0	24.0–26.0			Nb: 0.20–0.60 N: 0.15–0.35

*ASME, American Society of Mechanical Engineers; EN, European Norm; UTS, ultimate tensile strength; YS, yield strength. EN equivalents are approximate and indicative only.

The various codes and standards used for equipment designs in power plants throughout the world were originally introduced as voluntary safety standards.

generator pressure parts, their nominal compositions, their applicable material specifications, and their minimum tensile properties.

SPECIFICATIONS AND CODES

The grades of steels used in the construction of pressure parts are specified by governing codes—for example, the American Society of Mechanical Engineers (ASME) Boiler and Pressure Vessel code in the United States and the European Norm (EN) codes in Europe. The ASME code originated as a safety code to prevent boiler explosions, and today, it promotes the acceptance of properly designed equipment on a national and international basis by assisting in the standardization of safety rules. The rules of the code are kept up to date by continuing review. Section I, *Power Boilers*, of the ASME code provides the basic design rules and requirements, whereas Section II, *Materials*, provides specifications, properties, and design-allowable stresses for materials used in boiler and pressure vessel construction. Similar design rules and material specifications in the EN code are found in EN 12952, *Water Tube Boilers*, and EN 10216, *Seamless Tubes for Pressure Purposes*.

Another technical group, the American Society for Testing and Materials (ASTM), prepares and publishes specifications for the purchase, testing, and examination of a variety of materials. Similarly, the committees of the American Welding Society write specifications for welding practices and consumables. Such specifications are widely used to procure and acceptance-test materials in order to meet defined levels of quality. The ASME boiler and pressure vessel committees use the ASTM materials specifications to establish recognized grades of materials to which their code rules for design, allowable stresses, fabrication methods, and inspection apply. Both ASME and ASTM material specifications are therefore equivalent.

To supplement the rules of the boiler and pressure vessel codes, a number of other standards control the design and fabrication of associated components and systems. These include ASME B31.1 *Power Piping*, and ASME B16.34 *Valves Flanged, Threaded and Welding End*. The European equivalent of ASME B31.1 is EN 13480, *Metallic Industrial Piping*.

A basic limitation of all codes is that their rules must be expressed in sufficiently general terms in order to cover a wide range of applications. Because they define only reasonable minimum standards, cases in which a power plant designer must make further investigation and exercise additional effort are sure to arise. A great variety of supplementary information is available from publications of the various engineering societies and from technical bulletins of equipment suppliers.

CARBON STEELS

Carbon steels are the predominant materials used in boiler pressure part applications because of their low cost, excellent fabricability and weldability, and good combination of properties at low and somewhat elevated temperatures. In addition to carbon, these steels typically contain manganese and silicon in small amounts ($\leq 1\%$). Manganese combines with harmful residual sulfur in the steel to form benign manganese sulfide inclusions, and it also contributes somewhat to solid solution strengthening. Silicon is used in the steelmaking process as a deoxidizer and degasifier and can improve the oxidation resistance of the steel.

Carbon steels for boiler applications are further classed into low-strength, medium-strength, and high-strength grades, with commensurate increases in carbon content. Carbon contents range from 0.1 to 0.2% in low-strength carbon steels, from 0.2 to 0.3% in medium-strength carbon steels, and from 0.3 to 0.35% in high-strength carbon steels. Increased carbon content gives a higher fraction of cementite or pearlite in the steel, producing higher strength at the cost of reduced ductility and weldability. Still higher strengths can be obtained by further carbon additions, but such steels are seldom found in pressure parts because of weldability and ductility considerations.

The use of carbon steels as pressure parts in steam generating equipment ultimately is limited by their high-temperature strength and resistance to oxidation and corrosion. The maximum use temperature of carbon steels is approximately 850°F (454°C), which typically restricts their use to water-touched applications, such as feedwater piping, economizers, and furnace wall tubing. Carbon steels also are prone to degradation of their microstructure at high temperatures through a process termed *graphitization*, wherein iron carbides slowly convert to graphite (pure carbon) and iron. This process can be accompanied by a commensurate, marked reduction in strength and ductility if the graphite nodules concentrate and align, as can happen along heat affected zones associated with welds.

LOW-ALLOY FERRITIC STEELS

In terms of temperature capability, the class above carbon steels is low-alloy steels, which contain chromium and molybdenum. This class, the so-called "Cr-Mo steels," encompasses several alloys containing chromium in levels ranging from 0.5 to 2.25% and molybdenum in levels ranging from 0.5 to 1%. Molybdenum is a strong solid solution strengthening element, and 0.5% molybdenum originally was added to carbon steels in order to improve the high-temperature creep–rupture strength. This C-½Mo steel was prone to graphitization, however, and chromium subsequently was added to improve the high-temperature oxidation resistance and to prevent graphitization.

Further increases in high-temperature strength and oxidation resistance were realized by further chromium and molybdenum additions. The 2¼Cr-1Mo composition (Grade 22) gives an optimal combination of strength, weldability, and oxidation resistance for water- and steam-touched tubing and piping in the temperature range of 900 to 1,050°F (482–565°C). Above this range, however, oxidation limits the use of these steels, and alloys with greater chromium content must be used, such as 9Cr-1Mo-V-Nb steel or austenitic stainless steels.

Carbon steels and low-alloy ferritic steels are the principal materials for power plant equipment in order to maintain reasonable costs as multi-tonnage quantities are required.

ADVANCED FERRITIC STEELS

The desire for a ferritic steel with significantly greater strength and oxidation resistance compared with those of Grade 22 led to the development of creep strength enhanced ferritic steels, such as 9Cr-1Mo-V-Nb (Grade 91) and 9Cr-0.5Mo-W-V-Nb (Grade 92) in the 1980s. These alloys rely on a tempered martensitic structure and a fine dispersion of vanadium- and niobium carbo-nitrides for their excellent creep strength, which is as much as twice that of 2¼Cr-1Mo steel at 1,000°F (538°C). The higher chromium content also confers greater resistance to oxidation by steam and fireside combustion gases.

Because of the specific microstructure required for optimum creep strength, these alloys have more complex heat treatment and welding requirements than the low-alloy ferritic steels. First, they must be normalized at 1,900 to 1,970°F (1,040–1,080°C), air cooled, then tempered at 1,350 to 1,435°F (730–780°C). The hardenability (the ease with which martensite is formed) of these materials is such that the air cooling associated with the normalizing processes usually provides sufficient quenching to achieve the desired microstructure. However, this normalize-and-temper heat treatment must be repeated after any hot work and after cold work in which strains exceed 20%. Welding must be performed with a minimum pre-heat temperature of 300°F (150°C), and welds must receive a post-weld heat treatment (PWHT) in the range of 1,350 to 1,435°F (730 to 780°C).

These advanced ferritic steels are increasingly used for superheat and reheat tubing and headers as well as for main steam and hot reheat piping. The increased strength permits significantly reduced wall thickness compared to that of Grade 22, reducing the detrimental effects of thermal cycling on thick-walled components such as headers and piping.

Two advanced ferritic steels more closely based on the 2.25% chromium composition of Grade 22 also have been developed; these are designated as Grades 23 and 24. They are similar to Grades 91 and 92 in that greater creep strength has been achieved by additions of vanadium, niobium, tungsten, boron, titanium, or nitrogen, which form strengthening precipitates. They have lower carbon content than Grades 91 and 92, however, allowing them to be welded (in relatively thin sections) without a subsequent PWHT. Thus, they are well suited for use in waterwall applications where PWHT is difficult to perform. Despite their higher creep strength, which enables the use of lower wall thickness than Grade 22, the maximum use temperature of these grades is limited by the reduced steam oxidation resistance conferred by 2% rather than 9% chromium.

AUSTENITIC STAINLESS STEELS

As mentioned above, significant additions of elements such as nickel to steel result in stability of the FCC austenite phase at room temperature. Austenitic stainless steels use a combination of chromium in excess of 16% and nickel in excess of 8% to form very corrosion- and oxidation-resistant alloys with an FCC crystal structure and excellent creep strength. Typical alloys include 18Cr-8Ni (Type 304), 16Cr-12Ni-Mo (Type 316), and 25Cr-20Ni (Type 310). All of these alloys are strengthened

at high temperature by chromium carbides; stainless steels for high-temperature use typically have the "H" designation, signifying a higher carbon content and a coarser grain size.

Stainless steels typically are used as superheater and reheater tubing subject to the highest steam temperatures or severe fireside corrosion conditions. Despite their attractive combination of creep strength and environmental resistance, these alloys have drawbacks that prevent their more widespread use in boilers. They are considerably more expensive than low-alloy steels because of the high concentrations of chromium and nickel. Their thermal expansion coefficients also are considerably higher than those of ferritic steels, which limits their application in thick-walled components such as headers and piping. Austenitic stainless steels also are subject to stress corrosion cracking in certain aqueous environments, making them unsuitable for application as water-touched tubing and piping.

MECHANICAL PROPERTIES

Certain mechanical properties of steels affect their fabrication and service. Among these are tensile properties at low and elevated temperature, hardness, toughness, and creep–rupture strength. The allowable stresses used for the design of pressure parts are derived from these properties.

TENSILE PROPERTIES

The standard tensile test provides data concerning yield strength, tensile strength, and ductility. When metals are pulled (stressed) with a uni-axial, increasing load, the material stretches (strains). Diagrams such as the one shown in *Figure 8-7* depict the relationship between stress and strain for specific materials. With increasing load, the material strains elastically, and during this period of elastic behavior, no permanent deformation occurs. Strain is directly proportional to the stress.

Continuing to increase the loading results in plastic (permanent) strains and eventual breakage of the test specimen. The yield strength, which has several different definitions, describes the engineering stress (load divided by the original cross-sectional area of a test specimen) in the vicinity of this elastic-to-plastic behavior transition. The tensile strength is the engineering stress when the maximum load during the test is reached. Ductility is a measure of the amount of plastic deformation that a material will sustain before breaking. It usually is expressed as a percentage elongation or reduction in cross-sectional area of the test specimen. How much plastic strain a steel will exhibit is quite variable and generally is inversely related to the tensile strength of the material. High-strength steels typically will exhibit much less ductility than softer, lower-strength steels.

Most of the specifications covering the steels used in the construction of a boiler require room-temperature tensile testing with minimum specified values of tensile strength, yield strength, and ductility. For design purposes, however, the tensile and yield strengths of each grade of steel used need to be determined at temperatures up to the creep range of the grade. Various organizations, including the producers and fabricators of steel, perform such tests, and the data from these tests are used by codes to set maximum allowable stresses.

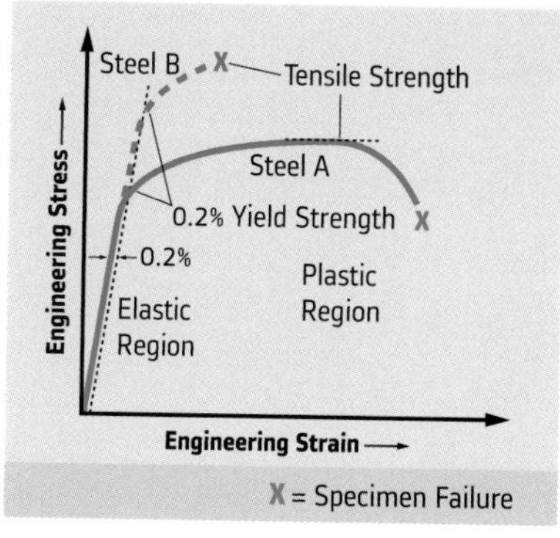

Figure 8-7 | Stress–strain curves for two steels with different strengths and ductilities. Steel A is weaker but more ductile than steel B

Some of the many product form specifications—most noticeably those for pipe and tube—require various deformation tests, such as flattening, flaring, or bending. These additional tests of ductility provide evidence for the ability of the steel to withstand fabrication or installation operations, such as bending, swaging, and tube expansion.

HARDNESS

The hardness of a material is a measure of resistance to plastic deformation and is related to the tensile strength. It also is used as an indicator of the machinability and abrasion resistance. Usually, hardness is determined by the Brinell, Rockwell, or Vickers test, in which a small ball or pyramid-shaped point is pressed into the surface of the metal with a specified force for a specified time. The size of the indentation is measured automatically or by microscope and is expressed as a hardness number. The smaller the indentation, the higher the hardness number.

The use of hardness testing is permitted in some material specifications to approximate tensile strength. The ASTM Specification A-370 and EN ISO 18265 contains hardness-to-tensile-strength conversion charts for different groupings of steels. In some material specifications, particularly those in which the ductility of the steel is important to its workability, maximum hardness values are specified.

Hardness testing frequently is used in the field as a check on material quality and as a means to assess the amount of degradation that the material has suffered as a result of high-temperature service. Extreme care must be taken in performing field hardness readings to ensure that a true measure of the component hardness is obtained, unaffected by surface conditions (e.g., oxidation or the presence of a soft, decarburized layer).

TOUGHNESS

Under most circumstances, steel can tolerate localized stresses above the yield strength by plastically absorbing and redistributing these stresses. Under certain conditions, however, even steels having considerable ductility are subject to a brittle (cleavage) mode of failure when subjected to concentrated stresses at low temperatures. The property of toughness is the ability of a material to resist this mode of failure.

Various impact tests evaluate toughness. One of the more commonly used tests is the Charpy V-notch impact test. In this test, a swinging pendulum strikes a single blow to a notched, horizontal specimen that is supported on both ends, breaking the specimen in two pieces. The energy absorbed by the specimen is related to the height that the pendulum reaches after breaking the specimen and is expressed in units of ft-lb (J).

For ferritic steels, the mode of failure in an impact test changes from ductile (shear) to brittle (cleavage) as the temperature is lowered. The temperature range at which this occurs is termed the *transition range*. Material within or below its transition temperature range may crack extensively if subjected to an impact load or if construction details are such that localized yielding is prevented.

The transition temperature range depends on the particular metal composition and melting practice as well as on the subsequent working and heat treatment. For many types of carbon or low-alloy steels, the transition temperature may be as high as 70°F (21°C) or above. The possibility of brittle fracture must be considered in the fabrication of materials (bending and forming in various manners), in testing the finished structure, and in any service involving operation at low the transition temperature. Care in the design, fabrication, inspection, and when necessary, field repair is required to eliminate conditions that might promote brittle fracture. This also is the reason why a minimum temperature of 70°F (21°C) is specified for hydraulic pressure testing of boiler components.

European codes and specifications place minimum toughness requirements on many steel grades used in boiler pressure parts. The ASME code does not; the compositional limits (especially restrictions on the content of sulfur and phosphorus) and required manufacturing processes are considered to be sufficient for ensuring adequate toughness.

CREEP–RUPTURE AND ALLOWABLE STRESSES

At temperatures exceeding approximately 650°F (343°C), most steels suffer a gradual decrease in tensile and yield strength. At still higher temperatures, the strain in a material is a function not only of the applied stress but also of the time spent under stress at temperature. In this high-temperature range, the metal will deform (creep) continuously even at stresses much lower than the yield strength. If held for a sufficient period of time under these conditions, the material will rupture.

Because no way has been found to predict this behavior quantitatively from short-time tests, it is necessary to perform tests of creep and stress-rupture at several stress levels and temperatures as well as over time periods as long as feasible. Such tests (and extrapolations as necessary) establish values of creep strength and stress-rupture strength. The creep strength of a metal at a certain temperature is the steady stress that produces a specified, low rate of elongation. For long-time service, such as in ASME Boiler Code applications, a creep rate of 0.01% over 1,000 hours is used. The stress-rupture strength is the steady stress required at a particular temperature to cause rupture within a specified, long period of time.

Figure 8-8 illustrates how creep and rupture strengths for a 2¼Cr-1Mo

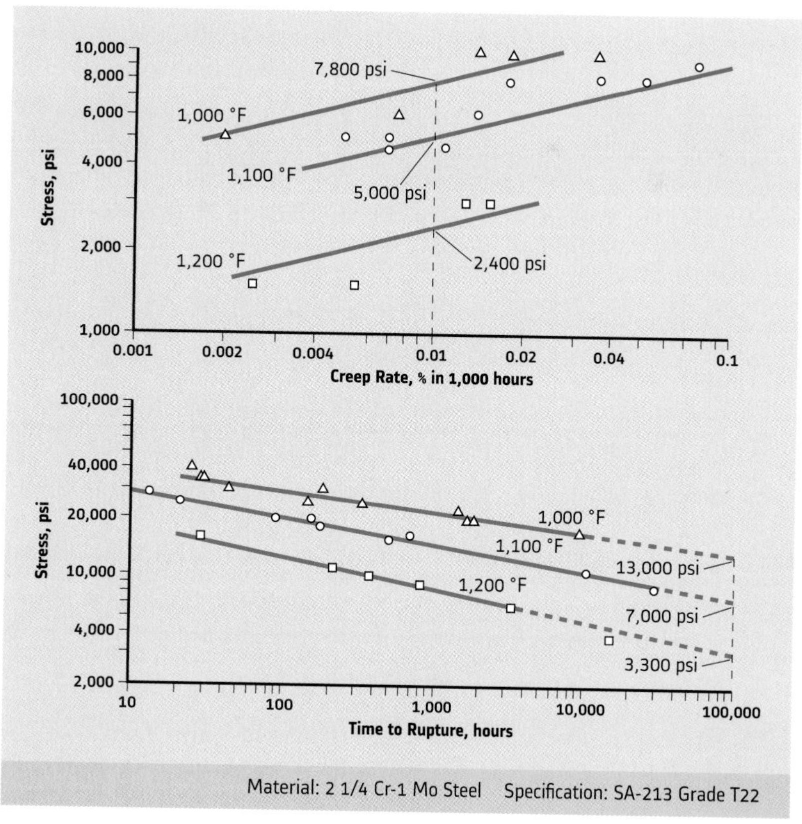

Figure 8-8 | Creep rate (top) and rupture strength (bottom) for a 2¼Cr-1Mo steel

steel are established from test data. In this figure, creep-rate data for 1,000, 1,100, and 1,200°F (538, 593, and 649°C) are plotted versus stress. The intersection of these data lines with that for 0.01% over 1,000 hours sets the respective creep strengths of 7,800, 5,000, and 2,400 psi (53.8, 34.5, and 16.6 MPa). The other curves in the figure show rupture life versus stress for the same three temperatures. Lines through these data are extrapolated to 100,000 hours to establish rupture strengths of 13,000, 7,000, and 3,300 psi (90, 48.3, and 22.8 MPa), respectively.

Table 8-3 lists the criteria used by the ASME and EN codes to determine the allowable stresses as a function of temperature. *Figure 8-9* applies these criteria to establish the allowable stress for 2¼Cr-1Mo steel as an example.

The relative influence of the different criteria varies with materials as well as with temperature. *Figure 8-10* shows the effect of temperature on ASME Boiler Code allowable stresses for a number of alloys used for high-temperature service. The carbon steels begin to lose strength above 700°F (371°C), and by 850°F (454°C), these steels are down to about one-half their room-temperature values. The low-chromium ferritic alloys start to lose strength above 800°F (427°C) and are down to half-strength at approximately 1,000°F (538°C). The austenitic stainless steels decline somewhat from room temperature to 1,000°F (538°C) because of reduction in yield strength; above 1,000°F, creep and rupture strength cause a rapid decrease to half-strength or less by 1,200°F (649°C).

TABLE 8-3 | SIMPLIFIED CRITERIA FOR DETERMINATION OF ALLOWABLE STRESSES BY AMERICAN SOCIETY OF MECHANICAL ENGINEERS (ASME) AND EUROPEAN NORM (EN) METHODS

ASME Methodology	EN Methodology
Non-creep regime, minimum of: · 67% Yield strength · 29% Tensile strength	Non-creep regime, minimum of: · 67% Yield strength · 42% Tensile strength
Creep regime, minimum of: · 67% of average stress to rupture in 100,000 hours · 80% of minimum stress to rupture in 100,000 hours · 100% of average stress to produce a creep strain of 0.01% over 1,000 hours	Creep regime, · 80% of average stress to rupture in 200,000 hours -or- · 67% of average stress to rupture in 100,000 hours (if 200,000-hour data are not available)

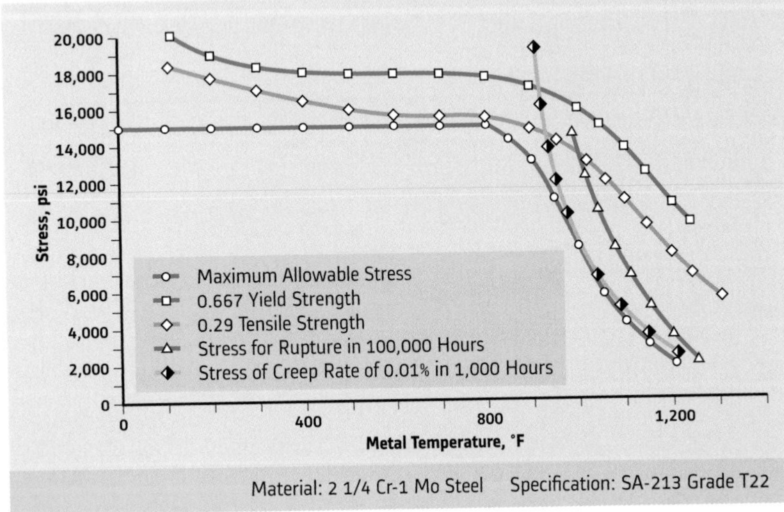

Figure 8-9 | Use of ASME Boiler Code criteria to establish allowable stresses for a 2¼Cr-1Mo steel

OXIDATION AND CORROSION OF STEELS

As described above, the allowable stresses of steels used in pressure parts are determined by their mechanical properties. The resistance of the steel to wastage by oxidation and corrosion processes, however, is just as important in the overall suitability of steels for a particular application.

Oxidation refers to the reaction of steels with oxygen in the air, flue gases, and high-temperature water or steam to form iron oxides (or, in the case of stainless steels, iron–chromium oxides). Corrosion refers to the attack on steels by combustion products (e.g., gases and ash) in the furnace (also known as fireside corrosion) and by corrodants in boiler water. Depending on the specific environment, iron or chromium oxides or sulfides may be formed as a result of fireside corrosion. Both processes result in wall loss (wastage), increasing the net stress in the tube or pipe. Severe wastage can result in premature rupture of boiler tubes. Oxides formed on the inner diameter of heat-absorbing tubes also serve to insulate the tube from the cooling action of the steam or water flowing through it, resulting in increased tube operating temperatures.

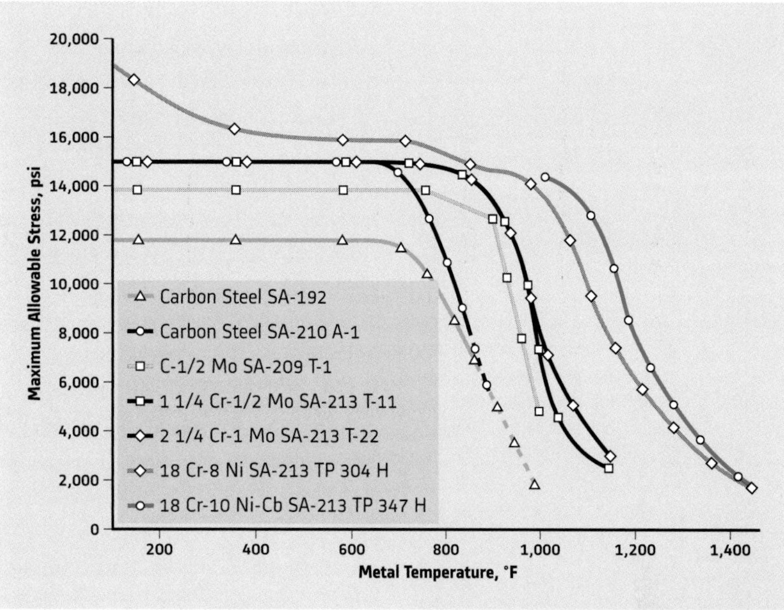

Figure 8-10 | Effect of temperature on ASME Boiler Code allowable stresses for grades of steel tubing: 1, Carbon Steel SA-192; 2, Carbon Steel SA-210 A-1; 3, C-½Mo SA-209 T-1; 4, 1¼Cr-½Mo SA-213 T-11; 5, 2¼Cr-1Mo SA-213 T-22; 6, 18Cr-8Ni SA-213 TP 304 H; 7, 18Cr-10Ni-Cb SA-213 TP 347 H

STEAM SIDE OXIDATION

Oxidation by water or steam is relatively predictable. Rates of scale growth have been measured for each alloy in controlled conditions, and as shown in *Figure 8-11*, the rate of growth decreases parabolically with time. For a given alloy, oxidation rates increase with increasing temperature. Oxidation rates decrease with increasing chromium in an alloy; stainless steels show very low rates of steam oxide growth. Because of the predicable nature of steam oxidation rates, the thickness of steam scales found on the inner tube walls can be used to estimate the local metal temperature, assuming that the number of operating hours is known. This can be useful in determining the cause of boiler tube failures.

Other than an increase in tube wall temperature, the primary concern with steam oxidation in the superheater and reheater sections is exfoliation (spalling) of oxides from the tube walls, which may collect in bends and block the flow of steam through a circuit or may pass into the steam turbine and cause erosion of the turbine blades and vanes. *Figure 8-12* shows an oxide layer attached to the base metal of a superheater tube. *Figure 8-13* shows a magnification of the tube with a double oxide layer. Factors that cause exfoliation are complex; thermal quenching of the oxide during start-up and shutdown operations is a potential cause. Limiting the thickness of steam side oxide scale by selecting an appropriate alloy for the specified steam temperature also will reduce the tendency for exfoliation.

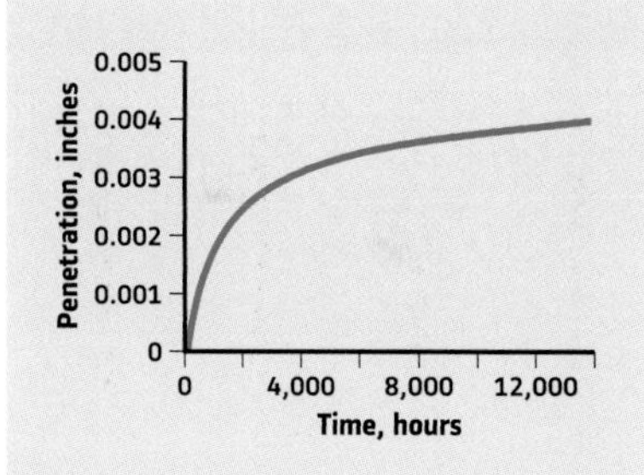

Figure 8-11 | Oxide penetration (metal loss) versus time for 1¼Cr-1Mo steel in steam at 1,100°F (593°C)

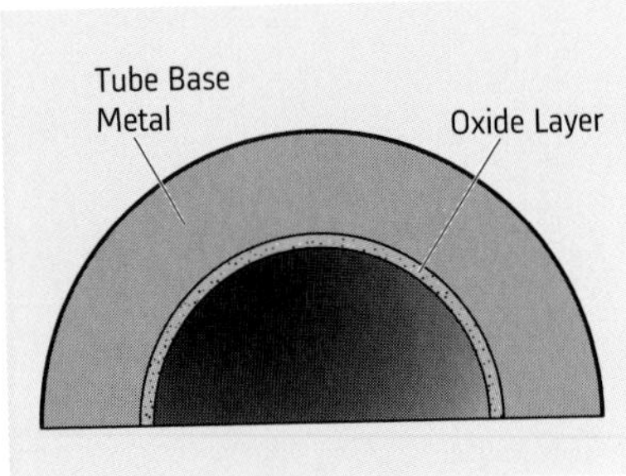

Figure 8-12 | Tube cross section showing typical two-layer oxide structure adhering well to the internal surface of a superheater tube. Tube base metal is the grey portion (original magnification, ×15)

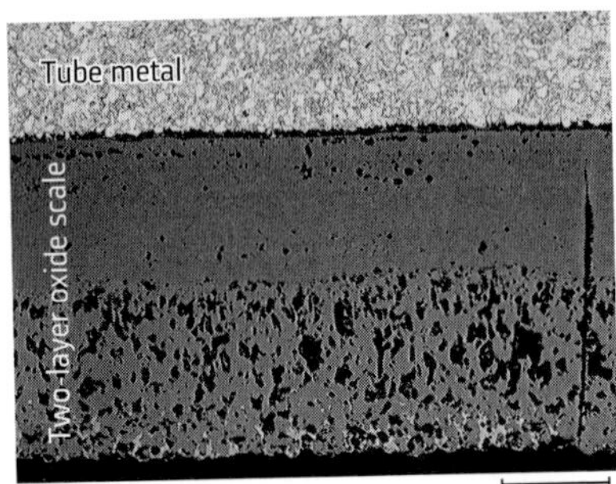

Figure 8-13 | Magnified tube cross section showing two layers of oxide scale

FIRESIDE CORROSION

Because of the wide variety of fossil fuels that are burned, corrosion occurring on the outside (fireside) of boiler tubes can vary greatly. Corrosion can range from simple oxidation in heat recovery steam generator units to heavy corrosion in plants burning coals or petroleum by-products that are high in sulfur and chlorine.

Specific rates of fireside corrosion are not well defined for all alloys and possible environments, but it generally is understood that combustion environments that are high in sulfur and chlorine are more aggressive and result in higher rates of attack. Areas where tubes are exposed to incomplete combustion products also may suffer greater rates of fireside corrosion. In these areas, local chemically reducing conditions allow enhanced attack by reduced sulfur species as well as carburization, which can disrupt protective oxide scales.

Alloys containing greater concentrations of chromium have a greater resistance to most forms of fireside corrosion. For this reason, stainless-steel tubes with 18% chromium or greater are used for superheater and reheater sections in units where aggressive fireside corrosion conditions exist. In some particularly severe environments, alloys with 25% chromium may be necessary.

Waterwall panels also may suffer from fireside corrosion, but stainless steels cannot be used for tubing because of the potential for stress corrosion cracking. For this application, protection can be provided by the application of corrosion-resistant coatings over the low-chromium ferritic tubing. The most common coatings in use today are weld-overlays, in which a thin layer (~0.070–0.100 inch [1.8–2.5 mm]) of stainless steel or nickel-base alloy with a high chromium concentration is welded onto the surface of the waterwall panel. Coatings also may be applied by other processes, such as thermal spray. In addition, coatings are applied to superheater and reheater tubes in order to provide protection against corrosion or corrosion–erosion mechanisms in the region of soot blowers.

MECHANISMS OF PRESSURE PART FAILURE

Pressure parts in fossil-fueled steam generators may fail by a variety of different mechanisms; *Table 8-4* presents a list of mechanisms and the components in which they are observed. A failure analysis investigation frequently is performed to verify the specific mechanism, which allows for a better understanding of the root cause of the failure and the actions that can be taken to prevent future failures. A full description of the various failure mechanisms and their features is outside the scope of this book; readers are referred to the Electric Power Research Institute's handbook on boiler and heat recovery steam generator tube failure for additional information.

MATERIALS FOR ADVANCED SUPERCRITICAL PLANTS

During the last decade or so, renewed emphasis on increasing the efficiency of fossil-fueled power plants has appeared. A significant feature of this higher efficiency is that the level of emissions per unit of power output is reduced; for example, an increase

in efficiency of 2 percentage points corresponds to a 5% reduction in CO_2 emissions. Moreover, because CO_2 capture and storage consumes energy that otherwise would contribute to the overall power output, increased efficiency of generation will reduce the future impact of capture-and-storage methods on the cost of electricity to the consumer.

Consequently, a serious worldwide effort is now underway to develop fossil-fueled power plants operating at higher steam temperatures to give greater generation efficiencies, and significant progress has already been made toward development of the advanced materials that are necessary for operation at these temperatures. *Figure 8-14* shows the substantial improvements in efficiency that can be gained by operation at higher temperatures and pressures. The current state-of-the art conditions are main steam temperatures of 1,110°F (600°C) and pressures in excess of 3,600 psi (25 MPa). Plants running at these conditions make wide use of the advanced ferritic alloys Grade 91 and Grade 92 described above as well as austenitic stainless steels for high-temperature tubing.

Research into ferritic alloys with temperature capability of 1,200°F (650°C) is ongoing. Attention currently is focused on alloys based on a 9% chromium composition, with additions of tungsten, cobalt, and very small amounts of boron. The maximum use temperature of ferritic steels, however, ultimately will be limited by the rate of oxidation in steam, particularly for heat-absorbing, in-furnace applications. Several advanced

TABLE 8-4 | TYPICAL BOILER TUBE FAILURE MECHANISMS

Failure Mechanism	Applies to: Water-touched tubes	Steam-touched tubes	Special case
Short-term overheating	X	X	
Long-term overheating/creep	X	X	
Corrosion fatigue	X		
Hydrogen damage	X		
Fatigue cracking	X	X	
Fireside corrosion	X	X	
Corrosion-enhanced thermal fatigue	X		
Low-temperature creep crack growth	X		
Acid dew point corrosion	X		
Acid phosphate corrosion	X		
Caustic gouging	X		
Stress corrosion cracking		X	
Pitting		X	
Dissimilar metal weld cracking		X	
Fly ash erosion		X	
Soot blower erosion		X	
Shockwave cracking			X
Strain-induced precipitation hardening			X
Liquid metal embrittlement			X

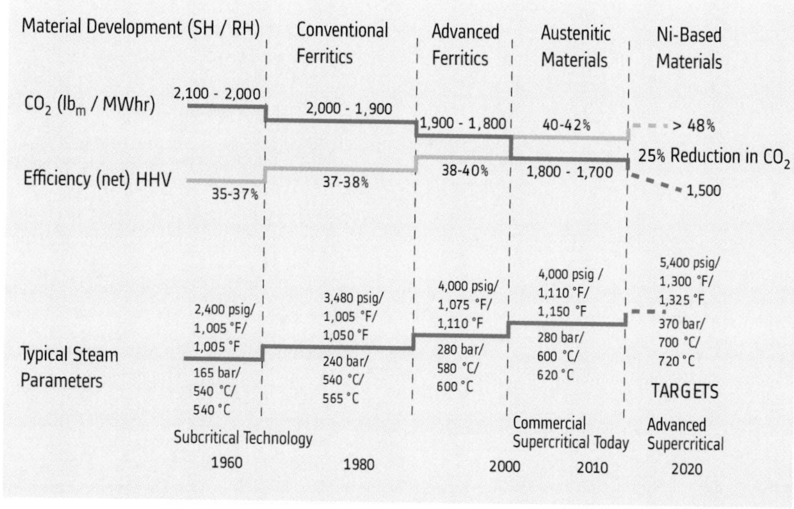

Figure 8-14 | Development of steam parameters, efficiency, and CO_2 reductions over time. Materials used in the highest-temperature steam sections are listed (HHV, higher heating value)

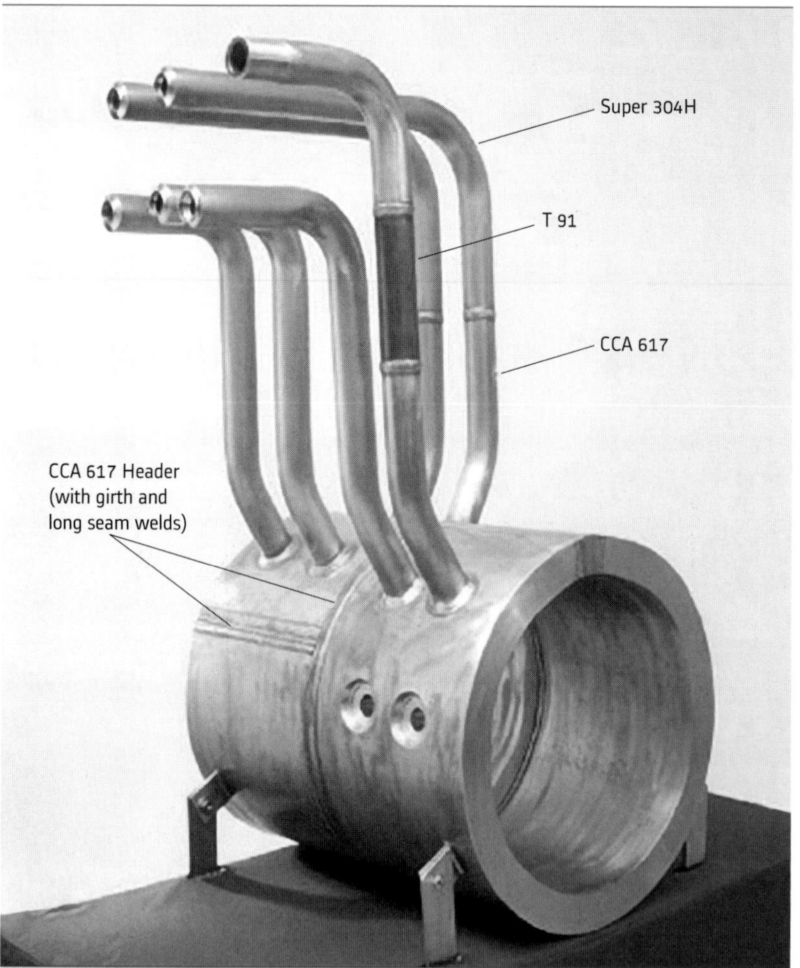

Figure 8-15 | Demonstration article fabricated by Alstom from nickel-base alloys and advanced austenitic and ferritic steels as part of a program to study materials for high efficiency boilers

austenitic stainless steels also have been developed that possess significantly higher creep strength compared with Types 304H and 347H. These include the 18% chromium alloy Super304H and the 25% chromium alloy HR3C (310HCbN).

In addition, a significant amount of work has been performed worldwide on developing materials for steam temperatures in excess of 1,300°F (700°C). These temperatures exceed the temperature capability of austenitic stainless steels, and development work has involved the use of nickel-based alloys for such conditions. Nickel-based alloys have been used extensively in gas turbine power plants and the petrochemical industry, but they have not been applied in fossil-fueled steam generators as a result of their cost, which is much greater than that of stainless steels. Typical nickel-base alloys for use at 1,300°F (700°C) are the solid solution strengthened alloys INCONEL® 617 and Haynes 230. The application of these alloys as tubing and piping in fossil boilers has been demonstrated through numerous programs (*Fig. 8-15*), including the COMTES 700 program, in which full-scale waterwall panels, superheater assemblies, main steam headers, and piping were installed in a commercial boiler (*Fig. 8-16*). Boiler designs with 1,300°F (700°C) main steam temperatures have been developed as well.

A similar materials development program in the United States is currently examining materials for steam conditions of up to 1,400°F (760°C), for which more complex nickel-base alloys will be required, such as INCONEL® 740, NIMONIC 263, and Haynes 282. These alloys use precipitation strengthening by the gamma-prime (Ni_3Al) phase, and they require additional heat treatment compared to the solid solution strengthened alloys INCONEL® 617 and Haynes 230. The more complex heat treatments and higher elevated temperature strength levels also make fabrication and welding more difficult. Despite these challenges, trial assemblies using these alloys have been manufactured and are being tested.

TERRY TOTEMEIER
IAN PERRIN

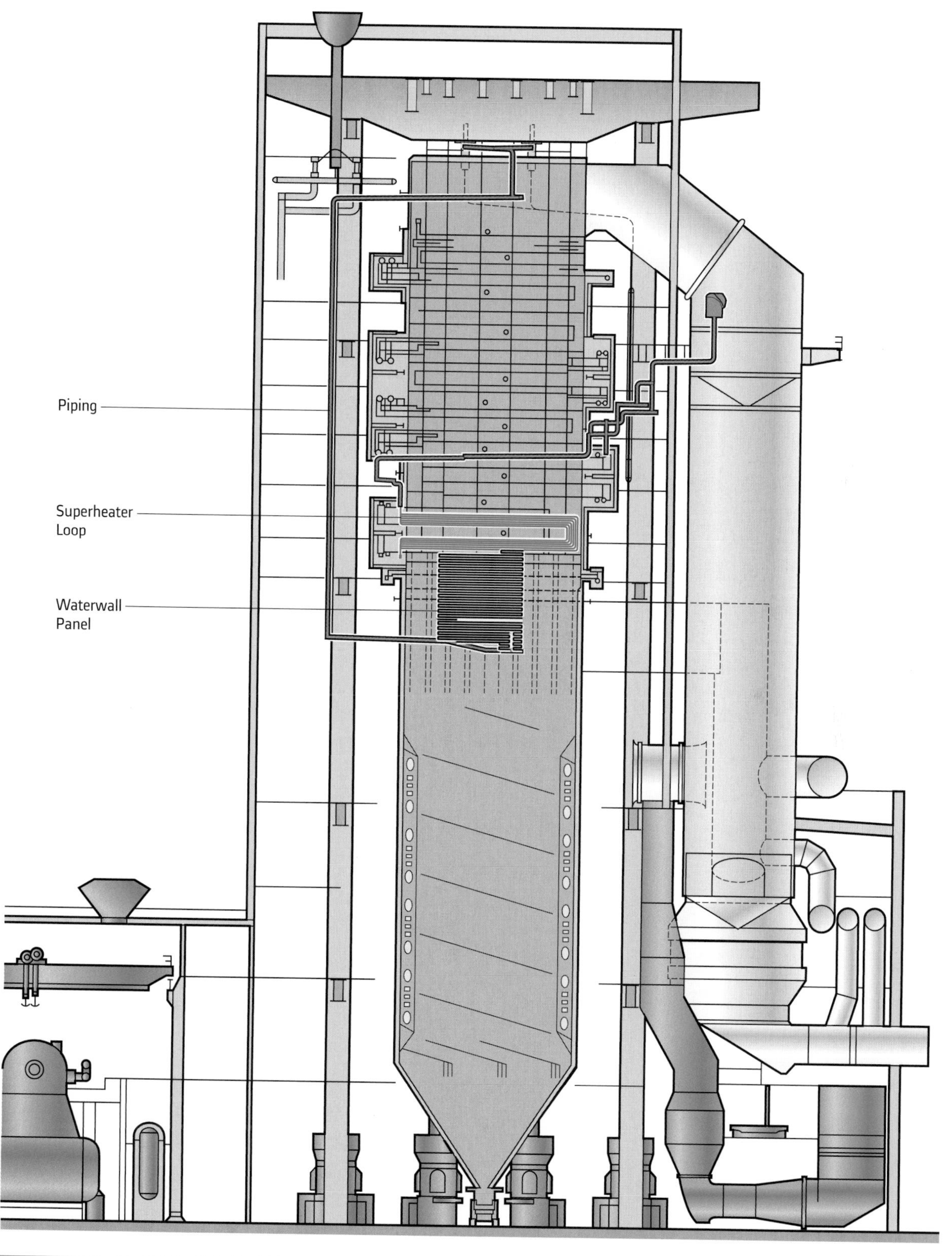

Figure 8-16 | Location of COMTES 700 components within the Schloven F boiler

Water Technology

Chapter **Nine**

Water is a basic engineering material used in the production of steam for power generation and process use. Effective treatment or conditioning of water has made possible more efficient steam cycles in the subcritical and supercritical pressure ranges. Many industrial processes have special requirements for high-quality water that is free of objectionable contaminants. These statements are indicative of the significant role of *water technology* as an interdisciplinary professional field, which comprises elements of basic chemistry as well as elements of chemical and mechanical engineering.

Water supplied to an industrial site can originate from a river or stream, mountain runoff, wells, or a lake. The composition of impurities in water varies over a wide range. Water may be contaminated with chemical or organic impurities, bacteria, dissolved gases, suspended mineral matter, and dissolved solids of both scaling and non-scaling composition.

When using water to generate steam for process or electric power, consideration must be given to water treatment in order to prevent corrosion of the construction materials, scaling of heat-transfer surfaces and other flow-related components, and contamination of steam. This involves treatment of the raw water that is available on that particular site and introduced into the cycle as well as conditioning of the water and steam while being utilized in the cycle. The extent of the treatment required before raw water is suitable for introduction into the cycle (make-up water) depends largely on the end use of the steam, the steam purity requirements, and the boiler design. The pressure of a boiler generally still is used to classify boiler designs. Therefore, the water quality necessary for a particular application has, by convention, been related to boiler pressure (and steam purity). This relationship between boiler pressure and water/steam purity has been reflected in the guidelines of the American Boiler Manufacturers Association (ABMA). It is recognized, however, that present-day water chemistry guidelines regarding plants providing steam for electric generation must reflect the steam purity requirements as specified by the steam turbine and gas turbine (if steam- or water-injected) supplier, because these require lower dissolved solids concentrations in the steam than are called for in the ABMA guidelines.

This chapter will discuss specific boiler applications of water technology, but many of the same considerations hold for various types of process operations. In practically every instance, a careful review of sources of water and of its conditioning is required to avoid economic losses because of a slowdown in production, damage to equipment, and increased costs of operation.

TECHNIQUES OF WATER TREATMENT

The extent of water conditioning or treatment depends on both the original supply source and the ultimate end use of the product. *Table 9-1* lists common impurities found in water, sets forth some of the resulting problems, and indicates common treatment methods. The techniques of water treatment cover a wide variety of raw-water preparation schemes. This is covered in detail elsewhere.[1–5]

TABLE 9-1 | COMMON IMPURITIES FOUND IN WATER

Constituent	Chemical Formula	Difficulties Caused	Means of Treatment
Turbidity	None—expressed in analysis as units.	Imparts unsightly appearance to water. Deposits in water lines, process equipment, etc. Interferes with most process uses.	Coagulation, settling, and filtration.
Color	None—expressed in analysis as units.	May cause foaming in boilers. Hinders precipitation methods such as iron removal and softening. Can stain product in process use.	Coagulation and filtration. Chlorination. Adsorption by activated carbon.
Hardness	Calcium and magnesium salts expressed as $CaCO_3$.	Chief source of scale in heat exchange equipment, boilers, pipelines, etc. Forms curds with soap, interferes with dyeing, etc.	Softening. Demineralization. Internal boiler water treatment. Surface-active agents.
Alkalinity	Bicarbonate $(HCO_3)^-$, carbonate $(CO_3)^{2-}$, and hydroxide $(OH)^-$, expressed as $CaCO_3$.	Foaming and carryover of solids with steam. Embrittlement of boiler steel. Bicarbonate and carbonate produce CO_2 in steam, a source of corrosion in condensate lines.	Lime and lime-soda softening. Acid treatment. Hydrogen zeolite softening. Demineralization. Dealkalization by anion exchange.
Free Mineral Acid	H_2SO_4, HCl, etc. expressed as $CaCO_3$.	Corrosion.	Neutralization with alkalies.
Carbon Dioxide	CO_2	Corrosion in waterlines and particularly steam and condensate lines.	Aeration. Deaeration. Neutralization with alkalies.
pH	Hydrogen ion concentration defined as: $pH = \log \frac{1}{[H^+]}$	pH varies according to acidic or alkaline solids in water. Most natural waters have a pH of 6.0–8.0.	pH can be increased by alkalies and decreased by acids.
Sulfate	$(SO_4)^{2-}$	Adds to solids content of water, but in itself, is not usually significant. Combines with calcium to form calcium sulfate scale.	Demineralization.
Chloride	Cl^-	Adds to solids content and increases corrosive character of water.	Demineralization.
Nitrate	$(NO_3)^-$	Adds to solids content, but is not usually significant industrially. Useful for control of boiler metal embrittlement.	Demineralization.
Silica	SiO_2	Scale in boilers and cooling water systems. Insoluble turbine blade deposits because of silica vaporization.	Hot process removal with magnesium salts. Adsorption by highly basic anion exchange resins, in conjunction with demineralization.
Iron	Fe^{2+} (ferrous) Fe^{3+} (ferric)	Discolors water on precipitation. Source of deposits in waterlines, boilers, etc. Interferes with dyeing, tanning, papermaking, etc.	Aeration. Coagulation and filtration. Lime softening. Cation exchange. Contact filtration. Surface-active agents for iron retention.
Manganese	Mn^{2+}	Same as iron.	Same as iron.
Oxygen	O_2	Corrosion of waterlines, heat exchange equipment, boilers, return lines, etc.	Deaeration. Sodium sulfite. Corrosion inhibitors.
Hydrogen Sulfide	H_2S	Cause of "rotten egg" odor. Corrosion.	Aeration. Chlorination. Highly basic anion exchange.
Ammonia	NH_3	Corrosion of copper and zinc alloys by formation of complex soluble ion.	Cation exchange with hydrogen zeolite. Chlorination. Deaeration.
Dissolved Solids	None	"Dissolved Solids" is measure of total amount of dissolved matter, determined by evaporation. High concentrations of dissolved solids are objectionable because of process interference and as a cause of foaming in boilers.	Various softening process, such as lime softening and cation exchange by hydrogen zeolite, will reduce dissolved solids. Demineralization.

TABLE 9-1 | COMMON IMPURITIES FOUND IN WATER—*continued*			
Constituent	Chemical Formula	Difficulties Caused	Means of Treatment
Suspended Solids	None	"Suspended Solids" is the measure of undissolved matter, determined gravimetrically. Suspended solids cause deposits in heat-exchange equipment, boilers, waterlines, etc.	Subsidence. Filtration, usually preceded by coagulation and settling.
Total Solids	None	"Total Solids" is the sum of dissolved and suspended solids, determined gravimetrically.	See "Dissolved Solids" and "Suspended Solids."

Adapted from Betz Laboratories, Inc., *Betz Handbook of Industrial Water Conditioning*, 8th ed. Philadelphia, PA.: Betz Laboratories, 1980.

Some of the basic chemical reactions involved in the treatment of raw water to produce suitable make-up water for boilers will be discussed in a general manner. Any evaluation of water conditioning for a power station must consider the impurities present in the raw water and in the make-up water in relation to tendencies toward scaling, corrosion, and deposits. Raw water contains many contaminating elements, including:

1. Mud, clay, and silt
2. Oxygen, carbon dioxide, and hydrogen sulfide
3. Organic matter
4. Scale-forming compounds of calcium, magnesium, and silica
5. Oil
6. Iron compounds
7. Normally soluble compounds, such as sodium bicarbonate, sodium carbonate, sodium hydroxide, and sodium chloride

The usual unit for reporting dissolved as well as suspended solids in feedwater and boiler water is parts per million (ppm). This is a rational unit that is easily understood and avoids misunderstanding. In other words, 1 million pounds of water will contain so many pounds of a particular substance. Boilers providing high-purity steam to a steam turbine will require make-up water and feedwater qualities for which the concentration of dissolved solids generally is below 50 *parts per billion* (ppb; 1 ppb = 0.001 ppm).

RAW-WATER TREATMENT PROCESSES

Raw water contains various gaseous and solid (soluble and insoluble) substances, which must be reduced before the water can be supplied as make-up water to a boiler. *Table 9-2* provides a typical analysis of lake water. To reduce the gaseous and insoluble substances, the processes of aeration, settling, coagulation, and filtering commonly are used. A brief description of each method follows.

AERATION

This process of aeration (*Fig. 9-1*) removes such undesirable gases as carbon dioxide and hydrogen sulfide from water by admixing water and air to reduce the solubility of the objectionable gas in water. The removal of gas follows Henry's law, which indicates that the solubility of a gas in water is directly proportional to its partial pressure in the surrounding atmosphere. The partial pressure of a gas such as carbon dioxide in air is low. Establishing an equilibrium between water and air by aeration results in saturation of the water with oxygen and nitrogen and in the practical elimination of such gases as carbon dioxide and hydrogen

TABLE 9-2 | ANALYSES OF TYPICAL SURFACE AND GROUND WATERS IN THE UNITED STATES

Analysis Number*	1	2	3	4	5	6	7	8	9	10	11	12	13
Silica (SiO_2)	2.5	0.4	2.3	8.2	13	8.0	8.4	9.6	16	23	34	12	39
Iron $(Fe)^{3+}$	0.03	0.05	.09	.12	0.04		0.15	0.04	0.0			2.1	.09
Calcium $(Ca)^{2+}$	5 .3	27	32	1.7	72	79	40	3.4	7.2	70	26	72	7.2
Magnesium $(Mg)^{2+}$	1.7	7	10	0.4	6.4	28	16	1.5	2.5	24	10	33	4.2
Sodium $(Na)^{1+}$	1.4	3†	3.5	1.9	41	99	94	5.6	147	12†	138	358†	7.5
Potassium $(K)^{1+}$	0.6		1.0	0.7	4.7	4			0.4		1.6		
Carbonate $(CO_3)^{2-}$	0	1	0	0	0	4	0	0	0		0		
Bicarbonate $(HCO_3)^{1-}$	10	99	138	3	174	137	46	21	328	179	170	293	50
Sulfate $(SO_4)^{2-}$	11	13	17	4.4	138	290	298	3.3	2.6	135	70	560	0.8
Chloride $(Cl)^{1-}$	2.6	7	6.5	2.6	9.5	79	14	3.6	51	8	139	195	6.8
Fluoride $(F)^{1-}$	0.1		0.1	0.6	0.4	0.4	0.1	0.2	0.8			2.5	0.0
Nitrate $(NO_3)^{1-}$	0.3	0.2		0.2	4.0	0.2	3.6	0.7	0.0		0.0	1.1	0.0
Dissolved solids	34	130	171	23	386	661	554	42	392	392	503	1380	90‡
Total hardness as $CaCO_3$	20	98	121	6	206	315	166	15	28	276	106	316	35
Noncarbonate hardness	6	16	8	3	64	197	128	0	0	126	0	76	0
Specific conductance (μS/cm at 25°C)	53.4		263	29.5	575	1,040	822	55.5	651		867		
Color	1		3	15	5		6	4	10			0	2.5
pH	6.9	8.1	8.2	5.8	7.7	8.4	7.6	7.0	8.0	7.6	7.9		7.5

* Analyses numbers are identified as follows. Values are in parts per million where this unit is appropriate:

1 = New York City, NY, Catskill supply (reservoir—finished).
2 = Detroit, MI, Detroit River (raw).
3 = Chicago, IL, Lake Michigan (raw).
4 = Fitchburg, MA, Pond (finished).
5 = Omaha, NE, Missouri River (raw).
6 = Los Angeles, CA, Colorado River (raw).
7 = Pittsburgh, PA, Monongahela River (finished).
8 = Macon, GA, Ocmulgee River (raw).
9 = Houston, TX, Well 1,932 ft deep.
10 = Jacksonville, FL, Well 1,064 ft deep.
11 = El Paso, TX, Well 703 ft deep.
12 = Galesburg, IL, Well 2,450 ft deep.
13 = Bremerton, WA, Anderson Creek.

† Computed by difference in epm and reported as sodium.
‡ Sum of determined constituents.
μS/cm = micro Siemens/cm
epm = equivalents per million

sulfide. Increasing the temperature, the aeration time, and the surface area of water improves the removal of gases.

COAGULATION

Adding coagulating chemicals reduces surface-water contamination in the form of coarse suspended solids, silt, turbidity, color, and colloids. The chemicals form a floc, which assists in agglomerating impurities. Settlement of the particles permits a clear effluent from the coagulating chamber. *Figure 9-2* illustrates a typical clarifier. Removal of colloids requires careful analysis of the impurities to establish the nature of their electrical charge, one of the principal factors that contributes to their remaining in the suspended state. Some chemicals used for coagulation are filter alum, sodium aluminate, copperas, Ferrisul, activated silica, and various proprietary organic compounds.

FILTRATION

Filters separate coarse suspended matter from raw water or remove floc or sludge components from coagulation or process softening systems. Generally, gravity and pressure-type filters are used for this purpose. Graded gravel or coarse anthracite are the materials commonly used in the filter bed. Diatomaceous earth and special pre-coat filters generally are used to remove oil and reduce color in feedwater make-up.

CHEMICAL SOFTENING PROCESSES

Non-scaling feedwater can be obtained with proper pretreatment of raw water. Various chemical combinations can remove hardness, silica, and silt from make-up water. Economics and boiler operating conditions dictate which technique is selected for the application.

REVERSE OSMOSIS

Reverse osmosis is based on the principle of osmosis. In osmosis, a membrane separates two solutions containing different amounts of dissolved chemicals. The membrane allows some compounds (like water) to pass through, but it does not allow larger compounds to do so (i.e., a semi-permeable membrane). Pressure differences cause pure water to pass through the membrane from the dilute to the more concentrated solution, as shown in *Figure 9-3*. The pressure is called *osmotic pressure*. The natural tendency is for water to move through the membrane from the dilute to the

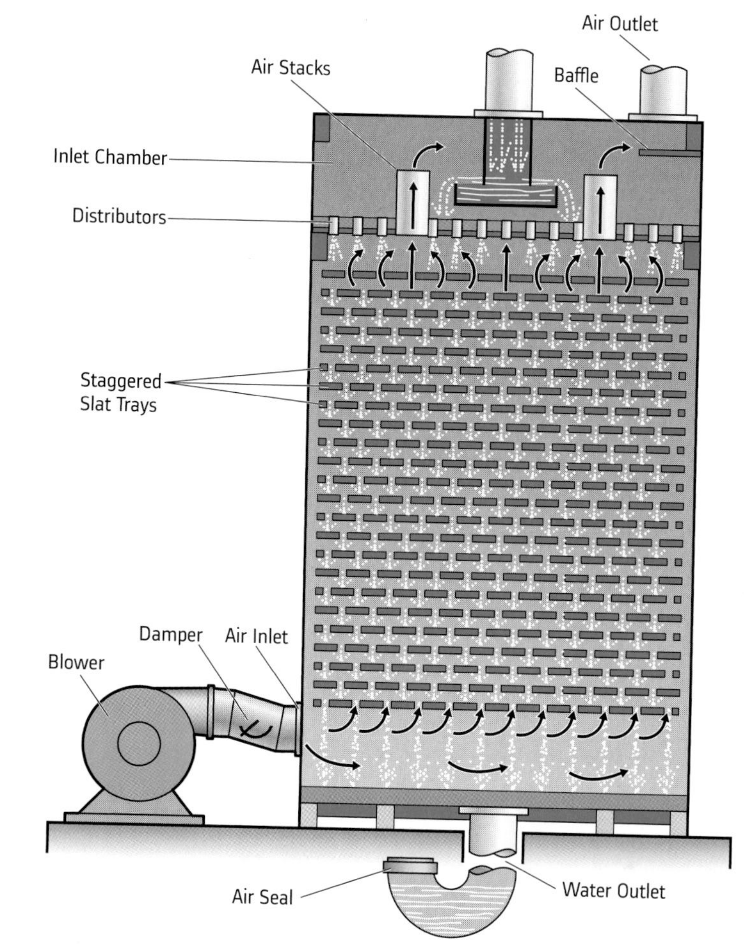

Figure 9-1 | Forced Draft Deaerator

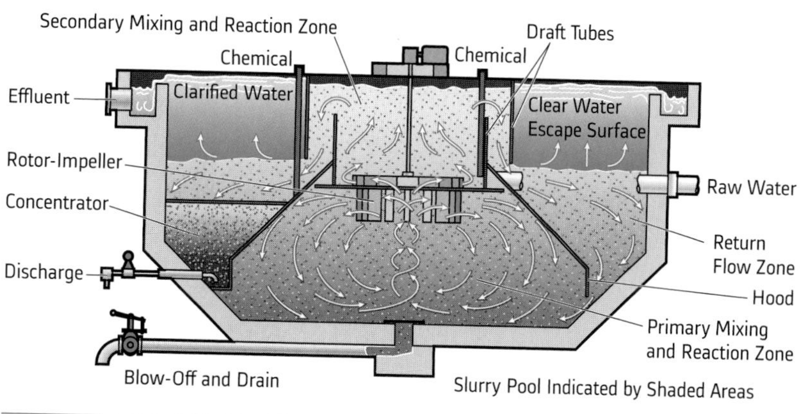

Figure 9-2 | Typical clarifier

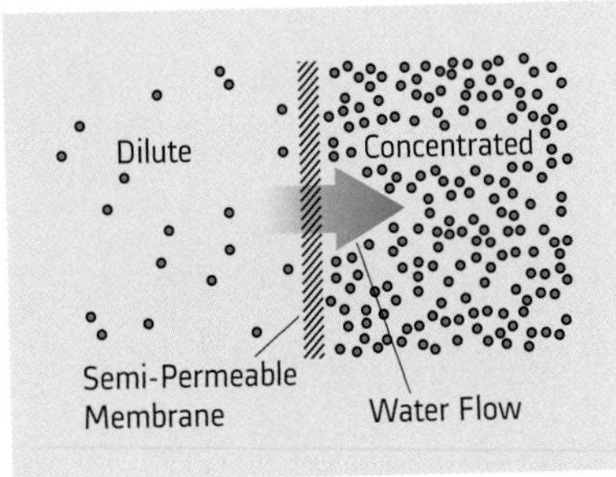

Figure 9-3 | In osmosis, water moves across the membrane from the dilute to the concentrated solution (Data from "Water Treatment Notes: Reverse Osmosis Treatment of Drinking Water," Cornell Cooperative Extension, New York State College of Human Ecology)

concentrated solution until the chemicals reach equal concentrations on both sides of the membrane.

In reverse osmosis, pressure is applied to the concentrated side of the membrane (i.e., the contaminated side). This forces the osmotic process into reverse so that with adequate applied pressure, pure water is forced from the concentrated (contaminated) side to the dilute (treated) side. Treated water is collected in a storage container. The rejected contaminants on the concentrated side of the membrane are drained as wastewater. *Figure 9-4* shows the process of reverse osmosis.

DEMINERALIZATION

In demineralization, ion exchange removes ionized mineral salts. Cations such as calcium, magnesium, and sodium are removed in the hydrogen cation exchanger, and anions such as bicarbonate, sulfate, chloride, and soluble silica are removed in the anion exchanger. Synthetic cation- and anion-exchange resins are used in demineralization of water. Sulfonic, carboxylic, and phenolic resins are used for cation exchange and amino or quaternary nitrogen for anion exchange. The cation exchanger is regenerated with acid; the anion exchange material is regenerated with caustic. If the cation resin is designated as Z and the anion material as R, the simple reactions in a two-stage demineralizer may be expressed as

Cation: $H_2Z + CaSO_4 \rightarrow CaZ + H_2SO_4$

Anion: $H_2SO_4 + R(OH)_2 \rightarrow R(SO_4) + 2H_2O$

Demineralization can yield a pure water that is equal or superior to the best evaporated vapor. The anion and cation resins can be arranged in various combinations to produce the best water most economically. Two-, three-, or four-bed units, or a single mixed-bed demineralizer, can be used to accomplish the required result. *Figure* 9-5 illustrates possible combinations of these systems to produce a specific water quality. Because strong base exchangers are temperature sensitive, they should not be used above 120°F (49°C). Cation-exchange resins can tolerate temperatures of 250°F (120°C).

Use of finely sized resins in demineralizers requires a water source that is low in turbidity and organic matter. Clarification, filtration, and chlorination generally are required to reduce organic matter to a low level. Failure to reduce the organic level in the water produces a marked reduction in the capacity of the exchangers because of fouling of the resins. The advance of demineralization to provide a high-purity make-up water may be attributed in part to the development of highly basic anion-exchange resins, which allow the removal of soluble silica from raw water. Mixed-bed demineralizers, in which the

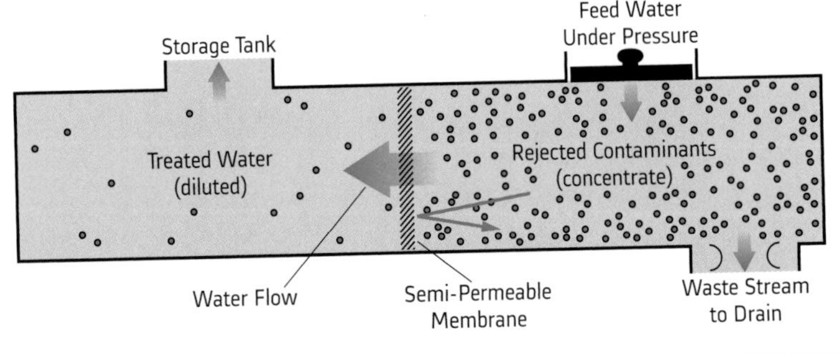

Figure 9-4 | In reverse osmosis, pressure is applied to the concentrated solution, reversing the natural direction of flow and forcing water across the membrane from the concentrated solution into the more dilute solution (Data from "Water Treatment Notes: Reverse Osmosis Treatment of Drinking Water," Cornell Cooperative Extension, New York State College of Human Ecology)

cation and anion resins are intimately interspersed (*Figs. 9-6* and *9-7*), have successfully provided high-quality make-up water as well as served polishing purposes in terms of cleaning up impurities in condensates of utility units. *Figure 9-8* is a schematic of a complete make-up water system for a utility power plant.

WATER TECHNOLOGY FOR BOILERS

Water technology for steam power plants encompasses the production of make-up water and the treatment of the water (boiler water and feedwater) after it enters the cycle. Requirements for make-up water quality and internal treatment may vary depending on many factors, such as system design, operating conditions, and type of construction materials. Modern, high-pressure power cycles require water of high purity, essentially free of soluble and insoluble solids. As described in previous sections, make-up water of excellent quality can be produced by ion-exchange systems at reasonable costs. The internal treatment is then designed to maintain a chemical environment that provides corrosion protection, deposit-free surfaces, and high-purity steam.

Plants with boilers operating below 600 psig (4 MPa) and where the steam is exported to a process generally have less stringent requirements. Therefore, it often is more economical to provide make-up water that has been only partially demineralized (softened) and to rely on internal chemical treatment to avoid potential problems resulting from the increased soluble solids concentration in the cycle. The greatest incidence of problems in steam generating equipment is related to scale or deposits, corrosion, and carryover of solids with the steam. In the next several sections, various chemical treatment schemes and the corresponding chemical agents will be reviewed.

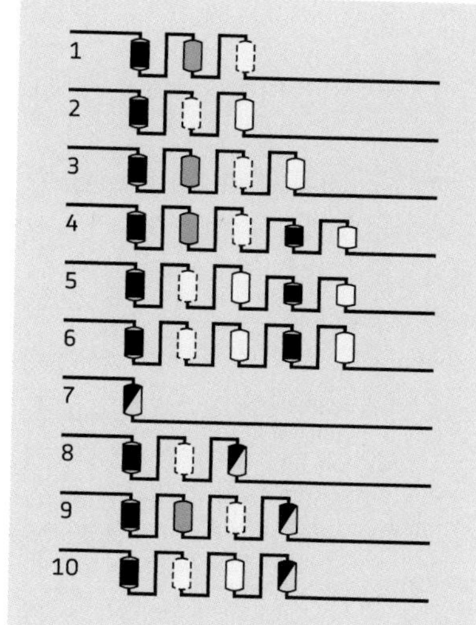

Figure 9-5 | Ten major demineralizer systems: black, strong-acid cation exchanger; white, strong-base anion exchanger; shaded, weak-base anion exchanger; half black and half white, mixed-bed demineralizer; broken rectangle, decarbonator or vacuum deaerator; 1, two-bed unit with weak base; 2, two-bed unit with strong base; 3, three-bed unit; 4, four-bed unit, primary with weak base; 5, four-bed unit, primary with strong base; 6, parallel two-bed units, as in system 2, or four-bed unit, as in system 5 (except for size of secondary unit); 7, mixed-bed mineralizer; 8, cation-bed unit, decarbonator, and mixed-bed demineralizer; 9, two-bed unit, as in system 1, and mixed-bed demineralizer; 10, two-bed unit, as in system 2, and mixed-bed demineralizer. The secondary units in systems 4 and 5, which are used only for polishing, may be smaller than the primary unit, as indicated

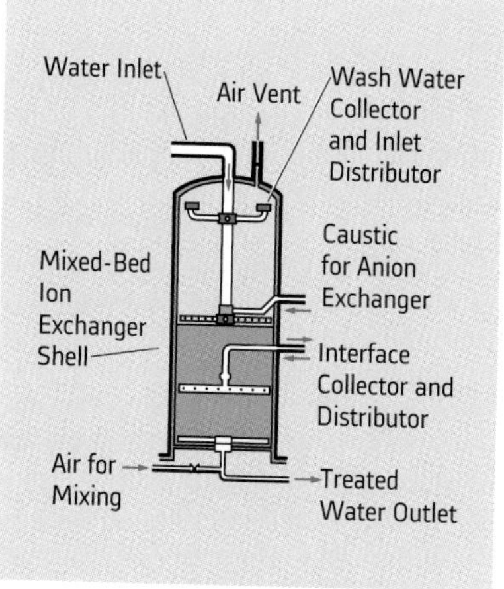

Figure 9-6 | A mixed-bed demineralizer houses a mixture of cation- and anion-exchange resins; air for mixing enters through the bottom distributor

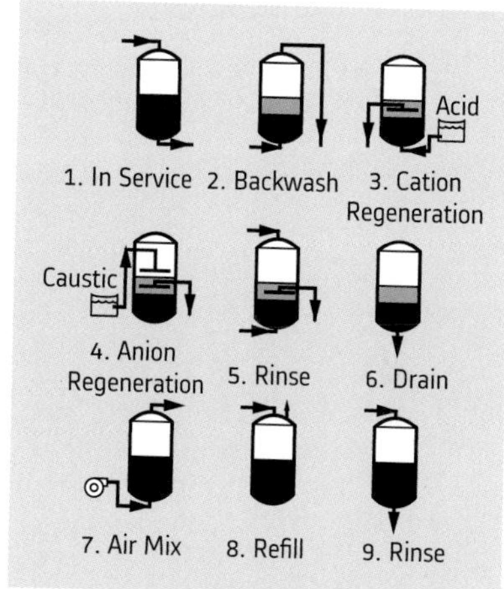

Figure 9-7 | Regeneration of the mixed-bed, from initial backwash to end of rinse and return to service, takes from 2 to 3 hours

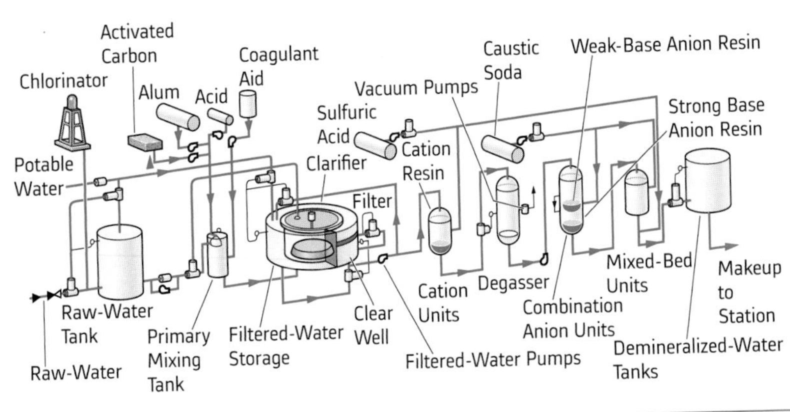

Figure 9-8 | Demineralizer and pre-treatment flow diagram

SCALE AND DEPOSITS

Major contributors to the formation of a heat deterrent scale or deposit are:

1. Contaminating elements present in the make-up water
2. Metal oxides transported to the boiler with feedwater
3. Contaminants from process equipment introduced into the condensate returned to the boiler
4. Solids in condenser leakage

Low-pressure boilers with high make-up water and a small, heat-recovering, pre-boiler system are more prone to deposits from the precipitation of chemical compounds. Substances such as calcium bicarbonate, if not properly removed from the make-up water, will decompose in the boiler water to form calcium carbonate as follows:

$$Ca(HCO_3)_2 \rightarrow CaCO_3 + CO_2 + H_2O$$

Calcium carbonate has a very limited solubility; thus, the precipitated particles will agglomerate at the heated surfaces to form a scale. Other substances, such as calcium sulfate, also produce scales. In this case, the scaling mechanism is a function of a retrograde solubility, or a decrease of solubility in water with an increase in temperature. These substances have a low thermal conductivity, and if left untreated, even a thin scale will overheat the boiler tube.

USE OF PHOSPHATES FOR INTERNAL TREATMENT

The work of R. E. Hall and associates[6] led to the use of phosphates as an internal boiler water treatment for converting residual concentrations of calcium and other hardness salts to their respective phosphate compounds. These compounds can be more readily dispersed and removed by blowdown, although if present in large concentrations, these will form scales on boiler tubes as well. Several phosphate compounds, such as trisodium phosphate, disodium phosphate, and monosodium phosphate, in conjunction with sodium hydroxide (caustic), can be used for this purpose. Some of these reactions are:

$$2Na_3PO_4 + 3CaSO_4 \rightarrow Ca_3(PO_4)_2 + 3Na_2SO_4$$
$$3MgCO_3 + 2Na_3PO_4 \rightarrow Mg_3(PO_4)_2 + 3Na_2CO_3$$
$$Mg(HCO_3)_2 + 4NaOH \rightarrow Mg(OH)_2 + 2Na_2CO_3 + 2H_2O$$
$$MgCl_2 + 2NaOH + SiO_2 \rightarrow MgSiO_3 + 2NaCl + H_2O$$

The phosphate–caustic treatment is limited to low-pressure boilers utilizing softened make-up water. It is recognized that for boilers using demineralized make-up, the need for high phosphate concentrations is greatly diminished. Also, the use of caustic is limited to 1 ppm because of its corrosivity at higher concentrations. With demineralized-quality boiler water, caustic (present either as a treatment chemical or a contaminant) can reach high concentrations because of the absence of large quantities of other competing ions.

Whirl and Purcell[7] recognized the ability of sodium phosphates to suitably alkalize and control pH in boiler water without the negative reaction associated with the use of caustic. They developed the pH control method known as "the coordinated phosphate pH control." This method is illustrated by the relationship of pH and the phosphate concentration in boiler water, as shown in *Figure 9-9*. Values noted on the curve represent pH values obtained by dissolving stoichiometrically pure trisodium phosphate (Na_3PO_4). Conditions below the curve represent solutions of trisodium phosphate and disodium hydrogen phosphate (Na_2HPO_4). The area above the curve represents solutions of trisodium phosphate and caustic. In the coordinated phosphate pH control, specifications can be maintained by adding trisodium phosphate (Na_3PO_4), disodium phosphate (Na_2HPO_4), or monosodium phosphate (NaH_2PO_4). Combinations of trisodium phosphate and disodium phosphate are preferred.

Alkalinity control is attained by the addition of phosphate ions to water to produce a captive quantity of hydroxide $(OH)^-$ by the reversed hydrolysis reaction as follows:

$$PO_4^{3-} + H_2O \rightarrow OH^- + HPO_4^{2-}$$

This reaction is complete at pH levels below 11.0. The hydrolysis reaction of hydrogen phosphate ion also proceeds in water as follows:

$$HPO_4^{2-} + H_2O \rightarrow OH^- + H_2PO_4^-$$

The latter reaction is complete at low pH (i.e., 5–7) but is less than 0.1% at pH 10. Thus, dibasic phosphate neither hydrolyzes nor dissociates in the normal boiler water pH range. Additions of disodium phosphate have little effect on pH in the range of 10 to 11. Monobasic phosphate dissociates to the dibasic form, and the addition of one mole of monosodium phosphate (NaH_2PO_4) is capable of neutralizing one mole of sodium hydroxide.

As discussed in later sections, the use of monosodium phosphate and even disodium phosphate is limited, because under certain conditions, a potential exists to form acid phosphate compounds, which can be corrosive. Trisodium phosphate therefore is the treatment of choice to ensure boiler water pH control in drum-type units.

SIGNIFICANCE OF IRON–WATER REACTION

A number of influences characterize the reaction of boiler steel and water:

- The chemical constituents present in solution
- The quantity of dissolved gases
- The structural characteristics of the steel
- The rate of heat input to the boiler metal

Although the reaction is understood, there generally is insufficient information to explain the mechanism in exact detail. Many theories have been forwarded to clarify this problem,

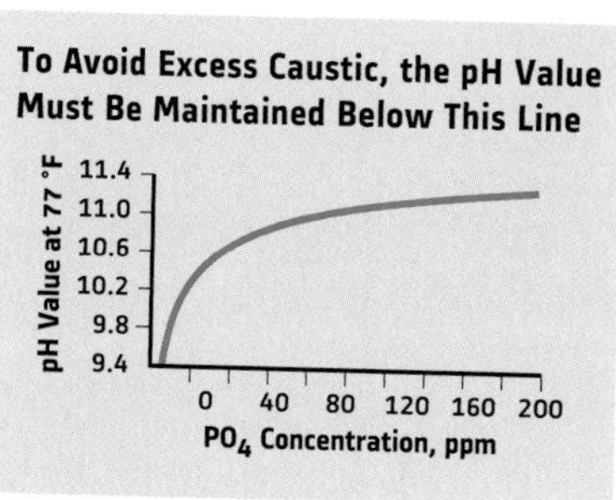

Figure 9-9 | Coordinated phosphate pH control

and despite a lack of fundamental data, experience and experimental evidence have permitted the development of controls that satisfactorily contain the corrosive activity. This section will deal with existing techniques developed to understand and control reactions in boilers.

The fundamental reaction of iron and water is to produce iron hydroxide and hydrogen as follows:

$$Fe + 2H_2O \rightarrow Fe(OH)_2 + H_2$$

It is an established fact that the end product of the reaction in boilers is magnetite (Fe_3O_4). The control of corrosion therefore is based on the knowledge of the rate-controlling step in the overall reaction.

Schikorr[8] established a mechanism that accounted for the production of magnetite. In the simplest form, the reactions would be:

$$Fe + 2H_2O \rightarrow Fe(OH)_2 + H_2$$
$$3Fe(OH)_2 \rightarrow Fe_3O_4 + 2H_2O + H_2$$

From a consideration of physical and chemical relationships, it can be shown that the formation of iron hydroxide is the rate-controlling step in the Schikorr hypothesis. Therefore, the rate of the overall reaction is based on the solubility and stability of this product. The initial reaction above is pH or alkalinity controlled, because by the laws of chemical equilibrium, addition of alkalinity would reverse the reaction to the left.

Corey and Finnegan[9] found that iron placed in contact with deaerated and chemically pure water will produce an equilibrium pH of approximately 8.3. Increasing the alkalinity reduces the solubility of the iron corrosion product and inhibits reactivity. The control of this reaction has been well established in the protection of metal surfaces existing ahead of the boiler.[10] The reaction of water and steel is spontaneous and rapid at high boiler temperatures. The only reason that boiler steel can survive normal operating conditions is that the corrosion end product, magnetite (Fe_3O_4), forms a protective barrier on the metal surface to stifle further corrosion.

In the simplest analysis, the function of alkalinity control is to maintain an environment in which this barrier is stable and protective. The objective of water treatment in boilers is to protect the barrier against the aggressive action of impurities introduced into the boiler with the feedwater. The work of Berl and Van Taack[11] (*Fig. 9-10*) has been used to relate corrosion of steel over a range of pH values. In interpreting the results of *Figure 9-10*, it may be concluded that the protective oxide is solubilized at pH values below 5.0 and above 13.0. Minimum corrosion is indicated at pH values of 9.0 to 11.0. It should be noted that in actual plant feedwater, other parameters, such as oxygen and dissolved solids or salts in the water, can influence the solubility of the protective oxide or corrosion of the metal.

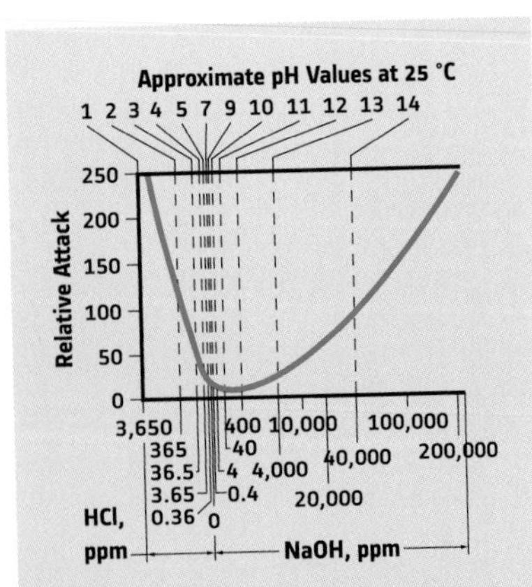

Figure 9-10 | Relative general corrosion rate of carbon steel versus pH

ROLE OF OXYGEN

The presence of oxygen in the feedwater influences the reaction of iron and water. Oxygen can react with iron hydroxide to form either a hydrated ferric oxide (hematite) or magnetite. This reaction is a function of the oxygen concentration, pH, and salt content (or cation conductivity) of the water.

Dissolved oxygen in water can cause general or localized corrosion. Oxygen reacts with hydrogen ions at the metal surface and depolarizes the surface locally, causing iron to dissolve. If the area becomes progressively anodic, it permits more iron to dissolve, gradually creating a pit. The most severe corrosion action occurs when a deposit covers a small area. Creation of a differential aeration cell about the deposit can lead to a severe local action. The metal beneath the deposit is lower in oxygen compared with areas surrounding it, becomes anodic, and is attacked. Pitting is most prevalent in stressed sections of boiler tubing, such as at welds and cold-worked sections and at surface discontinuities in the metal.

Generally, oxygen is excluded or removed from the feedwater of any power plant. Conditions exist, however, in which the cation conductivity (or salt content) is very low (not to exceed 0.3 μS/cm), so a small amount of oxygen (<1 ppm) can actually reduce the degradation of the protective oxide. Under these conditions, oxide layers consisting of hematite and magnetite are formed. These layers form an interlocking structure, which have a much lower corrosion product release rate. This mechanism forms the basis for a specialized treatment called "oxygenated treatment" (OT), which will be discussed in a later section.

Power plants employing tight cycles to prevent oxygen infiltration and condenser leakage generally are free of corrosion problems. On the other hand, many cycles are vulnerable to uncontrolled oxygen leakage into the feedwater as a result of design or operation. Efficient boiler operation requires the control of oxygen in the feedwater. The normal guaranteed value of oxygen leaving the deaerating heater or a deaerating condenser is less than 0.010 ppm. To achieve a low residual, it is necessary to[12]:

- Exclude air leakage into the condenser
- Judiciously control the addition of undeaerated water to the condensate or feedwater
- Prevent the addition of aerated heater drips into the condensate
- Ensure the exclusion of air into the feedwater cycle during short outages of the boiler

Boiler start-up is a likely source for a certain amount of oxygen infiltration into the feedwater. Normally, pressure in a deaerator is not attained until steam is admitted to the turbine and bleed steam is available for heating. It is possible to introduce more oxygen into the boiler at this time than it will be in a few months of normal operation. Admitting auxiliary steam to a deaerator to pressurize the unit to between 3 and 5 psig (0.2 to 0.35 bar) can prevent much of this problem, but the inclusion of auxiliary boilers or steam in a plant cycle is rarely done today. Plants that are designed to cycle and predict frequent starts and stops have been equipped with vacuum-type deaerators to better control oxygen ingress.

Removal of Residual Oxygen

Chemical agents added to the feedwater or, in some cases, to the boiler water are available to react with small residual quantities of oxygen. These are known as "oxygen scavengers." Two types of scavengers exist; volatile, such as hydrazine (N_2H_4) or its substitutes, and non-volatile, such as sodium sulfite (Na_2SO_3). The use of hydrozine has been problematical and, therefore, has been limited. However, it still provides

Control of oxygen in the boiler water is critical to avoiding corrosion problems. Efficient boiler operation requires control of oxygen in the feedwater.

TABLE 9-3 | SODIUM SULFITE LIMITS	
Boiler Pressure (psig)	Concentration (ppm)
<600 (4 MPa)	20–40
600–900 (4–6 MPa)	5–10

the best example when discussing the general behavior of oxygen scavengers. Sodium sulfite usually is added to the boiler water in low-pressure boilers that typically use softened water as make-up. Sodium sulfite, when added to the boiler water, reacts with oxygen to form sodium sulfate as follows:

$$2Na_2SO_3 + O_2 \rightarrow 2Na_2SO_4$$

Temperature affects the reactivity and stability of sodium sulfite (as well as hydrazine). Generally, a cobalt catalyst is added with the sodium sulfite solution to speed up the reaction at lower temperatures. Sulfite decomposition increases with temperature and local concentration in boiler water. Sodium sulfite decomposes in boiler water as follows:

$$Na_2SO_3 + 2H_2O \rightarrow 2NaOH + H_2SO_3$$
$$H_2SO_3 \rightarrow H_2O + SO_2$$

Sulfur dioxide (SO_2) is an acidic anhydride that increases corrosion of metals when it is dissolved in condensate films formed on wetted surfaces of a turbine or condenser. The concentration of sulfite must be controlled to minimize decomposition at elevated pressures. Recommended limits are shown in *Table 9-3*. This is one of the reasons that sulfite should not be used for reducing oxygen in high pressure boilers.

Hydrazine reacts with oxygen to form nitrogen and water as follows:

$$N_2H_4 + O_2 \rightarrow N_2 + 2H_2O$$

Hydrazine reacts with oxygen very slowly at temperatures below 350°F (180°C). Above 450°F (230°C), hydrazine is decomposed rapidly to nitrogen, hydrogen, and ammonia. The principal benefit of hydrazine is its ability to reduce the oxidized form of copper. In this state, the general corrosion of the copper alloy surfaces is reduced in the pre-boiler cycle. Copper oxide is reduced with hydrazine at temperatures as low as 150°F (66°C) (Iron oxide, or Fe_2O_3, also can be reduced at a temperature of 250°F [120°C]).

Normally, hydrazine or its substitutes, when needed, are added to the cycle at the outlet of the condensate pump at a rate not to exceed a residual of approximately 10 ppb at the inlet of the economizer. Reducing agents aid in curbing corrosion, especially copper alloys (oxygen > 10 ppb and cation conductivity > 0.3 μS/cm), but they will not prevent metal attack everywhere when oxygen is present in the boiler feedwater. At higher temperatures, the reaction rate of oxygen with steel exceeds that of the reducing agents.

FEEDWATER pH CONTROL

Besides the control of oxygen, it is important that the pH of the water be maintained in the proper range. In high-pressure units, feedwater is sprayed into superheated and reheated steam to help control final temperatures. Therefore, to ensure protection to pre-boiler equipment, volatile alkaline chemicals have been developed to control the pH of the water without forming solid residue in parts of the boiler where evaporation takes place. Classed as neutralizing amines, the most common of these are ammonia (NH_3), morpholine (C_4H_9NO), and cyclohexylamine ($C_6H_{11}NH_2$). These compounds volatilize with the steam and can react with gases like carbon dioxide to neutralize any acidity in the condensate system. The selection of any of these chemicals is based on obtaining an optimum fit between their chemical and physical characteristics (e.g., volatility, solubility, and stability) and the particular application.

Table 9-4 lists the stability characteristics of volatile amines. Both morpholine and cyclohexylamine have temperature stability limits. Ammonia, hydrogen, and carbon decomposition products are formed in the dissociation of these amines at high temperatures. Ammonia is stable and has been used at steam temperatures as high as 1,200°F (650°C). As a result, ammonia is the recommended compound for use in controlling the pH of condensate in high-pressure, high-temperature boiler systems.

It is important to maintain ammonia levels generally below 1 ppm in systems containing copper alloys to avoid copper alloy attack, because a copper ammonium complex is formed in the presence of high ammonia concentrations. The reaction can be further accelerated by the presence of abnormal concentrations of oxygen. Typical reactions are as follows:

$$Cu^{+} + 2NH_3 \rightarrow Cu(NH_3)_2^{+}$$
$$Cu^{2+} + 4NH_3 \rightarrow Cu(NH_3)_4^{2+}$$

It has been established that an ammonia concentration of less than 0.5 ppm will ensure a protective pH in the cycle without attacking copper surfaces. Morpholine and cyclohexylamine are preferred to ammonia for pH control in situations where excessive decomposition of these chemicals does not occur and an extensive condensing system or process piping network exist.

USE OF CHELANTS FOR INTERNAL CONTROL

Chelants are weak organic acids with the capability of complexing or binding many cations (calcium and magnesium hardness as well as heavy metals) into a soluble organic ring structure. Chelants are in the neutralized, sodium salt form. They hydrolyze in boiler water to an organic anion. Full hydrolysis depends on a relatively high pH level. The anionic chelant has reactive sites that attract coordination sites on cations. These coordination sites are areas on the ion that are receptive to chemical bonding. In this manner, cations (hardness salts) entering the boiler as contamination from the condensate system combine with the chelant to form a stable chelate. Deposition of hardness on boiler internal surfaces may therefore be prevented.

Although many substances have chelating properties, ethylenediaminetetra acetic acid is the most suitable for boiler feedwater treatment. As with any internal chemical treatment, however, the application and limitations must be clearly understood. Because of their thermal decomposition at saturation temperatures corresponding to higher pressures, chelants are limited to boiler pressures of less than 1,000 psig (0.7 MPa) and to those boilers typically using softened makeup water. In addition, overfeeding of chelants can lead to corrosion of boiler tubes, because chelation of the protective magnetite (Fe_3O_4) layer can occur (For a more detailed discussion, see references 1–5.).

TABLE 9-4 | STABILITY OF VOLATILE WATER-TREATING MATERIALS

Chemical	Formula	Pressure (psig)	Temperature (°F)	% Decomposed
Ammonia	NH_3	4,270 (29 MPa)	1,202 (650°C)	
Cyclohexylamine	$C_6H_{11}NH_2$	4,270 (29 MPa)	1,202 (650°C)	88
Morpholine	$O(CH_2)_2NH$	4,270 (29 MPa)	1,202 (650°C)	100
Hydrazine	N_2H_4	4,270 (29 MPa)	1,202 (650°C)	7,100

CORROSION DAMAGE IN POWER PLANTS

The major purpose of feedwater and boiler water treatment is to avoid corrosion and associated tube failures. Most materials that form boiler deposits originate in the pre-boiler system. Adherence to recommended operating procedures during power plant start-up, normal operation, shutdown, and outages is vital to minimize corrosion and to avoid the entry of corrosion products into the steam generator. Corrosion damage may be in the form of a general attack on the metal surface, pitting, or localized attack of the metal surface beneath internal deposits.

GENERAL SURFACE ATTACK

One type of corrosion is oxygen attack on ferritic materials of construction. Such corrosion may take place throughout the pre-boiler/boiler cycle. Corrosion from oxygen can occur during any period of the power plant lifetime, from erection to operation, as well as during standby conditions.

Another type of general overall corrosion is caused by lack of boiler water pH control during system operation. Improper condensate and feedwater pH levels also cause this type of general attack within the pre-boiler system.

PITTING AND LOCALIZED ATTACK

Pitting of various types can affect the internal surfaces of all tubes and components. Pitting is electro-chemical in nature, with the pitted area being anodic to the surrounding, non-pitted metal surface. If conditions favorable to pitting exist, such as excessive dissolved oxygen in the boiler water/feedwater or an acidic chemical environment, one of several normally innocuous factors can cause severe local attack. Crevices, such as those formed by deposits or minor variations in metallurgical structure, may act to promote localized corrosion. Normal, but higher than average, peak stress also can contribute to preferential pitting. Units that undergo peaking, variable-pressure, low-load, and two-shifting operations, with frequent shutdowns, are all susceptible to the peculiar corrosion patterns that are related to frequent introduction of oxygen during outage and start-up periods. A look at several instances of pitting attack will provide a better appreciation of the need for protection when the corrosion potential is high.

Examples of Pitting Corrosion

Figures 9-11 through *9-16* show a variety of corrosive attack attributable to pitting. Generally, the term *pitting* denotes localized, crater-like attack of a type shown in *Figures 9-11* and *9-12*. Failures do occur, however, in which individual pits join, producing crack-like penetrations. In the absence of a corrosion or metallurgical term describing this type of corrosion penetration, the condition has been included under the broad category of "pitting attack." The orientation and location of the crack-like indications can best be explained by pitting preferential to an area of somewhat higher strain compared with the surrounding metal. Differences in strain promote the formation of anode–cathode cells, and the resulting corrosion at the anode is oriented perpendicular to the direction of maximum residual or applied strain.

The pitting attack shown in *Figures 9-12* and *9-13* affected the entire tube circumference but was deepest under the welded fin. In this instance, differences in metallurgical structure also may have been a factor in promoting the electro-chemical cell. This type of pitting attack also has been found in some

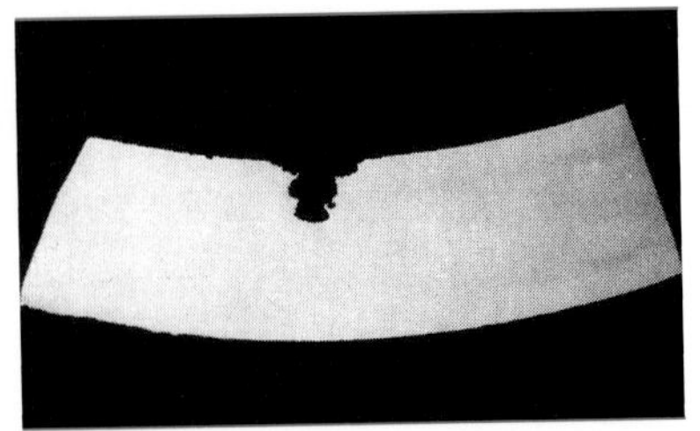

Figure 9-11 | Sectional view of one pit

lower waterwall drums. The overall character of these crack-like indications is not typical of fatigue cracking. The bottoms of the penetrations show no evidence of cracking, and the shape of the voids indicates they were formed as a result of corrosion.

When tubes exhibiting internal surface crack-like indications (*Fig. 9-14*) have been reverse flattened and bent to force fracture along these linear indications, the penetrations show themselves to be a series of aligned corrosion pits (*Fig. 9-15*).

The evidence strongly suggests that a pitting mechanism can initiate and propagate crack-like penetrations. In some instances, the penetrations appear to be a series of pits, one atop another, giving the impression of separate time periods when the pitting attack has resumed at the bottom of the penetrations, as shown in *Figure 9-16*. The pitting attack or crack-like penetrations, when influenced by residual or dynamic stresses, are also described as stress assisted corrosion or corrosion fatigue, respectively.

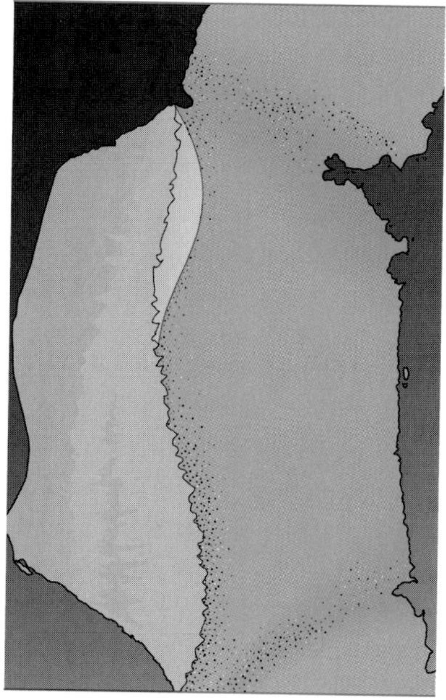

Figure 9-12 | General pitting attack from the inside surface of a waterwall tube. Pitting affected the entire tube circumference but was more severe under the external fin (original magnification, ×8)

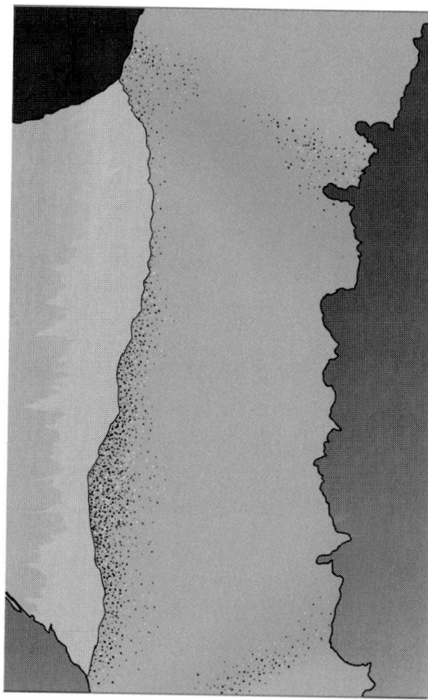

Figure 9-13 | Pitting attack similar to that shown in *Figure 9-12*, with deep, clearly corrosion-related, localized, crack-like penetrations under the external fin (original magnification, ×8)

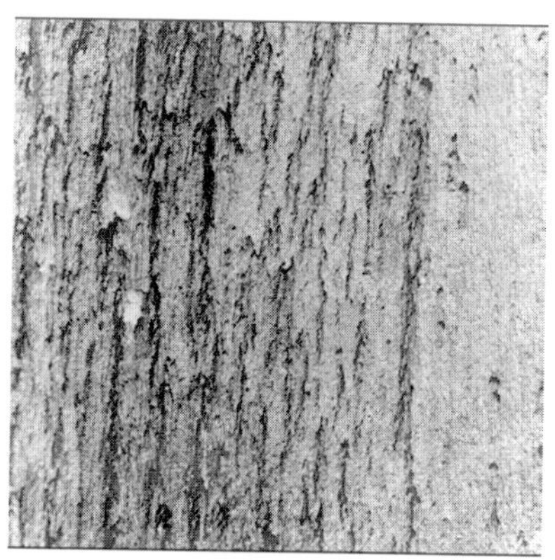

Figure 9-14 | Internal surface of tube with longitudinally oriented, crack-like indications (original magnification, ×3)

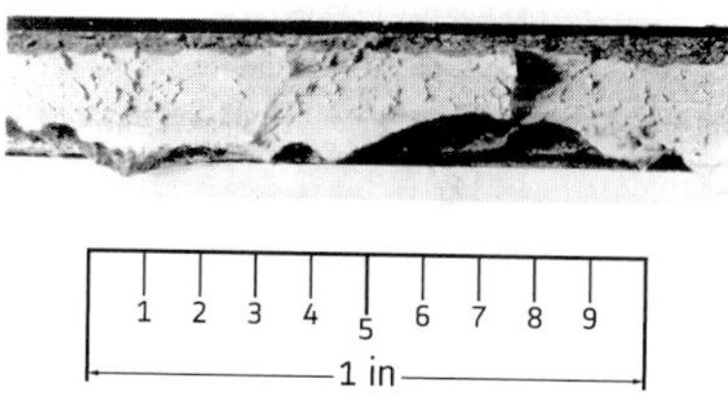

Figure 9-15 | Sectional, through-the-wall view of the tube shown in *Figure 9-14* after flattening and bending to promote fracture along a penetration. Inside diameter (ID) surface is at the bottom, and darker craters from the ID surface are pits. (The remaining wall portion is sound metal that fractured because of the flattening and reverse bending.) The crack-like penetrations result from aligned pits

BOILER WATER–RELATED CORROSION DAMAGE

Deviations from recommended chemistry limits, which result in depressed or elevated pH values, promote failures of boiler tubing. Although many variations exist, the majority of failures can be classified into one of the following two categories:

1. **Ductile gouging.** Normally, irregular wastage of the tube metal beneath a porous deposit characterizes this type of damage. The damage progresses to failure when the tube wall thins to a point at which stress rupture occurs locally. During this process, the microstructure of the metal does not change, and the tubing retains its ductility. *Figure 9-17* illustrates ductile gouging.
2. **Hydrogen damage.** This type of corrosion damage usually occurs beneath a relatively dense deposit. Although some wastage

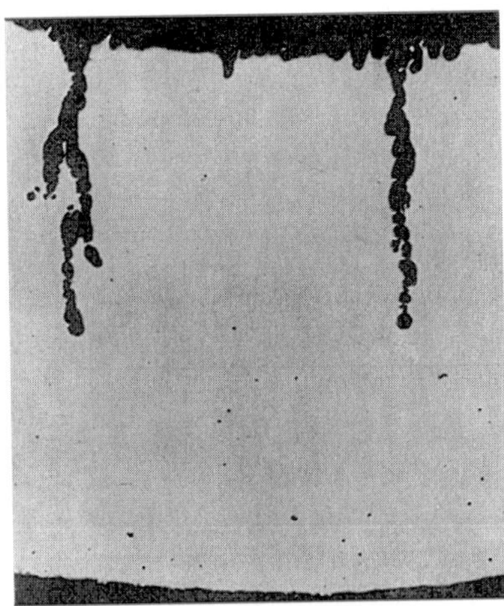

Figure 9-16 | Crack-like corrosion penetrations halfway through the tube wall, strongly suggesting that propagation results from separate time periods of pitting

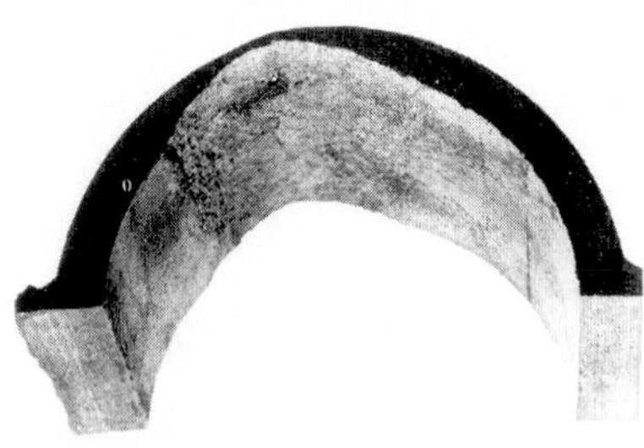

Figure 9-17 | Ductile gouging

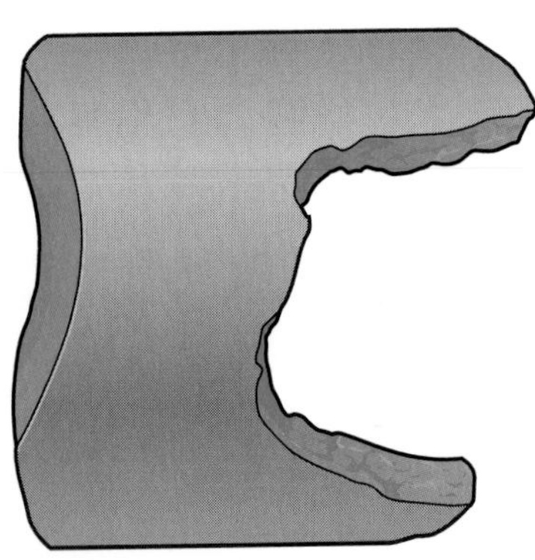

Figure 9-18 | Thick edge waterwall tube failure caused by hydrogen damage

occurs, the tube normally fails by thick-edge fracture before the wall thickness is reduced to the point at which stress rupture would occur. Hydrogen gas, produced in the corrosion reaction, diffuses through the underlying metal, causing fissuring of the structure. Brittle fracture occurs along the partially separated boundaries, and in many cases, an entire section is blown out of an affected tube. Examples of these failures are shown in *Figures 9-18* and *9-19*.

Internal metal-oxide deposits, which permit boiler water solids to concentrate during the process of steam generation, accelerate both types of attack. When the boiler water contains highly soluble alkaline treatment chemicals, such as sodium hydroxide or potassium salts, ductile attack is more probable. Hydrogen damage, on the other hand, is more likely to occur when a low-pH boiler water environment results from condenser leakage or some other type of system contamination.[13]

According to an American Society of Mechanical Engineers and Edison Electric Institute (ASME/EEI) sponsored laboratory research program,[14,15] clean tubes are not susceptible to corrosion even under high heat-transfer conditions unless unusually high concentrations of acid or alkali are present. In addition, fouled tubes do not appear to be susceptible to corrosion when contaminants are present if proper boiler water treatment is maintained.

These observations can be explained by the "concentrating film" theory. The Berl and Van Taack curve (see *Fig. 9-20*) illustrates the relative corrosion of carbon steel under various acid and alkaline conditions. Bulk boiler water concentrations are always well within the range of low corrosion rates. As heat is transferred through the boiler tube wall to a water–steam mixture, however, a temperature gradient is established, and the internal tube metal temperature must reach a value slightly higher than the bulk fluid temperature. As boiler water is converted to steam, the dissolved solids concentrate in a residual film, as shown in *Figure 9-20*. The solids concentration in this film increases until the boiling point of the solution is elevated to the temperature at the tube wall. It is improbable that such high concentrations can be reached in a clean tube under normal boiling conditions. Theoretically, the bulk of the film-temperature drop is experienced within a laminar film of approximately 0.001 inch (0.025 mm) in thickness. Free diffusion of ions into the turbulent fluid would prevent the establishment of a concentration gradient. Only when porous internal deposits are formed in areas of heat absorption is it possible to produce very high concentrations. The deposit itself acts as a diffusion barrier and, in so doing, increases the probability of high local concentrations being reached.

Because porous deposits may exist, boiler water chemicals should be of a type that will not become highly corrosive when concentrated. Experience indicates that sodium hydroxide and potassium salts are particularly objectionable. Alkalinity can be produced with sodium phosphate (coordinated phosphate treatment) without the risk of extremely high pH values being present on concentration. Control of boiler water pH also may be achieved by volatile amines, such as ammonia, entering with the feedwater (required for once-through units).

Condenser cooling waters represent a potential source for contamination of the boiler water. Depending on the chemical constituents dissolved in the cooling water, highly acidic or alkaline materials may be formed in the boiler environment as a result of condenser leakage.

Because of poor buffering capability, volatile treatment (amines) provides little protection against this type of contamination. On the other hand, coordinated phosphate treatment results in a more highly buffered boiler water, one in which acid-producing reactions from salt in-leakage are better suppressed. Optimum treatment programs based on this method are discussed in later sections.

Figure 9-19 | Another typical waterwall failure caused by hydrogen damage

FLOW-ASSISTED CORROSION

Flow-assisted corrosion (FAC) of carbon steel is defined as the acceleration or increase in the rate of corrosion caused by the relative movement between a corrosive fluid (either single-phase water or two-phase water and steam mixtures) and a metal surface. The dissolution of the protective magnetite layer is enhanced by the mass transport of soluble iron species (Fe(II)) away from the surface. The rate of mass transfer of these species to the bulk of the fluid is accelerated by flow/turbulence. This will increase the loss of metal as iron oxidizes to replace the dissolved film, repeatedly.

Flow-assisted corrosion imparts a distinct surface pattern, often called a "scalloped surface," as indicated in *Figure 9-21*. This physical feature helps to distinguish FAC, or metal "wastage," from other wastage corrosion mechanisms. Flow-assisted corrosion is not a mechanical abrasion- or erosion-related mechanism. It is a chemical/corrosion process mitigated by specific water-chemistry conditions within a particular fluid temperature range. Fluid temperature and fluid flow mechanics influence the location in boiler, or heat recovery steam generator (HRSG) components, where FAC could preferentially occur. A brief review of these parameters follows.[16,17]

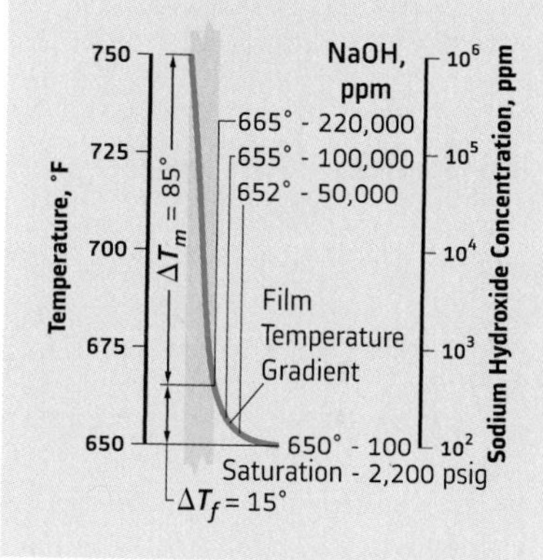

Figure 9- 20 | Illustration of "concentrating film" theory. Film temperature gradient of 15°F (8.3°C) is developed because of heat transfer. Soluble solids in boiler water are concentrated in the surface film during steam generation to produce "non-boiling equilibrium." Although the caustic concentration in the boiler water is only 100 ppm, the concentration in the surface film must equal 220,000 ppm to elevate the boiling point by 15°F (8.3°C)

pH and Oxidation–Reduction Potential

The pH and the oxidation–reduction potential (ORP) of the fluid affect the solubility of iron oxide/hydroxide, as typically represented by the Sweeton and Baes equilibrium reaction:

$$\tfrac{1}{3}Fe_3O_4 + (2 - b)H^+ + \tfrac{1}{3}H_2 \leftrightarrow Fe(OH)_b^{(2-b)+} + (\tfrac{4}{3} - b)H_2O$$

Ferrous hydroxide, on the right-hand side of the equation, is the soluble product. As indicated by this equation, the dissolution of magnetite is influenced by the ORP of the solution, as represented by the hydrogen molecule (H_2). It also is influenced by the pH, as represented by the hydrogen ion (H^+). Thus, lowering the pH and /or the ORP (toward negative potential or reducing conditions) will increase the dissolution rate of the protective oxide layer and accelerate corrosion.

Normally, oxygen or oxidizing conditions would be thought to cause additional corrosion, and in the presence of dissolved solids, corrosion is increased.

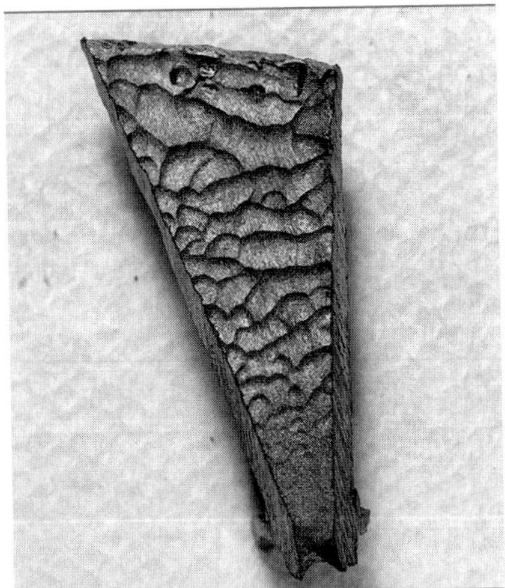

Figure 9-21 | Scalloped surface characteristic of flow-assisted corrosion

Figure 9-22 | Economizer inlet tube

In an environment of high-purity water (cation conductivity, <0.2 μS), oxygen acts to stabilize the protective coating and actually reduces the rate of metal loss. This is the same principle being exploited for feedwater OT.

Temperature

The effect of temperature on loss of metal parallels the effect of temperature on solubility of iron oxide (magnetite) in water. At low temperatures, the oxide formed is iron hydroxide. At high temperatures, this shifts to magnetite. These two materials have different solubility characteristics, accounting for a temperature peak of around 300 to 350°F (150 to 177°C). For the most part, minimum and maximum temperature limits have been reported in the range of 170 to 450°F (77 to 232°C), respectively. This parabolic solubility relationship with temperature is the reason why the low-temperature feedwater system and the intermediate- and high-pressure components do not normally experience FAC.

Velocity/Turbulence

Figures 9-22 and 9-23 show economizer inlet tubes/bends that have experienced FAC. The fluid velocity in economizer tubes typically is in the range of 1 to 3 ft/s (0.3 to 0.9 m/s). This is certainly not considered to be high. Whenever FAC has occurred in a system, however, the first general reaction of the operators has been that the velocity must be too high. Yet, as just indicated, experience indicates otherwise. The more important factor in all of these cases is turbulence.

Even at these low velocities, some tube configurations (e.g., bends and restrictions) and pipe fittings are intrinsic to any boiler systems in which turbulence or eddies are generated. Turbulent flow is characterized by a churning motion that can generate multiple increases in the transport properties of the fluid or, in this case, the diffusion (eddy diffusivity) of the chemical species involved in the surface reaction. The effect of turbulence increases the mass transfer rate of reactants and products both to and away from the metal oxide–water interface. Under adverse fluid chemistry conditions (discussed below), the metal/oxide equilibrium is disturbed, and the dissolution of the oxide, or corrosion rate, is increased. Without significant turbulence or eddy diffusivity, the process reaction would depend on molecular diffusivity (concentration differences between the bulk fluid and the metal–fluid interface), which is much slower and would not appreciably affect the equilibrium.

With advances in computational fluid modeling, tube locations/geometry and their impacts on fluid flow can be modeled (at least qualitatively). For example, *Figure 9-24A* compares a tube bend, which has been susceptible to FAC, and a straight section of tubing, which has not been susceptible. A 17° tube bend with a fluid velocity of approximately 3 ft/s (1 m/s) is shown. As seen, the increase in turbulence at the bend is approximately twice that in the straight section (i.e., the vertical tube section before the bend).

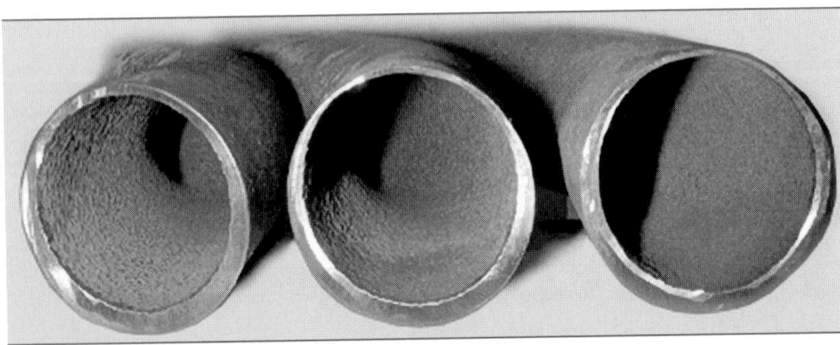

Figure 9-23 | Economizer tube bends at inlet header

Figure 9-24B shows an even higher increase in turbulence at a 45° tube bend. The degree of turbulence is represented or modeled by the kinetic energy that is generated by the turbulent fluctuations (or local velocity gradients). In other words, the generation of turbulence imparts an energy loss to the main flow. This energy loss must equal the mean kinetic energy of the turbulent fluctuations.

The change in flow direction at the bend generates additional turbulence beyond that generated just by the surface friction, as in the straight portion of the tube. The corrosion rate is influenced by the degree of turbulence. It is evident, however, that the relative magnitude of the turbulence does not need to be very high (or many times higher than that in the straight section for the same velocity) to generate higher mass transfer rates and cause FAC, as occurred in these types of tube bends. The contours of the turbulent field in the bend and just past it also simulate the corrosion pattern.

Modeling FAC Potential

Attempts have been made to develop a model utilizing field experience and observations, results from root cause analyses, and literature references. The ability of FAC models to quantitatively predict absolute wastage rates is limited. As learned from field experience, some of this limitation stems from the inability to adequately define the specific flow regimes, geometry, and chemical factors in the regions where attack has been observed. For this reason, the predictive potential of this model (and in others) is intended to be like a go/no-go gage; thus, the results are presented as an index. This is a "work in progress," and updates/revisions are considered/made as new information or experiences are collected.

The model initially considered all-volatile treatment (AVT) cycle chemistry using ammonia and a feedwater pH range of 7.0 to 9.4. Generally, ORP field data were lacking (and still are), so the most negative potential considered (in the formulations) was that represented by a zero oxygen concentration. Design parameters, such as temperature, flow rates, geometry or tube dimensions, and steam qualities, are those typical of HRSGs in combined cycles.

The model was derived from an empirical relationship that predicts FAC rates based on defined input for pH, oxygen concentration, fluid velocity, material composition, temperature, exposure time, and a Keller geometric factor.[18] The geometric factor was selected based on the location within the unit. These factors are related to velocity/turbulence, and a dimensionless value is assigned to varying geometries, such as straight tube sections, 90° bends, tees, and so on. Larger values (or factors) denote a greater propensity for flow disturbances.

In the case of single-phase flow, the average bulk velocity and bulk water chemistry were used. In locations of two-phase flow (low-pressure evaporator tubes), annular flow was assumed to be present. This flow type is characterized by a metal wall that is wetted by a constantly flowing, contiguous film of slower-moving water, and the two-phase mixture flows more rapidly through the center of the tube. For this case, a water film velocity was calculated and used as the input velocity for the model. Because the distribution of ammonia in water and steam is temperature dependent, the ammonia distribution factor was calculated.

(A) Contours of Turbulent Kinetic Energy (k) (m_2/s_2)

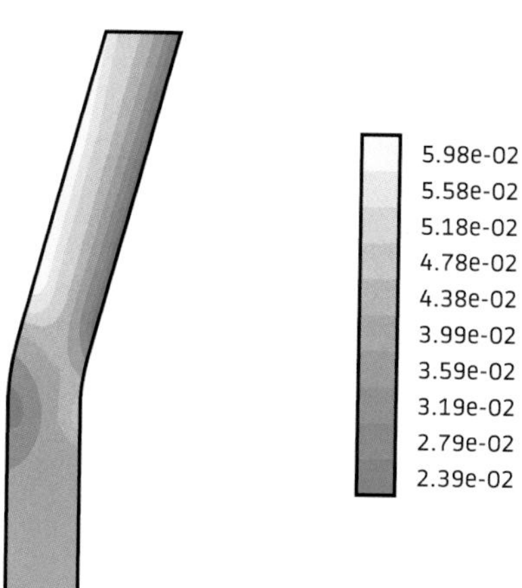

(B) Contours of Turbulent Kinetic Energy (k) (m_2/s_2)

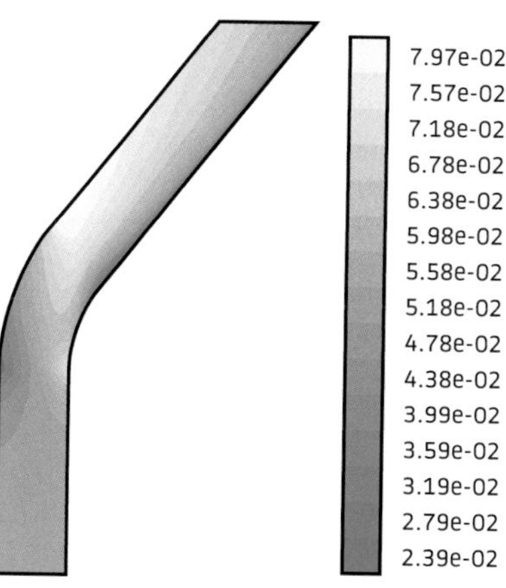

Figure 9-24 | Turbulent kinetic energy in a tube with (A) a 17° bend and (B) a 45° bend

This factor was used to determine the concentration of ammonia remaining in the liquid film of water. The pH of the liquid was based on this calculated value. Within the two-phase region, the most conservative approach was taken by assuming that the oxygen concentration resides entirely within the steam. The calculated values for the two-phase regions are based on 0 ppb of oxygen in the film of liquid water on the tube wall.

As stated earlier, the intent of the model is to provide an index or assessment of the potential for FAC, because the absolute corrosion rates have a high degree of uncertainty. The process for normalizing the data (to derive an index) utilized field experience (HRSGs and conventional boiler plants) as well as data from erosion–corrosion studies already referenced. The index values of greater than 1 indicate a potential for tube life degradation, whereas an index value of less than 1 indicates no significant reduction in tube life. Some of the model predictions or FAC potentials for specific areas are illustrated in *Figures* 9-25 and 9-26.

Flow-assisted corrosion has occurred in combined cycle plants where organic amines and oxygen scavengers (or hydrazine) are used for pH control in feedwater and low-pressure boiler water. In some of these plants, organic dispersive agents also were being used in the intermediate- and high-pressure boiler water. Of course, this resulted not only in lower pH values, because of organic acid by-products, but also in a very reducing environment, because of the high residual concentration of "hydrazine." In this regard, it seemed worthwhile to represent these very reducing conditions by empirically extending the model to low negative potentials (far lower than that represented by the zero oxygen concentration). Unfortunately, insufficient ORP data (field or laboratory) are available to even generate an index in the manner explained above. Based on the available information and field experience, however, the formulations and plots, such as those shown in *Figures* 9-25 and 9-26, were modified (in a qualitative manner) to include the higher negative potential region, and

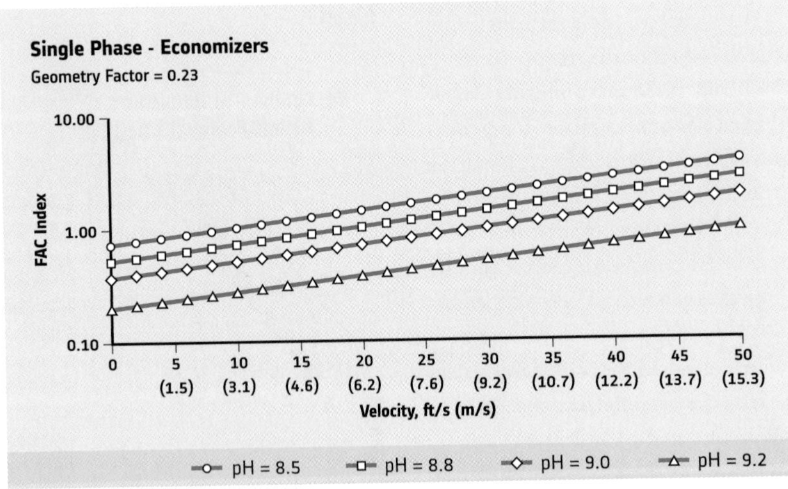

Figure 9-25 | Flow-assisted corrosion (FAC) index as a function of velocity for a single-phase fluid

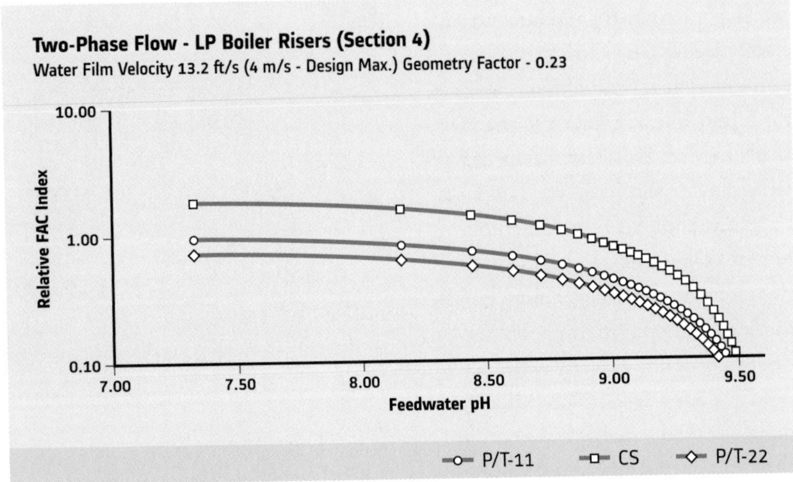

Figure 9-26 | Flow-assisted corrosion (FAC) index as a function of feedwater pH for a two-phase fluid (LP = low pressure)

the results are presented in *Figure 9-27*. It is evident that even with a feedwater pH of approximately 8.8, the presence of residual reducing agents (i.e., hydrazine or equivalent) will increase substantially the potential for FAC. It also is indicated, as commonly is agreed, that at a pH of greater than 9.3, the potential for FAC is low, even in a reducing environment.

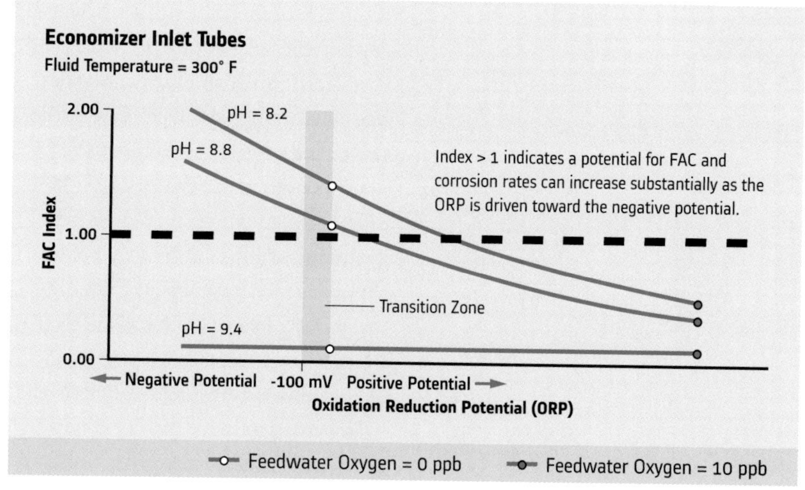

Figure 9-27 | Flow-assisted corrosion (FAC) index versus oxidation–reduction potential (ORP)

TUBE FAILURES CAUSED BY OVERHEATING

The preceding discussion on ductile gouging and hydrogen damage (under deposit corrosion mechanisms) focused on the role played by internal deposits in the corrosion of boiler tubes, but deposits also promote the majority of tube failures caused by overheating. *Figure 9-28* illustrates the temperature conditions existing in a typical furnace wall tube. The heat flux of 100,000 BTU/h-ft^2 (315,000 w/m^2) is established by the furnace flame temperature spectrum, and the bulk fluid temperature of 640°F (338°C) is fixed by the boiler pressure. The temperature profile is then established by the ΔT required to drive the 100,000 BTU/h-ft^2 (315,000 W/m^2) flux through each segment of resistance. With nucleate boiling on a clean tube, the ΔT across the fluid film is quite small (10°F [5.5°C]), and the overall temperature differential (90°F [50°C]) results from the resistance of the tube metal.

Figure 9-29 shows what happens to the tube temperature profile if an internal deposit exists. Approximately 60°F (33°C) is required to drive the 100,000 BTU/h-ft^2 (315,000 W/m^2) heat flux through the deposit, so both the inside and outside metal temperatures must rise correspondingly.

Figure 9-30 illustrates the temperature profile under a film-boiling condition. The reduced film coefficient increases the ΔT across the film to 310°F (170°C), and the metal temperatures rise correspondingly. It should be noted that the flux is constant at 100,000 BTU/h-ft^2 (315,000 W/m^2) for all cases.

STRESS RUPTURE

The strength of carbon steel tubing is nearly constant to approximately 840°F (444°C), at which point it begins to lose strength rapidly. If the tube metal temperature is increased gradually beyond this temperature, it will plastically deform (creep) and then rupture. The approximate time to rupture is a function of the hoop stress and of the temperature (*Fig. 9-31*). The hoop stress (*S*) equals the product of the internal pressure (*P*) times the tube radius (*r*) divided by the wall thickness (*x*):

$$S = P(r/x)$$

Simple visual examination of a failed section reveals a great deal

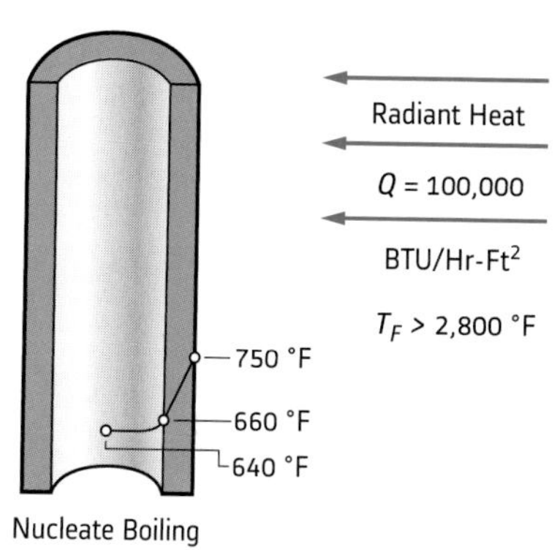

Figure 9-28 | Furnace wall tube—nucleate boiling

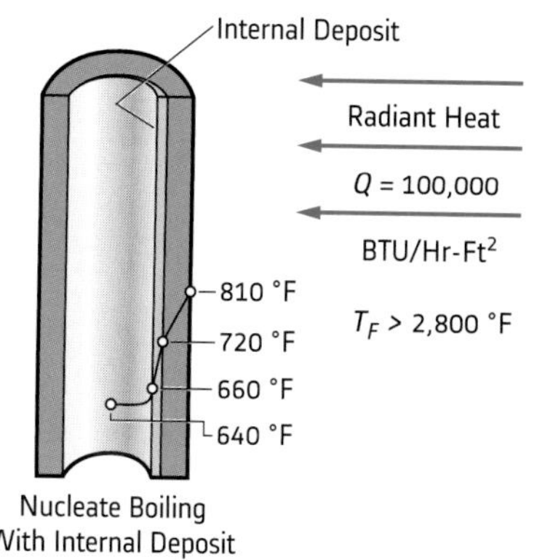

Figure 9-29 | Furnace wall tube—nucleate boiling with deposit

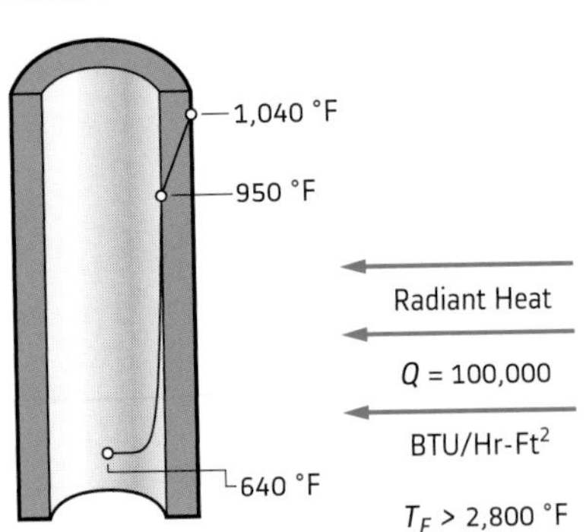

Figure 9-30 | Furnace wall tube: film boiling

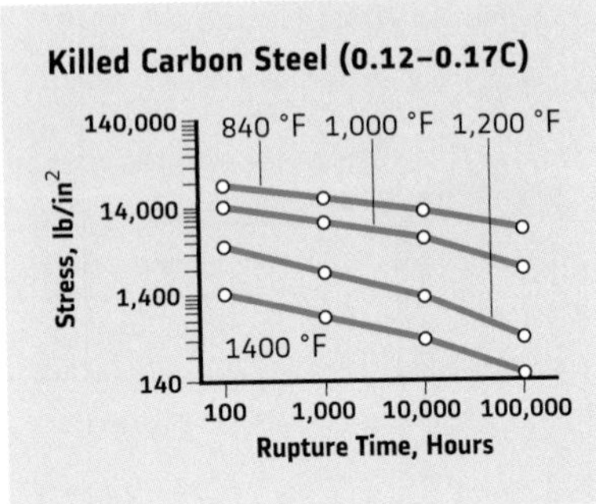

Figure 9-31 | Stress and temperature versus time to rupture

Figure 9-32 | Physical appearance of overheating failures

about the tube temperature history. In deposit-caused overheating, local tube temperatures rise gradually, and specific points begin to creep before others (blistering). Deposits tend to form non-uniformly, and even a 20°F (11°C) difference in temperature can have a pronounced effect on localized creep. Blistering is almost always caused by internal deposition, and conversely, overheating because of deposits will almost always be evidenced by blisters.

When an upset of boiling conditions, such as departure from nucleate boiling, elevates tube temperature, a temperature excursion will occur. Metal temperature will jump quickly from the normal condition to a higher value, consistent with the upset. If the temperature excursion is great, the tube may fail very quickly. For instance, if a tube is completely blocked during operation, the tube temperature will rise immediately to the failure-point temperature. The rapid plastic deformation of these very short-term ruptures produces very thin-edged fractures. In the case of major flow interruptions, the tube bulges over an extended length and fails like a balloon bursting. If a departure from nucleate boiling excursion places the tube metal temperature in the range of 840 to 1,020°F (450 to 550°C), the tube will take a longer time to fail. During this period, inter-granular oxidation of the metal will occur, and this will weaken the structure. Long-term failures, therefore, tend to be thick edged. The higher the temperature and stress conditions are above the creep limit, the shorter the time to failure and the thinner the metal edge at the fracture. *Figure* 9-32 presents examples of a short-, an intermediate-, and a long-term failure.

Metallographic analysis is an important tool for analyzing tube temperature history. The normal pearlitic microstructure of carbon steel boiler tubing can be seen in *Figure* 9-33. The light areas are iron, and the dark areas are pearlite, consisting of alternate layers of iron and iron carbide. The normal operating temperature of a boiler tube will not alter this structure. If the temperature of steel is maintained in the range of 930 to 1,340°F (500 to 730°C) for an extended period of time, carbon migrates from the pearlite to form spheres of carbon. This process, known as "spheroidization," progresses slowly at 930°F (500°C) and rapidly at temperatures near the lower critical range (1,340°F [730°C]).

Figure 9-35 shows carbon steel with various degrees of spheroidization. If the tube is heated to a temperature of greater than 1,340°F (730°C) and is then allowed to cool slowly to below 930°F (500°C), the normal pearlitic structure will be re-established. If the tube is heated to above 1,340°F (730°C) and then cooled very rapidly, however, a martensitic structure (*Fig.* 9-35) will be produced. This type of microstructure is likely to be found in very short-term overheating failures, in which the water escaping through the rupture suddenly quenches the overheated tube metal.

BOILER WATER AND FEEDWATER TREATMENT IN THE PREVENTION OF CYCLE CORROSION

DRUM-TYPE UNITS: UTILITY BOILERS AND HRSGs

The water chemistry guidelines for drum-type boiler are provided in *Tables* 9-5 through 9-11. Phosphate treatment is the prime choice for HRSG drum-type boiler water. All-volatile treatment is an alternative for special cases.

Boiler design criteria include:

- Mechanical carryover
- Blowdown: intermittent, up to 5%; continuous, 0.5 to 1%

In deviation to this specification, the following standards can be adopted:

- Verband derGrosskessel Besitzer (VGB) guideline R450L/2004
- Electric Power Research Institute (EPRI) guidelines TR1010438, TR1004188, and TR1004187
- Specifications from other organizations as approved by Alstom

General Remarks

These water chemistry guidelines are a general specification, valid only for the plant type mentioned above. The criteria will be reviewed for each specific application and at commissioning. This specification is valid for normal plant operation and for plant start-up. It is not applicable for commissioning and the following operating period until final cleanliness of the water–steam cycle is achieved. All conductivities and pH are in reference to 77°F (25°C). Possible contributions from carbon dioxide may be excluded, *at most,* to the extent of the following limits for the measured cation conductivity (see *Table 9-11*). The actual contribution of carbon dioxide has to be measured and regularly verified for every specific plant.

The specified values are maximum values. The actual values should be kept lower whenever possible, with the shortest and least frequent excursions.

The specification is related to the following conditions:

- Neither copper nor aluminum nor their alloys are in the system.
- Make-up water demand is less than 0.5% under normal conditions and up to 5% under maximum and intermittent conditions.
- Conditioning is done exclusively with injection of ammonia into the condensate and of trisodium phosphate into the drum boilers.
- Any possible process condensate returns shall have a quality compatible with high-pressure feedwater.

Except where defined otherwise in the footnote of a table, the following definitions apply to *Tables 9-5* through *9-11*:

- **N = Normal Value.** Values are consistent with long-term system reliability. A safety margin has been provided to avoid concentration of contaminants at surfaces.
- **A1 = Action Level 1.** The potential exists for the accumulation of contaminants and corrosion. Return to normal values within 1 week. Maximum exposure is 336 cumulative hours per year, excluding start-up conditions.
- **A2 = Action Level 2.** Accumulation of impurities and corrosion will occur. Return to normal levels within 24 hours. Maximum exposure is 48 cumulative hours per year, excluding start-up conditions.
- **S = Immediate Shutdown.** Immediate shutdown of the concerned system is required to avoid damage.
- **An = Analytical Supervision.**
- **C = Continuous.**
- **M = Manual (grab sample).**

The pH values are for a reference temperature of 77°F (25°C). These curves are approximations with sufficient accuracy for daily use. It is assumed that the feedwater pH is governed solely by the ammonia content. Typical distribution ratios for feedwater ammonia to boiler water ammonia have been used. The

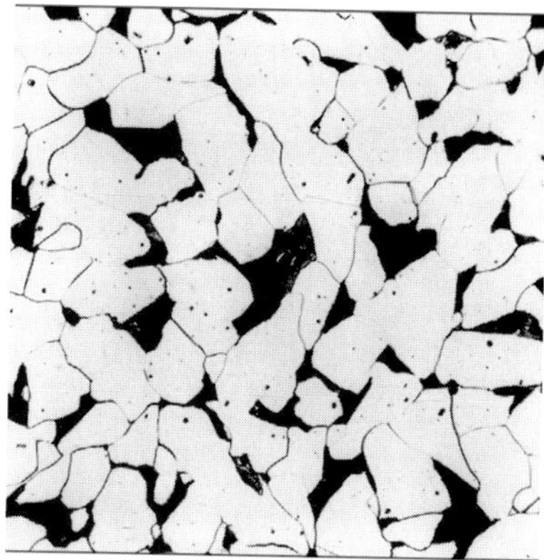

Figure 9-33 | Normal pearlitic structure of carbon steel

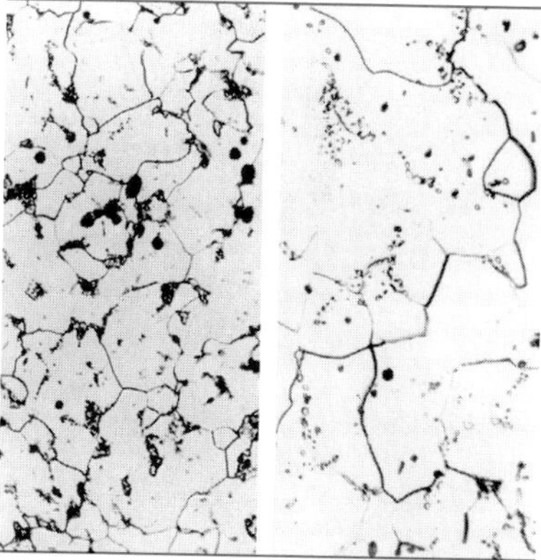

Figure 9-34 | Spheroidization: left, mild; right, extensive

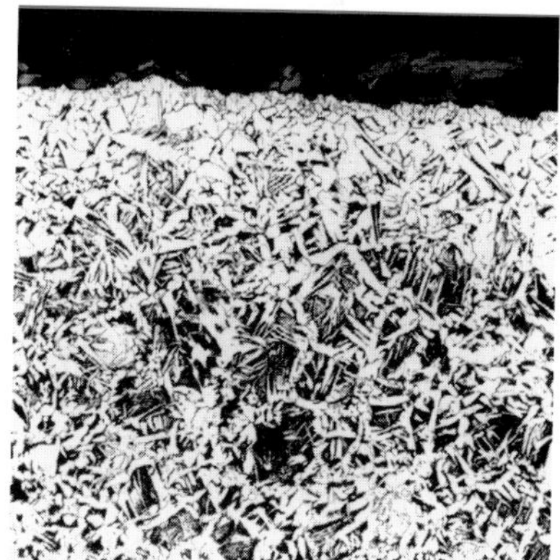

Figure 9-35 | Martensitic structure

WATER CHEMISTRY GUIDELINES FOR DRUM-TYPE BOILERS

TABLE 9-5 | DEMINERALIZED WATER

Parameter	Unit	N	A1	A2	S	An
Specific conductivity*	µS/cm	<0.20	—	0.2–0.5	>0.5	C
Specific conductivity†	µS/cm	<1	—	1–1.5	>1.5	C
Silica as SiO_2	ppb	<20	20–50	50–200	>200	M
Sodium as Na	ppb	<10	—	—	—	M
Iron as Fe	ppb	<20	—	—	—	M
Copper as Cu	ppb	<3	—	—	—	M
TOC‡	ppb	<300	—	—	—	M

*At demineralizer plant outlet (on-site demineralization plant or water from vendor).
†At demineralized water storage tank outlet.
‡TOC, total organic carbon.

TABLE 9-6 | CONDENSATE (AT CONDENSATE PUMP DISCHARGE)

Parameter	Unit	N*		A1	A2	S	An
		Cu	SS/Ti				
Specific conductivity	µS/cm	2–6	3–11	—	—	—	M
Conductivity after cation exchange	µS/cm	<0.20	<0.20	0.2–0.5	0.5–1	>1	C
pH		8.8–9.3	9.0–9.6	—	—	—	M
Silica as SiO_2	ppb	<20	<20	—	—	—	M
Iron as Fe	ppb	<20	<20	—	—	—	M
Copper as Cu	ppb	<3	<3	—	—	—	M

Cu, copper-alloy tubed condenser; SS/Ti, stainless-steel or titanium tubed condenser.

TABLE 9-7 | FEEDWATER (AT BOILER INLET)

Parameter	Unit	N*		A1	A2	S	An
		Cu	SS/Ti				
Specific conductivity	µS/cm	2–6	3–11	—	—	—	C
Conductivity after cation exchange	µS/cm	<0.20	<0.20	0.2–0.5	0.5–1	>1	C
pH		8.8–9.3	9.0–9.6	≠ N†	—	≤7, ≥11	M
Silica as SiO_2	ppb	<20	<20	≥20‡	—	—	M
Iron as Fe	ppb	<20	<20	—	—	—	M
Copper as Cu	ppb	<3	<3	—	—	—	M
Oxygen	ppb		<10	—	—	—	M

*Cu, copper-alloy tubed condenser; SS/Ti, stainless-steel or titanium tubed condenser.
†If outside N.
‡Time permitted above 20 ppb: [hours] × [ppb – 20] < 10^5. If this time has expired, silica deposits may be expected. Checking turbine pressure and efficiency as well as turbine cleaning should be considered. Normal feedwater quality should be achieved at 30% and higher unit load.

volatility of ammonia in the low-pressure boiler is so high that it does not influence boiler water pH significantly within the limits of normal phosphate treatment.

The water chemistry principles for drum-type utility boilers are similar to those for HRSG drum-type boilers. These chemistry guidelines reflect good industry practice and generally are in accordance with published guidelines from the EPRI, European Power Plant Suppliers Association, VGB, International Electrotechnical Commission (IEC), ASME, and ABMA. One notable exception is that the feedwater and boiler water qualities also reflect the steam purity requirements as specified by the steam turbine and gas turbine (if steam or water injected) supplier, as opposed to those provided in the ABMA guidelines, which are limited to the perspective of boiler chemistry. This guideline refers to normal plant operation. Higher impurity levels may be encountered during commissioning and the early operating period until the final cleanliness of the system has been achieved. Such condition must be analyzed on a project-specific basis in order to verify acceptance for operation during this period.

Feedwater chemistry control is based on the following general considerations:

- Ammonia is used to control pH.
- An oxygen scavenger is not needed if the feedwater oxygen concentration is less than 10 ppb. If the use of an oxygen scavenger becomes necessary, hydrazine is preferable if allowed by local safety regulations.
- To minimize the risk of FAC in the low-pressure systems, the pH range has a relatively high limit, and the use of organic treatment chemicals is not recommended.

Boiler water chemistry control is based on the following considerations:

- General and specific corrosion protection of the pressure part surfaces in the event of contamination ingress
- Achievement of the required steam purity.

There are several accepted methods for controlling boiler water chemistry. The majority of drum-type boilers, however, still use some form of phosphate treatment. The particular phosphate treatment (phosphate concentration and corresponding pH) should be selected based on the following main cycle considerations:

- Condenser cooling water chemistry
- Presence of condensate polishing system
- Phosphate hideout history or potential
- Sodium limit in the steam

The parameters of these guidelines cover the chemical species that are common in steam–water cycles. If, in a specific case, the cycle also may contain species that are not covered by these parameters, then the specification must be expanded accordingly. Such species may, for example, come from water treatment, return condensate, and so on.

Feedwater Quality and Steam Purity

DISSOLVED SOLIDS AND OXIDES. The water chemistry guidelines presented for drum-type boilers address the influence of both dissolved and suspended (i.e., oxides) solids. Because the feedwater is used for desuperheating (control of steam temperature), its level of dissolved solids must be limited in order to prevent fouling of steam-touched surfaces as well as to achieve steam purity requirements. It also should be recognized that metallic oxides transported to the boiler (or superheater/reheater/turbine) by feedwater can foul these surfaces such

WATER CHEMISTRY GUIDELINES FOR DRUM-TYPE BOILERS—*continued*

TABLE 9-8 | PHOSPHATE TREATMENT OF BOILER WATER

Parameter	Unit	N		An
		≤120 bar	121–197 bar	
Specific conductivity				C
N	μS/cm	<40*	<20*	
A1	μS/cm	40–80	20–40	
A2	μS/cm	>80	>40	
S	μS/cm	–	–	
pH				C
N		9.0–10.0†	9.0–9.8†	
A1		<9.0, >10.0	<9.0, >9.8	
A2		–	–	
S		<8	<8	
Phosphate as PO_4				M
N	ppm	2–6	1–3	
Silica as SiO_2				M
N	ppm	‡	‡	

Estimated value; must be compatible with steam purity.
†Within limits of Na/PO_4 :
≥ 3.0 (>2.6)
≤ Na_3PO_4 + 1 ppm NaOH
– min 0.1 pH above feedwater pH
‡See *Figure 9-36*.

TABLE 9-9 | ALL-VOLATILE TREATMENT OF BOILER WATER

Parameter	Unit	Value	An
Cation conductivity			C
N	μS/cm	<5	
A1	μS/cm	5–10	
A2	μS/cm	10–20	
S	μS/cm	>20	
pH			C
N		*	
A1		<9.0, >10.0	
A2		–	
S		<8, >10.5	
Na			M
N	ppm	<1	
A1	ppm	≥1	
Silica as SiO_2			M
N	ppm	†	M

*pH is controlled by feedwater pH.
†See *Figure 9-36*.

WATER CHEMISTRY GUIDELINES FOR DRUM-TYPE BOILERS—*continued*

TABLE 9-10 | LIVE STEAM AND REHEAT STEAM (AT BOILER OUTLET)

Parameter	Unit	N*		A1	A2	S	An
		Cu	SS/Ti				
Specific conductivity	μS/cm	2–6	3–11	—	—	—	M
Conductivity after cation exch.	μS/cm	<0.20	<0.20	0.2–0.5	0.5–1	>1	C†
pH		8.8–9.3	9.0–9.6	—	—	—	M
Sodium as Na	ppb	<10	<10	10–20	20–40	>40	C
Sodium as Na‡	ppb	<5	<5	5–10	10–20	>20	C
Silica as SiO_2	ppb	<20	<20	≥20§	—	—	M
Iron as Fe	ppb	<20	<20	—	—	—	M
Copper as Cu	ppb	<3	<3	—	—	—	M

*Cu, copper-alloy tubed condenser; SS/Ti = stainless steel or titanium tubed condenser.
†Switchable common monitor for high-pressure- and reheat steam.
‡Requirement in case boiler phosphate level is <2 ppm of PO_4.
§Time permitted above 20 ppb: [hours] × [ppb – 20] < 10^5. If this time has expired, silica deposits may be expected. Checking turbine pressure and efficiency as well as turbine cleaning should be considered.

TABLE 9-11 | MAXIMUM PERMISSIBLE TOLERANCE FOR CARBON DIOXIDE (ON-LINE INSTRUMENT CATION CONDUCTIVITY READINGS)

Type of operation	Type of condenser		Restrictions
	Water cooling	Air cooling	
Normal	<0.4μS/cm	<0.8 μS/cm	
Start-up	>2 μS/cm	>2 μS/cm	Steam production, <40% nominal. Do not pass steam to turbine
	1–2 μS/cm and decreasing	1–2 μS/cm and decreasing	Maximum of 30 min per start-up
	0.4–1 μS/cm	0.8–1 μS/cm	Maximum of 6 h per start-up

that damage and/or efficiency losses may occur.

OXYGEN. The feedwater guidelines (see *Table 9-7*) indicate that the oxygen concentration should be limited to less than 10 ppb. At the same time, the use of oxygen scavengers, such as hydrazine or hydrazine substitutes, has been omitted. This is based on the experience from plants using OT, in which less reducing conditions in low-cation-conductivity waters (<0.2 μS/cm) help to form a more adherent/less soluble oxide film. This further minimizes the potential for FAC. Oxygen scavengers such as hydrazine are not required (if copper alloys are present in the condensate system, the use of hydrazine can be evaluated). Organic-based treatment chemicals are not recommended and should not be required in a combined cycle power plant generating electricity in which no process steam is exported from the cycle.

CATION CONDUCTIVITY. The cation conductivity specification values given in the water chemistry guidelines do not include the influence of carbon dioxide. During normal operating conditions, levels of 0.06 to 0.2 μS/cm can be achieved. Higher values are observed during start-up. Carbon dioxide, having entered the system with air during shutdown, is dissolved in the water, and it requires some time to purge from the system. The removal rate depends on the efficiency of the deaeration devices (deaerator, condenser) as well as on cycle water pH. At cold start, normal specification values usually are obtained within a few hours for base loaded plants. Cyclic units with frequent cold starts require a significant proportion of the operating time to reach normal values. Therefore, the question is whether it is worthwhile to extend heat-up and bypass operation to achieve a low cation conductivity when solely influenced by carbon dioxide. In several combined cycle plants, start-up cation conductivity has been investigated using ion chromatography. One such example is given in *Figure 9-37*. In that figure, it is seen that cation conductivity started well above 1 μS/cm, but with exclusion of carbon dioxide, it was never larger than 0.3 μS/cm when the turbine was on-line.

Such analytical techniques normally are not available in a power plant. Even if the plant would have such equipment installed, it is doubtful if it could be brought to full operating conditions by the beginning of a cold start. The same applies to degassed cation conductivity measurements. Therefore, one must look at substitute parameters for evaluating steam chemistry. The boiler water is a good indicator for the ingress of any impurities, and its relation to steam chemistry is fairly well understood. The requirement for steam cation conductivity at start-up has been formulated as follows: The steam turbine can be kept in operation with boiler water purity within the specification and the conductivity of high-pressure steam showing a large decrease in conductivity within one hour from the beginning of turbine operation.

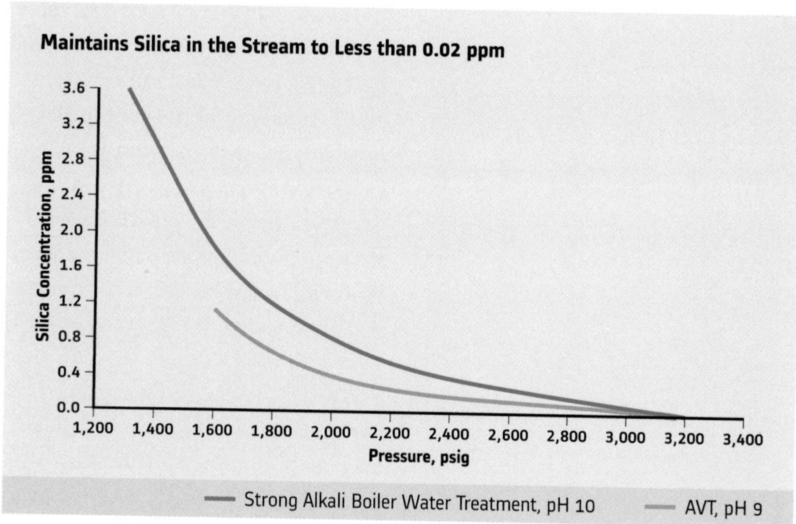

Figure 9-36 | Silica concentration in boiler water versus operating pressure (AVT, all-volatile treatment)

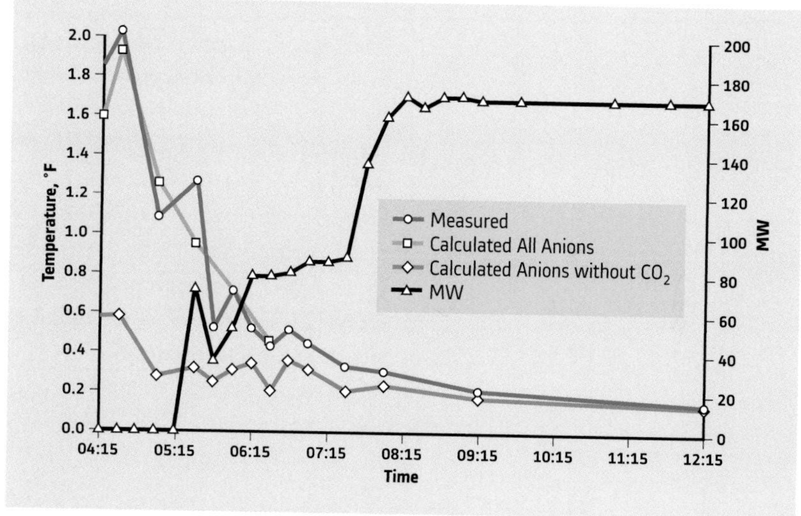

Figure 9-37 | High-pressure boiler steam cation conductivity at cold start

ALL-VOLATILE TREATMENT. The exclusive use of volatile conditioning agents is known as AVT. Volatile chemicals evaporate from the water into the steam in a gaseous form. When the steam condenses, the chemicals dissolve into the water. They do not form a solid phase; thus, they do not form a scale or deposit on heat-transfer surfaces. Common volatile conditioning agents are ammonia, amines, and hydrazine (or hydrazine substitutes).

With AVT, feedwater pH ranges from 8.8 and 9.8. Low-level AVT has a pH of between 8.8 and 9.3 (especially in plants with copper alloys), and high level AVT has a pH of between 9.2 and 9.8. Even though high-pH AVT provides better corrosion protection of steel, it has the disadvantages of questions regarding wastewater treatment, chemical consumption, and exclusion of ion-exchange resin to run in H^+ form.

AVT(R) is defined as AVT that employs a reducing agent, such as hydrazine or other oxygen scavengers. This results in a low (highly negative) electro-chemical potential.

In plants with copper heat exchangers in the feedwater train, AVT(R) is beneficial because it reduces copper corrosion and, therefore, the release of copper ions into the feedwater. In once-through systems, however, the cycle does not include copper or its alloys.

AVT(R) also favors FAC in the high-pressure feedwater system if it contains carbon steel alloys. Therefore, it is not used as a water treatment regime.

High pressure boiler practices and guidelines are applicable to both utility boilers and the high pressure boiler of an HRSG.

The use of hydrazine for wet lay-up is not relevant for operating conditions and therefore it is possible. Environmental aspects regarding the use of hydrazine, however, need to be considered.

AVT(O) is defined as AVT that does not employ any reducing agent. Even without use of an oxidizing agent, however, the electro-chemical potential will be substantially higher than that with AVT(R).

AVT(O) favors the formation of hematite layers, which are less soluble and, hence, more stable than the magnetite layers of AVT(R). As a result, it gives more protective margin against FAC, and it minimizes orifice fouling.

Boiler Water Quality

The boiler water quality and respective treatment is designed to prevent corrosion and deposits in the boiler as well as to produce steam with a sodium content that does not exceed specification limits. Therefore, a low-level sodium phosphate treatment has been selected. *Figure 9-38* is a plot of phosphate versus pH. This type of strong alkaline treatment provides good buffering capabilities in the event of impurity ingress. In those plants where phosphate treatment can be used in the low-pressure boilers, it will prevent the risk of FAC as well. The pH value (at 77°F [25°C]) is corrected from the contribution of ammonia and depends solely on the phosphate concentration. The heavy black line in *Figure 9-38* is the upper boundary for the saturated steam sodium concentration in high-pressure boilers with a mechanical carryover approaching 0.2%.

The listed phosphate range is 1 to 6 ppm (see also *Table 9-8*). This is limited by the sodium steam purity requirements and the steam drum mechanical or moisture carryover performance. The ABMA guidelines allow a higher level of dissolved solids (or sodium) in the boiler water; consequently, for these high operating pressure ranges, the resulting sodium level in the steam would be higher than that allowed by turbine suppliers. Therefore, the turbine steam purity requirements as specified by the turbine supplier controls the level of phosphates and other dissolved solids in the boiler water. The lower phosphate limit of 1 ppm for the high-pressure boiler water was chosen to provide sufficient general pH protection and buffering in case of impurity ingress. Because there generally is no problem with carryover at lower boiler pressures (these boilers are more in the critical temperature range for FAC), a lower phosphate limit of 2 ppm was chosen for low- and intermediate-pressure boilers.

Phosphate treatment, with a sodium/phosphate ratio of three, is applied as standard boiler water treatment. This treatment can be modified during periods of contaminant ingress to address either caustic or acid producing salts. Alternatives treatments, such as AVT, also may be applied. A guide for selection is given in *Table 9-12*.

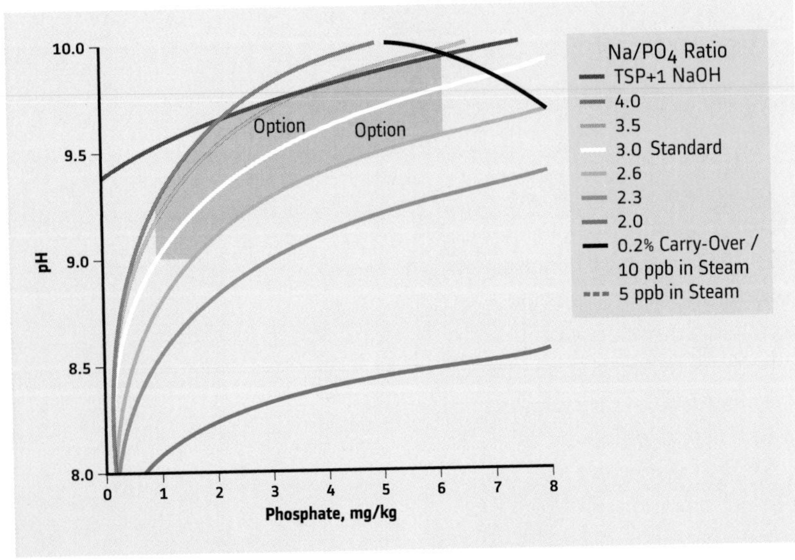

Figure 9-38 | Phosphate treatment zones (TSP, trisodium phosphate)

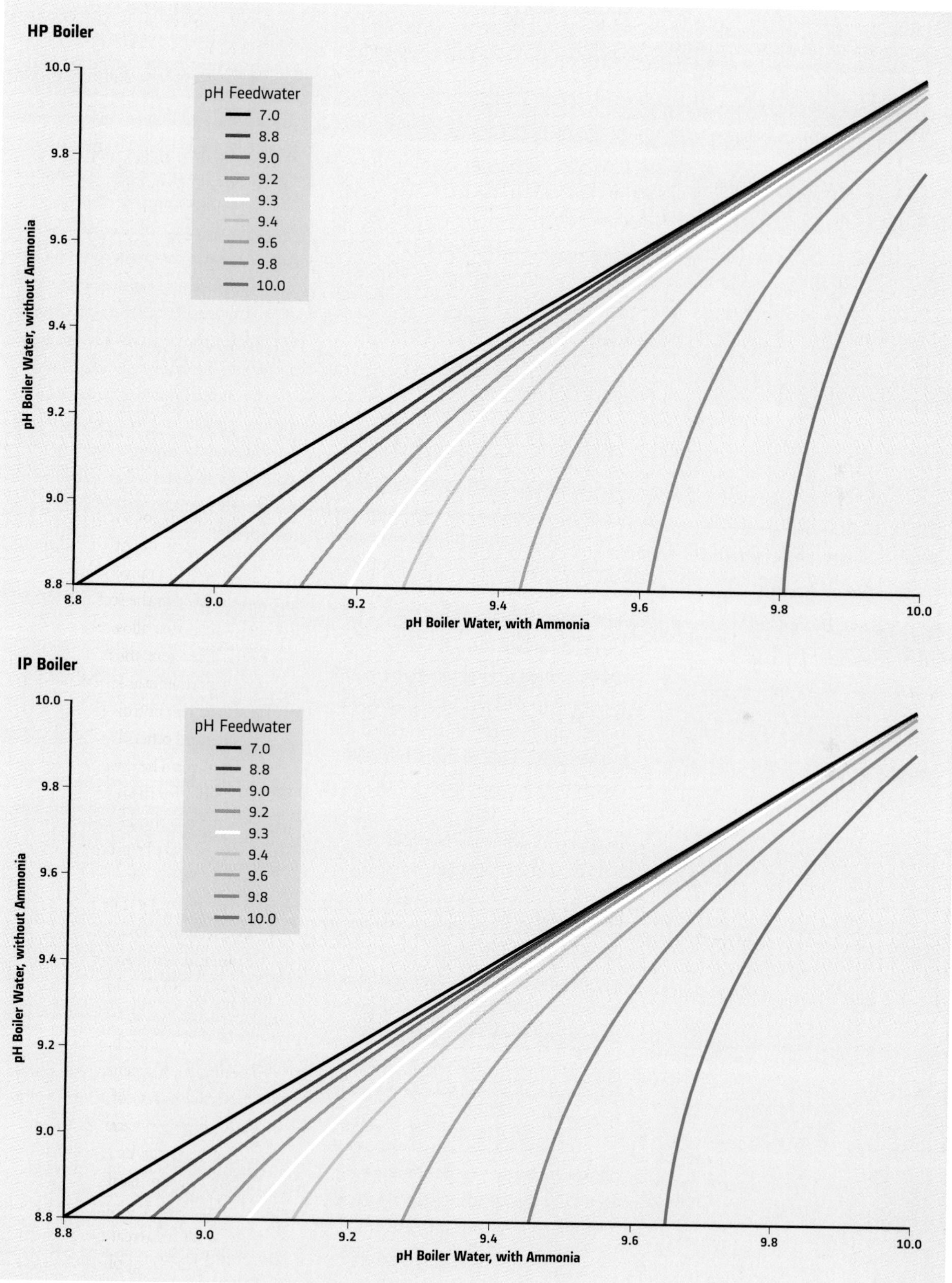

Figure 9-39 | Correction of boiler water pH for ammonia in feedwater

TABLE 9-12 | SELECTION OF BOILER WATER TREATMENT REGIMES

Treatment	Preference	Use
Na/PO_4 = 3	Standard	
Na/PO_4 = 3.0–2.6	Option	Where a buffer for caustic contaminants is required
Na/PO_4 = 3.0 – (3.0 + 1 ppm of NaOH)	Option	Where a buffer for acidic contaminants is required
All-volatile treatment	Option	Where phosphate hideout would occur
		Where solid alkalizers are not permitted
		Where boiler water is used for feed of other boilers
		Where boiler water is used for attemperation spray
		Where impurity ingress can be excluded

Intermediate and low pressure guidelines are applicable to lower pressure boilers and the intermediate and low pressure boilers of a multipressure HRSG.

Phosphate treatments should be applied within the range defined in *Table 9-8* and in *Figure 9-38*. It should be observed that in this figure, phosphate is related to pH after the contribution from ammonia has been subtracted. (A method for this calculation is given in Verib.[19]) *Figure 9-39* indicates the correction factors to be applied. For routine use, plant-specific empirical correction factors may be established and used. In specific cases, when phosphate hideout occurs, phosphate treatment with low phosphate concentration or AVT can be applied. Each boiler normally is controlled and treated independently, although the water chemistry guidelines presented here for drum-type boilers list the same level of treatment chemicals and conductivity. With demineralized feedwater, there really is no need to allow higher dissolved solids in low-pressure boilers just because the boiler can handle it without adversely affecting steam purity.

For phosphate treatment, trisodium phosphate is used as the conditioning agent. For the optional treatment with a sodium/phosphate ratio between 3 and 2.6, an adequate mix of trisodium and disodium phosphates can be used. The use of sodium hydroxide (>1 ppm) is considered to be risky for low-staffed power plants, because it requires much more attention and control in order to be safely applied.

In a typical combined cycle, the condensate, or feedwater, is relatively free of iron oxide during stable operation. Therefore, use of organic dispersants in the boiler water is not needed. These organic substances can decompose to carbon dioxide and produce organic acids. These acids can then circulate throughout the cycle. As a consequence, they could destabilize (if treated only with ammonia) the magnetite layer on the low-pressure boiler surfaces, which can increase the potential for FAC. *Table 9-13* provides some guidelines in the event of contamination ingress as measured by cation conductivity.

ONCE-THROUGH UNITS: UTILITY BOILER AND HRSG

The water chemistry guidelines for once-through units are provided in *Tables 9-14* to *9-18*.

General Remarks

All conductivities referred to in water chemistry guidelines for once-through units are for 77°F (25°C). Possible contributions from carbon dioxide may be excluded.

Operation is desirable at the lowest achievable impurity levels, with the shortest and least frequent excursions.

The specification is related to the following conditions:

- The system has no copper alloys.
- Conditioning is done with ammonia and oxygen injection.

The guidelines for once-through units presented here are a general specification, valid only for the plant type mentioned above. The criteria will be reviewed for each specific application and at commissioning.

TABLE 9-13 | CRITERIA FOR MAINTAINING HIGH-PRESSURE BOILER WATER CONDITIONS

Feedwater Conditions	High-Pressure Boiler Water Chemistry Control			Operational Limits
	Phosphate	Volatile	Options	
Cation conductivity, <0.2 μS/cm	Specific conductivity, <20 μS/cm pH* 9.0–9.8 PO_4^{3-}, 1–3 ppm	Cation conductivity, <5 μS/cm pH 9.0–9.6	See *Figure 9-38*	None.
Cation conductivity, 0.2–0.5 μS/cm	Specific conductivity, 20–40 μS/cm pH* 9.0–9.9 PO_4^{3-}, 2–6 ppm	Not suitable	See *Figure 9-38*	Monitor steam purity. Increase blowdown if required.
Cation conductivity, >0.5 μS/cm	Specific conductivity, >40 μS/cm pH* 9.1–10.1 PO_4^{3-}, 2–10	Not suitable	See *Figure 9-38*	Limited operation. Refer to turbine steam purity guidelines for abnormal conditions. Load will need to be reduced as will the use of desuperheating spray water. If feedwater cation conductivity increases above 1.0 μS/cm, prepare for orderly shutdown.

*Boiler water pH under phosphate control should be higher (by a minimum of 0.1 unit) than the feedwater pH.

Except where defined otherwise in the footnote of a table, the following definitions apply to *Tables 9-14* through *9-18*:

- **N = Normal Value.** Values are consistent with long-term system reliability. A safety margin has been provided to avoid concentration of contaminants at surfaces.
- **A1 = Action Level 1.** The potential exists for the accumulation of contaminants and corrosion. Return to normal values within 1 week. Maximum exposure is 336 cumulative hours per year, excluding start-up conditions.
- **A2 = Action Level 2.** Accumulation of impurities and corrosion will occur. Return to normal levels within 24 hours. Maximum exposure is 48 cumulative hours per year, excluding start-up conditions.
- **S = Immediate Shutdown.** Immediate shutdown of the concerned system is required to avoid damage.
- **An = Analytical Supervision.**
- **C = Continuous.**
- **M = Manual (grab sample).**

WATER CHEMISTRY GUIDELINES FOR ONCE-THROUGH UNITS

TABLE 9-14 | DEMINERALIZED WATER (AT DEMINERALIZER WATER PLANT OUTLET)

Parameter	Unit	N	A1*	A2	S†	An
Specific conductivity	μS/cm	<0.10	0.1–0.2	—	≥0.2	C
At storage tank outlet‡	μS/cm	<1	≥1	—	—	C
Silica as SiO_2	ppb	<10	10–20	—	≥20	C
Sodium + potassium as Na+K	ppb	<5	—	—	—	M
Iron as Fe	ppb	<20	—	—	—	M
TOC§	ppb	<300	—	—	—	M
Oxygen	—	Saturation				

*Indicates there is a problem. Action shall be taken to bring values to normal. Operation may be continued as long as feedwater/steam specifications are not jeopardized.
†Do not put this water into the demineralized water storage tank.
‡Conductivity as measured at demineralized water storage tank outlet, including carbon dioxide.
§TOC, total organic carbon.

TABLE 9-15 | CONDENSATE (AT HOTWELL OUTLET)

Parameter	Unit	N	A1	A2	S	An
Specific conductivity	μS/cm	2.5–11	—	—	—	M
Conductivity after cation exchange	μS/cm	<0.20	0.2–0.5	>0.5	>1	C
pH		9.0–9.6*	—	—	—	M
Iron as Fe	ppb	<20	—	—	—	M

*For oxygenated treatment, values are in accordance with those in *Table 9-17*.

WATER CHEMISTRY GUIDELINES FOR ONCE-THROUGH UNITS—*continued*

TABLE 9-16 | FEEDWATER (ALL-VOLATILE TREATMENT: MEASUREMENTS AT ECONOMIZER INLET)

Parameter	Unit	N	A1	A2	S	An
Specific conductivity	μS/cm	4.0–11	—	—	—	C
Conductivity after cation exchange	μS/cm	<0.20	0.2–0.5	>0.5	>1	C
pH		9.2–9.6	<9.2, >9.6	>10	≤7*	C
Sodium + potassium as Na+K	ppb	<5	5–10	10–20	>20	M or C
Silica as SiO_2	ppb	<20	≥20†	—	—	M
Iron as Fe	ppb	<20	—	—	—	M
Hydrazine	ppb	‡				M
Oxygen	ppb	<10	≥50	—	—	C

*If dosing is limited during system refilling, ammonia will be below normal. In such a case, pH ≥5.5 is tolerated.
†Time permitted above A1 (see "HP-steam"): (hours) × (ppb – A1) $<10^5$
‡Hydrazine or equivalent should not be used if O_2 is 10 ppb or less.

TABLE 9-17 | FEEDWATER (OXYGENATED TREATMENT INSTEAD OF ALL-VOLATILE TREATMENT)

Parameter	Unit	N	A1	A2	S
Specific conductivity	μS/cm	2.5–7.0	—	—	—
Conductivity after cation exchange	μS/cm	<0.20	0.2 - 0.5 *	>0.5 *	>1
pH		8.5–9.0	—	—	—
Sodium + potassium as Na+K	ppb	< 5	5 - 10	10-20	>20
Oxygen‡	ppb	50–150	—	—	—

*Discontinue oxygen injection.
‡Target for oxygen injection.

Once-Through Boiler Cycle: Guidelines for Initial Start-Up and Restarts After Long Outages

The guidelines for initial start-up are as follows:

1. Flush to waste until suspended solids in the condensate, feedwater, and boiler water are less than 3 ppm (permissible value depends on demineralizer performance/constraints). The feedwater (pH >9) can be pumped through the boiler into the start-up separator, flash tank (if present), and then to waste.
2. When this limit is achieved, circulate water through the boiler, start-up separator, flash tank, and then back to the condenser. Place condensate demineralizers in service.
3. When the total iron concentration drops below 1 ppm, silica is less than 100 ppb, and cation conductivity is less than 1 μS/cm (parameters measured at economizer inlet), unit firing can commence. Boiler and start-up system operation should be as per the instruction manual.
4. Proceed to normal feedwater control limits (parameters measured at economizer inlet). These should be obtained before exceeding one-third of the unit load.

Chemistry control in once-through steam generating units is based on the following features:

- The system has no phase-separating devices (i.e., steam drum).
- Feedwater, boiler water, and steam are the same fluid stream.
- Sliding pressure operation includes fluid conditions typical of both supercritical and subcritical operation.

The above design considerations require that the concentrations of feedwater contaminants be kept to a minimum and be within allowable turbine steam purity limits (as specified by the steam turbine supplier). Corrosion products transported to the boiler (or superheater/reheater/turbine) from the condensate and feedwater system must be kept at concentrations low enough to minimize fouling of heat-transfer surfaces and, thus, the potential for damage and/or efficiency losses.

For once-through systems, feedwater conditioning to minimize general corrosion and the production of iron oxide can be accomplished with either AVT or OT. Because of the greater concern for copper transport at supercritical pressures and its impact on turbine performance, feedwater systems in these once-through units consist primarily of ferritic alloys and do not contain copper alloys downstream of the condensate polishers. Keeping levels of feedwater contaminants to a minimum is critical in once-through units. There is no mechanism for their removal once in the feedwater (downstream of the condensate polishing system), nor can their aggressive behavior be arrested by the typical feedwater chemical treatments (OT or AVT). Contaminant ingress (e.g., from condenser in-leakage or make-up water) generally is controlled by a condensate polishing system. OT will provide a high electro-chemical potential that causes the formation of hematite layers, which are less soluble and, hence, more stable than the magnetite layers of AVT(R) and the mixed magnetite/hematite layers of AVT(O). As a result, the level of iron oxide in the feedwater is much lower. This gives an excellent protective margin against FAC, and it minimizes orifice fouling. As an additional bonus, OT has already been used successfully with very low-level AVT (i.e., feedwater pH 8.0–8.5). The related small ammonia concentrations permit a very long life of H^+ mixed beds and ease concern over questions of wastewater. Of course, OT also can be applied with higher-pH AVT, but it is not without problems. Oxygen, when coupled with

WATER CHEMISTRY GUIDELINES FOR ONCE-THROUGH UNITS—*continued*

TABLE 9-18 | HIGH-PRESSURE STEAM AND REHEAT STEAM (AT OTSG* OUTLET)

Parameter	Unit	N	A1	A2	S	An
Specific conductivity	µS/cm	2.5–7.0	—	—	—	M
Conductivity after cation exchange	µS/cm	<0.20	0.2–0.5	>0.5	>1	C
pH		9.0–9.6†	—	—	—	M
Sodium + potassium as Na+K	ppb	<5	5–10	10–20	>20	M or C
Silica as SiO_2	ppb	<20	≥20‡	—	—	C
Iron as Fe	ppb	<20	—	—	—	M

*OTSG: once through steam generator

†See *Table 9-17* if on oxygen treatment.

‡Time permitted above 20 ppb with an Alstom steam turbine: [hours] × [ppb] < 10^5.If this time has expired, turbine pressure and efficiency must be measured. If turbine capacity/efficiency has degraded, the turbine should be cleaned.

anions, will be corrosive. Therefore, OT requires strict control of feedwater impurities (i.e., condensate polishers).

The most frequent contributor to boiler water-side corrosion, fouling, and failures has been the accumulation of metal oxide deposits. These deposits form principally on heat-transfer surfaces but also can foul control orifices, which can then cause overheating of waterwall tubes. A reduction in the amount of debris and metal oxide deposition within the boiler can be accomplished successfully throughout its life cycle by:

- Good storage and on-site erection conditions
- Minimum metal oxide concentrations in the boiler feedwater during start-up operations as well as at load conditions
- Adherence to operational water chemistry guidelines
- Adherence to optimum lay-up procedures that prevent or reduce standby corrosion
- Periodic chemical cleanings

In order to minimize corrosion potential, a fluid environment must be provided that can promote oxide stability while meeting plant requirements.

Construction materials most commonly used in the condensate and feedwater systems of once-through utility cycles are ferritic alloys, stainless steels, and titanium. Copper alloys are not used in feedwater heaters, because copper oxides can dissolve in the supercritical fluid, resulting in turbine fouling. Carbon and stainless-steel tubes therefore are utilized in feedwater heaters, and stainless steels and titanium are used for condenser tubes.

Cycle Chemistry Considerations to Minimize FAC

In the steam–water system, FAC is observed mainly in the temperature range of between 170 and 450°F (77 and 232°C), with a maximum in the temperature range of approximately 300 to 350°F (150 to 177°C). Regions of concern are:

- Economizer tubes at high- and intermediate-pressure inlet headers
- Low-pressure evaporator surfaces at bends
- Low-pressure drum internals
- Low-pressure horizontal evaporative tube bends

To date, economizer, low-pressure evaporative tubes (at bends), and drum internals have experienced FAC in several HRSGs during combined cycle and operation. Economizer inlet tubes have experienced FAC because of low pH conditions (In three of these plants, steam purity requirements did not allow the use of feedwater pH control chemicals; thus, the pH was in the range of 6.5–7.0). Evaporative tubes and other low-pressure components, such as drum internals, with few exceptions normally have not experienced this type of attack with either AVT (pH 9.0–9.6) or with strong alkaline chemical additives (e.g., phosphates). Several plants experienced FAC of drum internals in low-pressure boilers and at economizer inlet tubes/bends. In these plants, an organic water chemistry program (e.g., organic dispersants, organic amines, and organic oxygen scavengers) was used.

In summary, a fluid environment that can promote oxide stability and, at the same time, meet plant requirements must be maintained. The construction materials in the feedwater system are protected from corrosion by controlling the pH and oxygen concentration with AVT. As the name implies, the treatment chemicals must be volatile, which means that when water is completely evaporated, no solid chemical residue must be present (i.e., zero solids treatment). This characteristic allows the use of feedwater for desuperheating (water is sprayed into the superheater to control steam temperature). When the boiler water also is on AVT, this means that no changes or chemical (i.e., ammonia) additions are made to it. Because some portion of this chemical will volatilize in the higher fluid temperature environment, the boiler water pH will be slightly lower than that of the feedwater. In combined cycle plants with three pressure levels, the cycle design quite often requires that the low-pressure boiler drum also serve as the feedwater tank and/or integral deaerator. In this case, the low-pressure boiler water becomes the feedwater to the other boilers as well as the source of desuperheater spray water. Thus, the boiler water as explained above must contain only volatile chemicals and have qualities similar to those of the feedwater.

Understanding the Limitations of AVT

pH CONTROL ADDITIVE. The recommended AVT in combined cycle plants consists primarily of ammonia injection into the feedwater to control

pH in the range of 9 to 9.6. An inherent characteristic of ammonia or other amines is the inability to buffer or effectively neutralize acidic agents at higher temperatures. This is the result of its decreasing ionic dissociation at higher temperatures. Consequently, if one were able to measure the local pH at high temperature, the pH would decrease as the fluid temperature increases, as illustrated in *Figure 9-40.*

For example, strong alkaline buffers, such as sodium phosphate and sodium hydroxide, do not exhibit this relationship with temperature. The pH remains relatively constant over the temperature range. Therefore, with AVT, relatively small amounts of salts or other acid-producing substances (organic contaminants or organic additives) can have a significant effect on pH in higher temperature regions. This relationship is taken into account when formulating the cycle water chemistry regime. Operators, however, also must realize that the AVT treatment scheme is less "conservative" and requires immediate attention should the feedwater/boiler water become contaminated by either acid- or caustic-producing salts or substances.

In this regard, *Figure 9-41* illustrates the effect on pH with temperature by salts such as magnesium chloride. This is the infamous salt in seawater that hydrolyzes to hydrochloric acid in high-pressure/high-temperature boiler water during a condenser leak incident. As shown in *Figure 9-41*, some effect on pH begins to occur in the temperature range of between 392 and 482°F (200 and 250°C).

Figure 9-42 shows a similar effect on high-temperature pH by organic acids. Unlike ammonia, strong alkaline substances, such as trisodium phosphate used in the boiler water, provide a high pH, unaffected by temperature, and can form stable/non-volatile compounds. In these cases, the potential for FAC is negligible even in the critical temperature range (low-pressure evaporative section) discussed above.

OXYGEN SCAVENGERS. Chemicals, such as hydrazine and other oxygen scavengers, are restricted or not used if the feedwater oxygen concentration generally is maintained below 10 ppb by mechanical deaeration. Hydrazine or hydrazine substitutes are reducing agents that will lower the ORP and increase the FAC potential in carbon steel components where fluid temperatures are in the range of approximately

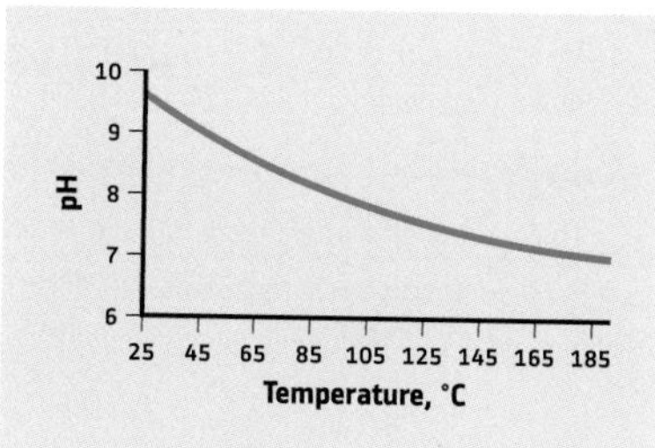

Figure 9-40 | Effect of fluid temperature on pH with 1.5 ppm of ammonium hydroxide

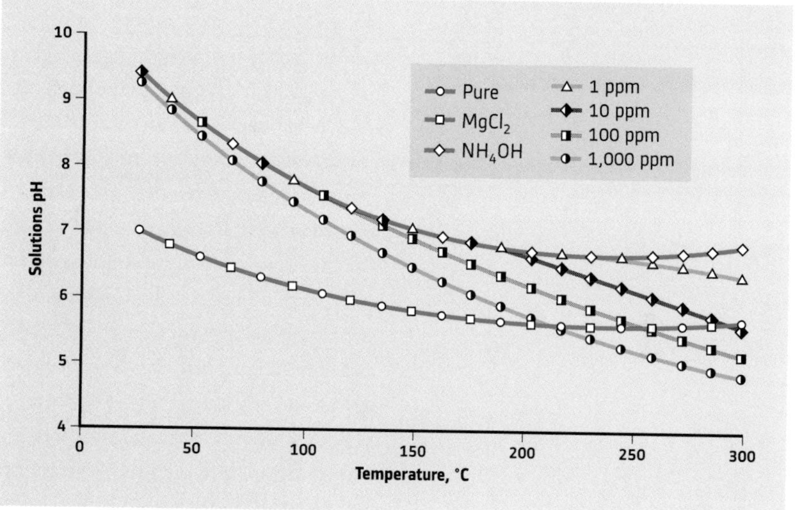

Figure 9-41 | Hydrolysis reactions

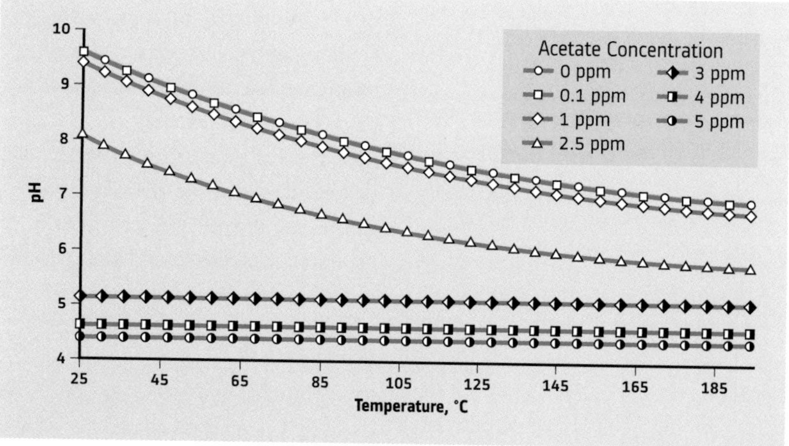

Figure 9-42 | Effect of organic acid (acetic) on pH with 1.5 ppm of ammonium hydroxide

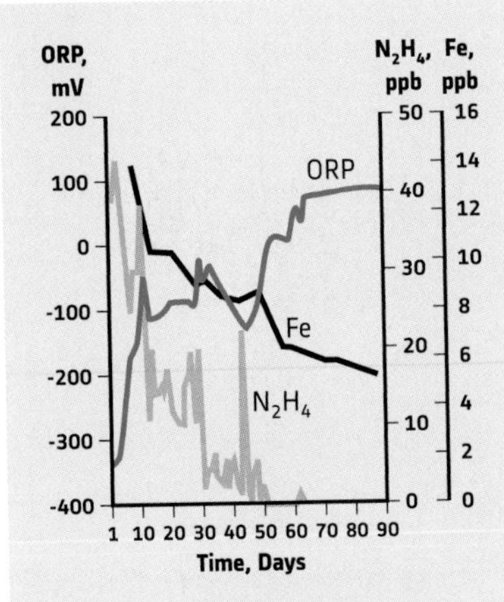

Figure 9-43 | Relationship of oxidation–reduction potential (ORP) versus hydrazine/iron concentrations (Data from D. Platt and D. A. Vinnicombe, "Operating of a Drum Boiler Without Hydrazine," ESKOM, Johannesburg, South Africa, June 1994)

170 to 450°F (77 to 232°C). *Figure 9-43* illustrates the influence of hydrazine on the ORP and the iron level in feedwater.[20] As hydrazine is reduced, the ORP increases toward the positive or oxidizing potential, and the level of iron decreases, thus indicating that the FAC rate also is being reduced.

Other studies[21] have shown the effect of oxygen or oxidizing potential in lowering the rate of FAC (*Fig. 9-44*). As little as 8 ppb oxygen can arrest FAC. In addition, even if hydrazine is present but the water contains residual oxygen, then oxygen is still controlling the reaction rate. If, however, oxygen is zero and hydrazine is present, then the ORP is driven to very negative potentials, which can substantially increase the corrosion rate, as already indicated in *Figure 9-43*.

In a combined cycle plant with no process steam requirements (i.e., cogeneration plant), ammonia is preferred/recommended over other amines as a feedwater pH control additive. All other amines (e.g., morpholine and cyclohexylamine) as well as hydrazine substitutes are organic chemicals. At higher fluid temperatures (boiler, superheater, and reheater), these substances in general will thermally degrade into carbon dioxide and organic by-products, which may include organic acids. These by-products are then recycled with the condensate and feedwater. In summary, high feedwater pH controlled with ammonia and no oxygen scavengers is recommended as long as the normal oxygen content is less than 10 ppb. The need to use organic amines/organic oxygen scavengers for feedwater and condensate chemistry control in cogeneration facilities should be evaluated carefully for each specific site.

Condensate Polishers

There are basically two options in terms of condensate polishers:

1. Deep-bed ion-exchange resin
2. Powdered resin pre-coat filters (powdered ion-exchange resin)

Both options will employ mixed-bed ion-exchange resins.

The ion exchange resin also will remove the conditioning agent ammonia from the water, which will then be replenished by the ammonia injection. At the same time, the cation-exchange resin will be exhausted by ammonia. This somewhat diminishes its capability to remove impurities like sodium, and it potentially releases residues from regeneration. In addition, the resulting alkaline pH in the mixed bed reduces the retention capabilities of the anion-exchange resin. Therefore, it becomes a plant- or customer-specific decision whether to operate the beds in the H^+ or NH_4^+ form (the NH_4^+ form is more common in the United States and the H^+ form is in Central Europe).

The size of the condensate polishers typically is for 100% or full condensate flow. This allows protection from a condenser leakage for a short period even at full load. Polishers also allow the removal of iron oxide, silica, and carbon dioxide during start-up. Powdered resin pre-coat polishers have less capacity overall, so they are easily exhausted by the treatment chemicals (ammonia). Therefore, the powdered resin usually will operate in the ammonia form. Because the powdered resin is purchased fully regenerated and rinsed, there are no further requirements for on-site regeneration and wastewater treatment. On the other hand, this throwaway resin may result in a considerable operating cost.

PROTECTION DURING OUTAGE CONDITIONS

If extensive corrosion during outage conditions is to be avoided, proper wet lay-up methods are essential. Because large utility boilers cannot be successfully dried to produce an internal atmosphere that is free of moisture, wet lay-up procedures are recommended even for long outage periods. For any outage longer than 4 days, the pre-boiler/boiler cycle should be filled, to the greatest extent possible, with a solution that is inhibited in order to prevent corrosion and should be pressurized with nitrogen to prevent air in-leakage. Excellent results have been obtained with condensate or demineralized water containing appropriate amounts of ammonia. Because this material is volatile, there is no objection to its use even in non-drainable superheater and reheater sections of the boiler. Where freezing is a problem, it sometimes is necessary to drain portions of the steam generator. This should be accomplished under a positive nitrogen pressure. Nitrogen blanketing is recommended even when the boiler can be maintained full of inhibited condensate. The success or failure of standby protection also depends on the proper design and selection of chemical feed equipment and on the ability to provide an inert gas blanket. Base loaded units may get along with simple, manual systems for the introduction of lay-up additives and nitrogen. Systems with load characteristics that require frequent boiler shutdowns require more elaborate, foolproof, wet lay-up protection systems.

INDUSTRIAL BOILER WATER TREATMENT

Internal chemical treatment systems are designed primarily to prevent scale formations resulting from residual amounts of calcium and magnesium hardness in the feedwater. External treatment and control must provide a feedwater that is low in hardness, alkalinity, silica, metal oxides, and oxygen.

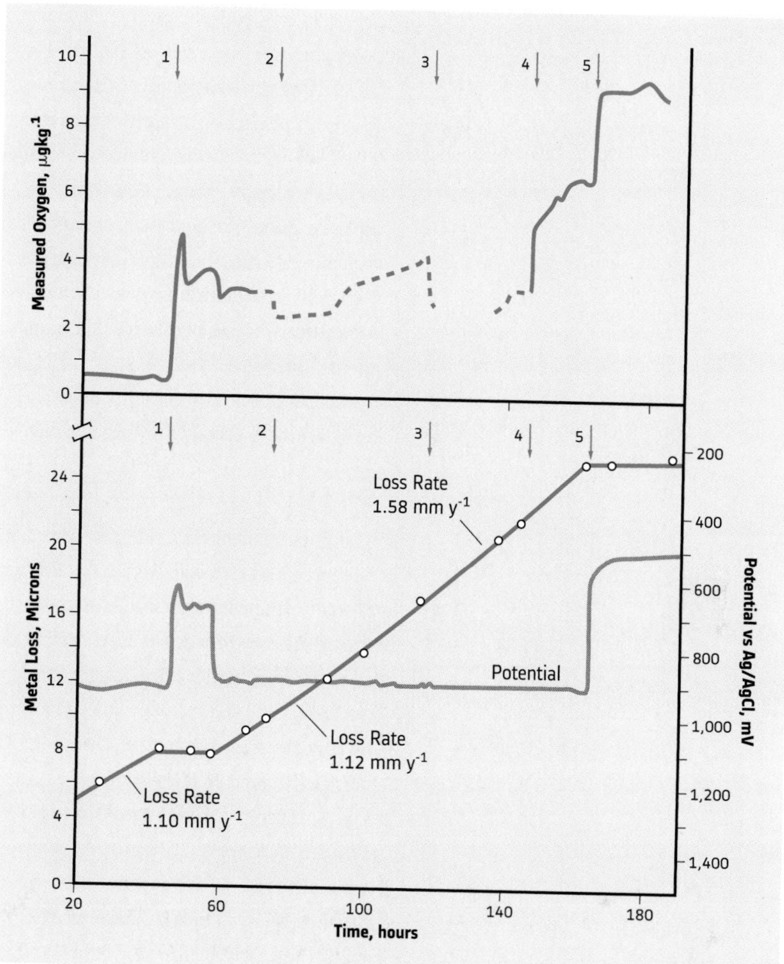

Figure 9-44 | Influence of oxygen on flow-assisted corrosion

Because of their extreme solubility, sodium salts are of concern only to the extent of their contribution to the total dissolved solids concentration.

Boiler tube scale consisting of calcium and magnesium components, however, is not uncommon in units operating below 600 psig (4 MPa) and using softened make-up water. These scales often are the direct result of loss of chemical control, permitting dense calcium precipitates, such as calcium sulfate or calcium silicate, to form. They also may be a more subtle result of a porous, hardness sludge or metal oxides, which permit boiler water to penetrate to the tube surface, precipitating complex silicate scales. Formation of scale below 900 psig (6.2 MPa) generally is more of a concern with respect to causing overheating failures than promoting corrosion attack.

Two basic systems are now available for prevention of internal hardness scales: the conventional phosphate–hydroxide methods, and the more recently adopted substitute systems involving chelating agents. Both are proven systems, but the success of either depends on the diligence with which they are applied.

PHOSPHATE–HYDROXIDE METHOD

The phosphate–hydroxide methods can be segregated into one that maintains an excess of hydroxide alkalinity and one that involves no excess or "free" hydroxide content. The former has a long history of use and is still the most prevalent system for low-pressure operation. *Table 9-19* presents typical control limits.

The intent of phosphate control systems is to provide conditions that are conducive to the precipitation of calcium as a calcium hydroxyapatite, $Ca_{10}(PO_4)_6(OH)_2$, and magnesium as serpentine, $3MgO{\cdot}2SiO_2{\cdot}2H_2O$. In contrast to low-pressure operation, boiler tube failures in units operating above 900 psig (6.2 MPa) can be caused by corrosion. Accordingly, the coordinated phosphate pH system is used to control boiler water chemistry as with utility high-pressure boilers.

CHELATION

Chelating agents have received wide acceptance as a substitute system for the conventional phosphate–hydroxide treatment methods. The most common is the sodium salt of ethylenediaminetetraacetic acid. As briefly explained previously, these organic agents act with the residual calcium and magnesium in the feedwater to form soluble complexes. Ideally, this should result in boiler surface conditions that are completely free of any hardness deposits. The soluble hardness complexes will be removed through the continuous blowdown line. With conventional phosphate treatment, it is difficult to maintain all of the hardness end products in suspension. As a result, some accumulations normally are found in drums and headers.

Most of the experience with this treatment method has been limited to operating pressures of 900 psig (6.2 MPa) and below. Economically, justification for its use is limited to feedwaters of low hardness concentrations (1–2 ppm). Such evaluation usually considers the savings realized by the elimination or reduced frequency of chemical cleaning.

Chemical additions are made in a continuous mode, with the amount based on the concentration of hardness salts in the feedwater. The chelants must be injected after the boiler feedwater pump to prevent corrosion of the pump components. Earlier attempts to utilize the chemical feed line to the boiler drum also resulted in severe corrosion of this line. High oxygen concentrations in the feedwater drastically increase the corrosivity of the chelants. Thus, it is imperative that good deaeration of the feedwater be maintained. A chelant program can be effective in preventing deposits or damaging boiler tubes, depending primarily on the knowledge and experience of the user. Of course, before initiating such a program on any boiler, the guidelines, control

TABLE 9-19 | CONTROL LIMITS FOR PHOSPHATE-HYDROXIDE METHOD

Pressure (psig)	450–600	600–900
Hydroxide alkalinity as OH (ppm)	50–100	25–50
Phosphate as PO_4 (ppm)	20–40	5–10
Sodium sulfite as Na_2SO_3 (ppm)	20–40	5–10
Silica as SiO_2 (ppb)	50 (maximum)	10 (maximum)

limits, and analytical procedures must be established with the cooperation of the chelant supplier or water treatment consultant.

CARRYOVER AND STEAM SAMPLING

This section deals with the phenomenon of carryover, methods of steam sampling, and techniques of steam purity determination. Once again, these subjects cannot be understood solely by rigorous theoretical analysis. Knowledge of laboratory testing procedures and ability to interpret field operating experience are required. Despite intensive research, our understanding in these areas is incomplete, and much empiricism remains in the techniques used for correcting problems that result from incomplete separation of steam and water in boiler equipment.

CLASSIFICATION OF CARRYOVER

Carryover of boiler water in steam leaving the drum provides a path for introducing solid materials into the steam. Modern separator designs can mechanically reduce the moisture content of the steam to 0.2% or less. In addition to mechanical carryover of boiler water, however, another mechanism exists that results in the contamination of steam with solid materials. As the operating pressures increase, the steam phase exhibits greater solvent capabilities for the salts that may be present in the water phase. These salts will be partitioned in an equilibrium between the steam and the water, a phenomenon known as "vaporous carryover." Vaporous carryover will contribute an additional quantity of boiler water solids directly to the steam, independent of the efficiency of steam–water separation components.

Silica was the first material found to exhibit significant vaporous carryover. Silica fouling of turbines was common until it was recognized that successful control of the amount of silica in the steam could be accomplished only by controlling the amount of silica in the boiler water. A similar solution will be required for other solids when operating at high pressures. Vaporous carryover contributes a significant proportion of total solids in the steam as the drum operating pressures increase above 2,600 psig (18 MPa).

Table 9-20 shows findings of a laboratory study on vaporous carryover.[22] For various salts, the table lists the percentage vaporous carryover, which is the ratio of the salt concentration in the steam and boiler water. In each case, sodium was measured and then converted to the appropriate salt concentration. When calculating total solids in the steam, vaporous carryover is assigned a value of 0.1% at drum operating pressures above 2,600 psig (18 MPa).

Mechanical carryover may be classified under four headings:

1. Priming
2. Spray
3. Leakage
4. Foam carryover

Each type of mechanical carryover results in troublesome deposits in the superheater or on the steam turbine blades.

Priming is the development of excessive moisture in the steam because of

TABLE 9-20 | SUMMARY OF LABORATORY RESULTS ON VAPOROUS CARRYOVER

Pressure (psig)	2,600		2,800		3,000	
Concentration (ppm)	15	500	15	500	15	500
Sodium sulfate	0.02%	0.03%	0.04%	0.07%	0.28%	0.48%
Disodium phosphate	0.01%	0.07%	0.03%	0.18%	0.41%	0.74%
Trisodium phosphate	0.02%	0.11%	0.04%	0.30%	0.35%	1.3%
Sodium chloride	0.04%	0.18%	0.09%	0.36%	0.39%	1.2%
Sodium hydroxide	0.02%	0.31%	0.08%	0.69%	0.55%	2.2%

spouting or surging of boiler water into the steam outlet. This is a rare, easily identified type of carryover. It usually is promoted by maintenance of too high a water level in the drum, spouting of a submerged riser, sudden swelling of the water in the boiler on a drop in pressure, or sudden increase in rating. Priming is rarely, if ever, associated with boiler water chemistry.

Spray, mist, or fog are degrees of atomization of the boiler water. Mist is carried from the drum by the steam, as dust is carried by air currents. This carryover is present to a degree in all boilers. It is the function of drum internals to separate and filter out such spray before the steam leaves the drum. Development of spray carryover indicates failure of the drum internals as a result of exceeding the velocity limitations of the purification equipment. It is characterized by initial development below the full rating of the boiler, and it continues to increase with boiler load. Spray carryover is not sensitive to boiler water concentration below the foaming range. Improved drum internals are capable of reducing the steam-borne mist to a value as low as a few parts per billion of solids.

The drum internals are designed to separate and filter out as much liquid water as possible before the steam leaves the drum.

Leakage is a general term applied to bypassing of impure steam or boiler water through the drum internals. Normally localized, this form of carryover is directly related to poor design or installation of drum internals. At times, the local contamination may not be sufficient in order to be reflected in steam purity measurements of total steam flow. A careful inspection of drum internals usually will reveal this source of carryover. Where the leakage is sufficient to register impurity tests of steam, it will be found that the impurity increases slowly with rating and is relatively insensitive to changes in water level and boiler water concentration.

Foam is the development of excessive moisture in the steam from carryover of foam from the drum. It is the most common form of carryover in low-pressure units, in which the boiler water may contain high concentrations of dissolved solids, and it also is the most troublesome and erratic type. Foam forms in the steam generating sections of the boiler when the water films around the generated steam bubbles are stabilized by the impurities in boiler water. Boiler circulation carries this foam up to the boiler drum, where it tends to accumulate at the water level. The foam produced may fill the entire steam space of the boiler drum, or it may be of a relatively minor depth. Although foaming in boilers has been recognized for many years, its causes are not clearly defined and are worthy of further investigation. The bulk water in the circulating mixture entering the drum is readily separated, but the wet emulsion of very small foam bubbles collects at the water level to a depth that largely depends on the drainage rate of excess water out of the foamy mass. A considerable amount of moisture is trapped in the foam. When foam carryover occurs, it frequently is sudden and excessive, and the steam sample registers a solids content that is characteristic of boiler water.

IDENTIFICATION OF CARRYOVER

A systematic field investigation can identify carryover. A variety of factors, which may be classified as mechanical, water, or operating conditions, affects the sources of carryover and the carryover itself to different degrees. As noted previously, foaming in the boiler is the most common type and the most troublesome and erratic form of carryover.

Special test methods have been devised to demonstrate the presence of foam blankets and for obtaining boiler performance without danger of serious carryover to the superheater and turbine.[23–26] Steam flow, water level, and total dissolved solids are the three major factors that can create carryover. By varying these three factors, one at a time, test results usually can be interpreted to determine the specific source of a carryover condition:

- Steam flow establishes the velocity distribution in the boiler drum. Excessive steam flow can increase steam velocity to a point that entrained moisture can overload the dryer.
- High water can create spouting and excessive carryover. This can occur at low steaming rates and boiler water concentrations.
- Foaming is a characteristic of boiler water concentration. With water level and steaming rate at recommended values, any carryover that can be precipitated or eliminated by a change in total dissolved solids can be attributed to foaming.

Figure 9-45 illustrates the development of foaming in a drum. The plot shown in this figure indicates purity values of steam samples taken ahead of the steam dryer and at the outlet of the boiler drum for a constant level of water in the drum and a typical steam load. The principal change is in the boiler water concentration. At a dissolved solids level of approximately 550 ppm, the sample ahead of the dryer was approximately 5 μS/cm (1 μS/cm is approximately 0.5 ppm of solids), and the sample at the boiler outlet was approximately 7 μS/cm. Increasing the boiler

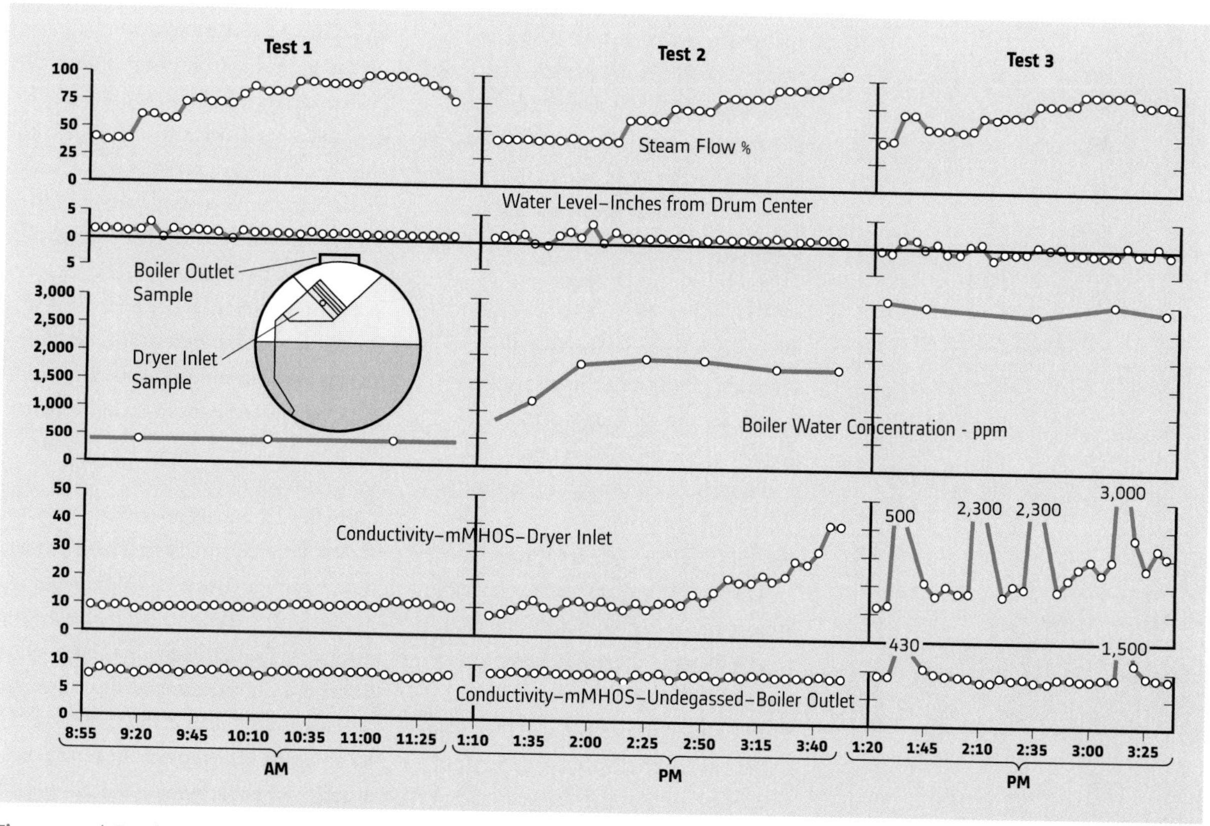

Figure 9-45 | Development of foaming in a boiler drum

water solids level to approximately 1,800 to 2,000 ppm did not alter the purity of the steam leaving the boiler drum. The sample ahead of the steam dryer, however, gradually increased to a value of approximately 40 μS/cm. Thus, with an established steam flow and a similar water level, a marked increase was found in the solids content of the steam entering the dryer. This is indicative of the presence of a mildly foamy condition in the boiler drum, because the only change was in the concentration of boiler water solids. Increase of boiler water solids to approximately 2,800 to 3,000 ppm in the boiler water, at the same steam load and water level as in the previous two tests, produced severe foaming in the boiler. The space between the water level and the dryer was practically filled with a foam blanket on the water, as evident in the high solids content of the sample entering the dryer. Severe foam carryover occurred when the water level in the drum was at or above drum center. This was not a factor in the previous tests. Thus, a small change in water level was sufficient to push the foam blanket into the drum internals, creating a severe case of foam carryover.

CAUSES OF FOAMING

Foaming is basically a result of chemical conditions. Boiler water concentration and composition are important factors. High total solids and high suspended solids aggravate the formation of foam. High-caustic alkalinity, oil, organic contamination, and excess phosphate also increase the foaming tendency in boiler water.

The general effect of a component on foaming may be anticipated, but it is impossible to predict whether foam will form based on a cursory examination of boiler water. Extreme cases are on record in which excessive foam carryover occurred with less than 650 ppm in one boiler; in another case, no carryover troubles developed with concentrations as high as 15,000 ppm. Although these inconsistencies exist, it is necessary to maintain a lower value of foam-producing chemicals in boiler water or to add foam-dispersing chemicals to the water. Organic anti-foam agents have been developed to dispel certain foams at higher steam pressures. Ordinary tannin and starch compounds are only effective at low pressures. Lignin sulfonates, alkaline polyamides, polymerized esters, and alcohols have been effective foam-dispersing agents. The function of an efficient anti-foam agent is to reduce the number of small bubbles and to confine steam-bubble formation to a small number of large bubbles, which will exhibit the tendency to coalesce and grow larger. Under these conditions, the bubbles are unstable and tend to break easily. Anti-foam agents are not equally effective with all boiler waters. It is necessary to select an anti-foam agent that is compatible with the chemical characteristics of the boiler water, and trial of several compounds may be necessary before the foam can be neutralized satisfactorily.

Foam will fill the free surface area of a separating device, increasing local velocities and promoting a serious carryover of boiler water. Foam carryover may be stopped by a quick reduction in boiler water concentration or by lowering the drum level. Centrifugal devices have shown a greater ability to handle foamy waters compared with that of simple internals. The basic function of a centrifugal device is to dehydrate the foamy emulsion. The dehydrated-foam bubbles can be easily broken up by screens or other simple devices. Foam in this type of separator will decrease the water separating efficiency of the device.

In general, foam carryover from a boiler can be avoided by keeping boiler water limits within the range suggested by the ABMA. These specifications, of course, cannot be a guarantee against foaming that, as indicated previously, is primarily a chemical problem.

Concentration limits as a function of pressure are shown in *Table 9-21*. This ABMA table has been modified to include boilers that supply process steam. In both utility and industrial plants, adherence to the ABMA specifications has produced satisfactory operation because of marked improvements in water technology and boiler design. Normally, the steam purity specification limit for low-pressure boilers is less than 0.5% moisture in the steam. With the use of superheaters and higher pressures, the boilers must deliver a steam product containing less than 1.0 ppm of solids entrained in the steam. Steam purity of high-pressure boilers has been markedly improved, and values of less than 0.01 ppm of impurity are achieved.

STEAM SAMPLING METHODS

Steam samples for measuring purity usually are taken ahead of the superheater. These are condensed and cooled. Collecting a true sample that is representative of a large mass of material always presents a difficult problem. The sample size, particle size distribution, and density relationship are some factors that must be considered where there is a question about lack of homogeneity. In a homogeneous sample of fine particle size, sampling is a relatively easy operation.[27,28]

TABLE 9-21 | RECOMMENDED BOILER WATER LIMITS AND ASSOCIATED PROCESS STEAM PURITY (AT STEADY-STATE, FULL-LOAD OPERATION)

Drum Pressure (psig, actual)	Drum-Type Boilers			
	Range of Total Dissolved Solids* in Boiler Water, (ppm, maximum)	Range of Total Alkalinity† in Boiler Water, ppm	Suspended Solids in Boiler Water, ppm (Maximum)	Range of Total Dissolved Solids†§ in Steam (ppm, maximum expected value)
0–300	700–3,500	140—700	15	0.2–1.0
301–450	600–3,000	120—600	10	0.2–1.0
451–600	500–2,500	100—500	8	0.2–1.0
601–750	200–1,000	40—200	3	0.1–0.5
751–900	150–750	30—150	2	0.1–0.5
901–1,000	125–625	25—125	1	0.1–0.5
1,001–1,800	100	‡	1	0.10
1,801–2,350	50	‡	N/A	0.10
2,351–2,600	25	‡	N/A	0.05
2,601–2,900	15	‡	N/A	0.05
ONCE-THROUGH BOILERS				
1,400 and above	0.05	N/A	N/A	0.05

*Actual values within the range reflect the ions in the feedwater. Higher values are for high solids; lower values are for low solids in the feedwater.

†Actual values within the range are directly proportional to the actual value of ions of boiler water. Higher values are for high solids and lower values for low solids in the boiler water.

‡Dictated by boiler water treatment.

§These values are exclusive of silica.

Source: American Boiler Manufacturers Association

In sampling steam, the impurities may be solid, liquid, and gaseous. The solid may be in the form of a finely divided sludge particle. Liquid impurity may be in the form of fog or mist in minute droplets, possibly having a solid particle as a nucleus. More adversely, it may be in a form of a surface film on a pipe wall. Moisture itself is not involved in the concept of steam purity except that it may carry solids in solution or suspension. Sampling impurities in steam is analogous to the difficulty of locating a needle in a haystack. At a sampling rate of 100 lb/h (45 kg/h), the impurity content of 1 ppm is represented by the withdrawal of 0.7 grain of solid per hour. Steam lines contain bends, elbows, valves, and other fittings that can disturb the flow and segregate the impurities.

Cross[27] has outlined the assumptions reached in the design of the steam sampling nozzle described in American Society for Testing and Materials (ASTM) Standards B 1066, Sampling Steam.[28] The velocity front must be reasonably flat, and the density difference of steam and mist or fog carried along with it must be of the same order of magnitude as that of water and steam at the pressure and temperature of the steam in the line. Basic prerequisites for use of the ASTM nozzle design are that the velocity of the steam entering the ports is the same as the line velocity of the steam and that each port of the sampling nozzle shall represent an equal area of the sampling section.

Turns and other irregularities of the steam line influence distribution of solid and liquid impurities. The sample point should be as remote as possible from a source of disturbance. It also should be located where there is a run of at least 10 diameters of straight piping. The preferred location with respect to position, in order of decreasing preference, is:

1. Vertical pipe, downward flow
2. Vertical pipe, upward flow
3. Horizontal pipe, vertical insertion
4. Horizontal pipe, horizontal insertion

DETERMINATION OF STEAM PURITY

Steam purity normally is determined by measuring either the electrical conductivity or the sodium content of the condensed steam sample. Measuring electrical conductivity is widely used to monitor steam purity in industrial low-pressure boilers. This method is described in ASTM Standards D 1125, Electrical Conductivity and Resistivity of Water.[29]

Gases dissolved in a condensed sample affect conductance and indicate an erroneous level of solid impurity. These gases may be removed by degasification. Methods suggested for establishing the content of solids impurity in steam are described in ASTM Standards D 2186, Deposit-Forming Impurities in Steam,[30] which provides four alternative techniques.

Determination of solids in steam by conductance is not sensitive to impurities in the parts-per-billion range, which is the range required for determination of steam purity in high-pressure utility boilers. Analysis of the steam sample to determine the sodium content is the primary method. A technical guidance document on steam purity or carryover test methods is published by the International Association for the Properties of Water and Steam (IAPWS). The guidance document is titled "Mechanical Carryover From Drum Boilers."

FRANK GABRIELLI

REFERENCES

1. E. Nordell, *Water Treatment for Industrial And Other Uses*, 2nd ed. New York: Reinhold Publishing Corp., 1961.
2. S. T. Powell, *Water Conditioning for Industry*. New York: McGraw-Hill, 1954.
3. Betz Laboratories, Inc., *Betz Handbook of Industrial Water Conditioning*, 7th ed. Trevose, PA.: Betz Laboratories, 1976.
4. P. Hamer et al., eds., *Industrial Water Treatment Practice*. London: Butterworths, 1961.
5. Nalco Chemical Company, *The Nalco Water Handbook*, 2nd ed. New York McGraw-Hill, 1988.
6. R. E. Hall et al., "Phosphate in Boiler Water Conditioning," *Journal of the American Water Works Association*, 21: 79–88, 1929.
7. S. F. Whirl and T. E. Purcell, "Protection Against Caustic Embrittlement by Coordinated Phosphate-pH Control," Proceedings of the Third Annual Water Conference, Pittsburgh, PA, November 9–10, 1942, pp. 45–60.
8. Schikorr, G, "Uber die Reakiionen zwischen Eisen, seiner Hydroxyden und Wasser," Z Elektrochemie. 35, 65–70 (1929).
9. R. C. Corey and T. J. Finnegan, "The pH, Dissolved Iron Concentration, and Solid Product Resulting from the Reaction Between Iron and Pure Water at Room Temperature," Proceedings of the American Society for Testing and Materials, Preprint 101,1939.
10. R. C. Corey and T. J. Finnegan, "The pH, Dissolved Iron Concentration, and Solid Product Resulting from the Reaction Between Iron and Pure Water at Room Temperature," Proceedings of the American Society for Testing and Materials, Preprint 101,1939.
11. E. Berl and F. van Taack, "Uber die Einwirkung von Laugen und Salzen auf Flusseisen unter Hochdruckbedingung und uber die Schutzwirkiung von Natriumsulfat gegen den Angriff von Aetznatron und von Chlormagnesium (The Action of Caustic and Salts on Steel under Conditions of High Pressure and the Protective Effect of Sodium Sulfate Against the Attack of Sodium Hydroxide and Magnesium Chloride)," Forschung sorbeiten 330. Berlin: VDI, 1930.
12. H. A. Grabowski, et al., "Problems in Deaeration of Boiler Feedwater," *Combustion* 25(9): 43–48, March,1955.
13. H. A. Klein and H. A. Grabowski, "Corrosion and Hydrogen Damage in High-Pressure Boilers," Presented at the Second Annual Educational Forum on Corrosion, National Association of Corrosion Engineers, Drexel Institute of Technology, Philadelphia, PA, September 15–17, 1964.
14. P. Goldstein and C. L. Burton, "Research Study on Internal Corrosion of High-Pressure Boilers," *Transactions of the ASME Journal of Engineering for Power*, 91, Series A: 75–101, April 1969.
15. J. A. Armantano and V. P. Murphy, "Standby Protection of High-Pressure Boilers," Proceedings of the 25th International Water Conference, Pittsburgh, PA September 28–30, 1964, pp. 111–124.
16. N. Henzel, W. Kastner, and B. Stellwag, "Erosion Corrosion in Power Plants Under Single- and Two-Phase Flow Conditions—Updated Experience and Proven Counteractions," *American Power Conference*, 50: 992–1000, 1988.
17. C. Cragnolino, "A Review of Erosion–Corrosion of Steels in High-Temperature Water," in *Environmental Degradation of Materials in Nuclear Power Systems—Water Reactors*, edited by G. J. Theus and J. R. Weeks. Warrendale, PA: The Metallurgical Society, 1987, pp. 397–406.
18. W. Kastner and K. Riedle, "An Empirical Model for Calculating Metal Loss due to Erosion Corrosion," *VGB Kraftwerkstechnik*, 66: 1171–1178, 1986.
19. G. Verib. "Sodium to Phosphate Ratios." PPChem 2002, 4(11), 687–690.
20. D. Platt and D. A. Vinnicombe. *Operating of a Drum Boiler Without Hydrazine*. Johannesburg, South Africa: ESKOM, 1994.
21. G. J. Bignold, C. H. de Whalley, K. Garbett, and I. S. Woolsey, *Water Chemistry of Nuclear Reactor Systems*, 3. Vol. 1. London: British Nuclear Energy Society, 1983, p. 219–226.
22. S. L. Goodstine, "Vaporous Carryover of Sodium Salts in High-Pressure Steam," *Proceedings of the American Power Conference*, 36: 784–789, 1974.
23. P. B. Place, "Carryover Problems and Identification of Carryover Types:" *Combustion*, 18(9): 29–34, 1947.
24. P. B. Place, "Steam Purity Determination. Part I. Evaluation of Test Results," *Combustion*, 25(10): 62–65, 1954.
25. P. B. Place, "Steam Purity Determination. Part II. Methods of Sampling and Testing," *Combustion*, 25(11): 41–44, 1954.
26. P. B. Place, "Steam Purity Determination. Part III. Interpretation of Test Results," *Combustion*, 25(12): 43–46, 1954.
27. B. J. Cross, "The Sampling of Steam for the Determination of Purity," Proceedings of the 11th Annual Water Conference, Pittsburgh, PA, October 16-18, 1950, pp. 71–82.
28. "Standard Practice for Sampling Steam," D 1006-06. In 2008 *Annual Book of ASTM Standards, Part 31: Water*. Philadelphia: American Society for Testing and Materials, vol. 11.01, 71–75.
29. "Standard Test Methods for Electrical Conductivity and Resistivity of Water," ASTM Standards D 1125–95(2005). In 2008 Annual Book of ASTM Standards, Part 31: Water. Philadelphia: American Society for Testing and Materials, vol. 11.01, 96–102.
30. "Standard Test Methods for Deposit-Forming Impurities in Steam," ASTM Standards D 2186-05. In 2008 Annual Book of ASTM Standards, Part 31: Water. Philadelphia: American Society for Testing and Materials, vol. 11.02, 103–109.

SUGGESTED READINGS

K. L. Atwood, "Solvent Selection for Preoperational and Operational Cleaning of Utility Boilers," *Combustion*, 42(3): 16–21, 1970.

K. L. Atwood and G. L. Hale, "A Method for Determining Need for Chemical Cleaning of High-Pressure Boilers," *Proceedings of the American Power Conference*, 33: 710–720, 1971.

K. L. Atwood and J. A. Martucci, "The Application of Hydrochloric Acid with Ammonium Bromate for Scale Removal in Utility Boilers," Proceedings of the 28th International Water Conference, Pittsburgh, PA, December 11–13, 1967, pp. 167–179.

R. J. Barto, D. M. Farrell, F. A. Noto, and S. L. Goodstine, "Intelligent Chemistry Management System (ICMS)—A New Approach to Steam Generator Chemistry Control," *Proceedings of the American Power Conference*, 48: 1025–1031, 1986.

R. D. Brown and D. A. Harris, "Large Coal-Fired Cycling Unit," Presented at the ASME-IEEE-ASCE Joint Power Generation Conference, Portland, OR, September 28–October 2, 1975.

B. Chojnowski and R. D. B. Whitcutt, "Corrosion Failure: One Cause and a Cure in an Operational Boiler," *Combustion*, 48(5): 28–33, 1976.

W. H. Clayton et al., "Design for Peaking Cycling," Presented at the Joint Power Generation Conference, Pittsburgh, PA, September 27–30, 1970.

F. Gabrielli and W. R. Sylvester, "Water Treatment Practices for Cyclic Operation of Utility Boilers," Proceedings of the International Water Conference, Pittsburgh, PA, October 31–November 2, 1978, pp. 193–208.

F. Gabrielli et al., "Contamination Prevention of Superheaters and Reheaters During Initial Start-Up and Operation," *Proceedings of the American Power Conference*, 38: 296–310, 1976.

F. Gabrielli et al., "Prevent Corrosion and Deposition Problems in High-Pressure Boilers," *Power*, 122(7): 85–92, 1978.

F. Gabrielli, N. C. Mohn, and W. R. Sylvester, "Water Chemistry Aspects of Cyclic Operation for Older High-Pressure Drum-Type Boilers," *Proceedings of the American Power Conference*, 45: 989–999, 1983.

F. Gabrielli, N. C. Mohn, and B. C. Teigen, "Deposit and Water Chemistry Studies with Rifled Tubing," *Proceedings of the American Power Conference*, 46: 973-984, 1984.

S. Glasstone, "Overvoltage and Its Significance in Corrosion," *Corrosion and Material Protection*, 3(6): 15–18, 1946.

S. L. Goodstine and J. J. Kurpen, "Corrosion and Corrosion Product Control in the Utility Boiler-Turbine Cycle," *Combustion*, 44(11): 6–18, 1973.

N. D. Greene and M. C. Fontana, "A Critical Analysis of Pitting Corrosion," *Corrosion*, 15(13): 41–47, 1959.

T. Hagewood et al., "The Control of Internal Corrosion in High-Pressure Peaking Units," *Proceedings of the American Power Conference*, 30: 939–948, 1968.

A. F. Kelly et al., "Modify Base-Load Turbines for Peaking Service," *Power*, 115(4): 62–63, 1971.

C. M. Kennedy et al, "Experience with High Rate Ammoniated Mixed Beds for Condensate Polishing of CIPSCO Coffeen Station." *Combustion*, 39(9): 19–30, 1968.

H. A. Klein, "A Field Survey of Internation Corrosion in High-Pressure Utility Boilers," *Proceedings of the American Power Conference*, 33: 702–709, 1971.

H. A. Klein, "Corrosion of Fossil Fueled Steam Generators," *Combustion*, 44(7): 5–20, 1973.

H. A. Klein, "Use of Coordinated Phosphate Treatment to Prevent Caustic Corrosion in High-Pressure Boilers," *Combustion*, 34(4): 45–52, 1962.

H. A. Klein and K. L. Atwood, "Chemical Cleaning of Utility Boilers," *Proceedings of the American Power Conference*, 26: 762–778, 1964.

H. A. Klein and P. Goldstein, "The Effects of Water Quality on the Performance of Modern Power Plants," Presented at the 24th Annual Conference of the National Association of Corrosion Engineers, Cleveland, OH, March 18–22, 1968, Paper 12.

J. J. Kurpen, "Externally Regenerated Condensate Demineralization Systems for Once-Through Steam Generators," Presented at the Liberty Bell Corrosion Course, Philadelphia, PA, September 16–18, 1969.

J. J. Kurpen and D. L. Dixson, "Operating Experience in Cycle Cleanup for Supercritical Pressure Units," *Proceedings of the American Power Conference*, 30:883–896, 1968.

J. A. Levendusky and L. Olejar, "Condensate Purification Applications of the Power Process in High-Pressure Utility Plant Cycles," *Proceedings of the American Power Conference*, 29: 840–856, 1967.

E. W. Lolir and S. K. Love, :The Industrial Utility of Public Water Supplies in the United States, 1952: Part l," Geological Survey Water Supply Paper 1299. Washington, D.C.: U.S. Government Printing Office, 1954.

E. W. Lolir and S. K. Love, :The Industrial Utility of Public Water Supplies in the United States, 1952: Part 11," Geological Survey Water Supply Paper 1300. Washington, D.C.: U.S. Government Printing Office, 1954.

H. M. Rivers, "Concentrating Films: Their Role in Boiler Scale and Corrosion Problems," Proceedings of the 12th Annual Water Conference, Pittsburgh, PA, October 22–24, 1951, pp. 131–145.

F. N. Speller, "Control of Corrosion by Deactivation of Water," *Franklin Institute Journal*, 193: 515–542, 1922.

D. G. Stocky and K. L. Atwood, "Non-Destructive Testing for Location of Corrosion Damage in High-Pressure Boilers," Presented at the Meeting of the Southeastern Electric Exchange, New Orleans, LA, April 29–30, 1971.

R. Svoboda, F. Gabrielli, H. Hehs, and H. Sandmann, "Combined Cycle Chemistry: Present and Next Generation," Presented at the Seventh International EPRI Conference on Cycle Chemistry in Fossil Plants, Houston, TX, June 3–5, 2003.

Ulmer, R. C. and H. A. Klein, "Impurities in Steam from High Pressure Boilers." Proceedings of the *ASTM*, 61:1396–1411,1961.

R. Svoboda, E. Liebig, H. Sandmann, and F. Gabrielli, "Cycle Chemistry Features in Advanced Combined Cycle Power Plants," Presented at the Sixth International EPRI Conference on Cycle Chemistry in Fossil Plants, Columbus, OH, June 27–29, 2000.

L. H. Vaughn and C. V. Runyan, "Corrosion Protection of Boilers and Associated Equipment During Idle Periods," *Proceedings of the American Power Conference*, 33: 721–729, 1971.

C. W. Wages and C. W, Smith, "Operating Experience of a Deep-Bed Condensate Polishing System," Proceedings of the 38th International Water Conference, Pittsburgh, PA, November 1–3, 1977, pp. 111–121.

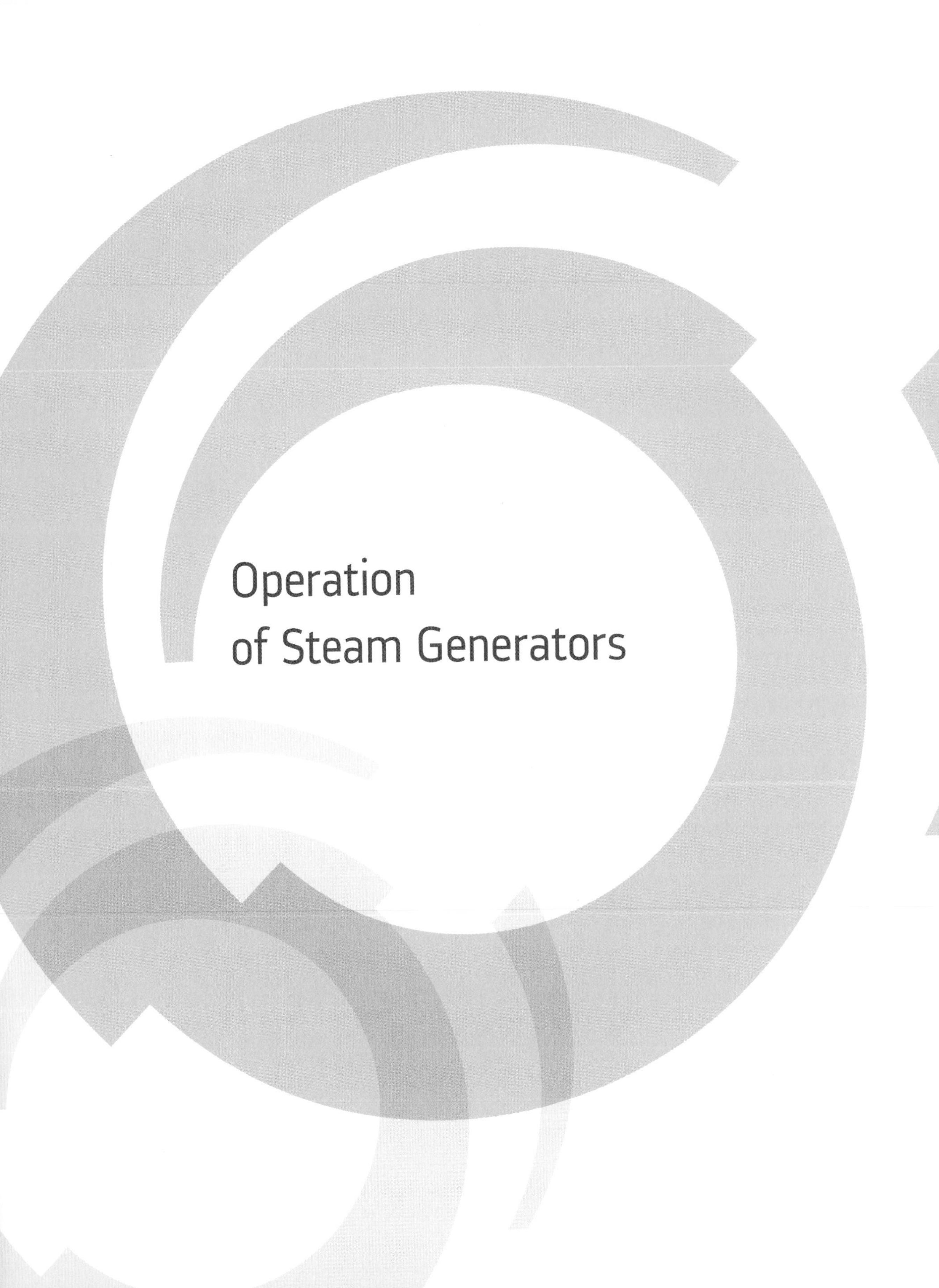

Operation of Steam Generators

Chapter **Ten**

The operation of a multi-million dollar steam generator and its associated power plant equipment requires the constant exercise of intuitive reasoning and sound engineering judgment. It is in operation that all the factors that went into the design and construction of the facility are put to the test. A principal objective of proper operation is sustained service between outages while, at the same time, obtaining the highest possible efficiency and availability from all the plant components.

Operation of a steam generator is a balance of inputs and outputs: the better the balance, the smoother the operation. Producing steam from a boiler requires that the weight of water entering the boiler equal the weight of steam leaving the boiler. Firing the furnace requires a balance of fuel and air. To equalize these inputs and outputs, one must understand the system, not just the network of hardware that comprises it. This understanding is the principal ingredient of successful operation. Too often operators have confused operation with control-system management. The operator must realize that a control system is hardware assembled to make operation easier, faster, and safer. All large steam generators require operators. The control of all major functions can be switched from automatic to operator control. To be effective an operator must know not only what he or she is doing but also why it is done and what results from the operator's action.

The prime consideration for all operation is the safety of people and equipment. Whenever there is any doubt about an unsafe condition, the operator must take immediate action to return the unit to a known safe condition, even if it means tripping the unit. Today, as throughout the history of steam generation, the two most dangerous conditions are the loss of water and the explosive mixture of fuel and air. Both result from an imbalance: the first is caused by less water coming in than steam produced, even if some of that steam is escaping through a tube leak; the second is caused by too little air for the fuel present.

Safe operation, then, is a result of comprehensive training programs for operators, well-designed furnace safeguard systems, and an effective preventive-maintenance program.

BASIC OPERATING PRINCIPLES

In this section, certain basic operating guidelines for overall effective operation of a large coal-fired unit are discussed.

STEAM TEMPERATURES

Maintaining the desired primary and reheat steam temperatures requires considerable operator attention. Even the best control systems do not anticipate all of the factors affecting steam temperature. Despite the equipment installed for controlling superheater and reheater steam temperatures, certain conditions may produce abnormal steam temperatures. For instance, with a new coal-fired unit, it may be necessary to operate for a considerable time before normal furnace seasoning allows the unit to produce predicted steam temperatures. "Normal furnace seasoning" is often defined as the condition of furnace wall slag or ash deposits that remain after soot blower operation. Low steam temperatures may also result from:

- insufficient excess air
- higher-than-design feedwater temperature
- reheater inlet temperature lower than specified
- externally fouled superheater or reheater
- leaking desuperheater spray water
- poorly adjusted controls

There are many potential causes for temperature variations in furnace operations. Often these are interrelated. A proper understanding of the system is needed to provide for proper and timely operator action.

On the other hand, high steam temperature may result from:

- an "over-seasoned" furnace
- too high an excess air level
- feedwater temperature lower than specified
- reheater inlet temperature higher than specified
- irregular ignition or delayed combustion
- poorly adjusted control equipment

An operating variable that has a very great effect on steam temperature is the cleanliness of the radiant and convective heating surfaces. Although all modern coal-fired steam generators are equipped with automatic soot blower systems, the judicious supplemental manual operation of certain blowers can improve overall unit operation. It can save valuable blowing medium and reduce required maintenance by minimizing the number of blowing cycles. To be most effective, a soot blower program requires periodic furnace observations. Based on such observations and performance results, selective soot blowing can lead to better control of the steam temperature and reduce the possibility of troublesome accumulations in the furnace and convection passes.

BOILER EFFICIENCY

An effective operator is constantly striving to obtain maximum efficiency from a unit. To do this, the operator must be aware of the effect of all operating variables, and the adjustments required to maximize efficiency. Two items within operator control that affect boiler efficiency are dry gas loss and unburned fuel loss.

Dry Gas Loss

Usually the largest factor affecting boiler efficiency, dry gas loss increases with higher exit gas temperatures or excess air values. Every 35 to 40°F (20 to 22°C) increment in exit gas temperature will lower boiler efficiency by 1%. A 1% increase in excess air by itself decreases boiler efficiency by only 0.05%. On most boilers, however, increased excess air leads to a higher exit gas temperature. Consequently, increases in excess air can have a two-fold effect on unit efficiency.

Usually, coal-fired units are designed to operate with 20 to 25% excess air. To operate a boiler most efficiently, an operator must have a reliable means of assessing the quantity of excess air leaving the boiler. In situ oxygen analyzers that measure the oxygen at the boiler or economizer outlet are the best information source. These must be checked regularly for proper calibration and maintained as necessary. The operator should maintain the required excess air level by making sure the controls are in the correct mode and tuned with respect to the fuel being fired.

Unburned Fuel Loss

On gas- or oil-fired units, unburned fuel loss should be negligible, whereas unburned loss on coal-fired units can be appreciable. The boiler manufacturer will predict unburned fuel loss. These values can usually be maintained with correct operation. There is no easy way to continuously monitor unburned carbon in the ash. Obtaining such values involves the time and manual effort of laboratory analysis of a fly ash sample. The significant point is that the laboratory should feed the information back to the operators in a timely manner. If values are consistently high, the plant operations department should develop a program to pinpoint what is causing the high level of unburned carbon and determine how to improve the condition.

Usually, high unburned carbon levels can be traced to the mixing process of the fuel and air in the furnace. Once the source is found, attention must be focused on what corrects it. For example, one cause of poor mixing of fuel and air could be inadequate windbox to furnace differential pressure. If this is so, monitoring the pressure to keep it in line is easier than waiting for the periodic feedback of laboratory results. There are two other items that have an effect on boiler efficiency about which an operator can do little. These are the moisture and hydrogen content of the fuel losses and the steam generator radiation loss.

Moisture Loss

Although the moisture loss of the stack gases is considerable, the loss comes from fuel moisture, the combustion of hydrogen, and the moisture in the air, which are not within operator control. The moisture in coal consists of inherent moisture and surface moisture. Although attention to the care of coal from the mine to the coal bunker can minimize the surface moisture pickup, with resultant increase in boiler efficiency, this is seldom within the boiler operator's control.

Radiation Loss

On large, well-insulated, steam generators, the efficiency loss due to radiation is about 0.2% at full load. Because essentially the same total heat is lost throughout the load range, radiation loss increases with decreasing loads. Considering only radiation losses, operating several units at low load may be less economical than taking one unit off-line. Other requirements must be considered, such as sudden additional load demands and fuel consumption required to return the unit to service. See Chapters 2 and 13 for further discussion of the above heat-loss items.

Availability of Equipment

Equipment availability is described as the status of a boiler, or its related equipment, that is capable of service, whether or not it is actually in service. In simple terms, this means a unit that can produce the desired output when it is called on to do so. Power plant boilers and their related equipment must be maintained in a state that makes them available as much as possible and at as high a load as reasonable. This dictates that equipment must be operated and maintained to the highest standards. It is the responsibility of the plant staff to be diligent in identifying problems and addressing them as the need and opportunity arises. This may mean taking a piece of equipment out of service for repairs during times of low-load operation. Another alternative could be taking a short unit outage during off-peak periods or taking an early maintenance outage for critical repairs.

Therefore, one of the most important components of diligent plant operation is being aware of equipment operation so that its maintenance needs can be addressed at the most opportune time. A plant operator should not wait for a piece of equipment to break down before making repairs, nor should equipment be purposely run until it fails, especially because of the potential for more critical damage or, worse, injury to personnel.

Air Heaters

As already noted, lower exit gas temperature is the most positive means for increasing boiler efficiency. The limiting factor is usually the air heater. For purposes of this discussion, observations will be focused on the Ljungström® type of regenerative air heater.

For maximum effectiveness the air heater must be kept clean, the baskets must be replaced when acid corrosion has deteriorated enough material to affect performance, and the seals must be adjusted to minimize air and gas leakage. Proper operation of the air heaters requires certain instrumentation. Pressure drop indicators across both the air and gas sides must be available to the operator, as well as temperature indicators for gas and air, both entering and leaving. Pressure drops are the best guide to when to operate the air heater soot blowers. Once pluggage progresses too far, soot blowers will not remove the deposits and the air heater will have to be removed from service for cleaning.

Faulty operation causes most air heater corrosion. The air heater manufacturer supplies a chart with recommended average cold-end temperatures to keep the metal above the acid dew point corresponding to the sulfur in the fuel. The "average cold-end temperature" is defined as the arithmetic sum of the temperature of the air entering the air heater plus the gas temperature leaving the air heater, divided by two. Consistent operation below the acid dew point rapidly corrodes air heater baskets. Steam or water air heaters or bypass ducts control the cold-end temperature.

High exit gas temperatures leaving the air heater can be an indication of air bypassing the air heater. This can result from poorly adjusted seals or excess pulverizer tempering air. Pulverizer systems, for example, are designed to dry coal of a specified moisture. If the coal has less than the "designed-for" moisture or the mills are at partial capacity, mill tempering air will bypass the air heater and result in higher exit gas temperatures leaving the air heater. See Chapter 6 for further details on pulverizers and air heaters.

The Economic Impact of Operation

The most effective way to achieve maximum boiler efficiency in day-to-day operation is to embark on an education campaign for plant management, supervisory staff, operators, and maintenance personnel. If everyone knows the economic impact of the operational variables on fuel costs, this knowledge can lead to significant fuel savings. Too often campaigns to improve efficiency are carried out by only one group. Tests are performed to collect data rather than to establish targets for day-to-day operation, and the people performing the tests communicate the results not to the rest of the plant, but rather to the company files. It is important, then, to review test results with the unit operators and to establish operating procedures that will take advantage of what is learned from the tests.

Plant restarts are expensive. They require considerable fuel to get a unit up to operating temperature and pressure and bring it online. Extra maintenance and online attention that keeps plant downtime to a minimum can pay off in fuel savings. Retaining heat in the boiler during a weekend shutdown when there is no demand for steam can save fuel. A boiler can retain a good deal of heat if its isolation dampers are in good condition and are closed tightly. Precautions should be taken to follow the purging requirements both before bottling and prior to light off. The loss of the unit because of an explosion will be infinitely more costly than any heat saving from failing to perform a proper purge.

START-UP FROM COLD CONDITION: GENERAL

Prior to light off of any boiler, a supervisor of operations should inspect the exterior of the unit. All doors should be checked, cleared of tags, and then shut. Valves should be correctly positioned for start-up in accordance with the steam generator manufacturer's valve operating diagram. All areas must be free of debris that will hinder unit expansion. If repair work was done during the outage, special care must be taken to ensure that no permanent ties were made to the furnace structure that will impair expansion. All personnel must be accounted for. Before light off, the operator should check all instrumentation and furnace safety systems. Because of the great differences in steam generating units, detailed start-up procedures cannot be given. The operator must be familiar with all of the manufacturer's instructions and the plant operating procedures.

At this point, safety tags can be removed from breakers. As the boiler is filling with treated water, all vents should be open, as noted on the manufacturer's valve operating diagram. On a thermal circulation unit, the water level should be brought to where it just shows near the bottom of the water glass. On a Controlled Circulation® unit, the water level should be brought near the top of the gage glass. This will prevent the water from dropping from sight when the first boiler-water circulating pump is started. The drainable portions of all steam circuit headers, connecting links, and piping should be drained through lines free from back pressure. Reheater drains and vents should be opened so that residual moisture will be boiled off. These reheater drains and vents will have to be closed prior to raising a vacuum in the condenser.

During warm-up and until the unit is carrying load, there will be little or no steam flow through the superheater and reheater. To protect the superheater and reheater metals, the temperature of the gas leaving the furnace should be limited to the manufacturer's recommendation, usually 1,000°F (540°C). The firing rate must be limited to satisfy this requirement. Thermal circulation boilers can be warmed up at a rate that does not exceed a saturated steam temperature rise of 200°F (110°C) per hour. Controlled Circulation® boilers have no limitation on the saturation steam temperature rise, only on the furnace exit gas, as previously stated. Most modern boilers have

Good operating and maintenance practices help to minimize downtime and, thus, the number of restarts. Restarts are expensive, consuming considerable fuel without contributing to increased efficiency. Minimizing the number of restarts improves overall efficiency leading to reduced annual emissions.

traversing thermocouples or optical pyrometers to monitor furnace exit gas temperature during warm-up. Older units may use temporary thermocouple probes for each start-up or have conservatively established firing limitations based on prior testing.

Safety first in any light off situation.

Usually the equipment will start in this sequence. Air heaters and boiler-water circulating pumps (on positive circulation units) will be started first. Next, the induced draft fans, followed immediately by the forced draft fans will be started. This will establish airflow through the plant equipment. On most units, the furnace draft will be established and then transferred to automatic draft control. Airflow is raised to at least 30% of the full-load airflow, and the unit should be purged for at least 5 minutes to remove any unburned fuel or combustible gases that may remain in the furnace. During start-up, airflow should be maintained at 30% of full-load airflow to ensure an air-rich furnace mixture and to prevent any settling out of explosive mixtures. Once the unit is purged, oil pumps may be started and gas or oil trip valves opened. At set intervals, the operator should check for the proper functioning of any furnace safeguard system. Regardless of the level of urgency for getting the unit returned to service, no interlock should be jumped or bypassed.

Light off of any fuel nozzle should never be attempted without the required ignition energy source for that nozzle. Any time an operator has any doubt about safe combustion in the furnace, the fuel should be tripped and the furnace purged before relighting.

As pressure is raised, periodic inspections are necessary to ensure that the unit is expanding as it should. If oil is the warm-up fuel, the air heater soot blowers should be operated frequently to keep the heating surface clear of any flammable deposits. Once the unit is online, the load may be picked up as swiftly, as pulverizers can be brought into service. The usual restrictions in most power plants are the warm-up and load increase limitations of the steam turbine. (See Chapters 4 and 9.)

Start-Up from Cold Condition: Drum-Type Units

On drum-type units, maintaining the drum water level is of prime importance. Normally, the operator carries out this function in the manual mode until pressure is raised. Before light off, the drum water level should be brought in sight. It is best to start firing with a low water level because, as the water starts heating, it will expand. Drum vent valves should be wide open so that the air will vent from the drum. The superheater and reheater should be drained of any condensate whenever possible and then the valves opened or closed according to the valve operating instructions.

For a Controlled Circulation® boiler, two of the circulating pumps are started to initiate water circulation. To minimize flashing of steam in the downcomers, additional pumps are not started until the boiler water reaches 250°F (120°C). The unit is now fired in accordance with the established furnace safeguards. During the warming period, the economizer recirculating line valves are open. The water will swell as it is heated and the operator will manually blow down the boiler as required to maintain sight of the water in the gage glass. The firing rate will be controlled to keep the furnace exit gas temperature below the recommended value, usually between 900 and 1,000°F (480 and 540°C).

When drum pressure reaches 25 psig (1.7 bar), it can be assumed that all air has been purged from the drum and water circuits. The operator can close the drum vent valves. As pressure increases, it is necessary to progressively throttle the superheater drains and vents and to increase the firing rate as required. If there is evidence of steaming in the economizer by erratic drum control during the feeding of the water, the operator must be certain that the recirculation line is open. On thermal circulation units it may be necessary to feed more water than required to maintain the level in the sight glass and to blow down to control the water level.

The turbine should start rolling as soon as the minimum permissible start-up pressure and temperature, specified by the turbine manufacturer, are reached. When bringing the steam turbine up to speed, the firing rate must continue to be controlled to prevent the furnace exit gas from exceeding its temperature limit. Once the turbine is synchronized and the minimum load established, this limit can be removed and the firing rate increased as required. Usually, by this time all superheater and reheater vents and drains are closed. If the steam drum water level is still under manual control, it should now be placed on automatic control.

Load and Pressure Control: Drum-Type Units

Opening or closing the turbine control valves increases or decreases the load on a drum-type unit. Changing the firing rate regulates the pressure. In theory, for increasing load, the operator will open the turbine control valve. If no other action were taken, the flow to the steam turbine would increase and the superheater outlet pressure would decrease. Upon seeing the outlet pressure drop, the operator would increase the fuel and air inputs to return the pressure to the desired level. Because of the increased steam flow, the water level in the drum would change. Initially, surging would cause the level to rise, but shortly thereafter, it would fall rapidly because more steam is removed than water enters. A trained operator will anticipate these interactions. As the turbine control valve is opened, the operator will simultaneously increase fuel, air, and feedwater flow. A well-designed and well-executed operational control system will perform the same procedure as will a trained operator. The more experienced and better trained the operator, and the more sophisticated the control system, the higher the expectation that smooth operation will result.

Shutting Down Drum-Type Units

Time requirements and procedures for shutting down a boiler depend on the nature of the shutdown (normal shutdown to cold, normal shutdown to hot standby, emergency shutdown) and whether the unit is to be entered. For a scheduled shutdown, steam pressure can be reduced to the limit of the turbine before the unit is taken off-line. Thermal circulation units should not exceed a cooldown rate of 150°F (80°C) per hour of saturated steam temperature decrease. Controlled Circulation® units can be rapidly cooled if the circulating pumps are left in service. Normally, the drum vents are opened at 25 psig (1.7 bar) and the

Very pure water is required for supercritical pressure operation as there is no separation of steam and water at these conditions. Any impurities in the make-up water will end up somewhere in the steam system.

boiler is not drained until the water temperature is below 200°F (93°C).

START-UP OF SUPERCRITICAL PRESSURE BOILERS

While there are many similarities between the operation of drum-type and supercritical-type boilers, there are also some specific and very significant differences. Supercritical boilers demand a very precise balance between inputs and outputs because they do not have the flywheel effect inherent in the boiler water circuits of drum type boilers.

Although the firing system start-up and operation are the same as for a drum-type unit, the fluid system start-up is completely different. The supercritical boiler is furnished with an integral start-up system. The unit is initially fired, warmed up, and brought to partial load on the bypass system. Current vintage supercritical boilers are of the sliding pressure design, which uses start-up separators and a separator storage-tank. The function of these components is to collect, separate, and then forward the steam to the superheater. At the same time, the separated water is returned to the boiler water circuit. The water level in the separator storage tank is monitored and tightly controlled within preset limits during all phases of operation. This has particular importance for boiler start-up during wet mode operation. Depending on the design, the start-up systems may or may not use a boiler water circulating pump (BCP). All designs use a flash tank whose function is to receive any excess/drain water that is removed from the boiler water circuit. That excess/drain water is subsequently returned to the condenser hotwell for recirculation through the condensate and feedwater systems.

Typically, at loads below 30%, the boiler operates in wet mode (and at subcritical pressure), with recirculated waterwall flow superimposed on feedwater flow. During wet mode operation, the feedwater flow must remain balanced with the superheater steam flow so that the separator storage tank water level is maintained within preset limits. If the feedwater flow is lower than the steam flow, the separator storage tank level will fall and eventually be lost. If the feedwater flow exceeds the steam flow, the separator storage tank level will rise and eventually flood the separators (in this case, corrective action is taken to prevent such flooding). In wet mode operation, the waterwall outlet is water and steam at saturated conditions.

Above 30% load, the boiler operates in dry mode (once-through mode). In dry mode operation, the waterwall outlet is steam only. All waterwall inlet flow is evaporated, and a small degree of superheat is added before reaching the waterwall outlet. The slightly superheated steam discharging from the waterwall is forwarded to the superheater with no water return from the separators to the separator storage tank. The boiler is now operating in once-through mode. At this point, the boiler pressure is still subcritical. As the firing rate and load increase, the pressure increases. Inherent in the boiler design, the pressure slides upward as the feedwater and firing rates are increased. The pressure ultimately increases through the critical pressure region and into the supercritical pressure region. Operation at supercritical pressure continues as long as the firing

rate and the feedwater rate remain sufficiently high. As these reduce during normal operation load changes, the pressure slides back down to the subcritical region. There is no bump or upset in boiler operation during these pressure changes. The pressure simply increases or decreases through these pressures as the firing and feedwater rates are changed.

Circulation Systems

The waterwall (evaporator) requires that a design preset, minimum inlet water flow be maintained (or exceeded) at all times. This is nominally 30% maximum continuous rating (MCR) feed flow. This is required to ensure proper cooling water flow through the furnace waterwall (evaporator) tubes at all times to prevent tube overheating. There are different designs used on the start-up systems and their method of waterwall (evaporator) circulation. One design uses a boiler water circulation pump and the other does not. (See *Figs. 10-1* and *10-2*.)

When the design uses a boiler water circulation pump (BCP), that pump remains in service until approximately 35% (or higher) load, after which it can be turned off. Up to 30% load, it recirculates water through the waterwall (evaporator). When the load increases through 30% and stable boiler dry mode operation is attained, feedwater flow will already be greater than the waterwall minimum inlet flow requirement, allowing the shutdown of the BCP.

When the design does not use a BCP, the boiler feed pump (BFP) provides the necessary minimum waterwall (evaporator) inlet water flow. With this design, when the boiler is in wet mode operation, there is a continuing requirement to drain water from the separator storage tank to prevent the tank level from increasing and flooding the separators, thus allowing water to enter into the superheater. With this design, the BFP provides the minimum waterwall (evaporator) circulation and excess water is continuously drained so as to maintain the separator storage tank level within preset limits. Prior to boiler firing, the waterwall (evaporator) outlet is water only, and 100% of this is drained, holding the separator storage tank level at the set point. As the firing rate increases, the waterwall (evaporator) outlet becomes water and steam, and the quantity of drainage from the separator storage tank decreases. As firing progresses, the waterwall outlet water/steam ratio progressively reduces and eventually becomes 100% steam with slight superheat. At this stage, there is no water drainage, and the boiler is operating in once-through mode.

Recommended Supercritical Unit Start-Up Procedure[1]

1. The BFP establishes a flow (5 to 10% of maximum continuous rating) for boiler filling through the economizer to achieve the normal separator storage tank level required to enable start of the BCP. After the BCP has been started, the BFP flow is reduced to 0%. As the firing rate increases and the waterwall (evaporator) generates steam, the feed flow increases to maintain separator storage tank level at the set point.
2. The BCP is running and maintaining the waterwall (evaporator) inlet minimum flow requirement and the separator storage tank level is steady and at the set point.

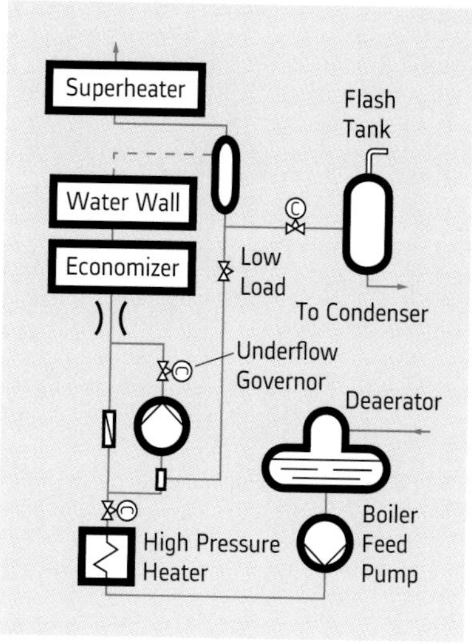

Figure 10-1 | Schematic diagram of a modern supercritical boiler with a BCP

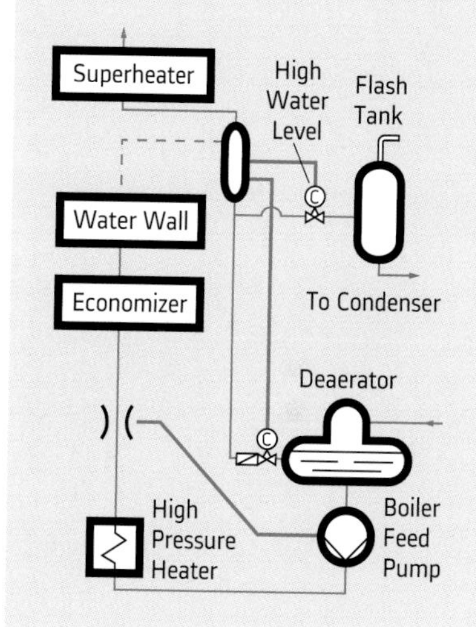

Figure 10-2 | Schematic diagram of a modern supercritical boiler without a BCP

3. The boiler is lit off, and gradually the pressure and temperature increase as steam is generated. During the start-up, the normal water swell that accompanies heating leads to an increase in the separator storage tank level, resulting in the requirement to drain some water from the boiler water circuit to prevent flooding of the separators. The drainage/excess water is discharged to the flash tank.
4. As steam generation continues, the pressure and temperatures increase further, and reach the point at which the steam turbine can be rolled, synchronized, and loaded. This occurs while the boiler is operating in wet mode. The pressure is still subcritical.
5. After the firing rate and load increase through 30% and stable dry mode operation is being maintained, the boiler circulating pump can be switched off.
6. A further increase in load results in a sliding pressure increase to the extent that the pressure eventually passes through critical pressure and into the supercritical region. The boiler continues to operate in dry mode (once through), with the feedwater flow operating well beyond the waterwall (evaporator) minimum inlet flow requirement.

Steam-Temperature Control

The superheater outlet temperature on a supercritical pressure boiler is controlled with the firing rate, which is increased to raise outlet temperature and decreased to lower it. Although this is an effective means of temperature control, the response time to correct a temperature deviation is too long for smooth operation. To improve the response, desuperheater water is injected between superheater stages. The injection water is taken from the economizer inlet at full boiler feedwater temperature, so there is no cycle efficiency loss. Although the injected water gives a fast response, the ultimate temperature control is balancing the firing rate with the feedwater rate.

The injection water bypasses the waterwalls and the economizer. When the superheater temperature is high, the operator or control system will open the spray valves until the temperature returns to the desired level. Usually, for a supercritical unit, adjusting the reheater outlet temperature follows the same procedure as for a drum-type unit. With a tangentially fired unit, the process involves tilting the fuel and air nozzles and maintaining furnace cleanliness by soot blowing.

Water Circuit Quality Cleanup

Because a supercritical boiler has no steam drum to separate the impurities in the waterwalls from the essentially pure steam in the superheater, a waterwall cleanup procedure must precede each start-up. The procedure involves circulating condensate through the polisher, feedwater heater train, economizer, waterwalls, separator, and drain system back to the condenser. The water iron concentration is monitored, and flushing is continued until the manufacturer's limits are obtained.

PULVERIZER OPERATION

Although several types of pulverizers are used to grind coal for power

plant service, the majority are of the rotating bowl type for use in direct fired systems. Refer to Chapter 6 for a description of this pulverizer. In operation, four areas must be understood and monitored: lubrication of the gears and bearings, airflow, mixture temperature leaving, and product fineness. Airflow, temperature leaving, and fineness are intertwined during mill operation.

LUBRICATION

With the exception of the roller journals and exhauster (if so equipped), the mill is completely lubricated from one system in the worm gear housing or from stand-alone lubrication systems. The circulation is either by an external pumping system or by an internal pump that is a part of the gearing system. The lubricant must meet the manufacturer's specifications and be non-foaming and non-corrosive. (See *Fig. 10-3.*)

Periodic inspection of the gear housing oil temperature is required. For most of the recommended lubricants, the oil temperature is maintained at about 150°F (65°C). If it is above this temperature, the oil level may be too low. If so, it should be promptly refilled with oil of the same manufacture and type as is already in the housing. High oil temperature could also result from a breakdown of the lubricant, or sludging. If the oil temperature is high, it should be changed. There could also be scale formation in the cooling coil, insufficient quantity of cooling water, or high temperature of the inlet cooling water. The operator should check the oil in the return glass on a daily basis and after each mill start-up, for mills in continuous service.

MILL OPERATION

To place a mill in service, the mill should be started and allowed to come up to speed. The mill outlet temperature should be brought up to the recommended level, before starting the coal feed. There should be proper ignition energy adjacent to the fuel nozzles supplied by the mill being put in service. The feeder should be started with a fairly high feed rate setting. After the mill begins to grind, the feed rate should be reduced to the desired amount. The feeder drive must be interlocked with the mill motor so that if the mill power is interrupted the feeder will shut down. The mill outlet temperature should be maintained as high as possible, without exceeding the safe limits of the type of coal ground. This temperature may be as low as 130°F (54°C) with lignite and as high as 180°F (82°C) for low-volatile, bituminous coals. Low mill outlet temperatures often indicate mill overload, which is usually accompanied by other indications, such as high motor amperage or high mill differential pressure.

Pulverizer Fires

Pulverizer fires can range from nondestructive to highly destructive, depending mainly on how soon the fire is detected and what action the operator takes. Basic causes of pulverizer fires are excessive mill temperatures, foreign combustible material (such as rags, paper, or wood), settling out of coal in the pulverizer, or excessive accumulation of pyritic material or coal in the mill base area. Early detection of fires enhances the safety of plant personnel; therefore, an automatic system is recommended. Using visual or other sensory means to detect such

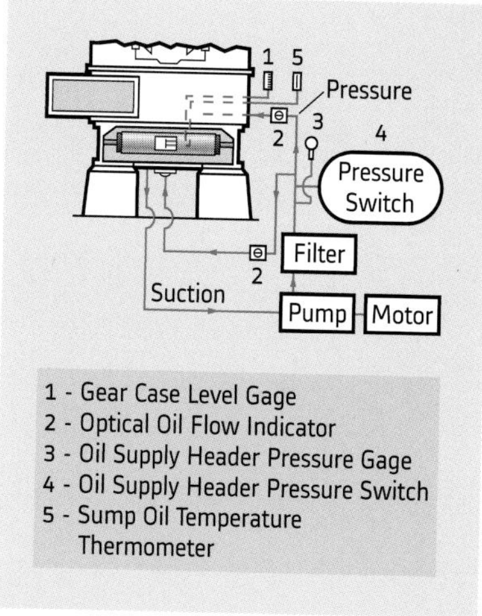

Figure 10-3 | Simplified pulverizer diagram showing lube oil system

fires is arbitrary, slow, and, worst of all, dangerous, as it requires the presence of a person in the immediate hazard area. Temperature detection devices should be used as the primary indicator of a fire in progress.

There are five types of pulverizer fires. These are categorized by where in the fuel preparation system they occur: feeder fires, above-bowl fires, under-bowl fires, exhauster fires, and fuel-piping fires. Upon detection of a pulverized fuel system fire, the fire extinguishing system must be activated. A spray of water is introduced into the system at multiple locations. The timing is usually at the discretion of the operator. However, the pulverizer must be kept inert until the water injection sequence is completed. When the pulverizer is empty of its contents, it can be shut off and isolated. Water injection should continue until all evidence of fire has disappeared. Entry for clean-up is allowable only after the mill and its contents have cooled to ambient temperature. Caution should still be exercised, as smoldering pockets of fuel may persist.

Pulverizer fires are a safety as well as equipment concern. Prompt measures should be taken.

Before restart, the entire milling system should be inspected and cleaned of any accumulations. The lubricants in the mill base and rolls should be checked for any evidence of carbonization. The compression of journal springs should be checked again by means of a hydraulic jack. If everything is satisfactory, the mill may be returned to service.

Explosions in Pulverizers

Pulverizer fires occur more often than pulverizer explosions. If properly handled, these fires are not overly dangerous. However, if a fire is not brought under control effectively and expeditiously, an explosive condition can occur. Explosions also can occur without the presence of an obvious fire, if the necessary conditions to support an explosion are present. All explosions are initiated by fires, but all fires do not result in explosions. Because of this difference, independently designed and operated systems are available to handle each condition safely. The explosion prevention system uses an automatic, steam-inerting sequence to reduce the potential for pulverizer explosions when hazardous operating conditions exist. The system can also safely transport the pulverized coal remaining in the mill to the furnace, while maintaining an inert atmosphere inside the pulverizer. The fire control system detects fires in operating pulverizers and alerts the control room operators. The operators can then initiate the fire extinguishing procedures, which include water spray injection, steam-inerting, and transporting. A combination mill inerting and firefighting system integrates the two subsystems into one complete package.[2–4]

SLAGGING AND FOULING

Chapter 2 and Appendix B describe ash characteristics and their effect on slagging and fouling. This section will cover what the operator can do to control slagging and fouling. Successful boiler operation depends to a significant extent on the ability of the operating staff to understand how certain operating variables relate to the fuel properties and furnace sizing criteria. Operating variables that influence slagging and fouling are unit load, excess air, fuel fineness, and secondary air distribution.

Load

The higher the load, the higher the heat input to the furnace, and the greater the potential for slagging and fouling. Therefore, the most direct way to reduce slagging is to curtail load. This is not always possible, as the current output may be necessary to meet demands for electricity generation or process requirements. Changes in excess air, fuel fineness, and secondary air distribution are less drastic methods for minimizing slagging and fouling.

EXCESS AIR

At high oxidation states, iron compounds in the ash melt at a higher temperature than they do at lower oxidation states. For bituminous coals, which are frequently high in iron content, there is a significant difference in ash fusion temperatures measured in reducing (oxygen-starved) and oxidizing (oxygen-rich) atmospheres. Sub-bituminous coals normally contain less iron and exhibit a smaller difference in melting temperatures produced in oxidizing and reducing environments. This means that, if slagging is a problem with coals high in iron, furnace deposits can be reduced dramatically by increasing the amount of excess air. As a rule of thumb, the higher the fusion temperature, the drier the slag in the furnace, and the easier it is to remove.

FUEL FINENESS

Slagging conditions often can be improved by proper control of pulverizer fineness and classification. Since coarse coal particles take longer to burn, they are more prone to producing slag. High retention on the +50 mesh often increases slagging tendencies. See Chapter 6 for a detailed discussion of the fineness recommended for optimal pulverized firing of various ranks of coal.

SECONDARY AIR DISTRIBUTION

Because several different types of firing systems are in use, it is difficult to generalize on the subject of air distribution in the combustion zone. Basically, the objective is to provide good mixing of fuel and air so that combustion is efficient and local zones with reducing atmospheres are avoided. For example, in units with tangential firing, sometimes slagging can be reduced by increasing the secondary airflow to fuel compartments. Some units provide air systems that attempt to provide an airflow to the waterwalls in order to maintain an oxidizing condition at the wall at all times (concentric firing, offset air, curtain air, etc.).

Other Operational Measures

If the coal contains a substantial amount of ash with a tendency to slag and/or foul heat-transfer surfaces, particular attention must be given to equipment capable of cleaning the furnace walls and convection-tube banks. Failure to remove deposits at the proper time may result in a chain reaction of deteriorating events. For example, excessive furnace slagging results from not using the wall blowers at proper intervals. This condition reduces the rate of heat absorption in the furnace, imposing higher gas temperatures in the convection sections. In turn, the higher gas temperature causes the fly ash to become sticky, increasing deposition in the convection sections. Depending on the gas temperature and ash properties, the retractable soot blowers may

Good water chemistry leads to reduced forced outages due to tube failures.

not be able to remove these deposits. Ultimately, sections of the convection pass may become plugged. Unless load is reduced at this point, it may not be possible for the induced draft fans to maintain the proper amount of excess air. This causes additional slagging, and the cycle repeats. Modern soot blower systems have programming techniques so that proper sequential operation of the blowers, on an automatic basis, can be established after ash deposition patterns are verified during preoperational tests. Through programming, ash deposits on the furnace walls generally can be held to a minimum, and combustion gases can be cooled sufficiently before they enter the convection pass.

Soot Blower Operation

A major guideline to reliable soot blower operation is that plant personnel should not wait until large deposits develop before operating the blowers. Waiting too long between operations can seriously hamper the effectiveness of soot blowers. Observation of furnace conditions at least twice per shift helps eliminate unexpected problems. For maximum effectiveness, the blowing sequence must be established to favor those sections of the furnace that foul most easily. Only by careful observation can these areas be identified. If some areas of the furnace are particularly prone to fouling, supplemental, remote-manual operation of selected blowers can save valuable blowing medium and reduce system maintenance by minimizing the number of blowing cycles.

Because the soot blower system is so important for reliable, full-power operation of a coal-fired unit, this equipment must be maintained in good operating condition. It should be noted that blowing pressure can change, especially in units in which valve travel is used for pressure regulation. Thus, air or steam pressure should be checked frequently with blowers of this type, especially when furnace observation shows a buildup in deposits. Soot blowers with adjustable orifices are not as sensitive and will usually retain their settings indefinitely.

FEEDWATER/BOILER WATER

Because internal tube corrosion and deposition are major causes of costly forced outages, operators must be continually alert to the hazard of water neglect. All plants must establish and adhere to a feedwater and boiler water treatment and control program for their system. Chapter 9 describes the chemistry of water treatment and corrosion prevention in detail. The following section re-emphasizes the cautions that must be taken to minimize corrosion and deposition.

OXYGEN CONTROL

There are specific circumstances, as discussed in Chapter 9, in which controlled oxygen residuals in the feedwater can actually further minimize the generation and consequently the transport of iron oxides. In this section, however, the discussion addresses the more common actions required to maintain feedwater oxygen concentrations below 10 parts per billion (ppb).

The oxygen concentration in the feedwater must be regulated to minimize the formation of pre-boiler corrosion products, which inevitably end up as deposits on the inside of heat-transfer surfaces in the boiler. Oxygen levels are more likely to exceed recommended limits during start-up, shutdown, and low-load operation. At these times, low pressure, feedwater heaters and related extraction piping are often under negative pressure, and any leaking valves, pumps, or flanges will provide a path for oxygen to get into the system. Excess oxygen is removed from the system by the deaerator, not through chemical additives. Such deaerators have manufacturer's guarantees for levels of oxygen leaving the deaerator. Oxygen leaving the deaerator should meet these guaranteed levels at all times. The manufacturer should be contacted for recommendations to bring the concentration back in line. In recent years, new plants may not have adequate amounts of auxiliary steam available to the deaerator during unit start-up so that oxygen is purged from the feedwater. Therefore, if adequate auxiliary steam is not available because there are no other sources of steam in the station, one option to consider is obtaining steam from the boiler drum until turbine extraction steam is available.

To minimize the formation of pre-boiler corrosion products, the oxygen concentration in the feedwater should be maintained at less than about 10 ppb during unit operation. Acceptable feedwater oxygen levels during steady-state operation do not necessarily mean that the oxygen concentration is within safe limits at all times. During various phases of operation, conditions can exist that may result in excessive amounts of oxygen. Thus, the use of dissolved-oxygen monitors is important. The cause of excessive oxygen levels must be identified and dealt with promptly. Periodically, plant procedures and controls should be evaluated to ascertain that all sources of oxygen contamination have been eliminated.

pH CONTROL

The control of boiler water and feedwater pH is essential to minimize general and local corrosion, which can lead to tube failures. Some of these localized corrosion mechanisms can lead to tube failure in a matter of hours. The primary cause of acidic and caustic boiler water is condenser leakage. Raw cooling water that leaks into the condenser eventually ends up in the boiler water. The water source determines whether the in-leakage is either acid-producing or caustic-producing. Fresh water from lakes and rivers, for example, usually provides dissolved solids that hydrolyze in boiler water to form caustic substances, such as sodium hydroxide. By contrast, seawater and water from recirculating, cooling water systems with cooling towers contain dissolved solids that hydrolyze to form acidic compounds.

Strict tolerance levels on condenser leakage should be established for all high-pressure boilers. A limit of less than 0.05 ppm (parts per million) dissolved solids or a cation conductivity of less than 0.2 uS (uS = micro Siemens)/cm in the feedwater is typical for normal operation. An excess of up to 1.0 uS/cm can be tolerated for only very short periods and actions should be taken to shut down the unit if the leak can not be contained or neutralized.

Another potential source of acidic and caustic contaminants is the make-up demineralizer, where chemicals used for regeneration, such as sulfuric acid and caustic agents, may inadvertently enter the feedwater system. Chemicals incorrectly applied during boiler water treatment also can be corrosive, as, for example, sodium hydroxide used in conjunction with sodium phosphate compounds to treat boiler water. Corrosion can occur if the sodium hydroxide and sodium phosphate are not added to the water in the proper proportion.

IMPORTANCE OF WATER ANALYSIS

A comprehensive water analysis program should be maintained to ensure that the feedwater and boiler water chemistries are held within prescribed limits. Continuous, automatic, analytical instrumentation is preferred. If automatic analyzers are unavailable or are not operational, water tests should be conducted daily or twice a shift; this information is provided in the water chemistry guidelines. Cation conductivity instrumentation or a sodium analyzer is of particular importance in detecting condenser leakages or contamination of the feedwater. The operator must remember that many potential tube failures can be avoided by continual attention to the control of the water and steam environment throughout the station.

COMMISSIONING FUNCTIONS

Before a new unit can be put in service, the entire system must be cleaned to remove oil, grease, siliceous material, mill scale, rust, and any other debris. The condensate and feedwater systems are cleaned before cleaning the boiler so that none of the debris or dirt is carried into the boiler. These two systems are mechanically cleaned then flushed. The economizer and boiler will be given an alkaline boilout or detergent flush. Operators may follow this flush with an acid cleaning. In some cases, a lone detergent flush may be used followed in a few years by an in-service acid cleaning. Also, some utilities have chosen to use a one-stage chemical cleaning. Finally, the superheater, steam piping, and reheater will be cleaned by steam or air purging. It is important that each of these processes be conscientiously undertaken and result in as clean a system as possible.

PRE-BOILER CYCLE

All pre-boiler systems of high-pressure boilers must be thoroughly flushed with alkaline or detergent solution to remove oils, siliceous materials, and particulate matter that are present following fabrication, storage, and erection. It is important that these materials be removed prior to initial operation. Otherwise, they will be carried into the boiler. Optimal plant operating conditions will be realized rapidly after start-up if the pre-boiler equipment is satisfactorily cleaned. The condensate system, the feedwater system, and the shell side of all heaters should be included in this cleaning operation. This cleaning involves the following basic operations:

1. Manual cleaning of the condenser, all feedwater heaters, and the deaerator storage tanks.
2. Gross flushing to waste to remove the bulk of any loose material.
3. Circulating cleaning solution throughout the system.
4. Rinsing to remove the cleaning solution.
5. Laying up to protect metal surfaces until initial operation.

Cleaning the pre-boiler system normally requires the installation of temporary piping to establish circulation through the system. It is also desirable to install temporary piping to bypass portions of the system, such as the boiler feed pump and deaerator storage tank, which may be damaged by or trap large quantities of loose particulate material. Circulation is normally established with a condensate pump, which takes suction from the condenser hotwell, or a special pump of equivalent capacity. Flow is through the condensate and feedwater systems and is returned to the hotwell through the temporary piping or through the shell side of the feedwater heaters. Strainers are placed at the suction of all pumps used during cleaning to protect them from suspended particles. The strainers are checked periodically during the circulation period and cleaned if necessary. The condenser, condenser hotwell, and deaerator storage tank have to be mechanically cleaned to remove loose debris before any flushing is started. Mechanical cleaning will consist of sweeping, hosing down all surfaces, and removing all loose material by vacuuming, shoveling, or any other convenient means.

CHEMICAL CLEANING OF BOILERS

The internal surfaces of a boiler in contact with water or steam must be kept clean to ensure efficient heat transfer in the generation of steam. Several cleaning procedures are available to ensure the removal of foreign matter introduced into the boiler during the manufacturing process, equipment construction, and operation. The general cleaning process is a detergent flush or an alkaline boilout. An acid wash may not be necessary in new boilers. Operational acid cleaning will be required periodically. A one-stage chemical cleaning process has been successfully used in place of multiple-stage cleaning.

A detergent flush or alkaline boilout removes contaminants commonly found in a boiler following its shop assembly or field erection, such as lubricants, oil, sand, metal fragments, and assorted debris. Acid cleaning removes oxide scales and deposits formed on internal heat-transfer surfaces that come in contact with water. This procedure dissolves compounds resulting from contaminants in the feedwater delivered to the boiler. Acid cleaning is also used to remove mill scale and corrosion products.

The cleaning of internal boiler surfaces ensures good heat transfer for the generation of steam and protects against corrosion and buildup of contaminants.

DETERGENT FLUSH/ALKALINE BOILOUT

The basic reason for a detergent flush or an alkaline boilout of a boiler is to remove water and alkali-soluble and saponifiable compounds from the water-side surfaces of the unit. These compounds may include lubricants used in the erection of the boiler and, in some instances, protective coatings applied to prevent atmospheric rusting following shop fabrication. Most lubricants used in boiler construction are water-soluble and are not difficult to remove during this stage of cleaning. Water-insoluble oils and greases are introduced in small quantities into the boiler from oil-lubricated equipment and workers' clothing. Every effort should be made to minimize the introduction of oil and grease into the boiler, because a greater quantity of these materials makes it longer and more difficult to obtain clean surfaces. Sand, loose mill scale, and corrosion products formed on the tube surfaces during construction and following the hydrostatic test are removed by blowdown during the cleaning process.

The chemicals used for a detergent flush are nothing more than a concentrated detergent readily available from major chemical vendors. A wetting agent is usually added to enhance cleaning effectiveness. Detergent is added to the boiler water during or after filling of the unit. Once filled, the solution must be circulated to be effective and until analytical results show that the oils are neutralized and turbidity has stabilized, which will usually occur within a matter of hours.

A fired boilout of the boiler is no longer common. However, when such a boilout is used, the chemicals are typically a combination of sodium phosphate compounds. Organic detergents are added to boilout chemicals to improve their effectiveness. These materials must be used with care and according to the supplier's recommendation. Their indiscriminate use may lead to foaming and carryover of chemical to the superheater. The temperature stability of the organic detergent should be ascertained before use in a boiler.

Detergent Flush Procedure

Detergent flush of a boiler can be done at ambient temperature using a detergent solution of 0.6% by volume. If the fluid temperature is >150°F (65°C), then 0.3% by volume may be used. In all cases, circulation must be provided by natural circulation, boiler water circulating pumps, or external pumps, if no pump is provided on the boiler. The detergent can be blended with the boiler water during or after filling. The detergent solution is usually circulated for 6 to 8 hours, or until the oils are emulsified and the turbidity has reached equilibrium. Following circulation, the solution is drained and the boiler rinsed. The boiler water surfaces should be checked to ensure cleanliness. The unit is now ready for the next stage of commissioning.

Boilout Procedure

If a fired boilout is to be conducted, then the chemicals to be added to the boiler should be dissolved completely before introduction into the unit. In thermal (natural) circulation units, these chemicals are most suitably introduced into the boiler by blending them with water as the unit is being filled. This ensures a homogeneous concentration throughout the boiler. In positive (pumped) circulation boilers, the boilout chemicals may be pumped into the boiler without concern about proper mixing with the fill water; the boiler water circulation pumps will ensure proper mixing. Gradual heating of the boilout solution in the boiler is accomplished by the use of ignitors and warm-up burners. This ensures a more even heating of the boiler surfaces. Steam pressure is raised to increase the saturation temperature and, thereby, the thermal circulation of the boiler water. This promotes good mixing of chemicals in the boiler circuits. The boiler pressure is raised to about one-fifth of the normal operating pressure or 300 psig (20 bar), whichever is lower. A pressure of not less than 100 psig (7 bar) is recommended for lower-pressure industrial boilers. Excellent results have been obtained in boiling out at a pressure range of a few pounds to 100 psig with positive circulation boilers, in which the ability to circulate the water is not related to boiler pressure.

The quantity of oil and grease found in a boiler determines the duration of the boilout, with boilout periods of 8 to 24 hours being common. During the pressure-holding period, boiler water solids are purged by blowdown at about 4-hour intervals. A chemical balance is reestablished at the end of each purging of the boiler water if the chemical concentration decreases to below half of the initial value. At the completion of boilout, the boiler is cooled slowly, drained, flushed free of residues, and inspected for cleanliness. If the boilout was unsuccessful and oil and grease are still present, subsequent acid cleaning of the boiler will be ineffective. If an internal inspection still shows oil or grease in the drum, the boilout procedures should be repeated.

The removal of all oil and grease during the boilout is essential to a successful acid cleaning.

ACID CLEANING

Manufacturing processes no longer produce a significant amount of mill scale on tube surfaces. A new unit may therefore require acid cleaning only if rust-type scale or fouling of the internal tube surfaces occurs during transportation, storage, or erection of the pressure parts. Since there will also be future needs for acid cleaning to remove operational deposits, the discussion incorporates both initial acid cleaning (if required) and future acid cleanings. Removal of preoperational and operational deposits from the internal surfaces of steam generator tubing and other components is an important maintenance activity. Because mechanical cleaning is virtually impossible in boilers, the effective application of flushing and chemical cleaning solvents is a necessary tool of the power plant operator. The primary reasons for chemical cleaning of an operational boiler are to prevent tube failures and to improve unit availability. Deposit-related tube failures are caused by either overheating or under-deposit corrosion. Caustic corrosion and hydrogen damage, which occur only in the presence of deposits, can cause tube failures at temperatures well below the creep limit. In other words, corrosion can occur without having excessive metal temperatures.

Mill and Operational Scale

Improvements in manufacturing methods, on-site storage, and construction techniques have all contributed to reduced mill scale on the inner surfaces of pressure parts. These cleaner surfaces reduce the need for performing preliminary (during commissioning a new unit) mill scale removal. However, an abundance of caution leads many owners to include this step. The type of operational scale found in steam generators is related to the quality of the feedwater supplied to the boiler. In industrial boilers, the principal deposits are calcium and magnesium phosphates, calcium and magnesium silicate, complex silicates such as acmite or analcite, quartz, oxides of iron and copper, and organic matter. In utility boilers, the principal deposits are corrosion products and iron and copper oxides.

Chemical Cleaning Procedures

Only experienced personnel with up-to-date equipment and a detailed procedure to follow should perform chemical cleaning operations. The procedure should include:

1. The system layout with proper identification of all equipment to be used
2. A step-by-step description of the functions to be performed, specific for the solvent used for the cleaning
3. Precautions to be taken against possible inadvertent contamination of equipment not included in the cleaning system

The boiler operators, cleaning vendor, and boiler manufacturer must cooperate closely for a successful operation. Mutual prior approval of cleaning procedures and assignment of responsibility are desirable. Although respective responsibilities may vary from job to job, they can be generally classified as follows:

1. Normally, the cleaning vendor will supply all the chemicals and equipment necessary to deliver the solvent to the boiler at a controlled concentration and temperature. Vendor personnel will generally operate the equipment and supervise the overall cleaning; they will perform the necessary chemical analyses during solvent introduction and monitor the spent solvent to determine when the cleaning has been completed.
2. Plant personnel must operate all permanent plant equipment. They are responsible for determining metal temperatures and maintaining proper temperatures throughout the cleaning period. The owner normally supplies the necessary water and steam and sets up the solvent-delivery and waste-disposal systems. An important operator responsibility is ensuring that the solvent is not inadvertently introduced to any other part of the steam plant.
3. The boiler manufacturer has the responsibility to provide a boiler that can be cleaned safely and effectively. The boiler must be designed with an adequate filling, draining, and venting capacity. The boiler manufacturer should establish a standard cleaning procedure for the specific boiler that emphasizes the hazards involved and the limitations on the use of specific components. The manufacturer should be informed of any unusual use of boiler components and be ready to review any cleaning procedures that involve unusual steps or solvents.

The precautions relative to acid cleaning are common to all solvents currently used in practice. The metal temperature of the boiler is raised either by heating water using auxiliary burners or by circulating water, which has been increased in temperature by the addition of live steam. To prevent destruction of any inhibitor from the localized application of heat, the addition of heat by the use of burners is prohibited when the boiler is filled with acid cleaning solvents. The boiler water and solvent temperatures are raised to approximately 150 to 180°F (65 to 82°C).

SELECTION OF CLEANING SOLVENTS. Solvents are selected for their ability to remove boiler deposits. In primary use today are organic acids and alkaline solvents, which are particularly useful in situations in which circumstances prohibit the use of hydrochloric acid. Some of the solvents that have been developed, extensively evaluated, and used in boiler cleanings are: (1) ammoniated citric acid (ammonium citrate), (2) formic and hydroxyacetic (glycolic) acids, (3) ammonium EDTA, and (4) sodium EDTA. In general, the criteria used to select solvents include:

1. *Materials of Construction.* The inhibited solvent must be compatible with the tube material. For example, hydrochloric acid cannot be used to clean superheaters and reheaters because of the possibility of stress corrosion cracking of stainless steel materials.
2. *Deposit Compositions.* Deposit compositions could include iron oxide, copper, zinc, nickel, aluminum, silica, as well as solids from condenser cooling water. Large amounts of silica in the deposit present problems. Ammonium bifluoride is one additional chemical (in conjunction with the solvent) used to remove silica-based materials. Copper complexors must be used with hydrochloric acid to avoid copper plating during the cleaning if small amounts of copper are present. If there is a large amount of copper in the deposit (greater than 10% by weight), a multi-step procedure will be necessary. Ammonium bromate has been shown to be effective in removing deposits with significant amounts of copper.
3. *Geometries.* Organic solvents are effective under dynamic conditions, usually when velocities are in the range of 0.5 to 1 ft/sec (0.15–0.3 m/sec). Hydrochloric acid is effective in a stagnant condition and can dissolve a variety of compounds and oxide scales so that it is still a primary solvent where circulation of the solvent is not available or practical. Complex circuits, found in some superheaters and reheaters, require special attention to ensure removal of all air pockets and positive flow in all circuits.
4. *Methods of Disposal.* Environmental regulations can greatly affect disposal. The costs and methods of disposing cleaning wastes have a strong influence in the selection of a solvent. Tube samples should be taken and given to a chemical cleaning vendor to allow determination of the best solvent and cleaning procedure. The thickness, porosity, texture, and composition of the deposit all may affect individual solvent effectiveness, and normal cleaning procedures may have to be modified. It is also a good practice to remove additional tube samples after the cleaning to verify that the cleaning was successful.

DETERMINING THE NEED FOR CHEMICAL CLEANING. Utility boilers should be cleaned approximately every 3 to 5 years. The empirical relationship given in *Table 10-1* correlates the amount of

TABLE 10-1 | RELATIONSHIP OF ANALYZED DEPOSIT QUANTITY TO UNIT CLEANLINESS

Boiler Type	Internal Deposit Quantity Limits, mg/cm²*		
	Clean Surfaces	Moderately Dirty Surfaces	Very Dirty Surfaces
Supercritical units	<15	15–25	>25
Subcritical units	<15 (≥1,800 psig)	15–40	>40

*All values are as measured on the furnace side of tube samples and include soft and hard deposits.
Note: For all practical purposes. 1 mg/cm^2 = ~1 g/ft^2.

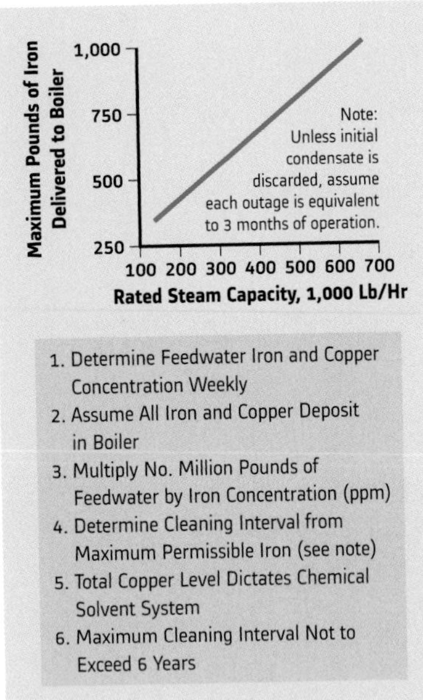

Maximum Pounds of Iron Delivered to Boiler
1,000
750
500
250
Note: Unless initial condensate is discarded, assume each outage is equivalent to 3 months of operation.
100 200 300 400 500 600 700
Rated Steam Capacity, 1,000 Lb/Hr
1. Determine Feedwater Iron and Copper Concentration Weekly
2. Assume All Iron and Copper Deposit in Boiler
3. Multiply No. Million Pounds of Feedwater by Iron Concentration (ppm)
4. Determine Cleaning Interval from Maximum Permissible Iron (see note)
5. Total Copper Level Dictates Chemical Solvent System
6. Maximum Cleaning Interval Not to Exceed 6 Years

Figure 10-4 | Operational chemical cleaning guide for industrial-type boilers (based on demineralized or evaporated make-up water)

deposit on a tube with the cleanliness of the boiler. Tube samples should be taken at yearly intervals from the high-heat-flux areas of the boiler (for example, several feet above the windbox) or other areas that have, in the past, been prone to accumulating deposits. The information obtained from inspecting the tube samples, in conjunction with operational factors, is used to decide the need for cleaning. These factors include the number of start-ups, the number of periods with condenser leakage, any chemistry deviations, and the length of outages.

Chemical cleaning of industrial boilers should also be performed on a periodic basis. The primary purpose for cleaning these units is to prevent buildup of deposits to the point at which overheating (or corrosion) may occur. In cases in which deposits consist of hardness salts, it is imperative to periodically examine tube samples from the unit to establish the need to clean. In units where iron oxide and copper are the main impurities in the feedwater, the information in *Figure 10-4* can be used as a guide in determining the need to clean. However, good practice would still dictate periodic examination of tube samples to confirm the analytical evaluation.

ACID CLEANING PROCEDURE. In thermal (natural) circulation boilers, no effective circulation can be obtained at the low solvent temperature of 150 to 170°F (65 to 77°C). Therefore, the distribution of acid strength and temperature is obtained by blending concentrated inhibited hydrochloric acid and hot water as the solution is injected into the boiler. Superheaters are flooded with condensate prior to the addition of acid to prevent the spillage of the solvent to this section. Thermal circulation boilers are generally cleaned by this soaking process. Samples are taken periodically to check the degree of reaction in the boiler. Boilers are soaked for 4 to 6 hours. The acid is drained by pressurizing with nitrogen. This step is taken to prevent the oxidation of the cleaned surfaces during this time. Water is used to displace nitrogen in rinsing the metal surfaces of the acid. The rinse water is subsequently displaced with nitrogen. Two rinses are usually sufficient to attain a pH between 5 and 6. The boiler is then filled with water containing a strong alkali (trisodium phosphate, soda ash, etc.) at a 1.0% solution. The water quantity is adjusted to the operating level, and the temperature is raised to correspond to a pressure of about 100 psig (6.9 bar). About 2 hours are required to effect neutralization of the acid and passivation of the metal. The boiler is drained and inspected at the conclusion of the wash period.

Controlled Circulation® and once-through boilers can be cleaned efficiently because the circulation pumps can be used to equalize acid temperatures and concentrations throughout the boiler. The acid is circulated intermittently with one pump during the cleaning, which normally requires 4 to 6 hours. Organic-type acids are frequently used to clean once-through boilers. At the conclusion of such a cleaning, the boiler is rinsed with water. When the system has then been purged of acid, condensate containing ammonia is circulated to effect neutralization.

Because of the close proximity of the superheater to the drum and the potential of corrosion from the cleaning solvents, particularly on the austenitic alloys, avoiding contamination of the superheater is important. If the superheater is known or suspected to be contaminated, the cleaning should be temporarily halted and the superheater flushed to remove the contaminants. The boiler should never be fired with possible contaminants in the superheater. For precautions necessary to avoid superheater contamination see below.

AVOIDING SUPERHEATER CONTAMINATION. The following steps should be taken to avoid superheater contamination:

1. The entire cleaning piping layout should be examined to identify all possible areas where solutions from the boiler could enter the superheater or reheater. Such connections should be eliminated so that contamination of the superheater does not occur. Possible leaking valves and pressure levels that might result in backflow must be avoided.
2. Control and monitoring of drum level is of paramount importance.
3. Water used to fill or "backflush" the superheater should be demineralized or of condensate quality.
4. Before starting the pre-boiler cleaning operation, the possibility should be considered that pre-boiler (feedwater train) cleaning solutions might "hide out" in lines, manifolds, or tanks, to be used, in, or interconnected to, water fill lines.
5. Suspicion of contamination warrants a careful assessment of water (or condensate) quality at appropriate locations in the superheater (e.g., locations nearest point of suspected entry). If evidence of contamination exists, firing should be discontinued until a judgment can be made as to the seriousness of the contamination. If doubt exists, the prudent course of action is to flush (condensate quality) the superheater and/or reheater with water.

SUPERHEATER/REHEATER CLEANING AND FLUSHING

Pre-operational solvent or detergent cleaning of the superheater and reheater is not required. The need to eliminate deposit-forming materials is related primarily to their effect on the corrosion problems common in waterwalls. There is little evidence that the presence of some initial mill scale has contributed to failures in superheaters and reheaters, or difficulties in turbines. Particulate matter and construction debris constitute the major portion of the foreign material present in any superheater or reheater at this point in its life. Because solvents do not efficiently dissolve most particulates, this method of cleaning is not considered completely satisfactory for placing a superheater and reheater in good condition for operation. Steam blowing has proven effective in removing particulate matter, debris, and loose oxide; therefore, it is recommended for any pre-operational cleaning of superheaters and reheaters, regardless of other procedures used.

The need to clean a superheater or reheater at some point in its operating life by using well-engineered programs containing solvent techniques or water flushing cannot be overlooked. Because

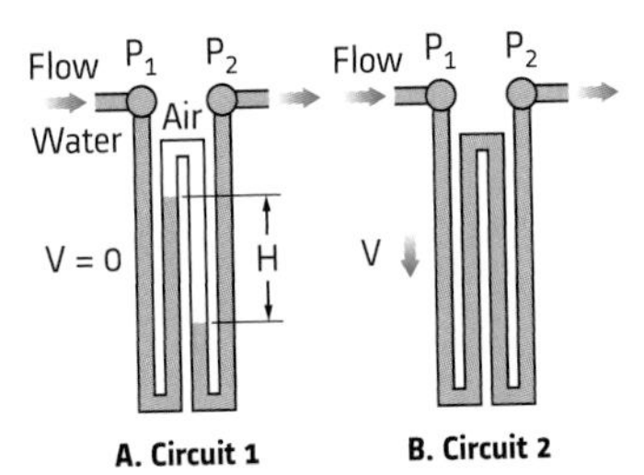

Figure 10-5 | Typical schematic of a non-drainable, non-ventable, superheater section where air blockage will occur. (A) The air-blocked circuit(s) remain stagnant because the unsupported water column H produces a pressure equal and opposite to the pressure drop between headers P_1 and P_2. (B) Air blockage is eliminated only when the flush rate is such that the pressure drop between the inlet and outlet headers because of flow exceeds the height of unsupported water column H.

of the geometry, superheater and reheater cleaning requires special attention. Frequently, these sections contain non-drainable, non-ventable sections that are difficult to clean unless the operator has a clear understanding of flow mechanics. In cleaning superheater or reheater surfaces it is necessary to ensure that there is positive flow through all of the parallel circuits. This is required for: (1) effective cleaning and (2) assurance that the solvent can be completely displaced at completion. This requirement applies even when simple water washing is used to remove soluble salts. Positive flow can be ensured with a relatively low flow of water if the entire section can be initially filled. When a portion of the loop is non-ventable, the main concern is trapped air. Air blockage, which develops in non-ventable areas, will prevent effective cleaning and make it impossible to completely flush the tubing, unless special procedures are used to ensure complete filling. *Figure 10-5* illustrates the filling problem. A well-engineered fill–flush program for the individual unit undergoing the cleaning and the confirmation of effective filling prior to the injection of cleaning solvent are required to obtain the desired cleaning results and prevent damage.

POST-ACID CLEANING ACTIVITIES

Before the main steam lines are blown, the steam and lower drums should be inspected and flushed of any loose sediment. The internals to the gage glass should be flushed and then blown out. Accessible headers should be inspected and flushed with clear water. If the primary and secondary separators were not placed in the drum, they are installed. On Controlled Circulation® units, each orifice and screen is installed in the lower drum. Each orifice is then checked with a go/no-go gage. Any header hand-hole caps, which were removed or not previously welded, are welded in place. Acid cleaning connections are removed or valved off, and temporary piping is removed. The chemical feed and continuous blowdown piping should be flushed and blown out. When all work is completed in the upper and lower drums, they must be inspected to ensure that no foreign material remains. New gaskets should be installed on all drum manholes before closing. Next, the boiler circulating pumps are prepared for operation as called for in the manufacturer's instructions.

STEAM-LINE BLOWING

Blowing the main steam lines and the reheat-steam lines before starting up a new unit is done to remove any foreign material remaining in the superheater, reheater, and steam piping after erection is completed. Considerable damage can result if such material enters the turbine during initial operation. On older units, steam-line blowing should be considered following major, pressure-part repairs, which introduce the possibility of foreign material in the system.

Responsibility

Because prevention of damage to the steam turbine is the prime concern, the responsibility for determining the effectiveness of the steam-line blowing operation rests with the turbine manufacturer's representative. During this process, the unit should be operated in accordance with recommended procedures, with all control systems and protective interlocks functioning. The design, fabrication, and installation of any temporary piping system for the purpose of steam-line blowing, as well as protection against overpressure or overtemperature, require careful attention by qualified engineers.

General

Ideally, to obtain optimal cleaning, the flow conditions in the system during steam-line blowing should equal those during normal operation at maximum load. Because it is impossible to exactly duplicate these conditions when blowing through the piping to atmosphere, it is desirable to produce equivalent conditions by using lower-pressure steam with a flow rate such that the product of steam flow times velocity will equal that under normal, full-load conditions. The determination of the total obtainable flow quantity must be based on flow resistances in the entire system, including the temporary piping. Customarily, the designer of the blowing system makes this determination. Most high-pressure units obtain satisfactory results with a blowing pressure in the 600 to 800 psig (41 to 55 bar) range. The actual steam blow is executed in three phases: main steam, cold reheat, and hot reheat.

To prevent foreign material from being transported from one section and deposited in the next, it is important that the system be blown by blowing each section separately. Particular care must be taken when blowing the reheater. If the reheater were to be blown immediately in series with the superheater, material too large to pass through the reheater tubes would remain lodged in the reheater inlet header and cause blockage of reheater tubes, with resulting overheating and failure of reheater tubing when the unit goes into operation. For this reason, it is recommended that the temporary piping be arranged such that the main steam lines can be blown to atmosphere first. Similarly, the cold-reheat lines should be blown to atmosphere before they are connected to the reheater inlet header. Only after these precautionary measures have been taken should steam be admitted to the reheater for blowing through the hot reheat lines.

The temporary piping is often equipped with shutoff valves, which are used as blowing valves. With this arrangement, the superheater and the upstream portion of the temporary piping are maintained at drum pressure at all times when not actually blowing. If the unit is equipped with main-steam stop valves, these may be used as blowoff valves if the valve design permits this type of service. When more than one steam line is provided in any section, consideration should be given to arranging the temporary piping so that each line may be blown separately. In such situations, the piping system should be inspected to ensure that flow unbalances and expansion stresses at the connections do not become a problem. Impact specimens, installed in the blowoff piping during the final blows, give an indication of the cleanliness of the section. Polished, square bar stock suitably mounted and supported has been used effectively for this purpose. The degree of pitting of the specimen surface following a blow determines the end point of the blowing cycle for the particular section.

Precautions During Steam-Line Blowing

1. The process of steam-line blowing imposes abnormal and severe conditions on the steam generator and steam piping. Large, rapid temperature changes occur during each blowing cycle. This cycling of temperature is far more severe than is incurred in normal operation. Thermal stresses may be excessive in the heavy-wall portions of the system, such as drums, headers, and piping. It is prudent to consider this fact when performing the blowing procedure and to limit the number of blowing cycles ("blows") to the minimum needed to clean the system.
2. Firing of all main fuel must be discontinued during all blows. It is permissible to keep ignitors and/or warm-up guns in service during the blows in order to speed up reestablishment of the desired blowing pressure after a blow is completed. On Controlled Circulation® boilers, circulating pump(s) must be kept in service during the entire blowing process. If a boiler circulating pump loses suction because of low drum-water level, it must be shut down. If all pumps are stopped because of loss of suction, the blow must be terminated immediately.
3. Since the temporary piping for steam-line blowing may be designed for lower pressure than the steam generator, care must be used to prevent overpressuring this piping during the entire steam-line blowing operation. The pressure in the temporary piping should be monitored continuously and the operators should be alert to prevent overpressure. It is recommended that a means for overpressure protection be provided in the temporary piping, such as safety valves set at the design pressure of the temporary piping.
4. It is difficult to avoid carryover from the steam drum to the superheater during the steam-line blowing operation. Therefore, to avoid deposits of solid materials in the superheater, boiler water should not be treated with non-volatile chemicals during this process.

Blowing the Main Steam Line—Phase I

The actual blow is started when the unit reaches the specified blowing pressure, usually 600 to 800 psig (41 to 55 bar). However, the first blow is always at reduced pressure to check out the temporary piping system and its supports and anchors. All main fuel firing is discontinued. The temporary valve, or main steam valve, is opened fully to blow through the superheater, the main steam piping, and the temporary blowoff piping to waste. When the drum pressure drops to about 200 psig (14 bar), the blowoff valve is closed. The firing rate is increased and the cycle repeated as often as necessary until cleaning is satisfactory, as indicated by inspection of the impact specimen.

Blowing the Cold Reheat Line—Phase II

The blowoff piping is now modified with a temporary connection from the main steam piping around the high-pressure turbine to the inlet of the cold reheat piping. Temporary blowoff piping is installed at the reheater inlet. Blowing is executed in the same manner as for the main steam line, but now the blow is through the superheater, main steam line, cold reheat line, and temporary blowoff piping to waste. Again, the first blow is at reduced pressure, with subsequent blows from 600 to 800 psig (41 to 55 bar) down to 200 psig (14 bar) drum pressure. This cycle is also repeated until the impact specimens are satisfactory.

Blowing the Hot Reheat Lines—Phase III

The temporary blowoff line at the outlet of the cold reheat piping is removed, and the cold reheat piping is permanently connected to the reheater. A temporary blowoff connection is installed at the hot reheat piping as close to the turbine as possible and piped to waste. The same blowing procedure is used as in phases I and II. When the specimen results are satisfactory, the steam blows can be considered successful.

Operating Procedures

The unit is started in the normal manner, following the cold start-up procedures. All normal recommendations and limitations with respect to pumps, fuel-firing equipment, ash-handling equipment, drains, and vents should be followed, as if the unit were being started for synchronizing the steam turbine. Before starting the first blow in each section, the economizer recirculating line valves should be closed. Because the steam blowing operation is the first occasion that the unit is fired at any significant rate, the start-up, as well as the steam line blowing, must be conducted with great care. The unit must be brought up much more slowly than during subsequent normal start-ups so that all equipment can be checked and expansion movements monitored closely. When the unit is fired, the furnace exit gas temperature limitation must not be exceeded.

During the blows, the drum-water level will be subject to extreme fluctuations. As the temporary blowoff valve is opened, the drum-water level will rise rapidly and may disappear from sight in the gage glass. As the blow progresses, the drum-water level will reappear and may drop out of sight. Consequently, it is important to establish the drum-water level at or slightly above normal operating level before the start of each blow. Feedwater flow must be established as soon as the water level drops back in sight to prevent an excessively low water level with resulting suction loss of the boiler circulating pumps. After the procedure is completed, the temporary piping is removed and final piping connections are made. The unit is now ready for the next commissioning function, setting the safety valves.

SAFETY-VALVE SETTING. All safety valves installed on boilers or other pressure vessels should be test-operated before the boiler or vessel is placed in service. This test should involve a check of the proper functioning of the valves as to correct opening pressure, correct blowdown, proper mechanical operation without chatter, and clean closure without leakage.

In checking opening pressure and blowdown, a calibrated pressure gage must be used. The location of its connection on the vessel, header, or other component must be such that the pressure it shows is a true indication of the pressure existing at the safety-valve inlet, both when it opens and when it closes. When valves are located on headers or steam lines through which steam is flowing, the test pressure gage should be connected near the valve to eliminate any effect of pressure drop resulting from the flow. In some cases the flow of steam being relieved through the valve itself could produce a significant pressure drop.

In order to avoid damage to the valves, maximum attention must be given to debris removal before testing and setting safety valves.

For high-pressure boilers (above approximately 1200 psig (83 bar) operating pressure) a manufacturer's representative should initially test and adjust safety valves. Certain local codes require that only licensed people may make adjustments on safety valves, so check with the insurance carrier before making any adjustments. The setting, or adjustment, of safety valves should be done by a competent person, familiar with their construction, operation, and maintenance. A written report should be made of all testing and adjustment, including the opening pressure, closing pressure, and/or blowdown and an indication of correct functioning of the valves as they are left. In addition, the report should include the name and title of the responsible plant observer and the name and title of any insurance inspector, or state or local boiler inspector, who witnesses the test and adjustment. The name of the valve vendor's representative making adjustments, if any, should also be included, as well as the nameplate data (serial number, set pressure, blowdown, and valve location) of each valve on the unit. The operating company should retain the report as a permanent part of their records.

Before testing safety valves for the first time on new units, the steam lines will have been blown to eliminate as much of the foreign material as possible from the superheater, reheater, and the connecting piping to prevent damage to the safety valves. Damage to the valve seating surfaces from grit blasting by mill scale, weld beads, and other such dirt is common during initial testing. Adequate steam blowing prior to popping valves will minimize damage. Valves mounted on the dead end of headers are particularly prone to this damage. Inspection and manual cleaning of the header by vacuum hose and/or magnets through the valve nozzle, with top works removed, is sometimes necessary. With maximum attention given to removing debris before initial popping of the valve, better success will be obtained with initial valve setting.

Leakage of safety valves in operation usually results from one or more of the following:

1. Seating-surface damage
2. Externally imposed stresses on the valve body, which distort the seating surfaces
3. Operation at pressure too close to the set pressure of the valve; the valve manufacturers recommend a minimum difference between popping pressure and operating pressure of 5% of the popping pressure. With less than a 5% difference on a continuous basis, problems with leakage and resulting frequent valve maintenance may be expected.

Safety of personnel and prevention of damage to the equipment should be the prime concerns when testing and adjusting safety valves. Tremendous forces are involved when these valves operate. All precautions necessary to contain these forces and prevent accidents must be taken. For the initial popping of each valve, all personnel should be kept at a safe distance. A rope should be attached to the manual lifting gear so that any uncontrollable valve chatter can be prevented from doing serious damage. Before starting the actual setting, refer to the latest section of the ASME Boiler and Pressure Vessel Code applicable to safety valves.

Procedures Prior to Safety-Valve Setting

Before firing the unit for setting the valves, check that:

1. Hydrostatic test plugs have been removed from the safety valves. If a problem of scheduling a valve vendor's representative for removal of hydrostatic test plugs is involved, the plug from one valve must be removed prior to the first fire. All plugs must be removed before the unit is brought up to full pressure for the first time.
2. There is no physical interference that would prevent functioning of the safety valves. Expansion of the unit should be considered in this check.
3. The exhaust stacks from the valves are firmly supported and restrained and that no physical interference that will put external stresses on the valves exists between exhaust stacks and the valves in the cold position, hot position, or in between.
4. The exhaust elbow attached to the valve body is not of excessive length in the horizontal run (maximum recommended, 24 inches [61 cm]) that may result in abnormal stresses being put on the valve body due to the reaction force when the valve is blowing.
5. The drain piping from the valve body and drip pans, elbow, etc., is installed and discharges into a location that will prevent injury to personnel when the valve is blowing.
6. If flexible hoses are used between the exhaust elbow and exhaust stack, they should be of sufficient length and installed so that they do not become "solid" in any position of the valve.
7. All components of the safety valves, such as manual lifting gear and adjusting ring pins, are in place and secure.

Hydraulic Jack Method for Safety-Valve Setting

The use of a hydraulic jack has made setting safety valves easier. These jacks can be bought or rented from the valve manufacturers. This method was developed originally for setting supercritical pressure valves so that the lift could be limited to reduce damage to the seating surfaces. The hydraulic jack system contains a pump, hydraulic piston, yoke, turnbuckle, and pressure gage. The hydraulic piston overcomes some of the safety-valve spring force so that the valve may be set at lower steam pressures. This method has also been used widely on reheater safety valves as well as with high-pressure valves (drum and superheater) on drum-type boilers. It must be remembered that this method tests only the popping pressure, not blowdown or the valve action itself. The disadvantages of not testing actual blowdown and valve operation are outlined below.

Problems Avoided by Blowdown Testing

1. Insufficient blowdown can result in chatter, which can produce extensive damage to the seating surfaces and other valve parts.
2. Excessive blowdown can result in operating problems in getting a valve to close above the normal operating pressure once it pops. The ASME Boiler Code requires that the low set drum valve have no more than 4% blowdown and that other drum valves have longer blowdowns but none lower than 96% of the set pressure of the lowest set drum valve.
3. The valve could fail to reach full lift because of some mechanical problem. This would not be known and, hence, its capacity might be restricted when it was really needed.
4. The valve could hang open because of a mechanical problem and bleed the pressure completely from the boiler during operation.
5. The exhaust stack arrangement would not be subjected to a full flow test before the unit goes on the line. Serious problems and possible damage can result if sizing is insufficient or the supports are not adequate.

In order to provide early detection of abnormal conditions before serious damage occurs, a checklist should be developed to assist in a periodic walkdown of the unit during operation.

Safety-valve manufacturers indicate that they check each valve with steam for blowdown. A cold setting of the blowdown rings can be made extremely close, if the instruction manual is followed closely. Nevertheless, it is usually recommended that the hydraulic jack method be used for supercritical or reheater applications.

After the unit has been chemically cleaned, steam lines blown, and safety valves set, the boiler is ready for supplying steam to the steam turbine. One of the necessities of effective operation is the periodic "walkdown" of a steam generator during operation. This requires that the operator keep his or her eyes and ears open for unusual conditions and report any findings. Potential damage to equipment can be avoided if abnormal conditions are detected in time. The operations department should develop a checklist specific to the station.

OPERATION OF FLUIDIZED BED BOILERS

Many operational aspects of fluidized bed steam generators are identical to those of other solid-fuel-fired units. This description, therefore, will be limited to the major differences in operation between fluid bed units and other solid-fuel boilers.

START-UP

Cold start-up times are generally 8 to 12 hours to full load. In a circulating fluid bed (CFB) boiler, this is because of the refractory lining that is integral to several components, such as the high temperature, refractory lined cyclones. The rate of refractory temperature change must be limited to no more than 250°F (121°C) per hour to avoid cracking and spalling from thermal shock. In a bubbling fluid bed (BFB) unit, start-up times are determined either by the refractory lining considerations or by the time needed to heat the bed material, which, in a multi-zone bed, requires the transfer of heat from a start-up zone to adjacent zones. Note that the boiler will not usually delay plant start-up on a cold start, because steam flow is available for turbine warming relatively quickly, and most turbines require many hours of thermal soaking.

Before start-up, if the bed had been drained for maintenance or inspection, a new charge of bed material is needed. This is usually sand, spent bed material (from the ash-disposal silo or a separate bed material silo), limestone, or a mixture of these. Fluidizing airflow is started and the bed is preheated—using overbed burners, underbed burners, or both—to the temperature required for fuel admission. Bed temperature is the principal permissive for main fuel firing. With sufficient bed temperature, burners or ignitors are not required to light off incoming solid, liquid, or gaseous fuels, as the heat of the bed will ensure fuel ignition.

NORMAL OPERATION

In normal operation, a fluidized bed boiler behaves similarly to other solid-fuel-fired boilers. Firing rate is a function of outlet steam pressure. Load swings will result in changes in pressure and, hence, in rates of fuel and air flows. In a CFB, combustor temperature is regulated by varying excess air, the primary air to secondary air ratio, total bed inventory, and (with a separate fluid bed heat exchanger) solids flow to the fluid bed heat exchanger (FBHE). The combustor inventory is set by the rate of bottom ash flow. Superheat and reheat outlet steam temperatures are controlled by desuperheater spray and solids flow to the superheat or reheat FBHE, if one is so provided. In a BFB, bed temperature control is accomplished by a change in excess air, bed level, and recycle rate. As in a CFB, bottom ash flow determines the bed inventory. Superheat and reheat steam temperatures are controlled by spray desuperheating and by biasing of gas dampers that direct gas flow to the reheat side of a split back pass, respectively.

In general, heat distribution is facilitated in a fluidized bed steam generator because the combustor temperature (equivalent to the furnace temperatures of stoker or pulverized coal [PC]-fired units) can be more easily regulated. Operation is usually very stable because of the large thermal flywheel effect of the bed mass. Thus, wider variations in fuel quality can be tolerated. The bed prevents gas-side transients occasioned by the loss or interruption of fuel flow, thereby improving boiler safety. There is no concern about furnace wall slagging, because bed temperatures are held below the ash softening temperatures to ensure fluidization and to optimize sorbent utilization. The importance of maintaining proper fuel sizing cannot be overemphasized. Fuel size strongly influences bed particle size, which in turn, affects most aspects of fluid bed boiler performance. The required fuel sizing and its influence on both design and performance of a fluid bed boiler are discussed in Chapter 3.

SHUTDOWN/RESTART

The shutdown procedure will depend on whether a hot restart is anticipated. If a hot restart is planned, the fuel and air are stopped. Bed temperature can remain above the firing permissive level for several hours, such that no purge is required on restarting. On a hot restart, the unit can be brought back to full load within a few hours, depending on the bed temperature level. If no hot restart is planned, the fuel and air flows are gradually reduced, so that the rate of refractory temperature change must be limited to no more than 250°F (121°C) per hour.

PLANT MAIN FUEL TRIP (MFT)

Stored heat in the bed material will continue to generate steam long after fuel flow stops. In a CFB, stored heat in the cyclone refractory system contributes to steam generation. Precautions must be taken to prevent damage to backpass, steam-cooled surfaces from this heat source. The drum level should be maintained by a slow feed of water to the drum following an MFT. If cyclone cooling is not possible in any other way, a small steam flow can be induced through the backpass by opening a steam vent to cool the backpass tubing. Steam-cooled surfaces in the combustor and/or FBHE are protected from the loss of steam flow in accordance with the manufacturer's instructions, which may call for depressurization or a small, cooling steam flow by means of a steam vent or turbine bypass.

LOSS OF POWER

During a power loss, feedwater flow to the boiler stops. As a result, stored heat can evaporate significant amounts of the water inventory. Whether this will damage the boiler depends on the specific design. The conservative approach is to provide an emergency feedwater pump, which allows water to be fed to the boiler during a power interruption.

TUBE RUPTURE

When limestone is used as the sulfur sorbent, the heated bed material will contain significant amounts of calcined, dehydrated calcium oxide. If this lime comes in contact with sufficient water, such as from a tube leak, it will harden when allowed to dry, and will make cleanup and repair difficult. The leaking water or steam may also damage relatively sensitive refractory linings. Quick action by the operators can minimize the duration of the outage and reduce the extent of cleanup. When a tube leak is detected, it is important to maintain fluidization and to drain the bed material as soon as possible. Acoustic steam leak detectors are an asset for the timely detection of tube leaks.

PROBLEMS IN OPERATION

In spite of adherence to the general procedures and observance of the cautions presented in this chapter, operational problems can still occur. Tubes may rupture for a variety of reasons. The size and location of the break will determine what action is necessary. On a drum-type unit, the best method for shutting down will be dictated by the ability to maintain normal water level in the boiler and the need for the boiler in service. If the water level can be maintained, the unit can be kept in service until after a peak, or service may be stretched to a weekend outage. There is, however, the danger of high-pressure water from a break cutting other tubes. If the rupture can be observed visually and it is ascertained that it is blowing out into the furnace

and not damaging other tubes, the unit may be able to operate for a long time provided that sufficient treated make-up water is available.

Unlike a waterwall tubing leak, a leak in a superheater, reheater, or economizer element requires greater attention. Because of the physical arrangement of such surfaces, steam cutting of adjacent tubes can result, making a major repair job out of what might have been a simple and short one. If left unattended, economizer ruptures can lead to plugging of the economizer and air heater because the water mixing with the fly ash can set, similar to concrete.

A leak in a waterwall of a super-critical unit can result in rapid and extensive damage, not only to the leaking tube, but also to nearby tubes. Thermocouples are installed on individual outlet tubes and representative inlet tubes to alert the operator to such leaks. Any decision to operate a once-through unit with a known waterwall tube leak must be made with the full knowledge of the serious damage that may be incurred.

FURNACE EXPLOSIONS

Furnace explosions usually occur during start-up, shutdown, or low-load operation. Generally, they result from the accumulation of unburned fuel in the furnace because of incomplete combustion, loss of ignition, or fuel-valve leakage. An explosion occurs when the proportion of unburned fuel and air is in the explosive range and some heat source increases the temperature of the mixture to the ignition point. Unburned fuel, which causes such fires, can accumulate in the furnace in several ways:

- at leaky fuel-inlet valves on idle wind box compartments
- when the fire is extinguished and the fuel is not shut off promptly
- when the fuel does not burn as rapidly as it enters the furnace
- if difficulty occurs in establishing ignition

Explosion Prevention

Because most explosions occur during periods of low fuel input, maintaining a minimum of 30% of full-load airflow is important to ensure an air-rich mixture in the furnace and to sweep out any accumulation of unburned fuel. Other preventive measures include:

- Ensuring that all liquid or gaseous fuel valves are tightly shut on idle fuel compartments
- Watching the fires closely at low loads and shutting off all fuel immediately if proper combustion is not maintained. Most modern units have flame scanners to trip the unit automatically when poor ignition occurs. The scanners must be properly maintained. They should never be removed from the safety system or their outputs defeated
- Always using the required ignition energy source when placing any pulverizer in service
- Keeping adjacent pulverizers in service during low-load operation
- Regularly checking the proper functioning of any furnace safeguard system
- Never defeating any portion of a safeguard or interlock system
- Purging the furnace before shutting off the fans on a unit trip
- Emptying the pulverizers of all coal before bottling up the unit

Good housekeeping helps prevent external fires. Oil spills are an especially dangerous problem and should be cleaned up immediately.

UNINTENTIONAL FIRES EXTERNAL TO THE FURNACE

One of the most destructive events in steam generator operation is the uncontrolled ignition of fuel in an area external to the furnace. Such fires have taken place in air heaters, ductwork, wind boxes, precipitators, hoppers, and fans. In the immediate vicinity of the boiler, such fires have occurred when oil is being burned. Generally, fires in air heaters, back-end ductwork, precipitators, and induced draft fans take place when a unit is being brought up to load after a cold start-up. With inadequate fuel oil atomization, poor mixing of the oil with the combustion air, or both, unburned oil distillates will carry to the back of the unit and deposit on the relatively cold back-end surfaces. Later, when the load is raised, these deposits will volatilize as the temperature increases and can ignite. Once such a fire starts, extinguishing it is difficult. The metal baskets in an air heater, for example, will continue to burn even after the oil is consumed. The only method of putting out such a metal fire is to flood it with as much water as possible. It is generally recommended that air-atomized light oil or steam-atomized heavy oil be used for light offs of a cold unit. If mechanical atomization of oil is the only means available, special observation of the furnace outlet is necessary when starting with a cold furnace. One method of detecting the carryover of distillates involves air-cooled probes at the furnace outlet, which can be periodically extracted and examined. Anytime there is doubt as to the quality of an oil fire during a cold light off, the air heater, and other back-end surfaces, should be examined. If oily deposits are found, all firing should cease until the surfaces can be thoroughly cleaned with a hot detergent solution. Uncontrolled ignition occurring around the wind box area, external to the unit, usually results from oil spills when the oil guns are removed or when valves or gaskets are permitted to leak. Therefore, oil spills should be cleaned and leaky oil valves or gaskets should be corrected immediately. Any plant that tolerates the accumulation of spilled oil around the burner area is in danger of a serious destructive fire.

COAL HANDLING IN POWER PLANTS

Improved coal storage and methods of loading bunkers can often result in substantial savings in power plant operations. Continuous production of steam requires a steady flow of coal from the bunkers. Interruption of the coal feed to the furnace not only causes a loss of production, but can also lead to furnace explosions. Perhaps the greatest factor impeding continuous coal flow is excessive moisture. Coals containing clays pack easily when moisture content increases. The packing can occur in bunkers, feeders, or pulverizers. In addition, foreign materials such as rocks, metal, slate, wood, and other debris in the coal can block or stall pulverizer or stoker feeders. Some plant operators learn to live with the problems associated with wet coal and foreign material by fighting stoppages inside the powerhouse with vibrators, manual sledge hammers, poke rods, sluice systems, air cannons, heaters, or coolers. These methods do not stop plugging, however; they only free them.

Other operators keep the problem out of the boiler room by limiting moisture pickup in the coal yard and removing all large debris before the coal arrives at the bunkers.

Coal usually arrives from the supplier reasonably dry and, if properly stored, will remain that way. If a small portion gets wet, it can be moved aside for drying and later use. On the other hand, to minimize fugitive dust, coal is sometimes wetted before shipment from the mine. Additional moisture pickup during transport can result from leaky barges or rain. Stations receiving coal with a substantial moisture increase from mine to plant should consult with the producer and the shipper to see if improvements are possible.

Guidelines on Coal Piling and Reclaiming

- Compact the coal. Loose coal picks up moisture and encourages fires in the coal pile
- Pile the coal for maximum runoff of rain. Piles should be rounded or pyramid-shaped, with the steepest slopes possible. Consider covering the coal pile if rain is a very frequent problem
- Keep the coal pile free of valleys and pockets. Water will collect in them and sink down into the coal
- Reclaim deep into the pile, not along wide areas of the top. When properly piled and compacted, only the top layers will be high in moisture. This top layer can be reclaimed during drier spells
- As coal is removed, rework the pile to fill in the reclaimed area and eliminate gulleys, pockets, and rivulets
- During reclaiming, avoid pushing the coal onto any water deposits or muddy coal in the area of the coal conveyor belt
- Minimize fine coal, as it absorbs water more readily than coarse coal. Wet, fine coal does not flow easily. It will stick to bunkers and feed pipes. Coarse particles will help to eliminate bunker plugging and keep the coal moving

Coal Yard Design and Management

Good coal yards should be carefully planned. Proper drainage is a must. The yard should be properly graded, and all rocks, wood, and metal removed. A base layer of coal should be spread, to a minimum depth of 2 feet. This base should never be reclaimed and should not be included in the stockpile records, even for emergency use. The coal yard should be fenced, or otherwise isolated, from material storage, scrap, or trash. Only coal, and the equipment needed to handle it, should be allowed in the area. Workers should be encouraged to look for foreign material in the yard and to remove it. The screens should not be depended on to remove all debris. Avoid crushing coal until it is ready to enter the bunkers. Wait until immediately before the boiler is ready to burn coal before filling the bunkers. There is a tendency in new plants to fill the bunkers as soon as the coal-handling system is ready. This is understandable, since start-up personnel want as much as possible of the equipment to be operational and ready. However, coal will gradually pack in the bunkers and will not flow easily when needed.

Also, coal stored in bunkers or silos for long periods can ignite and smolder. Finally, during initial operation, fill only those bunkers that feed the pulverizers required first.

In preparation for a scheduled long-term outage, all bunkers should be emptied, and should not be refilled until the unit is ready for restarting. If a unit has an unscheduled shutdown and it becomes apparent that it will be off-line for some time, serious consideration should be given to emptying the bunkers, especially if the moisture content of the coal is high. Temporary chutes to trucks can be provided in some plants. The coal can be returned to the stockpile. If major maintenance is to be done on a single pulverizer, its bunker should be run empty before being removed from service. It is important that the coal yard supervisor become familiar with the needs of the boiler operators, so that his or her responsibility is more than just filling the bunkers. It should include responsibility for the continuous feed of fuel to the pulverizers. In any case, the supervisor should be informed of all coal hang-ups.[5]

Operator training is key to obtaining maximum plant availability and optimum unit efficiency.

OPERATOR TRAINING

A well-trained operations crew leads to maximum plant availability and optimal unit efficiency. Such a crew is developed through a carefully designed training program, which should be a step-by-step learning process. First, there must be an understanding of the fundamentals and principles involved. The individual equipment components and subsystems that comprise the unit must be taught in detail. And, finally, overall generating unit operation must be discussed fully. To be effective, a program should be versatile. New operators, as well as more experienced personnel, should be able to benefit from it. Flexibility is important. A program that can be used individually or in classroom situations has a distinct advantage. Programs geared to specific equipment should be accurate and to the point.

THE SYSTEMS APPROACH

A well-planned, operator training program looks at energy supply as a system, not just as a network of hardware. Part of that system is the people who manage, operate, and repair the network of hardware and equipment. Many operating cost variables can be controlled by plant operating personnel throughout the useful life of the facility. Good operating techniques, for example, extend wear-part cycles. Fuel usage also depends on operating technique, as does effective preventive maintenance. The question of operating personnel quality is of great concern today, because of the increase in unit size, complexity, additional equipment, environmental consequences, and level of automation. The trend is for fewer personnel to be involved in the responsible operation of fossil-fuel power plants.

The elements necessary to establish a successful systems training program include prerequisite conditions, such as knowledge of the system—what it is, how it works, who uses it, and what it is for. This is followed by a needs analysis with regard to the specific requirements of the system and the student population; then the training program must be designed to meet these requirements. Systematic verification of the effectiveness of the training program is vital. Experience has taught that, if the above elements have been successfully applied, it is reasonable to expect student operating competence and a high level of student retention of new knowledge and skills. A prerequisite to a successful program is a cooperative understanding of the objectives and program goals. This is generally accomplished by giving presentations outlining the program goals and methods to station management personnel and officials of the production and maintenance unions. Experience has shown that these presentations have resulted in excellent dissemination of program information, a high degree of interest, and active participation and cooperation at all levels of plant personnel. The inclusion of union management has achieved the same resultant support and cooperation and helps to ensure cooperation and support for subsequent training activities.

THE NEEDS ANALYSIS

The analysis of training requirements is generally based on data gathered from questionnaires provided to all operating personnel and from a survey of the power station. The survey includes a review of plant configuration, technical documentation, operating procedures and directives, operator job requirements, and, where applicable, review of licensing requirements. These data are analyzed by educational psychologists and training specialists who then prepare a population description of the average student, identify job-knowledge requirements and performance objectives, and identify motivational factors to be considered in the design of training systems.

The availability of operators for training, with the exception of a new station starting up, represents a significant factor to be considered in the design of a training system. The complexities of current staffing levels, rotating shift schedules, and overtime opportunities complicate the arrangement of an effective training schedule. Performance measurement criteria applied to training program design are:

- Evaluate the effectiveness of instruction and course material
- Evaluate the level of each student's achievement and provide additional assistance, if required
- Review and reemphasize important areas of course material
- Establish procedures for scoring individual students to avoid possible union conflicts

THE ROLE OF THE POWER PLANT SIMULATOR

Training material, equipment, and facility requirements necessary to support the training program should be specified in the design of the program. Of great value to any operator training program is a power plant simulator designed to mimic a total operating plant. Simulators allow dynamic demonstrations of overall power plant systems operation: automatic combustion control system operation, turbine/generator control system operation, and feedwater and fuel control systems operation. Practice exercises can be provided through

The challenge of boiler operation comes from dynamics. Changes on the gas side happen relatively quickly. Changes on the steam/water side happen relatively slowly. The art of boiler operation is to properly time the manipulations so that their impacts will be coordinated.

TYPICAL OPERATOR WALKDOWN CHECKLIST

- Look for unusual traces of coal dust, oil, fly ash, or water.
- Look for leaks in valves and valve packing.
- Look for any unusual conditions, such as discoloration, hot spots on casing and ductwork, or vapor leaks.
- Open all inspection doors and note any slag accumulations.
- Listen for tube leaks in the furnace. (This is possible to do only on balanced draft units.)
- Check for unusual noises, overheating, and adequate lubrication of all motors and driven equipment.
- Look for leaks in gage glasses and water columns.
- Check that no soot blowers are stuck in the unit and that there are no leaks in the soot blower lines.
- On tilting tangential units, make sure that the tilt setting is the same on all corners.
- Check the secondary air damper settings to make sure that all dampers are the same on a given elevation.
- At the firing levels, check for coal, fuel oil, or gas leaks. See that warm-up guns are retracted. Note any fly ash leaks. Report any oil spills so that they can be cleaned up before a fire occurs.
- Check, with a hand touch, all vertical coal piping for possible plugging or overheating. A cold pipe on a mill in service is a good indication of plugging.
- Inspect the furnace just above the ash pit to make sure there is no bridging across bottom.
- Check the level of water in ash hopper and bottom seal trough.
- At the pulverizers:
  a. Check gear-case oil temperature, flow, and level.
  b. Check for excessive spillage or malfunction of pyrite system.
  c. Look for any indication of mill fires.
  d. Listen for unusual noises.
  e. Check for coal leaks.
- At the air heater:
  a. Check the air heater soot blower to make sure that it is not leaking when the control valve has closed.
  b. Check drive motor, support, and guide bearing lubrication and cooling water.
  c. Inspect the cleanliness of the air side through observation doors.
- At least once a week, a more extensive check should be done such as:
  a. Listen for badly leaking safety valves.
  b. Check the soot blower cycle by walking down the unit as each blower operates to make sure it is functioning correctly and the packing is tight. Make sure all blowers are blown during a cycle.
  c. Put all ignitors and retractable oil guns in service and check to make sure they are operating correctly.
  d. Start and stop any idle equipment to make sure it is ready if needed.

the insertion of selected malfunctions and load variations to improve operators' ability to diagnose abnormal conditions and initiate corrective action. The application of simulators to the training program is always in the context of specific power plant operating procedures and as a reinforcement of the training material being taught at the time.

OTHER SUPPORT MATERIALS

An audiovisual training program is also very effective. It combines sight and sound, which greatly increases retention. Such a program can be used throughout the life of the unit for retraining operators and initial training of replacement operators.

COMPLETENESS

The training program design is complete when the following components have been accounted for: curriculum, lesson plans, training aids, note-taking guides, simulator, study texts, quizzes, tests, practical exercises (plant walkdown and simulator operation), and demonstration of practice teaching exercises by the teaching team.

PROGRAM VALIDATION

The next step in the process is to provide for program validation. In general, an initial course instruction is provided to a "pilot" class. This is to validate the content, length of lessons, emphasis, and overall time schedules and objectives. Validation is accomplished by administration of pre-tests at the start of the course to establish the current knowledge of the operators; post-tests are administered at course completion to measure gains in knowledge. Evaluation of training effectiveness through course audit by technical specialists, analysis of test results, and review of student course critiques are additional validation measures. Course material should be revised as necessary based on the results of validation measures.

GARY MATTICE
FRANK GABRIELLI

REFERENCES

1. Edward S. Sadlon and Guenter Scheffknecht, "The Supercritical Steam Power Plant: Operational Success and Technological Advancement." Alstom, Windsor, CT, 2000.

2. S. E. Kmiotek and R. E Hickey, *Coal Pulverizer Inerting and Fire Fighting System.* Windsor, CT: Combustion Engineering, Inc., publication TIS-8256.

3. *Explosion Prevention Systems* (NFPA 69). Quincy, MA: National Fire Protection Association, 2008.

4. *Boiler and Combustion Systems* (NFPA 85) Chapter 9, Pulverized Fuel Systems. Quincy, MA: National Fire Protection Association, 2007.

5. George Thimot, "Want Better Coal Firing? Improve Coal Handling," *Electrical World*, August 1, 1972.

Construction and Maintenance

Chapter **Eleven**

FIELD CONSTRUCTION OF STEAM GENERATING EQUIPMENT

This section describes the field construction activities associated with erecting a coal-burning steam generator and some of the associated power plant equipment. The information is of a general nature, and it does not reflect the detailed design and construction of a specific unit. Rather, it represents features common to many of the large utility units being installed throughout the world. *Figure 11-1* shows such a large Controlled Circulation® coal-fired unit, which will be referenced repeatedly in this chapter. *Figure 11-2* shows a circulating fluidized bed (CFB) unit, which will be referenced later in this chapter.

PLANNING AND ORGANIZING FOR FIELD CONSTRUCTION

An electric utility company will prepare the design criteria and scope documents, the detailed engineering specifications, and other technical data needed for a complete plant. Much of this work is done by an engineering firm that is retained to perform the architectural and engineering design. On most projects, many different vendors supply equipment and services. Some of them do their own erection work on the plant site. As a result, the owner, or engineer, issues many specifications to the various suppliers of the plant components: steam generator, turbine generator, condenser, emission control equipment, ash-handling equipment, fans, pumps, piping, and valves. After equipment selection and purchase, the owner frequently will have the engineer/consultant continue as the constructor, supervising the several contractors and subcontractors.

Some of the crafts involved in the erection work are boilermakers, ironworkers, pipefitters, millwrights, electricians, insulators, operating engineers, sheet metal workers, carpenters, teamsters, and laborers. These personnel are hired at the local worksite either at the beginning of the project or as the work progresses, and they are released once the portion of work requiring their craft has been completed. A large utility project often involves up to 400 craft personnel on the steam generator field erection and up to 2,000 craft personnel for the total project.

The erection of a utility steam generator is a major portion of the work in building the full plant. In many instances, the company that supplies the boiler also constructs it. Early in the project, the erecting company sets up a field organization headed by a construction site manager who is experienced and knowledgeable in boiler erection and who holds the authority to make decisions necessary to the operation. *Figure 11-3* depicts a typical staff required for erecting a large steam generator. The number of people will be adjusted based on the size of the unit, the scope of the work to be performed, and the number of craft people planned.

Tender

A tender, or proposal, is developed based on the owner's inquiry. At this stage, an estimate is developed; this estimate is linked directly to a resource-loaded construction schedule. This schedule then becomes the basis for integration of the construction portion of the tender with the supply side. This integrates delivery of the various components with the erection plan, resulting in a complete offer to furnish and erect the end product. During the tender stage, labor availability, equipment pricing, and subcontractor quotes are procured and factored into the final price and schedule.

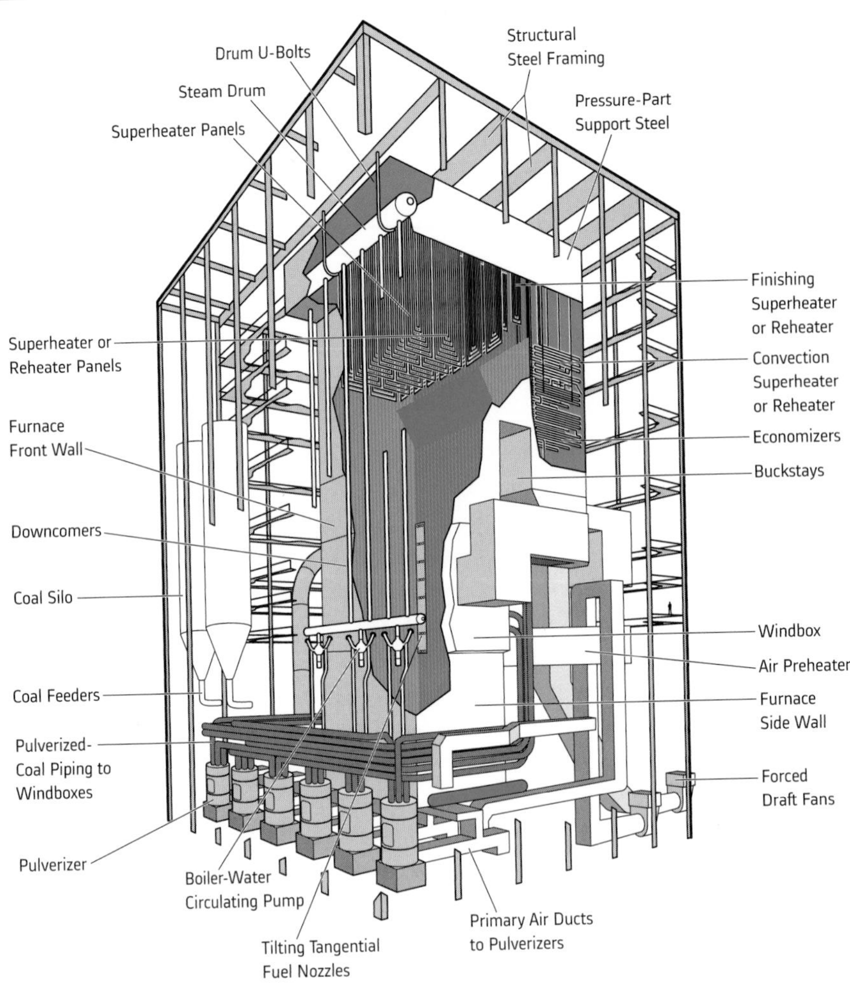

Figure 11-1 | Large pulverized coal-fired boiler

Pre-Construction

At the award of a contract to furnish and install a steam generating unit, the initial construction team, consisting of the Site Manager, Project Controls Manager, Scheduling Manager, and Construction Engineer, will be assigned at the start of engineering. The responsibilities of this team include:

- Interface with the client's and architects/engineers (A/E's) staff to establish site services.
- Interface with the engineering team to determine the sizes and configuration of the shippable pieces.
- Interface with the procurement team to ensure that shipments are synchronized with the construction sequence.
- Determine the site staff and select candidates.
- Interface with the applicable craft unions involved to coordinate labor demand.
- Determine work to be subcontracted, prepare bid packages, and negotiate contracts.

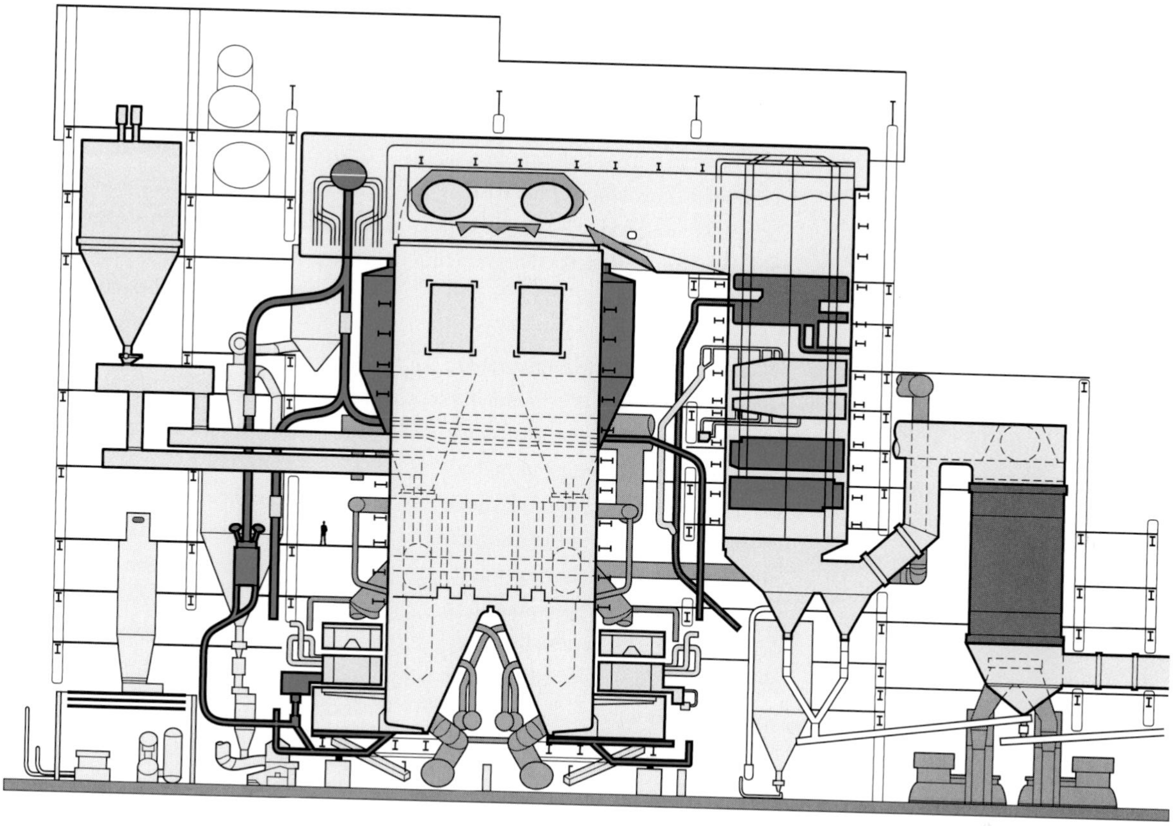

Figure 11-2 | Large circulating fluidized bed boiler

- Determining the major and minor equipment required, and negotiate contracts.
- Develop a resource-loaded schedule and site financial reporting package.

During the pre-construction planning phase, the site-specific services are finalized. The client normally specifies the general services to be furnished. At the pre-construction phase, details such as how much lay down area is available (normally, a large utility boiler requires 15 to 20 acres [6.1 to 8.1 hectares] to stage materials before erection), the availability of a rail siding to the site, where and how much

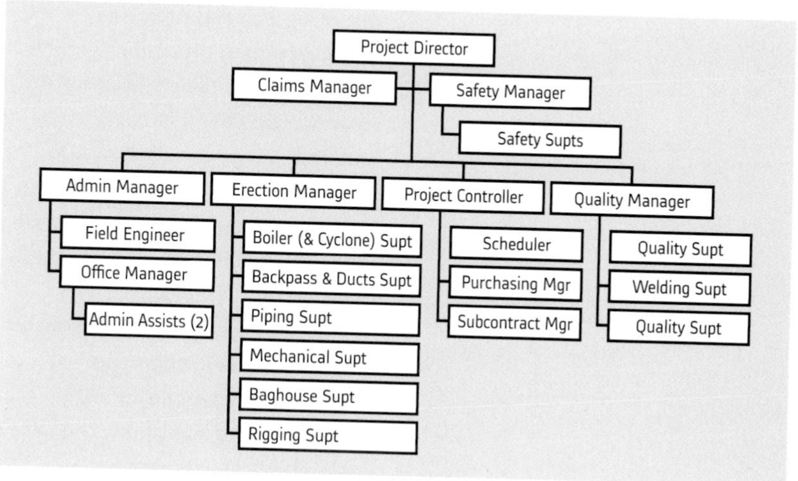

Figure 11-3 | Staff requirements for construction of a large steam generator

temporary power will be furnished, the installation and location of a construction elevator, and where cranes and other major equipment will be located are determined. At this time, the site coordination with other contractors is initiated. This will include such things as craft parking, office and craft buildings/trailer locations, movement of major pieces of equipment, craft working hours, and craft facilities.

The resource-loaded, integrated construction schedule developed during the tender phase is the primary document for planning and managing the interface between the client, other contractors, and the design and procurement teams. This schedule continues to evolve, capturing all the details of the project, and becomes the primary tool for tracking both schedule and costs throughout the project. With the links to the engineering, procurement, and delivery schedule, this creates an early warning system for flagging changes in the material supply side that will impact construction.

After labor cost, the payroll cost of employing craft and supervisory workers, the next most expensive item is the construction equipment. Selection of the crane, sized to erect the structural steel, and the crane (or cranes) to set the boiler components is a major activity. Once the minimum size is determined, a suitable crane is rented from a crane leasing company. This crane can be rented either "bare" (the lessee furnishes the operators and maintenance) or "operated" (the lessor furnishes the operators and maintenance). The location of the major cranes and the costs to move them to the construction site also need to be taken into account. A very large crane can require up to 40 trucks to transport it to the worksite. Other cranes and construction equipment are contracted for in the same way.

The major decisions regarding how the boiler components will be shipped as well as the general shipping sequence are made in the tender stage. The numbers and sizes of major components and shop assembly of parts and components into large modules are set before a contract is awarded. After the award, the construction team will work closely with the design and procurement teams to develop the details of shipping, the sequence of delivery, and the details about the physical lifting of the components into place. Large modules, as described later in this chapter, need to be handled during shipment, off-loading, and erection in such a way that they are not damaged. This is accomplished by designing specific fixtures and frames to off-load, upend, and erect the major components. In addition to the construction team, a Construction Engineer who specializes in large lifts will become involved in this phase of the planning.

Environment, Health, and Safety

The safety and health of employees and the protection of the environment are primary concerns for all involved, from the owner, engineers, and suppliers through the field labor required to execute the erection. Environment, Health, and Safety (EHS) planning begins in the pre-design phase and proceeds throughout construction and commissioning. The owner should set the EHS expectations that each stakeholder will be expected to deliver, establish a safety culture that adopts and encourages a "zero incident" philosophy, and then monitor safety performance.

Quality Assurance and Quality Control

As with the engineering and manufacturing of a utility steam generator to be installed in the United States,

Canada, and in some cases, other countries, the field erection must meet the requirements of the American Society of Mechanical Engineers Boiler and Pressure Vessel (ASME B&PV) Code. Specifically, the company must comply with the requirements of Section I (Power Boiler), Section V (Nondestructive Examination), and Section IX (Welding). Other sections may be required for other components of the power plant, such as Section VIII (Pressure Vessels). Companies must be certified to perform certain activities associated with the engineering, manufacture, and erection of the steam generator. They obtain their certification by providing evidence to a survey team, which is made up of a representative of the ASME B&PV Code and a representative of the National Board of Boiler and Pressure Vessel Inspectors (NBB&PVI), that their quality control program addresses the requirements of the Code and assures that the Code will be met. The ASME then issues the applicable Code Stamps and Certifications for the specific work the company wants to perform. Similar authorities and code bodies are found throughout the world.

The ASME B&PV Code addresses the specifics of the steam generator, but another quality-assurance program addresses even more, such as the tendering, planning, and business procedures of a company. This is the International Standards Organization (ISO) 9001 Standard, which Alstom follows. As with the ASME B&PV Code, the ISO 9001 also requires a quality-assurance program and certification. Alstom's quality programs for the ASME B&PV Code dovetail into the ISO 9001 quality program. The Alstom *Quality Systems Manual* meets the requirements of the ISO 9001, and the construction division's *Quality Assurance Manual for Code Compliance* meets the ASME B&PV Code for the erection of steam generators and more. Hartford Steam Boiler Inspection and Insurance Company serves as the third-party, authorized inspection agency for the ASME B&PV Code and also as the registrar for the ISO 9001. The quality program is implemented through a *Quality Systems Manual,* which meets the requirements of ISO 9001, and a *Quality Systems Manual for Code Compliance.* The latter manual is reviewed by the Hartford Steam Boiler Inspection and Insurance Company (Alstom's authorized inspection agency) and is certified to meet the requirements of ASME. The quality program manuals are supported by a subset of documented procedures, which include quality common procedures, work instructions, quality-assurance instructions, and quality plans.

The International Standards Organization (ISO) addresses quality assurance programs on a worldwide basis.

The quality control process begins in the negotiation stage with a review of the owner's and the engineer's specifications. After a contract has been awarded, a specific quality assurance program is established that meets the code requirements and any specific owner requirements. The specific quality-assurance program will address document control, purchasing control, process control, product ID and traceability, inspection and testing, nonconformance reporting, corrective and preventative action, material handling and storage, quality records, audits and training, and other areas as required by the contract and scope of work.

A significant percentage of the jobsite Quality-Control (QC) Superintendent's time is dedicated to assuring that field welding, inspection, and documentation meet the requirements of the ASME B&PV Code. Inspectors are trained and certified to stringent criteria to meet the requirements of the *Quality Systems Manual for Code Compliance*. The American Welding Society's Certified Weld Inspector program is a recognized national program that often is used to certify weld inspectors. The QC Superintendent's time is spent working with all parties at the jobsite to assure adherence to the requirements of the quality manuals. At the start of the field work, the QC Superintendent will meet with the local Authorized Inspector to identify which activities the Authorized Inspector wants to witness. The QC Superintendent also will work with the customer's quality-assurance/quality-control personnel to assure that their contract requirements are met. In addition to all the other activities of the QC Superintendent, assuring that required inspections and tests are performed is critical. At completion of the erection activities, the QC Superintendent will assure that the required ASME B&PV Code documentation is available, completed, and given to the Authorized Inspector for review and signing. This documentation is then registered with the NBB&PVI, as required by most states in the U.S.

FIELD CONSTRUCTION OF A BOILER

One of the first activities during the field construction phase is verifying the accuracy of all concrete foundations for the boiler. All column-to-column dimensions, anchor-bolt locations, and concrete elevations are measured and verified against the drawings.

Erection of Structural Steel

Because a boiler structure sometimes is 250 feet (76 m) high, very large cranes are needed for erection. Main cranes with boom heights of up to 400 feet (122 m) and lifting capacities of 300 tons (272 tonnes) or more are common. One crew of ironworkers can erect approximately 25 tons (23 tonnes) of steel a day with one such crane. Because of the large quantity of boiler steel (often >4,000 tons [3,600 tonnes] for a 600-MW unit), boiler components, and other plant equipment and materials, it usually is impossible—or at least uneconomical—to store all the boiler items within reach of the main crane. A multi-acre [multi hectare] storage yard and adequate warehouse storage are necessary for the material. Such additional equipment as lighter-capacity cranes, rough-terrain hydraulic cranes (cherry pickers), and flatbed trucks are required for moving the material to and from the storage areas and the erection site.

It is desirable for the boiler erector to also erect the steel structure. This facilitates the planning of erection sequences. Firm dates for finishing elevations can be planned with a minimum of coordination problems or schedule disruptions. If the steam generator supplier does not erect the structural steel, it is important that the boiler supplier and erector be consulted so as to avoid structural steel blocking installation of the boiler components.

The steel erection begins with the main boiler columns, usually starting on the turbine and steam drum sides of the unit. Then, the main girders are erected. They support the main boiler sections and the steam drum from the top of the unit. Usually, five or six main girders are spaced approximately 24 to 30 feet (7.3 to 9.1 m) apart. Girder sizes range from 6 to 15 feet (1.8 to 4.6 m) high and up to 100 feet (30 m) long, with weights of up to 160 tons (145 tonnes). For structural members of these sizes, shipping to the jobsite becomes a problem, because railroads and truck shipments have height and weight limitations. Boiler steel normally is erected in a modified tier method. The steel is erected

one tier, or to the first column splice elevation, at a time. The steel on the rear-column lines directly behind the boiler is left out for access to the main girders. As each tier is completed, it is checked for alignment and final bolted.

In terms of both efficiency and safety, it is advantageous that the platforms, staircases, and handrail be installed as each tier of steel is erected. Stair sections and platforms can be assembled on the ground to make installation easier and provide safe working platforms for the erection of the next tier. The large sizes of some of the boiler components, such as the ductwork, deaerator tank, and soot blowers, require that these components be installed as the building structure is erected. For this reason, close coordination between the material suppliers and the construction team is essential. In some cases, these components can be set directly in their final supports; in others, they need to be set on temporary supports until the structure and adjacent equipment is erected.

Figure 11-4 | Erection sequence of a main boiler girder: (A) main girder being lifted off the ground; (B) main girder at an angle to the steel; (C) main girder being set on the support columns; (D) main girder in place

Erection of Main Girders

When all of the tiers have been erected and bolted, the crane is located directly behind the boiler in order to erect the first girder. Because of the weight of the individual girders and the capacity of the crane, the crane may need to be relocated for each of the girder lifts. For the very heaviest girders and highest structures, it may be necessary to lift the girders using two cranes. Coordinating two cranes to share the load as planned and maintain safe working distances between the girder being lifted and the crane booms greatly increases the difficulty of this process.

Main girder erection is one of many rigging problems of the structural steel erection process. Lifting lugs are bolted to the top flange of the girder in order to attach it to the crane's load block. *Figure 11-4A* shows such a girder raised off the ground. Because the girder rests on top of the structural columns, its total length is longer than the open area between the columns. This requires the girder to go up at an angle in order to fit between the steel, as can be seen in *Figure 11-4B*. Once the girder has been raised above the column tops, the girder is rotated to its correct orientation. Then, the girder can be set down on the column tops, as seen in *Figure 11-4C*. At this time, the top flange of the girder is very close to the tubular framing on the boom. If the girders begin to swing and touch

Figure 11-5 | Lift of a steam drum in the boiler cavity

the boom, the boom could collapse. Once the girder is in place (*Fig. 11-4D*), intermediate steel, perpendicular to the girder, can be installed to tie all of the upper steel together. Coordinated radio communication, highly experienced operating engineers and rigging supervisors, and first-class equipment are imperative for successful girder erection.

Erection of Pressure Parts Support Steel

With all of the girders and intermediate steel in place, aligned, and bolted, the pressure parts support steel (see *Fig. 11-1, upper region*) can be installed. This steel, located at the top of the unit, supports all of the weight of the boiler. Unlike conventional structures that are built from the ground up, most modern boilers are built from the top down, with the whole boiler suspended by hanger rods from the main girder elevation. This permits the boiler to expand downward by as much as 15 inches (380 mm) as it heats up during the start-up of the plant. Correctly setting the pressure parts support steel is very important, because every part of the boiler is located with respect to this steel. It controls all elevations and is continually used as a reference to align the different components as they are erected.

Installation of Steam Drums

Supercritical boilers do not have steam drums. Therefore, this section is not applicable to supercritical boilers. Subcritical boilers, including CFBs, do have steam drums.

The steam drum can be raised into position at the top of the boiler once the main girder steel has been erected. As shown in *Figure 11-1*, this drum is hung just below the main girder steel by means of huge U-bolts that encircle the drum. Currently, utility boiler steam drums may be 7 feet (2.1 m) in outside diameter and more than 100 feet (30 m) in length, and may weigh as much as 330 tons (300 tonnes).

RAISING A DRUM. As shown in *Figure 11-5*, the drum is often raised at an angle to the ground, because the bay may not accommodate the full drum length. Based on the lifting lugs welded on the drum in the shop, the location of the support steel for the load blocks can be determined before construction begins. The drum lifting equipment is selected based on the weight of the drum, the angle of lift, the movement to the front of the boiler cavity that will be required after the drum has been lifted, and the configuration of the upper steel. Strand jacks, or block-and-tackle rigging, are used based on the conditions encountered.

The steam drum usually is brought inside the furnace cavity on a multi-axle carrier and off-loaded with the lifting equipment. In the absence of access for a carrier directly under the rigging, the crane used for steel erection can off-load the drum and "walk it" to the lift area. In some cases, additional rigging is required to maintain adequate clearances between the drum and the structure during drum erection. This is accomplished by installing block-and-tackle rigging to pull the drum horizontally during the lift. Proper location of all rigging is important because of the height of the boiler and the lifting distance, which can be well over 200 feet (61 m).

"DRIFTING" A DRUM. On some jobs, it is advantageous to erect the support and platform steel that is under the steam drum along with the boiler structural steel. This can involve more than 200 tons (180 tonnes) of steel that can be erected with the primary structure in a more efficient manner. When steel has been erected such that the drum cannot be lifted vertically from the ground, the steam drum must be raised up in the boiler cavity to a height just below its final elevation of installed steel and then rolled, or "drifted," into the drum bay area. This will require using strand jacks on rollers, so that they can move toward the front, or two sets of cat heads and blocks and an extra set of lugs on the drum.

ERECTION OF PRESSURE PARTS

INSTALLATION OF UPPER HEADERS AND LINKS. The upper headers and links are hung just below the pressure parts support steel. They may include the main steam lines to the turbine, the crossover links from the different stages of the superheat and reheat systems, the economizer lines to the steam drum, and the riser tubes from the waterwall outlet headers.

By the time these components are raised, the crane used to erect the boiler steel usually has been moved to the back of the unit and can only reach the areas where the hook can be lowered through the steel to reach the component on the ground directly under its final location. This access, however, is soon blocked by the installation of the links and headers. Therefore, most headers and links are raised from the ground inside the furnace cavity using block and tackle (a set of pulleys in a frame). The components are then hung on their respective hanger rods, which support the different boiler components, or are lashed temporarily to the pressure parts support steel.

The sequencing of component installation requires extra care with units having multiple riser tubes to the steam drum from the side wall headers. These pipe sections are usually 6 inches (150 mm) in diameter and up to 40 feet (12 m) in length. They are very flexible and may contain several compound bends. In some cases, with preplanning, the riser tubes can be installed in a lifting frame on the ground and then lifted into position as a group. This frame also eliminates the need for providing individual temporary support to each riser tube.

Other pipes between the various superheater and reheater headers often are 30 inches (0.8 m) in diameter, with sections weighing as much as 10 tons (9 tonnes). They require proper sequencing because of the difficulty in moving them once they have been positioned between the existing hanger rods. At this point in the installation of the boiler, no pressure part final welding has been started. All work has involved the placement of equipment.

On subcritical units, the downcomers connect the steam drum to the lower drum or headers, as shown in *Figure 11-1*, providing flow from the steam drum to the waterwalls. Usually arriving on the worksite in 60 foot (18 m) sections, downcomers are approximately 16 inches (40 cm) in diameter and weigh as much as 7 tons (6 tonnes) per section. Each downcomer requires three or four sections. Rigging must be located underneath the steam drum itself, because the downcomers are welded directly to the drum nozzles. Clips are welded on the ends so that threaded rods can be inserted to raise or lower the downcomer by a few inches (cm) and into proper positioning for welding. As soon as the downcomers are in place, boilermaker welders can begin the fit-up and welding procedures that will ultimately join the downcomers to the drum. A joint can be finished in about 1½ days if a two-person crew works on each weld.

On supercritical units, the steam separators, storage tank, downcomers, and circulating pumps replace the drum and downcomers. The storage tank is a single vessel oriented vertically and weighing up to 50 tons (45 tonnes). The separators and storage tank are hung in the steel during erection of the structural steel. Before the front waterwalls are installed, the downcomer manifold and downcomers are installed, starting at the storage tank and working down. Later in the construction sequence, the circulating pumps and links to the lower headers are installed.

INSTALLATION OF SUPERHEATER AND REHEATER MODULES. The next boiler components to be installed are the superheater and the reheater assemblies and modules. *Figure 11-1* shows their locations within the boiler. These modules, which require some of the most difficult rigging on the boiler, contain sections of tubes bent in complex configurations and welded together on a common section of header. Each module can measure as much as 10 ft × 10 ft (3 m × 3 m) and 55 feet (17 m) in length and weigh up to 70 tons (63 tonnes). They arrive on the jobsite partially encased in shipping rigs; these shipping rigs also are used to upend the module to a vertical position.

A large crane and a cherry picker are needed to off-load the modules from the railroad car to a flatbed truck, which brings them into the furnace area. A set of 75 ton (68 tonnes) capacity blocks are rigged above the final position of the module. The lower block is attached to a special spreader beam, as shown in *Figure 11-6*.

The lower end of the module is picked up with a cherry picker, and the main load blocks raise the header end. After the flatbed trailer is removed, the main blocks continue to raise the upper end of the module while the cherry picker lowers the other end, thus orienting the module in a vertical position for final raising. Rotation to the vertical position is accomplished quite easily with specially designed rods between the high-crown end bar of the module and the spreader beam. The cherry picker and shipping frame are then removed, and the module is lifted with the 75 ton (68 tonnes) blocks.

Because of the thick-wall tubes that are required to retain high-pressure steam, the superheater modules are much heavier than the reheater modules. When a complete section of superheater module is in place, the header sections are fitted together and prepared for welding. Girth welds, made on the

Main Lifting Device (blocks)
Front End Spreader Beam
Second Lifting Device (cherry picker)
Hanger-Rod Length
Tail End Spreader Beam
High Crown End Bars
Cables
Headers
Header End Lugs
Base Frame (shipping)
Tail End Lugs

Figure 11-6 | (A) Rigging for superheater; (B) raising of superheater module

header sections, connect the different superheater modules. Depending on the location of the modules in the furnace and the structural steel underneath them, it sometimes is necessary to drift a module into place. To transfer the load to its final position, this lift requires two sets of blocks attached to a steel plate that is pinned to the module. Generally, this procedure is required when the load is raised, or "picked," inside the boiler cavity, with the final location of the component being in the backpass of the boiler.

COMPONENT LIFTING CONSIDERATIONS. During erection of the boiler components, hundreds of lifts are made inside the furnace cavity. This necessitates changing the location of the rigging almost every time a pick is made. It often is helpful to locate a crane inside the furnace area that has the capacity to boom in and out and to swing around in order to change its location. A large, rough-terrain, hydraulic crane is very useful and can be employed throughout much of the steam generator construction. The elevation of the previously erected pendant sections, however, limits the extension of the crane boom, so upfront planning is necessary so that sufficient structural steel is left out to allow access for the crane into and out of the furnace. When most of the boiler is completed and no more headroom is available for the crane (about the time that the two lower headers are attached), the crane is removed.

ERECTION OF BUCKSTAYS. Once the crane has been installed inside the furnace, one of its first jobs is setting buckstays at different elevations. The buckstays are structural shapes that stiffen and restrain movement of the waterwalls caused by fluctuations in furnace pressure and temperature (see *Fig. 11-1*). Buckstays are horizontal beams that are tied at the corners in a method that allows each wall to expand horizontally while maintaining the overall shape of the boiler.

ERECTION OF SOOT BLOWERS. Soot blowers are mounted horizontally. They have a round tube, or lance, that is rotated by a driving motor. The soot blowers clean the walls and elements of the steam generator by periodically injecting high-pressure steam during operation. One type of soot blower is the wall blower, which extends into the boiler only 8–10 inches (20–25 cm) to clean the fire side of the waterwalls. A second type is the long, retractable blower, which can be inserted up to a distance of either the full boiler width or one-half the width of the boiler, depending on available space and owner preference. These blowers extend between the sections of the superheater, reheater, and economizer to clean the convection heat-absorbing surfaces. Soot blowers are set in the steel at their approximate elevation during steel erection utilizing the steel erection crane. They will remain in this temporary location until all of the waterwalls are erected and welded. The soot blowers are then mounted to "sealboxes," which are welded to the walls and support the waterwall end of the blowers. For retractable soot blowers, there will be a separate support on the other end. Wall blowers are fully supported from the sealbox.

ERECTION OF WATERWALLS. Once the soot blowers have been laid temporarily on the grating, the waterwalls, which form the sides of the furnace, can be erected. The waterwalls are sections of vertical tubes that are fusion welded together into a gas-tight panel. They conduct a mixture of steam and water upward as heat is applied from the furnace side. The walls extend from the base of the boiler (just above the ash hopper) up to the steam, or roof, level.

Waterwall panels may come from the shop with the upper headers already attached. When two panels are joined in the field, only one girth weld is then needed on the header. This eliminates the need for numerous field welds between header nipples and the panel tubes. Such shop prefabrication can reduce the construction schedule and costs by eliminating field welds, which often are performed under adverse weather or logistical conditions. Other examples of shop prefabrication of waterwall panels include welding of buckstay stirrups, installing insulation pins, and fitting sealboxes. Another helpful shop procedure is the application of white paint to each panel in order to brighten the interior of the boiler during erection; this technique improves working conditions.

Waterwall panels typically are approximately 12 feet (3.7 m) wide and up to 80 feet (24 m) long. They are brought into the furnace on a flatbed truck. Because they are so long and flexible, the biggest problem with these panels is upending them. This is performed by attaching either the fixed block-and-tackle rigging or the in-furnace crane to the upper end of the panel and then using a smaller hydraulic crane on the lower end to maintain clearance. Often, "spreader beams" are required to distribute the load during upending. This requires that several slots be cut in the welded web between the tubes. A bar welded to a small T-beam is inserted and pinned on the back; this device assists in keeping the panel straight along its width during the upending process. When the panel is vertical, the tailing crane is released, and the waterwall is lifted up to its final position.

Figure 11-7 | The structural framing between the furnace "nose" and the vertical front wall of the convection pass of a large, high-pressure steam generator

ERECTION OF ROOF TUBES. After the waterwalls are in place, the roof tubes can be erected, usually in one of two ways. One approach uses single tubes that fit between the vertical elements. In other areas with larger openings, full roof tube panels can be raised from the ground with a set of blocks and a tugger. While the roof tubes are being fitted into place, the intermediate waterwall panels are lifted and fitted below the upper panels. Generally, the intermediate waterwall panels are attached to the upper panels by a system of threaded rods and clips that are welded to the webs between the panel tubes. When this temporary hanging system is used, final panel spacing for welding can be done with the threaded rods.

SUPPLEMENTARY FRAMING. *Figure 11-7* shows the structural framing between the furnace "nose" and the vertical front wall of the convection pass of a large, high-pressure steam generator. All of the steelwork shown is supported by the pressure parts. Both the pressure parts and these structural members must be designed to withstand the loads imposed as well as both positive and negative gas pressures as dictated by codes and owner specifications. The horizontal tubing shown at the top of *Figure 11-7* forms the floor of the gas pass directly behind the furnace nose.

ERECTION OF AIR PREHEATER. Depending on the location of the air heaters with respect to the backpass and the specific plans for erecting the backpass, the air heater can be built early in the construction span or be left out and started after completion of the backpass. The air preheaters are heat exchangers made of heat-absorbing metal baskets assembled on a rotor that is turned by a drive. Hot flue gases leaving the boiler pass through one side of the heater. Incoming cold air from the forced draft fans passes in counter-flow through the other side. The "baskets" are heated by the hot flue gases and rotate into the cold air stream to raise the temperature of the incoming air. Various seals prevent the gas and air flows from mixing.

The air preheater most often is oriented with a vertical shaft. Its main parts are the bearing, bearing supports, baskets, oil circulating system, drive motor, seals, casing, and insulation. On some projects, it is economical to fabricate the main sections of the preheater on the ground and raise them into place in the structural framework with a crane from behind the unit. This method is very satisfactory if the same crane used for erecting the structural steel is available and access exists. The air heater baskets usually come assembled into the rotor sections, forming large, pie-shaped sections. These are raised with a crane and lock into place on the rotor shaft. After all of the pie-shaped sections are installed and welded together, the pin rack drive and the radial and axial seals are installed.

The extremely accurate measurements required to align this large, rotating component are performed by millwrights. These include setting the clearances between the rotor and seals, aligning the bearing and support structure, and setting the rotor motor and roller pins. Boilermakers erect the main housing and raise the air preheater into place. They also level and set the preheater in its final position within the boiler.

Extremely accurate measurements are required to align the air heater due to its large size, its rotation during operation, and its expansion and contraction due to temperature changes.

Erection of Backpasses

The backpass, like the furnace section, is made up of welded tube walls and internal-heat transfer surface. Unlike the furnace waterwalls, the backpass walls are normally 1¾- or 2-inch (4.4 or 5.1 cm) tubes on 4 to 5 inch (10 to 13 cm) centers. The surface is always horizontal elements. Superheater, reheater, and economizer surface is included in the backpass.

ERECTION OF BACKPASS WALLS. The backpass walls are erected in the same manner as the furnace walls. Because they do not extend as far as the furnace walls, they generally are shorter, lighter, and easier to handle. They usually are erected with block-and-tackle rigging, because a crane is not practical here. The sequence of erection is the sidewalls, front and rear walls, and then the roof. The backpass walls carry steam from the steam drum. Thus, they are the first stage of superheat and feed the horizontal surface in the backpass.

ERECTION OF BACKPASS SUPERHEATER, REHEATER, AND ECONOMIZER. The internal surface in the backpass is supported by economizer hanger tubes. These tubes extend from the outlet of the economizer elements through the superheater and reheater elements to the economizer outlet header above the roof. Hangers are attached directly to the roof tubes to support all of the weight hanging in the backpass. The superheater and reheater surface generally is in the upper section of the backpass.

Figure 11-1 identifies the location of the backpass components. These elements normally ship in assemblies of two elements attached to a hanger tube. If multiple elevations of surface are in the backpass, they can be welded together on the ground before installation. An upending jig is required to take the assemblies from horizontal to vertical in preparation for hanging. The assemblies are brought in under the backpass on a truck or transporter. The rigging will be attached to the assembly, an upending frame will be attached, and a tailing crane will be used to upend. Once the assembly is vertical, the upending frame is removed, and the assembly is raised to its final location. The assembly is then transferred to a threaded rod-and-bracket arrangement on the hanger tubes, where it is prepared for welding. The threaded rod allows minor adjustment for fit up of the weld joint. Normally, a two-bank assembly needs to have the hanger tubes welded before lower banks can be erected.

The economizer is a heat recovery device that transfers heat from the exiting flue gases to the incoming boiler feedwater. The economizer consists of an inter-connected, horizontal tube array. The upper ends of each economizer assembly connect to the outlet header, which is already in place above the roof tubes. The economizer banks are located in the backpass below the superheaters and reheaters. The economizer is supported on straps that are attached to the lower end of the economizer terminal tubes. The economizer normally ships in assemblies made up of two to six elements. These are upended and raised in the same manner as described for the superheater and reheater assemblies, except that the supports are mechanical, so pressure part welds are not required for support.

Two types of economizer heating surface are in common use on coal-fired units. One consists of a pair of longitudinal fins located 180° apart along the top and bottom of the horizontal tube. The second is bare tubing, similar to a horizontal, low-temperature, superheater surface. Spiral finned economizers are used on oil- and gas-fired units. Finned economizer tubes require careful handling because of the heat-absorbing fins. They are grouped together in modules of three to eight elements, each with saddle supports installed to hold them together. They are raised into place from the ground with a tugger, rigged in the area of the outlet headers. Pins and rods usually support the assemblies directly to lugs welded to the bottom of the intermediate headers. Because the economizer tubes often are fabricated in a staggered pitch to increase heat transfer and minimize space requirements, fitting the last few elements sometimes presents a rigging problem. It is difficult to pass hoisting falls through the staggered tubes. This often means that the already-installed elements must be spread apart and the side walls moved out.

Erection of Windbox Assemblies

After the intermediate waterwall panels are in place, the windbox assemblies (*Fig. 11-8*) can be brought into the furnace and positioned for lifting. The rigging of a furnace windbox assembly is one of the most difficult tasks on the project because of the weight, shape, and balance points of the assembly. When the windbox comes from the shop, sections of waterwall tubing are attached to it, with the bends in the tubing pre-fit around the windbox. These are welded into the already-erected wall panels and help support the windbox. Additional hanger rods support the back side of the assembly. The average weight of the assembly is 25 to 30 tons (23 to 27 tonnes). It is raised in place using the crane in the furnace. Because the back side of the windbox contains control arms, ductwork, and insulated panels, it must be cribbed up on the low-boy truck when it is brought into the furnace cavity. Special lifting lugs also are installed in the shop to make the windbox assembly hang as close to plumb as possible while it is being raised. To ensure that the tip of the crane boom does not hit the waterwall panel above, special care must be used when attaching the assembly to the hanger rods.

Figure 11-8 | Windbox assemblies being raised into place

Erection of Pulverizers

Coal feeders, coal pulverizers, and coal piping to the windbox usually are erected as part of the steam generator contract. If shipping schedules permit, coal pulverizers, such as those shown in *Figure 11-1*, can be set in place, in sections, as the structural steel is set. A large unit generally has 6 to 10 coal pulverizers, which are located on both sides or in front of the boiler at ground level. Generally, one pulverizer on each side is left out until most of the required components have been moved into the furnace cavity.

A typical bowl mill contains about six sections, the first of which is the poured concrete foundation with four large anchor bolts. The mill base, which contains the gear case on many mills, is set on top of the foundation. The mill side assembly, where the grinding bowl is located, is installed on top of this. The separator body, which contains the three roller journals and covers, goes on top of this. The separator, where the coal is classified cyclonically to the desired fineness, is next. The very top of the mill is the multi-port discharge assembly. Here, coal is fed into the mill from a central feeder pipe, and pulverized coal is discharged to the coal piping through the peripheral ports.

Mills weigh up to 150 tons (136 tonnes) and are up to 30 feet

(9 m) high. The crane that erects the structural steel can easily set the heavy sections of each mill. The lighter internals can be installed later. If the use of a crane is impractical, the different mill parts can be rolled into place on a track and then jacked into position. Ironworkers and millwrights do most of the construction work on the mills, with the latter doing all of the alignment and settings because of the close tolerances that are required. During the work on the bowl mills, hanging and setting of the coal piping to the furnace can be progressing as well. Welded joints and Victaulic couplings join sections of the pipe. *Figure 11-9* shows the final tightening of a Victaulic coupling on an elbow that connects to a windbox assembly.

Figure 11-9 | Fuel pipe connection being made to a furnace windbox

Erection of Suction Manifolds

The suction manifold, also shown in *Figure 11-1*, is raised into place next. It is the collecting header that distributes the water from the downcomers to the boiler circulating pumps. The suction manifold is hung from the downcomers, which are welded to the steam drum. The downcomer leads join the top of the manifold. Lugs are provided on the downcomers (and also on the nipples of the manifold) so that threaded rods can be inserted to hold the manifold after it is lifted. These also can be used to adjust the weld gap for proper fit.

The manifold usually is lifted into place using the crane in the furnace cavity. If the crane is not used, blocks must be rigged under the steam drum, with the rigging reaching down the full height of the boiler to hoist the manifold into place. The boiler circulating pump assemblies generally are raised and temporarily rigged before the manifold is raised. Because the lift is only about 8 tons (7.3 tonnes) for each pump assembly, the crane in the furnace can be used for this operation.

It often is advantageous to fit a number of pump components together on the ground first. The discharge valves can be welded onto the pump casings before erection. The pump casing is a volute-shaped chamber into which the pump impeller fits. The pumps force the water from the manifold through discharge links into the lower waterwall headers. Check valves at the pump

outlets prevent water from backing up into an idle pump. A rigging beam can be used to install the electric motors and pump rotors. Millwrights perform the critical alignment of motors and pumps.

Erection of Ductworks

Ductwork erection must be completely integrated with erection of the boiler in order to avoid problems in fitting ductwork sections into the structural steel framework. The boiler ductwork, as indicated in *Figure 11-1*, consists of two main systems: the air supply system, which includes the primary and secondary air and the furnace windbox ducts, and the flue gas system, which includes the backpass ash hopper and ductwork to the air preheater, precipitators, absorbers (if included), induced draft fans, and stack.

The hot air ductwork from the air preheater to the windboxes, along with the burner connection duct, contains some of the biggest pieces of equipment on the boiler. Because of the sizes involved, ductwork generally is assembled on the ground, with sections being installed simultaneously with the structural steel. Hanger rods and expansion joints in the ductwork allow thermal expansion. Some ductwork sections are 20 × 30 feet (6 × 9 m) in cross section. At this size, temporary internal stiffeners often are needed to provide strength during shipping and erection. The gas system ductwork extends from the bottom of the economizer to the exit side of the air preheater. It also includes the ductwork from the air preheater to the induced draft fans, to the gas cleaning equipment, and to the stack. Most of this ductwork is installed after the air preheater is in place, usually with the same crawler crane that set the air preheater. Dampers to isolate equipment or regulate air or gas flow to and from the boiler are installed with the ductwork.

Erection of Lower Waterwall Headers

Typically, the lower waterwall headers are the last major lifts made inside the boiler and are installed after most of the pressure part welding has been completed. The headers are up to 3 feet (0.9 m) in diameter, extend the full width and depth of the furnace, and weigh as much as 60 tons (54 tonnes) each. During boiler operation, once the water reaches the suction manifold from the downcomers, it is pumped into these headers and up the waterwalls. Because these headers are so heavy, and minimum head room is available, these are moved into place and lifted to position with rigging. Once headers are in position, they are hung with hanger rods from the waterwall structure.

Welding of Erected Components

Thus far, as erection of the boiler has proceeded, the different components have been raised and hung by hanger rods or by temporary rigging. After a group of components is installed, the fit-up and welding must be performed. Except for the structural steel, which most commonly is bolted together, almost everything else on the boiler is welded.

Several different welding processes are used in the field. One such process is gas tungsten arc welding (GTAW), in which a bare filler rod is fed into the molten weld. The tungsten electrode, which is not consumed, provides heat to the workpiece. An externally supplied shielding gas excludes the

Almost all metal parts on a boiler are welded. Machine welding improves the quality of the weld resulting from the repeatability of the machine.

atmosphere from the weld puddle. Argon usually is the shielding gas, although other gases, or combinations of gases, may be used. Historically, this relatively slow process is used to put in the root (first) pass in pressure part butt welds.

The most extensively used process is shielded metal arc welding (SMAW), more commonly referred to as the "stick electrode" process. In this process, the flux-covered electrode is consumed in the weld. The flux coating produces the shielding gas, which is supplied externally in the GTAW process. It also promotes electrical conductivity across the arc column, adds slag-forming materials that help prevent rapid oxidation of the weld metal, and in many cases, adds alloying materials to the weld. This process follows the GTAW root pass and completes the pressure part butt weld. It also is used to weld ductwork, waterwall seams, and other plate and pipe components.

The third process frequently used during the field construction of boiler components is gas metal arc welding. In this process, a machine feeds a base of flux-cored (flux-filled tubular) wire from a spool into the weld. The wire is the consumed electrode, as in SMAW. The shielding gas may be supplied externally (as with GTAW), or it may be supplied by the flux (as with SMAW) if flux-cored wire is used. This process also is used for ductwork, waterwall seams, and other plate welding.

With increasing frequency, machine welding is being performed in the field. In field machine welding, the equipment performs the welding operation under the constant observation and control of a welding operator. Machines that make pressure part welds are called "orbital welding machines." They usually employ the GTAW process, although the gas metal arc welding process can be used in the field as well. The main advantage of orbital welding is the higher quality of the deposited weld. This improved quality results from the repeatability of the machine and the decreased fatigue of the operators compared with manual welders.

Field welds are radiographically examined as required by code, contract, and self-imposed quality-control requirements. For this analysis, radiographic film is placed on one side of a weld, and a radioactive source is temporarily placed on the other side. (Sometimes, the source is placed inside a pipe weld for a panoramic shot, and other times, the source is placed on the outside of a tube or pipe weld for a double-wall shot.) When the film is developed, discontinuities may be revealed, requiring interpretation by a qualified radiographer. Any discontinuity, which is interpreted as a defect, must be ground out and rewelded.

Depending on the material specification of the component and on the diameter and thickness of the weld, post-weld heat treating may be required to reduce the residual stresses induced by the welding. This stress-relieving process involves the placement of electric elements (or coils) or gas burners around the weld area of the component. A band around the weld joint is brought up to a predetermined temperature, typically 1,100 to 1,300°F (590 to 700°C), at a controlled rate and then held there for a time period that is a function of the weld thickness. Thermocouples attached at the outside of the heat band, or temperature-indicating crayons, are used to monitor the temperature. The component is then lowered to ambient temperature at a controlled rate.

Additional Construction Work

Additional work that can proceed simultaneously in other sections of the boiler includes attaching the buckstays to the waterwalls, bolting the soot blowers to the waterwalls, connecting the piping for the soot blowers, and welding safety valves to the steam drum and outlet leads to the turbine. At this stage, a "punch list" of work that must be completed before the hydrostatic test should be compiled so that all responsible contractors can be aware of unfinished items.

ERECTION OF STEAM GENERATOR AUXILIARY EQUIPMENT. Other equipment that is worked on during erection of the boiler includes precipitators, absorbers, fans, and the stack. The precipitator (or fabric filter) is located downstream of the steam generator proper and removes the solid particulate from the flue gases. It rests on a structural steel frame that also is tied into the main support members for the precipitator. The hoppers are erected first and are lowered into the structural steel from above with a crawler crane. The hoppers usually are sub-assembled on the ground and then erected as one piece. The main supports, sides, and internal bracing are put up next, along with the inlet and outlet ductwork. The collecting and discharge electrodes, or other types of internals, are then erected. The inner roof, weather roof, and electrical components finish the main sections. Work on alignment, wiring, and checkout is required before the unit is complete.

Absorbers are installed as required by environmental regulations necessitating removal of sulfur oxides from the stack gases. Because of the large amount of ductwork and tanks, it usually is easier to erect the absorber at the same time as its structural steel support framing. Once the main sections are up, the internal piping and spray sections can be installed. Because of the potentially corrosive atmosphere inside the absorber, a non-corroding material, such as austenitic stainless steel, generally is used. Such stainless steel requires special handling and welding requirements not needed for carbon steel equipment.

Large utility units generally have two or more forced draft fans, which move combustion air through the air preheater and into the boiler through the windboxes, and two or more induced draft fans, which pull the hot gases from the boiler and direct them to the stack. Once the support foundations are poured, the lower rotor housing, bearing supports, and rotor are installed. Then, the remaining inlet chambers and outlet boxes are put together and connected to the supply and discharge ductwork. Millwrights set and align the rotor, a critical job because of the close tolerances required.

HYDROSTATIC TESTING AND INSULATION. During hydrostatic testing, water is pumped into the complete water and steam circuits of the boiler and raised to the pressure of 1.5-fold the maximum allowable working pressure (MAWP). This pressure is held for a specified period of time, after which it is lowered to the MAWP and held there for another period. The entire boiler, including piping, valves, wall panels, and drums, is then inspected for leaks. If any are found, the pressure is dropped, the water drained out, and the leak repaired. The entire process is

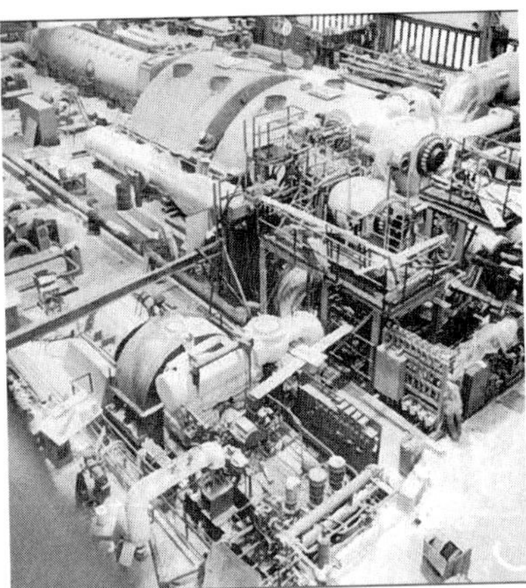

Figure 11-10 | Turbine pedestal with most components in place

then repeated until no more leaks are apparent.

A steam generating unit is "built-in accordance with the ASME Boiler Code" only when it has successfully passed such a hydrostatic test of the entire unit, either in the shop or in the field. The erector engages the services of a steam boiler inspection agent who is responsible for verifying the inspection and assuring the integrity of the boiler to the owner. The owner usually has its own insurance representative on the job at the same time to look over the records and to ensure that proper inspections and tests are performed.

Once the hydrostatic test is complete, the insulation and lagging installation can proceed. Insulation blankets, or blocks, are installed on all piping, waterwalls, drums, and ductwork. Metal lagging is installed over the insulation for protection of equipment and personnel. A coating of refractory is troweled on the top side of the roof tubes, and a steel "skin" casing is welded over the top. If the unit is an outdoor unit, the lagging serves to protect the boiler from the weather as well as to provide a satisfactory appearance. If the unit is an indoor unit, the boiler is completely enclosed by an outer building. This is desirable in cold climates, making initial erection and subsequent maintenance easier during the winter months.

ERECTION OF MECHANICAL EQUIPMENT. The installation of mechanical equipment proceeds while the boiler is being erected. Mechanical equipment includes the turbine generator, miscellaneous pumps and valves, the water treatment systems, the boiler feed pumps, and the condenser to name but a few. The turbine generator is a large section of the mechanical work and requires almost the same time span for erection as the boiler does. *Figure 11-10* shows a turbine under construction but with most of the components already in place.

The overhead gantry crane, one of the first pieces of equipment erected, is used to raise and set most of the turbine except for the stator. Because the stator is so heavy (200–400 tons [180–360 tonnes]), a special lifting rig is usually brought to the site just for this one lift. This rig uses a system of grip-type jacks with steel cables to lift the stator from the railroad car and up to the turbine-pedestal floor. Once the stator is up to elevation, special rolling beams are put under the stator. The stator can be lowered a few inches (centimeters) onto special, heavy-duty rollers and then rolled from the lift frame onto the concrete turbine floor. The stator is transferred to the generator hole and is lowered again using the upper section of the same lift rig. *Figure 11-11* shows a stator entering through an access opening from the ground.

ERECTION–COMMISSIONING INTERFACE. With most of the major work completed on the boiler, boilout and acid cleaning of the inside of the tubes can be done. Chemicals are circulated through the boiler for prescribed lengths of time and then drained from the boiler. These procedures remove internal scale from water-bearing systems and ensure free water passage in all tubes, headers, and drums. (See Chapter 10 for a description of boilout and acid cleaning of high-pressure steam generators.)

Installation of boiler drum internals may now be completed and access openings closed. The contractual responsibility for the erection phase usually is complete at this point; however, support craft personnel for assisting test and startup engineers may be necessary to take care of items that require modification and/or replacement during commissioning.

CFB BOILERS

The erection of a CFB boiler follows much of the same logic as the erection of a pulverized coal-fired unit. This section will only describe the major differences in the erection sequence and in erection of the additional components. Because the CFB has suspended solids in the combustor, which both enhance the capture and conversion of sulfur oxides and enhance the heat transfer, additional equipment (primarily the cyclones) is included. The other effect of the circulating solids is the potential erosion that can take place in the furnace, which in a CFB is referred to as the "combustor." This affects both the placement of radiant surface in the combustor and the preparation of the walls during construction.

Erection of Combustors

The erection of the combustor follows the erection of other units, but with the following exceptions: First, the potential for erosion requires that all surfaces inside the combustor, including all field welds and seams between components, be ground smooth. Second, the internal operating pressure in a CFB boiler is up to fivefold greater than that in a pulverized coal-fired unit. The higher pressure requires additional welding on the seams between waterwall panels and increased size and strength of the buckstay system.

Figure 11-11 | Stator lift rig

Erection of Cyclones

The addition of the cyclones is the biggest increase to the erection scope. Cyclones can either be manufactured plate or manufactured tubing and, thus, water or steam cooled. This section will address the erection of plate cyclones, which are more common.

Plate cyclones are ground assembled in the same manner as the coal silos and are erected in components as soon as the steel is erected to their support level. The cone section includes the support ring and weighs approximately 30 tons (27 tonnes).This section is set into the steel first, leveled, and bolted to the support steel. The barrel section is then set on the cone section and welded to it. Next, the inlet and top section are installed and welded to the barrel. Finally, the outlet section is supported independently from steel at a higher elevation and is erected after completion of the support steel to this point.

Solids Ducts and Fluid Bed Heat Exchangers

Depending on the size of the boiler and on the fuel burned, a fluid bed heat exchanger may be included. This is a refractory-lined box, set at grade, that contains evaporator, superheater, and/or reheater surface. A portion of the solids from the cyclone are routed through this device to transfer the heat from the ash to the appropriate surface. Because the fluid bed heat exchanger is at grade, is relatively heavy, and includes substantial heat-transfer surface, it needs to be erected in place at the beginning of support steel erection and before the cyclones and solids return system is in place.

Solids ducts return the solids from the cyclones to the lower combustor (for recirculating) or to the fluid bed heat exchanger. These ducts are manufactured from plate and are installed after the combustor is in place. Because the ducts are fixed and the combustor expands downward approximately 8 inches (20 cm), a slip-type expansion joint and/or a toggle section is used.

Refractory Linings

The cyclone and solids ducts have a refractory and brick lining that is designed to maintain the outer steel surface at acceptable temperatures. After the cyclone, the inlet duct and outlet are erected and welded. A specialty subcontractor is used to install the refractory and brick linings. Refractory is installed wet, using air-driven guns, starting at the bottom and working toward the outlet. The refractory will set up as gunned, but it needs to be "dried" in order to achieve the desired hardness. Dryout is accomplished when erection of the boiler is complete and at a point where heat can be introduced in the cyclones and surrounding components. This is done by installing temporary burners capable of bringing the refractory temperature to 700°F (370°C) and then holding this temperature for up to 24 hours to achieve the required dryout and hardness. The total time to perform dryout, including heat-up and cooldown, is 7 days.

Backpass

The CFB backpass can be similar to the pulverized coal-fired backpass. In some cases, a two-pass backpass is used, with reheat surface in the front pass and superheat surface in the rear pass. If the shipping dimensions are acceptable, the backpass can be shop fabricated into large, vertical modules. This moves much of the difficult field welding to the shop, and it shortens the amount of time needed to erect this section. This type of backpass module will weigh up to 50 tons (45 tonnes), be 60 feet (18 m) tall, 15 feet (4.6 m) deep, and 12 feet (3.7 m) wide. A rigging plan for rotating from horizontal to vertical (upending) and then raising to its final position is included in the erection plan. This can be accomplished with a crane, block-and-tackle rigging, or strand jacks, depending on the site conditions and equipment available.

MAINTENANCE AND REPAIR OF STEAM GENERATING EQUIPMENT

A good maintenance program is one of the keys to reliability of any steam generator. To be successful, such a program requires managerial ability, expertise, imagination, planning, training, and the commitment of top management. In addition, maintenance must be closely integrated with both the operation and power station engineering functions.

MAINTENANCE FORESIGHT

Because plant layout can either facilitate or impede a maintenance program, maintenance personnel should be a part of the initial design team to ensure the plant layout facilitates maintenance. Ideally, the person who will ultimately be responsible for plant maintenance should be a member of the design team, because only during the design stage can truly adequate space be allocated for maintenance.

As equipment is located, maintenance personnel must have space to easily remove the largest replaceable part. The steam generator should have enough access doors so that all areas may be entered easily for inspection. Access doors and aisles also must be large enough to accommodate components that must be moved to a maintenance area. Sufficient headroom is a must. Overhead trolleys and cranes for maintenance should be designed into the plant rather than retrofitted. All high-maintenance items should have adequate lay down and work areas adjacent to the equipment. Scale models, as well as three-dimensional modeling using virtual space, can help the designer plan for accessibility (*Fig. 11-12*). Thus, time can be saved not only during the installation of new equipment but also with component replacement during future maintenance.

Designers responsible for piping and electrical work must be aware of areas requiring accessibility for maintenance. Often, piping and wiring are field-run from drawings having notes advising construction personnel of special maintenance requirements.

Figure 11-12 | A scale model used to lay out a pulverizer bay for optimum maintenance access

EQUIPMENT MANUALS: AN ASSET TO EFFECTIVE MAINTENANCE

When equipment is purchased, it is important to also obtain operation and maintenance manuals that are complete, detailed, and specific to the piece of equipment supplied. Material that does not contribute to an understanding of the design, care, operation, and maintenance of the equipment should be excluded. Manuals should include:

- Step-by-step disassembly procedures
- Step-by-step reassembly procedures
- Preventive maintenance and lubrication instructions
- Lists of all special tools required, and instructions for their use
- Tabulated dimensional data on settings, clearances, and adjustments

The applicable plant department should contact the original equipment manufacturers on a periodic basis to verify if these procedures have been improved on or if service or technical bulletins have been issued on equipment still in operation. If so, copies of this documentation should be obtained for inclusion in their maintenance records and plant documentation.

DETERMINING THE NEED FOR SPARE PARTS

Often, a complement of spare parts is ordered with the initial equipment purchase. If this is not done, the spare parts should be purchased before the equipment is placed into service. Many times, the supplier of the new equipment will provide a Recommended Spare Parts list, with part numbers. Items critical to plant production should receive special consideration, and for those items, it may be prudent to maintain spare sub-assemblies. At the time of purchase, the applicable plant department should ask for complete instructions from the manufacturer for error-proof ordering of replacement parts. Catalogs specific to the equipment and with exploded-view drawings are helpful in selecting the appropriate spare parts.

There should be a system for tracking spare parts as well. Most plants maintain a computer-based, replacement parts inventory program. If establishing an in-plant program is not feasible, most equipment manufacturers have created inventory management programs that can effectively manage spare parts for planned and forced outages. Based on equipment history over the entire fleet, some manufacturers can create specialized sub-assemblies so that the correct parts will be available at the time of the outage, along with instructions for easy installation, thus reducing the inventory necessary at the plant site. Some manufacturers have Web-based systems with original drawings in order to simplify part identification and ordering. Even so, one must realize that all equipment of a given type does not wear at the same rate, because different local conditions can alter the wearing rate drastically. The use of manufacturer-supplied spare part sub-assemblies can provide significant time savings for repair work by eliminating time-consuming assembly of the individual parts by the plant personnel.

When parts orders arrive, responsible personnel should inspect the material carefully. A defective part may sit in a storeroom for years before the defect is discovered—often just at the time of need. Also, to ensure correctness and completeness, all incoming parts should be checked against purchase orders before those parts are stored. The inspections must be performed carefully to prevent damaging the preservative coating applied to many parts, such as bearings. This is critical to prevent the parts from deteriorating during storage. Installation instructions and assembly drawings supplied with the new parts and conversions must be forwarded to the applicable plant engineering and maintenance departments to enable the necessary tooling and work schedule to be prepared and the new part numbers to be added to the plant inventory system. Incorrect parts must be identified and action taken to delete them from plant inventory and prevent accidental reordering in the future. Maintenance records must be updated to identify these changes.

IN-SERVICE MAINTENANCE

To ensure that a unit is available on demand requires constant effort by the maintenance staff. They must implement a day-to-day, preventive maintenance program while the unit is in operation, establish a well-planned and properly executed inspection program for scheduled outages, and be prepared to handle all forced outages or equipment breakdowns as soon as they occur.

Online maintenance functions are just as important as those performed during an outage. If properly undertaken, not only do they add to unit reliability, they also save valuable downtime. Online maintenance includes lubrication, seal and packing replacement, and repair of any component that has been removed and replaced with a spare.

Proper lubrication is critical for all rotating equipment. Usually, the most complete part of any equipment maintenance manual is its lubrication instructions. The manufacturer's recommendations for lubrication should be followed, and substitute oils or greases should be used only if they meet all specified properties. Each plant must develop and adhere to routine lubrication schedules. Major lubricant suppliers will work with plant staff to develop a program that allows the most flexibility. Such a program would minimize the types of necessary lubricants and the amount of each kept at the plant as well as determine the best reordering schedules. Lubrication is such an important part of any maintenance program that records of work should be kept using check-off sheets.

Good communications between the operations and maintenance groups is essential. The day-to-day, in-service maintenance program must be closely coordinated with plant operators, who are to inform the maintenance crew of existing as well as potential problems. For example, maintenance should be informed of slight drops in pressure or temperature that could indicate inefficient operation or deterioration of machinery. In addition, operators inspecting equipment often can detect problems by unusual sounds, smells, or tactile sensations. Similarly, the maintenance crew must inform operators of any equipment being repaired. Often, in the case of several soot blowers needing repair, the operator decides which blower is crucial to operation and requests that maintenance staff give that blower priority.

Use of vibration analysis, oil analysis, and various non-destructive examination (NDE) procedures should be reviewed to assist in predicting equipment life and identifying potential future problems. Accurate analysis of each type of equipment is dependent on many factors, including the equipment design, installation location, type of analysis equipment, testing procedures used, and sampling or testing locations. Obtaining accurate results from each application may not be possible, but the results should be kept and compared to the equipment condition as discovered during each overhaul and to the equipment failure history.

Proper lubrication is essential for all equipment with moving parts and manufacturer's guidelines should be followed.

PULVERIZER MAINTENANCE

Pulverizers can be overhauled online or during a unit outage. The choice depends on the unit's ability to maintain load with the pulverizer out of service, scope of overhaul work, parts inventory, and availability of experienced maintenance personnel. When pulverizers are overhauled online, the work must be staggered so that all pulverizers do not require overhaul at the same time. In addition, the maintenance schedule should be arranged so that all pulverizers are ready for service when the unit's seasonal load demand increases.

An effective pulverizer maintenance program is adjusted on the basis of the actual plant operating experience and the service life of the pulverizer parts. An essential factor in this is to maintain an accurate log of each pulverizer's running time, including stoppages for removal of foreign material, maintenance work performed, and results of inspections, in order to predict when each overhaul is required. The life of pulverizer parts depends on many factors that can vary considerably from one plant to another. The main factors are the abrasive characteristics of the coal, operating hours of the individual pulverizers, coal fineness required for correct combustion, and pulverizer loading as a percentage of maximum capacity.

The grinding rolls and the bull ring (grinding ring) are the major replaceable parts. (Further discussion of grinding roll and bull ring wear is provided later in this chapter.) With good planning and preparation, it is possible to overhaul a pulverizer, replacing the grinding rolls and the bull ring as well as repairing or replacing other wear parts, in a few days. Exhausters (if used) can be overhauled in the same time period using the same process.

To aid a rapid overhaul, the plant should have ready for installation a minimum of three complete journal assemblies with the grinding rolls installed (*Fig. 11-13*). Often, such assemblies can be stored ready for use in the pulverizer overhaul area in order to reduce handling time. Frequently used bolts, nuts, and washers should be kept in bins in the overhaul area.

Figure 11-13 | Three complete journal assemblies stored on transport dollies

The remaining wear liners and other parts, such as the bowl extension ring and vane wheel segments, must be available in the event these are needed to replace parts found to be worn or damaged once the overhaul has started and the final scope of work has been established. If the pulverizer is equipped with an exhauster, a spare exhauster fan wheel assembly and spare casing liners must be available.

Once the pulverizer has cooled, it is locked out of service and isolated by closing the shutoff valves on the air inlet, the burner isolation valves, and the pulverizer/exhauster discharge valve. The access doors are removed, and to aid cooling of the pulverizer parts, an air mover may be used to ventilate the interior. Once the journal assemblies have been removed, there is free access to the inside of the pulverizer, and the worn bull ring or worn liners can be removed rapidly. When all obviously worn parts have been stripped from the pulverizer, the remaining parts and wear liners are carefully inspected for repair or replacement and any needed replacements are added to the final maintenance list.

When the repair work inside the pulverizer has been completed, the overhauled journal assemblies are installed. All access doors are closed. The pulverizer is cleared of all "hold" tags and then started, without coal, to facilitate adjustment of the grinding-roll-to-ring clearance. The pulverizer then is released for restricted service and tested by operating it with coal, during which the coal fineness test is performed to confirm that the pulverizer is operating correctly. Any required adjustments are made at this time, after which the pulverizer is released for normal operation.

The exhauster overhaul is performed in a similar manner. Once the pulverizer and exhauster have been isolated and locked out of service, the exhauster inlet elbow and inlet side are removed. The worn exhauster fan wheel and casing liners are inspected and replaced as required. When the repair work is complete, the inlet side and exhauster elbow are reinstalled. After the pulverizer is restarted and is running empty, the vibration of the new or reused exhauster fan wheel is checked using portable dynamic balancing equipment. If additional balancing work is required, it must be completed before the pulverizer is released for operation.

Following the overhaul, all worn journal assemblies that have been removed are rebuilt. The worn grinding rolls may be replaced or resurfaced with weld material to re-create the original shape. A weld material such as Combustalloy™ material can give four to five times the life of the original NiHard roll material. The journal rebuild and grinding roll hardfacing work can be performed by the plant or an Alstom Service Center. Hardfacing of the bull-rings is not recommended, because the process has the potential to damage or destroy the pulverizer gearbox bearings by electrical arc damage. In addition, if the finished, hardfaced bull ring is not built up to the correct angle and profile, it may create operational problems, such as grinding roll skidding, pulverizer vibration, coal spillage, and roll-ring clearance problems, that limit the pulverizer performance. Whenever any electrical welding and arc cutting work is performed on the pulverizer and exhauster, the welding ground cable must be placed at the location of the work to prevent accidental arc grounding through the gearbox bearings. Remote grounding to the plant structural steel must not be performed.

Pulverizer maintenance can be divided between normal, periodic replacement of grinding parts and wear liners and major gearbox overhauls. The latter includes replacement of bearings, gearing, and shafts or depending on the pulverizer type, replacement of the entire gearbox. When a major gearbox overhaul is performed, the use of manufacturer-supplied, spare part sub-assemblies can reduce the overhaul time significantly, often exceeding 40%, by eliminating time-consuming assembly of the individual parts by the plant personnel. An example of this is the use of a vertical shaft sub-assembly. This is composed of a new vertical shaft assembled to the gear, gear hub, locknut, thrust-bearing adapter, and thrust-bearing assembly, supplied ready for installation. For some pulverizer gearbox designs, a complete spare gearbox, ready for installation, can be supplied. In many cases, a number of the old removed parts can be refurbished and assembled with new parts to create another new sub-assembly for the next overhaul.

PLANNED OR SCHEDULED OUTAGES

For any power plant, the major part of its maintenance program is the scheduled maintenance outage. The objectives of the planned outage are to inspect equipment, perform previously planned and newly identified repairs, and verify which repairs have been completed. Then, it is important to update (or establish) a database from which to develop a preventive maintenance program. Although most outages will concentrate on repair work, a review of these three procedural items must be part of every outage.

Whether accomplished by plant personnel or a maintenance contractor, a well-planned outage program begins as much as a year before the scheduled downtime. The planning and the jobsite organization must include well-defined channels of communication (*Fig. 11-14*). When using an outside contractor, advance communication with the plant staff is crucial to the success of the operation. The plant staff must follow the contractor's activities closely so that spare parts, engineering changes, and new material selections are handled expeditiously.

Determining the duration between major and minor planned outages is a critical step in optimizing plant reliability. Excessive time between outages increases the risk of forced plant outages when generation is needed the most. If the period between outages is too frequent or extended, this can adversely impact the plant generation capacity factor. Often, longer outages are planned around major equipment retrofits, such as installation of low-NOx burners or emission control equipment. Major boiler outages can be scheduled with other large equipment requiring maintenance, such as turbine/generator sets. Shorter, minor outages usually are planned to repair equipment with known problem areas or items that cannot last until the next major outage. A list or database of known repairs that require a unit outage should be used to plan repairs during short, planned outages or, if possible, when the unit shuts down during a forced outage (as long as it does not impact the availability of the steam generator).

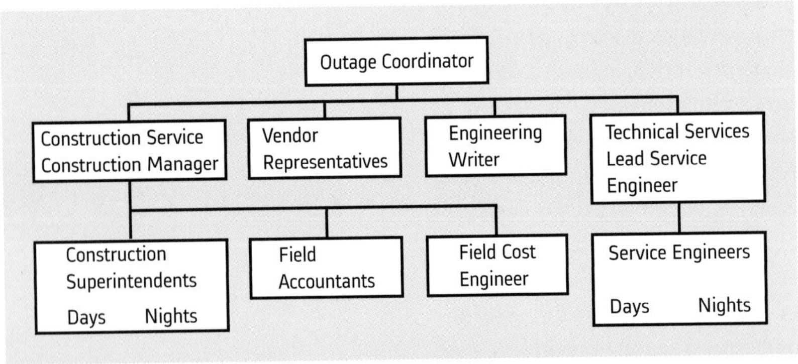

THE PRE-OUTAGE STAGE

Several months before a scheduled outage, the group responsible for the inspection and work activities must jointly plan the schedule with plant personnel. In preparation for the outage, personnel assemble the tools, scaffolding, spare parts, and other required materials. An equipment-specific, confined-space action plan needs to be established for all areas requiring this protection, including staff plans for hole watch and atmosphere testing personnel. Also during this period, the engineers in charge of the outage examine the unit operating and maintenance records and discuss with all plant personnel those areas requiring particular attention. Reviewing previous outage reports can be extremely helpful in verifying that past recommendations and authorized changes are on the schedule to be implemented. The use of computerized work documentation systems is another source for tracking and organizing previously recommended issues. All of these items play an important role in planning the pre-outage activities.

PRE-OUTAGE INSPECTION ITEMS. Usually, while the unit and its auxiliaries are still operating, a complete visual

Outage Coordinator
Construction Service Construction Manager
Vendor Representatives
Engineering Writer
Technical Services Lead Service Engineer
Construction Superintendents Days Nights
Field Accountants
Field Cost Engineer
Service Engineers Days Nights

Figure 11-14 | A successful outage must include a good organization, with well-defined channels of communication

inspection is performed to detect any obvious items requiring maintenance or more detailed investigation during the outage. All items are noted, and a list is compiled. Operational checks of certain equipment and systems also are conducted to determine whether each is functioning properly or requires adjustment, repair, or replacement. This includes:

- Fuel-burning equipment, such as burner tilt mechanisms, windbox dampers, coal gates, and oil or gas valves
- Burner management and ignition systems
- Combustion and feedwater control systems
- Soot blowing equipment

In addition, the settings on safety valves are checked. Control and isolation valve performance is verified, and any packing leaks are recorded. The condition of actuators is checked to confirm that oil seals are secure and lubricating oil is not contaminated with water or fly ash. Complete sets of unit performance data, near to or at full and control point loads, should be printed and analyzed. This review method can indicate items that may be out of calibration or problems with equipment or subsystems, and it can provide an important historical reference during future unit operation. Any problems should be noted and added to the outage activity list. All permanent thermocouples, such as those on superheater and reheater tubing as well as waterwall panel outlets, are checked to isolate any defects requiring repair during the outage. Readings from expansion trams in important areas should be recorded for comparison with readings taken during the outage, when the unit is cold, and after its return to service. These readings are used to confirm free and proper expansion of the unit.

SCAFFOLDING. For outages in which extensive inspection and repairs to the furnace are planned, fixed scaffolding, temporarily installed both outside and inside the furnace, can save time and money as well as improve safety and efficiency. When extensive repairs are planned for furnace and penthouse areas, scaffolding rental fees are more than offset by savings in working hours. Adapted for quick installation, such scaffolding is modular and made of tubular carbon steel with steel loops at the end of each section (*Fig. 11-15*). Fixed-length sections are safety-locked to one another by inserting steel wedges into the loops.

Figure 11-15 | Interior view of unit with modular scaffolding system. Note the easy entrance and access to all areas

Basically, the scaffolding for interior access provides a solid platform near the top of the furnace. Typically, 10 or more scaffold towers, each with three working platforms, are positioned at the front of the furnace, adjacent to each side of the superheater division panels. Scaffolding also is provided across the unit at the front and rear of the superheater or reheater pendant assemblies.

Furnace waterwalls are scaffolded from the lower slopes to a point approximately 6 feet (1.9 m) below the lowest-element tubing of the superheater division panels. Walkway levels are provided at approximately 7 foot (2.1 m) intervals, beginning at the bottom elevation of wall blowers and continuing to the top elevation of wall blowers. An extension of the waterwall platform at convenient working

Figure 11-16 | View of a vertical modular scaffolding system

Figure 11-17 | Tubing is measured ultrasonically for wall thickness

elevations provides interior access to the windbox. Exterior scaffolding also can be used at the penthouse front wall near the roof header and superheater links, at the soot blowers for lance removal, and at the economizer outlet ductwork.

As typical views of scaffolding show (see *Figs. 11-15* and *11-16*), maintenance and repair personnel have easy access to the unit during an outage. This provides three significant improvements over previous methods. First, repair personnel can enter the interior more safely than by using cable-hung equipment. Second, and equally important, continuous access to all areas is possible, and various crafts do not have to compete for access. This significantly reduces the time required to transport personnel and materials to the areas needing repair. Finally, scaffolding allows a more complete and thorough inspection.

The Outage Stage

During the outage, every portion of the unit requires inspection. Scheduled repairs are then accomplished by a critical path analysis to ensure that all repairs are completed. Key areas to be inspected are the pressure parts, the fuel firing and transport equipment, the boiler casing and structural supports, and such subsystems as ash-handling and soot blowing equipment.

Many locations in a power plant must be addressed as confined spaces, either permit or non-permit. National safety laws and local requirements and codes define these spaces and how personnel should be protected when entering these areas. The most current editions of these regulating documents should be reviewed closely to determine how they apply to specific plant locations and access points, and a plan should be created to properly protect these areas. Typically, a permit for a confined space will require regular ambient air testing and access points, monitored by trained hole watch personnel. The personnel and equipment needed to support this protection should be included as part of any outage plan.

PRESSURE PARTS: EXAMINATION OF EXTERNAL SURFACES. Within the furnace, the external surfaces of tubing are examined for erosion, metal wastage, swelling, or developing problems in critical areas, such as the firing zone and near the soot blowers. Suspicious areas are investigated further by cleaning with sandblasting, then checking the wall thicknesses by micrometer or measuring those thicknesses ultrasonically (*Fig. 11-17*). This type of inspection also covers:

- Critical superheater and reheater sections
- Economizer tubing
- Steam-cooled wall surfaces and waterwall hanger tubing in the gas passes

PRESSURE PARTS: EXAMINATION OF INTERNAL SURFACES. The steam drum must be entered and thoroughly inspected for deposits, loose parts, erosion, and areas that may allow internal bypassing of water or steam. Conditions found in the boiler drums may dictate inspection of waterwall headers and other internal surfaces for evidence of corrosion or deposits. Any lower waterwall headers large enough to have accessways should be inspected. Waterwall distribution orifices and screens are examined closely for deposits, and orifices are checked for proper size with go/no-go gages. Samples of furnace wall tubing may be removed from various locations a short distance above the uppermost fuel nozzles; such samples are examined internally to determine surface condition and to detect any deposits.

In the confined areas, a video recording borescope can be inserted into high-temperature headers, either through a terminal tube that is cut through and then sprung back for access or through a removed hand-hole plate or radiographic access plug. This permits inspection of the internal surfaces of the ligament and borehole surfaces for defective conditions, such as crazed cracking, borehole cracking, debris, girth weld cracking, and heavy oxide scale cracking (likely a thermal fatigue mechanism). This type of examination also is valuable in water-touched headers. For example, the economizer inlet header can be subjected to the effects of oxygen carried in with non-deaerated boiler feedwater. This can manifest into deep pits, which can link together to form line crevices or corrosion fatigue from the stop and start of feedwater flow during start-ups and other transient conditions. In general, all of these areas require periodic inspection to prevent failures and costly unplanned outages.

FIRING EQUIPMENT. During the internal inspection of the furnace, the condition of the fuel and air nozzles is determined, and any serious deterioration (*Fig. 11-18*) is noted for replacement or repair. This includes all low-NOx equipment and compartments.

During this stage of the inspection, oil guns should be inserted to their normal firing position to verify correct position in reference to the configuration of the windbox nozzle. Ignitor equipment should be checked to determine the condition of the horn and all internal components for deterioration and alignment. Any defective or questionable components should be replaced. Flame scanner alignment and orientation also must be checked to verify not only the remote viewing capabilities but also the position and condition of the guide pipe.

Any tilting fuel and air nozzles should be operated through their range of motion while being observed from inside the furnace. Binding, non-parallelism, or other malfunctions should be corrected. The tilt mechanism also is inspected from inside the windbox to determine the condition of the linkage. Windbox dampers are inspected from within to determine whether they operate through their normal stroke and if damper-blade movements correspond correctly to external linkage movement. No binding should be evident.

If there are retractable oil guns, the retracting cylinders must be operated to verify proper movement. A general inspection should be made of the ignitor control cabinet and associated piping. Any damaged or defective components should be noted and replaced.

A general inspection of the pulverizers and exhausters (if used) must be performed, and any repairs, including replacement of worn parts, should be preformed as required. The inspection should be made even if plant practice is to overhaul the pulverizers online because of the convenience of having them all out of service simultaneously along with the entire coal transport system. Each pulverizer, exhauster (if used), and coal feeder must be cleaned of all debris

Figure 11-18 | Fuel and air nozzles are inspected from inside the furnace

and spilt coal found inside it. This opportunity can be taken to inspect the gearing, change the gearbox oil, and inspect the condition of all major internal components sections. These include all shutoff dampers, control dampers, and inlet air ductwork. An NDE examination of the pulverizer gearbox vertical shaft can be scheduled at this time if the gearbox condition is suspect. Instrumentation lines should be checked and confirmed to be open and clean. Fire-extinguishing water spray nozzles and steam inerting lines should be cleaned and inspected. Thickness testing, using NDE, should be performed on the steam inerting lines and components to identify any items requiring repair or replacement. Exhausters must be inspected for wear to the fan wheel assembly, including the fan blades and fan spider. The exhauster casing liners must be inspected for wear, cracking, and impact damage that could result in pieces breaking off and falling into the rotating fan wheel. The feeders must be inspected as well, as recommended by the manufacturer, and any necessary adjustments and maintenance performed.

Coal pipe elbows are examined internally for wear. In particular, the final elbow at the coal nozzle must be inspected and the wear pattern noted. Coal pipe elbows fitted with deflector blocks ("kicker blocks") should be inspected for wear and damage in the vicinity of the deflector/kicker blocks and attachment bolts, and for wear on the elbow internal surfaces. Worn deflector/kicker blocks must be replaced. If the coal transport piping contains components made from brittle cast material, such as NiHard or cast iron, each one should be marked and scheduled for replacement at the next possible opportunity by an identical component that meets the National Fire Protection Association (NFPA) Code requirements. The couplings used to assemble the coal transport system components must be checked at assembly to confirm that the installation is correct, with the required engagement to each component.

Riffle distributors are inspected for wear and debris. The riffle elements are replaced or rotated as necessary. Coal pipe orifices are checked for wear and damage, especially if past clean airflow tests have indicated a flow imbalance greater than 5% of the average velocity in the subject coal transport line. If past clean airflow tests have indicated such a flow imbalance, the coal transport line in question should be opened and visually inspected for coal buildup, debris, and worn coal pipe orifices. Components out of tolerance are replaced as necessary. A new clean airflow test must be performed at the conclusion of the outage whenever components of the coal transport system or burners are replaced in order to confirm that the system is free of debris and that the flow balance is within the 5% limit.

CASING AND ROOF ENCLOSURE. The roof enclosure also is inspected, and the condition of pressure parts, hangers, and other pressure part supports is recorded. Any damage or leakage of the furnace roof casing and seals should be corrected. The condition of insulation and pipe seals should be recorded. The roof support steel and hanger rods within the air space between the roof deck plates and insulation are checked for corrosion. Any leaks or damage to the external casing of the entire unit noted during the pre-outage stage are repaired as necessary. The skin casing and seals within the dead air space behind the deflection arch are inspected, as are the casing, seals, and support

steel within the dead air space beneath the sloping furnace bottom. All are inspected to determine general conditions and to note any maintenance that should be performed during the current outage or in the future.

OTHER AREAS OF CONCERN. Drip shields and seal plates at the furnace bottom must be inspected and repaired. The bottom ash hopper and the balance of the ash-handling system are inspected as recommended by the manufacturer. To the extent possible, all gas and air ducts are examined both internally and externally for corrosion, erosion, and leakage.

The entire soot blowing system is checked. Any malfunctioning equipment noted during the pre-outage operational check is further investigated. During the internal furnace inspection, soot blower effectiveness and any tube erosion from soot blower operation are noted so that soot blowers can be adjusted as necessary. Boiler water circulating pumps are inspected according to the manufacturer's recommendations. Air heater elements, seals, bearings, drives, and lubrication systems are checked. Malfunctioning or leaking safety valves noted during the pre-outage operational check must be investigated and corrected. Repaired valves need to be reset when the unit is restarted.

The control system inspection includes calibration checks, stroking of drive units, and a general inspection of system components. Any malfunctioning components of the burner management system found during the pre-outage operational check are further investigated. Flame scanners are removed, inspected, and cleaned thoroughly.

All fans must be inspected (*Fig. 11-19*) for the condition of the bearings and their lubrication. The rotor and the associated dampers and/or inlet vanes must be inspected as well. In addition, the induced draft fans are examined for erosion, corrosion, and/or deposits.

Finally, all observation ports and access doors are checked for tightness.

The Post-Outage Stage

After the unit is returned to service, all repair work is checked under operating conditions. For example, another complete set of operating data is obtained under the same load conditions as the data recorded during the pre-outage stage. This should include all permanent thermocouples on superheater, reheater, and individual waterwall tubes to confirm proper operation. The data are analyzed, and comments are provided if deviations from the previous sets are noted. As the unit is brought online, all control systems should be observed functionally to make any necessary adjustments.

All valves that were repaired or repacked during the outage should be observed for proper operation and performance. Retighten all packing nuts with extreme care after each valve has reached normal operating pressure and temperature. Valves should not be touched if there is any indication that the valve was not packed properly. Repaired safety valves are tested to confirm that the relief settings have been set correctly. An inventory of all recommended new spare parts is prepared, along with a list of all parts and material shortages discovered during the outage. This information is forwarded to the plant purchasing department for reordering and upgrading of the plant inventory.

DOCUMENTATION. Documentation is an important phase of any maintenance program. All findings, both positive and negative, should be noted in a

Figure 11-19 | Fan rotor is removed for inspection

comprehensive report that covers all pre-outage, outage, and post-outage inspection and repair.

THE PRE-OUTAGE REPORT. The pre-outage inspection report contains a review of the unit history, the results of the visual inspections, the walk-down of the unit while in operation, and the pre-outage checkout of all thermocouples, ignitors, fuel-burning equipment, safety valves, and soot blowers. Any items requiring further inspection or repair during the outage are noted separately.

THE OUTAGE REPORT. The outage report contains the history of all work performed during the outage and forms the basis for the maintenance activity and spare parts required for subsequent outages. Outage documentation includes detailed inspection and work reports that describe the conditions of both pressure and non-pressure parts of the unit as well as the other plant equipment. The engineer in charge of the outage should compile the outage report. An effective report should include sketches, marked prints, or photographs, which can be useful when ideas or concepts rather than physical objects are being described for the record.

THE POST-OUTAGE REPORT. This post-outage report should include the status of all the maintenance activities that were scheduled and all additional items that were added during the outage. Each work item should include the final status of the system or component (i.e., a component replaced with one from the storage facility or required an emergency order). This method provides a gauge of the time spent in the pre-outage stage and identifies if greater time should be spent in a particular system or area before or during future outages. Emphasis should be placed on items that were not completed and on identifying the root cause for the failure. These uncompleted items should be recommended as a high priority on the next outage work list.

The post-outage documents should describe conditions immediately after restart and any changes in the operating parameters resulting from the maintenance performed during the outage. Operating data, including tube temperature measurements and expansion data, can help illustrate this item in the report. The final—and most important—documentation lists the recommendations of the inspection team as well as an engineering department review of those findings. Such recommendations should include which spare parts to order in preparation for the next outage.

After all the planning, inspection, and documentation have been completed, a critique provides all participants involved in the outage an opportunity to review their findings and determine improvements for future outages. A frank, open exchange sets the stage for the next outage and also the plan for continuing maintenance activities throughout the coming operating period.

Review and analysis of the damage found in many previous outages (as well as during forced outages) can help to determine typical problem areas. This analysis also can aid in identifying root causes to eliminate these problems in the future. Often, however, it is difficult to collect and analyze all these data when stored in individual records and reports. At a minimum, it is beneficial to keep track of these repairs in an electronic database or spreadsheet. Specialized equipment repair and failure tracking software

also is available, allowing easier tracking and more detailed cause coding for future analysis. Future maintenance plans can be recorded and tracked in such software. Most of these software programs also link the data entries to component arrangement drawings in order to provide a visual presentation of the problem locations. This allows better recognition of common problem areas to determine causes. Some of these programs are network or Internet based, allowing many users to view the results at any one time. This also allows a team to work together for outage planning and problem resolution. *Figure 11-20* illustrates examples of software entry and arrangement views.

FORCED OUTAGES

A forced outage requires as much or more planning than a scheduled outage, but by its nature, it allows the least time for planning. Consequently, a plant maintenance group must be prepared with an emergency plan, one that has been formulated before a failure occurs. This plan should be in writing and periodically updated. It should list alternatives, such as the use of manpower or parts from another division or utility, the use of alternate production methods, or the purchase of power. Because downtime is critical, the repair plan details and schedule must be worked out immediately. Plant personnel and the forced outage plan should have lists of other critical work that can be done during an outage. No items should be added to this list that will adversely affect the time during which the unit is out of service.

Pressure part failure is a major cause of forced outages. Because the steam generator must be cooled before it can be entered, the cooling time can be used for planning. The repair of the failure will be the critical path in returning the unit to service, so other maintenance may be performed only if it does not interfere with the repair. To save time during furnace cooldown, crews can move parts, tools, and scaffolds close to the steam generator access doors. Usually, it is possible to determine the area of the failure and its general magnitude from the outside, and if a leak is small, sky

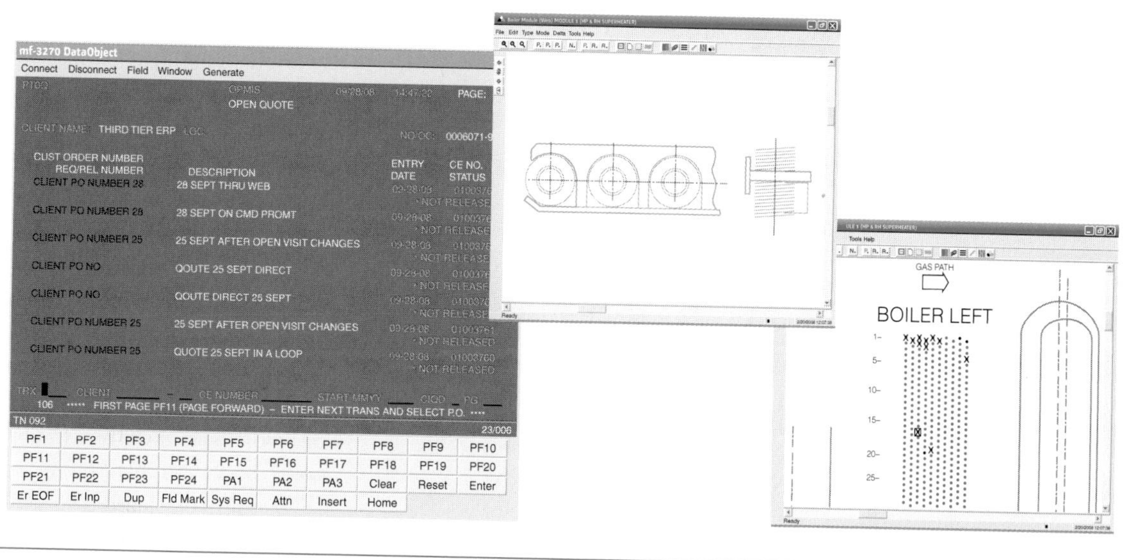

Figure 11-20 | Examples of software entry and arrangement views of maintenance activities on pressure part–related items.

climbers, bosun chairs, or two-man scaffoldings generally are adequate. If the furnace has cable holes extending through the roof enclosure, considerable time can be saved, because the roof enclosure does not have to be cooled for entry. For safety reasons, it is important that the cables be cooled if they are to pass through the hot enclosure. Compressed air is the usual cooling medium. If the damage is extensive and requires major repair work, more elaborate scaffolding may be necessary.

The importance of failure records cannot be over emphasized. The cause of a single failure may not always be determined, and an isolated, random failure may be of little significance. Several similar failures, however, may indicate serious problems that could affect future availability. Good maintenance, then, requires not only that a failure be repaired but also that every effort be made to determine the root cause of that failure.

To retrieve information easily, an effective record keeping procedure separates the logs for the superheater, reheater, economizer, and waterwall. Patterns and trends are easily spotted when presented graphically, such as on sketches showing elevation and plan views (*Fig. 11-21*).

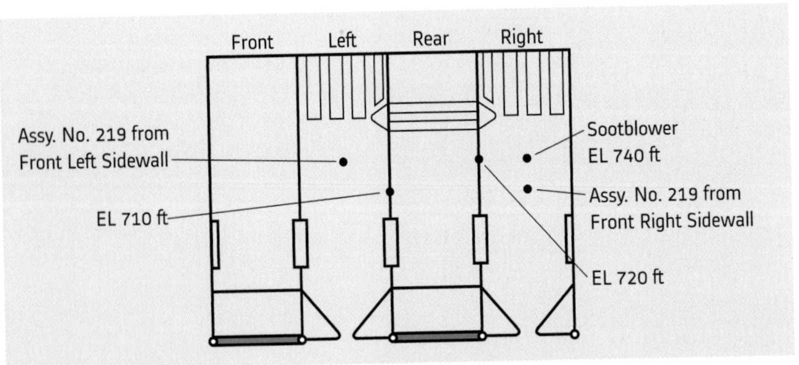

Figure 11-21 | Waterwall failure locations (viewed from inside the boiler)

Numerals or dates for the chronological occurrence of a failure can be added to this information. As noted under *Planned or Scheduled Outages*, modern boiler failure documentation software can be a valuable tool that easily documents the locations and causes of forced outages as well as other damage found during the outage. Common problem locations can be viewed on arrangement drawings with links to failure information. Common failure modes can be reviewed together in order to determine root causes and steps to eliminate the problem.

Repair Welding For Pressure Parts

Plant management and maintenance supervisors must bear in mind the legal formalities involved in the repair of boiler pressure parts. In the United States, the National Board Inspection Code (NBIC) provides guidelines and rules for repairs and alterations to boilers and pressure vessels after they have been placed into service. The NBIC rules, including the involvement of the Authorized Inspector, are only mandatory in those states and cities that have adopted the NBIC or where required by the owner or the insurance carrier. Jurisdictional requirements involving the Authorized Inspector vary widely. Most jurisdictions require the owner to obtain the Authorized Inspector's acceptance before making a repair or alteration. The NBIC, however, places the responsibility for coordinating the acceptance inspection on the contractor.

Anyone (owner, contractor, or manufacturer) preparing to perform welding on pressure parts or on attachments to pressure parts must follow the rules of the NBIC. For the most part, the NBIC refers the party making the repair back to the original code of construction for rules governing how to make a repair or alteration. When it is deemed impractical to follow the original construction code requirements, however, the NBIC has provided some special rules and guidelines for qualifying the repair procedures and welder performance training/testing when making the repair or alteration. Before the actual work begins, the Authorized Inspector and the owner must approve the repair plan and procedures.

GUIDELINES FOR WELDING REPAIR OF LOW-CARBON STEEL TUBES. When replacing a length of damaged tubing, the cut and weld prep should be located at least 2 inches (5 cm) beyond the end of the damaged area. If the new cut line places the new weld in the vicinity of an existing weld, the cut line should be moved so that the old weld falls within the removed section of tube. The minimum replacement tube length should be no less than 6 inches (15 cm).

The use of backing rings for a weld is permitted by code, but in some instances, they either cannot be used or must be removed after the welding is completed. For example, it may be an engineering requirement that a backing ring not be left in place, because it would create an orifice effect, an unacceptable stress riser, or a turbulent flow in the component. If the component is in a heat-absorbing area and is in contact with water or a mixture of water and steam, backing rings cannot be used. Without a backing ring, a welding process capable of producing a defect-free root weld (usually GTAW) must be used. After the root weld has been completed, the remainder of the weld groove can be made with any acceptable welding process (usually SMAW).

For instances in which the welds fall in areas where access to one side of the weld groove is difficult or impossible, it may be necessary to perform what is called a "window weld" (*Fig. 11–22*). This weld is completed by cutting a hole (window) in the front of the tube to allow access for welding the back side of the tube from the front. The first pass, or root, of the weld must be welded using the GTAW process. The remainder of the weld can be completed using either the GTAW or the SMAW process. Fit-up of the tube ends and the replacement plug for the window is critical to obtaining a satisfactory weld. Much care must be taken when cutting the holes and the plug. The side locations in which the two weld grooves form a 90° angle require close attention.

Fit-up of the weld joints is crucial to obtaining an acceptable final weld. Although it is difficult to make accurate cuts on furnace tubes, it is important to get the existing tube ends squared and correctly chamfered, cut the replacement tube to the correct length, and allow for weld shrinkage. A tube-end scarfing tool should be used when possible. Remember that the weld and parent metal are melted during the welding process and that molten metal shrinks as it solidifies. A butt weld in a tube will shorten the total tube length by approximately 1⁄16 inch (1.6 mm). The required preheat should be applied to the weld joint before welding. A clamp or guide lug should be used to hold one end of the replacement tube in alignment while the first weld is made (*Fig. 11-23*).

Both ends of the replacement tube should not be tack welded, particularly if the existing tubes are rigidly supported. The preheat requirements for the butt weld also apply to the tack welds. As a general rule, the weld at the lower

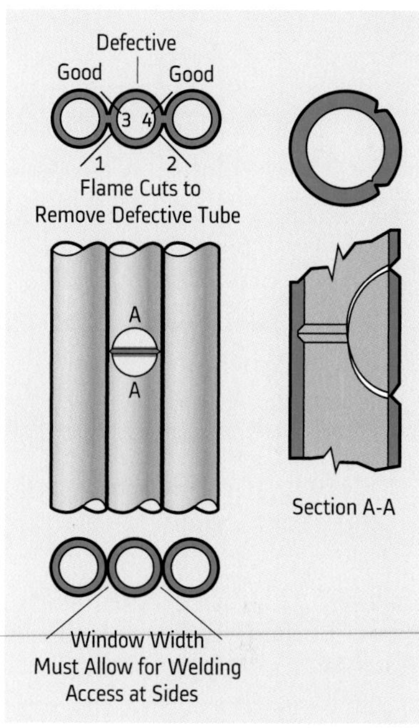

Figure 11-22 | Window welds may be used to repair damaged tubes when access is difficult

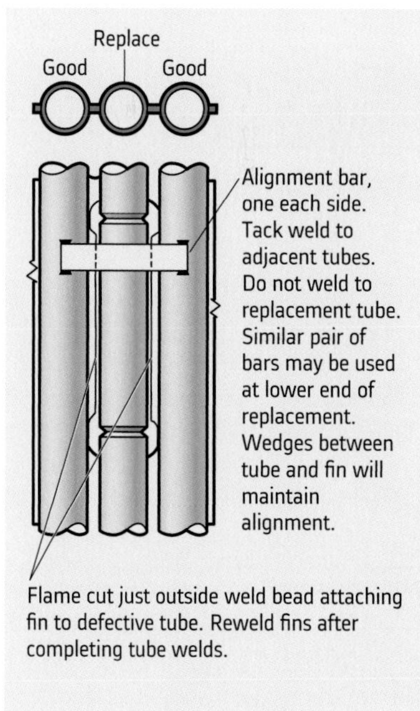

Figure 11-23 | Welding detail for replacing a tube length in a fin-welded furnace wall

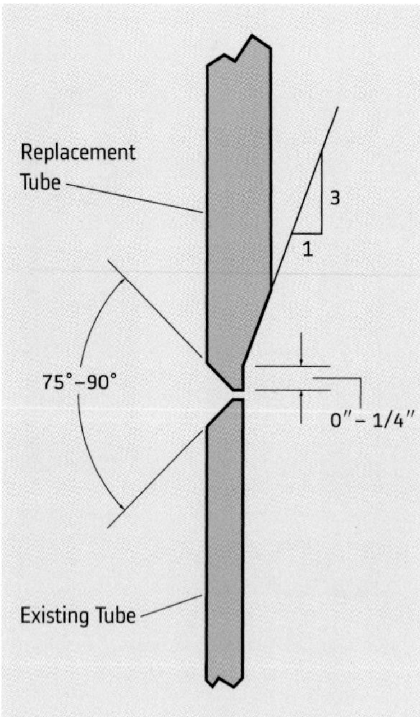

Figure 11-24 | Fit-up detail to install a replacement tube section with a wall thickness greater than that of the existing tube

end of the replacement tube should be completed first. The upper end of the replacement tube should not be welded until both the replacement tube and the existing tube have cooled to ambient temperature. The required preheat can then be applied and the welding performed in the same manner.

GENERAL GUIDELINES FOR ALLOY TUBE REPAIRS. If a tube is being replaced in an area in which the alloy being used changes, it is always preferable to make the weld cut lines in the same alloy material. The creation of dissimilar metal welds (e.g., ferritic to austenitic) should be avoided. In addition, the weld cut line should be made in an area where the wall thicknesses and diameters are the same. The manufacturer's material diagram will provide approximate locations of all material, wall thicknesses, tube diameters, and shop welds for specific areas in a panel. If possible, the new weld cut line should be made at least 6 inches (15 cm) back from the existing tube shop weld. This will allow a "safe end" with which to work.

CUTTING OUT A WELD. If it becomes necessary to cut out a weld, either shop or field, in which the two tubes being joined are of different alloys, wall thicknesses, or outside diameters, special attention must be paid to this type of operation. The tube inside diameters (IDs) must match up to ensure that an acceptable weld is made. If the IDs are not the same, it will be necessary to scarf out the ID of the smaller-ID tube in order to match the ID of the larger-ID tube (*Fig. 11-24*).

This operation reduces the wall thickness of the bored out tube, which could reduce its wall thickness to below the minimum required thickness for the operating temperature and pressure. The most common occurrence of this situation is when dissimilar metal weld (e.g., ferritic to austenitic) failures begin to appear. The ID of the ferritic tube should never be bored out to match the ID of the austenitic tube. This will result in the ferritic tube having less than the minimum wall thickness required for the design temperature and pressure at the butt weld location. There are two ways to handle this situation: Have a short spool piece machined out of the austenitic material, with the ends machined to the matching weld joint geometry, or have a short spool piece fabricated with two short pieces, one ferritic and one austenitic, that match the existing tubes, with the dissimilar weld being made in the center by the fabricator. The latter option is the preferred method. It allows the dissimilar metal weld (the most difficult to perform in the field) to be made in an environment where welder access and weld position can be controlled. If the tube IDs match up but the outside diameters (ODs) are different, additional weld material must be deposited on the weld joint to taper the larger-OD tube into the smaller-OD tube.

FIT-UP AND SHRINKAGE ALLOWANCE. Shrinkage resulting from welding in alloy tubes is similar to that in carbon steel tubes. Allowance must be made for expansion from preheating, which could close the root gap slightly. For SMAW with a backing ring, the root gap opening must be sufficient to allow full penetration and complete fusion with the backing ring during the first pass. For GTAW, the root gap needs to be sufficient to ensure complete fusion of the root without excessive concavity or convexity of the ID surface. The root gap should be within the range of 0 to ⅛ inch (0 to 3 mm) after the tubes are preheated. The two tubes should never be overheated (smoked) to close the root gap, nor should excessive force be used to pull the tube ends together.

REPAIR OF TUBES ROLLED INTO HEADERS OR DRUMS. If a tube that requires rolling into a header or drum is damaged in some way and requires repair, the normal practice is either to replace the entire tube or, if that is impracticable, to plug the tube holes in the header or drum and abandon that tube (or tubes, if there is damage to adjacent tubes). If replacement of the damaged tube is chosen, it usually is impossible to get the tube properly inserted into the holes. In this case, an option may be to cut the tube at some distance from the header or drum (2–3 feet [0.6–0.9 m]), making it possible to insert both ends into tube holes. A field weld can then be made in the tube before rolling the tube. Keep in mind that the replacement tube must provide the required installation length into the IDs of the headers or drums after welding. This would be a very difficult repair, because there will be very limited access for completing a field weld in the tube when it is in position. Most likely, there will be no visibility or access to the back side for welding.

REPLACING A TUBE LENGTH IN A FIN-WELDED FURNACE WALL. First, the fin is split along both sides of the tube section that needs to be replaced (see *Fig. 11-23*). The preferred method for splitting the fin is flame cutting. Because this leaves a very rough edge on the fin, the cut should be biased toward the tube that is to be replaced. This will allow the cut edge to be ground back to the desired location and a weld prep bevel placed on the membrane. Once the fin material has been split, the tube can be cut off at both ends. When laying out the cut line for the tube, keep in mind that an additional ½ inch (1.3 cm) of tube length on each end will be removed during the weld prep machining operation. The new tube length can be installed and welded according to the guidelines for fit-up outlined previously in this chapter. Once the tube butt welds have been completed, new fin material can be cut, fitted into position, and welded. It is important that the fin weld running in the axial direction between the tubes be a full-penetration weld, because this will prevent stress cracks during future operations.

REPAIR OF TUBE BLISTERS/SWELLING. Internal deposits cause swelling, often called "blistering," of furnace wall or boiler tubes. An internal deposit acts as an insulator on the tube wall, preventing the media inside the tube from cooling the metal at that spot. The increased metal temperature reduces the strength of the tube, allowing the tube metal to creep, which results in swelling. This swelling reduces the wall thickness in that area, eventually resulting in a rupture of the tube wall. Usually, a large number of tubes will be blistered and not noticed until the first one fails. The internal deposits generally occur when a high percentage of make-up water is used in the feedwater. Replacement of the swollen tubes should be performed according to the instructions given previously for replacing a tube in a fin-welded wall (see *Fig. 11-23*).

REMOVAL OF A TUBE SAMPLE FOR METALLURGICAL OR CHEMICAL EXAMINATION. It is always desirable to know the failure mechanism for the loss of a tube. Often, however, this mechanism is not readily apparent. Thus, a section of tubing must be removed and sent to a lab for analysis. For the lab to determine the cause, it is very important that the sample not be contaminated during the removal process. The most common ways for contamination to get into the sample during removal are from flame impingement and from cutting fluids. It is preferable to use mechanical cutting of a fin and tube when possible. If mechanical cutting is used to remove the sample tube, it should be a dry cutting method. If flame is used, the flame must be kept away from the area of interest. Once the sample has been removed, it must be clearly marked as to its orientation in the furnace (e.g., top end or furnace side). A memo identifying the location in the furnace (e.g., elevation and distance from sidewall) should be attached. Any other known, pertinent information that may be of interest to the lab also should be included (*Fig. 11-25*). Replacement of the sample piece should be accomplished by following the instructions previously given for replacing tubing.

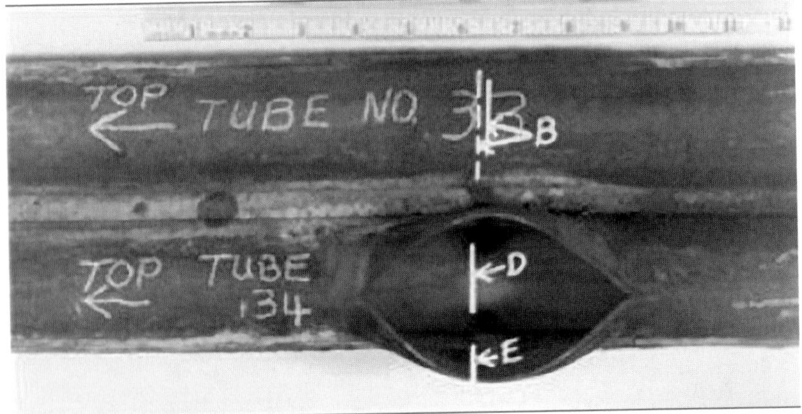

Figure 11-25 | Tube samples are clearly marked for proper identification and analysis

COMPONENT MAINTENANCE

Although it is beyond the scope of this book to describe the overhaul of all furnace and steam generator components and auxiliaries, a brief discussion of pump, fan, and control system maintenance is offered for general information.

Pump Maintenance

Various types of pumps are used with each steam generator design. For high-pressure, recirculation-type boilers, pumps of the single-shaft, centrifugal design driven by a wet-stator induction motor move boiler water at pressures and temperatures exceeding 4,000 psig and 650°F (28 MPa and 340°C). Because the motor is enclosed within the pump casing and is filled with boiler water at full system pressure, no seals are used between the pump and motor. A baffle (plus close clearances between the shaft and motor casing) prevents solids in the boiler water and hot water from passing into the motor. Through an external heat exchanger, recirculating water in the motor cavity cools the submerged motor. Although manufacturers generally recommend an annual inspection for such pumps, local conditions help to determine the proper interval for a given unit and installation. Periodic inspection of the pump in service usually reveals when an overhaul is needed. Some indications of this are an above-normal noise level, high motor temperature, vibration, unusual starting or fluctuating current, reduced head across the pump, leaks from the pressure casing, or drop in the winding resistance.

At most facilities, one of the pumps is dismantled every few years. Some plant maintenance departments prefer a rotating inspection schedule, in which one pump of a multi-pump installation is inspected per year, resulting in all pumps being inspected at least once in a three- or four-year period. During disassembly, the motor and pump impeller are lowered as one assembly. The impeller can then be removed from the shaft and the rotor assembly taken from the housing. The assembly is placed horizontally on V blocks at floor level. An inspection is made with as much disassembly of subsections as observation dictates.

Although other pumps on steam generators might handle a cooler liquid at essentially ambient conditions, they may require much higher maintenance if that fluid is more corrosive or erosive than pure boiler water. For example, heavy-duty centrifugal pumps are used to move a solution of lime or limestone in flue gas desulfurization (FGD) systems. The wear rate of these pumps can be substantial and is a function of the severity of the pumping duty and of the abrasive properties of the materials being handled. The life of wear parts, such as impellers and liners, varies greatly as well. For instance, steel impellers and bodies have had very short life with highly acidic and abrasive solutions. If a new make or different type of pump is used, it should be opened regularly and the parts inspected to establish the life of wear parts. When handling abrasive fluids, parts other than the impeller and housing also are subject to excessive wear. Shafts, gland seals, and even bearings must be inspected much more frequently. Bearing housings should be opened and inspected at least once a year.

Fan Maintenance

Steam generators require many types and sizes of fans. The largest fans are used for forced draft and induced draft service as well as for moving primary air to pulverizers for drying the coal. These fans can be either centrifugal or axial flow in design. Bearing failure—one of the biggest problems with fans—usually is caused by either poor lubrication or excessive vibration. As stated previously, it is important to follow the lubrication requirements specified by the manufacturer.

If a failure occurs when a fan is initially started, it may be related to vibration created by inadequate foundations or an unsuitable ductwork configuration or design. On the other hand, bearing failure that occurs soon after initial operation may be the result of rotor imbalance, which often causes vibration. The imbalance can be based on fly ash accumulation in eroded blades, water, blade erosion, or uneven thermal growth of the fan wheel. The possibility of changes in alignment or shifting foundations also should be considered. Another item of concern is the possibility of unbalanced gas flow into a dual-inlet centrifugal fan caused by unsynchronized dampers or inlet vanes. This will create an uneven flow volume, which in turn produces unbalanced loading on the bearing's thrust collar and, potentially, introducing vibration.

An outage inspection program permits correction before a dangerous condition exists. The fan blades and associated ductwork systems should be examined for erosion, corrosion, or cracks (*Fig. 11-26*). If cracks are found in any blade, it is wise to magnetic-flux all of the blades for cracks. Fan dampers are as important as the fan itself, because deteriorated dampers can cause poor fan control. Damper bearings are exposed to the same hostile environment as the fan wheel is. Because fly ash can penetrate the bearing lubricant, damper bearings must be inspected frequently and cleaned when the lubricant is contaminated. Dampers not in constant use, such as isolation dampers, may freeze in place and become useless; exercising idle dampers can avoid this condition.

Some erosion of induced draft fans on coal-fired steam generators is to be expected. Erosion generally is most severe at the leading edge of the blades. Axial-flow fans have the heaviest erosion on the front outer tip of the blade. For centrifugal fans, erosion generally is most severe at the joint between the blades and centerplate. Erosion at the fan's centerplate affects the structural integrity of the fan wheel. Blade erosion in either type of fan also may cause imbalance.

For severe duty, replaceable wear plates are bolted or welded to centrifugal fan blades. At each outage, the wear plates are checked and replaced when worn halfway through. If wear plates are allowed to erode to a point that damage occurs to the blade material, the repair cost and outage time can be greatly increased. Although wear plates can reduce the effects of erosion, it is best controlled by fly ash removal upstream of the fans. Again, an effective maintenance program determines and corrects the cause of the maintenance issue, which sometimes is initiated by equipment other than the equipment that is actually experiencing the problem.

An important part of any fan repair is the rebalancing and final cleanup. In addition to the normal dangers of rotating equipment, fans present an additional hazard in their ability to draw in not only air or gas but also loose material. Solid objects can pass through the fan and either damage the rotor or be discharged as projectiles. Therefore, on job completion, all ductwork must be inspected and all foreign material removed.

Figure 11-26 | Fan rotor blades with heavy erosion

Control System Maintenance

Historically, because of limited manpower and funds, maintenance of power plant control systems has been limited to the repair of known deficiencies. With greater emphasis on plant reliability and availability, however, preventive maintenance programs have grown. By relying on a redundant component, transferring a control loop to manual, or temporarily defeating the component's function, most control system components can be recalibrated, repaired, or replaced while the unit is online. This maintenance program of control system components should be a continuous process. Such periodic maintenance can prevent such issues as unit high or low furnace pressure trips caused by drifting calibration of transmitters and switches or by plugged sensing lines between the furnace tap and the transmitters.

An annual power plant outage offers the opportunity to perform a more complete overhaul of the control system. Usually scheduled well in advance, this work includes the recalibration of field devices, such as transmitters; pressure, temperature, and position switches; control valves; speed controllers; damper drives; and thermocouple inputs. If there are known problems in the control system, additional work is scheduled. For example, a dry run of the burner management system should be conducted if some control logic is not performing correctly, and the calibration, updating, enhancing, and retuning of a control loop may be in order if poor control is observed during previous system operation.

Because the control system is the power plant component that can trip a unit off-line based on input data, its role is critical to plant operation. Often, unit trips are attributed incorrectly to control system malfunctions when in fact the control system has sensed an abnormal condition and responded correctly.

Erosion And Abrasion

On coal-fired steam generators, one of the biggest maintenance requirements is the repair or replacement of worn parts resulting from erosion or abrasion by coal and ash. Abrasion is the "sandpaper" effect of solid particles moving parallel to, and in contact with, a wall or boundary surface. Abrasion tends to occur at the high spots on the boundary surface, and it has little effect on the surface matrix. Therefore, a boundary surface containing a small, hard particle matrix will give the best service life.

Erosion, on the other hand, occurs from the impact of hard particles. The solid particles strike the wall or boundary surfaces freely, and they cut portions of the boundary or wall material. Hard, or erosion-resistant, particles in the wall matrix will not protect the less-resistant balance of the matrix. Consequently, many abrasion-resistant materials are not resistant to erosion (*Fig. 11-27*).

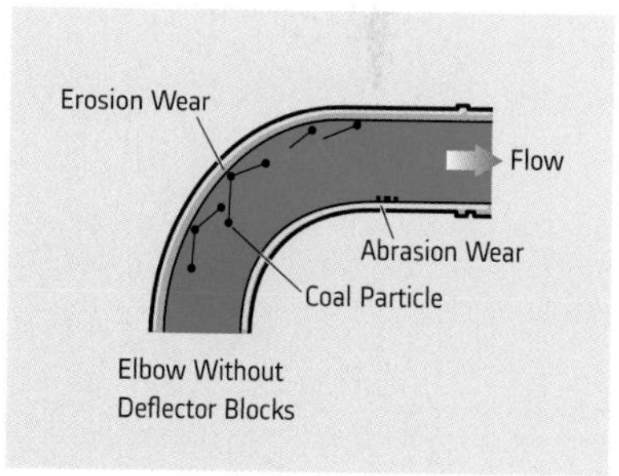

Figure 11-27 | Erosion and abrasion in coal piping

Pulverizer Wear

In coal pulverizers, the major wear is from a combination of abrasion and erosion. The grinding parts of the pulverizer wear principally from abrasion; the pulverizer classifier section and the components of the coal transport system wear principally from erosion. As discussed in Chapter 6, the different types of Alstom pulverizers

Figure 11-28 | Checking roll wear

perform the pulverizing process of the raw coal by subjecting it to attrition grinding between the segmented bull ring in the rotating bowl and the spring-loaded grinding rolls. When worn, both the bull ring and the grinding rolls can be removed and replaced. The rate of abrasive wear of the bull ring and grinding rolls, as well as all of the various wear liners, depends on the type and quantity of minerals in the coal, the required coal fineness, and the operational duty cycle of the pulverizer. It may be possible to obtain greater than twice the life from the bull ring as from a set of grinding rolls, or it may be necessary to replace both at the same time (*Fig. 11-28*).

The decision to replace parts is subject to the operational requirements of the pulverizer and the steam generator. These requirements can have an impact on plants that have switched coals and/or been retrofitted for low-NOx firing and now operate at fineness levels exceeding the original design specification. Because worn parts reduce the pulverizer capacity and coal fineness and can create unsafe operating conditions, such as coal spillage, it may be beneficial to replace the grinding parts before their useable life has completely expired in order to maintain the pulverizer at its required load.

Considerable laboratory research and field development of materials have reduced the wear rate and increased the service life of the pulverizer grinding parts and wear liners. The abrasion-resistant materials currently used for the bull ring are heat-treated, nickel-chromium white iron (Hi-Chrome), heat-treated white iron (Crown 700), and ceramic/metal composite (X-Win). For the grinding rolls, the materials include heat-treated white iron (Crown 700), ceramic/metal composite (X-Win), and hard-surface weld overlay. The hard-surface weld overlay is used to make new grinding rolls and to repair worn Crown 700 grinding rolls by building up to the original diameter and shape. Materials for the wear liners and other pulverizer parts subject to wear include abrasion-resistant plates, high-nickel castings, and various ceramic materials. Exhauster parts subject to wear include the entire fan wheel assembly (i.e., the fan blades and fan spider) as well as the various liners on the exhauster casing. Use of the large Alstom ceramic/steel open periphery and periphery liners on the exhauster casing simplifies maintenance of the required liner configuration.

If extensive application of block-type ceramic tile is made to the interior of the exhauster casing and exhauster cross-over pipe, the installation must be performed carefully to ensure that each tile is fastened strongly into place. Failure of even a single tile that subsequently falls into the rotating exhauster fan wheel can cause major damage to the fan blades and the bearing assembly and necessitate an emergency pulverizer outage to repair the equipment.

For whizzer wheel-type fan wheel assemblies, the service life of the fan blades can be increased by using ceramic tile-covered fan blades on which the edges are lined with tungsten carbide for increased impact protection and abrasion resistance. This design meets the fan blade weight requirement to prevent overloading the fan spider.

For High-Efficiency Exhaust Fan (HEEF)-type wheel assemblies, the application of tungsten carbide to the wear surfaces is often used.

Coal Transport Piping

With more frequent use of highly abrasive coals, wear to the pulverized coal transport piping can become a significant problem. The rate of wear generally is a function of:

- Particle characteristics (hardness, sharpness, and size)
- Particle velocity
- Angle of attack of the particles
- Properties of the piping material

The standard materials used for the coal transport piping system are ductile iron elbows (*Fig. 11-29*) at the pulverizer outlet or exhauster outlet and at the burner inlet, whereas all straight piping between these points usually is carbon steel pipe. The ductile iron elbows usually are designed to a two-pipe-diameter radius except for the burner inlet elbow, which has a one-pipe diameter radius.

The components of the coal transport system are assembled using mechanical couplings of either the Rockwell or the Victaulic/Graylok type. Both types provide strong assembly and can accommodate the thermal growth of the furnace/steam generator and piping components. An extensive arrangement of pipe hangers supports the components of the coal transport piping system.

Because the potential for erosion is greater at the elbow and in the first 2 to 3 feet (0.6 to 0.9 m) of straight pipe directly downstream of it, deflector blocks (kicker blocks) are installed in selected elbows both to absorb coal particle impingement and to redistribute thick air-coal flow streams (see *Fig. 11-29*). Experience dictates the initial location of the deflector/kicker blocks, but these blocks can be repositioned in the field to match the elbow wear pattern should it occur in a different location. System pressure drop considerations limit the number of deflector/kicker blocks that may be installed in each coal pipe. Sometimes, the coal transport system flow characteristics and erosion rates from use of highly abrasive coals are so complex that deflector/kicker blocks cannot be completely effective. In such areas, coal pipe components lined with special wear-resistant material are installed in place of the standard components in order to control the wear rate and extend the service life.

Experience with Wear-Resistant Coal Transport Piping Materials

To reduce the rate of erosion and maintenance to the coal transport piping, the practice of installing coal pipe elbows and other components made from brittle cast material, such NiHard and cast iron, often was used. These materials were adopted because they provided wear resistance superior to that of carbon steel. In 1988, however, the NFPA prohibited the use of brittle low-ductile materials in coal transport piping, because operating experience found the NiHard and cast iron components were subject to failure by fracture. Each failure had the potential to create a hazardous condition in the plant through the release of large quantities of pulverized coal. *Figure 11-30* is an example of an inlet elbow failure as the result of a coal transport piping fire.

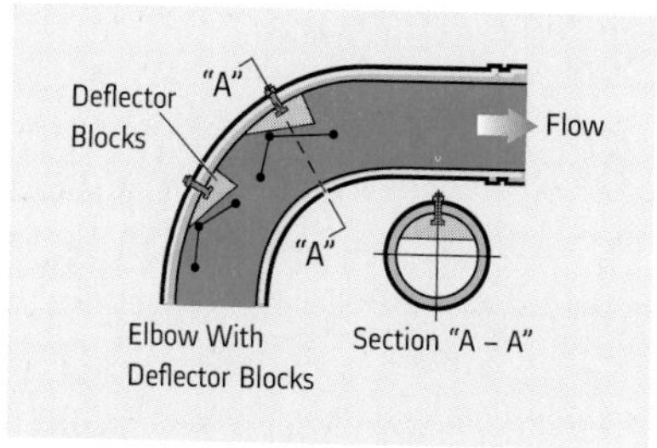

Figure 11-29 | Coal-piping elbow with deflector blocks

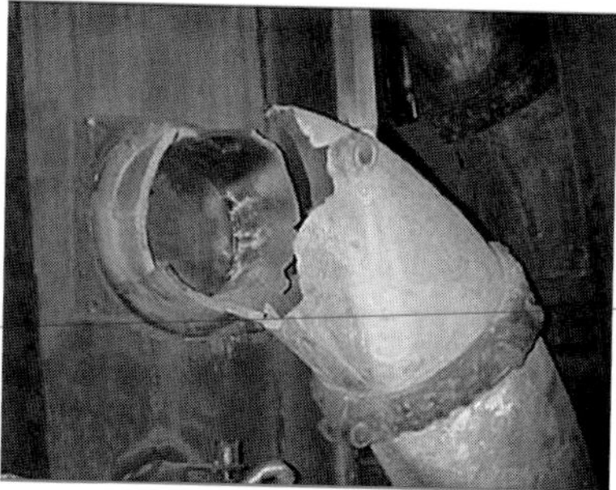

Figure 11-30 | Coal pipe elbow failure

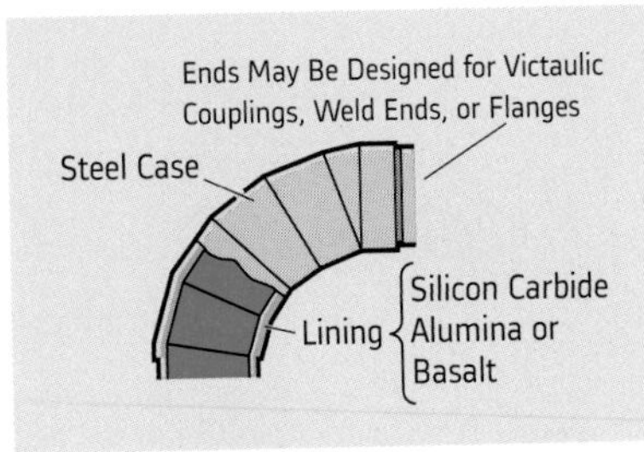

Figure 11-31 | Typical lined, 90° steel elbow

To comply with this regulatory change, components made from either ductile iron or carbon steel lined with ceramic tile are used. These new parts meet the NFPA requirements and provide service life that equals or exceeds that of the original brittle cast components.

Figure 11-31 shows a typical, ceramic-lined elbow. The steel casing, which may be made from fabricated steel mitered sections or from a modified steel pipe bend, encloses the wear-resistant ceramic tile lining and satisfies the code pressure requirements. The ceramic tiles are secured in place with a high temperature adhesive and may use weld plugs for additional attachment strength. The inside diameter of the elbow is identical to the pipeline ID, with the OD being substantially greater.

The most widely used ceramic for coal transport system applications is alumina (Al_2O_3). This material is capable of improving the wear life five- to seven-fold over that of plain carbon steel and nodular iron. Other ceramic materials, such as silicon carbide (SiC) and basalt, also have been used successfully, but alumina brick has been the most economical selection. The installation of replacement components in the coal transport system may, depending on the design used, require a review and changes to the coal pipe support network because of an increase in the component weight or outside diameter.

EROSION AND ABRASION FROM FLY ASH. Approximately 60 to 80% of the ash that results from burning coal exits the furnace with the combustion gases. Gas velocities must not exceed specified limits in order to control erosion from the ash particles. Depending on both the quantity of ash and its composition, the velocity generally is limited to between 50 and 60 ft/s (15 and 18 m/s). Two components in fly ash that appear to contribute most to fly ash erosion are silica (SiO_2) and iron oxide (Fe_2O_3), both of which are relatively hard, abrasive oxides. Ordinarily, silica is present at higher percentages than iron oxide, but iron oxide is denser and, consequently, produces a greater influence of impact.

In general use, the term *fly ash erosion* also includes fly ash abrasion. All tubing erodes when subject to a fly ash-laden gas stream. As long as the wastage rate (i.e., the loss of metal in a given time) is low, the polishing effect is not considered to be significant. When the wastage rate becomes excessive, however, premature tubing failures can occur. Although some erosion is experienced on superheaters and reheaters, most erosion occurs on economizers, which usually are horizontal tubes with closer spacing than the superheaters and reheaters.

ECONOMIZER EROSION. In general, predicting where excessive fly ash erosion might occur for any given unit is difficult, because such erosion is related to non-uniform flow of flue gas and uneven distribution of fly ash in the backpass area, associated with centrifugal forces acting on the ash particles during gas turning. Many factors affect fly ash erosion, which is a very complex process. It is directly proportional to ash loading and is influenced by the relative amounts of abrasive constituents (the silica, alumina, and iron oxide compounds) in the fly ash. Most investigators have found that the erosion rate is an exponential function of particle velocity to between the third and fourth power. Gas side pressure drop (a combined function of gas velocity, turbulence, and heating surface configuration) also influences erosion. Gas velocity through a tube bank is a function of unit operating load, excess air level, and amount of free (net) gas flow area within the bank. Therefore, operating the unit much above its maximum continuous rating and design excess air aggravates the potential for fly ash erosion. Also, any action that results in a reduced flow area, such as localized fly ash plugging, will increase the gas velocity and the potential for erosion by concentrating the fly ash in an area adjacent to the plugged area.

When a unit develops an economizer erosion problem, it is necessary to establish the cause. To add more localized baffling, tube shields, or other devices without regard for the causes may produce only short-term improvements. If examination of the steam generator and its operation indicates that such factors as operating load, excess air level, and presence of plugging are not abnormal, then the addition or modification of baffles, tube shields, or other devices is justified. On some economizers where excessive erosion has occurred across the rear of the backpass, a combination of erosion control methods has been used (*Fig. 11-32*); collectively, these methods have abated excessive erosion. Some of the methods used include:

- Adding filter baffles to obtain a more uniform fly ash distribution across the economizer
- Adding slag fences to prevent economizer plugging
- Installing plates or screens to block open areas and stop channeling of the fly ash
- Adding additional soot blower equipment to maintain cleanliness of the economizer section
- Sequencing the soot blower in the upstream convection sections to blow from top to bottom and rear to front

MAINTENANCE STAFFING

The size of a plant's maintenance staff varies with the number and size of units, fuel used, quality of the labor, and extent of available outside supplemental help. Large coal-fired stations may have several hundred people employed in maintenance and still hire contractors for major overhauls. Some utilities have roving crews to supplement plant labor when required. Plant management can only determine whether to use outside labor or to be self-sufficient. No matter how much outside contract labor is employed, however, the final responsibility must rest with the station staff. Unless they oversee the work that is done, little chance exists for a cohesive maintenance program.

Training for Maintenance

Training maintenance personnel is vitally important to the successful operation of any plant. Many months before a new plant goes into service, maintenance crews should be selected and trained. Although fewer programs are available for maintenance people than for operators, the plant should explore all training aids and methods. Many manufacturers have courses and workshops on equipment maintenance as well as the use of special tools and procedures.

The plant maintenance staff should be used for the initial set-up of equipment, because working with the

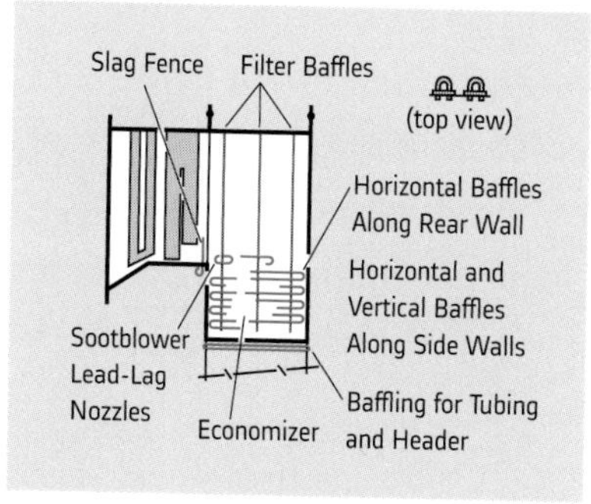

Figure 11-32 | Erosion reduction methods in economizer

Improved sensors, data acquisition systems, and software offer the possibility of predictive maintenance.

manufacturers' representatives provides invaluable training. Money spent on vendor servicing can be wasted if no one in the plant knows what is being done. Thus, a plant maintenance supervisor, as well as maintenance mechanics, should be assigned to each vendor representative.

Long-Range Planning and Scheduling

Nothing is more important in maintaining a plant than scheduling maintenance intervals. The more crowded and busy the maintenance chief's schedule is, the greater the need to take time for long-range planning and scheduling. Such forward thinking includes asking questions that define future needs, such as the following:

- What jobs are next in line?
- On what dates do the jobs have to be started or completed?
- Which person is going to do what?
- What equipment and material are needed to get the work done?
- What problems or roadblocks will the maintenance personnel encounter?

Equally important, an optimum maintenance program calls for replacing some parts before they are completely worn out in order to take advantage of scheduled outage time. A cost/benefit analysis is one way to decide when to change critical parts. The cost of replacing the component is weighed against the cost of the subsequent loss of production if that equipment is out of service again.

For fast-wearing or particularly vulnerable parts, substituting new materials or redesigned parts should be considered. Improved materials can prolong service life and lead to much less maintenance labor. With higher labor costs, materials once considered to be too expensive are now cost savers. Even plants that seldom rely on manufacturers' representatives for aid in maintenance should periodically ask manufacturers about new developments in materials and techniques. For instance, high-nickel material or tungsten-carbide overlays on steel have been most effective in prolonging the service life of steel parts. Although ceramics initially were used only on stationary parts, with improved epoxies they can now be used on rotating equipment as well and are found in many applications today.

Wise maintenance supervisors, then, will investigate new materials or other ways to cut maintenance costs. They will allot time for discussions with vendors' representatives to find out what new products may be a solution to difficult maintenance problems.

BEYOND MAINTENANCE AND REPAIR

Maintenance activities, as they have been addressed in this chapter, fall into three overlapping categories. These are maintenance and repair, anticipatory or preventive maintenance, and predictive maintenance.

The first type, maintenance and repair, has to do with the day-to-day, month-to-month, and year-to-year actions of inspection, monitoring, and testing (e.g., of oil or water) to ensure that a steam generating unit and its auxiliaries will keep running between scheduled outages. Strange sounds, visible leaks, and higher-than-normal pressures or temperatures all tell the alert operator or maintenance person that something must be done quickly or unit availability will suffer. Unfortunately, this type of maintenance is reactive, but it is vital to keeping equipment in service for extended periods of time.

The second type, anticipatory or preventive maintenance, is the kind that prevents the strange noises and other undesirable indications from occurring. Based on manufacturers' recommendations, in-plant experience, improved data acquisition and monitoring, and seat-of-the-pants judgment, preventive maintenance is done at planned intervals while the equipment is operating satisfactorily. Its purpose is to eliminate unscheduled outages resulting from component distress. With this type of maintenance, the timing is arbitrary. Empirical data and the accumulation of favorable experience provide the basis for those decisions.

The third type, predictive maintenance, has the same aim as preventive maintenance, but it employs more sophisticated, computer-assisted methods of timing the actions. It is intended to achieve the same or better results at lower cost.

Maintenance and repair activities beyond these three categories lead into the realm of life continuation, which is discussed in other chapters. Major efforts to obtain higher availability and indefinite continuation of equipment life are in the area of senior management decision making.

MAINTENANCE AND REPAIR OF STEAM TURBINES

Reliable operation of the complete plant is critical to the overall economics of a power station. Regular, planned inspections of plant equipment are carried out with the goal of avoiding unplanned shutdowns. This is particularly true of equipment that has moving parts subject to wear, such as a steam turbine. It is even more critical when the parts in question are obscured from view because of the high temperatures and pressures of normal operation.

Maintenance issues for steam turbines include solid particle impacts (from foreign materials introduced to the turbine), erosion, deposits, corrosion, water impacts (from valve leaks), electro-erosion, vibration, seal damage, and bearing wear (from contaminated or insufficient lubricating oil). Wear, erosion, and corrosion can be detected through proper inspection programs. These programs can be roughly divided into minor inspections (1–2 weeks in duration), intermediate inspections (2–4 weeks in duration), and major inspections (6–8 weeks in duration).

INSPECTIONS

Minor inspections preferably are conducted when the plant is shut down for reasons other than the steam turbine. Spot checks of control elements and systems are performed, along with inspections of the various safety devices. Any operational problems are reviewed, and corrective actions can be taken to minimize further impacts.

Intermediate inspections would be performed during a planned outage. Bearings are checked, and safety devices are tested. Steam valves are inspected, and condenser and feedwater heater systems are checked. The low-pressure, last-stage blades are visually inspected. Boroscopic examination of all accessible turbine components is carried out as well. All control systems, lubrication systems, and cooling systems are checked. If deemed to be necessary, the turbine casings can be opened. Finally, the alignment is checked.

Major inspections are comprehensive examinations of the entire turbine. All casings are opened. All blades and seals are examined. All of the checks and tests that are done in the intermediate inspection are carried out as well. During these inspections, any wear, corrosion, or erosion should be readily apparent. Repair and replacement are carried out as necessary.

TIMING OF INSPECTIONS

The timing of the first inspection and the interval between subsequent inspections are largely determined by the number of operating hours, the mode of operation, and the number of start-ups. These factors, especially the number of start-ups, influence component wear and metal fatigue. Typically, metal fatigue is insignificant before 100,000 hours of operation. The influence of the mode of operation on wear is expressed as

$$EOH = OH + NS \times HS$$

Equation 11-1

where

- EOH = equivalent operating hours
- OH = effective operating hours
- NS = number of start-ups
- HS = operating hours charged for one start-up

Typical values for HS might be 50 hours for critical components and 25 hours for other components. The value of EOH serves as a measure for the wear of the individual components, and it provides a basis for setting up the inspection intervals. A typical inspection interval chart is shown in *Figure 11-33*.

After an equivalent operating time of approximately 100,000 hours, the remaining life of critical components should be calculated (see Chapters 8 and 14). The inspection intervals are then determined on a site-specific basis. Approximately 12 months before the actual inspection is scheduled, the plant operator should determine the time, type, and duration of the inspection. Well in advance of the inspection, the "actual state" of the turbine should be determined by taking check measurements (e.g., pressure curves, vibration measurements, and foundation displacement) and comparing them to the design values. The results should be used to guide the inspection plan.

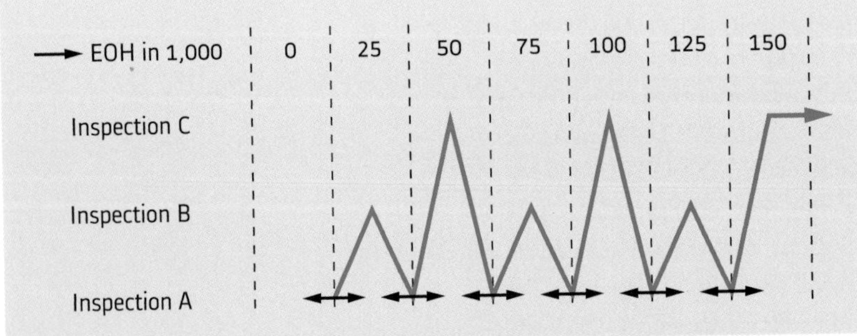

Figure 11-33 | Alstom equivalent operating hours (EOH)–based inspection schedule

SPARE PARTS

Spare parts play a key role in the maintenance of steam turbines. A variety of types of spare parts are maintained, depending on the type of unit involved, the anticipated impact of an outage, and the delivery time of different spare parts. *Table 11-1* shows some examples of the different categories and types of spare parts.

WATER QUALITY

The water quality of the water-steam cycle is an essential element for the lifetime of the condenser, the feedwater train, the boiler, the connecting piping, and the steam turbine (see Chapter 9). Because the water and steam are

TABLE 11-1 | CATEGORIES OF SPARE PARTS

Category	Definition	Examples
Daily maintenance spares (DM)	Material for daily maintenance	
DM1	Material for daily maintenance not related to specific engine. This material could be defined once for all steam turbine sets	Chemicals, lubricants
DM2	Material for daily maintenance, engine related	Filter inserts, carbon brushes
Operational spare parts (OS)	For optimization of plant availability without dismantling the turbine	
OS1	Small parts, but very important for high plant availability	Gaskets/O-rings for servo drives
OS2	Components/parts, necessary for high availability	Service kit for servo drives
OS3	Large components, necessary for high availability (Significant for customers with several units of the same type)	Reserve servo drive
Inspectional spares (IS)		
IA	Spare part recommendation for the relevant inspection according to Alstom instructions. Parts which will be damaged during dismantling have to be included	Gaskets
IB	IB includes IA	Gaskets, sealing rings and expansion sleeves
IC	IC includes IB	Gaskets, tensile bolts and expansion sleeves
Backup spares	Parts/components which could be only changed with dismantled turbine	

* Definition of the inspection types in accordance with the spare part category designations:
B-inspection: IB = OS + DM
C-inspection, complete: IC complete = OS + DM + IC
C-inspection after 150,000 equivalent operating hours: IC 150,000 = OS + DM + IC + BS1

enclosed in tubing and piping, it often is difficult to detect problems associated with water chemistry. Potential problems caused by poor water quality include magnetite deposition on the control valves, copper deposition in the high-pressure turbine, caustic embrittlement in the intermediate- and low-pressure turbines, and pitting corrosion and cracking in the low-pressure turbine. Cold-end corrosion diagnostics allow the operator to monitor the temperature and humidity inside the low-pressure turbine during operation. The operator can decide to shut down the unit if corrosive conditions persist. During shutdown, proper "lay-up" procedures (e.g., proper draining and nitrogen blanketing) need to be followed in order to minimize the potential for corrosion. By following the manufacturer's recommendations for shutdown and standby conditions, maintenance costs can be reduced over the longer-term operation of the plant.

MAINTENANCE AND REPAIR OF GENERATORS

Modern generators are very reliable and require limited maintenance. The main areas of concern are the insulation of the rotor and stator windings. This insulation ages with time according to the electrical, mechanical, and thermal stresses in service.

Critical components can be damaged by incorrect operation of the generator or nearby electrical faults on the transmission system. For these reasons, a regular program that combines inspection with both preventive and predictive maintenance programs should be utilized. Online measurements, inspections, and generator diagnostics are all part of a coordinated maintenance program.

Inspection intervals are based on the EOH for the generator and should be coordinated with the steam turbine inspections. Long-term trending that uses online monitoring will provide guidance to the maintenance team for inspections. During inspections, measurements are made (e.g., machine settings and shaft alignment) and then compared with the results from previous inspections and similar machines for indications of any problems.

During major inspections, the rotor should be removed. End covers, bearings, brush gear (or rotating exciter), and heat exchangers also are removed to allow comprehensive inspections of all generator components and auxiliary components. On hydrogen- and hydrogen/water-cooled units, purging should be performed before opening up the system.

Ultrasonic testing can be performed to assess the mechanical integrity of critical generator components, including the most highly stressed rotor retaining rings. Automated ultrasonic inspection of the retaining ring seating area allows condition assessment without the removal of the rings themselves. Natural frequency measurement can assess the condition of the stator end winding, and visual assessment can be made for the stator slot discharge. In situ inspection of the diodes and fuses on brushless exciters can provide reliable detection of faulty components within the rectifier bridge.

Online monitoring provides the opportunity for early detection of incipient faults. These include generator stator partial discharge monitoring, rotor condition monitoring, generator rotor flux monitoring, stator end winding vibration monitoring, and stator bar water temperature monitoring. This monitoring can detect a damaged part before it deteriorates to the point of causing a major failure that leads to a forced outage.

REPAIR ACTIONS

The generator stator core consists of steel sheets laminated with insulation that are insulated from each other to prevent harmful eddy currents from causing overheating and melting of the stator core. A generator flux test is used to detect and quantify any damage to the stator core. A repair can be made by carefully grinding out the damaged area and reinsulating the laminations by resin injection.

Stator windings of large generators are directly cooled by demineralized water. Imbalances in water chemistry can lead to copper oxide deposits inside the cooling tubes. A multi-stage chemical cleaning can first remove the excess oxides and then re-establish the surface chemistry.

After long periods of operation, the brazed connections on the waterboxes may decay, which can lead to leakage of generator cooling gas into the water circuit or of water into the stator bar insulation. A tungsten inert gas (TIG) welding process can be used to establish a permanent, impermeable coating

that covers the areas of the brazed connections between the waterbox and the hollow conductors.

The sealing ring and associated seal oil journals prevent leakage of hydrogen into the system. If the journal is damaged because of mechanical wear, it can be refurbished on site by using a metal spraying method and final machining.

Rotors or stators can be rewound on site or switched out with a spare unit while the damaged unit is sent to a shop for rewinding. Sparing philosophy is determined by the plant owner.

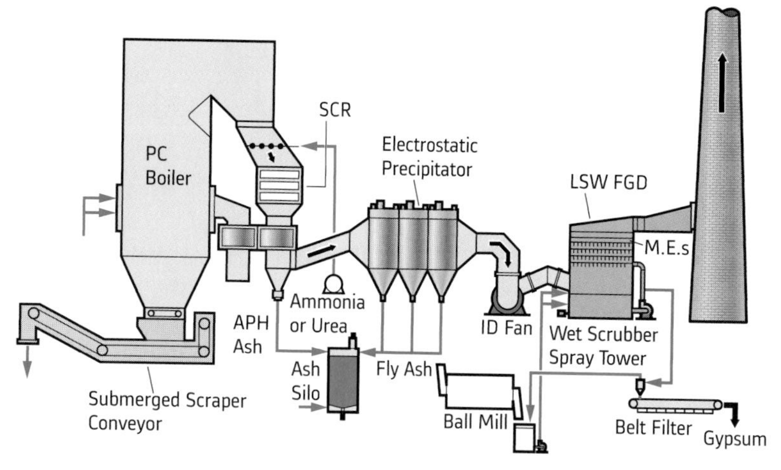

Figure 11-34 | Typical power plant configuration (APH, air pre heater; FGD, flue gas desulfurization; ID, induced draft; M.E.s., mist eliminators; PC, pulverized coal; SCR, selective catalytic reduction)

MAINTENANCE AND REPAIR OF EMISSION CONTROL EQUIPMENT

Fuel and air are required to produce energy (i.e., electricity and/or heat) from combustion. In addition to energy, organic components and particulates are produced. Legal restrictions on plant emissions exist in five areas:

1. Particulates (e.g., fly ash)
2. CO_2
3. SO_2
4. NOx
5. Mercury

The objective of this section is to give an overview of the major issues that need to be addressed during periodic maintenance of power plant equipment designed to remove particulates, SO_2, and NOx.

In general, wear, corrosion, and the heterogeneous nature of raw coal are the enemies in keeping emission control equipment operational. Each particular piece of equipment has its own nuances. Because many different control technologies from a wide group of equipment suppliers are currently in operation, the subject is very complex. In general, however, two major plant configurations exist for removing particulates, sulfur oxides, and nitrogen oxides.

A typical configuration for a power plant in which the main fuel is medium- to high-sulfur fuel, or in which wallboard-grade gypsum is the desired by-product, is shown in *Figure 11-34*. In this configuration, selective catalytic reduction (SCR) removes the NOx, an electrostatic precipitator removes the particulate matter, and a wet FGD system removes the SO_2. This configuration has many advantages. The SCR reliably removes over 90% of the NOx. The ESP removes over 99% of the particulate matter, and the wet FGD removes and converts at least 98% of the SO_2 into a usable by-product (wallboard gypsum) while also capturing any small particles that the ESP misses. The major disadvantages of this configuration are the capital cost of the wet FGD system and the large amount of water required to operate the FGD system.

A second configuration is becoming very important, particularly for firing lower-sulfur fuels (*Fig. 11-35*). In this configuration, NOx also is removed by SCR, but the SO_2 is removed by a dry process. The particulate control is by a fabric filter. The advantages of this configuration are lower capital cost, control of SO_3 as well as SO_2, very low particulate emissions, and lower H_2O consumption. This configuration typically results in slightly lower SO_2 capture (95% vs. 98% with wet FGD), and it does not produce a saleable by-product, such as wallboard gypsum.

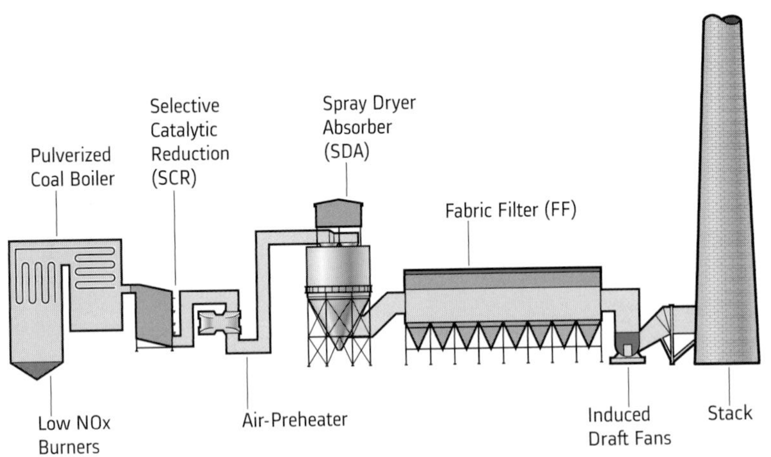

Figure 11-35 | Power plant configuration with dry scrubber

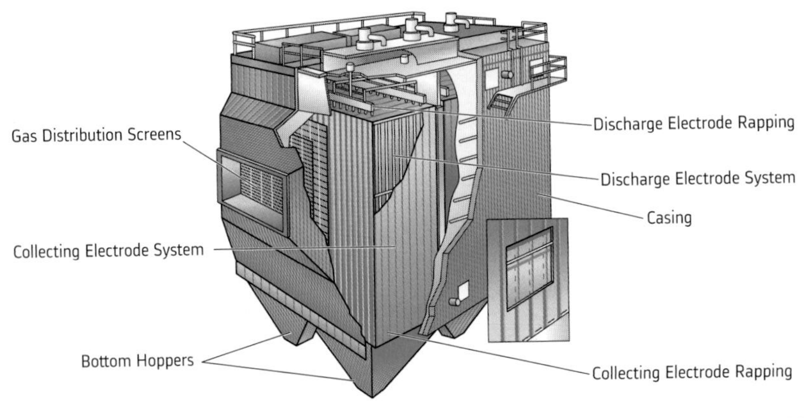

Figure 11-36 | Electrostatic precipitator

ELECTROSTATIC PRECIPITATORS

To effectively address maintenance and repair of an ESP, the operator needs to be concerned with the following issues:

- **Physical integrity and safety.** Physically, the mechanical components that make up the ESP must be structurally sound and safe for operation.
- **Particle charging.** Fly ash particles must be successfully charged by the high-voltage system.
- **Particle collection and cleaning.** Fly ash particles must be entrained on the collecting surfaces, which together with the charging system minimizes the effects of back corona. Particles held on the collecting surfaces must be periodically dislodged and moved to the ash hopper.
- **Ash transport.** The ash hopper must move its contents periodically to the ash disposal system. (See Chapter 6 for a detailed discussion.)

Physical Integrity and Safety of ESPs

The design of an ESP is specific to the application. Its height and width are selected to match the gas quantity to be treated and its treatment length to match the required precipitation efficiency. The number of fields is varied, depending on the amount of gas that will pass through the filter and on the electrical properties of the particulate

to be collected. The physical integrity and safety of the ESP is the first issue to be addressed when considering repair and maintenance.

Figure 11-36 identifies the major components of an ESP. All of these components are subject to wear and corrosion, particularly if the fuel being fired has a high sulfur content and if temperatures within the precipitator are not maintained above the acid dew point. The ESP cannot operate effectively if the key components are damaged. Consequently, periodic inspection of the key components, starting with structural integrity, is required.

Before beginning any inspection program, it is important that proper safety practices are understood and implemented. Dangers include electrocution, suffocation, engulfment, and exposure to toxic gas in confined spaces. Because the equipment is tall, a fall hazard exists, and open mechanical equipment represents various crush and pinch hazards. Experienced and trained inspection personnel, following documented safety procedures, are needed.

A safety plan that identifies hazards and preventive actions must be formed before entering the emission control equipment for a mechanical inspection. Alstom inspectors are equipped with the personal protective equipment necessary for dust, gases, and other hazards that could affect health. All plant safety procedures, such as "lock out tag out," must be followed to safely secure equipment for inspection and then for service. This requires communication with the control room to prevent the start of any equipment that could risk the safety of personnel working on the equipment. Specific procedures to follow include:

- Take all boilers joined to the ESP off-line, or bypass the ESP.
- Ventilate the ESP by opening hatches and running an induced draft fan for some hours at low speed.
- Switch off the ESP power supply.
- Lock out the power supply, and disconnect fuses. Alstom usually provides a sequential, keyed, interlock system to reduce the possibility that someone would be exposed to hazardous voltages. Before inspection, a key interlock is required for all equipment that would be tagged out based on operation or maintenance safety procedures. This includes safety switches, panel boards, electrical enclosures, molded case circuit breakers, medium-voltage switches, and circuit breakers or any other electrical device that is de-energized

Figure 11-37 | Ground switch with window

or disconnected and cannot be operated because of safety.

- Ground all internals directly to earth via suitable grounding devices. *Figure 11-37* is an Alstom grounding switch with a window to visually verify that the high voltage source has been disconnected.
- Start internal inspection when the temperature inside the ESP is low enough (maximum recommended temperature, 113°F [45°C]).
- Do not clean the ESP internals before inspection. An experienced inspector can determine much from looking at the dust behavior inside.
- The customer must supply one worker to assist and serve as the safeguard (hole watch) outside the hatch from which the inspector is working.

The first step in any periodic inspection plan is to ensure the fitness for service of the following key elements. Each element must be inspected for wear, corrosion, and physical damage. These elements include:

- Walkways, stairs, ladders, and safety equipment
- Casing and insulation
- Inspection doors
- Foundation rollers/slide plates/flex columns
- Hoppers
- Inlet and outlet elbow/breeching
- Expansion joints
- Dampers
- Bottom enclosure
- Penthouse

ESP Particle Charging Systems

The most important part of a precipitator is the discharge electrode system. The discharge electrodes provide the high voltage that generates the corona required for charging the particles in the flue gas. The electrodes are symmetrically placed in the electrical field to avoid excessive sparks or short circuits (*Fig. 11-38*).

Spiral discharge electrodes provide high reliability and are insensitive to the temperature difference that is required for optimized precipitator operation. The spiral electrodes are assembled in a rigid frame with one, two, or three levels of electrodes, depending on the ESP height. The electrode frames are hung and firmly bolted to a top frame, which in turn is suspended, via four support insulators located on the casing roof, outside the gas stream. At the bottom, the frames are connected to cross-guide irons and, after the discharge electrode system has been completed, form a rigid box

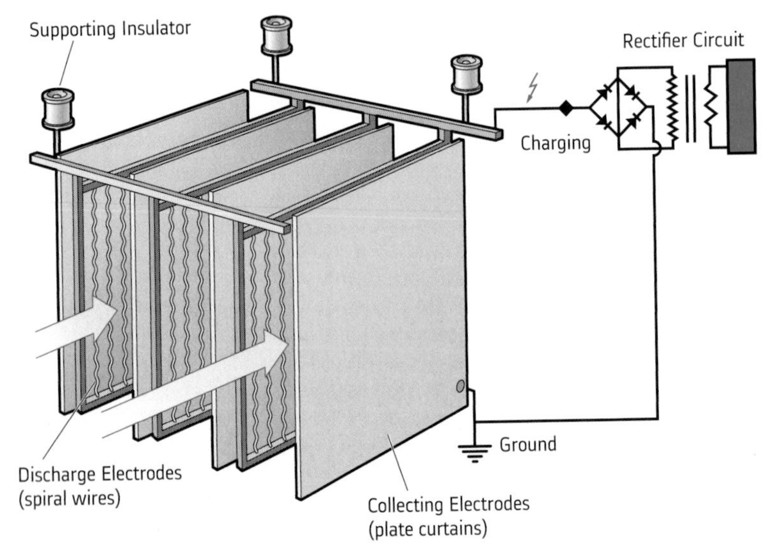

Figure 11-38 | Principal design of an electrostatic precipitator

structure. Because there is no potential for swinging of the frame, stabilizers are not necessary, and the structure is free to expand in any direction.

The multi-peak electrode has a tubular body of special quality to which barbs are stud welded. Each barb has two peaks directed toward the collecting surface. The barb peak has a special shape to generate the desired current/voltage characteristics without being sensitive to electrical erosion. Examples are shown in *Figure 11-39.*

The discharge electrodes are powered by transformer rectifiers, or Alstom high-frequency power supplies, known as "switched integrated rectifiers":

- Switched = high-frequency electronic power processing technique
- Integrated = transformer, power electronics, and controller integrated in the same housing
- Rectifier = alternating current (AC) input and direct current (DC) output

Alstom has found that in order to achieve low emission levels, it is very important to correctly energize the discharge electrodes. Several products for optimizing the flue gas cleaning are available.

By combining high frequency, solid-state power electronics and computer control, switched integrated rectifiers improve the collecting efficiency for different applications. They also substantially reduce installation and commissioning costs. The switched integrated rectifier is part of the EPIC system and communicates over a field bus. The field bus allows all units to share all available information in real time.

Maintenance and repair of the components that are required to charge particles is facilitated by routine mechanical inspection and trending the unit's performance over time. Discharge electrode wires are monitored by examination for excessive buildup, material loss, and pitting. Care also should be taken to clean and verify the integrity of the insulators that hold the discharge electrode frame. Problem areas are shown in *Figure 11-40.*

ESP Particle Collection and Cleaning Systems

For the charged particles to be collected effectively, the gas flow must be uniform and within the design velocity range of the ESP. The gas entering the precipitator must be uniformly distributed over the entire cross section to obtain optimum efficiency from the precipitator; acceptable distribution cannot be attained simply by the design of the inlet duct. Two or more screen plates in series are installed at the inlet nozzle (the actual number depends on the specific nozzle design and type of dust). The coefficient of variation in flue gas velocity, as measured over the cross section after the first field, should not be more than

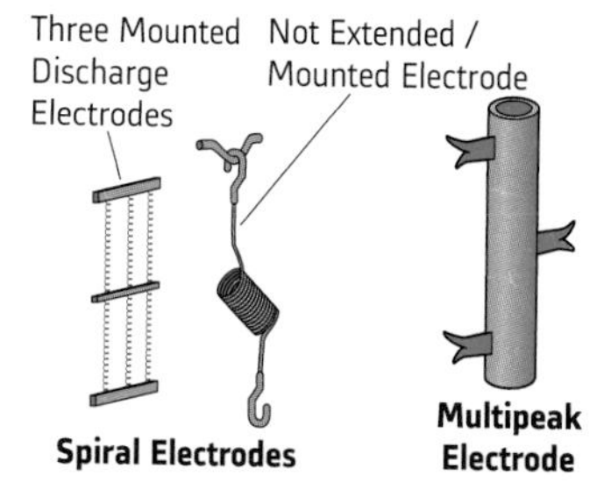

Figure 11-39 | Spiral and multi-peak electrodes

Figure 11-40 | Dust accumulation and cracked support insulator

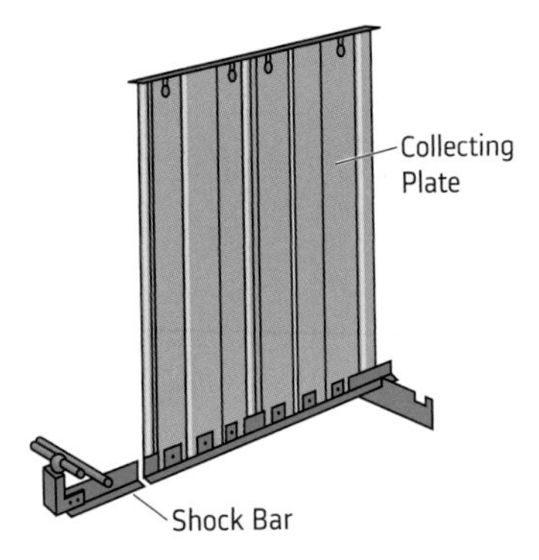

Figure 11-41 | Collecting plates with shock bar

20%. To achieve this, additional baffle plates may be added on the screens during the final checking of the gas flow pattern on site. The collecting electrodes are hung from a separate and adjustable roof structure. The suspension bar can be adjusted vertically for easy alignments of the whole system, if necessary.

Each collecting electrode is a 30 inch (750 mm) wide, profile roll-formed panel, in mild steel, with a special shape to provide satisfactory current distribution and stiffness. The profile edges are folded to improve stiffness and to eliminate possible sparks to sharp edges. The design is based on a concept that requires no welding.

Normally, there are three discharge electrodes per collector panel. The collecting plates are firmly connected at the bottom to shock bars (anvil beams), which ensures maximum transfer of the rapping energy (*Fig. 11-41*). The shock bars are properly guided on the sides to eliminate swinging or misalignment of the electrode curtain. Misalignment can cause electrical close clearances, which lower the efficiency of the filter. In severe cases, it will destroy the collecting plates.

In normal operation, the collecting electrode (CE) plates will collect the fly ash particles. Over time, the layer will build up and need to be cleaned by mechanically dislodging the agglomerated particles. Alstom's standard method for cleaning the CE plates is with "tumbling hammers," which are mounted on a staggered shaft with one hammer for each shock bar. As the shaft slowly rotates, each of the hammers in turn tumbles, hitting its associated shock bar. The shock bar transmits the blow simultaneously to all of the collecting plates on that row.

The design of the rapping mechanism gives a high, steeply ramped acceleration to shear off the dust cake in large agglomerates. The rapping intervals are adjustable and have to be optimized for each precipitator field. The measured minimum rapping acceleration for a 15 × 49 ft (4.5 × 15 m) curtain, with firm connection between the plates and shock bar, is approximately 150*g* at the upper far corner measured perpendicular to the plate. Each of the components listed below should be examined during periodic plant overhauls to ensure mechanical integrity. *Figure 11-42* gives some detail on the tumbling rapper hammer itself.

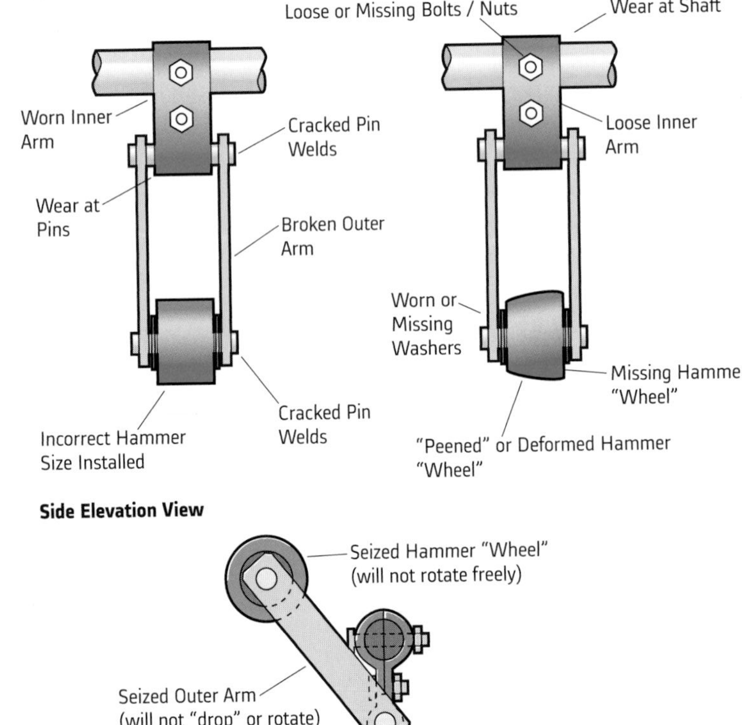

Figure 11-42 | Typical problems of rapper hammers

FABRIC FILTERS

Types of Fabric Filters and Safety Considerations

In a fabric filter, bag filter, or baghouse, the ash-laden gas is taken through a sieving textile media. The ash is collected on the surface of the media, and the deposited layer of ash becomes an integral part of the sieve. The pore size of the composite media-ash layer sieve is very small, typically in the range of 10 to 30 microns. Because of the sieving effect, the collection efficiency is high. The separation efficiency is, among other things, a function of the porosity of the media, the ash properties, and the cleaning technique. The smaller the pores, the higher the collection efficiency is in general terms.

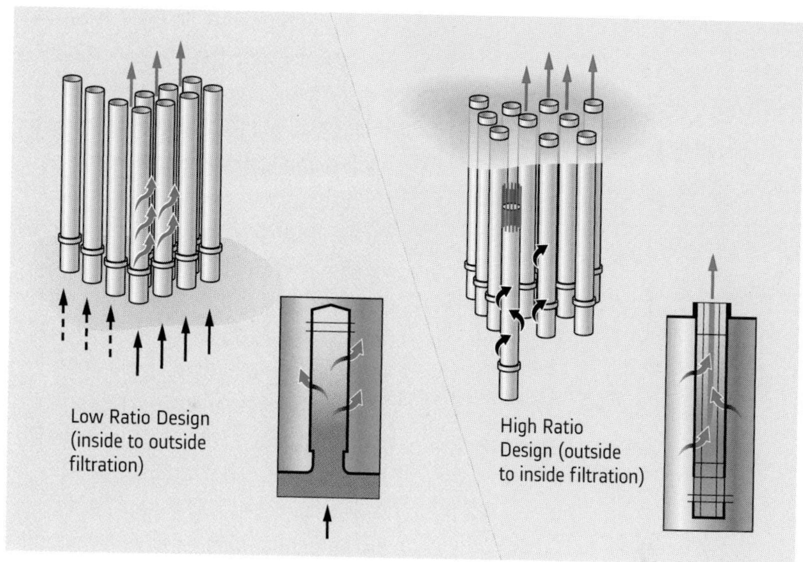

Figure 11-43 | High- and low-ratio filter designs

There are two major design concepts regarding fabric filters, with the difference being whether the ash is collected on the inside of the bags (the low-ratio design) or on the outside of the bags (the high-ratio design) (*Fig. 11-43*). For the high-ratio design, the soft and flexible bags are supported on the inside by a steel wire cage.

Irrespective of the type of filter used, the deposited ash layer must periodically be cleaned off the bags in order to control the pressure drop over the filter. Normally, both high-ratio and low-ratio filters are divided into a number of compartments. Each compartment is equipped with shutoff dampers in the inlet and outlet and, thus, can be isolated from the flue gas steam by closing the dampers. A high-ratio filter generally may be cleaned while online, without isolating the bags from the flue gas. A low-ratio filter is always cleaned off-line. The compartments are isolated from the flue gas periodically and sequentially. Filters cleaned in this way are designed with an extra compartment, because one compartment is always off-line for cleaning and, hence, does not take an active part in the filtration of the flue gas.

The cleaning method used for high-ratio filters is much more energetic than the cleaning mechanism used for low-ratio filters. This energetic cleaning method allows a high-ratio filter to operate at two or more times the air/cloth (A/C) ratio of a low-ratio filter. The A/C ratio is defined as the quotient between the actual flue gas flow (e.g., in actual ft^3/m [m^3/h]) and the total bag surface area of the filter (ft^2 [m^2]). It represents the flue gas mean approach velocity (ft/min [m/h]) to the filter bags. For high-ratio filters in power applications, the A/C ratio typically is in the range of 3.3–5.5 ft/min (60–100 m/h); for low-ratio filters, the A/C ratio typically is in the range of

1.7–2.8 ft/min (30–50 m/h). Consequently, the total bag surface area for a low-ratio filter generally is two-fold the total filter area for a high-ratio filter for a given application and gas flow.

A safety plan that identifies hazards and preventive actions must be formed before entering the equipment for a mechanical inspection. All plant safety procedures, such as "lock out tag out," must be followed to safely secure and release equipment. This requires communication with the control room to prevent the start-up of any equipment that could risk the safety of the personnel working on that equipment. Specific procedures to follow include:

- Take all boilers joined to the fabric filter off-line, or bypass the fabric filter.
- Ventilate the fabric filter by opening hatches and running an induced draft fan for some hours at low speed.
- Switch off the fabric filter power supply.
- Lock out the power supply and disconnect fuses.
- Start internal inspection when the temperature inside the fabric filter is low enough (maximum recommended temperature, 113°F [45°C]).
- Do not clean fabric filter internals before inspection. An experienced inspector can determine much from looking at the dust behavior inside.
- The customer must supply one worker to assist and serve as the safeguard (hole watch) outside the hatch from which the inspector is working.

Filter Media Lifetime

The filter media have a strong impact on the performance of the filter with regard to outlet dust emissions, bag life, and pressure drop over the filter. The most critical factor is the flue gas temperature, both continuous and peak. Other factors include material resistance to acid attack, hydrolysis, and so on. The development of new needle felt constructions and surface treatments have decreased emissions considerably over the last decade.

Fabric filters are applicable for solid fuel-fired (coal, lignite, biomass, and peat) power plants of all sizes and combustion techniques. These filters can be used for oil-fired boilers provided that a sorbent is injected upstream of the filter for gas absorption. Bags usually are replaced after approximately 24,000 to 32,000 operating hours for high-ratio filters, corresponding to between 3 and 4 years of operation with 8,000 boiler operating hours per year. Because each fabric filter has its own set of characteristics and system parameters, it is important to evaluate each of the following variables in order to choose the fabric that is best suited to the system:

- Temperature
- Moisture level
- Particulate size
- Gas stream chemistry
- A/C ratio
- Particulate abrasiveness
- Mechanical factors (e.g., cleaning style and installation)

In general, felt filter bags are used in pulse-jet collectors. Woven filter bags are used in reverse air or shaker baghouses. Limitations are associated with

TABLE 11-2 | PROPERTIES OF FILTER MATERIALS*

Fiber	Abbreviation	Temperature °C		Acid	Alkali	Hydrolysis (H_2O)	Oxidation (O_2)	Abrasion	Price Relative to PES
		Continuous	Peak						
Polypropylene	PP	90	95	5	5	5	3	5	1
Polyester	PES	135	150	3	2	1	5	5	1
Dolanit Ricem	PAC	125	130	4	3	4–5	3	3–4	1, 3
Ryton Procon Toray	PPS	180	210	4	4	5	3	3–4	4, 5
Nomex	APA	200	220	2	4	2	3–4	5	5
P84	PI	240	260	3	3	2	—	4	6
Teflon® Fiber	PTFE	230	260	5	5	5	5	3	15
Fiberglass	GLS	240	280	4	3	5	5	1	2–3

*1, low; 2, mediocre; 3, generally good; 4, good; 5, excellent.

each type of bag. *Table 11-2* summarizes the properties of the most common filter materials. The most important selection criteria for filter media are the flue gas temperature, both continuous and peak, and the flue gas and fly ash chemistry:

- **Flue gas temperature.** Power plants commonly operate at temperatures very near the maximum allowed by the fiber manufacturer. High temperature can accelerate oxidation of the fabric in conjunction with the effects of flue gas chemistry.
- **Flue gas and fly ash chemistry.** Recent laboratory analyses suggest that the fabric strength and lifetime will be reduced if there is chemical attack. In addition to the sources above, one possible source for the chemical attack is the sulfur trioxide (SO_3) in the flue gas, present either naturally or introduced as a flue gas conditioning agent. Combined with water, SO_3, a strong oxidizing agent, becomes sulfuric acid, a strong acid and also a strong oxidizing agent. Either of these sulfur compounds might degrade the bag material.

Bags, Cages, and Cleaning Trains

Normally, problems associated with fabric filers are confined to the fabric filter bags, the support cages, or the equipment to provide reverse flow cleaning. If an increase in particulate emissions occurs, there is a good chance that a hole has formed in one of the bags. The location of the hole can be found through analysis of the opacity signal compared to the firing of the cleaning system and inspection. *Figure 11-44* shows a photograph of a typical hole in a fabric filter.

As with gas sneakage, a single hole in a filter bag will significantly increase the dust emissions. For example, a hole with a diameter of 0.2 in (5 mm) will

Figure 11-44 | Hole in a fabric filter bag

increase the average emission rate by 100 fold for the affected bag and by 5 to 10% for a complete filter of 1,000 bags.

In high-ratio, pulse cleaned filters with an outside-to-inside filtration direction through the filter elements, the filter bags are attached to the separation plate between the inlet and outlet side of the filter with a cuff containing a spring-steel band. The grooved cuff fits into circular holes with narrow tolerances cut in the bag plate and can be installed and removed without tools.

In all designs, a bag cage is required to prevent the bag from collapsing under the pressure differential across the filter fabric. The bag fits on the cage with a certain looseness so that it flexes between its filtration position and the inflated shape at cleaning. This flexing is essential for the effectiveness of the pulse cleaning. It also, however, is a potential cause of failure because of concentrated fatigue. *Figure 11-45* shows the inspection of a bag cage.

Figure 11-45 | Inspection of a filter cage

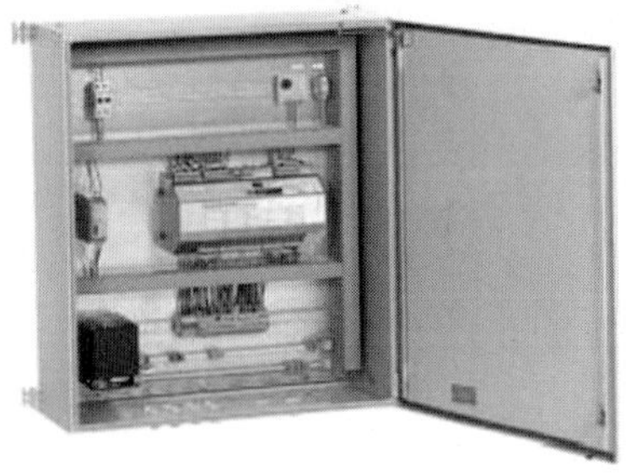

Figure 11-46 | Electronic fabric filter integrated controller (EFFIC) control cabinet

Fabric Filter Electronic Controls

The main function of most fabric filter controls is the control of the pulse cleaning in a fabric filter using compressed air. Alstom's electronic fabric filter integrated controller (EFFIC) is a cost-effective solution designed to be installed in new fabric filters or to replace and modernize control systems in existing fabric filters (*Fig. 11-46*). Several EFFIC control units can work together in a network to control larger fabric filters. In such cases, each EFFIC would control part of the filter, one line, one or more chambers, or even an individual pressure tank. One EFFIC is then configured to be the master controller for the others.

The functions of the EFFIC include:

- Minimizing dust emissions from the fabric filter.
- Optimizing the dust layer thickness on the bags for the best possible cleaning.
- Minimizing the pressure drop and, thus, the energy consumption.
- Reducing the total operating costs of the fabric filter.
- Bag failure analysis and valve fault detection.

Reasons for Emission Increases After Fabric Filters

A number of reasons exist for a slow increase in emissions in the exhaust gas path after a fabric filter that eventually results in excessive emissions:

- A gradual increase of gas flow over years. This could be caused by a gradual degradation of boiler performance and, quite often, by slowly increasing air in-leakage upstream of the filter.
- A production increase or changes in fuel or other chemistry changes that result in an increased gas flow and/or dust, which is more difficult to handle.
- Chemical or thermal degeneration of the textile in the fabric filter that results in a slow emission increase over time.

There are several reasons for rapid surges in emissions from a fabric filter:

- Holes made by mistake during installation (e.g., by a knife in unpacking the bags)

- Fault in the fabrication (e.g., a bad seam)
- Improper gas-tight welding of the plate in the filter between the inlet and outlet ducts
- Hot sparks in the exhaust gas, which cause a hole by burning or melting
- Wear damage in the textile because of poor gas and/or dust distribution

SPRAY TOWER ABSORBERS FOR SO_2 REMOVAL

Types of Open Spray Towers and Safety Considerations

Selection of SO_2 removal technology involves many considerations, including initial capital cost, long-term cost of reagent (lime or limestone), by-product requirements, landfill requirements, current and future SO_2 removal requirements, maintenance costs, long-term coal flexibility, and future emission controls (mercury, trace elements, and others). These multiple considerations lead to different site-specific equipment; however, the overall process and chemistry are similar.

Safety concerns with this equipment are similar to those with other plant equipment. Confined spaces potentially pose a suffocation or chemical exposure hazard. The physical size of the equipment creates fall hazards, and the strong chemicals in the process create potential for chemical burn hazards. All of these concerns need to be addressed in a site-specific safety plan before repair and maintenance operations are considered. As described previously, there are three major subsystems for the modern wet FGD process, as shown in *Figure 11-47*.

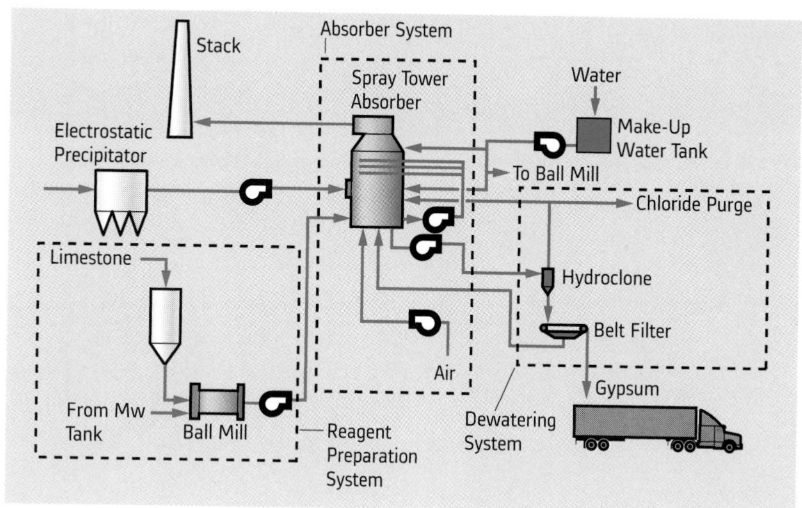

Figure 11-47 | Wet SO_2 scrubbing system with major subsystems

Reagent Preparation Circuit

The reagent preparation system generally is straightforward (*Fig. 11-48*). Usually, the reagent is limestone, which must be ground before addition into the absorber vessel to adjust pH. Repair and maintenance activities usually are focused on maintenance of the ball mill. Typical repair activities involve rubber lining replacement, gearbox overhaul, and classifier component replacement.

Figure 11-48 | Typical horizontal ball mill for grinding limestone

Recirculation Pumps, Headers, and Nozzles

Recirculation pumps are large, typically 50,000–65,000 gpm (3,200–4,100 l/s), and have a pump efficiency of between 87 and more than 90%. The pumps generally are centrifugal, with a rubber-lined casing and either a hard metal or rubber-coated impeller. The power required is 800 to 1,500 hp (~1 MW) per pump. Components of a typical pump are shown in *Figure 11-49*.

Wear generally is experienced on the seals, lining, and impeller. A typical impeller is shown in *Figure 11-50*.

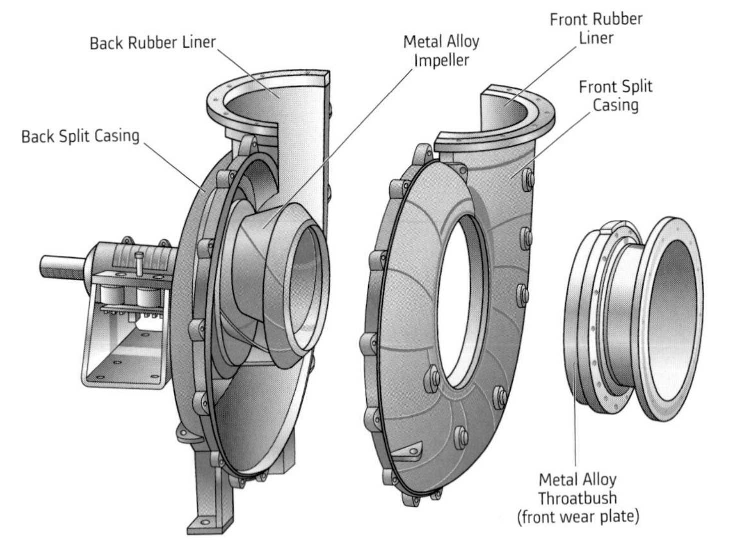

Figure 11-49 | Components of a typical centrifugal pump

Figure 11-50 | Typical impeller

Usually, headers and nozzles are provided in either fiber-reinforced plastic or stainless steel. From a repair and maintenance point of view, most problems involve pluggage or wear. Pluggage is minimized by control of the slurry pH, maintenance of proper chemistry, and minimization of the amount of fly ash entrained in the slurry. Nozzles should be nitride-bonded silicon carbide with flange connection, whirl-chamber type, hollow-cone spray, and 120° spray angle. These nozzles will support a slurry flow of 200–350 gpm at 8 psig (13–22 l/s at 0.6 bar). Nitride-bonded silicon nitride gives the longest-possible service but still needs to be periodically replaced. Over time, the benefits of "hollow core" nozzles have become apparent in preventing pluggage and delivering good atomization and flow characteristics. When replacing nozzles, strong consideration should be given to replacing older, spinner-type nozzles with the newer, hollow core nozzles.

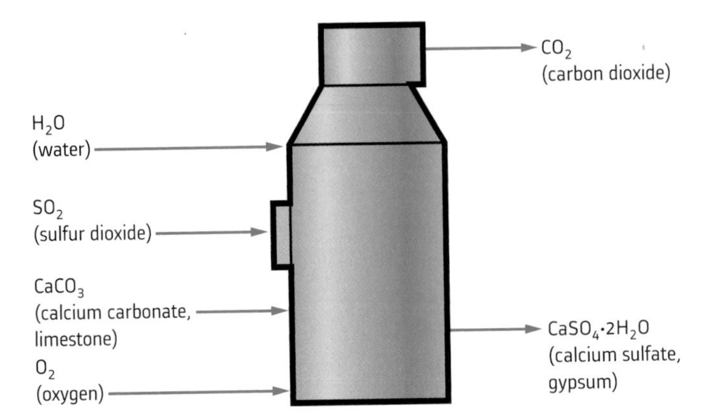

Figure 11-51 | Chemical input and desired output for a wet flue gas desulfurization system

Chemistry and Forced Oxidation

Flue gas containing SO_2 contacts alkaline (limestone) aqueous slurry in an absorber vessel. The slurry is continuously recirculated through the absorber from a reaction tank located below the absorber. The SO_2 absorbed into the slurry initiates a reaction with dissolved limestone. Several systems within the scrubber systems accomplish SO_2 removal and maintain the process. Close control of wet FGD chemistry is a vital component of reliable, cost-effective operation. *Figure 11-51* shows the desired chemical inputs and outputs for the absorber vessel.

Calcium sulfate gypsum generally is the desired product, because it often can be economically utilized as gypsum wallboard instead of a waste product. The wet scrubber chemistry can result in many chemical reactions other than those desired. For each reaction, there are other possible competing reactions. For example, if insufficient oxygen is

present, the main reaction will produce calcium sulfite. Additionally, pH levels, chlorides, SO_2 concentration, and additives such as dibasic acid and adipic acid also strongly influence wet FGD chemistry.

As mentioned previously, flue gas containing SO_2 contacts alkaline (limestone) aqueous slurry. The SO_2 absorbed into the slurry initiates a reaction with dissolved limestone. As a result of this reaction, sulfite crystallization occurs in the reaction tank, and the available alkalinity of the slurry is depleted. Fresh slurry is added to the reaction tank to maintain the desired alkalinity, and the slurry is again circulated back into the absorber section of the scrubber. The main determinant of SO_2 removal from a wet FGD is pH, as shown in *Figure 11-52*.

Unfortunately, competing chemical reactions can reduce the effectiveness of pH in controlling removal efficiency. If significant chlorides are in the absorber vessel, a lower pH will be required to achieve the same removal efficiency. For example, assume that a typical wet FGD system with a slurry pH of 6.0 achieves a 99% removal efficiency without chlorides present. If chlorine from the ash dissolves in the slurry over time to a level of 40,000 ppm, the removal efficiency might drop to 97.5%. This impact, known as "pH suppression," is shown in *Figure 11-53*.

Additives, as mentioned previously, also have a large influence on wet FGD removal efficiency. Additives improve the SO_2 removal efficiency by increasing the effective alkalinity of the slurry. Typical additives are adipic acid, dibasic acid, glutaric acid, succinic acid, and formic acid. Performance impacts are shown in *Figure 11-54*.

In addition to the above reactions that have a strong impact on SO_2 removal, other important events occur that are critical to operation. Particle size of the ground limestone has a strong effect on how easily the desired alkalinity can be achieved. Fly ash entrainment causes a myriad of negative consequences, including increased wear from abrasion, increased pluggage potential, and increased dissolved material in the slurry.

One final discussion on wet FGD chemistry concerns the role of oxygen in the absorber. *Natural oxidation* is the term used when no additional oxygen is added to the absorber vessel, whereas *forced oxidation* refers to the use of large air compressors to add oxygen. Natural oxidation was extensively practiced during the 1970s and 1980s. The by-product of natural oxidation is a sulfite sludge, which must be stabilized with fly ash and lime. This by-product can be economical if the end destination is a landfill, because slightly less mass of material is generated (SO_3 vs. SO_4). Thiosulfate has been identified as a free radical scavenger that inhibits sulfite oxidation effectively. Current practice is to apply thiosulfate to wet scrubbers using natural oxidation in order to enhance operating reliability. In addition to inhibiting sulfite oxidation, thiosulfate improves the dewatering characteristics of calcium sulfite/sulfate waste solids. Natural oxidation, however, generally has been abandoned because of the greater tendency of the naturally oxidized

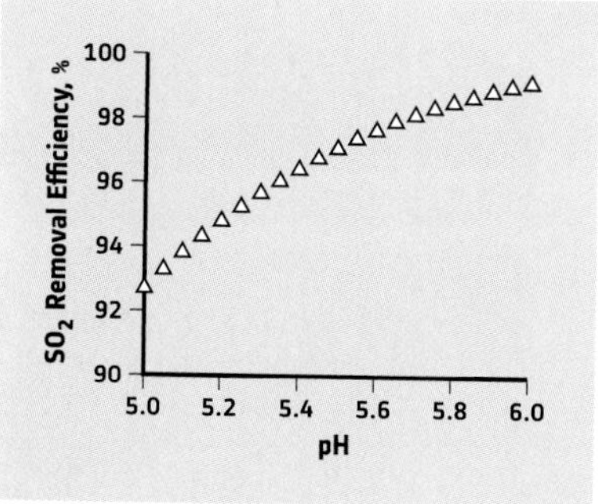

Figure 11-52 | Effect of pH on SO_2 removal efficiency

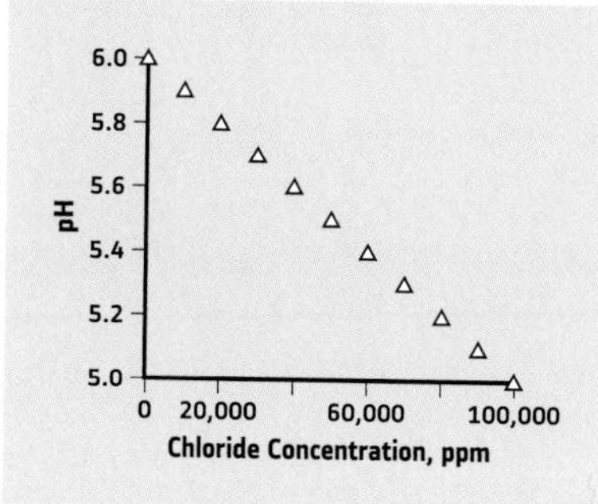

Figure 11-53 | pH suppression caused by chloride concentration

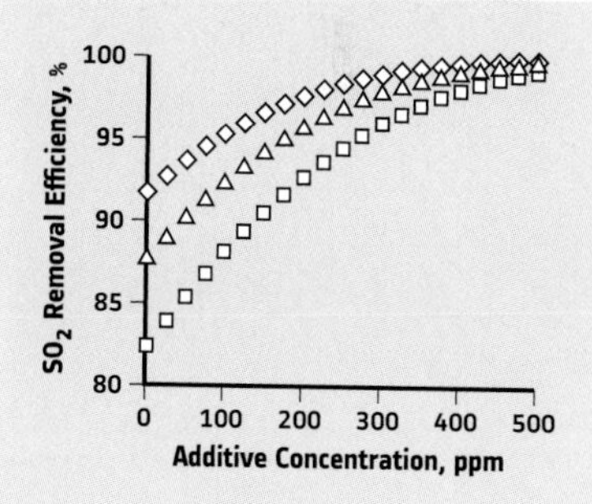

Figure 11-54 | Improved SO_2 removal efficiency by various additives

Figure 11-55 | Hydrocyclones used for dewatering

systems to form a scale on the walls of the absorber.

By-Product Removal and Dewatering System

The SO_2 removal process in the absorber produces by-products that must be removed in order for the system to prevent the reaction tank from becoming filled. The by-product treatment systems are tailored to the specific needs of that site. Some applications simply send the slurry to a pond, whereas others include primary dewatering with thickeners or hydrocyclones before ponding. Still others follow with a secondary system of vacuum filters or presses for further dewatering. The secondary systems are used when the output is saleable gypsum or the solids are stabilized before sending to a landfill.

Generally, the slurry primary dewatering system at a modern wet FGD system consists of hydrocyclones (*Fig. 11-55*). Hydrocyclones can take as input the slurry from the absorber that contains approximately 15% precipitated solids. Using a cyclonic action, the liquid leaving the cyclone is reduced to approximately 3% solids, whereas the lower discharge, often known as "underflow," has a much higher solid loading (55%).

Because commercial gypsum generally needs to have a moisture content of less than 10%, and because landfill gypsum is more economical if its moisture content is limited to 15%, an additional component, a vacuum filter, is required. The filtration cycle begins when vacuum is applied to the slurry that has been distributed on the vacuum belt filters. From a maintenance and repair point of view, particular attention needs to be paid to proper belt tracking and tensioning, control of cake thickness, and periodic measurement of cake moisture content.

There are two distinct operations in the filtration cycle: cake formation, and cake dewatering. Cake formation occurs as the free water is removed from the slurry. The end of the cake formation portion of the cycle is noted visually by the free water disappearing from the surface of the cake. The cake formation occurs very quickly after vacuum is applied. The cake washwater displaces dissolved contaminants from the formed cake. Cake washwater may be either recycled cloth washwater or make-up water. After cake formation and cake washing, cake dewatering begins and continues through the remainder of the cycle. In this portion of the cycle, water is removed from between the gypsum particles or crystals. The filter cloth and dewatered cake pass over a small-radius discharge roller that separates the dewatered cake from the cloth for discharge. The vacuum belt filter design can include a cloth wash after cake discharge.

DRY SCRUBBING SYSTEMS FOR SO_2 REMOVAL

Typical Spray Dryer Arrangement and Operational Issues

A typical dry scrubbing system is shown in *Figure 11-56*. From the standpoint of maintenance and repair, the dry scrubbing system can be

broken down into the major subsystems. These are the absorber vessel and atomizer, the lime preparation system, and the particulate removal system.

The repair and maintenance issues of the particulate removal system are addressed separately in this chapter. Safety concerns with this equipment are similar to those with other plant equipment. Confined spaces potentially pose a suffocation or chemical exposure hazard. The physical size of the equipment creates fall hazards, and the strong chemicals in the process create the potential for chemical burn hazards. All of these concerns need to be addressed in a site-specific safety plan before repair and maintenance operations are considered.

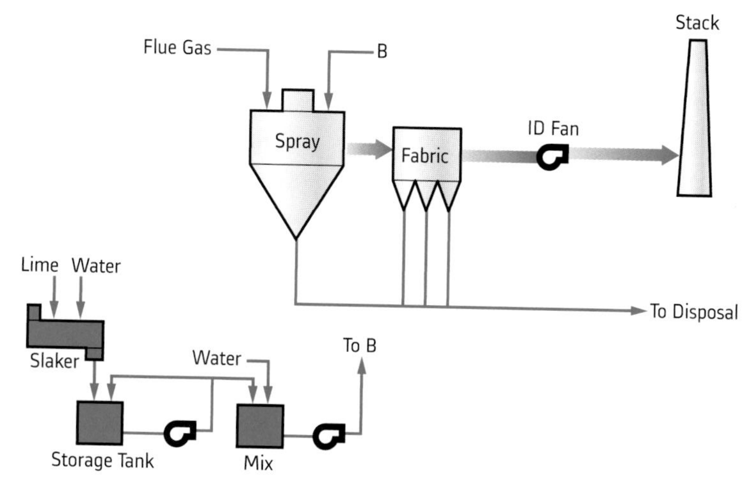

Figure 11-56 | Typical dry scrubbing system (ID, induced draft)

Absorber and Flexible Shaft Atomizer

As described previously, the absorber is where the slurry interacts with the flue gas to remove SO_2 and SO_3. From a maintenance and repair standpoint, the absorber vessel is straightforward. Maximum emphasis needs to be placed on ensuring that the atomized slurry droplets do not impinge on the walls and that process upsets are avoided. For example, concrete is formed by a mixture of sand, Portland cement, lime, and water. All these elements exist in the absorber vessel, and if control of the process is lost, the potential arises to plug the vessel with a very tenacious solid. To avoid this situation, flue gas flows and constituents need to be stable. The atomizer needs to provide a consistent, finely atomized product. Care also should be taken that the water supply for atomization is of sufficient quality that pluggage in the atomizer does not occur.

With this in mind, a key component of the dry FGD system clearly is the atomizer. The purpose of the atomizer is to supply the necessary fine droplets of liquid. Several styles of atomizers have been used in practice. Alstom provides as standard a 250 or 400 hp flexible-shaft atomizer. The slurry that is introduced into the spray dryer is atomized using flex-shaft atomizers mounted in the top of the spray dryer absorber. The slurry passes through ceramic nozzles, mounted in a disk rotating at 11,228 rpm. The high energy contained in the mechanical operation from the rotating disk produces fine droplets of slurry as the spray pattern expands into the spray dryer absorber. Slurry is delivered to the interior of the rotating disk under

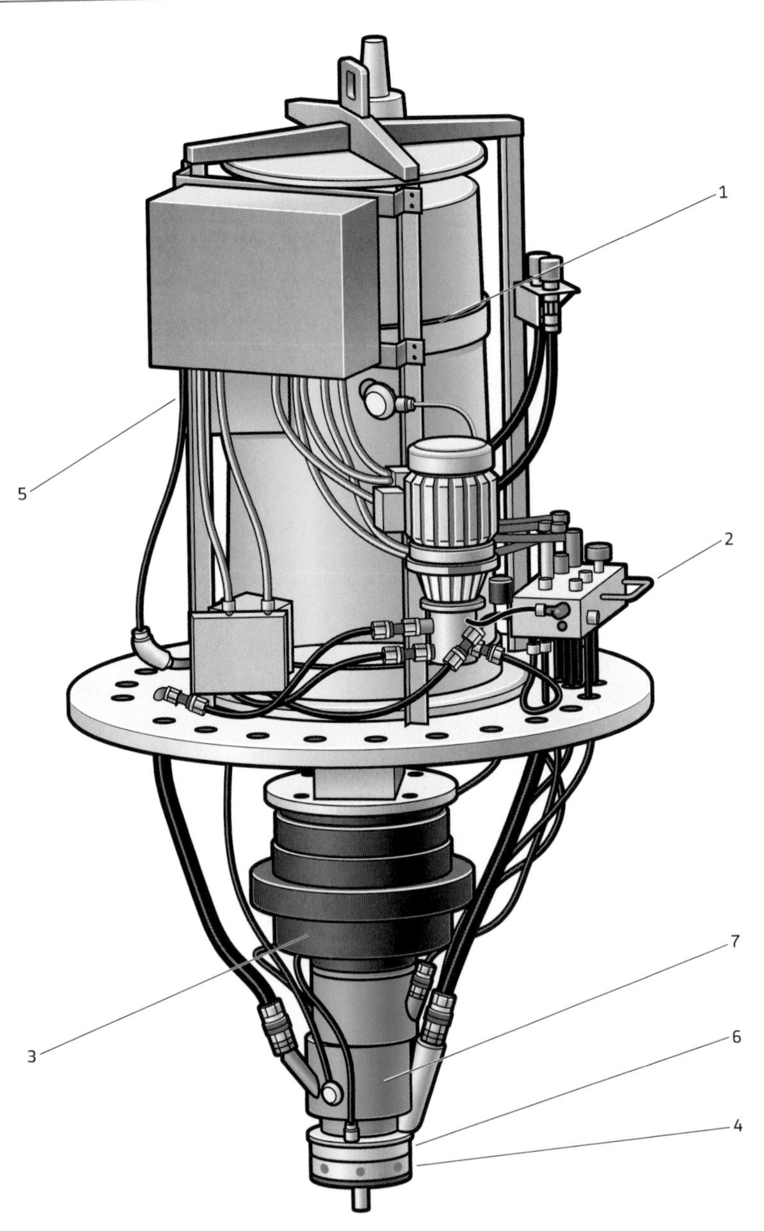

Figure 11-57 | Atomizer components: 1, electric motor; 2, atomizer lubrication system; 3, speed-increasing gearbox; 4, atomizer disk; 5, atomizer lubrication system; 6, scroll plate; 7, flex shaft

pressure. The diluted lime feed slurry is accelerated by the rotating disk and then forced through the perimeter nozzles. Ultimately, the accelerated slurry is atomized into droplets as it leaves the disk and enters the flue gas stream (*Fig. 11-57*).

Specifically, the components of the atomizer include:

- **Electric motor.** The electric motor usually operates at 3,600 rpm and furnishes 250 to 400 hp to its output shaft, which is oriented vertically and is connected to the gearbox input shaft with a flexible coupling. The motor can be a 480, 4,160, or 6,600 V(ac), three-phase, 60-cycle induction motor.
- **Speed-increasing gearbox.** The gearbox increases the rpm of the output shaft to finely atomize the lime slurry, thus increasing the contact area between the reagent and the flue gases.
- **Flex shaft.** The vertical output shaft of the gearbox operates at more than 11,000 rpm. All bearings and gears are lubricated. The drive is enclosed in a steel shroud that protects it from the flue gases.
- **Scroll plate.** The scroll plate is a non-rotating part that is used to introduce slurry into the atomizer disk. The scroll plate feeds the disk through a series of orifices.

- **Atomizer disk.** The atomizer disk is located below the scroll plate and extends into the flue gas path at the top of the spray dryer absorber. The disk is made of titanium, hardened tool steel, and ceramic components.
- **Atomizer lubrication system.** The bearings and gears of the gearbox and flex shaft are oil lubricated.

Generally, periodic maintenance on this machine is required to clean deposits from the scroll plate. An inspection is recommended every 8,000 hours of operation; this consists of an internal inspection of the mechanical seals, bearings, O-rings, and hardware inside the flex shaft. If needed, a rebuild of the flex-shaft atomizer should be done by a trained technician at the supplier's facility/shop. Every 16,000 hours of operation, the flex-shaft atomizer should be overhauled, with special attention to the speed-increasing gearbox.

Lime Preparation

The lime preparation system takes the quick lime and mixes it with water to form the lime slurry. The system includes:

- Bulk lime truck unloading station
- Bulk lime storage
- Lime slakers and make-up water controls
- Grit removal
- Lime slurry storage and atomizer feed pumps
- Atomizer lime slurry and dilution water controls
- Centralized Programmable Logic Controller (PLC) and controls

Handling bulk lime requires care and attention. Concentrated solutions of lime have a very high pH and are very caustic. The lime also tends to cake on exposure to moisture, making it difficult to handle. As with a solids handling system, wear can be an issue, although less so with lime.

PAUL LAFFERTY
PHIL LAFAVE
BRUCE CARNEY
JIM SUTTON
JIM GEYER
CHARLIE HART
RICHARD STONE
BILL HERMAN

Retrofits

Chapter **Twelve**

BOILER RETROFITS

Pulverized coal-fired power plants currently supply more than 50% of all electricity production in the United States. There is a large, installed base of plants throughout the world. As demand for power continues, existing plants must continue to operate while being mindful of environmental constraints. Existing plants have been operating at higher and higher capacity factors to facilitate this trend. In addition, many older boilers are subject to operating conditions for which they were not initially designed, such as cycling operation or the use of opportunity or spot market fuels. New regulations have been placed on power plants to reduce their environmental impact. There are myriad technical, political, economic, and environmental issues that must be considered when retrofitting an existing boiler.

Despite the uncertainties, the current trends in the market maximize output and revenues of the existing fleet through performance enhancements or maintenance upgrades. As a result, many plants have invested substantial capital to improve plant efficiency, lower plant emissions, increase output, switch to lower cost fuel, or increase plant reliability and availability. Retrofitting boilers for improved performance has been a recognized practice for decades. The plant must be studied to discover its strong points and weaknesses; that is, how well the designer has attacked the problem. What has been forgotten or left out and how can the omissions be corrected?[1]

The age of the plant will play a significant role in the economic and technical solutions available for that plant. Many boilers currently in service in the United States were constructed after 1950 with the largest number of MW being installed in the 1970s (*Fig. 12-1*).

This situation is similar in countries that began developing electric markets at the same time as the United States. In developing countries, this will not be the case. More retrofit opportunities

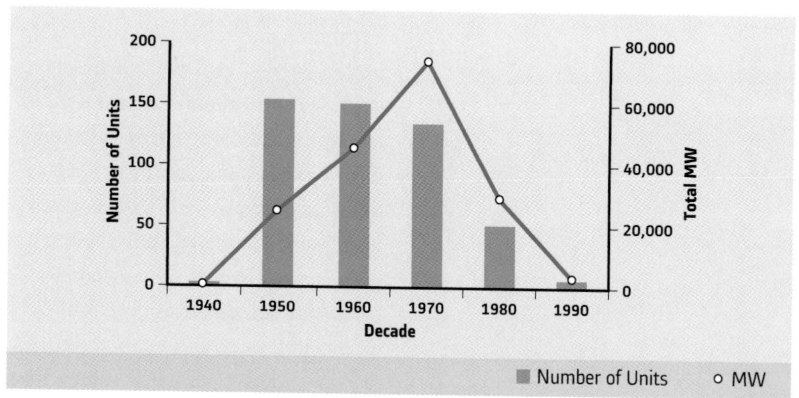

Figure 12-1 | Unit age of installed U.S. base for Alstom units

exist in areas that have a larger population of older boilers.

When retrofitting existing power plants, compromises are required between an ideal design and existing physical constraints. Different techniques and equipment may be required when retrofitting an existing design compared to a white paper design. In a retrofit situation, the existing envelope limits the space available for new equipment. When developing solutions for existing plants, the boiler designer must also account for the age-specific design issues and existing plant condition.

Tube failures are the number one cause for unscheduled boiler outages and account for almost 3% of all of the lost generation availability in the United States. All boiler components must be designed and maintained to ensure that the boilers are available when required. By reducing tube failures, a power generation owner can realize a positive return on investment through reduced operation and maintenance (O&M) costs, reliable and available generation capacity, and optimal selection of units to supply power based on lowest cost.

An important factor to ensure long term reliability of boiler pressure parts is the correct design to eliminate problem areas, while considering current and projected future operations. Boiler pressure part component replacements should be designed to minimize detrimental effects of highly corrosive fuels, heavy slagging fuels, cyclic (peaking) operation, longer run time between outages, higher temperature operation, and sub-stoichiometric tuning for environmental considerations, as well as upgrading the mechanical design to modern standards.

Even though the current competitive environment requires close attention to capital, operational, and maintenance costs, today's utility managers have increased their focus on total ownership cost; that is, what the expected cost is over the life of a component. All of the ingredients of long term cost have to be considered: lost generation due to forced outages, inspection costs, maintenance costs, outage cycles, outage length, unit efficiency, heat rate, and environmental considerations. Initial cost, although important, is not necessarily the overriding consideration. Consequently, this has put increased focus on providing solutions to long-standing problems.

The success of this approach relies on the support of operators and owners working closely with the mechanical and performance design engineers. This cooperation will facilitate the collection of invaluable service data as well as insight into maintenance and performance issues and operational goals and strategies. A systematic approach, using root cause analysis, will define the cause of failure(s). Continuous interaction with the customer complements the analysis by providing operational information that goes beyond service time and temperature to include fuel characteristics, possible fuel switches, and other operational variables. Evaluation of changes in operation and their impact on unit performance will allow utility management to make economically driven decisions to better meet performance expectations.

Based on recent market trends and forecasts in the United States, the most common retrofits fit into one of the following categories: unit uprating, emissions control, fuel switch/co-firing, and maintenance upgrades/performance improvement. Note that each plant will have its own

unique situation and resulting drivers. In retrofit situations, the use of best practices means that most of the available mechanical or performance upgrades would be used where applicable and economically feasible when components are replaced or redesigned.

UNIT UPRATING

The power generation market is becoming increasingly competitive and most utilities are looking to maximize the output of existing plants. The increased output is used to increase revenue or in some cases offset the parasitic power loss of new emission control technologies installed at the plants. There is also an emergence of potential CO_2 requirements, where avoided CO_2 emissions can be traded in emission trading schemes. As an example, for a 400 MWe coal-fired power station, a 3% efficiency improvement avoids approximately 100,000 tons of CO_2 emission per year.

To address these issues, a retrofit opportunity obtains more electrical output from an existing plant by using new technology for the boiler, the turbine-generator, or a combination of the two. Any attempt to increase existing generation capacity requires a system evaluation approach to ascertain and address all of the potential impacts.[2] As a result of original design tolerances built into the plant, many existing coal-fired plants have a hidden existing capacity. In addition, major boiler or turbine components may need extensive maintenance. A replacement component that increases the plant output almost always makes economic sense. By exploiting these hidden system capacities and retrofit needs, more generation can be achieved from an existing plant. Turbine specific aspects of the optimized plant retrofits are discussed in the turbine section. This section will discuss the boiler aspects of boiler and plant optimization (*Fig. 12-2*).

Plant specific turbine and boiler models are set up and run simultaneously to develop an accurate picture of the potential plant retrofit. The turbine supplier will lead the optimization process by modeling a turbine retrofit design. The boiler turbine interfaces are then calculated and the effects on the boiler are determined. The boiler turbine interfaces, main steam flow, temperature and pressure, cold reheat temperature, and final feedwater temperature are recalculated. The process is iterated to a converged solution and evaluated. The interface points are modeled in consultation with the customer during this iterative process in which combinations of main steam flow and pressure, as well as cold reheat (RH) steam temperatures and final feedwater (FW) temperature, are compared with relative costs, equipment changes, power output, and net plant heat rate. This allows the plant owner to make the best technical and economic decision regarding the plant.

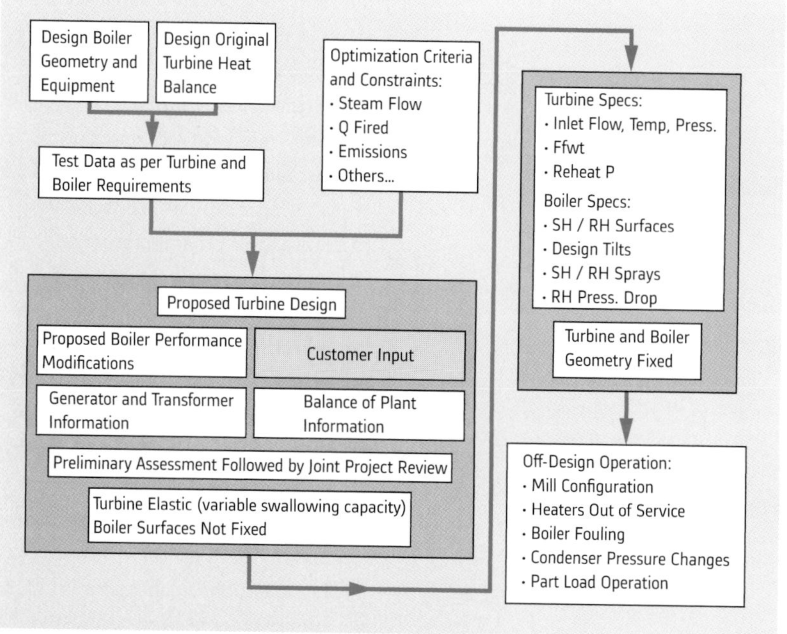

Figure 12-2 | The iterative thermal optimizing process

A major consideration at the time of retrofitting is whether or not to increase the main steam flow for the unit. Where environmental issues can be addressed, plant owners will usually increase the main steam flow as much as possible. There are many cases where units are unable to operate at the peak boiler flow, which usually corresponds to a 5% over pressure condition. Limitations may be related to safety valve operation, concerns over steam purity, or a conservative operating procedure. By designing a larger turbine with a bigger "swallowing capacity," this limitation can sometimes be eased.

The main steam and hot reheat steam temperatures are usually maintained at the original design condition, as it is cost prohibitive to modify all of the hardware to increase the temperature and it is rarely necessary to reduce the temperature.

High Pressure Turbine Retrofit Consequence on Boiler Operation

A high pressure (HP) turbine retrofit project is often responsible for power increases of about 2–3% that are a result of efficiency gains, not counting potential increases due to increased steam flow. Increasing the HP cylinder efficiency results in a decrease of the exhaust temperature (cold reheat). Hot reheat temperature is directly related to the cold reheat temperature and, therefore, all else being equal, an HP turbine retrofit results in a decrease in hot reheat temperature. Reheat temperature is a very important condition from both heat rate and power considerations. A reduction in hot reheat temperature affects power considerably more than the same reduction in main steam temperature.

The reduction is dependent on the efficiency levels both before and after the retrofit but is generally in the region of 15 to 20°F (8 to 11°C). In most retrofit applications the hot reheat temperature will be maintained at design levels, which requires extra heat to be added into the reheater. This is accomplished by increasing the size or effectiveness of the reheater. It is this additional heat added (in the region of 3–4% over the existing reheater duty) that contributes to the power advantage of HP retrofitting. The overall turbine heat rate is also improved due to the higher HP section efficiency, but the heat rate improvement is usually limited to about 60% of power increase.

The reduction of internal turbine leakages, particularly in the case of combined intermediate pressure (HP-IP) turbines, contributes significantly to the overall benefit of retrofitting. Turbine changes generally lead to an increase in reheater flow thus increasing the extra reheater thermal duty still further. In some cases the reheater flow has been increased by 2%.

If reheater spray water is currently being used, then the amount of spray required (assuming no other operational or plant changes) will reduce. The reduction in reheat spray water reduces power but does improve the heat rate.

Reheater sprays taken from the boiler feed pump discharge affect the turbine cycle by increasing the flow through the IP and low pressure (LP) turbines, with the main steam flow remaining unaffected. The increase in power is achieved at a worse heat rate and boiler firing is increased when compared to a plant designed for zero spray. Nevertheless, plant owners often are worried about reducing the spray quantity due to the associated reduction in power. In any case, a comprehensive boiler analysis is required to quantify the necessary changes. In many situations, the analysis highlights other areas of deficiency or shows modifications to other areas that may help reheater performance.

Intermediate/Low Pressure Turbine

When compared to the economics of modifying the HP turbine, an IP turbine retrofit is usually not as attractive with respect to the ratio of investment versus power gain. An important option when modifying the IP is the flow passing capacity. An increase in the flow passing capacity will, for example, reduce the IP inlet pressure and, therefore, the HP exhaust pressure.

In the case where the final feedwater heating is being tapped from cold reheat, the final feedwater temperature can be adjusted. Changes in the final feedwater temperature affect the heat input to the boiler and significantly affect the power and heat rate gain of the turbine cycle. The design of the IP turbine can, therefore, be used to optimize the cycle for either power or for heat rate. In general, low pressure turbine sections have minimal effect on the boiler operation and are not a factor that is accounted for when analyzing the boiler.

Steam Purity

As the boiler is pushed to produce higher steam flows, it is critical for the steam turbine operation that the steam purity is maintained. Steam purity basics are addressed in Chapter 9. However, the effects on unit uprating need to be considered. The steam drum is designed for a specific flow rate, pressure, and steam purity. Increasing the flow rate through the steam drum will either use any existing margin on the steam drying equipment or result in an increase in the amount of carryover. At constant drum level, the amount of mechanical carryover does not increase linearly with steam flow.

As the steam and water flow is increased through the drum, the velocities through the separation equipment increase above design. This results in a decrease in the efficiency of some of the mechanical separation devices, such as screens and chevrons. In general, mechanical carryover remains low as the steam flow increases. However, when critical values are exceeded, carryover increases abruptly and dramatically. As little as a 5% increase in load above the critical value may cause an order of magnitude increase in moisture carryover.[3]

At uprated conditions, the boiler is often run at overpressure conditions, which affects both the mechanical and vaporous carryover. As the pressure increases, the density difference between steam and water decreases, albeit only slightly at typical operating conditions. All else being equal, this results in an increase in steam carryover. Also, as the pressure increases, the amount of steam soluble material increases.

For these reasons, water chemistry control plays an increased importance in unit uprating retrofits. To address the steam separation and carryover issues, a thorough review of the existing design capacity of the drum as well as the condition of the separators, screens, dryers, and liners is the first step to ensure that the equipment is in optimum condition. In some cases, there is sufficient capacity in the original design to account for any increases in flow rates. Other times, an upgrade may be required in steam drying capacity. This can take the form of either larger size separator cans, when available, or an upgraded steam drum internal design. The upgraded steam drum internals improve the mechanical separation of the steam and water. The design of the upgrade will be dependent on the unique boiler application.

Water chemistry control becomes more important for retrofit applications as the boiler, turbine, and associated equipment have to operate at more stressful conditions.

Increasing the main steam flow to the original boiler design maximum continuous rating (MCR) and beyond needs to be considered carefully. The potential impacts to the boiler, turbine, generator, and balance of plant must be evaluated. A logical starting point is to review the current operating flow and, if below design, investigate ways to restore it. In some cases, fuel changes to lower rank fuels have reduced the output to below original design.

If the main steam flow is to be increased beyond the original rating with or without a steam turbine upgrade, the approach should focus on incremental increases. The point at which a particular plant item becomes the limiting factor can be more readily identified. Increased flow, therefore, involves the identification of major components and balance of plant items, the relationship between maximum component output and the main steam flow (which can be accepted with current equipment), and, finally, the modifications needed to increase the duty.

Safety Valves

Safety valves must be checked for relieving capacity and operating pressure based on current code. If the relieving capacity is exceeded, larger valve internals, larger valves, or additional valves will be required. Note that if the new operating pressure is within 3% of the closure pressure of that valve, excess leakage and subsequent maintenance can occur. In some cases the affected sections could be redesigned to reduce pressure drop. With a turbine retrofit, the best solution is to design the HP turbine for the required swallowing capacity at a lower throttle pressure. Another concern is that the low set superheater safety valve should lift before the low set drum safety valve to protect the superheater. This criterion may be the limiting factor in the amount of steam flow available through a unit. The same check is needed on the RH safety valves.

Water Circulation

An assessment is needed of the ability of drum type boilers to operate with adequate safety margin at the increased flow. The circulation ratio (CR) is defined as the mass flow ratio of the circulation fluid to steam leaving the circuit. A certain minimum CR value should be maintained in order for a waterwall circuit to operate in a safe zone for a given drum pressure and circuit fluid mass velocity (flow rate per unit area). Of course, this condition is very boiler specific and is not always a main concern.

Increased Firing Rate

The issues associated with increased firing cover boiler furnace, pressure parts, burners, pulverizers, air supply, emissions, etc. Evaluating the firing increases in incremental amounts and reviewing the margins in each of the associated pieces of equipment will allow an assessment to be made of the extent and cost of modifications necessary to reach a particular flow. An important performance goal for the boiler is to maintain main steam and reheat steam temperatures after the retrofit.

In certain boiler specific cases, boiler efficiency, flue gas temperature control, and firing rate issues may collectively point out a need for review of the thermal performance of the economizer. In several cases, upgrading the economizer has been a viable solution for (1) maintaining exit flue gas conditions for flue gas cleaning equipment, (2) lowering boiler heat input (Q_{fired}) rates to acceptable levels, or (3) increasing project justification via improvements in boiler efficiency. Economizer upgrades have also lowered system flue gas pressure drop and resulted in plant power savings, adding to the project justification.

EMISSIONS CONTROL

Emissions controls have been a major retrofit activity with most existing plants being upgraded over time to reduce nitrogen oxide (NOx) emissions, sulfur oxides (SOx), and, to a lesser degree, particulate emissions from the boiler. The unique impacts of retrofitting these systems to existing boilers are discussed here.

In-Furnace NOx Emissions Retrofits

The first combustion modifications strictly for NOx control were implemented in new boilers in the United States starting in 1971 under the New Source Performance Standards (NSPS). The Clean Air Act of 1990 required stricter emissions limits and required existing plants to reduce emissions.

Nitrogen oxide (NOx) emissions can be reduced in-furnace through combustion modifications such as low NOx burners, overfire air, or selective non-catalytic reduction (SNCR). The primary post-combustion systems for NOx control are selective catalytic reduction (SCR) systems. The basics of NOx formation and control are discussed in Chapter 5. The retrofit aspects are different, as there are often conflicting requirements when retrofitting for NOx emissions. Many times NOx retrofits are included as part of a fuel switching retrofit. In these cases, any changes due to the firing system modifications, such as furnace outlet temperature changes or excess air requirements, must be included in the overall boiler performance calculations.

NOx emissions are directly related to the fuel chemical characteristics as well as the physical and thermal properties of the unit being retrofitted. The final factor on NOx emissions is the type of low NOx firing system and its operation. Over the years, Alstom has developed a large database of coal properties by rank as well as contribution to NOx emissions under a wide variety of unit design and operational conditions. Alstom has low NOx firing system experience on practically every fuel and boiler type combination.[4]

These models use the laboratory fuel data as well as empirical field data to produce design criteria and NOx emissions predictions. The empirical field data accounts for the physical and thermal design effects on NOx emissions.

The critical boiler physical characteristics are furnace design heat input (NHI/PA [net heat input/plan area]) and residence time and staged or sub-stoichiometric residence time. In a new boiler design, these can all be matched with the fuel characteristics to produce the lowest NOx emissions possible from the combustion process. In retrofit situations, the physical dimensions of the existing firing system and furnace geometry compromise the ideal design. The low NOx firing system is designed to fit the existing constraints and then the fuel properties are used to develop emissions predictions for the specific application. *Figure 12-3* shows the NOx emissions from retrofitted plants based on the fuel type. The range within a fuel type is due to the type of low NOx firing system (how aggressive), physical and thermal boiler characteristics, and operational attention.

Tangentially Fired Boilers

Each of the tangential, low NOx firing system products utilizes the same basic

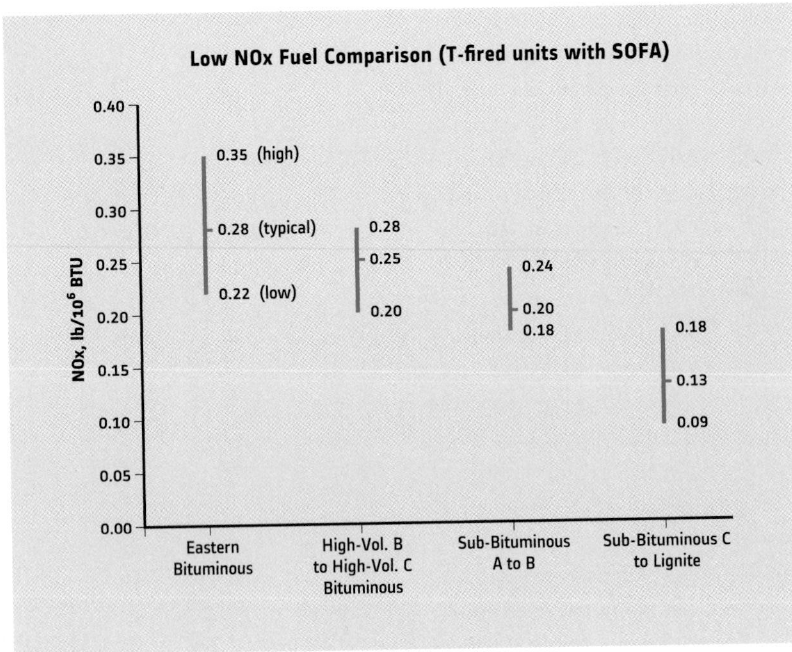

Figure 12-3 | Low NOx fuel comparison (T-fired units with SOFA)

design features of staged air combustion, early fuel devolatilization, and CFS™ concentric firing system for the secondary air. The differences among the options occur in the tradeoffs between the extent of NOx emissions reduction and the complexity and cost of material modification and retrofit requirements.

Overfire air, or staged combustion, is the key component of the low NOx tangential firing systems. The two types of overfire air utilized are the close-coupled overfire air (CCOFA), where the overfire air is introduced within the existing windbox, and separated overfire air (SOFA), where air is taken from the windbox and introduced into the furnace above the burner zone. Both are effective NOx reduction techniques. CCOFA is more economical on an installed cost with a moderate NOx reduction, whereas SOFA provides a more aggressive NOx reduction strategy. As the regulated levels of NOx emissions have decreased, most low NOx systems now incorporate SOFA as the primary means of NOx reduction. Each system incorporates a coal nozzle tip designed to promote early fuel devolatilization. The coal tip design is based on the fuel characteristics, system requirements, and unit operation.

The third common design aspect of tangential low NOx firing systems is the utilization of concentric firing. In a tangentially fired boiler, the coal and air are injected in the corners and are aimed tangent to an imaginary circle. In concentric firing, a portion of the air is aimed at a second imaginary circle that is larger than the primary circle. This promotes an oxidizing atmosphere near the waterwalls and changes the aerodynamics, which impacts the particle combustion time/temperature history and the ash characteristics. This combination has been shown to mitigate the potential for waterwall corrosion or wastage and to reduce the incidence of excessive ash deposition on the boiler waterwalls.

In combination with finer grinding, the cumulative effects of separated overfire air and concentric firing lead to the TFS 2000® R system for retrofit applications. This system can achieve the levels required for NSPS for the lower rank coals.

Wall Fired

There may be several different burner solutions for wall fired boilers. The chosen solution will be based on the fuels, original boiler manufacturer, and other considerations. The radially stratified flame core burner (RSFC™ burner) is a typical wall fired burner (*Fig. 12-4*).

This burner uses a three zone, swirling airflow to delay mixing in the near-burner zone. This produces the combination of a near field, high-temperature, fuel-rich core, followed

by a downstream, fuel-lean combustion zone that creates the required low NOx combustion conditions.

The RSFC™ burner achieves this flame pattern in a unique manner. The delay in mixing is achieved through stratification between the fuel jet and the surrounding, swirling combustion air. The stratification of the flame depends on turbulence and turbulent mixing dampening at the flame/air interface. The fuel enters along the centerline of the burner and is surrounded by three separate annuli of strongly swirling air as shown in *Figure 12-4*. The fuel jet penetrates into the central fuel-rich recirculation zone where the centrifugal forces of the swirling air pull the fuel jet apart and begin to mix the fuel with hot, recirculated flue gas.

The first flame region in the fuel-rich, high-temperature recirculation zone allows a large portion of the fuel nitrogen to be released in a low stoichiometric zone, where it is easily converted to molecular nitrogen. The internal recirculation zone also helps stabilize the flame by providing adequate energy to the root of the flame. This higher temperature zone along the centerline of the burner, surrounded by the cooler, swirling combustion air, creates the stratification that is characteristic of the RSFC™ burner flame structure. After passing through this initial stratified, low stoichiometric, combustion zone, the fuel quickly mixes with the remainder of the combustion air to complete the combustion processes. This has the effect of achieving a low NOx configuration in a shorter flame length when compared with a conventional low NOx burner.

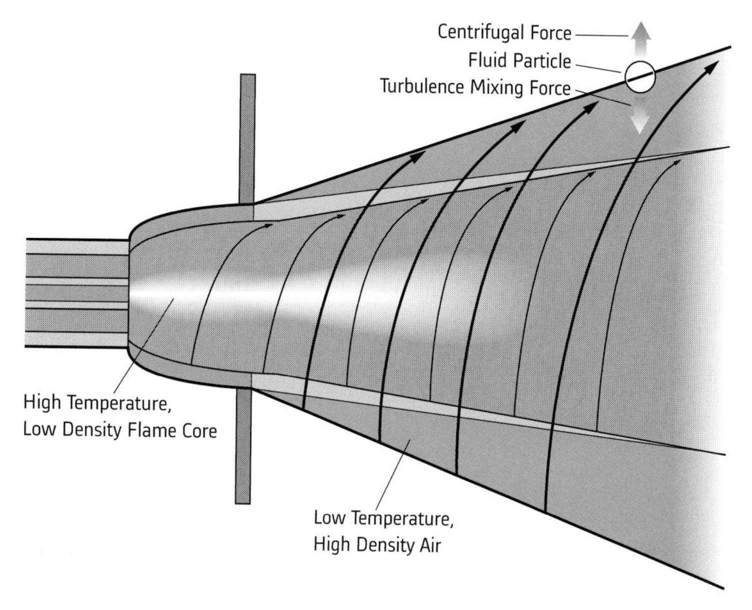

Figure 12-4 | RSFC™ concept

Low NOx Retrofit Additional Upgrades

Along with the performance concerns of the low NOx retrofits, the designer has to consider the condition of the existing equipment. Often, NOx projects will require replacement of older or marginal equipment for optimal fit and performance. Very often new or upgraded ignition and flame scanner equipment is installed as part of the low NOx retrofit to meet the current National Fire Prevention Association (NFPA) regulations for ignition support and safety requirements. One of the biggest concerns is the condition of the existing windbox, coal piping, and air ducting. In some cases, this equipment has been in service for 30 or more years and is in need of repair or upgrade.

For tangentially fired units, the waterwall tubes and windbox structure acts as a rigid vertical beam through which a series of vertical moments, horizontal forces, and dead loads from the connecting duct, buckstay system, and fuel piping pass. Over time these forces can cause the windboxes and/or air ducts to rack, rotate, or distort, creating equipment that does

Retrofits to the combustion system offer some of the lowest cost opportunities for reducing NOx emissions.

not conform to the original physical dimensions, clearances, or tolerances. This will either require repair or replacement of existing equipment. The decision to repair or replace this existing equipment is best determined by the end user based on age, condition, and economic factors.

Damper upgrades are another modification included in low NOx system retrofits. These utilize newer bearing designs and current sizing standards for optimal damper operation and air control. There are now fabric seal designs to replace older corrugated steel seals. Again, the existing design and condition will determine what upgrades or replacements are appropriate.

The furnace buckstay system configuration is designed to maintain the integrity of the waterwalls during pressure excursions. For existing plants, the buckstay design will be dependent on the waterwall construction (loose tube, tangent tube, or welded design), the furnace dimensions, as well as contract or code requirements in place at the time of the contract. The location of SOFA elevations can be affected by the size or location of the buckstays. In general, SOFA locations are chosen to avoid buckstays due to the extra cost involved in relocating or bracing them.

Post-Combustion (NOx, SOx, Particulates)

The installation of post-combustion controls such as SCR modules, scrubbers (wet or dry), electrostatic precipitators, or baghouse particulate equipment (collectively called "back-end equipment") usually requires the addition of a larger induced draft (ID) fan to overcome the additional pressure drop incurred by the installation of this equipment. This increase in the pressure capability of the fan will require that the furnace implosion capabilities of the boiler and ductwork be addressed. The implosion phenomenon is discussed further in the Chapter 7. The protection requirements are set by the NFPA code, which are currently based on either an absolute value of pressure (+/–35 inch WG [+/–6.5 cm Hg]) or the test block conditions of the forced draft (FD) and induced draft (ID) fans. This requires a total analysis of the boiler pressure part support system, including the air and gas ducts. Commonly referred to as a furnace pressure upgrade study, the analysis includes positive and negative pressure in the evaluation. In most instances, the negative pressure condition is the controlling factor. The modification required to satisfy the negative pressure condition will normally satisfy the requirements of the positive pressure condition.

For the analysis, the engineer makes two basic assumptions. The first requires the existing structure to be very near the original design. This implies minimal degradation of the structure. The second assumption requires the existing material to be in a "like new" condition. Although there is some minuscule degradation to be expected, this is usually acceptable due to material and design safety factors. The engineer will analyze every pressure load transfer point. The analysis process is very labor intensive, with minimal material requirements. The return to the utility is an increase in the ability of the furnace to resist the increase in furnace fan size.

The duct system of the unit is designed to contain the air and gas of the boiler. The duct's flat steel plate surfaces are stiffened to resist the internal pressure forces, the self-weight of the duct, wind loads, seismic forces, thermal expansion differential forces, and weight due to fly ash accumulation. The duct system is supported vertically and laterally to resist these forces. The expansion joints are designed to allow differential thermal expansion between the duct component and the support of the duct component.

Due to the use of expansion joints within the duct system, the internal air or gas pressure acting on the duct internal surface may result in unbalanced pressure forces, which must also be resolved. Each duct component section is reviewed to determine if unbalanced conditions exist. The unbalanced conditions are resolved by determining an acceptable load path to transfer the forces to the supporting structure.

The unbalanced condition may introduce forces directly into the structure, or create overturning moments, which must be coupled into a guide or the hanger rods. This can lead to reinforcement of the hanger rods, the duct guides, and/or the associated support lugs and brackets.

DUCT DESIGN CRITERIA. The analysis of the duct stiffener and plate stress is the most important aspect of the analysis. The stress in these components is limited to the values specified by the American Institute for Steel Construction (AISC) Code and standards developed by the manufacturer. The analysis reviews the deflection of the stiffener, limiting the deflection to 1/464 of the length of the member. Depending on the vibration criteria, deflections may exceed this limit. In cases where the stiffener ends at the corner without overlapping the stiffener from the other side, manufacturing design standards limit the reaction that is transmitted to the corner.

There are cases where the duct plate and/or stiffeners can be in resonance with the fan frequency. This typically requires the frequency immediately downstream from the fan to be 45 hertz or greater for the plate and the stiffeners. For areas downstream of flow restricting devices, the design requires the stiffeners to have a first natural frequency of 25 hertz or greater. Frequency is considered independent of pressure-induced stresses.

BUCKSTAY DESIGN CRITERIA. The buckstay system is required to limit the deflection of the furnace tube walls as a result of the pressure in the furnace due to operation. The buckstay system consists of a series of structural shapes attached to the furnace tube walls. The buckstay system bands the furnace tube walls at vertically calculated intervals. The buckstays minimize the tube wall deflections, maintaining the integrity of the furnace tube walls. During operation, the buckstay system provides horizontal support for the furnace tube walls, maintaining the integrity of the furnace tube walls and allowing the buckstay stirrups and buckstay corners to function as designed.

A system of stirrups transfers the furnace pressure load from the furnace tube wall into the buckstay system. The stirrup system is designed to allow horizontal expansion between the hot furnace tube wall and the cold buckstay. The furnace pressure load is resolved as an end reaction at each corner. The end reaction is canceled out across the width and depth of the furnace to the buckstay on the opposite side of the unit.

Furnace pressure imbalances can occur as the result of a fan malfunction, a furnace implosion, or a furnace explosion. Under positive pressure conditions, the furnace tube walls are pushed outward requiring the buckstay system to restrain the force of the pressure. The outboard flange of the buckstay goes into a tension load and the inboard flange of the buckstay goes into a compression load to resist the pressure load. The inboard compression flange has a tendency to buckle if adequate restraint is not provided at the required intervals. Alstom's design uses the stirrup system to provide the lateral support to prevent the buckstay flange from buckling. The outboard buckstay flange does not have a tendency to buckle, distort vertically, or twist as a result of the tension load. This case does not require any restraint system to limit the buckstay tension load.

Under negative furnace pressure conditions, the outboard flange of the buckstay can experience compression loading. Under this condition, the outboard flange can buckle. Alstom uses a system of vertical structural shapes to stabilize the buckstay against the compression load condition. Alstom designs the furnace buckstay system using criteria as defined by the AISC Code and Alstom standards to minimize the stress and instability of the buckstay system.

Beam Stress: Foremost among the criteria is stress and stability in the buckstay components and is limited to values as specified by the AISC code and Alstom standards.

Buckstay Deflection: Manufacturing standards limit deflection to 1/360 of the length of the member. The 1/360 standard is based on 8 inches H_2O of furnace pressure loading.

Yield Stress Values: Structural steel has a designated yield value (Fy) as indicated in AISC specification. For example:

Fy for A36 Steel = 36 ksi
Fy for A7 Steel = 33 ksi

Beyond these values the steel will theoretically take a permanent set.

Allowable Stress Values: Allowable stress values are simply a percentage of the yield values. This percentage provides a safety factor in the design. Allowable design stress for the bending is:

.6 * Fy = Bending Allowable

GAS TEMPERATURE CONTROL. As discussed in Chapter 5, the SCR is designed for a specific gas temperature window to optimize performance. Most of the first SCRs installed in the United States were designed to be operated within a narrow temperature window based on the May to September ozone season, when units are running at maximum capacity due to peak electrical demand.[5] Subsequent regulation changes required these SCRs to be operated all year long. This requires operation at off-design load and gas temperature conditions. As the exit gas temperature decreases with load, the challenge is to keep the temperature at near the design point as the load is reduced. There are several options available to maintain the temperature window including gas or water bypass systems, economizer resurfacing, split economizer, and hot water recirculation systems.

When the gas temperature available to the SCR is too low at full load, a reduction in economizer surface to increase gas temperature is a relatively easy solution. This addresses the SCR requirements but also reduces boiler efficiency at all loads. In addition, the reduction of economizer surface will be limited to the upper end of the control temperature range. This will result in a finite control range. If a larger control range is desired, then one of the following options should be considered.

SPLIT ECONOMIZER ARRANGEMENT. The split economizer arrangement is utilized with SCRs designed for higher inlet gas temperatures in the range of 725 to 800°F (385 to 430°C). With these high gas temperatures, the air preheater outlet gas temperature will be very high resulting in lower boiler efficiency. The split economizer design addresses these issues. The split economizer arrangement consists of one or two banks installed in the normal economizer location and another bank after the SCR but prior to the air preheater as shown in *Figure 12-5*. This arrangement allows the SCR designer to utilize a catalyst that has a wide operating temperature range (650 to 750°F [340 to 400°C]) while not compromising boiler efficiency. This also provides a wide SCR control range without requiring another system to control the gas temperature to the SCR at lower loads.

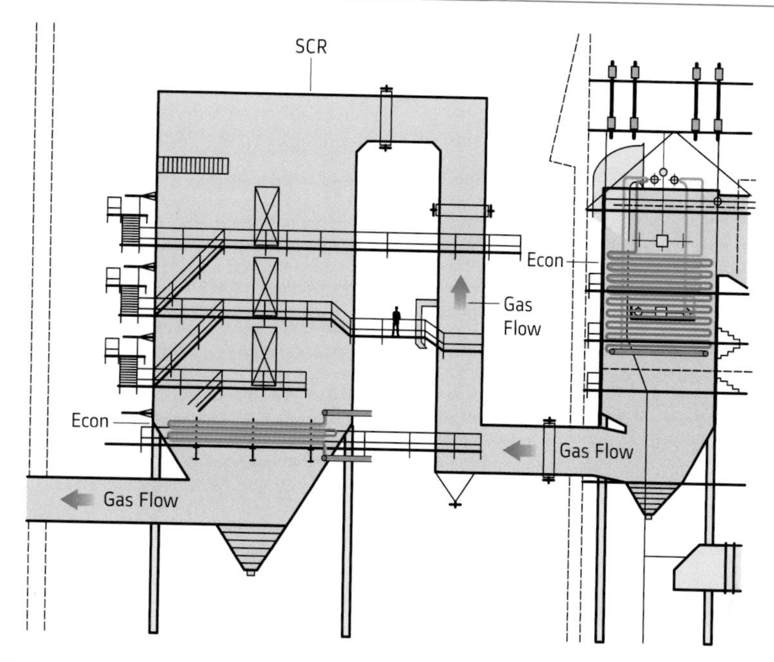

Figure 12-5 | Split economizer

ECONOMIZER FEEDWATER BYPASS SYSTEM. The economizer feedwater bypass system is generally only used on supercritical boilers. This system is not suitable for subcritical boilers for two reasons. The first is that when a large amount of feedwater is bypassed around the economizer, steaming occurs which can lead to overheating of the economizer tubing. In addition, the reinjection of the cold feedwater (water bypassing the economizer) combining with the steam mixture can cause water hammer, which can lead to tube or pipe failure. The second reason is that the economizer outlet fluid temperature can only get to saturation temperature, which is 686°F (363°C) for a 2,800 psig (19 MPa) operating boiler. With the entering fluid temperature (feedwater temperature) unchanged and the outlet fluid temperature being limited to a maximum of saturation, the condition only slightly reduces the economizer pickup. The expected reduction in economizer outlet gas temperature is only in the range of 20 to 30°F (11 to 17°C) before steaming occurs.

This system is ideally suited for Combined Circulation® (supercritical pressure) boilers, since the economizer outlet fluid can go to 800°F (430°C) without the fear of steaming. As the boiler operates at supercritical pressure, the fluid can never boil. In these cases, the system requires taking a large amount of feedwater flow, before it enters the economizer, and sending it to the economizer outlet into new junction/mixing headers. To ensure that the water bypasses the economizer at lower loads, a resistance valve is installed in the feedwater line and a control valve is used to establish the proper water flow. To obtain a 60°F (33°C) increase in economizer outlet gas temperature at lower loads (35 to 80% load) requires that about 70 to 80% of the water flow be bypassed around the economizer assemblies. Under these conditions, the fluid temperature leaving the economizer is close to 750°F (400°C). This fluid temperature translates to a tubing metal temperature close to carbon steel limits. If the economizer outlet gas temperature needs to be increased more, then more water bypass will be required. For example, if 85% bypass is used, the economizer outlet gas temperature can increase by 100°F (56°C). However, the economizer outlet fluid temperature could reach 1,000°F (540°C) in this case. Of course, if the entering gas temperature is too high (1,200°F [650°C] or greater), the economizer tubing could easily overheat and fail. These conditions limit how wide the range of gas temperature change is allowed.

If an economizer water bypass system were designed, junction headers would be needed to ensure sufficient flow and a low enough fluid temperature to the hangers that support the economizer banks to prevent hanger tube failure. At low economizer flows, flow instability and flow stagnation are a concern. If flow stagnation occurs, the economizer tubes without flow would reach gas temperature levels. A material grade of T-22 or higher may be necessary and possibly a thick-walled tube would have to be used in the upper economizer bank.

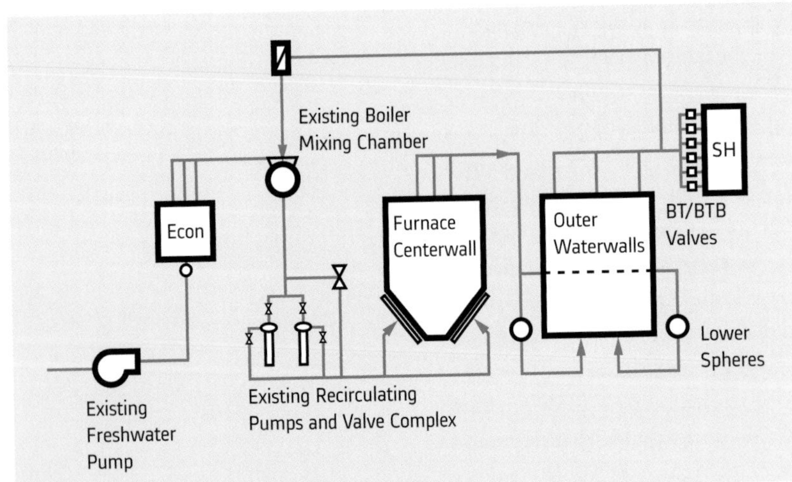

Figure 12-6 | Combined Circulation® with existing circulation line

HOT WATER RECIRCULATION SYSTEM. Hot water recirculation systems can be used on subcritical boilers or supercritical boilers. However, the design and costs of these systems are much different. The new hot water recirculation system will allow the operator of the natural and Controlled Circulation® (subcritical pressure) boilers to control exit gas temperature (i.e., economizer outlet) at loads below MCR so that the backend equipment can operate in the proper gas temperature range, which optimizes its performance.

Water at or slightly below saturated water temperature from the downcomer system is sent through a new recirculation pump so the water can be injected into the economizer inlet. By mixing these two fluids, the water temperature increases to the economizer, which decreases its ability to absorb energy (i.e., changes the log mean temperature difference). The result is an increase in economizer exit gas temperature. The cost of the hot water recirculation system for subcritical boilers is very competitive with any economizer flue gas bypass system.

Combined Circulation® (supercritical) boilers have an existing recirculation line from the waterwall outlet that connects the existing circulation pumps to the mixing chamber located after the economizer. This is shown in *Figure 12-6*. The new economizer waterwall outlet (hot fluid) recirculation system would replace the existing recirculation system by taking fluid from the waterwall outlet and mixing it with the feedwater flow in a new mixing chamber that connects to either new booster pumps in series with the existing circulation pumps or to new circulation pumps that discharge into the economizer inlet instead of the existing mixing chamber, as shown in *Figure 12-7*. The economizer waterwall outlet (hot fluid) recirculation system raises the economizer water inlet temperature at low loads so that the economizer heat absorption decreases and the exit gas temperature to the SCR increases. The water inlet temperature is increased by mixing hot, waterwall outlet fluid (765 to 780°F [407 to 416°C]) with the much colder feedwater (400 to 485°F [204 to 252°C]).

The pump head and flow requirements are specified to either add to or replace the boiler's two existing furnace wall recirculation pumps and to provide enough additional flow and head for the economizer recirculation duty. A control valve in the recirculation line will maintain the flow within the required performance range, as needed. Although the economizer outlet fluid temperature is higher, the change in waterwall outlet fluid temperature is minimal, because now the economizer outlet fluid temperature is about the same as the mixed temperature from the existing mixing chamber that enters the waterwalls.

The biggest change with the economizer waterwall outlet recirculation system is the increase in system resistance. The increases in pump head and pump horsepower may be two and a half to three times the original pump head and horsepower.

The amount of recirculated fluid is expected to be in the 20 to 30% range of the normal feedwater flow at the lower load points. The increase in flow through the waterwalls is expected to have a positive affect on the waterwalls. This system can be high in cost, but when compared with gas bypass systems designed with high-grade materials (high gas temperatures), the hot water recirculation system is competitive.

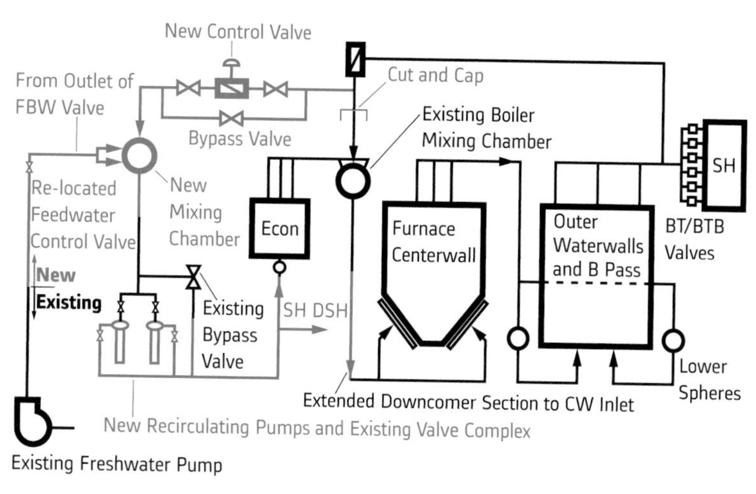

Figure 12-7 | Economizer waterwall outlet (hot fluid) recirculation system (B Pass, back pass)

FUEL SWITCHING

There are many reasons for a utility to consider fuels for a boiler that do not meet the original design specifications. In years past, fuel contracts were often signed for extended periods of time, as much as 20 years. In the current marketplace, contracted coal supplies are often supplemented or replaced by spot market purchases based primarily on a $/MMBTU consideration. Throughout the world, more and more coal is sourced outside of the original coal supply region (and coal rank) area due to a variety of reasons, including costs, environmental considerations, mine shutdowns, etc. In the United States, these drivers specifically include the decreasing supply and increasing costs of Central Appalachian coal that meets certain Clean Air Act sulfur levels. In addition, it has been shown that switching to low rank coals is also a viable NOx reduction technique.[6] This coal switch is the most common in the United States and is representative of the switch from higher rank, higher quality fuel to lower rank fuels that occur elsewhere.

When switching coals from different geographic locations or between coal ranks, it is important to remember that the existing boiler was designed for a specific coal heating value and ash quantity, as well as ash constituents and their resulting slagging and fouling characteristics. When switching coals, a thorough review of the boiler design effects on the fuel switch is in order. Many of the common traits on which coal is traded, such as higher heating value, sulfur content, and proximate analysis do not correlate well to the potential side effects in boiler operation. Two coals with similar heating values can operate very differently in the boiler, especially in terms of the fouling and slagging characteristics. Most fuel switch retrofit projects will start with an analysis of all components and systems that could be affected by the coal switch to identify any potential roadblocks. In general, switching from higher rank coal to lower rank coal creates more potential boiler-related issues. Therefore, the following description is based on that switch.

There is an emergence of CO_2 related retrofit projects in recent years. There is a developing market in biomass fuel as a source of energy for existing boilers, as biomass is considered carbon neutral.[7] In general, the biomass systems will be a co-firing application instead of a complete switch. Typically, up to 20% biomass will be fired in conjunction with the coal.

In any fuel switch or co-firing retrofit, there are three broad areas to be considered and accommodated.

1. Fuel selection and characteristics
2. Boiler performance and operation
3. Auxiliary equipment (fuel handling, ash handling, back end equipment, and fans)

TABLE 12-1 | INFLUENCE OF ASH CONSTITUENTS ON SLAGGING CHARACTERISTICS

Slagging Potential:	Low	Medium	High	Severe
Indices:				
CaO, %	< 10	10 to 20	20 to 40	> 40
Na_2O, %	< 1	1 to 3	3 to 5	> 5
Fe_2O_3	< 7	7 to 15	15 to 25	> 25
Fe_2O_3/CaO	variable when $Fe_2O_3 < 7$	0.5 to 0.7 or 1.4 to 1.8 and $Fe_2O_3 > 7$	0.7 to 1.4 and $Fe_2O_3 > 10$	
IDT, °F	> 2,190	< 2,190	< 2,100	< 2,010
FT, °F	> 2,550	2,280 < FT< 2,550	2,100 < FT < 2,280	< 2,100
Rs,°F	> 2,450	2,250 < Rs < 2,450	2,100 < Rs < 2,250	< 2,100

Coal Switching

FUEL CHARACTERISTICS. Each boiler is designed for a specific fuel or fuel range. If the coal switch retrofit utilizes fuels that are in the same American Society for Testing and Materials (ASTM) category with similar higher heating values and ash constituents, there are typically no issues in firing the new coal. As the coal properties vary from the original design properties, it is more likely that boiler or auxiliary equipment changes will be required to maintain design load.

In general, lower rank coals have a lower BTU and higher moisture contents. This results in lower boiler efficiency and higher gas and air flow rates through the boiler. In addition, lower rank coals often exhibit fouling and slagging characteristics that are worse than the original design coals (*Table 12-1*). For example, coals from the Powder

River Basin (PRB) in the United States all have high calcium contents and some fields also include high sodium contents. These coals will rank in the medium to high slagging index with some ranking as a high slagging index. For plants designed for a low to medium slagging index coal, this is an issue.

The higher calcium and sodium contents also lead to an increase in the fouling propensity of these coals. *Table 12-2* shows the fouling potential for these constituents.

TABLE 12-2 | FOULING POTENTIAL OF CALCIUM AND SODIUM IN COAL ASH

Fouling Potential	None	Medium	High	Severe
Na_2O (%)	< 1	< 2.5	2.5 to 5	> 5
CaO (%)	< 5	5 to 10	≥ 10	
$F = \% Na_2O \times B/A$	< 0.1	0.1 to 0.5	> 5	

BOILER PERFORMANCE AND OPERATION. The challenge for today's boiler designers is to competitively adapt steam generator systems for the low rank coals and to obtain the fuel cost and environmental benefits without limiting the output of the existing unit. The biggest issue during a boiler retrofit to a lower rank coal is to accommodate the fixed furnace size and heat transfer requirements versus the higher slagging and fouling characteristics typical of lower rank coals. Detailed analysis of furnace and boiler design is presented in Chapter 3, but the concepts important for retrofits are included.

FURNACE CONSIDERATIONS. For a new unit, the furnace sizing (width × depth) is based on the fuel heat input and ash quality, or the potential for ash to slag, which would inhibit waterwall heat transfer. In addition, the furnace height from the centerline of the top fuel elevation to the horizontal plane at the bottom of the panels (horizontal furnace outlet plane [HFOP]) and resulting furnace residence time is a key design factor. The combination of NHI/PA and residence time will determine the vertical furnace outlet plane (VFOP) gas temperature that enters the convective section. For new units, the design is based on maintaining a gas temperature that is lower than the ash softening temperature.

Since the 1970s, Alstom has built many units designed for lower rank coals. In addition, there have also been many retrofits of units designed for higher rank coals to the lower rank sub-bituminous C rank coals. Based on this experience, the ideal furnace size for a unit firing a typical high calcium, low sodium, sub-bituminous C would be on the order of $1.7–1.9 \times 10^6$ BTU/hr-ft^2 NHI/PA (*Fig. 12-8*). Units designed or modified based on this criteria have operations that are not limited by the waterwall slagging.

New units would be sized for an average residence time (with air-staging) of 1.3 seconds to the bottom of the panels/platens. Another way of expressing the height is as a multiple of the average furnace dimension (width + depth)/2 for relative comparisons across the range of unit capacities. A new unit designed today for a typical sub-bituminous C coal would have a height that is 1.0 to 1.15 times the average furnace dimensions, which results in the 1.3 second average.

For retrofit boilers that meet the size and residence time requirements described above, little additional equipment is required to maintain optimal furnace conditions. For these units, proper maintenance and operation of existing steam waterwall soot blowers is usually sufficient. For units

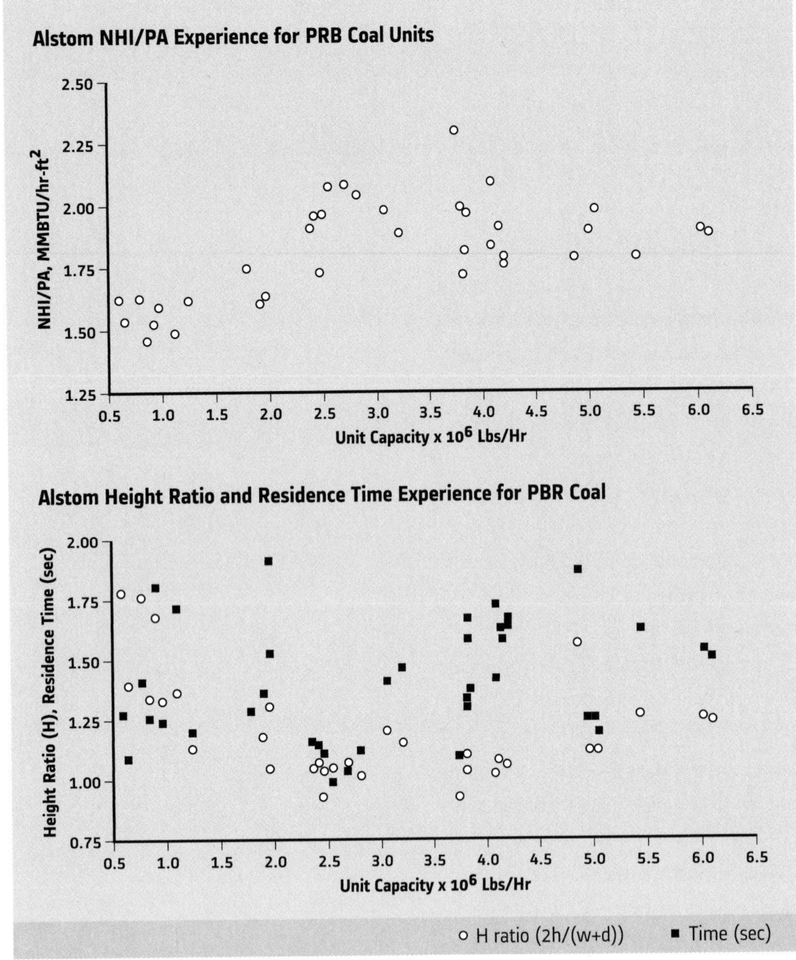

Figure 12-8 | Alstom experience with PRB coals (NHI/PA, height ratio, and residence time)

that don't meet the above criteria for temperature or residence time, careful considerations of retrofit designs and plant operational criteria are required to allow operation at these values that are not optimal.

Aggressive action is required inside the furnace to minimize the impact of slagging on the furnace walls. The addition of an aggressive low NOx firing system as discussed above, will result in a reduction in the furnace slagging due to the reduction of peak flame temperatures and the addition of concentric firing air directed at the waterwalls.

Although the addition of a low NOx system will assist in maintaining controllable slagging conditions, often it is necessary to retrofit new water cleaning devices that can more aggressively clean the walls. Water devices have been used successfully in applications where conventional steam and air blowers have been ineffective. They were slow to gain acceptance because of the potential risk of damage to boiler tubes. In general, conversions from higher rank to lower rank coals have shown that in many instances these devices provided the only economically justifiable mechanism for obtaining continuous full load operation. The advent of sophisticated microprocessor-based controls has greatly improved the "intelligence" required to safely operate these water-based, wall-cleaning systems.

CONVECTIVE SURFACES. The convective section of the boiler, like the furnace, is a fixed volume that is rarely altered. The two design concerns raised by lower rank coal conversions are ash bridging/plugging of surface over the furnace and just above the nose arch, and fouling/pluggage of surface in the "tunnel" and backpass. In both scenarios heat transfer suffers and draft loss increases can inhibit load if proper cleaning measures are not maintained. The design goal is to prevent gas temperatures from exiting the furnace at troublesome levels. Even with aggressive wall blowing in the furnace, this is not always possible.

Re-spacing of pendent section to prevent pluggage is usually not a realistic option due to cost and/or available

cavity volume, but several alternatives are possible. If the original assemblies are spaced surface (i.e., non-tangent in the direction of gas flow), then replacement with platenized surface will improve cleanability because ash cannot encapsulate the tubes. Platenized surface is less effective than spaced surface for heat absorption and typically 20 to 25% more surface is required to absorb a given amount of heat. However, when off-design conditions with troublesome ashes limit the cleanability of spaced heat transfer surface, cleanable platenized surface is the solution. Another means to improve surface cleanability is replacement of ferritic tubing with stainless steel. Sub-bituminous C coal ash high in calcium (typical of PRB coals) does not adhere to stainless steel tubing as it does to ferritic tubing. The lower stainless thermal conductivity is more than offset by cleaner surface and the effect is a higher overall heat transfer coefficient.

Backpass fouling will be dependent on the fouling characteristics of the coal. Deposits are easily removed with aggressive soot blowing. However, on many units designed for higher quality coal and close spaced surface (1 to 2 inch [2.5 to 5.0 cm] clear), the soot blower jet penetration is insufficient. There are several design options to address this situation. The first is to re-space assemblies on wider centers if there is adequate backpass volume to accommodate more square feet of surface area. Hanger tube spacing must be checked for compatibility with any other sections being supported. If assemblies cannot be re-spaced, then decreasing tube outside diameter (OD) to increase clear space is an option. Platenizing the surface to improve cleanability is also possible if steam temperature can still be achieved with a less effective surface (*Fig. 12-9*).

Modifying an easily fouled, staggered tube economizer arrangement to a more cleanable in-line design is not always possible because of the large increase in surface that is required. One option is installing a bare tube, in-line design with additional surface area. Most existing boilers typically do not have large open cavities available to install a new bank of economizer surface. Often, the only available location for new surface area is in the economizer hopper area. This can be accommodated with careful attention to design detail. There are many structural members in the hopper that may have to be modified to accommodate the new economizer bank. Of course, the economizer inlet header will have to be relocated even lower in the hopper area.

Another possibility is the replacement of the staggered arrangement with an in-line spiral fin surface (SFS) economizer surface. This has

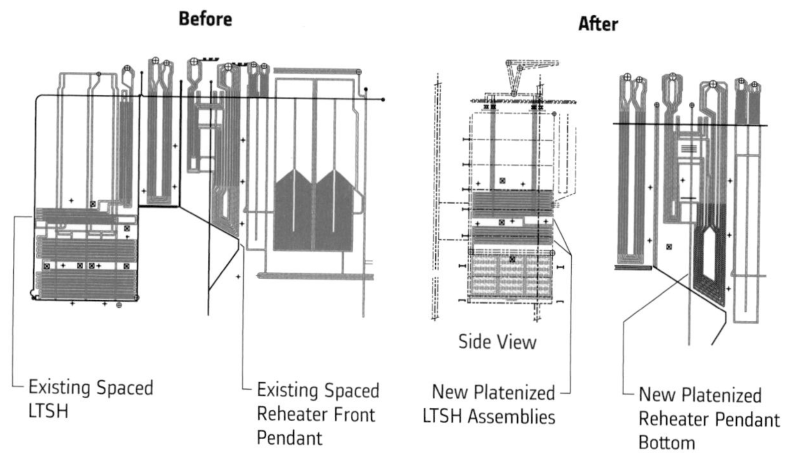

Figure 12-9 | Surface modifications to allow for better cleaning

been a very successful application for units firing lower rank coals with low sodium content. The SFS economizer is not recommended for coals with higher levels of sodium due to the very high fouling tendency of the ash. A typical SFS economizer consists of inline tubes with a spiral fin pitch of approximately two fins per inch and a maximum fin height of 0.75 inches (1.9 cm) with a thickness of 0.060 inches (0.15 cm). Clear space between fin tips is maintained at 2 inches (5.0 cm), while the assembly depth is limited to approximately 5 to 6 feet (1.5 to 1.8 m) to ensure complete soot blower coverage (*Fig. 12-10*).

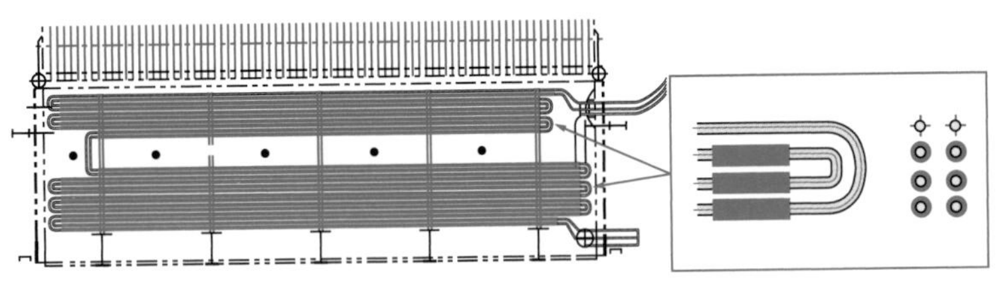

Figure 12-10 | Spiral finned economizer application with soot blower locations

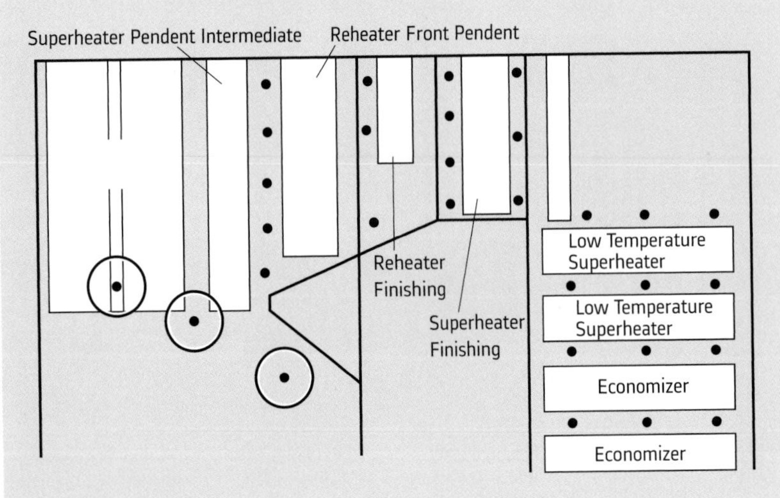

Figure 12-11 | Example of soot blower coverage

CONVECTIVE PASS SOOT BLOWER COVERAGE. To compensate for the nonideal gas temperatures entering the convective section and the limited space for surface in the backpass, convective soot blower coverage is usually 100% for the low rank sub-bituminous C coals. This is necessary to maintain or regain all superheater (SH), reheater (RH), and economizer thermal performance. An example of the coverage is shown in *Figure 12-11*. In many cases these blowers will be used more frequently than pre-conversion, i.e., once or twice per shift. Due to the increased frequency, steam or air sources should be evaluated for the increased duty and tube shields or thicker wall tubing should be installed to offset the possibility of increased tube erosion.

FIRING SYSTEMS. In most cases, the existing firing equipment has sufficient flexibility to handle the change in coal quality. Windbox and SOFA damper operation will change, but will usually be within the control capabilities of the system based on the windbox to furnace pressure set point. The notable exception for the firing system flexibility is the coal nozzle design itself. In some cases, especially in boilers that are wall fired, increases in moisture, throughput, and mill airflows will result in velocities through the fuel nozzle that are unacceptably high. This can result in flame fronts that are unacceptably detached or unstable flames. In these cases, the fuel nozzles can be changed out with suitably sized nozzles that meet the velocity requirements of the system.

AIR HEATERS. During conversions to lower rank coals, air heater performance usually deteriorates. Increased air and gas flows increase their respective draft losses through the machine. Many of the lower rank coals have a higher fouling tendency, which will increase draft loss and decrease thermal performance. Typical remedies to improve these conditions include the installation of hot and/or cold end soot blowers, if they do not already exist, as well as off-line water washing devices for removal of long-term fouling/plugging with minimal outage time. In vertical shaft air heaters, loose pack baskets can be installed. These baskets are constructed from wider-spaced plates that are slightly loose in the bundle to resist plugging and improve cleanability.

FANS. When switching coals, if the coal has higher moisture than the design coal (as is often the case for lower rank coals), the moisture content increases the mass flow of the flue gas. In addition, the moisture content decreases the boiler efficiency by as much as 5 percentage points, requiring the same percentage increase in coal flow and higher air and gas flows. Thus, forced draft (FD), primary air (PA), and induced draft (ID) fans must be evaluated for both flow and head capacity increases.

Often times, the FD and ID fans can sustain full load operation by using the original design margin for both head and flow. If the margins are insufficient or have been used in unit upratings, then changes to add head and flow will be required. Typically re-tipping the fan blades and upgrading the motors will obtain the necessary uprate in fan capacity. In a few cases, new rotors and motors have been required. The PA fans have to supply an increase in hot airflow to the pulverizers for coal drying. Typically this is within the margin of the fan(s), but in rare cases, re-tipping along with motor upgrades is a viable option.

MILLING SYSTEMS. The switch to lower rank coals also has to be accommodated by the coal handling and pulverizing systems. The heating value of subbituminous coals can be as much as 30% less than high-volatile bituminous coal. This requires that the fuel processing equipment be modified to handle this fuel quantity increase. This requirement directly affects the pulverizers.

Any given size coal pulverizer has a finite maximum capacity expressed in throughput, lbs/hr (Kg/hr). This can be either a mechanical limitation or thermal limitation depending on the coal characteristics. During any retrofit that involves increasing the coal throughput requirements of the pulverizers or changing the coal source requires an analysis of the milling system to determine the coal throughput capacity and options for increasing the throughput if required.

MECHANICAL CAPACITY. There are two primary characteristics of the coal being ground that are integral parts of determining the mechanical capacity of a pulverizer. They are grindability, which is the measure of the difficulty with which a coal is reduced in size, expressed as Hardgrove Grindability Index (HGI), and product fineness, which is expressed as the percentage of the pulverizer output that can pass through a 200 mesh sieve. In some cases with bituminous coals, moisture is also a factor in determining mechanical capacity.

When evaluating pulverizer performance, the required mill throughput in lbs/hr (Kg/hr) at MCR is compared to the expected maximum mill throughput for the given HGI and desired fineness. Alstom recommends that the throughput at MCR does not exceed 90% of maximum capacity to ensure that the pulverizer is capable of processing the required amount of coal when in a worn condition.

For coal blends, all of the mechanical capacity is done using the grindability of the lowest HGI fuel. Due to the propensity of the lower HGI coal to collect in the pulverizer and make up the majority of the recirculating load, HGI values are not averaged.

DYNAMIC™ CLASSIFIERS. Dynamic™ classifiers use a variable speed conical rotor in place of the existing dual cone static classifier. The addition of a Dynamic™ classifier will increase pulverizer capacity due to a reduction in the recirculation load created by the classifier for a given coal flow and fineness. The reduction in recirculation load represents an increase in classifier efficiency, reducing the unnecessary over-grinding of the very fine (200 mesh) particles and discharging the properly sized particles quicker. The capacity increase can be used to increase coal flow for a given product fineness or increase product fineness for a given coal flow.

MILL BLUEPRINTING. Over the course of a pulverizer's operation, regular maintenance includes parts replacements, mechanical adjustments, and operational changes for a variety of reasons. It is common for a variety of non-original equipment manufacturer (OEM) parts to be installed during this period. In addition, plant practices over time may differ from recommended pulverizer operational or mechanical set points. These changes from original design conditions may occur over the course of many years and can result in mill throughput limitations. Quite often these limitations are not noticed due to the spare capacity designed into the milling system. When there is a fuel switch to a lower rank, lower BTU, higher moisture coal, the required increase in throughput will highlight any mill mechanical weaknesses due to nonstandard or optimum parts as well as incorrect set points. To eliminate these choke points, the mill can be "blueprinted" with OEM parts, usually upgraded, and all original tolerances and spring tensions as per recommendations for the current fuel being fired. This will result in the maximum mechanical throughput of the milling system.

THERMAL CAPACITY LIMITATIONS. Pulverizer thermal capacity is the amount of raw fuel the pulverizer can effectively dry. The thermal capacity is primarily a function of fuel rank, available primary air inlet temperature, available primary air mass flow, and desired pulverizer outlet temperature. During initial pulverizer selection the thermal capacity is typically higher than the mechanical capacity and is rarely an issue. Thermal capacity can become an issue at a later time, particularly when a fuel switch is being considered. Thermal capacity is determined using a mathematical heat balance model. Pulverizers are usually sized up to 100% of the thermal capacity value, since wear has no effect on a pulverizer's thermal capacity. Standard airflow, recommended outlet temperatures, and specific heats are used to generate the required primary air inlet temperature for each operating case. These temperatures are then compared to the available primary air temperature leaving the air heater to determine if there is adequate thermal capacity. Generally a 50°F (30°C) margin is desired between the required primary air temperature and the available primary air temperature. If the thermal capacity of the pulverizer is lacking, there are several options available to increase the drying capacity of the pulverizer and throughput.

HIGHER HOT AIR TEMPERATURES. Hot air temperatures to the mill can be increased by the use of in-duct gas or oil-fired heaters. Alternatively, duct modifications can be made to take hotter air off of the air heater.

LARGER EXHAUSTER FAN WHEELS. For exhauster style mills, larger diameter exhauster fan wheels will add head and airflow to the system. Often times, a larger, conventional open paddle wheel design can fit within the existing housing. There is also an option of using a newer style high efficiency fan (HEF) within the existing fan casing. Using the HEF has an added benefit of higher operating fan efficiency, minimizing fan power consumption at the higher head and airflow. Higher airflow also helps with the mechanical capacity of the mills.

FAN SPEED INCREASES. Increased fan speed can provide additional airflow through the mill for greater drying capacity by the following methods:

1. Add a higher speed motor and new gear for bowl, which requires mechanical analysis for bearings, shafts, structure and lubrication
2. Decouple the fan from the pulverizer and add a second separately driven fan

Higher airflows increase the power requirements from the fans. If the existing motors are to be used, they must be checked. Sometimes they can be rewound for increased power.

Biomass Co-Firing

FUEL CHARACTERISTICS. Biomass firing often involves locally obtained material as the cost to transport the lower heating value fuel can become economically untenable with large distances. The economics of biomass firing are currently closely tied to the CO_2 constraints and economic incentives to reduce CO_2.

Biomass does not have classifications similar to coal due to the wide variety and local nature of the fuels. An incomplete list of biomass includes wood and wood products, bagasse, straws, agricultural wastes, construction wastes, and animal waste including derivatives of these products. *Table 12-3* contains an example project where the fuels were

TABLE 12-3 | RAW BIOMASS FUEL PROPERTIES

Fuel	Wood Pellets	Palm Kernels	Olive Pellets	Olive Cake
Proximate Analysis				
H_2O%	8.38	6.78	11.45	ND
Ash%	1.43	5.06	10.12	ND
VM%	68.19	70.79	59.62	ND
FC%	22	17.37	18.81	ND
Ultimate Analysis				
C%	46.41	45.14	44.18	42.8
H%	5.15	5.75	4.92	5.75
N%	1.87	2.6	1.71	1.88
O% by diff	36.44	34.24	27.25	
S	0.21	0.23	0.14	0.19
Cl%	0.11	0.2	0.23	0.31
GCV kJ/kg	18,906	19,235	18,691	17,588

GCV = Gross Calorific Value

all cellulose-based and thus have a calorific value on a weight basis that are similar.

However the volume fired varied dramatically as the bulk density of these fuels varied by a factor of two. For comparable heat inputs, different volumes of fuel must be processed, even though the heating value on a weight basis may be the same. Other differences from coal include the high amount of volatile matter. As can be seen, the volatile matter of the products in the table are all 60% or higher. Coal contains around 30% volatiles.

Biomass fuel ash often contains alkaline metals. When these inorganic compounds are in the form of salts or bound in the organic material, these elements are easily released. This creates a concern for the heat transfer sections of the boiler. In addition, the high chlorine content in some biomass fuels represents a concern for boiler tubing. Chlorine attack can occur on the tubing metal and create wastage issues. For these reasons, in retrofit situations, biomass is usually limited to a percentage of the total fuel heat input. In limited cases where biomass is retrofitted to fire at 100%, the boiler usually must be derated to account for the operational issues.

BOILER PERFORMANCE AND OPERATION. As with coal switching issues, the addition of biomass co-firing will be highly dependent on the original design of the boiler, age, and maintenance of the equipment. Biomass co-firing effects on the boiler are dependent on the type of biomass and the quantity fired. In general, the higher hydrogen content of biomass, as well as the moisture content, will usually lead to a boiler efficiency decrease and a subsequent increase in total heat input required. In a 20% co-firing scenario, the air and gas weights are not significantly different and, therefore, the effect on fans and downstream equipment is minimal.

As the blended ash increases in the alkali elements such as calcium and sodium, the rate of tube deposition can increase. In addition, the fusibility characteristics of ash can vary as the chemical constituents change. By limiting the heat input to a nominal 20% co-firing, the slagging and fouling potential, although increased, can usually be managed. In some scenarios, additional cleaning equipment may be required.

FIRING SYSTEMS. For new boilers firing biomass, the boiler design would be based on the characteristics of the fuel. Biomass fuels have different handling, transport, and combustion characteristics compared to coal. Based on these characteristics, steam output and conditions, etc., the firing system will usually be either a stoker system or a fluidized bed boiler.

With existing plants, the choice of firing system is limited. If a unit is to be converted to 100% biomass firing, a stoker can be installed in the bottom of the boiler and traditional stoker feed systems utilized. The total heat input to the unit will be directly related to the grate heat release rate and will usually result in a significant unit derate.

For a co-firing installation, the new biomass burners typically are placed near the top of the windbox between adjacent burners. The design generally must address the following considerations:

- Existing arrangement of windbox and physical restriction
- Ensuring burnout of larger particles, which might fall through the furnace

- Allowing biomass firing at lower loads, when only the upper mills are in service for steam temperature control
- Operating in a higher temperature region of the furnace to ensure stability of the biomass flames at lower loads

The burner management and combustion control systems operation will be specific to the unit, but usually a minimum level of firing in the furnace is required as with adjacent coal mills in service. Biomass co-firing at the 20% level generally results in no to slight reductions in NOx emissions from the plant.

AUXILIARY EQUIPMENT. Fuel handling is a key component of the successful retrofit of biomass firing into a coal designed boiler. Unlike coal, the material is low density and often has high fiber content. These properties must be considered in the proper development of fuel handling, storage, milling, and fuel transport systems.

All of these systems should be based on the best practices and local regulations for handling material that creates a fine dust and can constitute a dust explosion hazard. Additionally, the material is likely to decompose during prolonged storage causing self-heating, which can lead to rapid spontaneous combustion. Silos need to be emptied if the unit is not firing biomass to ensure that the material is not stored for long periods.

For co-firing applications, the biomass is usually ground to allow efficient combustion. A hammer-type mill is utilized for this type of application, as a roller mill will create buildup inside the mill, reducing output. A typical design would include a relatively small milling chamber to reduce the opportunity and effect of any potential explosion. An example of a duplex hammer mill with screw feeders is shown in *Figure 12-12*. The fuel is transported through either a dilute or dense phase, depending on the unique situation.

Figure 12-12 | Duplex hammer mill with screw feeders

MAINTENANCE UPGRADES

As noted in the introduction, the trend is to improve the performance and reliability of existing plants. This can often be accomplished by retrofitting existing boilers with the newest design standards and performance enhancing products.

Updating SH and RH Alignment Attachments

Maintaining alignment from tube to tube in vertical assemblies is vital to the overall operation of the unit. When the tubes are out of alignment, the tube-to-tube stress increases, giving way to potential tube failures at the attachment, failure of the support or alignment attachment, increased pressure drop across the assembly, and potential slag buildup, further reducing gas flow and heat transfer across the assembly. There are many different types of attachments used for maintaining tube-to-tube alignment and tube-to-tube support. Depending on the customer's preference, the alignment and tube supports are installed during fabrication.

Alstom's preferred alignment attachment is a flexible tube connector. The tube connector consists of three parts, two "L" shaped "female" lugs and one "T" shaped "male" lug. The lugs are designed to be low mass to minimize heat absorption. The lugs are shop welded to adjacent tubes. This design allows the lugs to operate at a much lower temperature than earlier generations of attachments. Due to the operating temperature of the assemblies, there is an axial expansion of the tubing. Adjacent tubes will operate at slightly different temperatures, resulting in different expansions. The design of these lugs allows the tubes to move axially independent of each other, while at the same time, maintaining alignment.

Alignment attachments that are not welded to the tubes must be selected to operate at the gas temperature of the component. In most applications, a higher quality material must be specified, therefore increasing the cost of the attachment.

Changing SH and RH Fluid Cooled Spacers to Modern Design

The preferred method of controlling side-to-side movement of vertical assemblies employs the use of a steam- or water-cooled tube circuit. The main function of the tube spacer is to prevent the assemblies from swinging in the path of the gas flow. If the assemblies are not restrained, over time the vertical assembly could experience failure between the assembly tube and the seal where the assembly penetrates the roof. The failure could be a tube leak or the failure of the gas seal, allowing superheated gas into the roof enclosure area. The early spacer support system consisted of four lugs on the spacer tube for each assembly tube. The spacer tube was located between the first and second tube of the assembly. The system was a very flexible system. The downfall of the system is that the spacer tube and the assembly tube are free to come into contact with each other. Over time, failures have occurred in one of the tubes due to the rubbing. The failure would result in a tube leak.

The current spacer support system replaces the four lugs on the spacer tube with two interlocking lugs. The interlocking lugs prevent the spacer tube and the assembly tube from coming into contact. The arrangement prevents the tube failures due to the tube-to-tube contact.

The interlocking support lugs provide a positive restraint, preventing the assembly side-to-side movement. Because of the positive restraint, the vertical portion of the spacer tube generally requires an expansion loop. The vertical assemblies may operate at a different temperature or be of a different material than the spacer tube. This difference introduces a thermal expansion differential between the assembly and the spacer tube. The expansion loop resolves the differential.

Additional modifications include:

1. Reduce number of tube changes in components to reduce shop welds, minimize cost, simplify design, and minimize customer's inventory requirements
2. Change pendant section support arrangement to eliminate tie welds
3. Upgrade to split ring casting alignment design
4. Upgrade economizer and horizontal SH and RH support systems
5. Modularize components (with or without new headers) to improve constructability and reduce outage length and manpower requirements

Furnace Bottom Replacement

In addition to the daily wear due to erosion and corrosion, the furnace bottom slope tubes experience tube failures as the result of slag fall from the upper furnace. The impact of the slag fall can result in the crushing of the tube, creating a tube leak; failure of the sidewall seal between the slope tube and the sidewall, creating a tube leak; failure of the sidewall seal that allows the superheated gas to escape into the coutant slope support system, resulting in a support failure; or failure of the support system due to the impact of the slag fall. It is possible to address these failures due to the slag fall with several different improvements.

The first improvement involves redesigning the coutant slope tubes using a "fat" tube design. The tube wall thickness is increased to improve the tube's ability to absorb the impact of the slag fall. The increase in the tube wall thickness is accommodated by reducing the clear space between each tube. The tube-to-tube centers are maintained to ensure matching to the tubes above the coutant slope. In some cases, a flow analysis is performed to determine if the inside diameter of the slope tube may be decreased.

A second option involves welding a rectangle-shaped wear bar to the furnace side of the slope tube to increase the tube's ability to resist the impact of the slag fall. The combination of the tube strength and the strength of the wear bar increases the resistance to the crushing affect of the slag fall. It is also possible to combine the wear bar construction with the fat tube design.

Once the ability of the slope tubes to resist the slag fall is addressed, the framing system for the slope tubes must be evaluated. Somewhat like the slope tubes, as the slag fall impacts the tube, the force of the slag fall is passed through the tubes into the structural framing system. The slag fall may crush or deform the existing structural shapes, reducing the ability of the structure to support the slope tubes. The attachment between the slope tube and the structural support may fail, resulting in the force of the slag fall finding a different load transfer path. The resultant load path also may not be designed to accept the new forces. All of these failures potentially can lead to the failure of a tube.

The structural supports can be redesigned in a manner that reinforces the ability of the slope tube to resist the slag fall. If the existing structure is not deformed, it may be reinforced with the addition of new material. The existing structure can be reinforced locally to spread the impact of the slag fall into a larger area. The connections between the slope tubes and the structure may be redesigned or the number of connections increased; again, redistributing the force of the slag fall.

The final area to be considered when updating the furnace slope involves the seal between the slope tubes and the sidewall tubes. Alstom employs a "soft" seal design, which allows the seal to flex between the movements of the slope tubes and the sidewall tubes. In earlier designs, the seal was a more rigid design. The impact of the slag fall or the day-to-day furnace operation could result in the failure of the seal or the failure of the tubes.

As the source of the fuel may change over the operating life of the plant, the safety implications need to be factored into any retrofit plan.

Flexibility Analysis

The original design of header terminal tubes was considered to be a base load type condition. The base load design included what was considered at the time to be a number of normal start-ups and shut downs per the guidelines of the American Society of Mechanical Engineers (ASME) Code. As a utility attempts to maximize the use of the

Good maintenance practices and well planned retrofits lead to improved operating availability, increased output, and reduced emissions.

units to meet demand and economic conditions, it may now operate the unit through a more severe cycle of partial shutdowns and, in some cases, complete shutdowns. Although the system is exposed to other factors contributing to the total stress, if the stress due to thermal differentials can be reduced, the life of the components may increase.

While operating at low loads, hot restarts, and/or cold startups, flow unbalances are created between each circuit at the headers. The flow unbalance restricts the flow to the different circuits, resulting in the circuits operating at larger temperature differentials. When adjacent circuits operate at different temperatures and the circuits are rigidly attached, increased thermal expansion stresses occur between the circuits. The buildup of the thermal stresses over time reduces the strength of the system, allowing outside factors to attack. The attack of the outside factors eventually leads to a failure.

When performing a flexibility analysis, the thermal expansion stresses are evaluated based on the geometry of the system, the different component materials, the different temperature conditions, and the different start-up or shutdown conditions. The major contributor to failures at the connection to the header is internal corrosion. Areas exposed to high stresses are prime targets for internal corrosion. As the unit cycles, the thermal stress is repeated, accelerating the internal corrosion, eventually leading to a failure. Increasing the flexibility of the system reduces thermal expansion stress. Flexibility can be increased by the addition of bends to the component, offsetting the component, and/or increasing the distance between the fixed points of the component. The relationship between the temperature differential and the thermal expansion stress is a linear relationship. Therefore, any reduction in the temperature differential will result in an improvement of the system's ability to resist the attacks by outside factors.

As the current competitive environment requires close attention to capital and operational and maintenance costs, today's utility managers have increased their focus on total ownership cost. That is, what is the expected cost over the life of a component. All of the ingredients of long-term cost have to be considered: lost generation due to forced outages, inspection costs, maintenance costs, outage cycles, outage length, unit efficiency, heat rate, and environmental considerations. Initial cost, although important, is no longer the overriding consideration and consequently, this has put increased focus on providing solutions to long-standing problems.

The success of this approach relies on the support of operators and owners that, through working closely with the mechanical and performance design engineers, will allow the collection of invaluable service data and insight into maintenance and/or performance issues plus operational goals and strategies. The systematic approach using root cause analysis will define the cause of failures. Continuous interaction with the customer complements the analysis by providing operational information that goes beyond service time and temperature but also includes fuel characteristics, possible fuel switches, and other operational variables. Evaluation of changes in operation and their impact on unit performance will allow utility management to make economically driven decisions that better meet their expectations. An example of the total plant concept is shown in *Table 12-4*.

In the United States, a 600 MW plant over the course of years implemented a fuel switch and a unit uprating with a new HP turbine. During this time, the unit realized an increase in output and availability while firing a lower rank fuel. NOx and SOx emissions decreased and the outage interval was increased significantly. This multiyear ongoing improvement project consisted of an HP turbine optimized plant retrofit (OPR), a PRB coal switch, a low NOx firing system, and mill modifications.

TABLE 12-4 | RESULTS FROM A 600 MW RETROFIT PROJECT

600 MW Plant Example	1977	1985	2001
Coal heating value	11,000 BTU/lb (25,586 kJ/kg)		8,600 BTU/lb (20,000 kJ/kg)
Generation (MWhrs)	12,200,000	13,100,000	16,700,000
Max. Unit Capacity (MWe)	580	580	630
NOx	0.7 lb/MBTU (0.3 kg/kJ)	0.6 lb/MBTU (0.26 kg/kJ)	0.115lb/MBTU (0.05 kg/kJ)
SOx	6.0 lb/MBTU (2.6 kg/kJ)	4.8 lb/MBTU (2.06 kg/kJ)	0.52 lb/MBTU (0.22 kg/kJ)
Operating Availability	75%	77%	90%
Pulverizer Capacity *t*	90,000	90,000	120,000
Outage Interval (months)	12	18	36

STEAM TURBINE RETROFITS

Technological advances have led to the potential for realizing substantial improvements in older generation plants by retrofitting steam turbines with blade path components of advanced design. The principal of retrofitting existing steam plants in order to achieve cost effective increases in output, efficiency, and reliability is becoming well established. This has been driven not only by the trend toward deregulation of the supply markets and the associated increase in competition, but also by the advances in technology that have been made in recent years by OEMs. Continuous research and development has focused on computational fluid dynamics (CFD) coupled with rigorous testing. This has resulted in real improvements in blade path design that, although initially intended for the new machine market, can offer significant benefits in the retrofit market. Upgrading older generation plants with the modern technology has the potential for realizing the substantial advances made over the past 10 to 20 years. Improvements in guide blade profile design alone have yielded improvements in the region of 2% on stage efficiency, with even greater improvements coming from advanced 3-D profiles and improved design techniques in all parts of the turbine (*Fig. 12-13*). Efficient, modern blade paths also benefit from larger numbers of stages than were possible in the past, and, thus from lower root diameters, improved blade aspect ratios, and lower steam velocities.

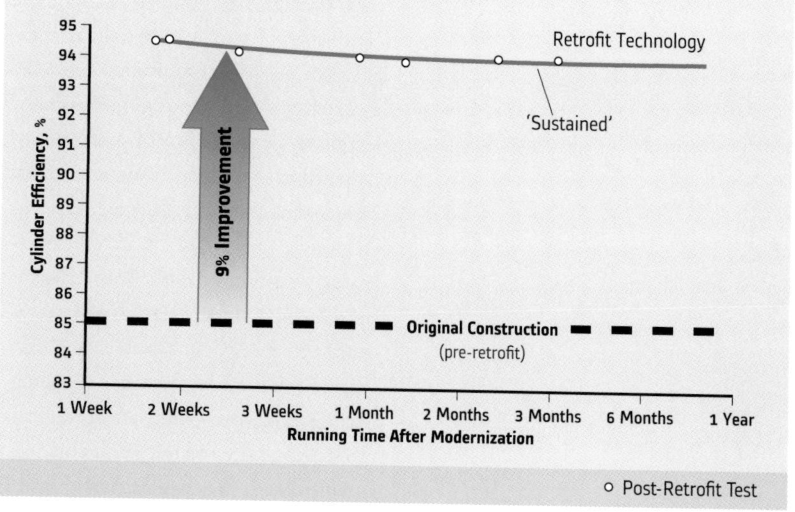

Figure 12-13 | Efficiency improvements after modernization

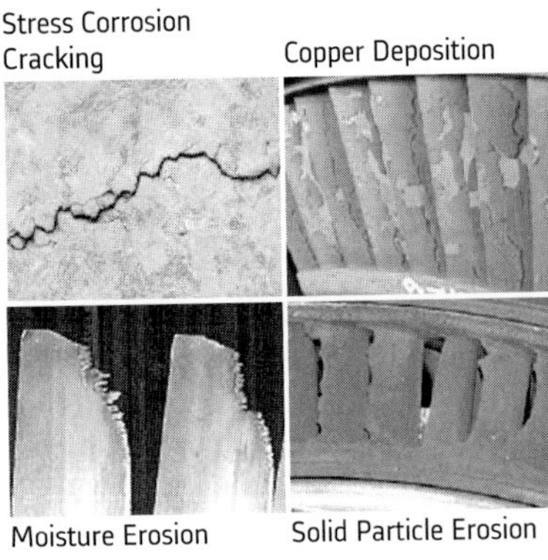

Figure 12-14 | Examples of maintenance issues

RETROFIT DRIVERS

When considering why to retrofit, the concept of asset optimization must be considered. There are many older units still in operation that may be facing serious mechanical deficiencies as they reach the end of their design lives. They are likely to have efficiency levels that are less competitive than today's advanced technology turbines. Often, the original driver for a steam turbine retrofit is maintenance or reliability issues and, of course, the elimination of these issues is one of the key benefits of the retrofit. These maintenance issues often include (*Fig. 12-14*):

- Solid particle erosion (SPE)
- Water droplet erosion
- Flow accelerated corrosion
- Copper oxide deposition
- Stress corrosion cracking (SCC)
- Leaking inlet connections
- Casing cracking and distortion leading to joint leakage.

Sometimes maintenance issues have been with the plant for so long that the routine repairs and inspections that are needed to keep the unit running are regarded simply as normal maintenance. The maintenance team is unaware that these problems are abnormal and can be eliminated, or significantly reduced, by a retrofit. In such cases, it can be much more attractive to advance the operating life of the whole plant by retrofit, rather than to decommission and build a complete new station. This old plant can be brought up to modern day efficiency levels by retrofitting with newly designed components. Modernization of a generating plant, through a steam turbine retrofit, can provide a variety of benefits including improved component life, improved reliability, reduced maintenance, and increased efficiency with increased output capacity, ultimately producing improved revenues due to increased generation or reduced fuel consumption.

The drivers for retrofitting include the following:

- Efficiency
  - Reduced fuel costs
  - Reduced emissions, heat rejection
  - Improved competitive position in deregulated markets
  - Improved environmental performance
- Capacity
  - Increased MW output
  - Delayed new generating plant construction
  - Optimized steam turbine and boiler/reactor capacity
- Reliability
  - Increased reliability
  - Reduced spare parts replacement
  - Increased plant life
  - Resolved existing maintenance issues

Usually, improved thermodynamic efficiency is important for the plant owner. A steam turbine retrofit can provide a short payback period on this basis alone. However, increasingly, customers are recognizing the benefits of a performance retrofit that also solves existing plant reliability issues, such as rotor SCC, SPE, or persistent blade integrity issues, each of which may require reduced maintenance intervals and associated costs, which can be designed out as a result of the retrofit. A good relationship with the customer, making all relevant information available, leading to clear identification of the retrofit drivers, will provide an excellent basis for generation of the concept design.

Enhancing Efficiency

The improvement in unit heat rate has become the strongest retrofit driver in many countries. Deregulation, more stringent environmental regulations, and CO_2 concerns have placed new challenges on power plant operators. These changes have resulted in competitive markets for electricity and a strong drive to reduce generating costs and emissions. Retrofitting of existing steam turbines with the latest steam path technology offers attractive returns on investment with a reduction in fuel costs and plant emissions.

Increasing Capacity

Increased demand for power and the high market price during peak periods are powerful drivers for increasing the MW capacity of existing generating plants. A steam turbine retrofit offers the most cost-effective means of increasing capacity in many cases.

Improving Reliability

Many older types of steam turbines suffer from reliability problems requiring frequent and extensive repairs or component replacement. Even without major operational problems, a unit with high service hours represents an availability risk as it reaches the end of its lifetime. Retrofitting solves all existing maintenance and lifetime problems.

Retrofit or Refurbishment?

If the plant operator selects a refurbishment solution, existing components are renovated or replaced with components of similar design. This will overcome the plant degradation and lifetime problems, but will not provide increased performance. A turbine retrofit will provide additional power beyond that which is gained by a standard in-kind replacement.

RETROFIT DESIGN FEATURES

Each turbine retrofit is unique in that it is customized to suit each customer's operating parameters. The steam path is designed around the volume of steam provided by the boiler. Therefore, the more steam the boiler can provide, the more power output will be provided by the retrofit. When retrofitting non-Alstom units, an on-site survey is required. The first part of the survey starts in the design area with an assessment of the most likely retrofit options, so that the engineer supervising the survey has a clear understanding of which components are likely to be replaced. The engineer is then responsible for concentrating on obtaining the necessary data on all interfaces between those components that will be retained and those components that will be replaced. The second part of the survey requires dispatching a measuring team to the site. The necessary data is obtained by measuring either the component that will interface with the new parts, or the component that will be replaced. In general, when available during a survey, both components will be measured to ensure the reliability of the data. However, this may not always be possible, if some components are not accessible. Measurements are ideally taken during planned outages, when the cylinder is being opened for routine inspection.

The measurement exercise requires careful coordination with the station maintenance team to ensure that the timing allows access to all components and has a minimal impact on the outage program. Measurement would normally take three to four days for a fossil HP or IP turbine. In the event that there is no suitable overhaul outage, then it is generally possible to obtain all of the necessary measurements with minimal strip down, consisting of removing the top half outer casing and the pedestal covers (*Fig. 12-15*).

Figure 12-15 | Turbine measurements

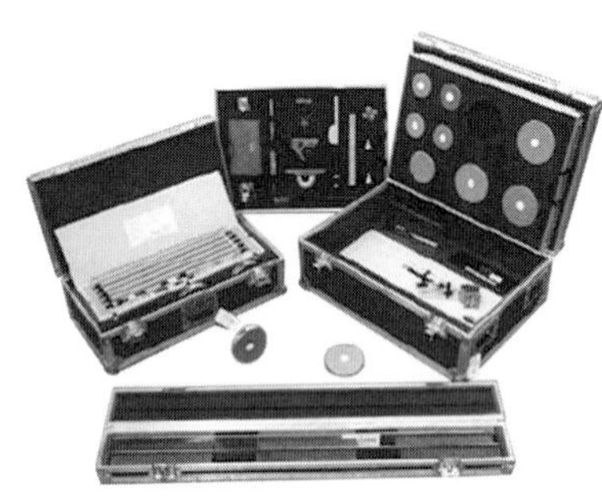

Figure 12-16 | Measurement tools

For making conventional measurements, Alstom engineers are equipped with specially equipped HP/IP measuring boxes (*Fig. 12-16*), containing all the measuring tools necessary to measure full speed fossil HP and IP parts, e.g., straight edges, digital calipers, inside micrometers up to 126 inches (3.2m), pi tapes up to 60 inches (1.5m) in diameter, etc. For the larger "half speed" nuclear HPs and LPs, the HP/IP boxes are supplemented by an LP box to increase the range of measurements, with pi tapes up to 192 inches (4.9m) and inside micrometers up to 252 inches (6.4m).

In addition to the conventional measurements, modern, coordinate measuring methods are deployed. The portable coordinate measuring machine (CMM) and the Faro arm are such systems. The larger Faro arm will measure directly anything within 6 feet (1.8 m) of its base, or 12 feet (3.6 m) spherical diameter. Magnetic datum spheres, attached to the object being measured, allow the arm base to be repositioned beyond the 6 foot (1.8 m) range while still retaining the original coordinate references, thereby, extending the working range of the arm. The computer aided design (CAD) based, software package allows geometric shapes (e.g., planes, bores, etc.) to be measured easily and is ideal for machined surfaces. The arm can also be used "paint brush" style to sweep complex surfaces to give a 3-D map of the area, ideal for cast surfaces or complex forms such as turbine blades. The Faro model has the advantage of recording measurements recorded directly into a CAD system as CAD entities, so that no further interpretation is required for use during the design phase.

The design process can be roughly divided into two main parts, these being the concept generation and optimization phase and the detailed design phase.

Concept Generation

A dedicated team that includes all the core competencies of thermodynamic and mechanical design, together with customer liaison, handles the generation of the retrofit concept for a specific project. Thus, members of the team deal directly with the client's representatives in order to achieve the best possible understanding and, hence, optimal retrofit solution for the client's needs. This successful design approach has been based on the application of proven design features that are assembled into new design solutions for retrofit applications. Thus the client can have confidence that all the features of a retrofit are proven by service experience. For example, a given moving blade of the current, advanced profile, is tailored to a specific application in terms of axial width for mechanical strength and height and root diameter for optimal thermodynamic performance. It is then married with the design using standard root designs and integral shroud design. The result is a stage that effectively has the benefit of considerable service experience and also the design and manufacturing advantages of a standard design.

The design process has evolved from the "inside out" process of new machine development to an "outside in" process for retrofit. That is, whereas the traditional design process focused on starting with a blade path and rotor and designing the successive casings around it, the retrofit process must focus on working both from the blade path outward and from the original components inward. In a typical HP cylinder retrofit, only the outer casing may be retained. However, it is equally possible that the inner casing may be retained or, indeed, that the outer casing is replaced. The choice will be based on the relative benefits in terms of performance, reliability, and cost.

Concept generation revolves around the requirement to fit the optimal blade path design within the constraints of the existing hardware. These constraints are not just the axial and radial space available within an existing casing or foundation, but also those factors that affect the running of the machine. Both the new retrofit components and the existing components, for example, can impact rotor dynamic behavior and rotor axial thrust. The "concept" of the existing frame (single flow or double flow, "reaction" or "impulse") also impacts on the selection of the most effective retrofit solution. Operating conditions (temperatures and pressures) must remain substantially unchanged for existing components between the original and retrofitted situation. Interface loads and thermal differential allowances are all matched so that, in effect, the retrofitted parts will be invisible to the remaining parts and the operator.

The design activity is based on computer tools within the concept design area, which permit rapid iteration to determine optimal solutions, and allow assessment of "what-if" situations both in a short time and without the need for large teams. These core tools consist of a thermodynamic suite, which can handle heat balance and cylinder through-flow and stage efficiency calculations, and a mechanical design suite, which communicates directly with it. The mechanical design suite includes contract analysis methods, material data, and built-in design rules to allow rapid design of precise and reliable rotor and diaphragm designs. It can also interface with the more detailed design calculations, such as the shaft-line dynamic analysis suite. When coupled with the CAD system, the final design and modeling can be completed (*Fig. 12-17*).

The key success factors within this process are reliability and speed,

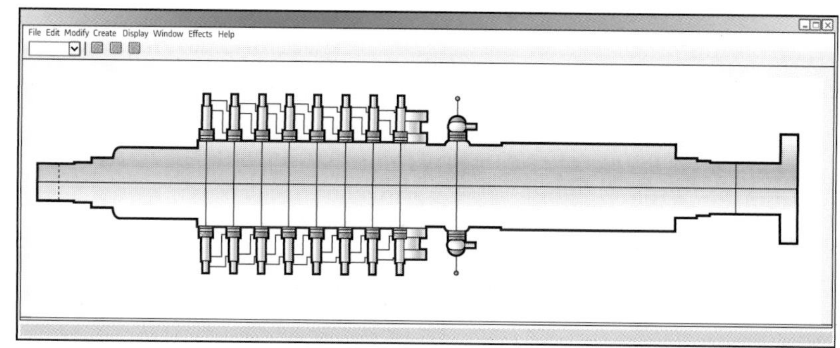

Figure 12-17 | Computer-generated drawing

ensuring that the engineer is able to establish a reliable and optimal design. In general, the most efficient design will have the maximum number of stages, with the associated reduction in root diameter, leading to low steam velocities and long, efficient blade profiles. At the concept stage, however, the number of stages must be optimized against other considerations, such as available axial length, rotor dynamics, and the economic evaluation of each additional stage. Most of this "concept" work can be done with minimal dimensional information on the existing machine. This work will form the basis of an effective and efficient measurement survey.

Retrofit Design

The basis of the retrofit design is the concept design, which exists, not only as a concept, but also as a reliable and detailed model in the CAD system and a detailed analytical model in the rotor design suite. This will be married with final thermodynamic data and detailed dimensional data on the components to be retained from the existing turbine. The detailed design is, therefore, a process of "adding" detail to the concept. As discussed above, dimensional data will consist of 3-D data from either Faro or 3-D laser CMM equipment, which is imported into the CAD system in use. In addition, the manual measurements are also transferred into the CAD system. At this point, a thorough consistency check can be made in appropriate areas. It is also worth observing that data from other similar machines can be cross-referenced quickly and easily, to provide additional confidence and make maximum use of previous design work. Thus, at an early stage in the process, a consistent model containing the available dimensional data is established. Should there be any conflicts or omissions, they can be identified and dealt with. The design, thus, develops as a "virtual assembly" of the new components under development with the detailed model of the components that already exist. The existence of this assembly ensures that there is no risk of the late discovery of a misfit or of any clash when the module is finally assembled.

The details of the design itself are based on well-established practices that have been refined on new modules, with some evolution to suit the needs of the non-OEM retrofit market. The "modifications" are made in order to provide the increased degree of adjustment necessary for retrofitting, but are applied in such a way that the elements of the proven design features are unchanged. Standard established features will correct known "type" problems with the original equipment. For example, the commonly used inlet seal arrangements with "high-low" rings are known to give problems due to distortion and wear in service and are commonly replaced at outages. The design, which replaces this as part of the retrofit, consists of piston rings fitted into the inlet stub of the new inner casing that work against a new stellite sleeve fitted into the existing outer casing. This arrangement provides a "fit and forget," reliable, proven, and totally leak-free arrangement (*Fig. 12-18*).

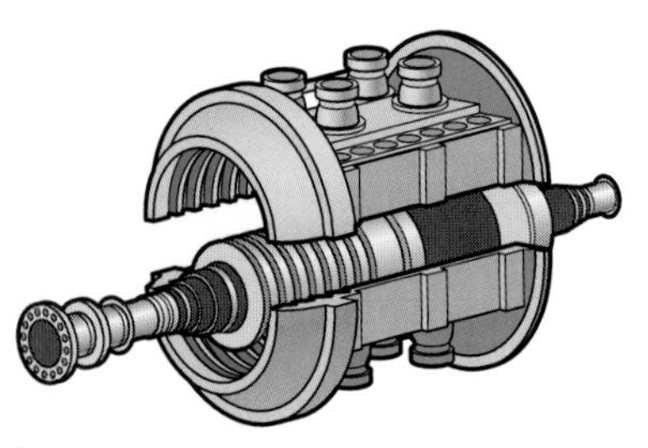

Figure 12-18 | Casing and rotor fit up

TURBINE RETROFIT TECHNOLOGY

Steam turbines fall into the category of either "reaction" or "impulse" design. Alstom is in the unique position of producing designs that include the best of both types by selecting the best components from the combined technologies. This is made possible by having retained the expertise of design and manufacture of both types of turbine designs, and having created a culture of sharing of technology and know-how across product lines. Steam turbines are not mass produced. Failures are rare and expensive. Statistical feedback from operations is limited. Therefore, the sharing of design knowledge and available operating experience from both technology backgrounds has led to an improved understanding of the fundamental physics of steam turbine design. Analytical tools are extremely sophisticated today. When design teams apply such tools to both impulse and reaction designs, then issues which, in the past, have relied on empirical correlation can be understood directly. Only with this combined experience base and expertise is it possible to "mix and match" components safely. Combinations of features must be done with care. These must be properly designed and analyzed.

Design Features

At the heart of the retrofit, and a fundamental requirement in its justification, is a high efficiency steam path. Alstom has continuously invested in airfoil development for both impulse (low reaction) and reaction blading technology. This includes both HP/IP blades and LP front stages together with new, retrofit-specific, penultimate LP (L-1) and last stage LP (L-0) blades. This has been achieved through extensive use of advanced computational fluid dynamics techniques, including fully 3-D viscous analysis combined with laboratory testing for both aerodynamic and mechanical verification. For different machines, either impulse turbine blades (ITB) or reaction turbine blades (RTB) or a combination of both can provide an optimal solution (*Fig. 12-19*).

IMPULSE (LOW REACTION) TECHNOLOGY BLADING. The impulse technology (*Fig. 12-20*) consists of a bladed disc

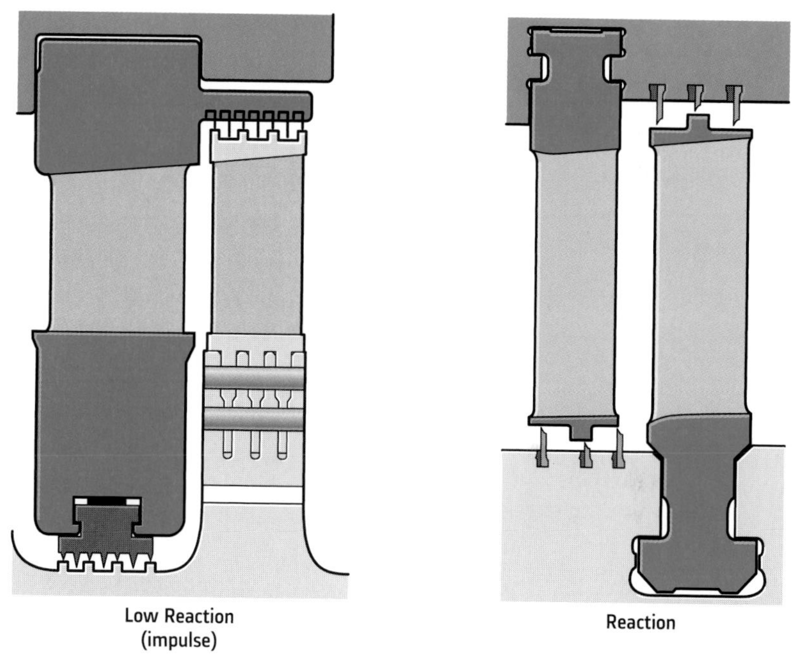

Figure 12-19 | Impulse and reaction blades

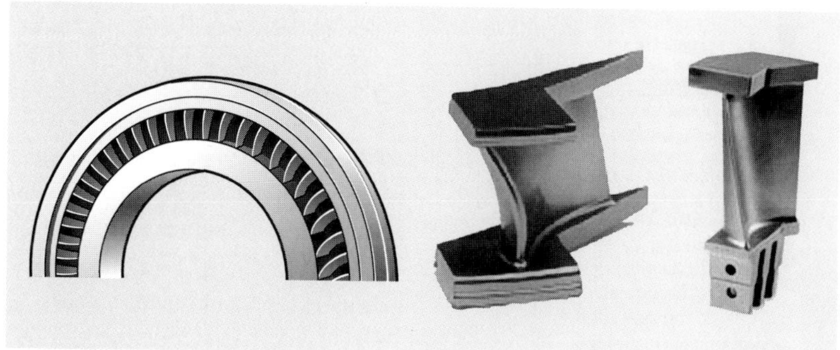

Figure 12-20 | Impulse blading

and diaphragm construction. The moving blades are machined from a single bar and include the following features:

- 3-D airfoil design, scaled for specific application, maximizing height while minimizing root diameter and axial width for performance
- Robust pinned root fastening, parametric design with two or three pins, two to six fingers, and an efficient load-carrying mechanism
- Integral tip shroud, with pre-twisted assembly, providing row continuity with no requirement for closing blade and ideal for vibration control and sealing design

The fixed blades are also machined from a single bar and then welded in the diaphragm rings with the following features:

- 3-D airfoil design, scaled for specific application, applying "controlled flow" technology where appropriate
- Robust section profiles for SPE resistance
- Integral root and tip platforms with integrated fillet radii features and accurate control of steam channel definition
- Welded diaphragm construction, with low blade numbers per row. Kinematic support enables small radial clearances as the component remains circular

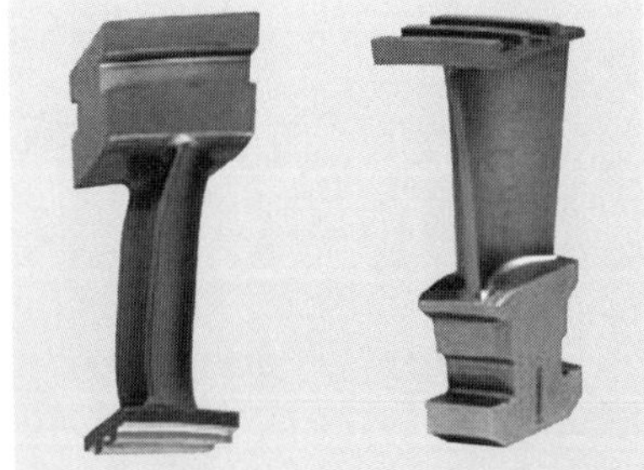

Figure 12-21 | Reaction blades

REACTION TECHNOLOGY BLADING (RTB). The reaction technology consists of a drum-type rotor and separate moving and fixed blades (*Fig. 12-21*). Both the moving blades and fixed blades are machined from a solid bar and include the following features:

- 3-D aerofoil design, scaled for specific application, maximizing height while minimizing root diameter and axial width for performance
- Robust hook root fastening and parametric design with two or four hooks
- Integral shroud, with pre-twisted assembly where applicable, providing row continuity with no requirement for closing blade and ideal for vibration control and sealing design

For impulse and reaction technologies, aerodynamic improvements continue. Mechanical innovations, for example in root fastening design and materials developments, are allowing longer blades to be employed. As a result of improved components, improved analysis methods, and greater flexibility in design, increased numbers of stages relative to the original design can be accommodated within the retained casing equipment, thus providing another lever to generate performance improvements.

LAST STAGE BLADES (LSB). The last stage blading in operation is likely to be of an old vintage, developed without the benefits of the latest computational tools and optimization techniques. These older blades can have efficiencies that are several percentage points lower than is achievable today. Equipment often is not ideally optimized to the output and condenser pressure. Often there is scope for increasing the exhaust flow area by fitting longer last stage blades, even within the existing casings. There are many different designs of last stage blading in operation around the world. In order to be able to offer an efficient retrofit solution for such a diverse technical market, it is valuable to have a number of efficient designs available. Again, for any given application it is appropriate to select the optimum last and L-1 stage blades from the best of both impulse and reaction designs.

Steam turbine manufacturers build their range of LSBs by scaling them from one rotational speed to another. By doing this, the operational conditions of one last blade of the range are identical to those of the derived blades and the references in operation are those of the full family of blades it generated. Traditionally, suppliers have made use of their range of new equipment LSBs for best fit to retrofit applications. More recently, industry has recognized the benefit of developing LSBs specifically for retrofit applications in order to gain most advantage through optimization. For example, *Figure 12-22* gives the range of large, LSBs available at 1,800 rpm, offered by suppliers. As explained above, scaled versions of these blades may also be applied for 1,500 rpm applications.

From the measurements carried out on standard LP modules of non-OEM equipment, it has been possible to define the maximum LSB length that the module can accommodate, taking into account the existing geometry of the outer casing. Again, this is an example of how flexibility and innovation have provided further

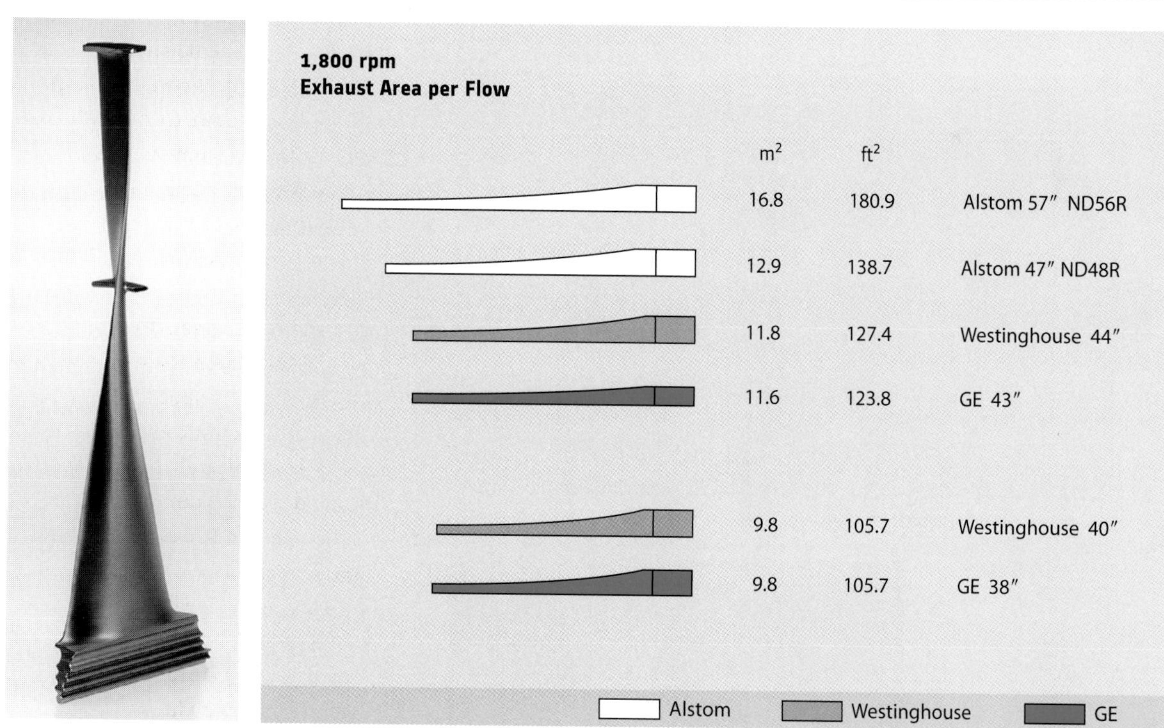

Figure 12-22 | Range of last stage blades

optimization of the retrofit product. At the concept design stage, a greater range of LP options tailored specifically to both OEM and non-OEM equipment enable a suitable option to be identified with maximum benefits.

PARTIAL ADMISSION CONTROL STAGE. Another area of the steam path where significant benefits can be obtained through the retrofit design is the control stage HP stage one. The control stage can suffer the most arduous loading in the turbine as a result of high temperatures and pressures, together with the shock steam loading associated with partial arc admission and the potential for fatigue damage. Depending on the architecture of the existing equipment, either a welded "impulse wheel" construction or a special control stage integral shroud, pinned root blade design may be employed. For larger HP cylinders, some OEMs utilize reverse flow double stage one designs that have very poor efficiencies and take up valuable space in the steam path. By replacing this with a single forward flow stage, not only is the stage performance improved but extra axial space is made available for further additional stages. In addition, for the most highly loaded stages operating at elevated temperatures, specially developed, high-creep strength materials may be applied.

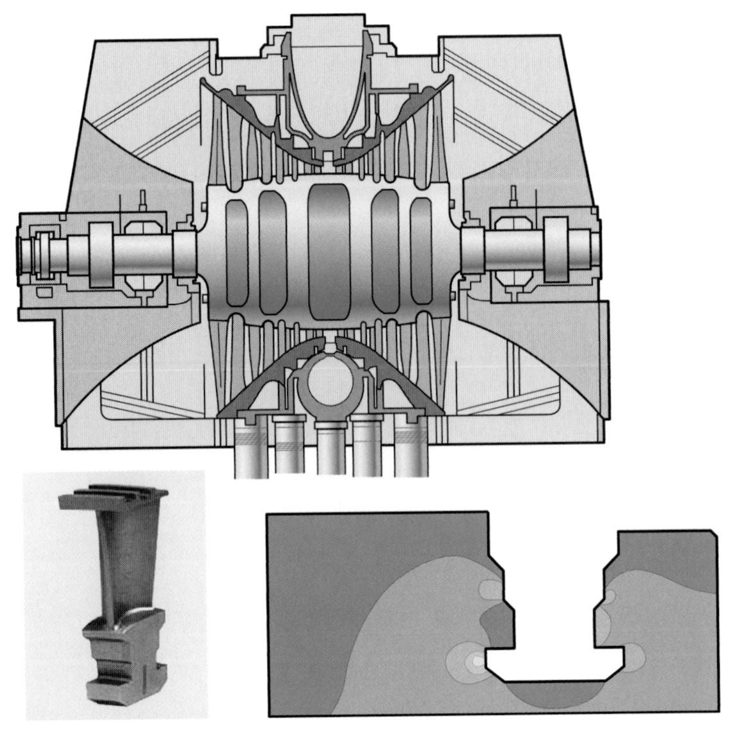

Figure 12-23 | Welded rotor technology with optimized root

WELDED ROTOR CONSTRUCTION. Regardless of the blading technology that is applied, Alstom's LP rotor design is based on the welded rotor technology. LP retrofits are frequently driven by reliability concerns, particularly relating to SCC, as well as moisture erosion problems. There is a risk of SCC when high strength materials are exposed to high stresses in a wet steam environment. Many large rotors with shrunk-on disc construction have suffered SCC at the disc bores and disc rims due to the combination of high blade fastening stresses and residual, shrink-fit hoop stress. The welded rotor technology, together with optimized root fastening details (*Fig. 12-23*) eliminates the need for high strength rotor material, which ensures immunity from SCC.

FLEXIBLE DESIGN AT INTERFACES. An essential aspect of the retrofit design is to correctly account for the interface points between the old and new components, so as to ensure a trouble-free installation. Not only does the design need to cater to manufacturing tolerances for the replacement components, but also to variations in the positional accuracy of the retained features. Examples of this are:

- Inlet connections, inlet sleeves—where original "high/low" ring designs can be replaced with the sleeve and piston ring design. The new sleeves are supplied to site with a machining allowance, allowing the diameter to be adjusted to fit during installation. This can then deal with any misalignment of casing bores that have occurred due to original manufacturing tolerances or casing distortion.
- Inner casing alignment keys and packers—where alignment packers (shims) are included in the existing design, these are retained in the retrofit design. Where they are not included on the existing design they are provided in the retrofit to aid installation and allow easy adjustment.
- LP extraction connections—for LP retrofits, it is often necessary to replace the complete inner casing. This necessitates cutting and re-welding the extraction pipes. To ease this process, standard practice is to add short lengths of pipe that can be readily cut to the length required during the installation. This approach also provides the facility to accommodate misalignment between the new connection and the existing pipe.

RADIAL SEALING TECHNOLOGY. Damage to radial seals caused by rotor instability during run up through critical speeds or through casing distortions (where inadequate arrangements are provided to maintain concentricity between the rotor and stationary elements) is a common source of efficiency loss. Steam turbines using impulse (low reaction) blading in disk and diaphragm construction incorporate kinematic support and location of fixed blade diaphragms, gland casings, and inner casing to ensure that stationary parts are free to expand radially. Relatively fine radial clearances can be maintained in this arrangement, irrespective of casing distortions.

Steam turbines using reaction type blading use circumferentially uniform, high-temperature casings, incorporating a shrink-ring closure system to ensure that casing circularity is maintained under all operating conditions to avoid damage to radial seals.

The development and application of advanced, high-efficiency, steam path technology has been discussed in this section. In summary, the intelligent use of computerized fluid dynamics tools, complemented by confirmatory aerodynamic laboratory testing, has accelerated the development of steam turbine blading and steam path sealing technology (as well as steam valve designs and turbine inlet and exhaust configurations, etc.). As a direct consequence of this work, it is now entirely feasible to achieve up to 5–6% improvement in HP section efficiency on many fossil fired, utility steam turbines, which entered service in the mid-1980s. This efficiency gain translates to an output improvement of about 12 MW on a typical 660 MW unit. For LP turbines, the availability of improved fixed and rotating blade profiles, better sealing technology, longer last stage blades, and improved exhaust hood designs provides both an increase

More output for the same steam flow means lower emissions/kW-h.

in LP section internal efficiency and a reduction in exhaust leaving losses. The combination of these benefits can provide a heat rate/power improvement in the range of 2–4%, depending on the age and type of the original unit.

RETROFIT INSTALLATION

With all retrofits, it is important to consider installation from the beginning of the design process. The time to complete the installation of a retrofit is often of paramount importance, with large cost implications to the customer. Even when the retrofit outage is extended for other reasons and the retrofit installation is not on the critical path, it is important to design for short installation, because a short and simplified installation usually means lower installation labor hours and lower installation cost. As far as possible, machining requirements for the retrofit installation are limited to small components that can be machined on machines that are available in the site workshop or can be easily brought to the site. Perhaps the most important aspect of "design for installation" is to ensure that flexibility is designed into the interface points between the old and new components so that the effects of manufacturing tolerances and, to a degree, original manufacturing errors can be accommodated as routine. This is particularly important on non-OEM retrofits where only one unit is being measured and other nominally identical units at the station are being retrofitted based on the single measurements. Examples of this are:

- Inlet sleeves
- Inner casing alignment keys and packers
- Casing baffles
- Blowdown and pressure taps
- LP extraction connections

Inlet Sleeves

On units where the inlet connections between the outer casing and the inner casing/nozzle boxes utilize high/low rings as seals, the outer casing "high/low" rings often remain in position during the measurement outage and, therefore, it is not possible to determine the bore diameters in the outer casing accurately. The Alstom design replaces the high/low rings with a sleeve and piston ring design. The new sleeves are supplied with a machining allowance on the outside diameter. During installation, the high/low rings are removed, the bores cleaned and measured, and the outside diameter of the new sleeves machined to match.

By providing additional material on the outside diameter, over and above the normal machining allowance, it is possible to machine the outside diameter of the sleeve eccentric to the bore, thereby accommodating any of the inlet bores being significantly out of position. A similar arrangement is used in the case of "bell seal" inlets (*Fig. 12-24*). A new "floating" ring is provided with excess material in the bore for machining as required during installation.

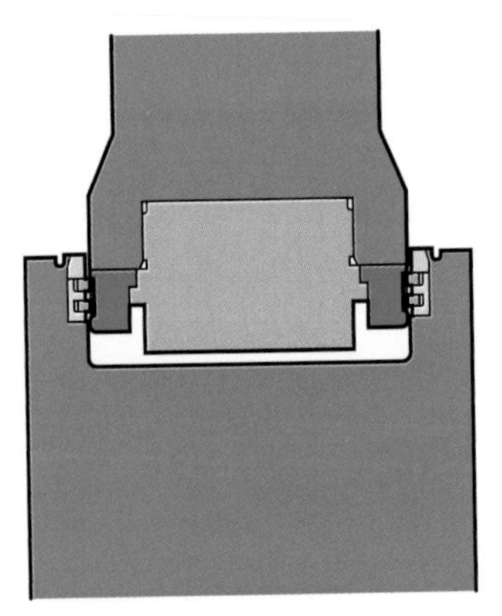

Figure 12-24 | Bell seal inlet

Inner Casing Alignment Keys and Packers

Where alignment packers (shims) are included in the existing design, these are retained for the retrofit. In other positions, such as axial location keys and transverse location keys where packers were not provided as part of the original design, the retrofit design includes packers to permit easy adjustment.

Casing Baffles

Where small gaps with close tolerances are required for control of steam flows, as in the case of casing inter-space baffles, the design accommodated a "bolt-on" baffle, (see *Fig. 12-25*), that could be easily adjusted on site with available machine tools. Experience over a number of retrofit projects has shown that the extent of adjustment provided by the bolt-on baffle has not proved to be necessary.

As a result of this experience feedback, the design for the casing baffle has been simplified (see *Fig. 12-26*), so that the restriction is achieved from a combination of axial and radial clearances that are not so critical, resulting in cost savings on original manufacture and time and cost savings during installation.

Blowdown and Pressure Taps

In some cases, it is not practical to obtain certain measurements during a routine maintenance outage. These would typically be parts that require the removal of the bottom half inner casings, such as blowdown connections on combined HP-IP cylinders, or pressure taps and extraction connections on HP cylinders. In such cases, a flexible design is used with final adjustment at the site during the installation outage. An example would be the small bore pressure connection for stage one pressure in the bottom half of a casing. Parts are provided such that the length of the connecting pipe can be adjusted by cutting and welding.

LP Extraction Connections

For LP retrofits it is often necessary to replace the complete inner casing. This necessitates cutting and rewelding the extraction pipes. To make this easier, standard practice is to add short lengths of pipe that can be readily cut to the required length during the installation, (see *Fig. 12-27*). This approach also provides the ability to accommodate misalignment between the new connection and the existing pipe by bending the new pipe spool in the required direction.

The process for dealing with the interfaces during installation is fully detailed on the interface drawings, including tolerances. The interface drawings are specific to the retrofit being installed and are in the customer's preferred units. Site installation is facilitated by the design practices discussed earlier. These practices have proven very successful and retrofits of two, three, and four units at a station have been completed without problems, based on the measurements taken on one unit. In some cases, the only measurements taken were on spare components.

Alignment

The Alstom alignment philosophy for new units is to set all bearings on the rotor natural catenary such that, at all couplings, the coupling gaps are parallel. When changing from shrunk-on disc LP rotors to the much stiffer, welded rotors, the natural catenary is significantly different. Realigning the complete unit to match the new, natural catenary would be a major undertaking, requiring large bearing/pedestal, generator, and exciter moves, with significant program and cost implications. Experience has shown that it is often possible to stay with the original shrunk-on disc catenary, or at least minimize the height changes required, provided this

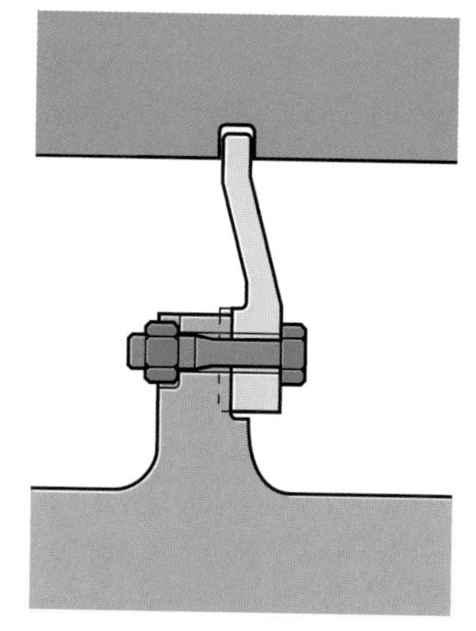

Figure 12-25 | Bolted baffle design

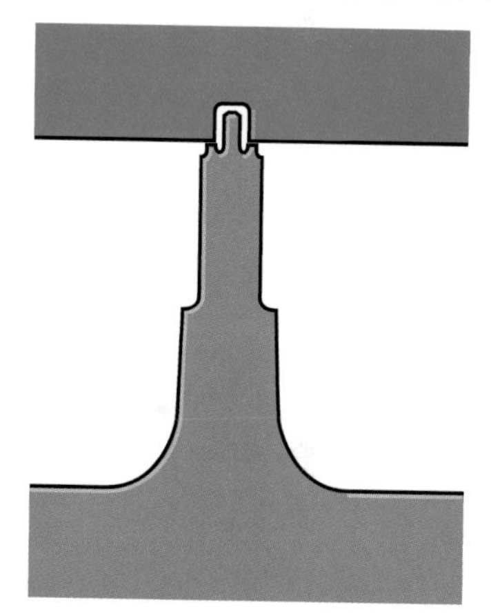

Figure 12-26 | Simplified design

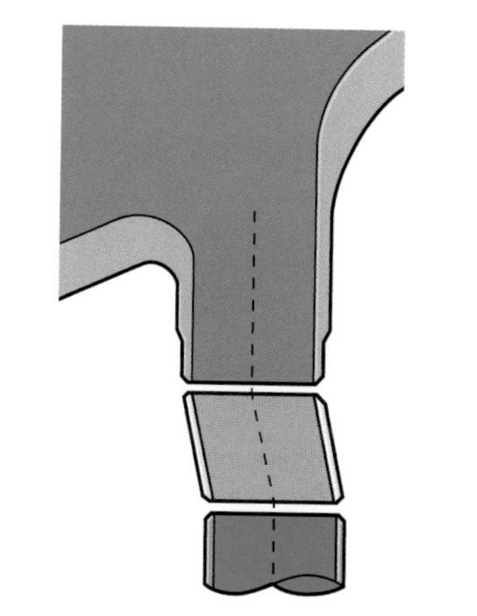

Figure 12-27 | Short pipe lengths for extraction connections

is known in the design phase and rotor stresses and bearing loads are confirmed to be acceptable. Where a new retrofit is being coupled to an existing rotor with a shrunk-on coupling (such as an LP/generator), then the goal is to maintain the parallel coupling gap philosophy at this position. This ensures that the bending loads across this coupling are minimized and there is no increase in the risk of fretting between the shrunk-on coupling and its rotor. Minimizing alignment changes is a particularly important part of the "design for installation" process, since alignment changes will have a major impact on the installation duration and cost.

Planning for Installation

An essential part of any installation, as with any overhaul work, is the up-front planning for the activity. Coordination with the site is critical and should be initiated at an early stage, to assist and advise on the installation requirements and installation planning. A part of this process is to visit the site to meet key personnel and run through the features of the installation requirements to ensure that all are familiar with the product and any special requirements of the installation.

Installation

On steam turbine retrofits, it is not necessary that the equipment supplier carry out the installation of the retrofit. The customer can decide, either when placing the retrofit hardware contract or during the supply phase, whether to install the new equipment, to contract with a third party, or to contract with the equipment supplier. The supplier will usually require that a representative (a technical field advisor, or TFA, for Alstom) be on-site during the installation to ensure that the installation is carried out in accordance with the drawings and other instructions provided. The cost of these advisors is generally included in the hardware supply contract. The TFA's role is to provide technical advice on disassembly, inspection, adjustment, and re-assembly. This includes:

- Providing advice and assisting with the outage scheduling
- Providing the technical link between the site and the home office during the installation
- Providing analysis of all strip down measurements and non-destructive examination (NDE) results
- Providing approval of all reassembly settings and clearances
- Compiling and issuing the final installation report

There are usually clear advantages to the customer in carrying out the installation using the customer's own labor force when this is available:

- It is invariably less expensive than using a third party or OEM.
- It familiarizes the supervision and labor force with the product and practices of the supplier .
- It is without doubt the best form of training.

Start-Up and Operation

As a general rule, the retrofit should be made transparent to the operators. A major part of this transparency is to minimize changes to the existing operating instructions and procedures. This philosophy becomes particularly important on multiunit stations, where operators move from unit to unit.

For a time there will be some units retrofitted and others not retrofitted. If the customer has specific concerns with the existing instructions, these often can be addressed and corrected or improved as part of the retrofit supply. For example, on some units, the start-up is extended by the original requirement to hold for prescribed periods after achieving a required reheat steam temperature. By supplying additional instrumentation to monitor rotor stresses during the start-up and modifying the start-up procedure, the time taken to start these units can be significantly reduced.

Balancing

All new rotors are high speed balanced to a high standard before shipment to site. During installation, it is essential to ensure that the rotors are coupled together so that they rotate on the same centerline as when balanced in the factory (the centerline of the journals). The coupled concentricity of rotors is the single most important parameter that ensures rotors operate with a low level of vibration, without the need for in situ balancing. Alstom installation practice requires measurement of journal/journal coupled concentricity as well as the more usual coupling/coupling coupled concentricity using high accuracy dial indicators (0.0001 inch/division). The acceptance standard is primarily on the journal/journal concentricity, since this is clearly the most important parameter.

EMISSIONS CONTROL EQUIPMENT RETROFITS

As previously discussed, the requirements for minimizing emission of combustion byproducts from electric power plants have changed over the years. Additionally, wear and tear on older equipment, after 20 years or more of operation, creates situations where major renovation of the equipment must occur. In both of these situations, a major renovation and upgrade, as opposed to the routine maintenance and repair described in Chapter 11, must be considered. Typically major upgrades involve particulate removal or SO_2 removal equipment, as only this type of emissions control equipment has been in service long enough to fall short of current performance requirements.

When considering upgrades, the customer is typically faced with a complex analysis with the following factors:

- Current and anticipated air quality legislation at the target plant
- System-wide strategy for minimization of emissions
- Capital cost of procuring and installing an upgraded system
- Length of time to install the upgrade and its effect on lost electric generation
- Future operation and maintenance costs

Each of these items is unique to each plant and to each corporate entity, with the result that there is not a single "one size fits all" approach to the correct answer.

UPGRADES FOR ELECTROSTATIC PRECIPITATORS

Most power plants are equipped with electrostatic precipitators. Over years of service, this equipment has reliably proven that it can remove more

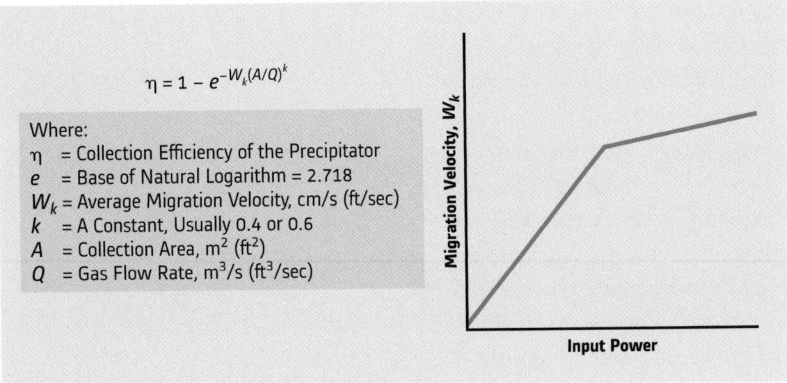

η = 1 – e^{-W_k(A/Q)^k}
Where:
η = Collection Efficiency of the Precipitator
e = Base of Natural Logarithm = 2.718
W_k = Average Migration Velocity, cm/s (ft/sec)
k = A Constant, Usually 0.4 or 0.6
A = Collection Area, m² (ft²)
Q = Gas Flow Rate, m³/s (ft³/sec)
Migration Velocity, W_k
Input Power

Figure 12-28 | Collection efficiency of the precipitator

than 99% of the particulates from the flue gas exiting the boiler. While the fundamental principles of electrostatic precipitation are unchanged, over time some major improvements in design concepts have occurred, especially in the area of high voltage controls and plate spacing. Collection efficiency is generally predicted by the Modified Deutsch equation, developed by Matts and Ohnfeldt (1963)[8] (*Fig. 12-28*).

Determining in detail the critical component, W_k, involves both art, in interpreting historical data, and scientific understanding of electrostatic principles. Some equations from electrostatics can be useful in understanding the operation of the equipment (see below).

Examining these equations in total, we can see the collection efficiency is driven by gas flow, migration velocity (which is affected by charge on the particle), electrical field strength, and collection area. These parameters become the focus of upgrade efforts. Typical upgrades to improve collection efficiency are listed in *Table 12-5* and described in greater detail in subsequent paragraphs. The table is grouped from lowest to highest cost for convenience.

Electrical Sectionalization

An electrostatic precipitator (ESP) is divided into a series of independently energized fields in the direction of the gas flow. Precipitator performance depends on the number of individual fields installed. *Figure 12-29* shows an ESP consisting of four fields, which is typical of a commercial ESP in the power industry.

Figure 12-29 introduces the terminology for cells and chambers. Each section can be considered an independent precipitator and be adjusted and operated accordingly. As a rough rule of thumb, each field removes roughly 80% of the particles. Most applications have at least three fields in the precipitator. However, to attain a collection efficiency of more than 99%, some ESPs have been designed with seven or more fields. Previous

SOME USEFUL EQUATIONS FOR UNDERSTANDING PRECIPITATION

Charge on a given particle of size $d_p > 1$ micron is given by an equation from electrostatics:

$$q = \left(\frac{3\varepsilon}{\varepsilon+2}\right)\pi\,\varepsilon_0 E_c d_p^2$$

where ε_o is the permittivity (8.85 × 10^{-12} C/V .m), ε is the dielectric constant of the particulate (usually between 2 to 8) and E_c is the electric charging field strength (V/m).

Electrostatic force on the particle:

$$F_e = q \cdot E_p = \left(\frac{3\varepsilon}{\varepsilon+2}\right)\pi\,\varepsilon_0 E_c\, E_p\, d_p^2$$

where E_p is the field at collection plate (V/m).

The drag force on the particle:

$$F_d = 3\pi\mu_g\, d_p\, w \frac{1}{K_0}$$

Usually E_p and E_c are the same.

Equating and rearranging we get

$$w = \left(\frac{3\varepsilon}{\varepsilon+2}\right)\frac{\varepsilon_0 E_c^2 d_p}{3\mu_g} K_0$$

experience with a particular application is required to determine how many fields are necessary to meet the emission limits.

Each field has individual transformer-rectifier sets, high voltage controls, and electrodes that, when energized, establish a current flow in the section. Since the particle loading varies so much across the ESP, the ability to adjust the power input requirements of each field becomes very important in achieving optimal performance.

The first field of an electrostatic precipitator has very high particle concentrations. As these particles become charged, they create an electric field that inhibits the flow of current from the discharge electrode to the collecting plate. This is known as space charge. Space charge is overcome by applying the highest voltage possible, without spark over, and by using electrodes that maximize corona current. Moving further downstream in the precipitator, the particulate loading is usually much lower, allowing the corona current to be relatively easily established. In each section however, the voltage and current need to be adjusted for optimum performance. From these principles, it is relatively easy to understand the following upgrades.

Modification of Plate Height

The footprint of an electrostatic precipitator is generally fixed between the air heater and the stack. It is very difficult to extend the length of the precipitator, but relatively easy to raise its height. Increases in plate height result in an increase in collection area and a decrease in gas velocity and, consequently, have a very positive impact on collection efficiency.

TABLE 12-5 | TYPICAL UPGRADES TO IMPROVE COLLECTION EFFICIENCY

Issue	Type of Upgrade	Typical Best Fit
Particulate emissions from ESP are greater than allowed or limit operational flexibility	ESP electric or controls upgrade	Most cost effective way of achieving 30–50% reduction in particulate emissions. Cost roughly 5% of complete new ESP with minimal to no downtime.
	Flue gas conditioning	Low capital cost method of adjusting the collection efficiency of the ESP by modifying the surface resistivity of the fly ash.
	ESP sectionalization and mechanical upgrades with wide plate spacing, new electrodes, increased plate height	50–100% improvement in performance. Makes best sense when ESP casing, foundation, and support steel is in good condition. Cost is 50–90% of a new ESP. Implementation takes 8 to 15 weeks depending on ESP size and crane access.
	Addition of an another field to the ESP	An additional section can typically result in an 80% removal efficiency improvement. The cost varies and is driven by the mechanical complexity and interferences with other plant equipment.
	Total ESP replacement	Considered when condition of ESP is poor or where major change in performance is required. New ESP cost can often be $5 million or more. Installation time is 20 weeks or more. Often the new ESP is built adjacent to the existing ESP to minimize plant outages.
	Conversion of ESP to fabric filter (FF)	Considered where lowest particulate emissions are required and limitations of the FF operating envelope (pressure drop, temperature sulfur content, among others) are not prohibitive.

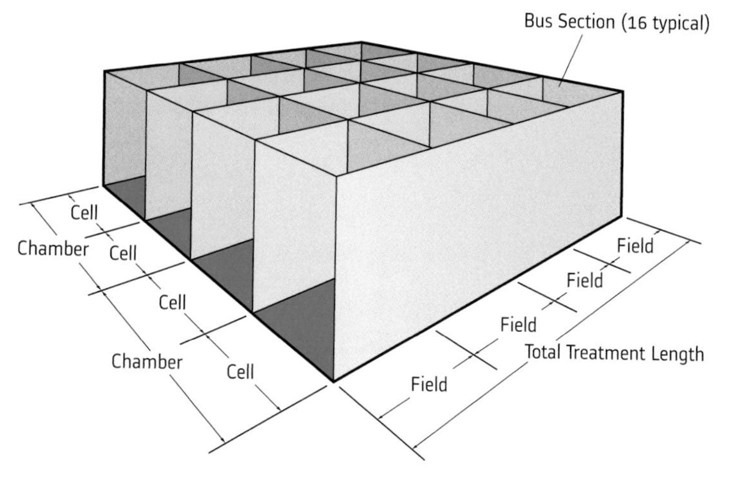

Figure 12-29 | Fields in an electrostatic precipitator

Modification of Electrodes

The discharge electrodes provide the high voltage, which generates the corona required for charging the particles in the flue gas. The electrodes are symmetrically placed in the electric field to avoid sparks or short circuits.

Spiral discharge electrodes have high reliability and insensitivity to temperature differences required for optimized precipitator operation. The spiral electrodes are assembled in a rigid frame with one, two, or three levels of electrodes, depending on the ESP height. The electrode frames are hung and firmly bolted to a top frame, which in turn is suspended, via four support insulators located on the casing roof, outside the gas stream. At the bottom, the frames are connected to cross guide irons. After erection, the discharge electrode system forms a rigid box structure. Since there is no potential for swinging of the frame, stabilizers are not necessary and the structure is free to expand in any direction.

The multipeak electrode has a tubular body of special quality to which barbs are stud welded. Each barb has two peaks directed toward the collecting surface. The barb peak has a special shape to generate desired current/voltage characteristics without being sensitive to electrical erosion.

Conversion of older precipitators with basic "bare" or "weighted" wires to electrodes of the above design generates significantly better performance due to a greater and more uniform flow of corona current.

Wide Plate Spacing

Over time, industry experience, combined with the availability of power supplies with voltage capability of 100KV and above, has caused a change in typical plate spacing from about 9 inches (23 cm) up to 12 inches (30 cm) (in the 1980s), and 16 inches (41 cm) between plates for new construction. The wider plate spacing allows for a significant reduction in weight along with improved performance.

Additional Electrical Field

As described previously, additional electrical and mechanical fields will substantially improve the performance of the ESP. Generally, this can be done only if additional space behind or in front of the precipitator is available. Often the air preheater and stack will prohibit expansion. In this case, the only way of adding an additional electrical field is by taking one of the existing fields and splitting it to form the additional field. This may be especially helpful in the first field, where particulate loading and space charge conditions vary dramatically.

Electrical and Control System Upgrades

As previously discussed, the fundamental mechanism for collecting particulates in an ESP is applying an electrical charge to the particle. The more effectively the particles are charged, the more efficiently the particles can be collected. The easiest way to improve the particle charging is to provide better controls for the high-voltage power supplies that are the source of the charging current.

Most ESPs are equipped with transformer rectifiers that provide a voltage ranging between 40 and 100KV, while providing current capability to

2 amps or more. This technology has functioned very reliably but is limited in three important ways:

1. Conventional transformer rectifiers produce a DC output voltage with up to 40% ripple. This means that during the valley period, less voltage and current is available to charge the particles.
2. Conventional transformer rectifiers must be controlled so that they produce maximum voltage without excessive sparking between the emitting electrodes and the collecting plates. If excessive sparking occurs, the transformer rectifier voltage must be briefly reduced to a low level to allow the spark to clear. This process of clearing the spark takes 80 or more milliseconds, during which the ESP is not functioning at full capability.
3. Some dusts are very resistive and the layer of dust on the collecting plates can achieve a very high charge that limits the corona current. This situation is known as back corona and can dramatically reduce the effectiveness of particle charging and collection.

There are two products to address these issues. The first is a control system that retains the conventional transformer/rectifier known as the EPIC (electrostatic precipitator intelligent controller) and the second which is a replacement for the transformer rectifier (T/R) known as SIR (switched integrated rectifier)

EPIC

The EPIC controller is designed to efficiently control one section of the ESP as shown in *Figure 12-30.*

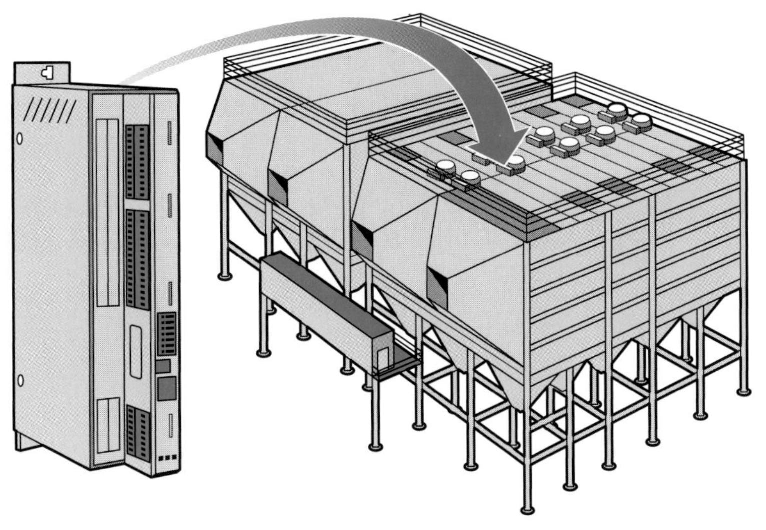

Figure 12-30 | Electrostatic precipitator intelligent controller (EPIC)

The EPIC uses microprocessor technology to monitor corona current hundreds of times per second to detect sparks, automatically adjust the transformer rectifier output to its optimum level, and use proprietary algorithms to minimize the effects of back corona.

SIR

By combining high frequency, solid state, power electronics, and computer control, SIR improves collecting efficiency for different applications (*Fig. 12-31*).

SIR also substantially reduces installation and commissioning costs. Conventional ESP rectifiers generate peak voltages, which can be as much as 25% above the average voltage. The peak voltage triggers the sparking in the ESP field. Sparking quenches the ionization and effectively limits the average voltage applied to the electrodes and thus the efficiency of the ESP. SIR provides an almost

Figure 12-31 | Switched integrated rectifier (SIR)

ripple-free DC output compared with conventional T/Rs, which allows the ESP to operate at full voltage up to the point at which sparking occurs. SIR therefore increases useful ESP current, which provides substantial ESP emission reduction for processes that generate very fine and low-resistive dust (*Fig. 12-32*).

ESP TO FABRIC FILTER CONVERSION

In some applications the major benefits of fabric filters (high removal efficiency, small size particulate removal, and potential mercury removal) necessitate that the original ESP be converted into a fabric filter. As described in the section on new fabric filters, there are two major design concepts for fabric filters. For the low ratio design, the dust is collected on the inside of the bags. In the high ratio design, the dust is collected on the outside of the bags. The deposited dust layer is periodically removed from the bags to control pressure drop. Both low and medium pressure pulse jet designs have been successfully utilized for conversion of utility ESP casings into fabric filters.

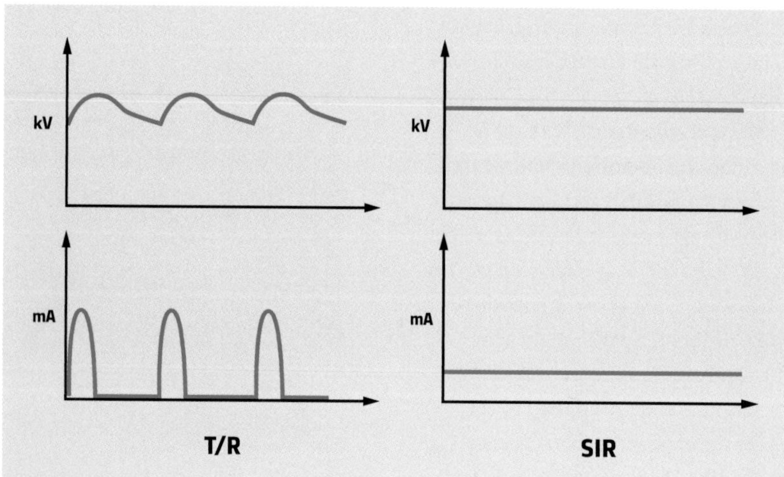

Figure 12-32 | Voltage and current comparison

There has been a significant amount of conversion experience around the world with the majority of units located in either South Africa or Australia. Generally, a minimum ESP SCA (specific collection area) of 250 to 300 is typically required for full conversion of the casing with some degree of sectionalization. Currently the largest U.S. project is 450 MW.

The required outage time and overall cost is impacted by:

- Condition of the existing ESP casing
- Ability to utilize existing side walls and hoppers
- Degree of compartment sectionalization desired
- Degree of access for cranes and pre-assembly work for modular sections
- Ability of existing fans to support the additional pressure drop of the fabric filter
- Structural upgrades of boiler and ducts to prevent implosion from new fans

UPGRADES TO EXISTING FABRIC FILTERS

Fabric filter upgrading possibilities include gas and dust distribution improvements, modulating pulse jets, and improved monitoring.

Gas and Dust Distribution

An uneven distribution will increase the emissions due to high local gas/dust loading. An uneven distribution will also increase the wear of the bag textile. Reasons for poor gas distribution can be found both upstream of the fabric filter or inside it. Installation of, or repairing of, guide vanes can improve the situation.

Modulated Pulse

The emissions from a filter are concentrated in a short period following the removal of the ash layer, and the disturbance of the media structure during cleaning. The emissions during cleaning of bags, especially of sub-micron particles, can be significantly reduced if the cleaning pulse is modulated. This will enhance the re-entrainment of fine particles into the media in connection with bag cleaning.

The modulated pulse cleaning (MPC) is mainly an adjustment of the pressure of the compressed air at the end of the pulse. Mechanical wear can be reduced and the emissions can be decreased, especially the emission of small particles. By keeping the normal pressure of the compressed air at the beginning of the pulse, the cleaning efficiency can be maintained.

Monitoring

By monitoring the real-time data from plant operation, an analysis can be done of the changes in fabric filter status and filter bag condition. Together with laboratory analysis of bag textile properties, an early warning can be given of bag degeneration and other process influences on fabric filter performance.

Fabric Filter Type LKP-PLUS

A method to reduce the emission at cleaning is to take the gases from the newly cleaned bag compartment back to the filter inlet until the filter cake has been sufficiently reestablished. It requires a recirculation fan and outlet damper on each compartment. As some of the gas is recirculating after cleaning, the filter load will increase and a minor extension of filter area might be necessary.

EFFIC

Alstom has developed the EFFIC, efficient fabric filter integrated controller. EFFIC is used as a service tool to detect valve and bag failures. It can also increase fabric filter availability and improve performance with respect to emission and operating cost. MPC is a more efficient cleaning pulse than a conventional cleaning pulse. MPC has the potential to significantly reduce the emissions while the need for pressurized air is reduced and bag life is increased by approximately 25%. Another useful feature is the filter drag control, which allows a more optimized cleaning frequency than simple differential pressure operation. The filter drag control allows optimization with respect to dust emission, additive consumption, pressurized air consumption, bag lifetime, and total pressure drop (fan power).

UPGRADE OF SO_2 REMOVAL BY OPEN TOWER SPRAY ABSORBERS

Early SO_2 removal systems did not treat the entire flue gas process stream, and were often equipped with elaborate damper systems to allow the flue gas to bypass the SO_2 removal system. Systems typically processed only 70 to 80% of the total flue gas stream, with the remaining 20 to 30% bypassing the absorber vessels. By recombining the streams before the stack, the flue gas exit temperature remained high enough to prevent condensation in the stack. Systems frequently were designed with several absorbers so that if one absorber was out of service, production could still continue.

For the flue gas that was treated, early systems were typically designed for 80 to 90% SO_2 removal and used various reagents including sodium and calcium-based additives. As time and

Time and experience have proven the performance and reliability of SO_2 removal systems.

experience have progressed, the new system standards for SO_2 removal efficiency and operational reliability have dramatically increased. As discussed in the new wet fuse gas desulfurization (WFGD) sections, 100% of the flue gas is now typically treated with operational reliability of more than 99% and SO_2 removal efficiencies of greater than 98%.

This large gap between the performance of the earlier technology and current state-of-the-art technology has given rise to numerous upgrade options. Improvements that are now generally possible include:

- Increase in the percentage of flue gas treated
- Increased SO_2 removal rate
- Improved operational reliability and reduced number of outages for cleaning
- Lower operation and maintenance costs
- Creation of a saleable by-product to reduce or eliminate disposal costs

These improvements to the existing SO_2 scrubbers are made possible by the following equipment change options:

- Modification of reagent supply system to use limestone, lime, or other reagent
- Change in the internal components of the scrubber including new spray headers, addition of trays, and elimination of wall sneakage with performance enhancing plates
- Use of organic acid to improve removal efficiency
- Addition of air compressors to force higher oxidation levels in the reaction tank to produce gypsum
- Complete teardown of the existing multiple absorber vessels and replacement with a single larger vessel

Owners of the SO_2 removal equipment have to determine the most cost effective and technically feasible method to achieve the desired performance and reliability improvements. The analysis can be somewhat complex and site specific. For example, we can consider the options for the following older SO_2 removal system:

Year put into service	1982
Reagent	Lime (90% available CaO)
Absorber SO_2 Removal Efficiency	90%
Overall SO_2 Removal Efficiency	81%
Flue Gas Bypass	10%
Design Coal Sulfur	3%
Absorber Diameter	22 feet
Recycle Pump Quantity	16 (4 per absorber)
Liquid to Gas Ratio	100 gpm/kacfm
Spray Levels per Absorber	3
By-Product	Fixated landfill

On quick inspection, there are numerous possible improvements and results that can be achieved. These range from doing virtually nothing beyond normal maintenance to complete change-out of the entire absorbers as shown in *Table 12-6*.

The upgrade options will be presented in further detail focusing on upgrade options for the absorber itself, the inputs to the absorber, and, finally, upgrades to by-product removal. Prior to beginning this discussion, for the hypothetical unit described above, the following results were obtained (*Table 12-7*).

TABLE 12-6 | UPGRADE OPTIONS FOR HYPOTHETICAL OLDER SCRUBBER

	Upgrade Options Retaining Existing Lime-Based WFGD
Option 1A	Restore the existing system with in-kind replacement. While probably not desirable from an operational standpoint, this option can be evaluated and serve as a baseline, minimum capital cost option. The process design would retain the use of lime reagent and fixated landfill production.
Option 1B	Restore the existing system retaining lime as the reagent but resulting in a saleable gypsum by-product. Retain the reagent storage/feed system and absorber island with changes/upgrades limited to those required to achieve reliable operation. Supply new oxidation and dewatering system and retire the older existing dewatering/fixation in place.
Option 1C	Same as Option 1B except that only landfill-grade gypsum is produced.
	Upgrade Options That Include Converting to Limestone Reagent
Option 2A	Conversion to limestone/wallboard gypsum operation and internal components upgraded. Limestone storage/preparation and gypsum dewatering systems would be added. Absorber island would be upgraded to add forced oxidation and organic acid feed equipment. New internal components would include new slurry header system, possibly a tray (depending on pressure drop), new mist eliminators, and new mist eliminator wash system.
Option 2B	Same as Option 2A except that organic acid enhancement is not used.
Option 2C	Same as Option 2B except that landfill gypsum is produced.
	Limestone-Based WFGD/Gypsum Byproduct: New Absorber
Option 3A	Completely new organic acid-enhanced limestone/wallboard gypsum system. Existing absorber island, lime storage/preparation, and dewatering/fixation systems were abandoned in place.
Option 3B	Same as Option 3A except that organic acid enhancement is not used.
Option 3C	Same as Option 3B except that landfill gypsum is produced.

Based on the site specific issues, availability of capital, need to keep outages minimized, and customer long-term strategy, virtually any of the upgrades can be justified as optimum. In general, where highest reliability and removal efficiency is required without the use of organic acids, customers should consider complete replacement of older WFGD equipment. Where high reliability and good removal efficiency is required, cost-effective upgrades can be made to meet plant operating requirements. Typically, 98% removal efficiency can be achieved, often without the use of additional additives.

TABLE 12-7 | UPGRADE OPTION RESULTS

Type	Option	Reagent	By-product	Organic Acid	SO_2 Removal Efficiency (%)
Refurbish	1A	Lime	Fixated sludge	No	98
	1B	Lime	Wallboard gypsum	No	98
	1C	Lime	Disposal gypsum	No	98
Refurbish	2A	Limestone	Wallboard gypsum	Yes	98
	2B	Limestone	Wallboard gypsum	No	90
	2C	Limestone	Disposal gypsum	No	90
New	3A	Limestone	Wallboard gypsum	Yes	98
	3B	Limestone	Wallboard gypsum	No	98
	3C	Limestone	Disposal gypsum	No	98

Upgrade Options within the Absorber Vessel

IMPROVED SLURRY SPRAY SYSTEM (HEADERS AND NOZZLES). Over the years, the design concepts of various components within wet scrubber systems have been evaluated, analyzed, and redesigned as new products, materials, and information become available. From these efforts new solutions and design standards were developed. The recycle spray system has received a large amount of attention, since improvements here can be translated into substantial improvements in performance, operation, and maintenance. The recycle system is the single largest power consumer in the wet scrubber system and can require high levels of maintenance. Starting in the mid 1990s, the new design standard became higher velocity spray towers with a greater number of lower flow, lower pressure drop spray nozzles to ensure optimal liquid/gas contact. The net result was much higher performance at a lower pumping horsepower. The lower flow nozzles, although smaller in size and flow than the nozzles provided on earlier systems, have free passage through nozzles that are larger and less prone to pluggage than the older nozzles, with higher pressure drop and smaller free pass areas. With a larger number of nozzles, tower spray coverage is much better. There is sufficient overlap of the sprays so that should a nozzle plug, the effect is much less than a plug in one of the old style, large volume nozzles. Applying this concept to older wet scrubber systems yields many benefits and allows the owner some choices on how to take advantage of those benefits, whether it be power savings, additional SO_2 removal efficiencies, or both (*Fig. 12-33*).

Essentially the recycle system header/nozzle upgrade consists of redesigning the spray elevation nozzle placement to maximize liquid gas contact. This upgrade typically includes all new spray nozzles and replacing or modifying the spray elevations to accept the new nozzle arrangement. The extent of spray header replacement or modification depends on the age, condition, materials of construction, and layout of the existing headers. Many plants have headers that are metal and most likely in good condition. In this situation, the typical upgrade does not require many header laterals to be replaced. In any case, the headers and installation procedures are always designed to minimize field labor while ensuring full coverage. A final benefit of upgrades to spray nozzles and header systems is the potential improvement in slurry flow that can result from lower backpressure (*Fig. 12-34*).

PERFORMANCE ENHANCEMENT PLATES (PEP). The PEP, U.S. Patent No. 6531104, was developed as a result of in-depth flow pattern and absorption studies of open spray tower systems to combat the well-known gas sneakage problem at the walls of spray towers. However, the full effect on performance enhancement was not quantifiable until the development of a unique measurement method to verify this phenomenon. Gas velocities at the wall can be 2 to 3 times higher than that in the balance of the absorber. This phenomenon is primarily a result of the lower spray liquid density at the absorber walls that, when combined with the lower liquid levels, yields lower SO_2 removal efficiencies at the walls. The PEP is essentially a guide vane strategically placed along the perimeter of the spray contact zone to improve the liquid/gas contact. PEP plate sizing and placement is specific to each installation to maximize process improvement. Aspects that differentiate PEP from other in situ process improvement devices are:

- Easily installed—low labor costs and short down time
- Minimal impact on absorber pressure differential (typical 0.2 to 0.5 inches WG [0.4 to 0.9 mm Hg])

Figure 12-33 | Hollow cone nozzles and headers to enhance performance

Figure 12-34 | Tapered header showing placement of nozzles

- Located in lower removal/efficiency area of the absorber cross section below each spray level (redirecting the gas into a higher liquid density area)
- Incremental installation (one absorber at a time as time and budgets permit), therefore does not require a plant outage to make the conversion
- Due to minimal effect on absorber pressure drop, absorbers with and without PEP can be operated together without the need to bias gas flows between absorbers while the remaining conversions are accomplished
- No moving parts
- No maintenance requirements and improved process control typically reduces other maintenance requirements

FLOW DISTRIBUTION TRAY. The flow distribution tray is a well proven device to enhance the SO_2 removal efficiency in existing scrubber modules. The counter current gas/liquid flow through the perforated sections of the baffled tray has resulted in a significant increase in SO_2 removal at the expense of about a 2 inch increase in system pressure drop. Flow distribution trays are typically located above or below the lowest spray levels in the spray tower depending on site specific issues including access and potential for pluggage (*Fig. 12-35*).

The important benefits of tray design can be summarized as follows:

- Easily installed—low labor costs and short down time
- No impact on recycle pumps
- Incremental installation (one absorber at a time as time and budgets permit), therefore does not require a lengthy plant outage to make the conversion
- No moving parts
- No maintenance requirements

Figure 12-35 | Flow distribution tray developed and proven at Alstom's pilot scale test facility in Karlshamm, Sweden

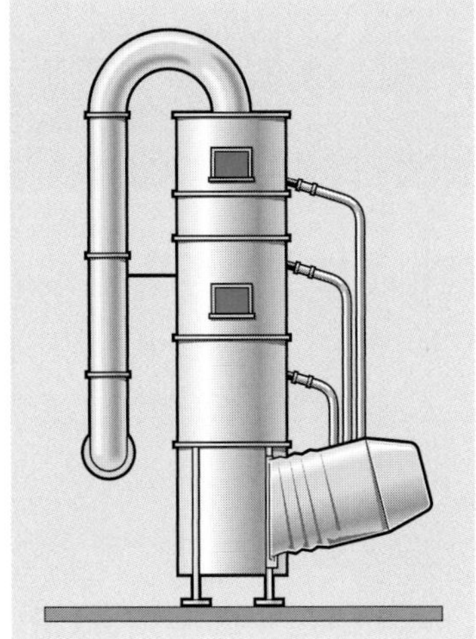

MIST ELIMINATION. Typical mist eliminator upgrades consist of a stage system made up of three to nine vane assemblies designed to utilize the existing scrubber mist eliminator (ME) supports. This is a high performance system that is designed for the typical gas velocities ranging up to 12 ft/sec (3.7 m/s), but is capable of continuous operation of gas velocities of more than 16 ft/sec (4.9 m/s) without adverse effect on moisture carryover, should the need arise (*Fig. 12-36*).

These mist eliminators are of proven design and are used extensively throughout the scrubber industry. Key advantages of the high performance ME include:

- High droplet breakthrough velocity—The gas velocity at which there is an onset of mist

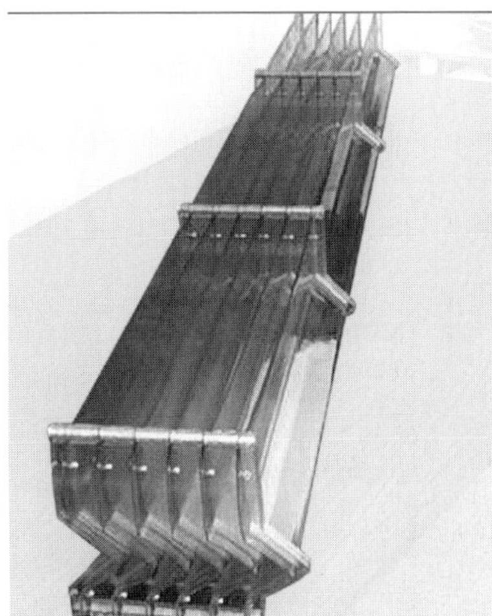

Figure 12-36 | Mist eliminators

breakthrough (carryover) is over 18 feet per second (fps) (5.5 m/s) through the vanes. This is among the highest breakthrough velocities of any vertical flow mist eliminators.

- Excellent online cleaning—Another design feature is that the high performance ME was specifically designed to facilitate online cleaning. The design varies from manufacturer to manufacturer. However, the most successful design contains no ridges, channels, or hooks that can trap solids.Furthermore, with two stages and only two passes for each stage, all ME surfaces can be easily washed online. Improved online cleaning will reduce the need for manual cleaning.
- Low operating pressure drop—The total pressure drop of the Alstom 2×2+ ME is approximately 0.30 inches WG (0.6 mm Hg) at the specified system design gas flow rate.
- Reliable and low maintenance—When washed as recommended, the high performance ME can operate indefinitely without the need for manual cleaning. A fixed grid wash system, designed to provide 150% coverage of the mist eliminator face, will perform well. When an absorber is taken out of service for an inspection/maintenance outage (typically at 12 to 18 month intervals), the only ME attention required is to hose down the trailing edge of the second stage ME to remove any trace deposition that may have occurred. The deposit is typically less than 1/16 inch. A complete (hose) washdown can be performed in less than one shift for typical absorbers. Furthermore, there is no need to dismantle the 2×2+ ME system to reach an intermediate stage.
- Materials of construction—The high performance ME can be constructed in several different materials. The most common and reliable are extruded polysulfone or polypropylene thermoplastics and extruded fiberglass reinforced plastic (FRP). Both thermoplastic and FRP ME materials have been used extensively in WFGD service. Polysulfone, a homogeneous thermoplastic, has the added benefits of a high (continuous) temperature rating, increased corrosion resistance (due to its homogeneous nature), and high impact strength, increasing vane/assembly life even further. Polypropylene (with glass filler) characteristics are similar to the polysulfone with somewhat less heat resistance, but more than sufficient for the specified temperature ranges. Both plastics would provide good service life in this application.

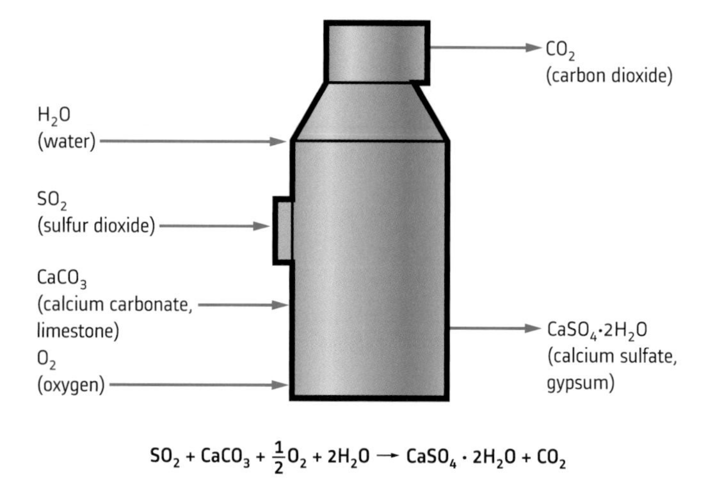

Figure 12-37 | Forced oxidation system

FRP vanes would also be a suitable selection for this application.

Upgrade Options for Systems Supplying the Absorber

FORCED OXIDATION. Forced oxidation of the recycle slurry in a limestone wet flue gas desulfurizatin (FGD) system produces a more manageable, easily handled byproduct. To produce the oxidized byproduct (at least 99% sulfite oxidation), two 100% capacity centrifugal blowers supply air to the reaction tank. The oxygen in the air converts the dissolved calcium sulfite ($CaSO_3$) to calcium sulfate ($CaSO_4$), which then crystallizes as $CaSO_4 \cdot 2H_2O$, otherwise known as gypsum (*Fig. 12-37*).

The size of the blower is selected based on SO_2 loading, removal, and tank depth. Typical size ranges from 10,000–25,000 scfm (4.7–12 Nm^3/s) at 17–27 psig (1.2–1.9 bar) and requires motors of 1,000–3,500 hp (1–2 MW). Pumps are typically single stage, centrifugal types, but alternatives that have been used include rotary lobe type or multistage blowers.

The oxidation air injection system utilizes either a set of lances located below the operating liquid level in the reaction tank or a side entry agitator with air injection. Newer designs use the side entry agitator, but many retrofit and upgrade projects require the lances because of equipment layout and access issues. When required, an oxidation lance is a simple, reliable design with minimal maintenance requirements. In addition, the design allows for optimization of oxidation air flow and compressor power consumption at lower boiler loads and reduced inlet SO_2 loadings. The oxidation air is quenched and saturated with a stream of water prior to discharge into the reaction tank in order to prevent solids buildup in the lances.

ORGANIC ACID ADDITIVE SYSTEM. Organic acids have the ability to significantly enhance the performance of limestone WFGD systems by increasing the absorption capacity of the scrubbing slurry. See Chapter 5.

LIMESTONE SLURRY STORAGE AND FEED. A uniform slurry of limestone of 28–30 wt% solids and particle fineness of 90% less than 45 microns is provided to the reagent feed tank. One reagent feed tank with an effective storage capacity of 13 hours is typically provided, complete including agitator and feed pumps. Limestone slurry is transported from the transfer tank to the absorber through the use of a recirculating feed loop. Slurry velocities are constantly maintained in the loop, while at the same time providing the required reagent feed to the absorber. Control valves regulate the flow of reagent slurry to the reaction tank. Limestone slurry is added to the reaction tank, at the base of the absorber, in response to control signals based on the pH of the slurry in the reaction tank and boiler load. The pH in the reaction tank drives a feedback loop that trims the limestone slurry feed valve. The pH-trimmed system responds rapidly, is essentially independent of plant load, and is therefore highly stable. A feed forward signal using boiler load is also used to further control the addition of reagent during excursions and start-up periods.

Upgrade Options for Systems Removing Product from the Absorber

PRIMARY DEWATERING. Upgrade primary dewatering consists of equipment to process gypsum slurry containing 15–20 wt% solids. The slurry is pumped from the reaction tank to hydrocyclone classifiers, which split the slurry into a low density stream of fines (the overflow) and a high density stream of coarse crystals (the underflow). In so doing, the hydrocyclones also classify the slurry chemically: unreacted limestone is relatively fine and reports to the overflow; the product gypsum is a coarser material and it preferentially reports to the underflow. The hydrocyclone underflow product flows by gravity to rotary drum vacuum filters for further dewatering. The hydrocyclone overflow is directly returned to the absorber reaction tank by gravity. A small portion of the hydrocyclone overflow is directed to the FGD purge tank to maintain the steady state chlorides at the desired level. The chloride purge stream is transferred from the FGD purge tank to the ash pond by the FGD purge pumps. The gypsum slurry, hydrocyclone underflow containing approximately 40–50% solids by weight flows by gravity to rotary drum vacuum filters. The rotary drum vacuum filters dewater the underflow slurry to produce a gypsum cake of 85 wt% solids. A liquid ring vacuum pump provides the suction needed at the drum filter cloth. A small amount of fresh water is needed for vacuum seal water and for cloth washing.

CHLORIDE PURGE. The hydrocyclone overflow is divided into two streams as it leaves the overflow collection launderer. The majority of the overflow returns by gravity to the absorber reaction tank. A portion of the overflow is diverted to the FGD purge tank, where it is combined with a portion of the filtrate from the belt filters. These combined streams make up the system purge that is sent to disposal for control of chlorides and fines. The relative amounts of the two inputs to the FGD purge tank are determined to provide enough removal of fines and impurities (limestone inert matter, fly ash, and calcium fluoride) to ensure the desired gypsum quality, while not burdening the disposal system with excess solids.

PAT JENNINGS
KEITH BERGER
JIM SUTTON
PHIL LAFAVE
WALT LACEY

REFERENCES

1. R. Fernald, and G. Orrok, *Engineering of Power Plants.* New York McGraw Hill, 1927.

2. "Maximizing Economic and Environmental Performance of Existing Coal-Fired Assets," P. Bartley, et al, 2008, Alstom.

3. F. Gabrielli and S. Goodstine. *Utility Boiler Steam Purity Considerations.* 1991 ABB Combustion Engineering Systems, Inc.

4. R. MacWhinnie and N. Nsakala, et al. *NOx Emissions Performance of Powder River Basin (PRB) and Reference Coals.* Alstom Power Internal Report, 2003.

5. "Project Shows Potential for Optimizing SCR and Boiler Operations." Lehigh Energy Update, August 2006, Vol 24(2), Lehigh, PA.

6. P. Jennings, *Low NOx Firing Systems and PRB Fuel; Achieving as Low as 0.12 Lb NOx/MBTU.* Institute of Clean Air Companies Forum 2002.

7. "Case Study of a Dedicated Biomass Firing System at Fiddlers Ferry Power Station, UK," 2007, Alstom.

8. S. Mathis, et al. *Efficient Gas Cleaning with SF Electrostatic Precipitators.* Fläkten, 1963/4, 1–12, pp. 93–110.

SUGGESTED READINGS

A. Lord, *Features of turbine retrofit design,* Alstom Retrofit Conference, San Francisco, 2003.

S. Glover, *Conceptual Mechanical design of a steam turbine retrofit,* Alstom Steam Turbine Conference, Prague, 2005.

P. Hemsley, *Building on the best of both worlds,* Alstom Retrofit Conference, San Francisco , 2003.

J. McCoach, *Steam turbine retrofits for improved performance,* Power Gen Europe, Barcelona, Spain, May, 2004.

A. Holmes, *Retrofit Installation,* Alstom Retrofit Conference, San Francisco, 2003.

M. Oates, *Economic justification of a steam turbine retrofit,* Alstom Retrofit Conference, Chicago, 2006.

Performance Testing of Power Plants

Chapter **Thirteen**

The performance testing and analysis of power plants is a vital tool in the ongoing process of maintaining optimum performance, reliability, and profitability of the plant. Understanding how the unit as a whole is performing and then examining the individual components is the first step in maintaining the system at peak performance. Performance testing is the key to gaining this insight. Performance testing can be utilized to meet several objectives:

- Monitor ongoing unit performance
- Evaluate the unit for potential modification or upgrades
- Evaluate the unit for potential maintenance needs
- Demonstrate guaranteed improvement as a result of modification or initial unit acceptance

OBJECTIVE OF TESTS

Testing is used to gather information about the current condition of the plant, unit, or component. This information may be used for a variety of purposes.

PERFORMANCE EVALUATION/ ROUTINE MONITORING

Probably the most important type of testing is the ongoing performance monitoring of a unit. This type of testing enables the unit to stay at peak performance on a continual basis. This type of program combines online monitoring with periodic tests at specific conditions. The key aspect is repeatability more than absolute accuracy. The objective of this effort is to identify changes in performance and component degradation.

COMPONENT EVALUATION

When the routine performance monitoring indicates a problem with a specific component or in a certain area of the unit, component testing may be required to correctly diagnose the problem. This type of testing is specific to the component being tested and the issues associated with that particular component.

DESIGN MODIFICATION

When major changes are being considered for a unit, current operating data is used to evaluate the unit. The proposed modifications are then factored in and the new unit performance is predicted. Common design modifications are fuel change, uprating, turbine upgrade, and environmental control equipment additions.

CONTRACTUAL GUARANTEES VERIFICATION

After first commissioning or the modification of a unit, a performance guarantee test is required to demonstrate that the unit has achieved its goal. This type of test requires the most accuracy, since the guarantees are absolute values. This type of test will usually follow closely the applicable American Society of Mechanical Engineers (ASME) Performance Test Code.

ASME PERFORMANCE TEST CODES

For more than 100 years ASME has been developing Performance Test Codes (PTCs). ASME, in cooperation with the American National Standards Institute (ANSI), has issued PTCs for overall plant performance as well as for many individual plant components. These Codes are recognized as the American national standard for the determination of performance. While many of these Codes are written from the perspective of an acceptance test, the basic methodology detailed in the procedure may be used for other types of tests. An acceptance test to determine absolute performance usually requires the most stringent attention to measurement accuracy and testing detail. Similar codes in Europe include EN 12952-15: 2003 for steam generators and IEC 60953-2 for steam turbines. Much of the testing methodology that is presented below is based on ASME PTCs.

PTC 46 OVERALL PLANT PERFORMANCE

ASME PTC 46 Overall Plant Performance addresses the corrected net power output, corrected heat input, and corrected net plant heat rate. The corrections are applied for variations of the boundary conditions such as ambient conditions, heat sink conditions, and fuel composition. PTC 46 covers both Rankine cycle plants as well as combined cycle plants.

PTC 4 FIRED STEAM GENERATORS

ASME PTC 4 Fired Steam Generators covers the determination of boiler efficiency. This Code was revised in 1998 to reflect fuel efficiency, i.e., the percentage of the heat energy in the fuel that is converted to energy in the steam and water. The previous Code, which was replaced with PTC 4, ASME PTC 4.1, was based on total energy inputs, considering energy that was not part of the energy in the fuel. Since most users of the Code used the "short form" and considered only the fuel energy, they in fact were calculating the fuel efficiency. When the Code was revised, the committee evaluated more than 16 different definitions of efficiency, all technically correct, and selected the current PTC 4 method. This method allowed the boiler efficiency determined using PTC 4 to be used to calculate the heat input for the overall plant heat rate as determined by PTC 46. The 1998 Code also included procedures to address fluidized bed combustion, as well as other environmental equipment within the boiler envelope.

The primary method for determining efficiency is referred to as the energy balance method, formerly called the heat loss method. This method is based on the energy balance relationship:

$$\eta_{blr} = \frac{Output}{Input}$$

$$Output = Input - Losses + Credits$$

Thus,

$$\eta_{blr} = 1 - \frac{Losses}{Input} + \frac{Credits}{Input}$$

The following Codes are included in the 1998 revision:

PTC 4.2 Pulverizers
PTC 4.3 Air Heaters
PTC 4.4 Heat Recovery Steam Generators

PTC 6 STEAM TURBINES

ASME PTC 6 covers the determination of steam turbine performance for steam turbines in a regenerative cycle where feedwater heaters are present. The performance parameters that may be determined from a PTC 6 test include the following:

- Heat rate
- Generator output
- Steam flow
- Steam rate
- Feedwater flow

PTC 6.2 STEAM TURBINES IN COMBINED CYCLE APPLICATIONS

ASME PTC 6.2 covers the determination of steam turbine performance for steam turbines in a combined cycle or cogeneration application. This Code provides procedures for testing and calculating turbine generator output corrected to reference conditions as a measure of overall steam turbine performance.

ASME PTC 19 series outlines the requirements for instrumentation and includes the following codes:

PTC 19.1 Test Uncertainty
PTC 19.5 Flow Measurement
PTC 19.10 Flue Gas Analysis

OTHER TEST METHODS

U.S. ENVIRONMENTAL PROTECTION AGENCY (EPA) REFERENCE METHODS

The EPA has a number of standard methods for measuring emissions from power plant stacks. These methods include the following:

Method 5 Particulate Matter
Method 6 SO_2
Method 7 NOx
Method 9 Opacity
Method 10 CO
Method 25 Gaseous Organics
Method 26 Halogens
Method 29 Metals

In addition, the EPA has provided specifications for continuous emissions monitoring systems (CEMS) for the above listed materials. For most power plants subject to EPA emissions regulations, such CEMS are required to demonstrate continuous compliance with the appropriate regulations.

HIGH PRESSURE-INTERMEDIATE PRESSURE (HP-IP) PACKING LEAKAGE

On steam turbine designs where the HP and IP turbines are of an opposed design within a single shell, there is a packing seal that has a leakage of steam from the HP bowl to the IP bowl. If the packing is worn, this leakage may be excessive, resulting in higher reheater (RH) temperatures or an increased RH spray flow. Engineers at General Electric[1] developed a simple test methodology to estimate this flow. The method is known as the Booth-Kautzman Temperature Shift Test. It is important to keep this testing option in mind when evaluating the performance of the boiler's reheater. Since the steam leaks from the HP to the IP, it bypasses the reheater, reducing the flow to the reheater. With less flow, the reheater outlet temperature rises and may incorrectly be interpreted as an oversurfaced reheater.

AIR HEATER LEAKAGE

The measurement of oxygen with the corresponding computation of flue gas weight provides a powerful tool in the analysis and diagnosis of several boiler-related issues.

Reducing air leakage into the boiler improves overall efficiency, as this additional air is merely heated by the boiler and pumped up the stack by the fan.

FURNACE OUTLET TEMPERATURE

The most common devices for measuring temperatures, including furnace outlet temperature, are thermocouples. Information on the proper applications of thermocouples is found in ASME PTC 19.3, Supplements on Instruments and Apparatus.

TESTING RESULTS

Testing is more than just taking a snapshot of data in time and running some calculations to determine the performance. Testing involves a methodology of establishing the proper unit operating conditions, ensuring the unit is operating in a steady-state condition, and collecting representative data to suit the test objectives. There are a number of methodologies available to the user to evaluate various components or the entire unit. While the ASME PTCs are the most prevalent, there are several others that are available for certain components or desired results. The methodologies listed previously should be viewed as the test engineer's toolbox, a variety of methods to determine operating characteristics of a particular unit. Some of the typical results that an engineer may want to test for are described below, with more detailed discussion in the validation and analysis section.

HEAT RATE

Heat rate is a measure of the efficiency of the cycle. The units for heat rate are BTU/kWh, which represents how much thermal energy is required to produce a kilowatt of electric energy for a one-hour period. Heat rate is the inverse of efficiency, in that it measures the energy required to produce a unit of electricity. If the ratio were inverted and the thermal energy converted into kilowatt hours, the cycle efficiency would result.

Cycle efficiency:

$$\eta_{cycle} = \frac{P}{3412.14 \times Q_{in}}$$

where

P = power in kilowatts

Q_{in} = thermal heat supplied to the cycle in BTUs per hour

$$HR = \frac{Q_{in}}{P}$$

There are several different variations of heat rate used in a typical power station: turbine cycle heat rate, gross unit heat rate, net unit heat rate, and corrected heat rate. The differences in these heat rate calculations are based on different boundary envelopes around the cycle. The prefixes "gross" and "net" typically refer to where the power is determined. Gross usually refers to the power at the generator terminals, while net usually refers to the power sent to the grid, and is determined after the auxiliary loads have been taken. The difference between turbine cycle and unit refers to where the heat input is determined. A turbine cycle heat rate uses the heat supplied to the turbine as the heat input and, thus, measures the efficiency of the turbine feedwater heater and condenser cycle. The unit heat rates include the boiler and, thus, the total heat input to the cycle. The net unit heat rate considers the total fuel heat input to the boiler divided by the net power sent to the grid and reflects the true energy conversion efficiency. Any one of the previously defined heat rates can be corrected to reference conditions. These corrections adjust the current measured heat rate to the heat rate that would be present if specified external boundary conditions were present. Ambient conditions represent a good example. If the cooling water into the condenser was colder than the reference condition, the condenser would perform better and the calculated heat rate would be lower (better) than the reference value. These corrections are useful when comparing heat rates measured at different times, when ambient conditions were different. Another example is correcting boiler efficiency for fuel variations such as moisture content or the ambient air conditions for the inlet to a gas turbine in a combined cycle plant. These corrections allow the user to determine changes in performance that have occurred with the unit. ASME PTC 6, ASME PTC 46, and ASME PTC 4 all provide details of the corrections to be applied and how to apply them. Refer to those Codes for further reference.

The primary equation for corrected heat rate is:

$$HR_{corr} = \frac{Q_{corr}}{P_{corr}}$$

where

HR_{corr} = corrected heat rate
Q_{corr} = corrected heat input
P_{corr} = corrected net power

For Rankine cycle plants, especially solid fuel-fired, the heat input is usually defined as:

$$Q = \frac{Q_{turb}}{\eta_{blr}}$$

where

Q = calculated heat input
Q_{turb} = measured heat supplied to the turbine
η_{blr} = energy balance boiler efficiency per PTC 4

BOILER EFFICIENCY

Boiler efficiency is determined using the energy balance method, formerly called the heat loss method, as detailed in ASME PTC 4.

This method is based on the energy balance relationship:

$$\eta_{blr} = \frac{Output}{Input}$$

$$Output = Input - Losses + Credits$$

Thus,

$$\eta_{blr} = 1 - \frac{Losses}{Input} + \frac{Credits}{Input}$$

The energy balance boiler efficiency has a number of advantages over the input–output method:

- Higher accuracy
- Ability to be corrected to reference conditions
- Identification of energy losses

The increased accuracy in the energy balance method is derived from the fact that only the losses and credits are measured. Since the boiler efficiency is typically around 90%, the losses and credits are approximately 10% of the total energy involved. Thus, a 1% error in the measurement of a loss results in only a 0.1% error in the efficiency. In the case of the input/output efficiency calculation, the input and output are being measured directly. A 1% error translates directly into a 1% error in efficiency. Solid fuel flow measurements are notoriously inaccurate, typically greater than 5%, and would result in an unacceptably high uncertainty in the resulting calculated efficiency.

The input/output method of boiler efficiency uses the measured fuel flow and heat output to the turbine to determine the efficiency. Since the fuel flow is measured directly, there is no way to correct back to reference conditions for deviations in fuel quality or ambient conditions. In the energy balance method, the losses and credits are calculated on a per pound of coal basis based on the fuel analysis. Substituting the reference fuel analysis into the equations for determining gas weight and composition provides the correction to a reference fuel. There are also corrections to air heater performance for variations in air heater air inlet temperature. ASME PTC 4 specifies that to correct the input/output efficiency to reference conditions, the user should calculate the energy balance efficiency at test conditions and then at reference conditions (i.e., apply the corrections). The difference is determined and added to the measured input/output efficiency.

Possibly the most important aspect of the energy balance method is that it determines the losses. Comparing the measured losses to the design losses will quickly identify where the inefficiencies have crept into

Temperature measurements are a critical element of controlling and operating a power plant. The steam temperature delivered to the steam turbine is typically a guarantee requirement for the boiler.

the boiler (or plant), as opposed to merely knowing that the efficiency is 1% lower than design.

MEASUREMENTS AND INSTRUMENTATION

TEMPERATURE

Temperature measurement techniques differ depending on temperature level, fluid stratification, physical accessibility, and accuracy desired.[2] Generally, two methods are common in steam generator testing:

1. Filled-system thermometers
2. Thermoelectric and electrical resistance effects

These two methods are direct in that they involve fluid temperature level attainment by the sensing element. On the other hand, calibration difficulties, arising from variations with different fuels and furnace equipment, prevent frequent use of indirect techniques, such as utilization of optical or radiation effects accompanying temperature level of the fluid. The most common of the filled-system thermometers, mercury and other liquid-in-glass thermometers, use volume expansion. Their use in gas and air ductwork is restricted to ambient level temperatures and, when stratification does not exist, in ducts. As a variation of the volume-expansion class, gaseous-bulb type instruments, commonly found in operating instrumentation, also measure accompanying pressure change. Although this type of instrument permits remote indication, it is a fixed-position device, usually requiring field calibration by another means.

The most versatile temperature measurement devices are those in the second group. Both thermoelectric and electric resistance type techniques are readily adaptable to remote measurement, thus enabling monitoring of many points from a single location. Of the two, the thermocouple is more widely used because of its simplicity and low cost.

The Thermocouple

Thermocouple measurement employs the thermoelectric effect, a phenomenon whose alternate effects were first observed respectively by Seebeck and Peltier in 1821 and 1834. An electromotive force (emf) is developed if a circuit comprising two different wires has the two junctions at different temperatures. The magnitude of the emf depends on the wire materials and is proportional to the temperature difference between the junctions. Thus, knowing the temperature at one junction and considering the wire materials, the temperature at the other junction can be determined. Special laws govern the effects of intermediate metals and temperatures.[3]

Numerous metals are available for thermocouple materials with selection being based on the emf developed, the expected mechanical life in the atmosphere and temperature involved, calibration constancy, and cost. The most common types are copper-constantan, iron-constantan, chromel-alumel,[4] and platinum-platinum-rhodium. Their upper limit temperature ratings for general service are 400, 1100, 1800, and 2700°F (204, 593, 982, and 1,482°C) respectively.

Several engineering societies[5] have developed detailed specifications covering temperature-emf relationships and standard accuracy limits. Experience with chromel-constantan thermocouples also indicates suitability of this combination for measurements up to 1,600°F (870°C) with high emf developed. Thermocouple emf can be measured with either a millivolt galvanometer or a null-balance potentiometer. However, in the galvanometer system, the thermocouple circuit resistance is an additional factor and complicates the measurement, whereas in the null-balance system, no current flows in the thermocouple circuit, the measurement being of the opposing emf. Being simpler, the latter system is more widely used.

The Resistance Temperature Detector (RTD)

The resistance-bulb method involves the known temperature-electrical resistance change characteristic of a material, usually nickel or platinum, using a Wheatstone bridge type measuring circuit. This method can be made extremely accurate and is used in temperature standards work. There are two versions of RTDs: three wire and four wire, with the four-wire version being more accurate.

Using Thermocouple Probes

Generally, flue gas temperature measurement is made with thermocouple probes. Such measurement requires that the hot junction of the thermocouple reach the fluid temperature level. Thus, the fluid contacting the thermocouple must be flowing at a sufficient rate to supply heat lost by conduction from the hot junction along lead wires and by radiation to colder surfaces. The magnitude of these heat losses will depend on the probe design, including the probe temperature and the relative orientation of the hot junction, and the temperature differential between the hot junction and the heat receiving surfaces. Thermocouple measurement of gas-air temperature in most ducts is simplified for the following reasons:

1. The temperature level is below 700°F (370°C) and does not require water cooling of probes for mechanical strength.
2. The ducts are insulated to prevent heat loss and the interiors of ducts are essentially at fluid temperature.

At a temperature level of 700°F (370°C), an error of 15°F (8.3°C) is commonly found with bare thermocouples in proximity to economizer heat transfer surfaces at 500°F (260°C).

Grounded thermocouples should be used in flue gas ducts, especially downstream of an electrostatic precipitator, to dissipate any static charges.

FURNACE OUTLET TEMPERATURE PROBE—HIGH VELOCITY THERMOCOUPLE (HVT) PROBE. At gas temperatures higher than 700°F (370°C), water cooling of probes is necessary for mechanical strength reasons. The leadwire conduction heat loss increases. More significantly, higher temperature levels correspond to areas with heat transfer surfaces such as economizer, waterwalls, superheater, and reheater, the surface temperatures of which vary between 500 and 1,100°F (260 and 590°C). As a result, the radiation error of a bare thermocouple junction increases significantly until, at the furnace outlet (with gas temperatures over 2,000°F [1,100°C]), the bare thermocouple error is about 200°F (110°C). To compensate for radiation and conduction heat loss in furnace gas-temperature work, the thermocouple junction is shielded with a thin ceramic cylinder through which a high gas flow is induced. In turn, the shield is subject to the same heat loss effects. By increasing the number of annular shield layers, the thermocouple junction can be brought to within ± 5°F (2.8°C) of true gas temperature. Usually the fuel determines the limit to the size and number of shield openings. With high ash coals, serious plugging can occur in a short time when shields with small openings are used.

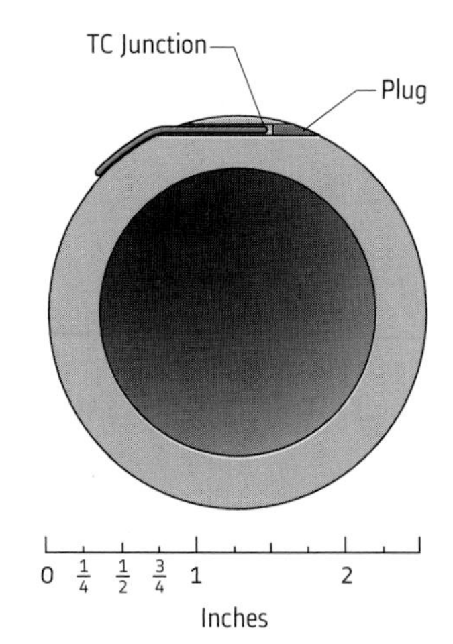

Figure 13-1 | Thermocouples are used for surface-temperature measurement of tubing containing fluids at high pressure

THE ORIFICE PROBE. Another type of furnace gas temperature measuring device is the orifice probe. The hot gas is drawn through two metering orifices in series, with deliberate cooling of the gas occurring between them. By measuring the two orifice flow rates and the cold gas temperature, the initial gas temperature can be calculated, since the weight flow is constant and the orifice flow differentials indicate volume flow, which is a function of temperature. The advantage of this type of measurement is that it eliminates thermocouple radiation error.

Measurements Related to Heat Absorption

Heat absorption values are used in developing the surface heat transfer relationships and are determined from test steam temperature and flow measurements, together with gas temperatures and flows. Additional performance items in the water-steam cycle are pressures, pressure drops, and quality/purity determinations. Circulation studies in furnace waterwalls and flow distribution between circuits are other examples of water-steam cycle testing.

THERMOWELL MEASUREMENTS. Some aspects, however, present more serious problems than in the gas-air work. Due to the high fluid pressures, the measuring elements are rarely exposed directly to the fluid stream. Measurement is commonly made by bottoming contact with a metal well that projects into the stream and provides the necessary mechanical strength. Several well designs are shown in the ASME *Performance Test Code, Supplements on Instruments and Apparatus,*[6] PTC 19.3 and in a paper by J. W. Murdock.[7] In a well application, spring loading of the element is more practical.

SURFACE-TEMPERATURE MEASUREMENT. Another method of fluid temperature determination is surface-temperature measurement of the tubing containing steam or water. This method is only possible where there is no heat transfer, because of temperature gradient effects from the hot gas or the steam film. In these zero heat flux areas, the tube wall gradient usually presents no problem in measurement, although even here precautions should be taken against boundary effects. Thermocouples are commonly peened directly into the tube metal or attached by welding the hot junction to the metal. In both cases, the thermocouple is grounded and measurement of a number of points must be made by separate circuits since series connections can form unknown loops using boiler metal as a third wire.

CHORDAL TEMPERATURE MEASUREMENT. Chordal thermocouples are used to determine heat flux in a waterwall tube. A 1⁄16 inch (1.6 mm) diameter thermocouple with a tip surface ground flat, is inserted into a hole drilled into the chord of a tube (*Fig. 13-1*). The junction of the thermocouple is placed at the crown of the tube a known distance below the surface. Knowing the TC location in the tube wall and the inside wall temperature (due to the saturated steam conditions), the heat flux can be determined.

The Electrical Resistance Mapping (ERM) Intelligent Sensor

Waterwall temperature monitoring for slagging detection or wastage detection are two major applications using ERM. ERM has been installed at four plants in the United States to detect wastage. Plant personnel at three large utility companies were interested in waterwall temperature monitoring for slagging detection.

Each ERM module provides a temperature map of a large area of the waterwall, typically 40 feet by 40 feet (12 m by 12 m). Within this measurement area, the ERM system provides a grid of approximately 120 waterwall temperature measurements. The ERM system views the boiler waterwall as a large metal plate and measures its electrical resistance. The electrical resistance of the tube sheet metal changes with temperature in a known, predictable manner. Using online resistance measurements, compared to a baseline measurement, the ERM system calculates the average metal temperature of the waterwall tubes. When a fixed, known, DC electrical current is passed through the waterwall panel, the electrical resistance of the metal generates a very small electrical field in the waterwall panel. This is the two-dimensional version of Ohm's Law. Although the voltages are very small, they can be measured with a microvoltmeter (*Fig. 13-2*).

The ERM module injects an electrical current into the waterwall and measures the resulting voltage at more than 100 locations. The data acquisition modules are designed by Alstom Power Plant Labs and built with sophisticated electronics that can accurately measure voltages within a few millionths of a volt. The electrical resistance of the panel is proportional to the metal thickness and to the electrical resistivity of the metal. Erosion of the waterwall material reduces the amount of metal available for the electrical current to pass through and increases the electrical resistance (just like running water through a smaller pipe). Increasing the temperature of the metal also increases the electrical resistance by making it harder for the electrical current to pass through the metal. Increasing the electrical resistance for any reason increases the voltage differences between measurement locations, given that the current is constant.

Special software in the ERM system uses the grid of voltage measurements, along with a few local temperature measurements from thermocouples mounted on the waterwall. The two-dimensional grid of voltages is processed using mathematical deconvolution. A reference set of measurements (voltages and thermocouple temperatures) is taken at plant start-up. The software computes the temperature profile or metal thickness loss on the waterwall by comparing each set of new measurements to the reference measurements. Using the independent temperature measurements from several thermocouples,

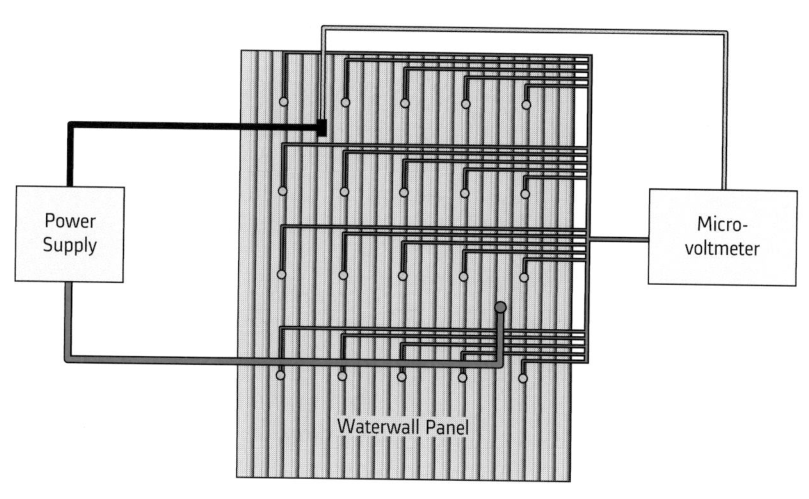

Figure 13-2 | Schematic for ERM sensor

the software separates the increased electrical resistance due to higher metal temperature from the increased electrical resistance due to metal erosion.

Since the ERM detects voltages at the microvolt level, attention must be paid to electromagnetic interference. ERM sensor wires may need to be shielded. A site ERM test procedure should check for ambient electrical noise. Solid-state electronic motor controls, such as those used on variable speed pumps, may create noise that disturbs the ERM. When an outage is still in progress, electrical welding on the waterwall induces stray currents that are detected by the sophisticated and sensitive ERM circuitry. Therefore, reference testing is often done during quiet hours in the outage schedule.

From a physical viewpoint, the ERM system uses wires connected in a two-dimensional grid to the insulation pins on a waterwall section. The ERM power supply establishes a 50-amp direct current flow in the grid. The resistivity curve of the metal waterwall is known. The current is constant, and thus the ERM sensor wires become the terminals of a microvoltmeter. The typical grid is 11 pins by 11 pins, with pins on four foot (1.2 m) spacing to give a coverage area of 40 by 40 feet (12 × 12 m). The ERM principle is patented by Alstom Technology, Ltd. as U.S. Patent number 6,288,528.

PRESSURE

The fundamental reference pressure and pressure-differential measuring device is the deadweight tester. Deadweight instruments employ incremental weights acting on a given-sized piston that floats when the liquid and weight pressures are equal. In deadweight gages, the liquid pressure is line pressure, its value determined from the weight total. In deadweight testers, the liquid is in a closed system, with the pressure acting on the instrument to be calibrated and on the weight piston, from which the pressure value is determined. Pressure measurements are typically made using electronic smart transmitters. Their sensitivity, linearity, repeatability, and accuracy are very good. Experience has shown that these devices either work accurately or do not work at all. These devices come in a variety of ranges to match the application pressure.

FLOW

Water and Steam Flow

Both steam and feedwater flow are obtained by pressure-differential measurement across flow nozzle or thin-plate orifice sections. The flow element accuracy is usually in the range of 0.6-1% of full scale, dependent upon the flow element design. Refer to ASME PTC 19.5 on flow measurement accuracy. Some plants have test flow nozzles installed on low pressure, low temperature condensate points in the feedwater cycle to avoid undue extrapolation of the original calibration data. Their calibration is performed with laboratory weigh tanks. Extrapolation of flow coefficients to the condensate conditions of flow, temperature, and pressure is usually accomplished on the basis of the Reynolds number and other dimensionless criteria. While a few central stations have reheat steam flow meters, it is more common to determine this quantity from primary steam-water flow, extraction flow to the high-pressure heater (heat bal-

ance), and the appropriate turbine leakage corrections.

CALCULATION OF FLOW THROUGH AN ORIFICE OR NOZZLE. This procedure calculates flow through a differential metering element in accordance with ASME PTC 19.5-2004.

$$Qm = 300\left(\frac{\pi}{4}\right)d_a^2(\epsilon)C\sqrt{\frac{2\rho(\Delta P)32.17405}{(1-\beta_a^4)}}$$

where

Qm = calculated mass flow rate in lb/h
d_a = element bore diameter at actual flowing conditions
ϵ = expansion coefficient for flowing fluid ϵ = 1 for water
C = coefficient of discharge
ρ = fluid density in lb/ft^3
ΔP = differential pressure in psi
β_a = beta ratio at actual flowing conditions
D = tube diameter

$$\beta = \frac{d}{D}$$

$$\beta_a = \frac{d_a}{D_a}$$

$$D_a = D + \alpha_p D(T - 68)$$

$$d_a = d + \alpha_e d(T - 68)$$

where

α_p = pipe thermal expansion factor
α_e = element thermal expansion factor
T = temperature

Flue Gas Velocity and Flow

This information is included because of the profound effect that the quantity of gas being handled has on the sizing and cost of the gas treatment equipment. The determination of total quantities of gaseous and solid constituents in the gases leaving a steam generator depends on an accurate quantification of the gas flow itself. For instance, in the sampling of dust, the amount of material caught in a sampler is reduced to a dust concentration of, say, pounds (kg) of dust per 1,000 pounds (kg) of gas. The total quantity of dust being emitted by the source, then, is the product of dust concentration and total gas flow by weight.

BOUNDARY LAYER EFFECTS. *Measurement of Solids in Flue Gases,* by P. G. W. Hawksley, defines the approach of the British Institute of Fuel.[8] This publication discusses the effects of nonsymmetrical gas flow distribution and boundary layer profiles. It should be noted that the equal-area zone method, as typically used, can easily miss the boundary layer flow profile. Very small incremental areas would be required for the velocity probe device to "see" all of the boundary layer. However, traversing time can be reduced if the boundary layer is evaluated in detail for one test only and then used to correct coarser subsequent traverses. This approach is justifiable since each flue or stack will have its own characteristic boundary layer, which is a function of the specific system geometry and flow turbulence. There have been occasions where boundary layers representing 5% of the flue diameter have produced flow errors of about 10–20%.

VARIATION IN RESULTS USING PITOT STATIC MEASUREMENT. Pitot static tube velocity measurements have been coupled with the equal-area technique for many

Flow measurements are often crucial for understanding what is happening in a power plant. Errors in flow measurements can lead to unnecessary shutdowns or load reductions due to emissions constraints.

years. The results of total gas flow can be quite varied and misleading, if care is not given to the selection of the measurement plane, or consideration not given to the selection of the proper type of flow measurement device for the flow directionality that is present. *Table 13-1* presents the results of several total gas flow measurements using the pitot static tube and equal-area techniques as called for in ASME PTC 27. The results listed are derived from a typical utility steam generator installation operating at constant load. Observe the gross divergence of measured values and the necessity for careful choice of measurement point. As noted, the flow as measured can vary from 104 to 150% of rated value.

Power Plant Flow Patterns

Industrial ductwork and flues are designed to connect pieces of equipment at minimum cost and minimum space requirements. The resultant flow patterns quite often deviate from the desired uniform and unidirectional condition required for accurate quantification of flow. Flow separation and reverse flows, often found in the major runs of flues, are corrected only by major pressure drops, such as an air heater or excessively long runs of ductwork. Flow patterns in stacks and fans frequently display high levels of vortex energy. A basic problem associated with vortex formation is that vortices will persist for many diameters downstream from the source. The vortices have a very strong effect on dynamic flow measurement devices.

Occasionally, reverse (or negative) flow may be encountered. A question then arises as to how to calculate the total volume flow rate from this type of data. Fluid flow continuity requires that all velocity points, both normal direction and reverse flow, be arithmetically averaged and applied to the total, cross sectional area of the plane of the measurement. If this is not done, the recirculated gas flow (the negative values), which can represent 5 to 15% of volume throughput, will increase the positive flow values by the same amount and produce a "measured" flow that is high.

TABLE 13-1 | GAS FLOW MEASUREMENT

Gas flow measured at different locations in accordance with methods given in *ASME* PTC 27 and by using a pitot static tube. Observe the gross divergence of measured values and the necessity for careful choice of measurement point.

Measurement Point	Gas Flow CFM	Percent Rating
Rated Value	300,000	100
Mechanical-Collector Inlet	383,000	128
Mechanical-Collector Outlet	449,000	150
Induced-Draft Fan Inlet (Precipitator Outlet)	313,000	104
Induced-Draft Fan Outlet	424,000	141

CFM, cubic feet per minute

Velocity Measurement

The classical approach to the measurement of fluid velocity has been by pitot tube. Several references are available which describe the developing history of this device. Appendix E of *Combustion*, 3rd edition, 1981, titled "Velocity Calculations by Graphical Methods," presents graphs that can be used for quick determination of gas velocities from pitot tube readings.

THE PITOT TUBE. The typical flow measurement device is the pitot tube shown in *Figure 13-3*. The impact, or total pressure hole, is the most useful part of the probe. Hydraulically, the impact pressure is the true sum of the local static and dynamic (velocity) heads. Also, the impact hole can have a cone of response of about 60 to 70°. Therefore, accurate angular positioning of the probe for total (impact) pressure measurements is not critical. However, positioning of the probe parallel to the flow direction is very critical for static pressure measurement. The static pressure tap reference surface should be parallel to the flow stream lines. Also, ideally, the flow stream lines should be straight and parallel. Any flow stream line that is not parallel to the static surface will induce an impact or reverse-impact, dynamic pressure at the static hole and create an associated error.

One practical problem associated with the pitot tube is the right-angle bend and probe tip length. This configuration requires large holes in the flue (or duct) wall, or some awkward probe handling by the user. The bend also makes it difficult to probe the flow at the near side, or access wall, of the flue. Large holes in the flue wall are, in turn, difficult to seal to prevent leakage errors. Another problem associated with the standard pitot tube is the tendency for the small holes to plug in flues with heavy dust loadings.

THE STAUSCHEIBE PITOT TUBE. To eliminate such problems, stack samplers have used the "Stauscheibe," or Type S, pitot tube shown in *Figure 13-4*. Because the reverse-impact method is used to read the static pressure, this probe will produce a new velocity head reading, $h = KV^2/2g$, where K will be greater than 1.0. A velocity correction factor, C_v, where $V = C_v\sqrt{2gh}$, is 0.855. However, C_v is not constant, but it is a function of velocity. Cole[9] recommends C_v = 0.870 at 10 ft/sec (3 m/s) and 0.885 at 3 ft/sec (0.9 m/s). Alstom has found that C_v is 0.855 only for velocities of 20 ft/sec (6.1 m/s) and higher. Cole shows that there are many variations of manufacture. Thus, each Type S pitot tube must be calibrated in a known flow and a curve of C_v versus velocity prepared.

THE FECHHEIMER PROBE. A directional pitot tube (*Figure 13-5*) has been developed using the work of Fechheimer.[10] This probe is basically a reverse-impact probe, but makes use of properties of the flow field around a cylinder. Two additional static, or Fechheimer, taps are located on the "forward" face of the cylinder. Two sets of differential readings are required. The probe is rotated in the gas stream until the velocity taps read positive and the two additional static taps are nulled. The probe is then "looking" directly at the flow-velocity vector and the angle can be recorded.

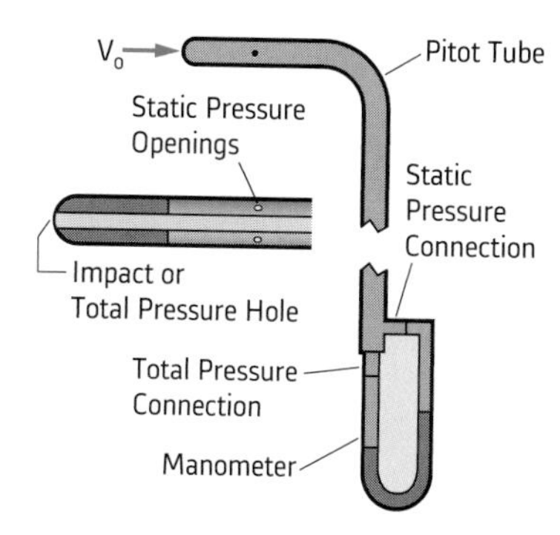

Figure 13-3 | A pitot tube for fluid-velocity measurement with pressure connections and readout shown schematically

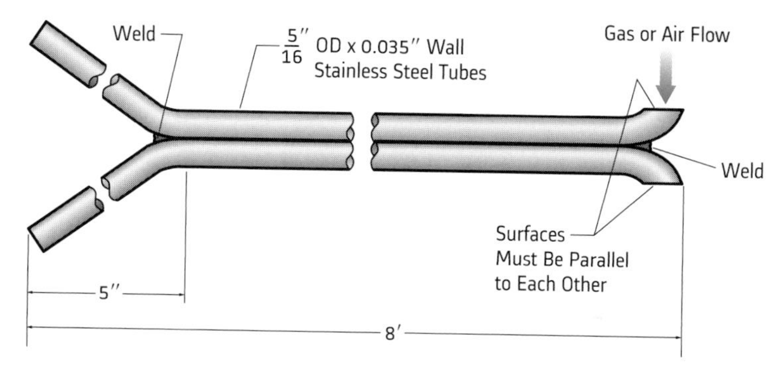

Figure 13-4 | The Stauscheibe or Type S pitot tube

The Fechheimer probe is very sensitive to the problem of flow moving along the length of the stem when the stem is not exactly perpendicular to the flow field. Folsom evaluates this condition, called "stem effects," in reference 11. The probe, used in Alstom's Power Plant Laboratory, places the sensing cylinder at the end of the airfoil stem, which will tend to bleed off stem flow before it reaches the pressure sensing holes. This modification minimizes, but does not eliminate, the induced stem errors. The velocity correction factor, C_v, for this probe is not as dependent on small differences in manufacture, as is the Type S probe. In this case, the value

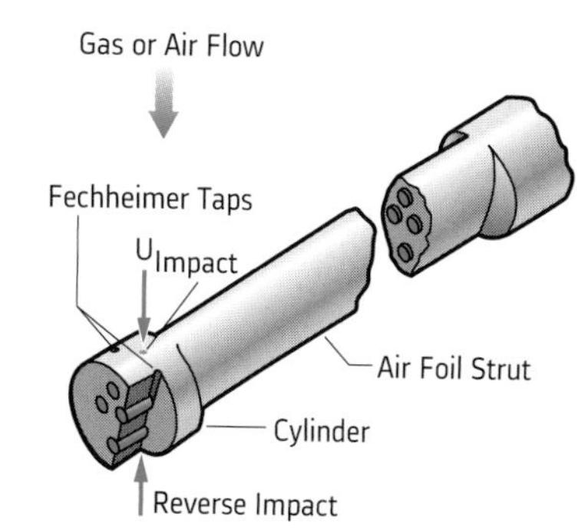

Figure 13-5 | A Fechheimer directional pitot tube

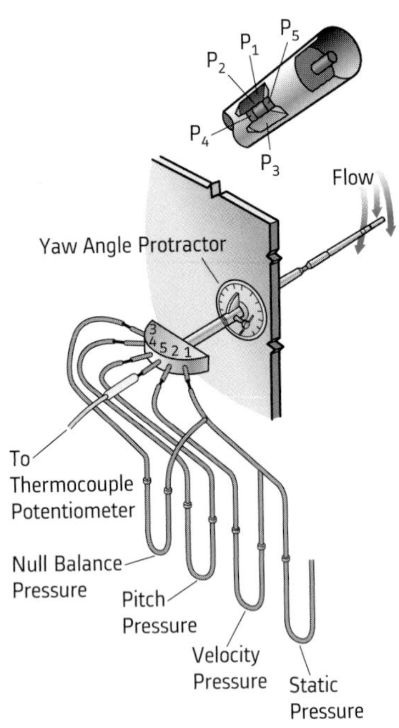

Figure 13-6 | Five-hole probe

of C_v is typically 0.78 for Reynolds numbers in excess of 100.

THE FIVE-HOLE PROBE. Another type of directional pitot tube is the five-hole or three-dimensional probe. See *Figure 13-6.* This probe is similar to the Fechheimer probe. However, it has an additional two pressure-sensing taps, which allow measurement of the pitch angle of the velocity vector. As with the Fechheimer probe, the static pressure taps are nulled so that the probe is "looking" directly at the flow-velocity vector. The pitch angle is determined from a calibration curve that relates pitch angle to a pitch pressure coefficient, C_v. This coefficient is the ratio of the pitch tap differential pressure over the flow-velocity pressure.

$$C_{\phi}=\frac{P_4-P_5}{P_1-P_2}$$

Each probe head has its own calibration curve, which is a function of Reynolds number.

The use of a five-hole probe is most important where there is significant directionality of the gas flow. That is, the flow-velocity vector is not parallel to the duct axis. Most pitot probes are insensitive to flow directionality less than 15%. The Fechheimer probe measures directionality only in the plane normal to the probe. A five-hole probe measures directionality in planes normal and parallel to the probe.

If the flow vector at a point is known, then the component of flow normal to the plane of traverse can be calculated. The duct gas flow can then be expressed as:

$$Q_n = A\frac{1}{n}\sum_{i=1}^{n} V_i\,(\cos\phi)(\cos\psi)$$

where

Q_n = gas flow rate normal to the plane of traverse
A = duct cross-sectional area
V = gas velocity at one point
ϕ = yaw angle of flow-velocity vector
ψ = pitch angle of flow-velocity vector
n = total number of traverse points
i = any one point

As shown by this equation, pitot probes that do not account for flow directionality can indicate gas flow rates that are higher than those actually present. Selection of a probe should be based on the directionality of the flow stream at the measurement plane. Typically, in most large boiler installations, the stack is the only location where the directionality of the gas flow in both planes is less than 15%. However, if a duct has less than this amount of flow directionality along the pitch plane, the Fechheimer probe can be used.

THE HOT-WIRE ANEMOMETER. A device now often used for measurement of industrial fluid velocities is the hot-wire, or hot-film, anemometer. A single hot-wire system is described in PTC 19.5. The hot-wire anemometer has the advantage of high sensitivity at very low velocities, producing an electric readout and a measurement of turbulence. A disadvantage is its incapability of measuring directional flow in complex flow fields. It is also fragile and can easily be broken in flues with heavy dust loading. This last problem can be overcome by the use of a hot-film anemometer. The hot-film anemometer operates with the characteristics of the hot wire, but sacrifices the ability to measure very high turbulent frequencies. Since high-frequency response

is typically desirable only in aerodynamic wind-tunnel studies, it is rarely needed for industrial flow evaluation.

INSTRUMENT CALIBRATION. All devices should be calibrated to ensure a reasonable level of accuracy. The standard pitot tube will deviate from the theoretical Bernoulli response of $C_v = 1.0$ as a function of wear. The Stauscheibe and Fechheimer probes produce values of C_v that will also vary as a function of velocity and wear. The hot-wire and hot-film response is typically some function of V, where n is less than 1.0 and will vary with dirtiness. Also, each device is dependent on gas composition. Using these dynamic devices requires that the gas density be known. The hot-wire device requires the further evaluation of gas thermal properties. Fortunately, the probes can be calibrated in air and analytically corrected for gas properties.[10]

Probe Dynamics and Turbulence

To simplify energy calculations, flow turbulence is usually considered to be a random, but isotropic process. Typically, flow in industrial flues produces two distinct turbulence characteristics described as rolling and vortex flow.

ROLLING FLOW. Many installations include sharp corners and other abrupt discontinuities that will produce the turbulent roll. This roll is characterized by fluctuating velocity components, μ and v, usually coplanar with the major flow vector. A third component, w, is perpendicular to the main flow vector, and is usually of smaller magnitude. Isotropic turbulence, which is defined as $\mu = v = w$, is difficult to find in industrial work.

VORTEX FLOW. Vortex flow can be produced by stack entrances and fan discharges, as well as by two rolling turbulence patterns intersecting at an angle. It is difficult to characterize vortex flow in linear-velocity, vector notations. Typically, all turbulence is characterized when possible by the combined values of intensity (μ), frequency, and scale or size of the major eddies.

EFFECTS ON VELOCITY MEASUREMENTS. Turbulence, when applied to a dynamic device such as the standard pitot tube, will introduce a series of basic errors in the interpreted reading. The first is mathematical in that the reading produced by the pitot tube is a "head" of $V^2/2g$, while the result required is the velocity, or V. *Figure 13-7* shows that, when measuring a turbulent or fluctuating velocity, the head measured will be the root mean square (RMS) value of the wave form and will always be higher than the head produced by the "average" velocity. Second, this problem is complicated by the flow dynamics of the resistance of the small size pressure taps and tubing, the compressibility of air or gas in the tubes (where applicable), and the inertia of the indicating fluid. These effects are additive such that, in turbulent flow fields, when using fluid dynamic devices, the velocity as read will always be higher than the actual velocity being measured.

VELOCITY READOUTS. The problem of flow resistance can be partially corrected by using large sensing holes in the probe, close coupling of the readout device to the probe, and using a readout device of low displacement volume and inertia. The readout device should also be capable of producing an electrical output signal. The signal can be recorded for later analysis of the mathematical RMS effect on the velocity reading. An approach to the mathematical evaluation of turbulent effects on velocity readings is given in

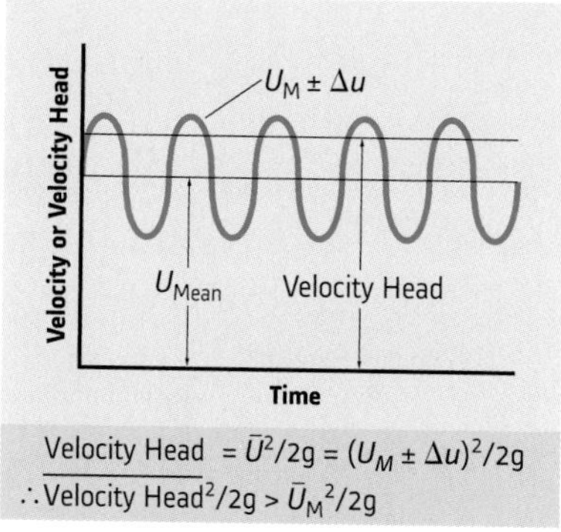

Velocity Head $= \bar{U}^2/2g = (U_M \pm \Delta u)^2/2g$

$\therefore$ Velocity Head$^2/2g > \bar{U}_M{}^2/2g$

Figure 13-7 | Pulsing-flow wave forms obtained in measurements of fluctuating velocities

a prior version of ASME PTC 19.5 which specifies isotropic turbulence and the RMS approach. It is relatively easy to apply this guide if the signal is sinusoidal. However, if the signal is not sinusoidal, turbulence effect is difficult to evaluate. This problem can be resolved by using a true RMS voltmeter to produce a true RMS reading independent of the applied wave form.

The effect of flow-stream vorticity has just the reverse effect on the velocity readout. Vorticity represents a well ordered flow field of significant curvature. Flow curvature, in turn, produces a very definite radial pressure gradient. If the radius of curvature of the flow is of the same order of size as the measuring device, the device will not be measuring either the correct dynamic or static pressures. Vorticity of small size and high intensity can, therefore, contain a significant amount of dynamic, or pressure, energy that will not be read if the measuring device is physically larger than the size of the turbulent vortices being produced. Unfortunately, there is no easy way to evaluate the effect of vorticity on measurements of dynamic flow. Therefore, vorticity should be minimized or eliminated by egg crates or screens if no other flow traversing station without vorticity is available. Recommendations on reducing the major sources of error in obtaining total gas flow rates, based on the above, are given in *Quantification of Stack Gas Flow*, by C. L. Burton.[12]

POWER

Electric power is typically measured using a watt-hour meter connected to metering class, current transformers, and potential transformers. For a detailed discussion of the measurement of three phase, electric power, refer to any one of several ASME PTCs: PTC 6, PTC 6.2, or PTC 22.

FUEL ANALYSIS

Analyzing Fuel Characteristics

In its broadest sense, fuel analysis refers to determination of all physical and chemical properties of a fuel.

SOLID FUELS. The basic type of chemical analysis for coal is the proximate, which describes the fuel in weight percentage of fixed carbon, volatile material, ash, and moisture content. In the ultimate analysis, the fixed carbon and volatile material contents are reported in terms of total carbon, hydrogen, oxygen, nitrogen, and sulfur, this form being required for the calculation of air quantities. Fuel analysis and higher heating value (HHV) determination are made in accordance with the Test Code for Solid Fuels PTC 3.2 and *ASTM Standards*.[13] This is a constant volume determination. Because the fuel is burned at constant pressure in the steam generator, the HHV at constant volume, as determined in the bomb calorimeter, must be converted to a constant pressure HHV. Throughout the Codes, this HHV for constant pressure combustion is referred to as the HHV. (When testing by the input/output method, only the HHV and the moisture content of the fuel are required.)

Generally, fuel sizing refers to crusher-prepared coal sizing measured with screens of one inch (2.5 cm) opening and larger, and is of importance mainly for fuel bed distribution problems in stoker firing. Coal fineness usually refers to suspension burning sizes and, for pulverized coal, involves sieving of 50 to 200 mesh (openings per inch) particle sizes. In both cases, a series of screen sizes is used, with the fractions retained or passed by each size being reported. Knowledge of the size consist or overall fraction relationship, rather than just one size, is required. For example, in

pulverized coal firing, combustion efficiency (carbon loss) can be more affected by larger size consist, whereas grinding power is more closely related to the finer size percentages. Another physical property related to pulverizer performance is ease of grinding, or grindability index. This is determined from the amount of power required to pulverize a prepared sample of the test coal in the laboratory. The results are then compared with a standard sample. In the Hardgrove method, the standard is 100, with decreasing numbers indicating progressively harder grinding coals.

LIQUID FUELS. Oil fuels are reported in an ultimate analysis together with HHV and sample density, viscosity, and flash point. Density can be stated as either standard specific gravity, referred to water, or degrees American Petroleum Institute (API), the two terms being readily convertible. Additional properties are pour point, sediment, and presence of solid impurities such as metallic salts. These properties may influence pumping, storage, slagging, and corrosion problems. In general, the ultimate analysis is sufficient to determine fuel-air relationships for byproduct liquid fuels such as pulp-mill black liquor, refinery wastes, pitch, and others. Operating problems may require special tests in addition to the standard physical property determinations.

GASEOUS FUELS. Gaseous fuels are usually combinations of saturated and unsaturated hydrocarbons. Their analysis is reported as a mole, or volume, percentage of these constituents. Common analyses include low-temperature distillation, mass-spectrometer, and adsorption methods. From this constituent analysis, the HHV, at standard volumetric conditions and saturated or dry, can be calculated by using the standard heating values of the constituents. Where gas samples of large volume can be provided easily, the classical method of heating value determination, by calorimeter, is feasible. For instance, recording calorimeters are often found at transmission-line entry points to a user's plants for billing purposes. Many plants have their own calorimeters.

VALIDATION AND ANALYSIS

The most important part of the testing of a unit is the review and validation of the test data. Validation of the data is accomplished by evaluating the data collected as a whole and by using engineering relationships and mass and energy balances to confirm the data.

COMBUSTION CALCULATIONS

The combustion calculations allow us to determine the pounds of theoretical air required to burn a fuel of a given composition per million BTUs, or per pound of fuel. This information provides the ability to compute the majority of the heat losses for boiler efficiency on a percentage basis, based on the fuel fired.

$$TDA = \frac{11.51C + 34.3\left[H - \frac{O}{7.937}\right] + 4.335S}{HHV \times 100}$$

where

TDA = theoretical dry air lb air/million BTU
C = carbon in fuel percentage by weight
H = hydrogen in fuel percentage by weight
O = oxygen in fuel percentage by weight
S = sulfur in fuel percentage by weight
HHV = higher heating value of fuel BTU/lb

$$\text{Combustible in Refuse} = C_r = \%FA \times \%CFA + \%BA \times \%CBA$$

$$\text{Dry Refuse} = D_r = \frac{A}{1 - C_r}$$

$$C_b = C - D_r \times C_r$$

where

%FA = percentage of fly ash
%CFA = percentage of carbon in fly ash
%BA = percentage of bottom ash
%CBA = percentage of carbon in bottom ash
C_b = carbon burned

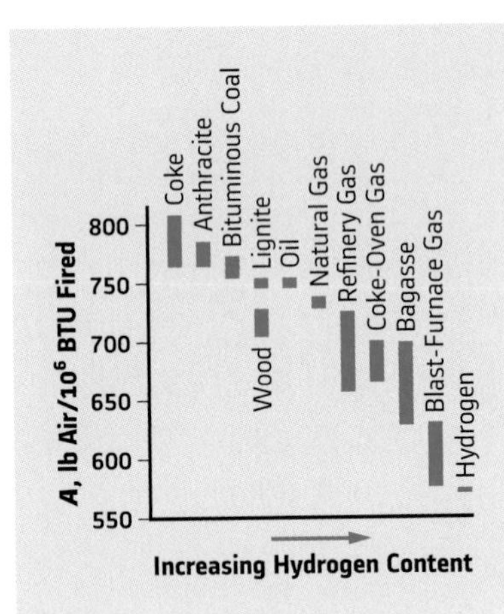

Figure 13-8 | Combustion-air requirements for various fuels at zero excess-air—a range of values as an approximate function of hydrogen content

If the carbon loss is significant (greater than 1%), C_b should be used in lieu of C in the above equations and those for excess air.

Calculating the theoretical air on a wet basis can be used as a check on the fuel analysis.

$$A_{wet} = \frac{11.68C + 35.03\left[H - \frac{O}{7.937}\right] + 4.38S}{HHV \times 100}$$

The calculated theoretical air should be within the dark blue areas as shown in *Figure 13-8*.

EXCESS AIR

$$R = \frac{\left[31.32C + 11.528S + 13.334N\right]}{HHV \times 100}$$

$$EA\% = \frac{O_2\left[R + 10.338 \times TDA\right]}{TDA\left(2.73 - .130680_2\right)}$$

where

O_2 = percentage of oxygen measured in the flue gas on a dry volume basis.

CALCULATING FLUE GAS ANALYSIS

Moles of O_2 required

$$AO_2 = \frac{C}{12.01} + \frac{H}{4.032} + \frac{S}{32} - \frac{O}{32}$$

Moles of N_2 from fuel

$$AN_2 = \frac{N}{28.02}$$

Excess air as a fraction

$$EA = \frac{EA\%}{100}$$

Moles of N_2 in flue gas

$$PN_2 = AO_2(1 + EA)3.785 + AN_2$$

Total moles of dry flue gas

$$TotM = \frac{C}{12.01} + \frac{S}{32} + AO_2(EA) + PN_2$$

Mole fractions

$$O_{2_{dvmf}} = (AO_2 \times EA) / TotM$$

$$CO_{2_{dvmf}} = \frac{C/12.01}{TotM}$$

$$SO_{2_{dvmf}} = \frac{S/32}{TotM}$$

$$N_{2_{dvmf}} = 1 - O_{2dvmf} - CO_{2dvmf} - SO_{2dvmf}$$

Weight fractions

$$TotP = 44.01CO_{2dvmf} + 32O_{2dvmf} + 64.07SO_{2dvmf} + 28.02N_{2dvmf}$$

$$O_{2dw} = \frac{32O_{2dvmf}}{TotP}$$

$$CO_{2dw} = \frac{44.01CO_{2dvmf}}{TotP}$$

$$N_{2dw} = \frac{28N_{2dvmf}}{TotP}$$

Calculating the products of combustion—lb/lb fuel basis

Air to combustion

$$TDA_{lb} = \frac{TDA \times HHV}{1000000}$$

$$DryAir = TDA_{lb}(1 + EA)$$

$$MoistAir = SpecHum \times DryAir$$

$$WetAir = DryAir + MoistAir$$

$$SpecHum = \text{Specific Humidity, .013 for 60\% relative Humidity}$$

Fuel in products

$$Wet_{prod} = WetAir + 1 - D_r$$

D_r is dry refuse from above

Moisture from fuel

$$MF = (M + 8.936H)/100$$

Moisture in products

$$M_{prod} = MoistAir + MF$$

Dry products

$$Dry_{prod} = Wet_{prod} - M_{prod}$$

ENTHALPY EQUATION CONSTANTS FROM ASME PTC 4.4

The enthalpy is calculated for each constituent in a gas stream as a function of the gas temperature. The enthalpy correlations for each constituent are dual range correlations with a change at 1,800°R. The correlations require the temperature to be in °R. *Table 13-2* provides the appropriate constants for the constitutive equation.

$$T_R = \text{Temperature [°R]} = (\text{Temperature [°F]} + 459.67)$$
$$h_i = -A_1/T_R + A_2\ln(T_R) + A_3{*}T_R + A_4{*}T_R^{\,2} + A_5{*}T_R^{\,3} + A_6{*}T_R^{\,4} + A_7{*}T_R^{\,5} - A_8$$
$$T_R > 1{,}800°R$$

BOILER EFFICIENCY

The primary method for determining efficiency is referred to as the energy balance method, formerly called the heat loss method. This method is based on the energy balance relationship:

$$\eta_{blr} = \frac{Output}{Input}$$
$$Output = Input - Losses + Credits$$

Thus,

$$\eta_{blr} = 1 - \frac{Losses}{Input} + \frac{Credits}{Input}$$

TABLE 13-2 | CONSTITUENT ENTHALPY EQUATION CONSTANTS

A Values	Constituents					
	N_2	O_2	CO_2	H_2O	Ar	SO_2
T_R<=1,800°R						
A_1	5076.903444	−6888.073538	7227.711078	−14100.39482	0	−5333.964877
A_2	−48.72474552	54.14599817	−50.87920389	114.2053432	0	50.72160967
A_3	0.431208942	0.069447256	0.239235281	0.102713623	0.124279476	−0.073060273
A_4*10^4	−16.79893331	7.402341031	3.138394549	22.11623913	0	18.98189113
A_5*10^4	100.9860003	−4.364913417	−0.987579956	−83.27114025	0	−80.07268636
A_6*10^{11}	−2925.146767	−538.2934954	148.749738	2341.441933	0	1921.86454
A_7*10^{15}	34031.29176	12285.5047	2449.873977	28077.80325	0	−19897.19608
A_8	−123.5670205	406.9617332	−199.50475	844.3000544	64.58431507	330.8196608
T_R>1,800°R						
A_1	134989.0343	208707.2821	17207.41433	369646.9091	3.238297928	−11325.49719
A_2	−285.7350587	261.9417179	−145.2915082	−478.7281864	−0.005362306	−46.04550381
A_3	0.43008964	0.112934906	0.374147054	0.512156854	0.124282926	0.236090695
A_4*10^4	−1.209016552	2.185673559	0.115607258	7.018191588	−5.51268E-05	−0.172156415
A_5*10^4	1.088015054	−1.397060777	0.022579091	−7.753574689	6.16422E-05	0.180366793
A_6*10^{11}	−5.844054022	5.463669086	−0.365792061	44.54356391	−0.000387631	−0.724777306
A_7*10^{15}	14.34281709	−9.687873053	5.44194572	101.277945	0.001021528	1.723497991
A_8	−1809.588277	2037.040157	−758.4598037	−3313.267173	64.54706733	−151.4826348

At low temperatures, the enthalpy changes in the flue gas can be estimated with a reasonable degree of accuracy through the use of the specific heat of the flue gas, which is dominated by the nitrogen content of the gas. At higher temperatures, there are more non-idealities. The constitutive equations provide a more accurate estimate of the enthalpy of the flue gas at a given temperature.

A good fuel analysis is the basis for all combustion and efficiency calculations.

The ASME PTC 4 Code considers 16 losses:

1. Dry gas
2. Water from fuel
3. Moisture in air
4. Unburned combustible
5. Sensible heat in residue
6. Hot Air Quality Control System (AQCS)
7. Air infiltration
8. NOx
9. Surface radiation
10. Additional moisture
11. Calcination
12. Water in sorbent
13. Wet ashpit loss
14. Recycled material
15. Cooling water
16. Heat internally supplied to air preheater (APH) coils

and 7 credits:

1. Dry air
2. Moisture in air
3. Sensible heat in fuel
4. Sulfation
5. Auxiliary power
6. Sensible heat in sorbent
7. Energy in additional moisture

In PTC 4, a series of worksheets are provided that walk the user through the calculations. There are three main advantages to using the energy balance method for boiler efficiency versus the input–output method:

- Greater accuracy—Since the losses and credits are measured and they represent only 10-15% of the total energy, the impact of measurement errors are significantly less than those made in measuring the input or output.
- Ability to correct to reference conditions—When attempting to compare results on a unit from different time periods, a correction to a reference fuel analysis or ambient condition is possible when using the energy balance method.
- Identification and quantification of losses—Since each of the losses are determined, a comparison to the design condition quickly reveals the source of degradation.

The detailed calculations for PTC 4 follow.

Boiler Efficiency Calculation Methodology by ASME PTC 4

The methodology is as follows:

1. Use the ultimate analysis of the fuel and the carbon in the ash streams to determine the carbon burned, theoretical air, and theoretical air corrected using stoichiometric calculations. These calculations are done on either a lb per million BTU basis or a lb/lb fuel basis. Most losses are determined on a percentage loss per lb of fuel. Some losses are determined on a total BTU lost basis and are converted to a percentage per lb of fuel by dividing the fuel flow and heating value. This will require iteration using an initial estimate of the fuel flow and recalculation when the efficiency has been determined.

   Coal Ultimate Analysis (mass percentage in fuel):

   $MpCF$ = percentage carbon
   $MpHF$ = percentage hydrogen
   $MpNF$ = percentage nitrogen
   $MpOF$ = percentage oxygen
   $MpSF$ = percentage sulfur
   MpH_2OF = percentage moisture
   $MpAsF$ = percentage ash
   HHV = higher heating value BTU/lb

Combustibles in refuse

$$CR = MpFA \times MpC_{FA} + MpBA \times MpC_{BA}{}^{*}$$

where

$MpFA$ = percentage of ash to fly ash (mass percentage of ash)
MpC_{FA} = percentage carbon in fly ash (mass percentage of carbon in fly ash)
$MpBA$ = percentage of ash to bottom ash (mass percentage of ash)
MpC_{BA} = percentage carbon in bottom ash (mass percentage of carbon in bottom ash)

*Note: Additional ash sources may be included by using their carbon content and the percentage of the ash flow that is collected there.

Dry refuse

$$DR = \frac{MpAsF}{(1-CR)}$$

Carbon burned

$$MpCb = MpCF - \frac{DR \times CR}{100}$$

Theoretical air

$$MFrThA = 0.1151 \times MpCF + 0.3430 \times MpH_2F + 0.0431 \times MpSF - 0.0432 \times MpO_2F$$

where

$MFrThA$ = theoretical air lb of air per lb of fuel

$$MqThAf = \frac{MFrThA}{HHV}$$

where

$MqThA$ = theoretical air lb of air per BTU

Theoretical air corrected for carbon burned

$$MFrThACr = 0.1151 \times MpCb + 0.3430 \times MpH_2F + 0.0431 \times MpSF\,(1 + .5MFrSc) - 0.0432 \times MpO_2F \text{ lb/lb fuel}$$

$$MqThACr = \frac{MFrThACr}{HHV} \text{lb / BTU}$$

$$MoThACr = \frac{MFrThACr}{28.963} \text{moles / mass fuel}$$

2. Compute the wet and dry products of combustion

Moles of dry products

$$MoDPc = \frac{MpCb}{12.01} + (1 - MfrSc)\frac{MpSF}{32.064} + \frac{MpNF}{28.013} + MoCO_2Sb$$

Moles of moisture per mole dry air:

$$MoWA = 1.608 \times MFrWA$$

where

$MFrWA$ = specific humidity lb H_2O/lb dry air

Moles of wet products of combustion

$$MoWPc = MoDPc + \frac{MpH_2F}{201.6} + \frac{MpWF}{1801.5} + \frac{MFrWAdz}{18.015} + MoWSb$$

3. Use the measured percentage of oxygen in the flue gas at both the air heater inlet and outlet to determine the excess air level using the ASME equation.

Excess air based on oxygen volume dry basis

$$XpA = 100\frac{DVpO_2(MoDPc + .7905 \times MoThACr)}{MoThACr(20.95 - DVpO_2)}$$

where

$DvpO_2$= percentage oxygen dry volume basis

Excess air based on oxygen volume wet basis

$$XpA = 100\frac{VpO_2(MoWPc + MoThACr(0.7095 + MoWA))}{MoThACr(20.95 - VpO_2(1 + MoWA)}$$

where

VpO_2= percentage oxygen wet volume basis

4. Calculate the products of combustion and the flue gas composition at both the air heater inlet and outlet using stoichiometric calculations. Subscript z denotes location specific information.

Dry air entering the boiler ahead of location z:

$$MqDAz = MqThACr(1 + \frac{XpAz}{100})\ \text{lb / BTU}$$

$$MFrDAz = MFrThACr(1 + \frac{XpAz}{100})\ \text{lb / lb fuel}$$

Wet air entering the boiler ahead of location z:

$$MqAz = (1 + MFrWA)MqDAz\ \text{lb/BTU}$$
$$MFrAz = (1 + MFrWA)MFrDAz\ \text{lb/lb Fuel}$$

Wet gas from fuel

$$MqFgF = \frac{(100 - MpAsF - MpUbC - MFrSc \times MpSF)}{100 \times HHV} \text{ lb/BTU}$$

Moisture from H_2O in fuel

$$MqWF = \frac{MpWF}{100 \times HHV} \text{ lb/BTU}$$

Moisture from combustion of H_2 in fuel

$$MqWH_2F = \frac{8.937 \times MpH_2F}{100 \times HHV} \text{ lb/BTU}$$

Gas from sorbent (if applicable, such as for a circulating fluidized bed (CFB) type unit)

$$MqCO_2b = \frac{MFrCO_2b}{HHV}$$

Product gas weight is an important boiler design parameter as well as a necessary factor in efficiency calculations.

Water from sorbent (if applicable)

$$MqWSb = \frac{MFrWSb}{HHV}$$

Additional water (from soot blowing, atomizing steam, etc., if applicable)

$$MFrWADz = \frac{MrStz}{MrF}$$

where

$MFrWADz$ = mass fraction of moisture added per pound of fuel fired
$MrStz$ = mass flow rate of steam/water added
MrF = mass flow rate of fuel (estimated initially)

$$MqWADz = \frac{MFrWADz}{HHV}$$

Total moisture in flue gas

$$MqWFgz = MqWF + MqWvF + MqWH_2F + MqWSb + MqWAz + MqWADz$$

Total wet flue gas weight lb/BTU

$$MqFgz = MqDAz + MqWAz + MqFgF + MqCO_2Sb + MqWSb + MqWADz$$

The dry flue gas weight

$$MqDFgz = MqFgz - MqWFgz$$

5. Determine the enthalpies.

Enthalpies are determined based on the Journal Army, Navy, Air Force/ National Air & Space Administration (JANAF/NASA) correlation. Enthalpies for dry flue gas are based on a composition of 15.3% CO_2, 3.5% O_2, 0.1% SO_2, and 81.1% N_2. Errors due to variation from this composition for combustion of fossil fuels are not significant if the excess air level is less than 300%. For nonstandard fuels individual components of the flue gas should be used and combined on a weight basis.

Water vapor

$$Hwv = 0.4408 \times T + 2.381E^{-5} \times T^2 + 9.638E^{-9} \times T^3 - 34.1$$

Steam/water

$$HSt = 0.4329 \times T + 3.958E^{-5}T^2 + 1062.2$$
$$HW = T - 32$$

Residue

$$HRs = 0.167 + 1.09E^{-4}T^2 - 2.843E^{-8}T^3 - 12.95$$

Dry flue gas

$$Tk = T + 459.7$$
$$HDFg = -0.1231899E^3 + 0.4065568 \times Tk + 0.5795050E^{-5}Tk^2 + 0.631121E^{-7}Tk^3 - 0.2924434E^{-10}Tk^4 + 0.2491009E^{-14}Tk^5$$

Flue gas

$$HFg = (1 - MFrWFg)HDFg + MFrWFg \times Hwv + MFrRsFg \times HRs$$

6. Calculate the temperature of the flue gas leaving the air heater corrected for no leakage.

Mean specific heat of air

$$MnCpA = \frac{HATFgLv - HAEn}{TFgLv - TAEn} \text{BTU/lb F}$$

Mean specific heat of flue gas

$$MnCpFg = \frac{HFgTFgLv - HFgTFgLvCr}{TFgLv - TFgLvCr} \text{BTU/lb F}$$

$$TFgLvCr = TFgLv + \frac{MnCpA}{MnCpFg}\left(\frac{MqFgLv}{MqFgEn} - 1\right) \times (TFgLv - TAEn)\,°\text{F}$$

where

$HATFgLv$ = enthalpy of air at flue gas leaving temperature
$HAEn$ = enthalpy of air at air entering temperature

$TAEn$ = temperature of air entering
$TfgLv$ = measured temperature of flue gas leaving the air heater
$HfgTFgLv$ = enthalpy of flue gas at flue gas leaving temperature
$HfgTFgLvCr$ = enthalpy of flue gas at flue gas leaving corrected temperature
$MqFgLv$ = total wet flue gas leaving air heater lb/BTU
$MqFgEn$ = total wet flue gas entering air heater lb/BTU

This is an iterative calculation since the corrected temperature is used to determine the mean specific heat of the flue gas.

7. Calculate the efficiency losses.

Dry gas loss percentage

$$QpLDFg = 100 \times MqDFg \times HDFgLvCr$$

where

$MqDFg$ = lb dry flue gas per BTU
$HDFgLvCr$ = enthalpy of dry flue gas at the corrected temperature leaving the air heater.

Water from fuel loss

The water from fuel loss

(1) Loss due to water formed from combustion of hydrogen in fuel

$$QpLH_2F = 100 \times MqWH_2F(HStLvCr - HW\,\mathrm{Re})$$

(2) Loss due to liquid water in fuel

$$QpLWF = 100 \times MqWF(HStLvCr - HW\,\mathrm{Re})$$

(3) Loss due to water vapor in a gaseous fuel

$$QpLWvF = 100 \times MqWvF \times HWvLvCr$$

where

$MqWH_2F$ = moisture from combustion of H_2 in fuel
$HstLvCr$ = enthalpy of steam at the corrected temperature leaving the air heater
$HW\,\mathrm{Re}$ = enthalpy of water at reference temperature
$HwvLvCr$ = enthalpy of water vapor at the corrected temperature leaving the air heater

Loss due to moisture in air

$$QpLWA = 100 \times MFrWA \times MqDA \times HWvLvCr$$

where

$MFrWA$ = specific humidity of air lb H_2O/lb dry air
$MqDA$ = lb of dry air per BTU
$HWvLvCr$ = enthalpy of water vapor at the corrected temperature leaving the air heater

Loss due to unburned combustibles

(1) Loss due to unburned carbon

$$QpLUbC = MpUbC\frac{HHVCR}{HHV}$$

where

$MpUbC$ = lb of unburned carbon per lb of fuel
$HHVCR$ = higher heating value of carbon in refuse = 14,500 BTU/lb
HHV = higher heating value of fuel

Correctly estimating the losses from the system provides a more accurate calculation of the efficiency.

(2) Loss due to unburned hydrogen in residue (not normally present)

$$QpLH_2Rs = \frac{MrRs \times MpH_2Rs \times HHVH_2}{MrF \times HHV}$$

where

$MrRs$ = mass rate of residue
MpH_2Rs = percentage of H_2 in residue (mass weighted for multiple streams)
$HHVH_2$ = higher heating value of H_2 61,100 BTU/lb
MrF = fuel flow lb/hr
HHV = higher heating value of fuel

(3) Loss due to carbon monoxide

$$QpLCO = DVpCO \times MoDFg \times MwCO\frac{HHVCO}{HHV}$$

where

$DVpCO$ = CO percentage dry volume
$MoDFg$ = moles of dry flue gas per lb of fuel
$MwCO$ = molecular weight of CO 28.01
$HHVCO$ = higher heating value of CO 4,347 BTU/lb
HHV = higher heating value of fuel

(4) Loss due to pulverizer rejects

$$Mq\mathrm{Pr} = \frac{Mr\mathrm{Pr}}{MrF}$$
$$QpL\mathrm{Pr} = 100Mq\mathrm{Pr}(HHV\mathrm{Pr} + H\mathrm{Pr})$$

where

$Mr\ \mathrm{Pr}$ = mass rate of pulverizer rejects
MrF = fuel flow

$HHV\,Pr$ = heating value of pulverizer rejects from lab analysis
$H\,Pr$ = enthalpy of pulverizer rejects (use enthalpy of residue at mill outlet temperature)

(5) Loss due to unburned hydrocarbons

$$QpLUbHc = VpHc \times MoFg \times MwHc \frac{HHVHc}{HHV}$$

where

$Vp\,Hc$ = total hydrocarbons percentage dry volume
$Mo\,Fg$ = moles of dry flue gas per lb of fuel
$Mw\,Hc$ = molecular weight of hydrocarbons (use MW of reference gas used for analysis typically propane 44.096)
$HHVHc$ = higher heating value of reference gas used
HHV = higher heating value of fuel

Loss due to sensible heat in residue

$$QpLRs = 100 \sum MqRsz \times HRsz$$

where

$MqRsz$ = residue lb/BTU at specific location
$HRsz$ = enthalpy of residue at temperature of location

Loss due to hot air quality control systems (AQCS)

$$QpLAq = 100[MqFgEn(HFgEn - HFgLv) - (MqFgLv - MqFgEn)(HAAqLv - HALvCr)]$$

where

$MqFgEn$ = lb flue gas per BTU entering AQCS
$MqFgLv$ = lb flue gas per BTU leaving AQCS
$HFgEn$ = enthalpy of flue gas at entering temperature
$HFgLv$ = enthalpy of flue gas at leaving temperature
$HAAqLv$ = enthalpy of wet air at temperature of gas leaving the AQCS
$HALvCr$ = enthalpy of wet air at corrected temperature of gas leaving the air heater

Loss due to air infiltration between the normal boiler exit (typically the gas economizer outlet) and the air heater exit not included in the leakage into hot AQCS:

$$QpLALg = 100MqALg(HALvCr - HALgEn)$$

where

$MqALg$ = lb air per BTU entering air heater
$HALgEn$ = enthalpy of wet air at temperature of air entering air heater
$HALvCr$ = enthalpy of wet air at corrected temperature of gas leaving the air heater

Loss due to formation of NOx

$$QpLNOx = DVpNOx \times MoDFg \times MwNOx \frac{HrNOx}{HHV}$$

where

$DVpNOx$ = NOx percentage dry volume
$MoDFg$ = moles of dry flue gas per lb of fuel
$MwNOx$ = molecular weight of NOx 30.8
$HrNOx$ = heat of formation of NO 38,600 BTU/lb and heat of formation of NO_2 35,630 BTU/lb
HHV = higher heating value of fuel

Loss due to surface radiation

Use the larger of

$$Hcaz = 0.2(TDi)^{1/3}$$

or

$$Hcaz = 0.35VAz^{0.8}$$

$$Hraz = 0.847 + 2.637E^{-3}TDi + 2.94E^{-6}TDi^2 + 1.37E^{-9}TDi^3$$

$$QpLSrc = \sum(Hcaz + Hraz)Afz(TMnAfz - TMnAz)$$

$$QpLSrc = 100\frac{QrLSrc}{MrF \times HHV}$$

where

$Hcaz$ = convection heat transfer coefficient
$Hraz$ = radiation heat transfer coefficient
TDi = temperature of surface–temperature of ambient assumed to be 50 unless for surfaces known to be higher
VAz = air velocity near surface, assumed to be 1.67

Note: TDi and VAz may be measured for the test and multiple areas or they may be assumed as noted above.

Loss due to additional moisture

$$QrLWAd = \sum MrStz(HStLvCr - HW\,Re)$$

$$QpLWAd = 100\frac{QrLWAd}{MrF \times HHV}$$

Loss due to calcinations

$$QrLClh = \sum MrSbk \times MFrClhk \times Hrk$$

$$QpLClh = 100\frac{QrLClh}{MrF \times HHV}$$

Proper calculation of efficiency includes estimates of both losses and credits.

Loss due to water in sorbent

$$QrLWSb = MrWSb\left(HStLvCr - HW\,\mathrm{Re}\right)$$

$$QpLWSb = 100\frac{QrLWSb}{MrF \times HHV}$$

Loss due to wet ashpit

$$QrLAp = 10000 \times ApAf$$

$$QpLAp = 100\frac{QrLAp}{MrF \times HHV}$$

Loss due to recycled streams

(1) Recycled gaseous streams

$$QrLRyFg = MrRyFg\left(HFgCr - HFgEn\right)$$

$$QpLRyFg = 100\frac{QrLRyFg}{MrF \times HHV}$$

(2) Recycled solid streams

$$QrLRyRs = MrRyRs\left(HRsLv - HRsEn\right)$$

$$QpLRyRs = 100\frac{QrLRyRs}{MrF \times HHV}$$

Loss from cooling water

$$QrLCw = \sum MrCwn\left(HWLv - HWEn\right)$$

$$QpLCw = 100\frac{QrLCw}{MrF \times HHV}$$

Loss due to internally supplied air preheating

$$QrLAc = MrSt36\left(HW36 - HW24\right)$$

$$QpLAc = 100\frac{QrLAc}{MrF \times HHV}$$

8. Credits

Credit due to entering dry air

$$QpBDA = 100MqDA \times HDAEn$$

where

$MqDA$ = lb dry air per BTU
$HDAEn$ = enthalpy of dry air at air heater entering temperature

Credit due to moisture in air

$$QpBWA = 100MFrWA \times MqDA \times HWvEn$$

where

$MFrWA$ = specific humidity
$MqDA$ = lb dry air per BTU
$HWvEn$ = enthalpy of water vapor at air heat entering temperature

Credit due to sensible heat in fuel

$$QpBF = \frac{100}{HHV} HFEn$$

where

$HFEn$ = enthalpy of fuel entering
HHV = higher heating value of fuel

Credit due to sulfation

$$QpBSlf = MFrSc \frac{MpSF}{HHV} HRSlf$$

where

$MFrSc$ = mass fraction of sulfur capture
$MpSF$ = mass percentage sulfur in fuel
$HRSlf$ = heat of formation for sulfation
HHV = higher heating value of fuel

Credit due to auxiliary equipment power

(1) Steam driven equipment

$$QrBX = MrStX \frac{HStEn - HStLv}{100} EX$$

$$QpBX = 100 \frac{QrBX}{MrF \times HHV}$$

where

$MrStX$ = mass rate of steam supplied to the equipment
$HStEn$ = enthalpy of steam to the equipment
$HStLv$ = enthalpy of the steam leaving at the exit pressure and the entropy entering
EX = overall drive efficiency

(2) Electrically driven equipment

$$QpBX = 100 \frac{3412 \times QX \frac{EX}{100}}{MrF \times HHV}$$

where

QX = energy input to devices kWh
EX = overall drive efficiency

Credit due to sensible heat in sorbent

$$QpBX = 100\frac{MrSb \times HSbEn}{MrF \times HHV}$$

where

$MrSb$ = mass rate of sorbent entering
$Hsb\ En$ = enthalpy of sorbent entering
MrF = mass rate of fuel entering
HHV = higher heating value of fuel

Credit due to additional energy supplied by additional moisture

$$QrBWAd = \sum MrStz(HStEnz - HW\,\mathrm{Re})$$

$$QpBX = 100\frac{QrBWAd}{MrF \times HHV}$$

where

$MrStz$ = mass flow rate of additional moisture
$HStEnz$ = enthalpy of additional moisture entering
$HW\,\mathrm{Re}$ = enthalpy of water at reference temperature
MrF = mass rate of fuel entering
HHV = higher heating value of fuel

9. Calculate efficiency.

$$EF = 100 - \sum QpL + \sum QpB$$

Spray water needs to be accounted for in the overall efficiency calculation.

BOILER HEAT OUTPUT—TURBINE CYCLE HEAT INPUT

The energy absorbed by the steam in the boiler and sent to the steam turbine plus the energy added in the reheat section is the boiler output.

$$Q_{blr} = (M_{fw} - M_{blowdown}) \times (h_{ms} - h_{fw}) + M_{spray}(h_{ms} - h_{spray}) + M_{CRH}(h_{HRH} - h_{CRH}) + M_{RHSpray}\,(h_{HRH} - h_{RHSpray})$$

Spray Flow by Heat Balance

The spray flow to both the superheater and the reheater may be measured directly or be calculated by a heat balance around the spray station. Determining the spray flow using both methods is a good verification of the data around the spray station.

$$M_{spray} = M_{StmIn}\frac{(h_{stmOut} - h_{stmIn})}{(h_{stmOut} - h_{spray})}$$

The goal of a clean, modern power plant is to minimize overall net plant heat rate to reduce fuel use and minimize emissions.

The calculation of RH spray flow, in cases where there is a high flow rate, can be influenced if there is spray impingement on the downstream thermowell. The liquid droplets vaporizing from the well will reduce the indicated temperature below that of the true average steam temperature leaving the desuperheater station.

Calculation of Reheat Flow

In many steam cycles, there is a small percentage of the steam sent to the high pressure turbine that is sent to the seals and leaks and, thus, is not returned to the boiler for reheating. In addition, there is usually a top feedwater heater, to which extraction steam is sent from the HP exhaust. There may also be, in some cycles, another heater that receives steam from an HP extraction.

$$M_{CRH} = M_{MS} - M_{TurbLeak} - M_{HPExt}$$
$$M_{HRH} = M_{CRH} + M_{RHSpray}$$

Determination of HP-IP Leakage

In many cases, the leakage in the turbine is estimated from the design heat balances. This value is used in the calculation of the cold reheat flow. With certain turbine designs, where the HP and IP are in a single shell, and are separated by a packing gland (sometimes referred to as an "N2" packing), the steam leakage may be significantly higher than expected, due to a worn packing. This situation will usually manifest itself by high RH steam temperatures or excessive RH spray flow and a lower than expected RH pressure drop, turbine flange to turbine flange.

Overall Plant Heat Rate

The overall plant net heat rate can be defined as

$$HR_{Net} = \frac{Q_{blr}}{\eta_{blr}\left(P_{Gross} - P_{Aux}\right)}$$

where

HR_{Net} = net unit heat rate
η_{blr} = boiler efficiency
Q_{blr} = heat absorbed in the boiler and sent to the turbine cycle
P_{Gross} = power, gross
P_{Aux} = power, auxiliary load

By defining the heat rate in this manner, one can dissect the different components to determine where there are deviations from the design. As discussed earlier, calculating boiler efficiency by the energy balance method yields the boiler output. Now dividing the Q_{blr} by the P_{Gross} will yield the turbine cycle heat rate, which can be compared with the design case. A comparison of the current auxiliary load with the design, or reference, auxiliary load will indicate higher than expected losses in that area.

MATT DOOLEY

REFERENCES

1. J. Booth and D. Kautzman, "Estimating the Leakage from HP TUIP Turbine Sections," EPRI Power Plant Performance Monitoring Conferance, 1984, EDRF, Palo Alto, CA.

2. *ASME Performance Test Codes*, PTC 19.3, "Temperature Measurement." New York: American Society of Mechanical Engineers, 2004.

3. P. H. Dike, *Thermoelectric Thermometry*, 3rd ed. Philadelphia: Leeds and Northrup Co., 1958.

4. Chromel and alumel are chromium-nickel and aluminum-nickel alloys respectively. Constantan is a copper alloy.

5. *Annual Book of ASTM Standards*, Section 4, "Magnetic Properties; Metallic Materials for Thermostatic; Electrical Resistance, Heating, Contacts; Temperature Measurement; Illuminating Standards." Philadelphia: American Society for Testing and Materials, 1999.

6. "Orifice Metering of Natural Gas." *ANSI/API 2560. AGA Report No. 3.* New York: American Society of Mechanical Engineers, 1960.

7. J. W. Murdock, "Power Test Code Thermometer Wells," *Transactions of the ASME. Journal of Engineering for Power*, 81, Series A: 403–416, 1959.

8. P. G. W. Hawksley, et al., *Measurement of Solids in Flue Gases*, 2nd ed. London: The Institute of Fuel, 1977.

9. E. S. Cole, "Pitot Tube Practice," *Transactions of the ASME*, 57: 281–294, 1935.

10. C. J. Fechheimer, "Measurement of Static Pressure," *Transactions of the ASME*, 48: 965–977, 1926.

11. R. G. Folsom, "Review of the Pitot Tube," *Transactions of the ASME*, 78: 1447–1460, Oct. 1956.

12. C. L. Burton, "Quantitation of Stack Gas Flow," Reprint from *Journal of the Air Pollution Control Association*, 22(8): 631–635, Aug. 1972.

13. *ASTM Standards*, Part 26, *Gaseous Fuels; Coal and Coke; Atmospheric Analysis*. D 2015, "Test for Gross Calorific Value of Solid Fuel by the Adiabatic Bomb Calorimeter"; D 2961, "Test for Total Moisture in Coal Reduced to No. 8 Top Sieve Size (Limited Purpose Method)"; D 3172, "Proximate Analysis of Coal and Coke"; D 3173, "Test for Moisture in the Analysis Sample of Coal and Coke"; D 3174, "Test for Ash in the Analysis Sample of Coal and Coke"; D 3177 "Test for Total Sulfur in the Analysis Sample of Coal and Coke"; D 3178, "Test for Carbon and Hydrogen in the Analysis Sample of Coal and Coke"; D 3180, "Calculating Coke and Coal Analyses from As-Determined to Different Bases"; D 3286, "Test for Gross Calorific Value of Solid Fuel by the Isothermal-Jacket Bomb Calorimeter"; D 3302, "Test for Total Moisture in Coal"; Philadelphia: American Society for Testing and Materials, latest edition 2008.

Maintaining Availability: Condition Assessment and Remaining Life Analysis

Chapter **Fourteen**

In many respects, the electric utility or independent power producer is unique. Its product, the day-to-day output of electric energy, is supplied on demand, with no opportunity to be inventoried or stored. Thus, the network of generation, transmission, and distribution equipment through which the electricity is delivered must have high operating integrity to ensure optimum reliability of supply, which is one of the power industry's highest priorities.

In addition, because of the long lead time required to add or contract for new capacity, it is necessary for the industry to plan to build generating equipment years in advance of the required service dates to supply future electric loads. Further, the power industry ranks among the most capital intensive, in terms of dollars of investment per dollar of revenue. This chapter explores the implications of reliability of supply and plant availability in the generation of steam electric power by fossil fired plants.

AVAILABILITY

The availability of an electric power plant is important to both system reliability and generating company profit. Improving availability only slightly can save considerably on reserve generating capacity and costly replacement power. As one measure of reliability, published availability statistics are of considerable interest, as the power industry emphasizes producing the most energy for the least cost.

The importance of high plant availability and reliability has spurred the U.S. Department of Energy (DOE), the Edison Electric Institute (EEI), and the Electric Power Research Institute (EPRI) to pursue programs that identify means of improving plant performance.[1] Some state and federal laws concerning electrical plant reliability already have been enacted. As world demand for electricity continues to increase steadily, the industry places tremendous importance on power generating plant availability. Fluctuations in fuel costs are felt in virtually all energy sources with a significant impact on political, social, and economic activities.

PRODUCTIVITY INDICES

The utility industry uses several indices to evaluate electric generating unit reliability, availability, and productivity, which, in essence, is a measure of the ability of a plant to produce electricity on demand. The North American Electric Reliability Corporation (NERC) defined the following performance indices as the principle measurement values for the power industry. The performance indices for an individual unit are based on the standard definitions by IEEE Power Engineering Society Standards 762-2006.

Net Capacity Factor (NCF), percentage =

$$\frac{\text{Net Actual Annual Generation (NAAG) in MWh}}{\text{Period Hours (PH)} \times \text{Net Maximum Capacity (NMC)}} \times 100$$

Service Factor (SF), percentage =

$$\frac{\text{Service Hours (SH)}}{\text{Period Hours (PH)}} \times 100$$

$$\text{Availability Factor (AF), percentage} = \frac{\text{Available Hours (AH)}}{\text{Period Hours (PH)}} \times 100$$

$$\text{Equivalent Availability Factor (EAF), percentage} = \frac{[\text{Available Hours (AH)} - (\text{Equivalent Unit Derated Hours} + \text{Equivalent Seasonal Derated Hrs})]}{\text{Period Hours (PH)}} \times 100$$

$$\text{Commercial Availability (CA), percentage} = \frac{\text{Available Hours when market price of power is greater than the cost of fuel}}{\text{Period Hours (PH)}} \times 100$$

$$\text{Forced Outage Rate (FOR), percentage} = \frac{\text{Forced Outage Hours (FOH)}}{\text{Service Hours (SH)} + \text{Forced Outage Hours (FOH)}} \times 100$$

$$\text{Equivalent Forced Outage Rate (EFOR)} = \frac{\text{Forced Outage Hours (FOH)} + \text{Equivalent Forced Derated Hours (EFDH)}}{\text{Forced Outage Hours (FOH)} + \text{Service Hours (SH)} + \text{Equivalent Forced Derated Hours (EFDH) during Reserve Shutdown}} \times 100$$

where:

Net Maximum Capacity (NMC) = the capacity that a unit can sustain when not restricted by ambient conditions.

Available Hours (AH) = the period of time during which a unit or major piece of equipment is capable of providing service, whether it is actually in service or not, and regardless of capacity level that is provided.

Period Hours (PH) = the number of clock hours that the unit is in the "active state" (usually taken as one year). The active state includes both the available condition (with the unit operating from zero to full load) and the no-load condition during forced or scheduled outages. It does not include any period in which a unit is on inactive reserve, mothballed, or retired

Service Hours (SH) = the total number of hours the unit is electrically connected to the transmission system and performing generating functions.

Forced Outage Hours (FOH) = the sum of all hours during which a boiler or other major equipment is unavailable because of a forced outage

(component failure or other condition requiring that the unit be removed from service immediately, or up to and including the next weekend).

Equivalent Forced Derated Hours (EFDH) = the product of the hours when the unit was forced to reduce load due to unforeseen maintenance issues and the amount of the reduction in capacity, divided by the rated capacity.

Planned Derated Hours (PDH) = The product of the hours when the unit was scheduled to reduce load and the amount of the reduction in capacity, divided by the rated capacity.

MEASURING AVAILABILITY

Each equation identifies only a portion of the performance measurement for a generating unit. No single index tells the overall performance story for a unit, a fact that is apparent from *Figure 14-1*. Capacity factor, for instance, is not a true indicator of a unit's reliability, because actual generation may be limited by economic or environmental dispatch, as well as forced and scheduled outages and deratings. This is particularly true with older units, which typically have higher heat rates (lower thermal efficiencies) than more modern units. The annual availability factor (AF) establishes only the percentage of time during the year that the unit was capable of producing power. This factor includes time when the unit was capable of generating power but was not in service because more efficient units were being used. Thus, the AF does not measure the ability of a unit to operate at a specific power level when called on by the dispatcher. Rather, it measures only the capability of the unit to produce at a power level ranging from 0–100% of its rated capacity. The equivalent availability index provides for an AF adjustment to account for the effect of partial deratings (losses in electrical power output capability) from partial forced and scheduled outages. Essentially, the index is equivalent to the percentage of the year during which the unit was available for operation at full capacity.

What equivalent availability does not indicate is whether an outage was forced or planned. A forced outage is generally more costly in terms of both replacement power and load supply ability. The forced outage rate (FOR) measures this performance. Net capacity factor (NCF) is, in effect, the "bottom line" result and also includes

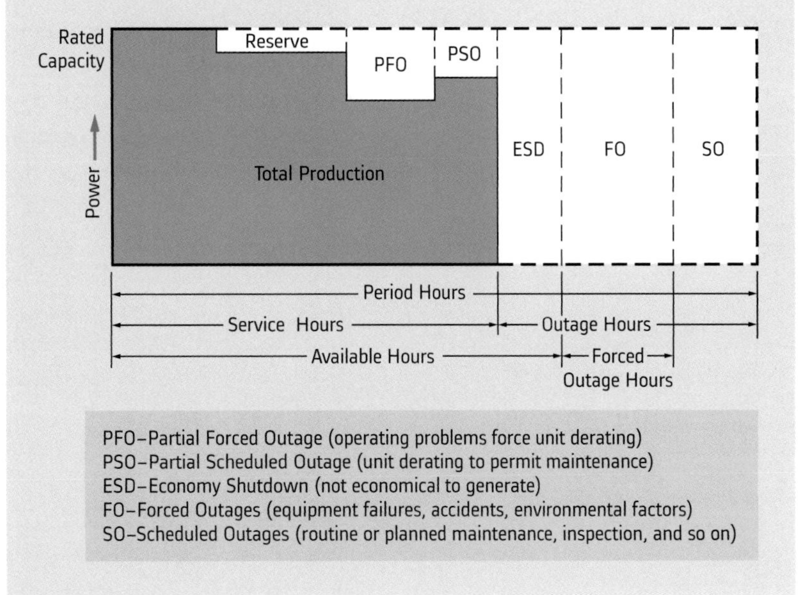

Figure 14-1 | Factors affecting productivity of power plants

discretionary cutbacks in output by a generating company.

A relatively new index called commercial availability (CA) attempts to measure the financial impact of plant availability. A power plant produces net revenue for the owner when the plant operates while the market price of power is greater than the variable cost of operating the plant. For most utility power plants the major contributor to variable costs is the cost of fuel (usually greater than 95% of variable costs). The magnitude of this difference between the market price of power and fuel costs (in $/MWh) is measured by an index called the "spark spread" for gas-fired units and "dark spread" for coal-fired units. If the spark spread or dark spread is positive, an owner can make a net revenue gain by operating the plant. The larger the spark spread or dark spread, the more profitable it is to operate the plant. Because of this, some owners measure CA by weighting the operating hours by the spark spread or dark spread. In either case, CA is gaining wider use as a measure of power plant performance by independent power producers and utilities that are operating in a deregulated, competitive power market environment.

Another index that is easier to calculate, and can be used as a financial indicator of plant performance, is the equivalent forced outage rate (EFOR). Since EFOR includes forced outages and forced derates when the unit is asked to be available, it is often used as a measure of financial performance.

Each index, therefore, is limited to defining a specific aspect of power plant performance. To evaluate the overall performance of a power plant requires subjective and collective review of these and other indices.

TABLE 14-1 | 1990–2007 GENERATING UNIT STATISTICS FROM THE NORTH AMERICAN ELECTRIC RELIABILITY COUNCIL (NERC) GENERATING AVAILABILITY REPORT (GAR)

Unit Type	No. of Units	NCF, %	SF, %	AF, %	EAF, %	FOR, %	EFOR, %
Fossil-Steam	1,808	54.65	64.63	86.47	84.02	5.44	7.74
Nuclear	136	78.43	81.36	82.53	79.43	6.80	8.87
Gas Turbine/Jet Engine	1,901	2.91	3.43	91.98	87.85	41.12	44.82
Diesel	236	3.14	2.92	95.55	95.35	47.36	48.05
Pumped Storage/ Hydro	1,712	38.86	55.98	89.63	89.20	3.70	3.76
Fluidized Bed	11	61.30	72.85	82.18	76.99	8.14	10.84
Multi-boiler/ Multi-turbine	94	48.41	58.10	89.86	84.52	5.39	9.84
Geothermal	43	60.30	86.50	92.67	73.58	1.78	19.95
Combined Cycle	538	37.85	50.27	89.38	85.51	6.11	8.24
Cogenerator	102	53.83	71.77	91.65	88.46	4.16	5.62

NCF - Net Capacity Factor
SF - Service Factor
AF - Availability Factor
EAF - Equivalent Availability Factor
FOR - Forced Outage Rate
EFOR - Equivalent Forced Outage Rate

AVAILABILITY STATISTICS

Table 14-1 is a sample of the Generating Unit Statistics given by the Generating Availability Data System (GADS) of NERC for the period 1990 to 2007. IEEE Standard 762 and equations and definitions are taken from the short-form summary of its Generating Availability Report.[2] This tabulation illustrates the differences in six performance factors for equipment currently chosen for electrical power generation in the United States during this time period.

Note that fossil-fired steam generators (units that use coal, oil, or gas as the primary fuel) have lower AFs than jet engines (aircraft-derivative gas turbines), gas turbines (stationary industrial type), and diesel engines. This is because of the extended planned outages taken on such units for repair, maintenance, and upgrading, usually in anticipation of major, power generation campaigns. The internal combustion equipment, which is smaller on average than the steam generators, is closer to the ground, often has many replaceable modules, and has inherently shorter preventive maintenance time. The lower downtime for maintenance translates into a higher AF.

There has been a trend in recent years to extend the time between major, planned outages for coal-fired utility power plants. Up until the mid-1980s, it was common practice to have annual maintenance outages for most utility coal-fired plants. Since then, a number of utilities have extended times between major maintenance outages to 18, 24, and in some cases 36 months. This improves plant availability. However, there is a trade-off with increases in forced outages rates, FOR, and EFOR. If these forced outages occur at times of high power demand and/or high market prices for electricity, then the benefits of extended time between planned outages can be more than offset by the costs of replacement power or lost energy revenues.

THE POWER PRODUCER'S VIEW OF AVAILABILITY

A major reason for improving availability in electricity production is a matter of economics, which essentially relates to the high cost of constructing power generating facilities. The basics of power plant economics are discussed in more detail in Chapter 1. Better plant availability could have a significant effect on plans for the construction or deferment of new plants. On the other hand, long-term outages from repeated boiler tube leaks, turbine blade losses, or other plant equipment problems could force a utility either to install additional capacity or to purchase replacement power (if it is available) at high cost.

RESERVE MARGINS

One measure of adequate generating capacity is the reserve margin in excess of the peak load demand. This margin offers protection against unanticipated demand growth, forced outages, derating, and other contingencies. In the United States, a reserve margin of about 20% is generally considered acceptable. Because of regulatory and/or political factors, certain geographical regions have much less reserve than others, accentuating the requirement for highly reliable generating facilities and adequate transmission interconnections. In all cases, outages of large, highly efficient, base load equipment increase generating costs.

PROBLEMS AND THEIR ROOT CAUSES

The underlying causes of equipment problems producing forced outages and load restrictions may be difficult to isolate, but their correction requires identification. Treatment of the symptoms will neither cure a power plant "disease" nor correct a disorder that may, in some instances, be a design or construction deficiency. Chapter 11 emphasizes the importance of determining the root cause of incidents causing forced outages and load restrictions. The following are some brief but commonplace examples.

In the case of waterwall tube ruptures, poor feedwater quality is often the major contributing factor. With higher operating pressures, feedwater quality becomes even more critical. This issue is discussed in more detail in Chapter 9.

Degradation of coal properties adversely affects the capability of boiler auxiliaries. Its direct effect on availability is difficult to quantify. When a fossil fuel fired steam generator uses a lower quality fuel than the original design fuel, the capability of components such as pulverizers, fans, economizer, and air heaters frequently limits unit capacity and reduces generating reserves. If auxiliaries are operated continuously at or near their peak capability without proper maintenance, problems generally will develop.

The addition of air quality control systems may require increased induced draft fan capacity. Furnace framing structural design to withstand negative pressures can be increased significantly to provide greater protection against implosion.[3] Usually the cost of the upgrade is worth the investment due to the degree of protection it provides.

Damage to fan housings, ductwork, and stack liners, resulting from fan-induced duct vibrations caused by pressure pulsations in centrifugal fans, can be a significant problem. In large fans, it is a common practice to specify equipment that does not emit damaging pulsations. An example of this type of design is the requirement of vane-controlled instead of louvered-damper-controlled fans whenever possible. A second example is the specification of dorsal fins or an equivalent in all vane-controlled fans. The dorsal fin assembly eliminates high pulsations by destroying the vortex precession. Without this corrective device, some installations experience destructive levels of vibration. Stipulating equipment with these features limits the selection, but markedly reduces fan/duct vibration incidents.[4]

A commonly overlooked resource in trying to determine the root cause of a problem can be plant or equipment supplier personnel who have practical knowledge of the complete steam generator cycle or individual equipment. Although analysis based on computer systems can pinpoint or isolate the problem area, many times it is the experienced-based knowledge of personnel, even at the lowest levels of an organization, who can be more effective in resolving the problem. Their deductive reasoning is usually based on empirical data, such as operational experience, noise levels, unusual smells, or visual changes in a given area. This type of data usually cannot be designed into a computer program. This information, even if it is considered trivial, should not be overlooked when trying to determine the root cause of a problem.

AVAILABILITY/RELIABILITY AND LIFE CONTINUATION

In consideration of many factors, electric utilities and owners of large industrial boilers have often redirected their resources to the improvement and the continuation of life of existing equipment.[5,6]

Many large fossil plants were originally designed as base load units, intended to run steadily with as few starts and stops as possible. However many of these large units have been relegated to cycling duty, which requires an increase in the number of start-ups, shutdowns, and load swings above those contemplated in the original design. As the cost and difficulty of building new units has increased, many coal-fired steam generators have returned to base loaded operation. However, some of these units are older and age is taking its toll on them. Thick metal parts, for example, experience substantially increased thermal stress due to cycling. These stresses, in turn, affect the material properties of the components and make them more susceptible to failure through fatigue, creep, and other conditions. Water chemistry effects on internal corrosion, external gas-side corrosion, erosion, and other mechanisms can also significantly affect boiler life.

Owners, therefore, need to have qualified engineers inspect for the presence of these anomalies on existing plant equipment and determine how they might influence the performance of both individual components and the system in general. Once this is done, a judgment can be made as to the remaining life of the critical components and whether or not it would be economically feasible to keep the unit operational for some additional period of time.

While there are uncertainties with any life prediction method, an objective assessment is a prerequisite in any plant life continuation program. The combination of sound preplanning, inspection, examination, and utilization of the best available life-prediction methodology will permit meaningful conclusions to be drawn about the current condition of a steam generator and its ancillaries, and of its capability to operate beyond its originally planned retirement date. Often the most effective approach is a combination of operational and maintenance changes and material or component modifications.[7]

MAINTAINING AVAILABILITY

In this section, techniques of continuing the intended life of power plant equipment are introduced. As intimated earlier, a decrease in the availability of any mechanical or electrical equipment is most often the result of a conscious decision by the owner. The process of life continuation (keeping a steam electric plant in good condition so that it can continue to operate in active and

Good operating maintenance practices lead to higher availability.

Obtaining more use out of existing equipment provides for lower cost electricity to the customer.

efficient base load or peaking service for some undefined length of time) is a management decision to repair, replace, rebuild, or upgrade only as necessary to accomplish that end. Any activities exceeding that represent a judgment to extend life to, say, 55 or 60 years, which is probably greater than the executives originally purchasing the equipment contemplated.

WHY A NEED FOR LIFE CONTINUATION?

For a variety of reasons, the construction of new base load type, electrical generating capacity can be difficult to implement. There are often competing concerns. Permits may be difficult to obtain. Costs may be too high. There may be public opposition to a new plant. Thus, power producers have to evaluate the cost of life continuation, which may include the cost of environmental compliance equipment, versus the investment for replacement equipment. The engineering analysis that precedes a life continuation program must be very thorough and positive in its prediction of remaining life of the components that are not to be modified or replaced. The engineers responsible for the replacement or upgrading of pressure parts and other components subject to thermal or pressure stress, or to corrosion or erosion, must assure the owner that the life of the unit will in fact continue as intended. It behooves owners to continue in-service, preventive, and planned maintenance on a timely basis, in order to prevent any loss in capacity of power plant equipment that might result from the deferral of such work. Any temporary reductions in capacity must be avoided because they effectively could be made permanent through legal interpretations of environmental regulations.[8]

ASSESSMENT OF REMAINING LIFE OF STEAM GENERATOR COMPONENTS

Condition assessment, the evaluative process that precedes any actual life continuation activity, is essentially a review of plant operational and maintenance records plus engineering evaluation of findings from component inspection. This can lead to a prediction of expected safe operating life from the date of the inspection. The process might pinpoint the most sensitive component, the one that will probably run out of life first, but the estimate of remaining life is strictly an engineering judgment and is not a calculated value. Any repairs that are indicated, or any upgrading of components or subsystems to the state-of-the-art level that are recommended, are only to allow the unit to continue to operate in what is felt to be a safe manner.

A condition assessment study will identify components having time independent or time dependent characteristics that will affect their service life. Life predictions in the time independent regime involve knowledge of when effective tube-wall thickness or metal characteristics will be reduced to the point of failure. Essentially, there is no deterioration of material strength properties over time; that is, creep does not occur. The rate of corrosion, erosion, or crack propagation must be

established to predict life, taking into account safety factors in the American Society of Mechanical Engineers (ASME) Boiler Code as well as realistic, long term, future operating conditions. In instances where observable distress is incident related (rather than time related), such as with caustic attack, hydrogen damage, or pitting, life predictions are not practical.

The situation in the time dependent regime is much different. Because of creep damage along grain boundaries, components in the time dependent temperature range can rupture with essentially no wall loss. Such components have a finite life because their strength-retaining capability is diminishing with time. Uncertainties in life continuation studies often relate to predicting metal behavior in the time dependent regime, especially for thick walled, pressure containing elements.

Design Code Aspects

Before discussing what is involved in the remaining life analysis of thick walled components, it is important to understand what is not involved. Life analyses are not a simple review of the design vis-à-vis the ASME/American National Standards Institute (ANSI) Codes and a rubber stamp to say that the design meets the Code and is, therefore, satisfactory. The fact is that, if the unit met the Codes when it was designed, then, unless there are such effects as thinning present, it will meet the Codes now. The reason for this is that the Codes (to which thick components are built) do not explicitly consider the effects of time, nature of service, and fluctuations in load. To understand the reasons for this, it is necessary to consider some of the philosophy behind their development.

First, the Codes are design tools. They are also, in a very real sense, some of the earliest expert systems. Their purpose is the enforcement of design rules that ensure a low probability of failure by specifying the minimum allowable thicknesses of components made of approved materials fabricated in a stated manner.

Second, the philosophy of the Codes is based on such concepts as:

- Allowed materials are ductile and, therefore, in many cases, forgiving.
- Life, operational effects, material variability, local stresses, and other similar effects are not directly considered but are expected to be accounted for by the conservatism applied in setting the allowable material properties.

Design rules are developed by consensus within groups of acknowledged experts and are subject to multiple levels of review. Being developed in this way, there may be no precise physical justification for some of the rules.

The result of this type of approach is that the actual stress in a local region of a properly designed component may exceed the allowable stress given in the Code being used. This does not mean that the component is unsafe, but only that the published values of allowable stresses for the material are sufficiently conservative to ensure that the resulting component will be safe, even without considering local effects that may occur in design, manufacture, field construction, or operation.

Unfortunately, the simplifications that make for an excellent design tool destroy the usefulness of the Codes as devices for predicting the life of a component with any precision. The fact is that the life of a component is intimately related to the actual local stresses, temperatures, and material properties. Ignorance of any one of these has a significant effect on the accuracy with which life can be predicted. The Codes ignore all of these and, as a result, while it is possible to manipulate such a Code to obtain a value for the life of a component, any life obtained from such an approach may be in error by orders of magnitude.[9,10]

Failure Mechanisms

In a well designed and well manufactured, high-pressure component, unexpected loading and/or environmental situations can cause failure. A simple design review and an evaluation of inspection results generally will confirm the quality of the design and manufacturing.

The loading and environmental situations that can adversely affect components are:

1. Water chemistry effects
2. External corrosion
3. External wastage due to erosion
4. Change in thermal conductivity due to scale buildup
5. Service at temperatures and/or pressures above design conditions
6. Changes in the behavior of support structures
7. Abnormal conditions such as temperature and flow misdistributions or defective support systems
8. In-service origination of corrosion sites
9. Non-linear temperature and pressure start-up ramps
10. Faster-than-design start-ups and shutdowns
11. Excessive cycling

Items 1 and 2 are not in general amenable to analytical approaches as discussed in previous chapters, and are beyond the scope of the present treatment. Items 3 and 4, although they can be analyzed, are usually associated with tubular components in the gas pass and, as such, are not generically considered as relevant to thick walled components. The principal situations to be considered are therefore Items 5 through 11. Some of these, such as thermal transients resulting in cracking of internal scale and exposure of corrosion sites, are not currently capable of being analyzed, and will therefore not be considered here.

The parameters that affect the life of a component are the local values of stress and temperature, and its material properties. Component life not only depends on these parameters, it is extremely sensitive to variations in them. The effects of stress can be appreciated if one considers a component designed such that its thickness is just equal to that required by the Code for operation at 1,000°F (540°C). If, in any part of such a component, the local stress is a mere 12% greater than the Code allowable value, then the life of the component will be halved. As an example, consider both unpenetrated and penetrated cylinders designed such that their thicknesses are precisely that

required by ASME Section I. As far as the Code is concerned these two components are equivalent. However, a detailed stress analysis shows that the local stresses are significantly different. High local stresses will be somewhat relaxed over time by creep effects and, in fact, the location of the high stress areas will move from the inner surface to the outer surface. However, it is a fact that the lives of the two components are not the same and are probably significantly different.

Assuming the same parameters as in the previous example, then a 17°F (9.5°C) increase in local temperature above the design assumptions will also reduce the life of the component by half. This is due to the change in material properties with temperature. As an example, temperature variations along a header can be significant and some allowance is made for this in the design process. However, this temperature distribution is not precisely predictable, nor is it reproducible between similar units. Aside from the safety aspect, from the user's point of view it is just as bad to underestimate the remaining life as it is to overestimate it. The percentage of deviations from design stress and design temperature required to halve the life of a typical component are shown in *Figure 14-2* as functions of design temperature.

The third variable involved is the material of the component itself. The properties of any single material specification are extremely variable, particularly those that affect the life of a component. For instance, at 1,000°F there is a factor of five between the predicted life of a component obtained using minimum properties and that obtained using mean properties. The difference between mean properties and maximum properties would involve an additional factor of five.

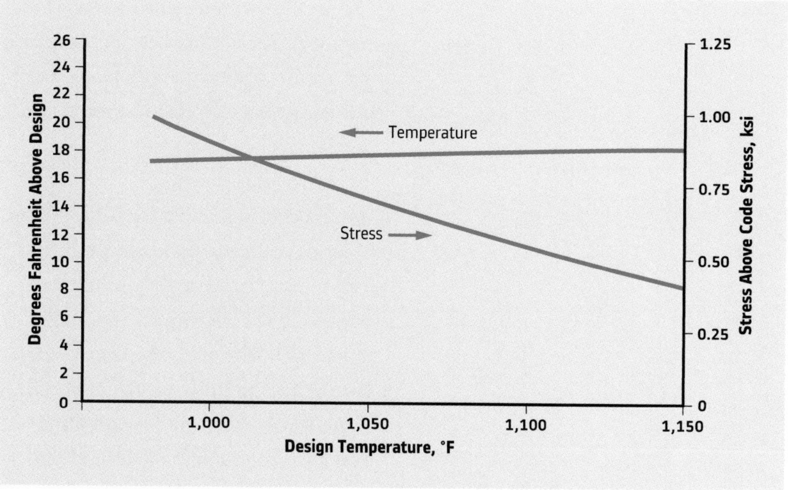

Figure 14-2 | Effect of deviations from design for 2¼% Cr, 1% Mo steel, to reduce component life by half

If one has no information about the material other than its specification, then the minimum material properties have to be used to predict life. Using this approach, the predicted life may be underestimated by as much as a factor of 25, purely as a result of the variability of material properties. *Figure 14-3* shows the minimum and mean lives of a component as a function of operating temperature assuming the actual stress is the allowable ASME Code value.

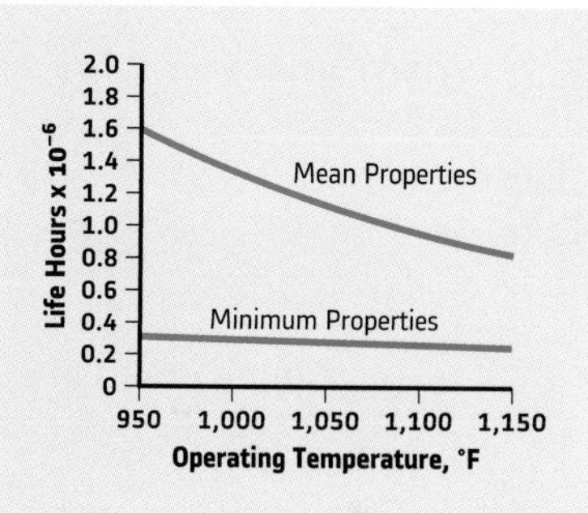

Figure 14-3 | Life versus temperature at ASME code allowable stress (material: 2¼% Cr, 1% Mo steel)

The above effects apply even if the component is operated purely in steady state, that is, with no variation in thermal, mechanical, and/or pressure loadings. In fact, the component undergoes fluctuations in these loadings both in a gross fashion during start-up and shutdown of the system and, in a minor way, during operation. Although the Code does not require it, the manufacturer of a steam generator specifies a start-up rate to limit potential damage to the system. However, this start-up is assumed to be smooth and, for stress analysis purposes, linear. In fact, the change in loadings during start-up can be extremely nonlinear as various subsystems are modulated. In addition, although the shutdown is assumed to be a mirror image of the start-up, the transients in this situation are often even more severe than in the start-up. The effect of transient loadings, particularly in temperature, can be very severe and result in local cyclic plastic deformation that can lead to fatigue failure in a relatively low number of cycles.[9,10]

As described earlier, there are two principal types of situations that can be considered in the determination of the life of thick walled components. The first, in the time-dependent regime, is the high temperature pseudo-steady-state loading where the creep of the material is the phenomenon that leads to failure. The second, in the time-independent regime, is the cyclic plasticity that occurs during start-up and shutdown that can lead to low-cycle-fatigue failures.

CREEP. Creep is the degradation of material properties that occurs with time at temperature. It happens even at low temperatures and somewhat differently in the heat-affected zone of a weld than in the base metal. An analysis that does not correctly include the effects of creep may well predict failure in an incorrect location. This is because the damage resulting from creep occurs throughout the life of a component and is exhibited as permanent deformation. This permanent deformation allows a highly stressed area to shed load to a less highly stressed area. Such a redistribution of load can be significant. In the case of a cylinder under internal pressure, if creep is not present the highest stress will be on the inside surface. If the cylinder is operating at creep temperatures, however, the highest stress area will, after time, be on the outside surface and that is where failure will originate.

FATIGUE. Fatigue is the process in which materials fail under cyclic loading. For thick walled components of high pressure steam generators, the transient thermal effects that occur during start-up and shutdown produce the principal loading that can cause damage. These events are severe but, fortunately, relatively infrequent. When the transient events within a start-up or shutdown are considered, the total number of cycles during the life of a unit tends to be below 10,000. If failure occurs in fewer than 10,000 cycles, it is termed "low-cycle fatigue." It is characterized by local strains in the region of failure that are in excess of the yield point of the material, with the result that the material undergoes plastic flow.

Whenever fatigue failure occurs, it is initiated at a free surface even though this free surface may be at a subsurface flaw. In low-cycle fatigue, this initiation is followed by crack growth through a region of previously plastically strained material. Finally, the

crack propagates through the rest of the component, through regions that originally saw only elastic strains, and the component fails. Crack initiation occurs at a very early time in life (less than 5% of the number of cycles to failure). The surface defect is usually located at a persistent slip band where material extrusions or intrusions occur as a result of cyclic plastic flow. These slip bands occur on planes of maximum principal shear stress although the direction of opening will be that of the maximum principal normal stress. Although slip bands occur adjacent to the crack, as soon as the crack starts to open, the stress on these adjacent defects is relieved and crack growth is generally limited to a single crack. This is different from the creep situation where gross material degradation occurs throughout the region adjacent to the main crack.

METAL-TEMPERATURE DETERMINATION. Without reasonably accurate estimates of metal temperature, stress-rupture life predictions, whether based on minimum or average strength properties, cannot be accurate. There is research data on the growth of steam-side oxide scales on the low alloy, ferritic steels used in steam generators.[11] At elevated temperatures, the internal surfaces of pressure parts will slowly oxidize and form an indigenous oxide scale. The rate of oxidation is a function of the internal surface temperature, the type of material, and the time at temperature. It is possible to infer a "historical" metal temperature of a tube sample by measurement of the oxide scale thickness, when there is knowledge of the rate of heat transfer, scale conductivity, scale growth rate, and the length of service. Using such data, the past temperature exposure of a tube can be approximated if the age and thickness of the oxide scale are known. Estimates of this kind, of necessity, assume unchanging heat input to the tube, and constant steam-side conditions.[11]

Determination of Critical Components

A life continuation study is not solely a boiler inspection program, or just nondestructive testing of unit components, or only a prediction of remaining life of critical items. Although elements of these are present, timing is also an important issue in the plant life continuation concept. Also, component assessment should not be considered a one-time event. Life evaluation efforts should be a continuing process, especially on units that are operating in excess of their original design life. Instead of inspecting all components at the same time, a plan should be created to continually inspect critical components periodically as the plant continues to operate. This information should be documented, tracked, and obtained once again in a continuing assessment plan.

Component assessment is not a one-time event. Remaining life evaluation is an important safety analysis as well.

It is not feasible, for economic reasons, to evaluate in detail the life of every component in a steam generator; nor is this necessary. The first step in any life continuation study, whatever the level of complexity involved, is therefore the determination of what are the critical components. The initial step in the determination of criticality is an assessment of the consequences of a failure. If the consequences of the

Experience is a key factor in judging which components are of critical importance and need further analysis.

loss of a component are significant, then that component meets the first test of criticality.

If the component is one of many similar components with similar loadings and the failure of any one of these components does not result in significant consequences, then it may be that this class of component need not be considered critical. The reasoning behind this is that there will be a distribution in the actual lives of these components and the actual failure rate can be used as the input to the decision as to whether or not it is necessary to replace a system made up of these components. This is usually the case in systems that consist primarily of tubing. The failure of most other components containing high pressure water or steam would be considered significant.

DESIGN PARAMETERS. The basic parameter to be considered in evaluating the criticality of a component is its design temperature. The fact that a part is designed to operate in the time-dependent regime identifies it as having a finite life and tentatively places it within the class of critical components. Generally, this includes the final superheater outlet header and the hot reheater outlet header.

GEOMETRIC PARAMETERS. Components that are excessively thick may well be sensitive to even relatively slow transients. This is generally not a problem with components fabricated by steam generator manufacturers, but there may be a problem with purchased fittings (tees and elbows) and components such as valves and pump casings.[12]

A second geometric consideration is that of configurational complexity. Geometrically simple components often can be eliminated from the list of critical components because of an adjacent one that is more geometrically complex. The reason for this is that, because of the way that design codes handle these, a more complex geometry will generally have higher local stresses than a simple one.

EXPERIENCE. The principal guide to determining which of the components that passed the first tests of criticality are, in fact, critical is experience, either generic or plant-specific. Generic experience is that knowledge that has been gained from other studies and from observations within the operating company, the manufacturer's organization, and the technical community as a whole. Plant-specific experience involves contractors' personnel and records, as well as those of the owner, and includes such items as knowledge of previous failures and over-temperature operation. It also involves any inspection results. This suggests that the criticality of a component can change following the inspection portion of a life continuation program. Evidence of distorted or discolored components, cracks in unusual areas, and missing or defective support structures would all cause reassessment of associated components.

PRINCIPAL CRITICAL COMPONENTS IN STEAM GENERATORS. Experience indicates that there are a number of components that should be considered as critical items. The first three of these have experienced difficulties very frequently and should always be considered. An examination of plant records may remove some of the others from the list.

- The final superheater outlet header and the main steam piping system
- The economizer inlet header
- The high temperature reheater outlet header and the hot reheat piping system
- Other reheater outlet headers and piping
- Other superheater outlet headers and desuperheater systems, particularly where there are indications of higher-than-design levels of desuperheating
- Superheater and reheater inlet headers

Approaches to Remaining Life Evaluation

There are many different ways to evaluate what has happened to a component and what its expected remaining life will be, with different strategies for pressure vessels and piping. There are five general levels of complexity:

- The design-basis approach
- The operating-records approach
- The pressure and temperature test-data approach
- The material-sampling approach
- Online monitoring and analysis

As the level of analysis increases, confidence in the results increases, as does cost.

DESIGN BASIS APPROACH. Manufacturers design steam generators to the customer's specifications of pressure and temperature. Each manufacturer has its own design procedures. As with the ASME Boiler Code (or equivalent international codes), this process is an expert system in that it uses constants and coefficients based on experience. Using this procedure, a design is made with the Code used as a design tool to ensure that its requirements are met. In other words, the stresses for the design conditions, calculated in the way that the Code requires, are confirmed to be no greater than the Code-allowable stresses for the specified material at the design temperature. What this means is that the sections will always be at least as thick as the Code requires and often much thicker. In particular, it is frequently standard practice to make the thickness of a cylindrical component equal to the next commonly available size above the precise thickness required by the Code. Fabrication requirements may also impose a thickness requirement.

Having arrived at the design criteria for any given component, and what should be its minimum allowable thickness, a first-order assessment of plant life can be made with some confirmation from plant records of operational conditions. In most cases, this will say that the majority of high temperature components are close to, or have passed, their useful life and that the low temperature components are satisfactory, in spite of possible physical evidence of damage. In most instances, this approach is just a screening tool at best.

OPERATING RECORDS APPROACH. This level uses the design basis approach with augmentation by plant records. With the advent of reasonable costs of analytical modeling, this type of evaluation is included, although it uses assumed linear ramp rates as input loading data. Minimum material properties and nominal sizes are used.

The analytical tool used is a sophisticated heat-transfer and stress analysis computer program that includes the effects of creep and plasticity. As such, it can overcome the problems of the design-based approach by evaluating the effects of start-ups and shutdowns. However, since these transients are assumed to be linear, this level still ignores their nonlinear nature and is, therefore, nonconservative. This problem can be overcome to some extent by using generic data taken from similar units but, because of the idiosyncrasies of individual units, a high level of uncertainty remains. In general, this approach is not recommended because it is frequently assumed that, since a sophisticated analysis is performed, a reliable answer is obtained. This is not the case and care should be taken to understand this concern.[13]

THE PRESSURE AND TEMPERATURE TEST DATA APPROACH. This approach uses transient pressure, temperature, and flow data, taken during operation, as input for the computer program mentioned above. Installing thermocouples and pressure transmitters on the components under consideration and operating the unit specifically to obtain this data would be desirable. A more cost-effective approach is to install a temporary data acquisition and analysis system so that the evaluation can be done online during normal operation. Such an approach avoids the costs of a special test and the associated data handling, and provides the owner with immediate information about what aspects of unit operation are most damaging.

This analysis also uses the measured thickness of components and incorporates the other results of an inspection program.[14] Apart from the uncertainty that the test data may not be representative of past operations, the only other question in this type of approach is the lack of actual material data. As a result, minimum material properties have to be used to provide a lower bound for remaining life. The use of actual test data allows the prediction of the effects of changes in future operation and also identifies possibly unknown sources of problems such as condensate flow events.

THE MATERIAL SAMPLING APPROACH. The next level of sophistication is to take samples of the material present in the components and, after performing accelerated creep tests on these samples, to incorporate this data into the evaluation. This testing is fairly expensive and care needs to be taken to ensure that these results are used correctly.

One requirement for applying accelerated creep test results to actual components is that creep testing be performed at the stress level that the component sees during operation. It therefore introduces errors to perform these tests at stresses that derive from a design approach. The difficulty is that, during operation at elevated temperature, the stress in the component is redistributed by creep relaxation and as a result the operating stress will be significantly different from the design stress. Another aspect of this approach is that, in general, to avoid creating problems with the component, the material sample has to be taken from an area removed from geometrical discontinuities. Unfortunately, in most cases, the critical areas are precisely those areas that have to be avoided during sampling. As a result, unless miniature samples can be taken from the highly stressed areas, it is necessary to translate the results of the accelerated creep testing into the remaining life at the critical areas. This means that, by the use of plant history and analytical techniques, the original creep properties of the material have to be obtained. These can then be applied to the analysis of the critical areas.

Finally, it is, unfortunately, a fact that high pressure components are fabricated from substructures made up of different heats of material. Unless the material sample is taken from the critical substructure, the use of accelerated creep test results is inappropriate. In the worst case, if the accelerated creep test results indicate that the material properties are at the top end of the scatter band, and the critical area is in another substructure where the material properties happen to be at the bottom end of the scatter band, then the life estimate will be nonconservative by a factor of about 25. Although an analysis might indicate that the component has many years of remaining life, the critical area may have totally exhausted its useful life. Despite these cautions, when applied properly, this approach does provide the highest level of confidence currently possible for a single-outage evaluation.

ONLINE MONITORING AND ANALYSIS. The ultimate level of assessment is similar to that described previously, except that online monitoring, analysis, and evaluation can be accomplished by a boiler stress and condition analyzer described in Chapter 10. Such a device monitors temperature, pressure, and flow and uses this data together with material and geometry information to assess damage on a real-time basis. It makes no assumptions about repeatability of operations. An option to the use of this device is to incorporate "what-if" capabilities such that the effects of changing operational modes can be evaluated.

Proper operation is an important factor in achieving maximum life expectancy of the plant.

ASSESSMENT DOCUMENTATION AND TRACKING. Once condition assessment steps have been performed and summaries provided, all the information should be kept in an available documentation and planning tool. Specialized software programs exist to keep track of past assessment locations and results as well as to store recommendations for future assessments. This data tool can provide a living document that can be used for maintaining continued plant reliability.

SUMMARY

Life continuation of a steam generating system implies an objective of operating the equipment beyond the originally intended life, with these considerations in mind:

- Through rehabilitation or upgrading techniques, the steam generator can be restored to an operational level of availability, reliability, and capacity factor as practically close to "as new" status as possible
- Currently available state-of-the-art component designs can be incorporated, in full or in part, to improve the performance level and safety of a steam generator
- Sophisticated analytical techniques can be applied to estimate the remaining life of boiler components
- Future operational requirements may change from past or current practice. Design changes may, therefore, be indicated for some of the components subject to rehabilitation
- Because of aging or service-related destructive mechanisms, replacement of some parts may be required. Such replacement can be programmed over a period of time based on the calculated remaining life of specific components

A life continuation study is not solely a boiler inspection program, or just non-destructive testing of unit components, or only a prediction of remaining life of critical items. Although elements of these are present, timing is also an important issue in the plant life continuation concept. A proper program is an ongoing process in which the owner and the equipment manufacturers work together closely over a long period of time to solve technical and operational problems. Any modifications that are decided on should be phased over as long a time period as possible, for maximum economy. Recommendations for any steam generator will be owner and site specific, and will require a significant degree of owner participation to result in a productive outcome.

PHIL LAFAVE
CHARLIE HART
JACK MATTON
BRIAN MORRIS
CHARLES MCDARIS
DAN GELBAR
JIM GEYER
MICHAEL ROGERS
JERRY CHASE

REFERENCES

1. "Availability Patterns in Fossil-Fired Steam Power Plants," EPRI Report No. FP-583-SR. Palo Alto, CA: Electric Power Research Institute, November 1977.
2. Generating Availability Report (GAR), Princeton, NJ: North American Electric Reliability Council. Data compiled following IEEE Standard 762 – Revised 2006, (Revision of IEEE Std 762-1987. IEEE Standard Definitions for Use in Reporting Electric Generating Unit Reliability, Availability, and Productivity, 15 March 2007.) Tabulated results calculated from the Annual Unit Statistics for Years 1990–2007, Periods 01–12.
3. S. S. Blackburn and D. E. Lyons, "Design for Availability— An Update," Proceedings of the American Power Conference, Chicago: Illinois Institute of Technology, 1975, vol. 39, pp. 349–368.
4. C. H. Gilkey and J. D. Rogers, "A Summary of Experiences with Fan-Induced Duct Vibrations on Fossil-Fueled Boilers," Proceedings of the American Power Conference, Chicago: Illinois Institute of Technology, 1975, vol. 37, pp. 728–734.
5. "Extending the Lifespan of Fossil Plants," *EPRI Journal*, June 1983.
6. "Generic Guidelines for the Life Extension of Fossil Fuel Power Plants," EPRI Report No. CS-4778, Palo Alto, CA: Electric Power Research Institute, November, 1986.
7. D. E. Gelbar and S. J. deMello, "Assessing Boiler Life Continuation Needs," Proceedings of the 1988 Joint ASME/IEEE Power Generation Conference, Philadelphia, PA, September 25–29, 1988, ASME Paper No. 88-JPGC-Pwr-37.
8. J. S. Baylor, "Acid Rain Impacts on Utility Plans for Plant Life Extension," *Public Utilities Fortnightly*, March 1, 1990.
9. J. D. Fishburn et al., "Approaches for the Determination of Remaining Life in High Energy Piping Systems," Proceedings of the American Power Conference, Chicago: Illinois Institute of Technology, 1988, vol. 50.
10. T. McColloch, J. D. Fishburn, G. E. Roberts, and G. Hunter, "Evaluating the Structural Integrity of High Energy Piping Systems on Fossil Boilers," presented at the Second EPRI Fossil Plant Inspections Conference, San Antonio, TX, November, 1988.
11. R. P. Aubrey, B. A. Hawkins, and T. D. Jamison, "The Use of Oxide Scale Thickness Measurements in Life Extension Analysis," presented at ASNT 1989 Spring Conference, Charlotte, NC, March 22, 1989.
12. J. D. Fishburn and R. W. Loomis, "Life Extension of Thick Walled Components," presented at 11th International Conference of the AMIME, Irapuato, Mexico, November 2–4, 1988.
13. F. V. Ellis, R. W. Loomis, and S. Tordonato, "Life Extension: The C-E Approach to the Analysis of Thick Walled Components," presented at Conference on Life Extension and Assessment of Fossil Plants, EPRI, Washington, DC, June 1986.
14. B. W. Roberts, F. V. Ellis, and R. Viswanathan, "Utility Survey and Inspection for Life Assessment of Elevated Temperature Headers," Proceedings of the American Power Conference, Chicago: Illinois Institute of Technology, 1985, vol. 47, pp. 259–301.

SUGGESTED READING

"IEEE Standard Definitions for Use in Reporting Electric Generating Unit Reliability, Availability, and Productivity," IEEE Power Engineering Society, IEEE STD 762™ 2006 15 March 2007, IEEE, New York, NY.

Alternative Fuels

Chapter **Fifteen**

Whether because of the increased costs of conventional fossil fuels, environmental constraints, or the recovery of valuable chemicals, many industrial and utility boilers use alternative fuels, either to supplement their existing fossil fuel sources or to burn as a stand-alone fuel. Alternative fuels can be defined as energy-containing materials that are not expressly produced for energy production. Rather, they are the by-products and wastes from a variety of industries and processes from all parts of the modern economy. They are the unconventional sources of energy that can minimize the use of premium fuels. Industries that produce large quantities of these alternative fuels include agriculture, mining, forestry, petroleum refining, primary metals production, chemical manufacturing, pulp and paper production, waste treatment, and construction, to name a few.

Alternative fuels can essentially be broken into three distinct categories: solid, liquid, or gaseous. *Table 15-1* shows a number of by-products and wastes commonly used as alternative fuels in boilers. Because these alternative fuels originate from a wide range of industries and processes, they have a wide range of physical and chemical properties. As a result of the extensive number and diversity of these fuels, a detailed discussion regarding the characteristics and associated combustion issues of each is not practical. Therefore, a select number of alternative fuels will be discussed, along with general comments regarding combustion issues.

SOLID FUELS

Solid alternative fuels can be further divided into several subcategories: biomass fuels, municipal waste sources, and fossil-fuel derived products. The types of boilers and combustion systems used vary with the characteristics of type of solid alternative fuel.

BIOMASS

The most common category of alternative fuel is biomass. Biomass encompasses all types of plant material, paper, and wood products as well as bio-derived fuels, such as municipal solid waste, sewage sludge, and animal waste. *Figure 15-1* shows some examples of biomass fuels.

Hybrid Poplar

Wheat Straw

Alfalfa

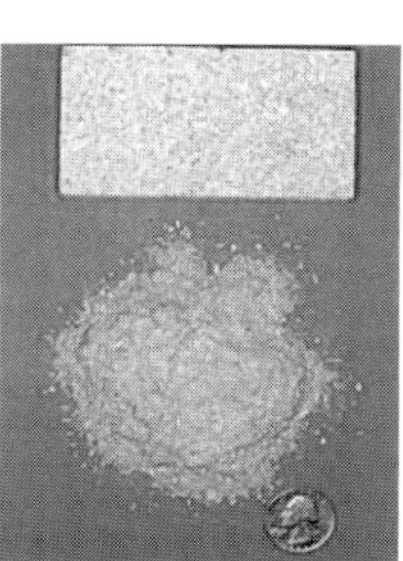

Wood Residue

Sunflower Hulls

Figure 15-1 | Examples of Biomass

TABLE 15-1 | EXAMPLES OF ALTERNATIVE FUELS

Non-Fossil Fuel/Material Burned	Physical Form		
	Gaseous	Liquid	Solid
Agricultural residues			X
Agricultural waste–cotton and corn			X
Alcohol (ethanol)		X	
Alcohol solvent		X	
Almond shells			X
Almond tree prunings			X
Animal fats		X	X
Ash pile char			X
Bagasse			X
Balsa wood			X
Bark			X
Barley dust and chaff			X
Barley needles			X
Bio-liquids		X	
Bio-gas	X		
Biomass			X
Bitumen		X	X
Bituminous coke			X
Black liquor		X	
Blast furnace gas	X		
Blond fiber			X
Cardboard			X
Carpet scrap			X
Clarifier residuals, primary			X
Clarifier residuals, secondary			X
Coal refuse, anthracite culm			X
Coal refuse, bituminous gob			X
Coal tar oil		X	
Coal tar plus soil			X
Coating residues		X	
Coke oven gas	X		
Composite water		X	
Compressed paper			X
Conforming waste materials			X
Construction/demolition wood/debris			X
Corn fiber			X
Corn gluten feed			X
Corn mill dryer off-gas	X		
Corn starch residue			X
Corn stover			X
Cotton gin residues			X
Cotton stalks			X
Cottonseed hulls			X
Cow manure			X
Crankcase oil		X	
Deinking residuals		X	X
Dewatered combustible residues		X	X
Diaper scraps			X
Digester gas	X		
Distillers dry grains			X
Distillers grains			X
Distillers grains stillage		X	
Engineered wood plant scrap			X
Envirofuel Pellets			X
Filters			X
Foam residues			X
Fruit pits			X
Fuel cubes (paper diaper clippings/refuse)			X
Fuel oil solids (tank clean-out residue)			X
Fume filter oil		X	
Gear oil (virgin and used)		X	
Gluten feed pellets			X
Grain dust			X
Glycerol distillation by-product		X	
Hardboard dust			X
Hardboard residues			X
Hardwood pellets (hammer-milled, dried, pelletized; sold as fuel)			X
Heavy recycle		X	
High caustic fuel		X	
Hog fuel, hard wood			X
Hog fuel, soft wood			X
Hog fuel, urban			X
Hogged bark			X
Hydro-pulper refuse			X
Industrial plastics			X
Ink solvents		X	

Most biomass fuels are cellulose-based, which makes them physically and chemically very different from other solid fossil fuels, such as coal. Compared to coal, most biomass fuels contain a higher proportion of hydrogen and oxygen and typically are low in ash, high in volatile matter, and highly variable in moisture content. Specific constituents within the biomass fuel, especially nitrogen, sulfur, and chlorine, give rise to variations in combustion and emission behavior unless considered in the design and operation of the boiler. The lower sulfur and nitrogen contents of most biomass fuels, however, have a positive implication for gaseous emissions. Some types of biomass contain relatively high chlorine levels, which result in high HCl concentrations in the boiler flue gases and, possibly, in high temperature corrosion.

Biomass ash contains a number of inorganic minerals (SiO_2, CaO, MgO, K, Na, Fe_2O_3) and trace elements of heavy metals (Hg, As, Pb). The high proportion of alkali metals within the ash, such as K and Na, is a good indicator for potential slagging and fouling problems within a boiler. Another major mechanism for ash deposition is dependent on the ash fusion temperature of the particular biomass being burned and on the combustion conditions. *Table 15-2* shows some typical ash compositions of biomass fuels.

Raw biomass fuels, such as energy crops (switchgrass, miscanthus, and short-rotation crops), can contain up to 60% moisture. They also have significantly different properties with respect to storage, bulk handling, volume flow, milling, combustion, slagging, corrosion, and gaseous emissions. Biomass fuels can be delivered to the site in a number of forms, ranging from pelletized fuels to chipped fuels and bales. The issues regarding delivery, storage, and preparation of the biomass fuels differ from those with other solid fuels, and this presents the first obstacle to overcome regarding the continuous, long-term use of biomass. Biomass pellets typically will have lower moisture contents (and, thus, higher calorific values) as well as increased bulk densities compared to raw biomass, and they generally are easier to handle.

Biomass tends to be more reactive than other solid fuels, but in almost all cases, it requires milling in order to achieve a size that is suitable for transportation and complete burnout within the furnace. Because the cost of milling biomass is high, knowledge of the maximum acceptable particle size that will still burn is of great importance. This size will depend on the specific biomass being considered, because the milling behavior and ultimate shape will vary among the biomass fuels. In addition, the furnace in which the biomass is burned, and how that furnace is being operated, also will affect the aerodynamic and combustion effectiveness. The ignition process of biomass is similar to that of coal except that more volatile matter is available. In some biomass fuels, however, high moisture and ash contents can cause ignition and combustion issues.

Firing of biomass fuels in large power boilers can be achieved by either co-firing with the conventional fossil fuel or by firing as the primary fuel source in suspension, on a stoker, or in a fluidized bed combustor. With co-firing, as the proportion of biomass increases, the overall average fuel analysis to the furnace varies according to the proportion fired. In general, the average calorific value and amount of ash that is produced generally will decrease as the quantity of biomass increases. In addition, the lower the quality of the biomass fired (i.e., biomass with a

TABLE 15-1 | EXAMPLES OF ALTERNATIVE FUELS—*continued*

Non-Fossil Fuel/Material Burned	Physical Form		
	Gaseous	Liquid	Solid
Knots and knotter rejects			X
Laminate production scrap dust			X
Laminated wood			X
Lamination finishing plant residues			X
Lamination plant residues			X
Landfill gas	X		
Latex paint water		X	
Lightweight asphalt		X	
Lignin			X
Liquefied chicken fat		X	
Livestock manure, bedding and yard residues		X	X
Log yard cleanup			X
Low carbonate corn fiber			X
Lube oil (virgin and used)		X	
Lumber refuse (hogged pallet boards/other non-treated scrap)			X
Malt sprouts			X
Manure			X
Mechanical pulp mill rejects			X
Medium density fiber board sander dust			X
Medium density fiber board trim (some with water-based primer)			X
Mill trash			X
Millfeed			X
Mixed liquid residues		X	
Mixed wood residues			X
Municipal sewage residues			X
Neutralene			X
New and used solvent, Acetone		X	
Non-condensable gas (includes stripper offgas)	X		
Non-halogenated solvent		X	
Non-hazardous by-product solvent		X	
Nut shells			X
Oat hulls			X
Oil booms			X
Oil residues/excesses/by-products (no. 6, asphalts)		X	X
Oilseed (rapeseed, canola)		X	
Oil spill cleanup residues		X	X
Oilseeds (canola, corn, beans)			X
Oily rags			X
Old corrugated container rejects			X
Olive cake			X
Olive kernel			X
Orchard prunings			X
Oriented strand board trim/dry residuals			X
Orimulsion		X	
Other biomass			X
Paint rags			X
Paint residues		X	
Palm oil plantation by-products (palm kernel exfoliate, fiber, shell, empty fruit bunch [EFB])			X
Paper			X
Paper broke			X
Paper cores			X
Paper fines			X
Paper, office waste			X
Paper wrapper and packaging trimmings			X
Particleboard sander dust			X
Particleboard trim			X
Paunch manure			X
Peat			X
Pecan hulls			X
Petroleum coke			X
Petroleum distillation solvent		X	
Petroleum-refining residue oil		X	
Pine and cedar trees, chipping and residues			X
Pine and fir			X
Pine tar		X	
Pitch/woodwaste		X	X
Plywood trim			X
Post-harvest biomass residues			X
Poultry litter			X
Process-derived liquid fuel		X	
Process gas	X		
Pulp liquor		X	
Pulp mill gas	X		
Railroad ties			X

TABLE 15-1 | EXAMPLES OF ALTERNATIVE FUELS—*continued*

Non-Fossil Fuel/Material Burned	Physical Form		
	Gaseous	Liquid	Solid
Railroad ties, chipped			X
Reclaim ink solvent		X	
Recovered gaseous butane	X		
Rectified methanol		X	
Red oil (steam stripper, steam condensate, including terpenes, terpenoids, methanol, total reduced sulfur [TRS])		X	
Redwood and fir			X
Refinery gas	X		
Refuse			X
Refuse-derived fuel			X
Reinjection char			X
Reprocessed oil		X	
Resin solid			X
Restaurant oils and greases		X	
Rice hulls			X
Sander dust			X
Sawdust			X
Sawmill scrap			X
Scrap x-ray film			X
Screen rejects			X
Sewage gas	X		
Shredded cloth			X
Silvicultural wood			X
Sludge		X	X
Sludge without water			X
Solid paraffin			X
Solvents		X	
Soybean hulls			X
Spent coffee grounds			X
Spent oxide			X
Straw			X
Stripper condensate		X	
Sulfur-free organic by-product			X
Sunflower hulls			X
Sunflower husks			X
Sunflower pellets			X
Sunflower seed hulls			X
Sunwax (diatomaceous earth with sunflower oil wax)			X
Switchgrass			X
Synfuel coal			X
Tall oil and tall oil derivatives		X	
Tallow		X	X
Tar		X	X
Tire chips			X
Tire-derived fuel			X
Tires (whole)			X
Toluene		X	
Turkey brood woodwaste			X
Turpentine		X	
Used hydraulic oil		X	
Used motor oil		X	
Used oil		X	
Used thermal oil		X	
Vegetable oil		X	
Virgin hydraulic oil		X	
Waste alcohol		X	
Wastewater treatment residues		X	X
Wax and cellophane wrapper and packaging trimmings			X
Wet distiller grains			X
Wheat fiber			X
Whole-tree chips/harvest residue			X
Wood			X
Wood bark			X
Wood briquettes			X
Wood char			X
Wood chips			X
Wood chips, fines			X
Wood chips, old			X
Wood fuels, bark			X
Wood pallets			X
Wood shavings			X
Woodwaste, clean			X
Woodex pellets			X
Woodworking residuals (cabinet manufacturing)			X
Yellow grease (used cooking oils; sold as commercial fuel)		X	

higher moisture content), the lower the overall boiler efficiency.

As the boiler efficiency decreases with lower quality biomass fuels, the flue gas flows will increase and lead to an increase in gas loading on the induced-draft fans and back end equipment. For units that were not originally designed to burn higher-moisture-content biomass and that have little or no fan margins, load reductions can be expected. In addition, the desuperheater spray flow, air heater gas outlet temperature, main steam to reheater outlet steam temperature differential, and reheater outlet steam temperature can be affected.

Corrosion can be another major issue in co-firing applications. Elements of concern include alkalies (Na and K), chlorides, sulfur, lead, and zinc. High concentrations of alkalies lead to low-melting-temperature ash components. Molten ash compounds tend to be more aggressive in attacking metals because of the high ion mobility in the liquid phase. Low-melting ash components also lead to sticky deposits that attract other ash material, leading to a high buildup of deposits on tube surfaces. The stickiness makes the deposit hard to clean. Potassium compounds tend to be more corrosive than sodium compounds. *Figure 15-2* shows a deposit from the co-firing of wheat straw and coal.

Chlorides can combine with alkalies to form compounds with very low melting temperatures. These compounds can cause very rapid corrosion of boiler tubing. Lead and zinc can be contributing factors. These materials can be absorbed from soils by the biomass during the growing process depending on the location, types of soils, and types of fertilizers being used. *Figure 15-3* illustrates some of the eutectic mixtures of

chloride compounds and their melting points.

In most cases, burning biomass produces lower emissions compared with other, conventional fossil fuels. Therefore, many larger power boilers look to offset some or even all of their fossil fuel with biomass. Biomass can reduce the amount of greenhouse gases, particularly CO_2, being generated from the combustion of fossil fuels. As part of the process called *photosynthesis*, living plants utilize CO_2 and water in the presence of light energy to form glucose and oxygen. And although CO_2 is released into the atmosphere during the combustion of biomass, it also is taken from the atmosphere during growth. Therefore, biomass fuels often are considered to be carbon neutral.

The lower sulfur contents of most biomass fuels will result in lower SO_2 emissions compared with most coal- or oil-fired boilers. If the biomass fuel contains a high level of chlorine, this can form HCl in the flue gas, which will impair the operation of the flue gas desulfurization system. An increased presence of heavy metals, such as mercury, arsenic, or lead, in the flue gas could be concentrated in the flue gas desulfurization residues.

The situation regarding NOx emissions when firing biomass is more complex than the situation regarding SO_2 emissions. Unlike the situation with sulfur, which directly forms SO_2, not all of the nitrogen in the biomass will ultimately end up as NOx. Fuel properties influencing the formation of NOx include nitrogen content, volatile matter, and release rate of the nitrogen. The nitrogen content in biomass can vary significantly depending on the source. Nitrogen released with the volatiles is reduced to molecular nitrogen under reducing conditions and can be controlled by near-field aerodynamic changes, whereas the remaining nitrogen in the char phase is released at a slower rate and is influenced by the furnace environment. In some cases, firing certain biomass materials may produce NOx emissions that are similar to, if not higher than, those of some coal- or oil-fired units.

The unburned carbon from certain biomass-fired systems, such as older suspension-fired units or stoker-fired units, can be relatively high. This results from the low-density and high-drag-coefficient char particles that often are associated with biomass.

TABLE 15-2 | TYPICAL ASH COMPOSITIONS OF BIOMASS FUELS

	Illinois No.6	Cordero Rojo	Wheat Straw	Alfalfa	Hybrid Poplar	Sunflower Hulls	Wood Waste
SiO_2	54.7	30.0	66.5	30.4	4.7	4.8	28.4
Al_2O_3	20.9	22.1	0.0	0.5	1.5	1.6	11.3
Fe_2O_3	14.6	7.4	0.4	0.7	2.0	0.7	10.3
TiO_2	0.9	1.9	0.1	0.1	0.1	0.1	0.5
P_2O_5	0.2	1.2	1.4	8.8	7.9	8.0	1.4
CaO	3.5	29.9	3.5	25.4	49.6	12.8	29.2
MgO	1.6	5.5	1.8	4.4	8.6	9.9	6.1
Na_2O	1.3	1.7	2.8	1.5	0.4	0.0	5.0
K_2O	2.2	0.4	23.5	28.2	25.2	62.1	7.8
Cl (ppm)	340	57	2,120	2,340	93	588	649

Figure 15-2 | Ash deposit of wheat straw and coal blends

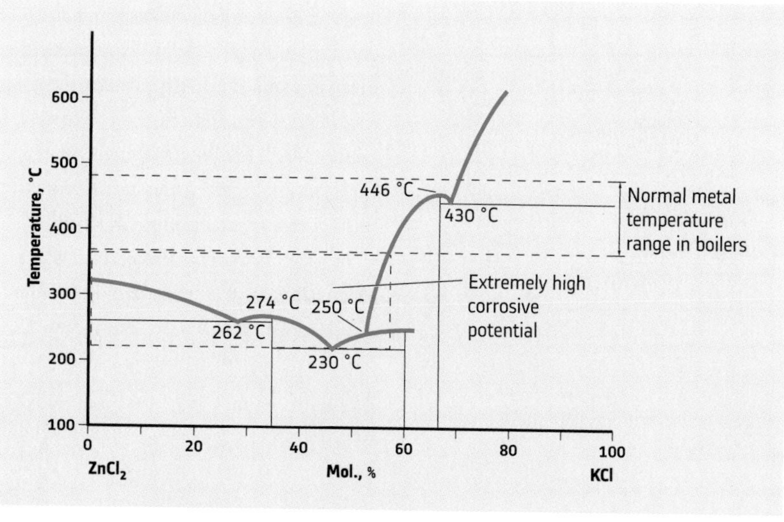

Figure 15-3 | Phase diagram for potassium and zinc chlorides

Wood/Woodwaste

Wood is a complex vegetable tissue that is composed principally of cellulose, an organic compound having a definite chemical composition. Because of the presence of resins, gums, and other substances in varying amounts, the heating values of different woods can differ significantly. This is also a reason why the Dulong formula is not reliable at predicting their respective heating values.

The moisture content of freshly cut wood can vary from 30 to 50%. Wood that has been allowed to sit for a period of time may have its moisture content reduced to between 18 and 25%. This impacts the gas weight that results from combustion.

Most wood or woodwaste is a result of specific manufacturing processes. These sources can provide the same ash constituents in the fuel that lead to the corrosion issues described previously. Examples of woodwaste include sawdust, wood pallets, furniture discards, lumber rejects, cuttings, and others.

Bark/Hog Fuel

Bark is a common waste product in the paper mill industry. As logs come in, they are fed through a debarker. Bark is peeled off the tree trunks in large strips and chunks. The bark usually contains a high moisture content and often entraps sand and dirt from the logging process. The high moisture content (i.e., low heating value) and high mineral matter can cause issues with conventional boiler designs.

Hog fuel is a term that is used when discussing the manufacture of lumber. A fair amount of waste results when producing lumber from a tree trunk, such as the bark, the sawdust and shavings, and the remaining larger-sized pieces of material. These waste products require further size reduction in a "hog" in order to make them more conducive to handling and burning. Hog fuel typically contains a moisture content of approximately 50%. This high moisture content results in high gas flow weight from combustion. This higher gas flow can be accommodated in the design of a new boiler intended for bark fuel. When such fuels are co-fired in existing units, however, the amount of these fuels may be limited by the fan system. Fines from processing of the wood can be carried up into the upper furnace, which leads to higher unburned carbon loss for such fuels.

Bagasse

Bagasse is a waste fuel that is produced when extracting sugar from cane. After the sugarcane is harvested, it is shredded into much smaller pieces in order to facilitate squeezing the juice out of the cane through a series of rollers. After this primary pressing occurs, the issuing fiber, called "bagasse," typically is sent through another series of rollers for further extraction. Although the bagasse has a high volatile matter content, it also usually contains high moisture (upwards of 55%). Pure bagasse has little to no ash. Because of increased mechanization in the sugar manufacturing industry, however, a higher quantity of ash, usually high in silica, often is present, because as opposed to manual harvesting, the machines that harvest the bagasse often pull up the roots.

Bagasse usually is fired in suspension in a conventional power boiler over a grate. The fuel's high moisture content, high reactivity, and ash content are issues that require consideration.

Switchgrass/Miscanthus

Switchgrass and miscanthus are both considered to be renewable, high-energy crops. Switchgrass, or thatchgrass, is a tall grass native to North America. It is a hardy perennial grass that can reach heights of between 2 to 6 feet (0.6 to 1.8 m) in a single growing season. It is resistant to many pests, diseases, and drought, and it often is used to prevent soil erosion. Because of these advantages, it often is considered for use in supplementing traditional fossil fuels in power plants. The low density, high volatility, and fibrous content make the feed and transport of the material the biggest challenge.

Miscanthus, or elephant grass, is a very tall perennial grass that is cultivated primarily in Europe as a biofuel. It can grow up to 12 feet (3.7 m) in height. The use of miscanthus as a biofuel is becoming more popular as a result of environmental regulations to reduce CO_2 emissions from fossil-fueled boilers.

FOSSIL-FUEL BASED PRODUCTS

This broad category of alternative fuels consists of waste products in the production of petroleum refining or the overburden, underburden, and mineral layers separated from the as-mined coal and then discarded. Many of these alternative fuels contain substantial thermal energy when burned, but they also may contain significant contaminants and often are difficult to burn. Several examples are petroleum coke, coke breeze, and culm.

Petroleum Coke

Petroleum coke is a by-product of the process in which residual hydrocarbons are converted to lighter, more valued distillates. There are two basic types of petroleum coke: delayed and fluid. The process of producing fluid coke is more complex than that for delayed coke, and fluid coke typically has a lower volatile content compared with delayed coke. The heating value of the petroleum coke can be as high as 15,000 BTU/lb (34,900 kJ/kg).

The analysis of the petroleum coke is very dependent on the base petroleum product from which it is produced. Certain petroleum cokes can have very high sulfur, sodium, vanadium, and asphaltene contents. Each of these constituents can affect the combustion process within a boiler. In addition, vanadium can form highly corrosive compounds, such as vanadium pentoxide and vanadyl sulfate, during the combustion process. These compounds can be very corrosive. Another characteristic of petroleum coke is its low reactivity and low ash content.

Typically, petroleum coke is used either as a supplemental fuel in a conventional boiler firing typical fossil fuels or as a fuel in a fluidized bed combustor. Fluidized bed combustors have an advantage in burning petroleum coke. The solids have a long residence time, which overcomes some of the problems with the low reactivity of the fuel. In addition, the combustion temperature is considerably lower

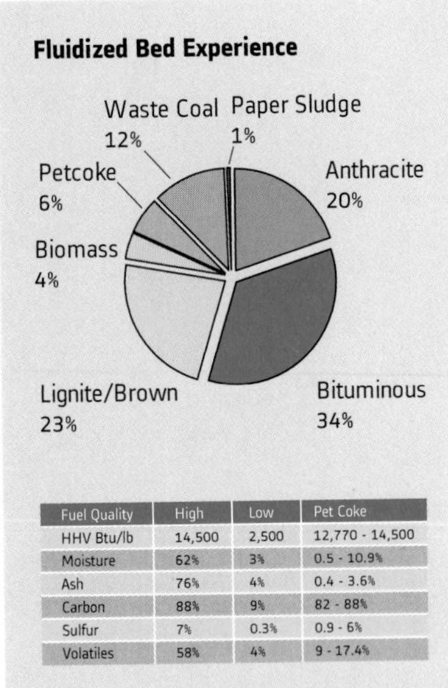

Fuel Quality	High	Low	Pet Coke
HHV Btu/lb	14,500	2,500	12,770 - 14,500
Moisture	62%	3%	0.5 - 10.9%
Ash	76%	4%	0.4 - 3.6%
Carbon	88%	9%	82 - 88%
Sulfur	7%	0.3%	0.9 - 6%
Volatiles	58%	4%	9 - 17.4%

Figure 15-4 | Experience with alternative fuels in circulating fluidized bed boilers (HHV, higher heating value; Pet, petroleum)

than that of suspension firing, which prevents the formation of some of the compounds that melt at low temperatures. The use of limestone in the fluidized bed provides for the capture of sulfur during the combustion process; this feature greatly reduces the amount of sulfur that is available to form low-melting-temperature compounds. *Figure 15-4* shows the variety of fuels that have been burned in circulating fluidized bed combustors.

Culm and Gob

Coal mines often yield an impure product, and the raw coal must be further processed to remove much of the undesirable materials. This waste material is termed *culm* in the case of anthracite coal and *gob* in the case of bituminous coal. Coal producers accumulate this material in large piles. Because culm and gob often contain a percentage of the parent coal, it does have some intrinsic energy within it. The majority of these fuels exist in Pennsylvania, West Virginia, and other locations that mine either bituminous or anthracite coals.

Some of the issues associated with culm are the high ash content, high mercury concentration, and significantly lower calorific value compared with those of the parent coal. For these reasons, circulating fluidized bed technology permits these coal mine wastes to be burned efficiently and with lower emissions than other types of combustion systems. The properties of coal mining waste are measured using a combination of standardized coal tests and other physical test methods that reveal both combustion characteristics and the nature of its ash.

The high ash content presents some special issues. As the ash content of the fuel increases, the capacity required of the ash-handling equipment goes up in a non-linear fashion. This is because more fuel is needed to provide the same relative heat input. This additional fuel contains more ash, resulting in the need to handle that ash as well.

The additional ash also impacts the feed system, because more fuel is needed to provide the same level of heat input. For the higher-ash fuels (ash content, >20%), when the level of ash in the fuel doubles, the amount of ash that is produced to obtain the same output (in MW) increases by nearly a factor of four. The split between bottom ash and fly ash also may be affected. The ash may contain materials that are more resistant to crushing, which leads to higher wear on the fuel preparation system and, often, an increase in the amount of larger particles entering the bed. In turn, these typically end up in the bed drain system rather than as fly ash.

Ash also includes "tramp" material that happens to come along with the fuel. When these coal piles have existed for any length of time, many other materials (e.g., welding rod, tramp metal, and rocks) may have been sent to the same pile. These materials give rise to problems in transporting and preparing the fuel. The variability regarding the existence of these materials in a given pile requires equipment that is more tolerant than conventional equipment designed to handle conventional fuels.

MUNICIPAL WASTE FUELS

Another broad category of solid alternative fuels is that from the waste of the human population. These can include such sources as municipal solid waste, refuse-derived fuel, various sludge sources, tire-derived fuel, and railroad ties. These materials are discarded as waste but contain energy within the product. Many facilities are using these materials to reclaim that energy as well as to reduce the disposal volume. As landfill space becomes scarce, these "waste-to-energy plants" are becoming more common and, in some cases, a requirement.

Municipal Solid Waste

Solid residential, commercial, or industrial waste is termed *municipal solid waste*. This waste derives most of its heating value from its paper, plastic, wood, and other smaller, contributing materials. It is a highly time-, geography-, and weather-dependent fuel. Its characteristics also vary widely with the economic status of the people generating it. It is extremely heterogeneous, and the heating value is heavily dependent on the amount of paper and plastics discarded. Because of the heterogeneous nature of the fuel, the ash content and characteristics can vary widely as well, influencing the design requirements of the boiler as well as the emissions.

Municipal solid waste is burned in specially designed furnaces on stoker grates. Emissions restrictions for municipal solid waste plants are more stringent than those for conventional units because of the variety of potential emissions and the likelihood of higher levels of heavy metals and organic emissions (dioxins and furans).

Refuse-Derived Fuel

Refuse-derived fuel is similar to the parent municipal solid waste but is without many of the non-combustible materials and other impurities. The remaining product is then shredded into a more homogeneous product, which can then be pneumatically conveyed to the boiler and fired partially in suspension and partially on a stoker grate. Many of the same issues regarding municipal solid waste also exist for refuse-derived fuels.

Tire-Derived Fuel

Tires can be a problem in terms of landfill disposal, increased mosquito population, and other environmental or health issues. Some facilities shred the tires to make them easier to transport and store as well as to simplify the necessary boiler and combustion system. Tire-derived fuel can have a heating value of approximately 15,000 BTU/lb (24,900 kJ/kg). Many issues can arise with the imbedded wire, high sulfur content, zinc chloride, and particulate emissions.

LIQUID FUELS

Liquid alternative fuels include a wide variety of oils, greases, fats, solvents, sludges, process solutions, and slurries of various kinds. The pulp and paper industry has utilized combustion technology for more than a century to recover chemicals that are used in the pulping process. Chemical recovery boilers burn black liquor (a slurry of lignin, unused pulp, and cooking chemicals) to recover sodium and sulfur compounds for reuse. Bark-fired boilers provide steam for processing. Deinking sludge from the recycling of newspaper provides fuel for some of these boilers.

Heavy oils, greases, fats, and solvents also are hydrocarbons of a nature similar to that of conventional oils. Typically, however, these hydrocarbons are of higher molecular weight and heavier in nature. They may be solid at room temperature and need to be heated to remain as a pumpable liquid. Atomization may be a problem. High asphaltene contents can lead to soot formation and relatively high unburned carbon levels. Because some of these materials may have been used for other purposes, they often contain other, non-combustible materials that must be accounted for in the combustion and handling processes. Solvents in particular tend to have an adverse impact on seals and other material-handling systems.

The majority of these fuels represent only a small amount of the total fuels burned. Some fuels, however, either exist in potentially large quantities or can potentially be produced in large quantities. Two such fuels are very heavy oils (e.g., orimulsion) and alcohol fuels (e.g., ethanol and methanol).

VERY HEAVY OILS

Very heavy oils are found in the Orinoco fields well inland in Venezuela. The cost of producing, processing, and transporting these fuels is rather high. One process to assist in the commercial utilization of these fuels is emulsification. A water–oil emulsion can be prepared that allows the material to be pumped. The goal is to be able to burn the fuel in a manner similar to oil. These fuels tend to be high in sulfur, so appropriate emission controls would be required for proper utilization. Several large utility units have been retrofitted to use this fuel.

ALCOHOL FUELS

Alcohol fuels can be produced from plant material (primarily ethanol) or other hydrocarbon materials via gasification (primarily methanol). Current production of ethanol is from corn or sugar manufacture, but substantial research is underway regarding the production of cellulosic ethanol. Most plants (i.e., biomass) consist of approximately 25% lignin, 45% cellulose, and 30% hemicellulose. The lignin is not suitable for conversion to oils or alcohols; however, the cellulose and hemicellulose can be converted to sugars, and then to alcohols, fairly easily. The life-cycle energy balance for this biomass fuel is favorable compared to the conversion of corn to ethanol.

Full utilization of biomass materials that are currently left behind could provide as much as 40% of the current oil requirement of the United States. Current programs include genetic engineering of microorganisms that convert the sugar to ethanol. Additional work on improving the utilization of incident sunlight by photosynthesis also would contribute to the potential of this process. Although alcohol fuels are similar to solvents, their current utilization in gasoline provides some experience in the

types of materials that would be needed for wide-scale application.

GASEOUS FUELS

Gaseous fuels include refinery gases, blast furnace gas, coke oven gas, non-condensable gases, and landfill gas. These gases currently are utilized as long as the heating value of the fuel can be maintained above approximately 60 BTU/ft^3 (2,250 kJ/m^3). Gases with lower or more variable heat contents usually are thermally oxidized, either by flare or thermal oxidizer.

Design considerations are concerned primarily with the fuel delivery and burner systems. The low heating content of the gases generally requires larger fuel piping and special burner design features. Once the fuel has been burned in the furnace, the resulting flue gas is comparable to more conventional gas firing. One area of concern would be with those gases having a high hydrogen content. Hydrogen combustion tends to be associated with higher NOx production. For the more dilute gases, the temperatures usually are low enough that this is not a problem. For gases with some concentration of methane or ethane, the heating value tends to be higher, and measures need to be taken to ensure that NOx regulations can be met.

DOUG HART
WILLIAM BAILEY
CARL BOZZUTO

SUBJECT INDEX

Page numbers for tables, graphs and illustrations are in italics.

A

B

D

E

F

G

H

I

J

K

L

M

N

O

P

R

S

U

V

W

Z